WE DESIGN, BUILD, RETROFIT AND REPAIR

Naval and governmental authority vessels

PERMANENT CONSIDERATION OF THE STATE OF THE ART, PRECISION AND QUALITY OF WORK AND DELIVERY ON SCHEDULE ARE THE MAINTAINED TRADITION OF ABEKING & RASMUSSEN.

SAR cruisers

- COMPREHENSIVE KNOW-HOW APPLIED TO THE CONSTRUCTION OF COMPLEX SHIPS AND COMPONENTS OUT OF WOOD, FRP, ALUMINIUM, STEEL AND NONMAGNETIZABLE STEEL.
- ABILITY TO PERFORM ALL KINDS OF SHIP- AND COMPONENT REPAIRS.
- CONSULTATION, COMPUTER AIDED DESIGN AND MANUFACTURING AND CALCULATION WITH FINITE ELEMENTS.
- ASSEMBLY OF COMPONENTS TO ENTIRE CONSTRUCTIONS.
- QUALITY MANAGEMENT ACC. ISO 9001 AND MILITARY STANDARDS.
- UP TO 70 M AND 1.500 T

High performance yachts

Fast patrol boats and ferries

ABEKING & RASMUSSEN

—— SINCE 1907 ——

Abeking & Rasmussen, P. O. Box 1160, D-27805 Lemwerder, Germany, Phone 49-(0) 421-67 33 -0, Fax 49-(0) 421-67 33-112

Jane's
HIGH-SPEED
MARINE CRAFT

Edited by Stephen J Phillips
BSc (Hons) CEng MRINA

Twenty-eighth Edition
1995-96

ISBN 0 7106 1266 4
"Jane's" is a registered trade mark

Copyright © 1995 by Jane's Information Group Limited, Sentinel House, 163 Brighton Road, Coulsdon, Surrey CR5 2NH, UK

In the USA and its dependencies
Jane's Information Group Inc, 1340 Braddock Place, Suite 300, Alexandria, VA 22314-1651, USA

I(T)P An International Thomson Publishing Company

British Library Cataloguing-in-Publication Data.
A catalogue record for this book is available from the British Library.

Printed and bound in Great Britain by Biddles Ltd, Guildford and King's Lynn.

The World's only Foilcat in commercial operation

Westamaran Foilcat 3000

The World's fastest diesel driven passenger ferry
Max speed 50 knots
Proven comfort in up to 4 metres significant wave height

30 years experience – builders of more than 100 fast ferries
We create opportunities at sea

Head Office:
Swede Ship Invest AB
S-440 64 Rönnäng
Sweden
Phone   +46 304 66 22 20
Telefax +46 304 66 25 75

Sales Office Far East:
Swede Ship Representative Office
Permata Plaza
Jakarta 10350 Indonesia
Phone: +62 21 390 3324
Fax: +62 21 390 3325

[2]

Contents

ADMINISTRATION

Publishing Director: Robert Hutchinson

Managing Editor: Keith Faulkner

Yearbook Editorial Production Manager: Ruth Simmance

Production Editor: Tarquin Acevedo

EDITORIAL OFFICES

Jane's Information Group Limited, Sentinel House,
163 Brighton Road, Coulsdon, Surrey CR5 2NH, UK

Tel: 0181 763 1030 International +44 181 763 1030
Telex: 916907 Janes G
Fax: 0181 763 1006 International +44 181 763 1006

SALES OFFICES

Send enquiries to International Sales Manager:
Fabiana Angelini (UK/MoD, Europe)
David Eaton-Jones (Middle East, Asia Pacific, Africa, Austria,
Germany, Greece, Switzerland, Eastern Europe)
Jane's Information Group Limited, UK address as above

Tel Enquiries: 0181 763 1030 International: +44 181 763 1030
Fax Enquiries: 0181 763 1006 International: +44 181 763 1006
Fax Orders: 0181 763 0276 International: +44 181 763 0276

ADVERTISEMENT SALES OFFICES

Advertisement Sales Manager: Richard West

Australia: Brendan Gullifer, Havre & Gullifer (Pty) Ltd, Level 50,
101 Collins Street, Melbourne 3000

Tel: +61 3 696 0288
Fax: +61 3 696 6951

Benelux: Annabel Chisholm, Jane's Information Group (see UK/Rest
of World)

Brazil: L Bilyk, Brazmedia International S/C Ltda, Alameda Gabriel
Monterio da Silva, 366 CEP, 01442 São Paulo

Tel: +55 11 853 4133
Telex: 32836 BMED BR
Fax: +55 11 852 6485

France: Patrice Février, Jane's Information Group — France,
BP 418, 35 avenue MacMahon, F-75824 Paris Cedex

Tel: +33 1 45 72 33 11
Fax: +33 1 45 72 17 95

Germany and Austria: Annabel Chisholm, Jane's Information Group
(see UK/Rest of World)

Hong Kong: Jeremy Miller, Major Media Ltd, Room 1402, 14F
Capitol Centre, 5-19 Jardine's Bazaar, Causeway Bay

Tel: +852 890 3110
Fax: +852 576 3397

Israel: Oreet Ben-Yaacov, Oreet International Media, 15 Kinneret
Street, IL-51201 Bene-Berak

Tel: +972 3 570 6527
Fax: +972 3 570 6526

Italy and Switzerland: Ediconsult Internazionale Srl, Piazza Fontane
Marose 3, I-16123 Genoa, Italy

Tel: +39 10 583684
Telex: 281197 EDINT I
Fax: +39 10 566578

Japan: Intermart/EAC Inc, 1-7 Akasaka 9-chome, Minato-Ku,
Tokyo 107

Tel: +81 3 5474 7835
Fax: +81 3 5474 7837

Korea, South: Young Seoh Chinn, JES Media International, 6th Floor
Donghye Building, 47-16 Myungil-Dong, Kangdong-Gu, Seoul
134-070

Tel: +82 2 481 3411
Fax: +82 2 481 3414

Scandinavia: Annabel Chisholm, Jane's Information Group (see UK/
Rest of World)

Singapore, Indonesia, Malaysia, Philippines, Taiwan and Thailand:
Hoo Siew Sai, Major Media (Singapore) Pte Ltd, 6th Floor, 52 Chin
Swee Road, Singapore 0316

Tel: +65 738 0122
Telex: RS 43370 AMPLS
Fax: +65 738 2108

South Africa: Annabel Chisholm, Jane's Information Group (see UK/
Rest of World)

Spain: Jesus Moran Iglesias, Varex SA, Modesto Lafuente 4,
E-28010 Madrid

Tel: +34 1 448 7622
Fax: +34 1 446 0198

UK/Rest of World: Annabel Chisholm, Jane's Information Group,
Sentinel House, 163 Brighton Road, Coulsdon, Surrey CR5 2NH

Tel: 0181 763 1030 International +44 181 763 1030
Telex: 916907 Janes G
Fax: 0181 763 0643 International +44 181 763 0643

USA and Canada: Kimberley S Hanson, Advertising Sales and
Marketing Director
Kristin Schulze, Regional Advertising Sales Manager (Air Transport)
Jennifer Felix, Advertising Sales Representative (Land and Marine
Transport)
Jane's Information Group Inc, 1340 Braddock Place, Suite 300,
Alexandria, Virginia 22314-1651

Tel: +1 703 683 3700
Telex: 6819193
Fax: +1 703 836 0029

USA West Coast: Anne Marie St John-Brooks, Regional Advertising
Sales Manager, Jane's Information Group Inc, 1523 Rollins Road,
Burlingame, California 94010

Tel: +1 415 259 9982
Fax: +1 415 259 9751

Administration: UK: Tara Betts
                   USA and Canada: Maureen Nute

[4]

How To Use This Book

The purpose of this book is to provide a comprehensive reference yearbook covering the design, construction and operation of high-speed marine craft, worldwide.

Entries in this book cover all organisations involved in this industry and are divided into four main sections as follows:

Builders

Civil Operators

Principal Engineering Components

Services

These main divisions are further divided into subsections containing entries for organisations arranged under more specific headings. For example the Builders section of the book is divided into six types of craft built: Air Cushion Vehicles, Hydrofoils, Multihulls, Swath vessels, Monohulls and Wing-in-ground-effect craft. The Principal Engineering Components section is divided into seven types of principal components: Engines, Transmissions, Air propellers, Marine propellers, Water-jet units, Air cushion skirt systems and Ride control systems.

Under each of these subsections, entries are arranged alphabetically into countries and thereafter into organisation names.

An Addenda is included at the rear of the book so that developments occurring during the main publication process are not excluded.

A comprehensive Bibliography is also included which lists all the relevant books, technical papers and presentations that have been made public over the last five years.

Any particular entry may be located by using one of the three indexes covering Organisations, Craft types or Craft names.

To help users of this title evaluate the published data, Jane's Information Group has divided entries into three categories:-

● **VERIFIED** The editor has made a detailed examination of the entry's content and checked its relevancy and accuracy for publication in the new edition to the best of his ability.

● **UPDATED** During the verification process, significant changes to content have been made to reflect the latest position known to Jane's at the time of publication.

● **NEW ENTRY** Information on new equipment and/or systems appearing for the first time in the title.

We have also added dates to the pictures included in this edition. All pictures will be dated with the first year of publication. This year's pictures will be dated *1995* and next year's *1996* and so on.

We hope these measures increase the value of this title to our thousands of customers worldwide. If you have any comments or suggestions for further enhancements, the Publisher would be pleased to receive them.

This edition of *Jane's High-Speed Marine Craft* contains a total of 240 new or updated photographs and drawings.

Alphabetical list of advertisers

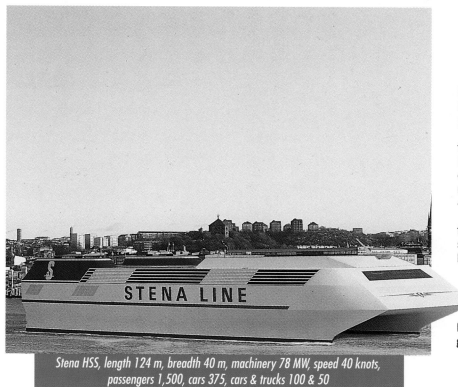

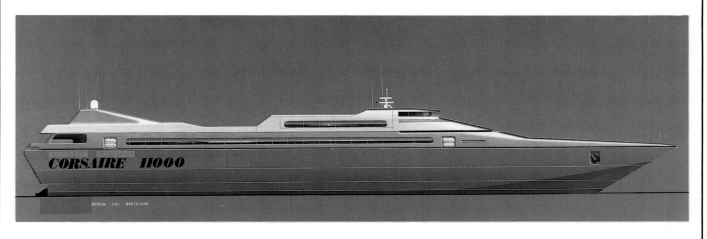

Mjellum & Karlsen 95m Monohull Kattegat on trials

Jane's

HIGH-SPEED
MARINE CRAFT

1995-96

Jane's Information Group Limited, Sentinel House, 163 Brighton Road, Coulsdon, Surrey CR5 2NH, UK
Jane's Information Group Inc, 1340 Braddock Place, Suite 300, Alexandria, VA 22314-1651, USA

Foreword

With the value of high-speed marine craft deliveries and orders surpassing last year's record, this has been another outstandingly active and interesting year. The technology of transportation by high-speed marine craft has now evolved to such an extent that fast ferries are not only replacing many conventional ferries but are forming the basis of a substantial new industry: fast marine transportation. It is hoped that this reference book will assist all its readers in the successful development and implementation of their contribution to this industry sector.

Speed at Sea

Throughout history there has been an enthusiasm and urgency for transportation at higher and higher speeds over land, sea and in the air. With the relatively recent development of fast, reliable and cost effective marine vehicles, this pressure has led to the very rapid development of the fast ferry market which includes new operators, new routes, new ship construction, increases in the demand for relevant materials and equipment and a new level of interest in the research and development of the associated technologies. Like so many transportation and communication industries, once started, the momentum for further development appears to increase and become almost self-sustaining. The only barriers to its continuing expansion are issues of safety and the environment, technological limitations and saturation of the market. Judging by the present status of conventional ferrying operations, the market for these fast ferries is a long way off saturation and so there is currently very little to slow this momentum of growth.

At present the difference between fast ferries and conventional ferries is quite clear, not only in their speed and rather marked styling but also in their construction and principal particulars. However as time progresses the conventional ferries are likely to change and incorporate much of the technology that is being developed within this industry. These developments include regulatory advances, where both construction and operational issues are traded against a given safety level, as well as the introduction of new materials and equipment alternatives. However, the trade-off between speed and vessel size (or operating costs against capital costs) to meet a given operational demand is likely to remain the principal design issue and will determine the speed of the vessel.

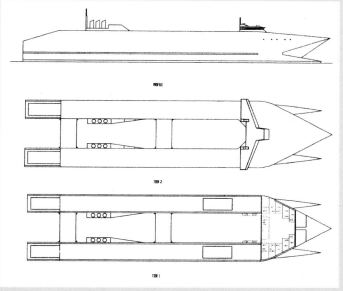

The InCat-designed 130 m fast catamaran freighter proposal which is to be constructed from two slender monohull craft joined with a large truss arrangement. This design has a deadweight capacity of 1500 tonnes and an operational speed of up to 50 knots. Negotiations are reported to be nearing agreement for this craft to be built at the newly formed South Australian Ships shipyard.

The massive structure of one hull of the Stena HSS being constructed at Finnyards. The first vessel is now due for delivery in Autumn 1995.

Although efforts have been made to numerically define the meaning of 'high speed' and 'fast' in relation to marine transportation (as discussed in earlier editions of this yearbook), it remains more useful to consider these as relative terms and not to try and fix a numerical definition which inevitably leads to confusion. However, with this in mind, the benefits of increased speed for the commercial transportation of passengers, vehicles and light cargo are numerous and include:

The opening of new routes that would otherwise be considered unworkable due to the block time involved if serviced by conventional vessels.

The flexibility within one craft to operate economically at low, medium and high speed to suit variations in payload demand, thus minimising capital investment for a given demand profile.

The ability to substantially reduce crewing costs by eliminating shift work and/or associated accommodation requirements.

The ability to serve the ever growing niche market for those wishing to get from A to B in as short a period of time as possible where a cost premium for very fast transit speeds is not a barrier.

Based on these benefits, investment in increased speed at sea is growing. Examples of this emphasis on speed can be seen in two of this year's deliveries which include the first of five 50 knot, 45 m, FBM Group Ltd Tricat catamarans delivered to Hong Kong and the 55 knot, 78 m, InCat K55 car carrier delivered to South America. Oceanfast in Australia is also known to be developing an air-lubricated system for its range of fast ferries in an attempt to radically increase speed over current state of the art designs.

The Fast Ferry Market

The size of the world market for fast ship construction was quantified recently at approximately 100,000 tonnes (displacement) over the last five years (1990 to 1995). This compares to a figure of half this value for the period 1985 to 1990. Indeed over the last 20 years the market size has doubled over every five year period. Current predictions are for this rate of growth to be maintained for the next five year period and it is the growing confidence in this assessment that is causing so many suppliers and businesses to look at this new industry.

Operation of fast ferries is now a multinational business. Hong Kong, with about 14% of current world operations, operates the greatest tonnage. Italy is close behind with 10% and the UK a close third with 8.5%. With the introduction of the large Stena

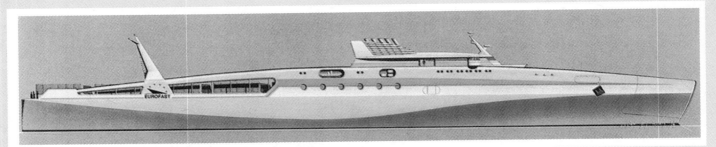

The EUROFAST EF80 design. This is a 30 knot, 177 m fast freight carrier designed by a European shipyard consortium, to carry 80 trailers with the 100 accompanying drivers. This design consortium is aiming to exploit the potentially large European market for fast short sea shipping vessels.

HSS craft and the Hoverspeed Super Seacat into UK waters later this year, this will make Europe the main centre by far for fast craft operations.

Looking at the type of craft constructed over this 20 year period and those currently on order, the semi-displacement catamaran vessel is overwhelmingly dominant, accounting for over half the total tonnage constructed. Due to the ever developing technology and changing requirements of the industry, this observation may not necessarily represent the future trend in craft types and indeed many of the larger vessels now on the drawing board are of a more conventional, but fast, monohull form. However the advantages accrued from multihull configurations, particularly stability and powering benefits, are such that they will undoubtedly continue to be built in large numbers.

Looking at the current new buildings and designs, it is obvious that there is an increasing emphasis being placed on the fast transportation of vehicles and freight as well as passengers. In the 1985 to 1990 period, fast ferries carrying vehicles were almost non-existent, with the notable exception of the Cross-Channel hovercraft. In the 1990 to 1995 period nearly half the fast ferry tonnage constructed had vehicle carrying capabilities. It is clear that this trend is having a dramatic effect on conventional ro-ro ferry operations with established operators considering very seriously the competition from fast ferries.

Fast freight carriers are also being very actively investigated on the basis that, if their economics can be favourably arranged, the market for such craft could be huge. Levels of interest in this area are high with very credible designs already on offer in many countries. One interesting design being proposed by International Catamarans is made up from two very slender monohull craft joined with a lightweight truss arrangement to form a catamaran structure. This reduces the structural weight over a conventional catamaran and improves the propulsion efficiency, redundancy and safety over an equivalent monohull arrangement.

Research and Development

Often a good pointer of things to come, research and development (R&D) into fast ship technology has been steadily increasing since the mid-1980s. Norway, Netherlands, Germany and Japan have recently completed substantial national research

programmes with subsequent research in these and other countries developing rapidly.

The UK has initiated a series of government funded research projects to be undertaken in the universities. Australia held a national shipbuilding 'workshop' in November 1994 bringing together government, academia and industry, with the result of focusing a series of diverse government R&D grant systems into one formal programme aimed at making fast ship construction a core export from Australia. Funding from the European Union for the study of fast ships for short sea shipping is being made available to a European consortium and some other substantial programmes have been privately funded by large shipbuilding concerns, particularly in Europe where a large slice of the potential market for these craft clearly exists.

The main areas of research in all these programmes includes the development of basic analytical design tools and techniques, the understanding of safety and economy of operation, developments of new materials and production techniques, industrial implementation of those developments and the production of a range of conceptual ship designs for market testing.

The 78 m InCat/AMD K55 on sea trials prior to delivery. With a maximum speed of 55 knots and carrying 63 cars and 450 passengers, this is the fastest car carrying catamaran built to date.

Fast Freight Carriers

There are three main bodies of interest pursuing the development of fast freight carriers. Firstly there are the technologists who now feel they have sufficient technology and experience for the successful development of these craft. Secondly shipyards, new and old, are looking to fill their orderbooks for the future and fast freighters present a potentially large and interesting market. Thirdly, industry in general is looking at ways of reducing the ever increasing 'interest' payable on cargo in transit. These pressures, combined with the general interest in being able to offer and receive a faster transportation and delivery service, have produced a flurry of design proposals for fast freight vessels over the past year.

The emphasis to date has been on the carrying of containers, particularly on short sea routes. Scandanavia has identified specific requirements with the export of fish and paper products from Norway and the import and export of car parts into and out of Sweden. Japan and Korea have a more general fast cargo transport requirement with the urgency in Japan for an alternative to road transport becoming daily more critical. Italy is already using relatively fast conventional shipping along its east and west coasts as an alternative to overland transportation.

With the need to keep weight to an absolute minimum on these fast ships, and with a general need to substantially speed up and

Hayabusa, at 100 m overall length, is the largest wave-piercing catamaran built to date carrying a modest 450 passengers and 94 cars at speeds of up to 36 knots. Perhaps a more interesting statistic is that this vessel was built by Kawasaki in Japan in six months from cutting of the first plates to final sea trials.

The TSL A70 is the 55 knot, 70 m trials craft for the proposed 127 m Techno Super Liner being developed in Japan to meet the needs of the country's modal shift from land to sea transportation.

improve cargo handling operations in port, it is likely that a container design and handling revolution will precede or at least run concurrently with the development of these new vessels.

When will this revolution in fast sea cargo transportation occur? This year in particular has demonstrated that the future introduction of fast freighters is no idle prediction. With Japan having recently completed a US$150 million study into fast freight transport to satisfy its domestic requirements, businesses in the USA are now involved in a US$11 million study into fast trans-Atlantic container transportation. Expectations are that large fast freight carriers will be operational within the next five years.

Regulations

With the new Code of Safety for High Speed Marine Craft having been finalised in June 1994 as IMO Resolution MSC.36(63) and scheduled for inclusion under SOLAS in January 1996, it is too early to judge the effect that this will have on vessel safety. However many of the fast ferries that have been built within the last two to three years have been designed on the basis of early drafts of this new code and further more, the code in its present form has been implemented on a voluntary basis since June 1994 by a number of marine administrations, including the Marine Safety Agency in the UK. Thankfully the number of serious accidents involving high-speed craft has to date been relatively small, although each incident is of course cause for concern and reflection. One issue which has become of particular interest is the performance of these craft in collisions, particularly groundings. With the 78 m wave-piercing catamaran Condor 11 being driven onto a low reef at 30 knots in Tasmania late in 1994 and with the bottom damage to the 42 m Saint Malo at high speed off Jersey in April 1995, it is evidently clear that bottom damage regulations are of paramount importance. The current regulations define a given, rather modest, damage length at which the vessel must retain an acceptable level of stability: it is hoped that this part of the new rules will come under close scrutiny before their final implementation to ensure that sufficient allowance is made for this type of incident.

The Next Five Years

With a projected fast ferry tonnage of 200,000 tonnes being constructed over the next five years, the industry is clearly maturing and providing a new challenge to established maritime thinking and operations. Not only is it replacing some existing tonnage but it is opening up new marine transportation opportunities. Whilst fast passenger ferries have been well established on many sheltered routes, fast passenger and vehicle ferries are now becoming established on relatively exposed routes in many parts of the world and it will not be long before fast freight carriers are also built and tested for short sea operations.

The knock-on effect for ship operators, shipyards, equipment and service suppliers and the technological research organisations is and will continue to be significant. Indeed it is clear from the contents of this book that many are already taking full advantage of this industry's rapid expansion.

We at Jane's wish all of you the very best for your particular contribution to this industry and hope that this yearbook is of interest and assistance to you. As always we are grateful to receive all comments, ideas and criticisms that you may have since we are committed to providing you with an informed, balanced and comprehensive reference source for this industry sector.

S J Phillips BSc(Hons) CEng MRINA
Seaspeed Technology Limited
The Old Mill
Botley
Hampshire SO3O 2GB
UK
Tel: +44 (1489) 795222
Fax: +44 (1489) 795333

Although not covered in this book due to the vessel's small dimensions, the 15 m VSV 50, designed and built by Paragon Mann, has a maximum speed of 55 knots in Sea State 3 and a range of up to 1200 nautical miles. Whilst this small vessel is of particular interest to military and paramilitary organisations, larger versions of this VSV (Very Slender Vessel) concept are now being developed for fast ferry operations.

The first gas turbine propelled 50 knot, 45 m FBM Group Ltd Tricat craft delivered to CTS-Parkview Ferry Services of Hong Kong. Four other Tricat craft are due for delivery later in 1995 and early 1996.

Preface

This annual reference book is aimed at providing a single balanced, informed and comprehensive data source for all those organisations with an interest in high-speed marine craft. There is no charge made for editorial entries in this book.

If your company or product is not included but you feel that it should be then please do contact me: I would be delighted to find a way to include all relevant information.

Whilst every effort is made to standardise and rationalise the information presented in this book, it is nonetheless not always possible to ensure that all the information is based on a common standard. For example the operational speeds quoted for each craft may be for slightly different displacement definitions. However, each year we spend a considerable time in rationalising the data and hope that in the future this will lead to still further improvements in data quality.

What constitutes high speed in the marine world has been the subject of much debate. It is clearly a relative term and for the purposes of this book, need not be defined quantitatively. However craft with speeds of less than 25 knots and with a length of less than 20 m are only included if they represent a development of particular interest.

It may be noted that the new International Maritime Organisation's Code of Safety for High Speed Marine Craft defines high speed on the basis of a speed to displacement coefficient. In this Code a high-speed craft is a craft capable of a maximum speed equal to or exceeding $V = 3.7(Displ)^{0.1667}$, where Displ is the maximum displacement in cubic metres and V is the speed in metres per second. Thus for a 100 tonne craft this speed is 15 knots, for a 1000 tonne craft it is 23 knots and for a 10,000 craft it is 35 knots.

Sea—General		Wind							Sea					
Sea State	Description	(Beaufort) Wind force	Description	Range	Wind Velocity	Wave Height			Significant Range Periods	Periods of Maximum Energy of Spectra Tmax=Tc	Average Period Tz	Average Wave Length Lw	Minimum Fetch	Minimum Duration
						Average	Significant	Average of One-Tenth Highest						
	Sea like a mirror	U	Calm	1 knot	—	—	—	—	—	—	—	—	—	—
0	Ripples with the appearance of scales are formed, but without foam crests	1	Light airs	1-3 knots	2 knots	0.04 ft	0.01 ft 0.01 ft	0.09 ft	1.2 s	0.75	0.5	10 in	5 n miles	18 min
1	Small wavelets; short but pronounced crests have a glossy appearance, but do not break	2	Light breeze	4-6 knots	5 knots	0.3 ft	0.5 ft	0.6 ft	0.4-2.8 s	1.9	1.3	6.7 ft	8 n miles	39 min
2	Large wavelets; crests begin to break. Foam of glossy appearance. Perhaps scattered with horses	3	Gentle breeze	7-10 knots	8.5 knots 10 knots	0.8 ft 1.1 ft	1.3 ft 1.8 ft	1.6 ft 2.3 ft	0.8-5.0 s 1.0-6.0 s	3.2 3.2	2.3 2.7	20 ft 27 ft	9.8 n miles 10 n miles	1.7 h 2.4 h
3	Small waves, becoming larger; fairly frequent white horses	4	Moderate breeze	11-16 knots	12 knots 13.5 knots 14 knots 16 knots	1.6 ft 2.1 ft 2.3 ft 2.9 ft	2.6 ft 3.3 ft 3.6 ft 4.7 ft	3.3 ft 4.2 ft 4.6 ft 6.0 ft	1.0-7.0 s 1.4-7.6 s 1.5-7.8 s 2.0-8.8 s	4.5 5.1 5.3 6.0	3.2 3.6 3.8 4.3	40 ft 52 ft 59 ft 71 ft	18 n miles 24 n miles 28 n miles 40 n miles	3.8 h 4.8 h 5.2 h 6.6 h
4	Moderate waves, taking a more pronounced long form; many white horses are formed (chance of some spray)	5	Fresh breeze	17-21 knots	18 knots 19 knots 20 knots	3.7 ft 4.1 ft 4.6 ft	5.9 ft 6.6 ft 7.3 ft	7.5 ft 8.4 ft 9.3 ft	2.5-10.0 s 2.8-10.6 s 3.0-11.1 s	6.8 7.2 7.5	4.8 5.1 5.4	90 ft 99 ft 111 ft	55 n miles 65 n miles 75 n miles	8.3 h 9.2 h 10 h
5 6	Large waves begin to form; white crests are more extensive everywhere (probably some spray)	6	Strong breeze	22-27 knots	22 knots 24 knots 24.5 knots 26 knots	5.5 ft 6.6 ft 6.8 ft 7.7 ft	8.8 ft 10.5 ft 10.9 ft 12.3 ft	11.2 ft 13.3 ft 13.8 ft 15.6 ft	3.4-12.2 s 3.7-13.5 s 3.8-13.6 s 4.0-14.5 s	8.3 9.0 9.2 9.8	5.9 6.4 6.6 7.0	134 ft 160 ft 164 ft 188 ft	100 n miles 130 n miles 140 n miles 180 n miles	12 h 14 h 15 h 17 h
7	Sea heaps up, and white foam from breaking waves begins to be blown in streaks along the direction of the wind (Spindrift begins to be seen)	7	Moderate gale	28-33 knots	28 knots 30 knots 30.5 knots 32 knots	8.9 ft 10.3 ft 10.6 ft 11.6 ft	14.3 ft 16.4 ft 16.9 ft 18.6 ft	18.2 ft 20.8 ft 21.5 ft 23.6 ft	4.5-15.5 s 4.7-16.7 s 4.8-17.0 s 5.0-17.5 s	10.6 11.3 11.5 12.1	7.5 8.0 8.2 8.6	212 ft 250 ft 258 ft 285 ft	230 n miles 280 n miles 290 n miles 340 n miles	20 h 23 h 24 h 27 h
7	Moderate high waves of greater length; edges of crests break into spindrift. The foam is blown in well-marked streaks along the direction of the wind. Spray affects visibility	8	Fresh gale	34-40 knots	34 knots 36 knots 37 knots 38 knots 40 knots	13.1 ft 14.8 ft 15.6 ft 16.4 ft 18.2 ft	21.0 ft 23.6 ft 24.9 ft 26.3 ft 29.1 ft	26.7 ft 30.0 ft 31.6 ft 33.4 ft 37.0 ft	5.5-18.5 s 5.8-19.7 s 6-20.5 s 6.2-20.8 s 6.5-21.7 s	12.8 13.6 13.9 14.3 15.1	9.1 9.6 9.9 10.2 10.7	322 ft 363 ft 376 ft 392 ft 444 ft	420 n miles 500 n miles 530 n miles 600 n miles 710 n miles	30 h 34 h 37 h 38 h 42 h
8	High waves. Dense streaks of foam along the direction of the wind. Sea begins to roll. Visibility affected.	9	Strong gale	41-37 knots	42 knots 44 knots 46 knots	20.1 ft 22.0 ft 24.1 ft	32.1 ft 35.2 ft 38.5 ft	40.8 ft 44.7 ft 48.9 ft	7-23 s 7-24.2 s 7-25 s	15.8 16.6 17.3	11.3 11.8 12.3	492 ft 534 ft 590 ft	830 n miles 960 n miles 1110 n miles	47 h 52 h 57 h
9	Very high waves with long overhanging crests. The resulting foam is in great patches and is blown in dense white streaks along the direction of the wind. On the whole, the surface of the sea takes on a white appearance. The rolling of the sea becomes heavy and shocklike. Visibility is affected	10	Whole* gale	48-55 knots	40 knots 50 knots 51.5 knots 52 knots 54 knots	26.2 ft 28.4 ft 30.2 ft 30.8 ft 33.2 ft	41.9 ft 45.5 ft 48.3 ft 49.2 ft 53.1 ft	53.2 ft 57.8 ft 61.3 ft 62.5 ft 67.4 ft	7.5-26 s 7.5-27 s 8-28.2 s 8-28.5 s 8-29.5 s	18.1 18.8 19.4 19.6 20.4	12.9 13.4 13.8 13.9 14.5	650 ft 700 ft 736 ft 750 ft 810 ft	1250 n miles 1420 n miles 1560 n miles 1610 n miles 1800 n miles	63 h 69 h 73 h 75 h 81 h
	Exceptionally high waves. Sea completely covered with long white patches of foam lying in direction of wind. Everywhere edges of wave crests are blown into froth. Visibility affected	11	Storm*	56-63 knots	56 knots 59.5 knots	35.7 ft 40.3 ft	57.1 ft 64.4 ft	72.5 ft 81.8 ft	8.5-31 s 10-32 s	21.1 22.4	15 15.9	910 ft 985 ft	2100 n miles 2500 n miles	88 h 101 h
	Air filled with foam and spray. Sea white with driving spray. Visibility very seriously affected	12	Hurricane*	64-71 knots	>64 knots	>46.6 ft	74.5 ft	94.6 ft	10-35 s	24.1	17.2	—	—	—

* For hurricane winds (and often whole gale and storm winds) required durations and reports are barely attained. Seas are therefore not fully arisen

DEFINITIONS OF SYMBOLS AND UNITS

Four of the seven base units of the SI (Système International d'Unités) which are used in this book are:

length	metre	m
mass	kilogram	kg
time	second	s
electric current	ampere	A

Decimal unit	Quantity	Formula
Pa (Pascal)	pressure or stress	N/m^2
N (Newton)	force	$kg.m/s^2$
W (Watt)	power	J/s
Hz (Hertz)	frequency	$1/s$ (1 Hertz = 1 cycle per second in previous British practice)
V (Volt)	electric potential difference	W/A

Other units		Quantity
dB	(decibel)	sound pressure level, re 0.0002 microbar
dBA	(decibel)	sound level, A-weighted, re 0.0002 microbar

CONVERSIONS

Length
1 km = 0.6214 statute mile = 0.540 nautical mile
1 m = 3.281 ft
1 cm = 0.3937 in
1 mm = 0.0394 in

Area
1 ha (hectare = 10 000 m^2) = 2.471 acres
1 m^2 = 10.764 ft^2

Volume
1 m^3 = 35.315 ft^3
1 litre = 0.220 Imperial gallon = 0.264 US gallon

Velocity
1 km/h = 0.621 statute mile/h = 0.540 knots
1 m/s = 3.281 ft/s

Acceleration
1 m/s^2 = 3.281 ft/s^2

Mass
1 t (tonne) = 1000 kg = 0.9842 long ton = 2204.62 lb = 1.1023 short tons
1 kg (kilogram) = 2.205 lb
1 g (gram) = 0.002205 lb

Force
1 MN (meganewton) = 100.36 long ton force
1 kgf = 2.205 lbf
1 kp (kilopond) = 2.205 lbf
1 N (newton) = 0.2248 lbf (The Newton is that force which, applied to a mass of 1 kilogram, gives it an acceleration of 1 m/s^2.)

Moment of force (torque)
1 Nm = 0.7376 lbf.ft

Pressure, stress
1 atm	(standard atmosphere)	= 14.696 lbf/in^2
1 bar	(10^5 pascal)	= 14.504 lbf/in^2
1 kPa	(kN/m^2)	= 20.885 lbf/ft^2
1 Pa	(N/m^2)	= 0.020885 lbf/ft^2

Power
1 metric horsepower (ch, ps) = 0.7355 kW = 1.014 horsepower (550 ft lb/s)
1 kW = 1.341 horsepower (1 horsepower = 550 ft lb/s) = 1.360 metric horsepower

Nautical mile
The International Nautical Mile is equivalent to the average length of a minute of latitude and corresponds to a latitude of 45° and a distance of 1852 m = 6076.12 ft.

Fuel consumption
Specific fuel consumption, 1.0 g/kWh = 0.001644 lb/hph (hp = 550 ft lb/s)
1.0 litre/h = 0.220 Imperial gallon/h
= 0.264 US gallon/h

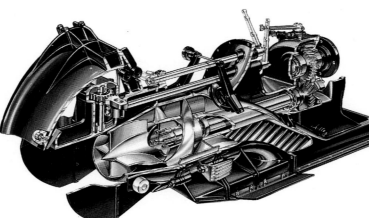

Classified list of advertisers

The companies advertising in this publication have informed us that they are involved in the fields of manufacture indicated below:

Their editorial entries appear on the pages detailed in brackets.

Craft Builders

Air cushion vehicles
The Cincinnati Gear Company .... (411)
Oceanfast Ferries .... (134, 212)
Royal Schelde .... (39, 157, 250)

High-speed multihull vessels
Abeking & Rasmussen .... (228)
A Fai High Performance Ships .... (145)
The Cincinnati Gear Company .... (411)
Fincantieri .... (27, 90, 238)
Finnyards .... (142)
Oceanfast Ferries .... (134, 212)
Royal Schelde .... (39, 157, 250)
Swede Ships .... (171)

High-speed monohull craft
Abeking & Rasmussen .... (228)
A Fai High Performance Ships .... (145)
The Cincinnati Gear Company .... (411)
Bazan, Empresa Nacional .... (255)
Fincantieri .... (27, 90, 238)
Finnyards .... (142)
Leroux & Lotz Naval Division .... (226)
Mjellem & Karlsen .... (251)
Royal Schelde .... (39, 157, 250)

Trinity Marine Group .... (282)

Hydrofoils
A Fai High Performance Ships .... (145)
The Cincinnati Gear Company .... (411)

Swath vessels (semi-submerged catamarans (SSC)
Abeking & Rasmussen .... (228)
The Cincinnati Gear Company .... (411)
Finnyards .... (142)

Civil operators

Principal engineering components
Engines
Bazan, Empresa Nacional .... (255)
The Cincinnati Gear Company .... (411)
Fincantieri .... (27, 90, 238)
GEC Alsthom Ruston Diesels .... (381)
GE Marine & Industrial Engine & Engine
  Services .... (394)
MAN Nutzahrzeuge .... (364)
Vosper Thornycroft Controls .... (261)

Marine propellers
Bazan, Empresa Nacional .... (255)

Fincantieri .... (27, 90, 238)
KaMeWa .... (428, 440)
Vosper Thornycroft Controls .... (261)

Ride control systems
Vosper Thornycroft Controls .... (261)

Transmissions
The Cincinnati Gear Company .... (411)

Water-jet units
Castoldi .... (434)
KaMeWa .... (428, 440)
Lips Jets .... (426, 436)
MJP Waterjets .... (445)
Vosper Thornycroft Controls .... (261)

Services

Consultants and designers
Abeking & Rasmussen .... (228)
A Fai High Performance Ships .... (145)
Bazan, Empresa Nacional .... (255)
The Cincinnati Gear Company .... (411)
Fincantieri .... (27, 90, 238)

New Entries in this Edition

Company	Section	Country
Aero-Marine Engineering	Consultants and Designers	USA
Air Craft Corporation	Consultants and Designers	USA
Alaska Travel	Civil Operators	USA
Albadria	Civil Operators	Italy
Alufast International Pty Ltd	High-Speed Multihull Vessels	Australia
Astra Bay Enterprises	High-Speed Multihull Vessels	Australia
Australian Maritime Engineering Crc Ltd	Consultants and Designers	Australia
Bahtera Segara Persanda	Civil Operators	Indonesia
Bali Hai Cruises	Civil Operators	Indonesia
Bar Harbor Whale Watch	Civil Operators	USA
Bintan Resort Ferries	Civil Operators	Singapore
Blue and Gold Fleet	Civil Operators	USA
City Jet	Civil Operators	Estonia
Dalian Yuan Feng Ferry Company	Civil Operators	China, People's Republic
Dodecanese Hydrofoils	Civil Operators	Greece
Dong Bu Express	Civil Operators	Korea, South
Ferries Australia	High-Speed Multihull Vessels	Australia
Ferry Lineas	Civil Operators	Argentina
Forma Ltd	Consultants and Designers	CIS
Geraldton Boat Builders	High-Speed Monohull Craft	Australia
Gråhunbus	Civil Operators	Denmark
Hallig-Und Inselreederei	Civil Operators	Germany
Hang Tong High Speed Ship Development Co Ltd	High-Speed Multihull Vessels and Addenda	China, People's Republic
Harbor Bay Maritime	Civil Operators	USA
Hermes	Civil Operators	Greece
Holen Mek Verksted A/S	High-Speed Multihull Vessels	Norway
Iris Catamarans	Addenda	France
Isle of Man Steam Packet Company	Civil Operators	UK
JCL High-Speed Marine Craft Consultancy	Consultants and Designers	UK
Kenai Fjords Tours	Civil Operators	USA
Korea Research Institute of Ships and Ocean Engineering	Consultants and Designers	Korea, South
Kumsan Hungup	Civil Operators	Korea, South
Kyushi Ferry Boat Company	Civil Operators	Japan
Kyushu Railway Company	Civil Operators	Japan
Lada Langkawi Holdings	Civil Operators	Malaysia
Leprado	Civil Operators	French Polynesia
Lineas Fred Olsen	Civil Operators	Spain
Mackenzies Marine	Civil Operators	Australia
Marinteknik Shipbuilders (S) Pte Ltd	Addenda	Singapore
Maritime Services Ltd	Consultants and Designers	UK
Nevesbu	Consultants and Designers	Netherlands
Nichols Brothers Boat Builders Inc	Small-Waterplane-Area Twin-Hull Vessels	USA
Niigata Engineering Co Ltd	Engines	Japan
North American Marine	Water-Jet Units	USA
Paradis Nautica	Consultants and Designers	Norway
Peterson Builders Inc	High-Speed Multihull Vessels	USA
Quadrimaran International	Consultants and Designers	USA
Quicksilver	Civil Operators	Indonesia
Robert Allen Ltd	Consultants and Designers	Canada
Rottnest Express Pty Ltd	Civil Operators	Australia
Royal Schelde BV	High-Speed Multihull Vessels and High-Speed Monohull Craft	Netherlands
SPI Maritime	Civil Operators	French Polynesia
Samsung Heavy Industries Company Ltd	Air Cushion Vehicles	Korea, South
Santa Lines	Civil Operators	Greece
Semo Company Ltd	Addenda	Korea, South
Stolkraft Pty Ltd	Consultants and Designers	Australia
Sukkula	Civil Operators	Estonia
Sun Island Cruises	Civil Operators	Trinidad
Tallink Express	Civil Operators	Estonia
Techni Carène	Consultants and Designers	France
Tirrenia Navigazione	Civil Operators	Italy
Transal-Aks Engineering Co	Consultants and Designers	CIS
UR Tekniks S.L.	Consultants and Designers	Spain
WaveMaster International Pty Ltd	Addenda	Australia
Westamarin A/S	High-Speed Multihull Vessels and Addenda	Norway
Won Kwang Shipping	Civil Operators	Korea, South
Yantai Marine	Civil Operators	China, People's Republic

AIR CUSHION VEHICLES

Company Listing by Country

Australia
Austal Ships Pty Ltd
International Shipyards Pty Ltd
NQEA Australia Pty Ltd

Belgium
Scheepswerf SKB
Polyship NV

Canada
Canair Hovercraft Inc

China, People's Republic
Bai Hai Shipyard
Cactec
Dagu Shipyard
Dong Feng Shipyard
Huangpu Shipyard
Hudong Shipyard
Maric
Shanghai Aircraft Factory
Zhong Hua Shipyard

Commonwealth of Independent States
Almaz Shipyard
Astrakhan Shipyard
Gorkovski Philial CNII im akad.
A N Krylova
Krasnoye Sormovo Shipyard
A A Zhdanov
Marijski Polytechnical Institute
Neptun CDB Corp
St Petersberg Shipyard

Sosnovskaya Shipyard
Vympel Central Design Bureau

France
Ackerman Industrie
DCN
DRET
ACH
CMN

Germany
Blohm+Voss AG

Italy
Fincantieri Cantieri Navali Italiani Spa
SEC

Japan
Mitsubishi Heavy Industries Ltd
Mitsui Engineering & Shipbuilding Company Ltd
Technological Research Association of Techno-Superliner

Korea, South
Korea Tacoma Marine Industries Ltd
Samsung Heavy Industries Company Ltd
Semo Company Ltd

Netherlands
Hovertrans BV
Royal Schelde BV
Koninklijke Maatschappij de Schelde
Tille Shipyards BV

Norway
Kværner A/S Fast Ferries
Kværner Mandal A/S
Ulstein International A/S
Westamarin West A/S

Singapore
Singapore Shipbuilding and Engineering Ltd

Spain
Chaconsa SA
FM-Aerodeslizadores

Sweden
Karlskronavarvet AB

United Kingdom
ABS Hovercraft Ltd
Air Vehicles Ltd
Aluminium Shipbuilders Ltd
British Hovercraft Corporation
Griffon Hovercraft Ltd
Hovermarine International Ltd
Ingles Hovercraft Associates Ltd
Osprey Hovercraft UK Ltd
Slingsby Aviation Ltd

United States of America
Avondale Boat Division
Neoteric Hovercraft Inc
Textron Marine & Land Systems

AUSTRALIA

AUSTAL SHIPS PTY LTD

100 Clarence Beach, Henderson, Perth, Western
Australia 6166, Australia

Telephone: +61 (9) 410 1111
Telefax: +61 (9) 410 2564

John Rothwell, *Managing Director*
Christopher Norman, *Director, Marketing and Sales*
Garry Heys, *Director and General Manager*
Kevin Stanley, *Director and General Manager*

Although Austal Ships have yet to build an air
cushion vehicle, the 38 m ACC is being marketed as
their fastest passenger ferry design. This design is
the result of extensive research and the construction
of a large scale prototype.

38 m AIR CUSHION CATAMARAN
Principal Particulars

Length overall	38.5 m
Beam	11.8 m
Draught, hullborne	2.0 m
Draught, on-cushion	0.6 m
Passengers	334
Fuel capacity	7000 l
Water capacity	1000 l
Propulsive power	2 × 2000 kW
Lift power	2 × 400 kW
Maximum speed	50 knots

UPDATED

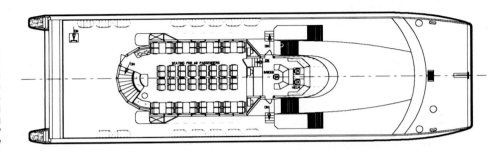

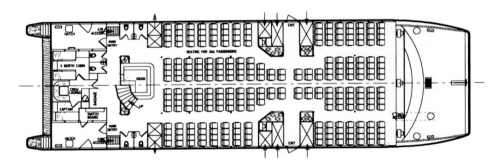

*38 m air cushion catamaran, general
arrangement*
1995

NQEA AUSTRALIA PTY LTD

62-90 Cook Street, PO Box 1105, Portsmith, Cairns,
Queensland 4870, Australia

Telephone: +61 (70) 527222
Telex: 48087 AA
Telefax: +61 (70) 352812/352520

D G Fry, *Chairman*
E W Graham, *General Manager, Commercial*
R Bannah, *Marketing Manager*
R D Rookwood, *Senior Design Engineer*
M Richards, *Chief Naval Architect*

In 1964 NQEA entered the shipbuilding industry
with the construction of a range of vessels including

Australia's 'Attack Class' patrol boats, and the construction of several medium-sized craft, including
tug boats, fishing trawlers and 22 workboats for the
Australian Defence Department.

In 1977, NQEA was the successful tenderer for 14
(of a total of 15) 42 m 'Fremantle Class' patrol craft
for the Australian Navy, the lead vessel being built in
the UK by Brooke Marine. Taking 85 weeks to con-

NQEA-built AP1-88

struct the craft, NQEA was delivering at a rate of one every 14 weeks.

NQEA has built a number of high-speed catamarans under licence from International Catamarans Designs Pty Ltd and AP1-88s under licence from British Hovercraft Corporation, the first order for the latter having been received in February 1986.

AP1-88 300 MODEL

In 1990 NQEA converted and delivered to Chominco, a Canadian mining company based in British Columbia, the AP1-88 previously known as *Hover Mirage II*. Chominco has renamed the craft *Hover Freighter*. The passenger cabin has been significantly reduced in size, only allowing for 16 passengers. The reduced cabin size creates a well-deck capable of lifting up to 11 tonnes in its remodelled form. The modification was formally approved by

Craft built	Name	Seats	Launched	Operator/Owner
BHC AP1-88	*Benidorm* (ex *Courier**)	81	December 1986	Hovertravel Ltd
BHC AP1-88	*Hover Mirage*	70	March 1987	Anfibios, Uruguay
BHC AP1-88	*Hover Freighter*	16	April 1987	Chominco Co, Canada
BHC AP1-88	*Tienpengyang I*	94	November 1989	Tien Peng Yang Hovertravel Corporation
BHC AP1-88		101		(not completed)
BHC AP1-88		101	July 1990	(not completed)

*Arrived UK December 1988 from Australia, GH 2108, fitted with 100 seats and later sold to Real Maritima de Cruceros, Spain. Bought by Hovertravel Ltd in UK June 1992

BHC, which designated the NQEA design the AP1-88 300 model.

VERIFIED

OCEANFAST FERRIES PTY LTD

18 Clarence Beach, Henderson, Western Australia 6166, Australia

Telephone: +61 (9) 410 1866
Telefax: +61 (9) 410 1927

David Browning, *Manager*

Oceanfast Ferries is a member of the Oceanfast Marine Group which includes Oceanfast International, Motor Yacht International and Ferries Australia.

The company signed an agreement with Ulstein International of Norway in February 1994 to transfer the technology developed by Ulstein for the UT 928 Air Cushion Catamaran, and by early 1995 had completed the construction of two UT 928 vessels, one with Ulstein Z drives and one with KaMeWa 63SII waterjets.

UT 928 AIR CUSHION CATAMARAN

This design has been arranged to accept water-jet or Speed-Z propulsors, with the Speed-Z configuration offering more than a 2 knot advantage.

Principal Particulars

Length overall	37.6 m
Beam	11.8 m
Draught, on-cushion	2.4 m
Draught, off-cushion	3.3 m
Passengers	350
Crew	9
Fuel capacity	14 000 l
Water capacity	1500 l
Main engines	2 × MTU 16V 396 TE 74L diesels
Lift fans	2 × MTU 12V 183 TE 72
Generators	2 × MTU 6V 183 AA 51
Propulsors	2 × Ulstein Speed-Z drives
Maximum speed	48 knots
Operational speed	45 knots

UPDATED

Oceanfast Ferries' first UT 928 fitted with Ulstein Speed-Z drives   *1995*

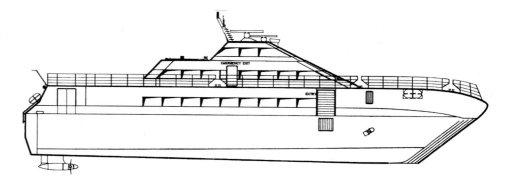

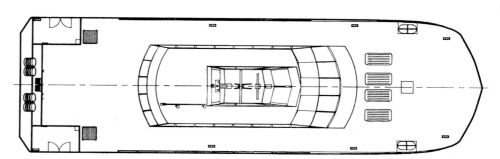

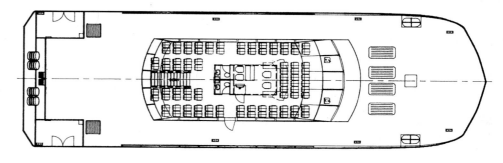

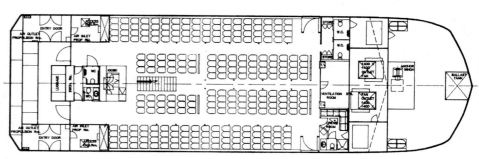

Oceanfast Ferries UT 928 air cushion catamaran   *1995*

BELGIUM

SCHEEPSWERF SKB POLYSHIP NV

H. Baelskaai 6, 8400 Ostend, Belgium

Telephone: +32 (59) 324720
Telefax: +32 (59) 325938

L Longueville, *Chairman and Managing Director*
J C Renault, *Sales Manager*

NV Scheepswerf 'Béliard' Polyship was taken over in 1994 by SKB which now markets the SES designs.

29.6 m/32.6 m SES FERRIES

Constructed in composite materials for the fast transport of passengers on routes of 400 to 448 nm in sheltered waters. Adapted versions (SES and/or Catamaran) are offered for navigation on large lakes and major rivers, and mixed passenger/freight versions of craft can also be offered.

The hull is built in single skin GRP with longitudinal stiffeners and web frames. The main deck, with deckhouse, is built in a sandwich material construction. An automatic ride system is provided.

Passenger accommodation is divided into two classes although standard outfitting of both passenger saloons can also be offered. Both the passenger saloons and wheelhouse are fully air-conditioned.

29.6 m SES FERRY
Principal Particulars

Length overall	29.6 m
Beam	10.8 m
Draught, hullborne	1.7 m
Draught, on-cushion	0.9 m
Crew	6
Passengers	192
Fuel capacity	5900 l
Water capacity	1200 l
Maximum speed	40 knots
Range	448 nm

Classification: Lloyd's Register of Shipping + A1 Air Cushion Vehicle Group 2 + LMC UMS for machinery. These vessels are built and outfitted to the IMO-code of Safety of Dynamically Supported Vessels Res. A 373 (x) and BZI (Belgian Maritime Inspectorate) regulations.
Propulsion: Engines, propulsion: 2 × Deutz MWM TBD 604 V16.
Engines, lift: 2 × Deutz MWM TBD 234 V8.
Propulsion: 2 × KaMeWa 63 SII water-jets.
Gearboxes: 2 × ZF BW 755.
Lift fans: Air Vehicles Ltd.

32.6 m SES FERRY
Principal Particulars

Length overall	32.6 m
Beam	10.8 m
Draught, hullborne	1.85 m
Draught, on-cushion	0.9 m
Crew	6
Passengers	224
Fuel capacity	9450 l
Water capacity	2000 l
Maximum speed	40 knots
Range	400 nm

Propulsion: Engines, propulsion: 2 × Deutz MWM TBD 604 V16.
Engines, lift: 2 × Deutz MWM TBD 234 V8.
Propulsion: 2 × KaMeWa 63 SII water-jets.
Gearboxes: 2 × ZF BU 755.
Lift fans: Air Vehicles Ltd.

UPDATED

SES Manto   *1994*

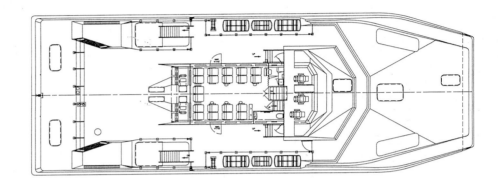

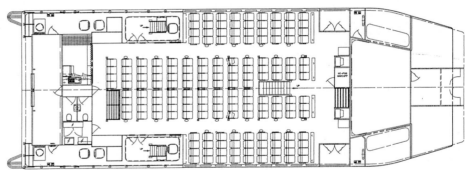

General arrangement of 29.6 m SES Manto   *1994*

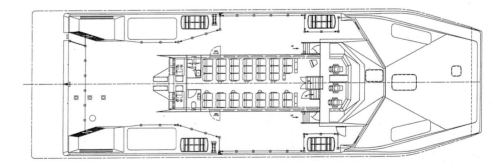

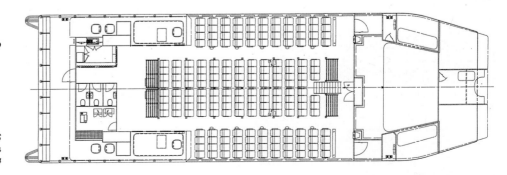

General arrangement of 32.6 m SES
Alexandros
1994

CANADA

CANAIR HOVERCRAFT INC

PO Box 478, 110 Industrial Avenue, Carleton Place, Ontario, Canada K7C 3P5

Telephone: +1 (613) 257 8332
Telefax: +1 (613) 257 7948

Ron Fishlock, *President and Technical Director*
Jim Wells, *Marketing and Sales Director*
Peter Howe, *Manager of Manufacturing*
Ron Johnstone, *Manager of Field Service and Training*

Canair was founded in 1964 on the basis of its market research that showed a global market existed for a range of utility/commercial grade light hovercraft. The Canair series of modular structured hovercraft can perform many duties currently not possible with traditional surface craft. Canair hovercraft can also provide a more cost-effective transportation solution in many areas where helicopters are now being used.

Some unique and effective features shared by all Canair models are: the quickly deployable folding sides that can be used as storage compartments; the simple rudder/reverse system that provides control in forward flight and when braking and reversing; the anti-snag skirt attachment system; the modular structure that reduces the down time and costs associated with major structural repairs; this later

Canair 504 L   **1995**

feature provides the flexibility needed for configuration changes so that all the models can be adapted to a range of individual roles.

Construction of the first Canair 504 L model was completed in the early Summer of 1994 and is being evaluated for certification by the Canadian Coast Guard.

A second Canair 504 L is being built to order and the first Canair 509 LT has been ordered and is scheduled for delivery in the Spring of 1995 to HoverTour Canada in Quebec.

UPDATED

CHINA, PEOPLE'S REPUBLIC

BAI HAI SHIPYARD

Qing Dao, People's Republic of China

A Type 7217 craft was completed at Bai Hai Shipyard in December 1993 and operates as a passenger ferry at Qiao-Zhou Gulf, near Qing Dao City.

VERIFIED

CACTEC

CHINA AIR CUSHION TECHNOLOGY DEVELOPMENT CORPORATION

41 Changdi Road, Tianjin, People's Republic of China

Telephone: +86 (22) 311984/313544
Telefax: +86 (22) 3333

Hu Wenliang, *Manager*

Branch office: 132 Jichang Road, Shanghai, People's Republic of China

Zhu Bi Yu, *General Manager*

Telephone: +86 (21) 377 0539
Telex: 33157 CSQXS CN

(DESIGN, RESEARCH, DEVELOPMENT AND PRODUCTION ASSISTANCE ORGANISATION)

Formed in 1984, CACTEC is a subsidiary of the China State Shipbuilding Corporation (CSSC). It is a specialised business corporation, working jointly with MARIC on a wide variety of applications of the air cushion principle with emphasis on the research, development, design and production of amphibious and sidewall (SES) hovercraft. Craft operated by CACTEC are given in the Operators section of this edition.

VERIFIED

DAGU SHIPYARD

Yangzhabei, Xigu, Tang-gu, Tianjin, People's Republic of China

Telephone: +86 (22) 3901 Ext 98
Telefax: +86 (22) 3128

Young Tze-Wen, *Director*

Building of various types of hovercraft (amphibious and sidewall), and design and building of medium and small size steel vessels.

TYPE 7203

Derived from Types 713 and 717 (built in the 1970s), Type 7203 is a high-speed passenger ferry for use on coastal and sheltered waters. Alternative applications include coastguard patrol and port/harbour fire-fighting duties.

Built at the Dagu Shipyard, Tianjin, the prototype was launched in September 1982 and underwent trials on the Hai river and in Tang-gu in late 1982.

Principal Particulars

Length overall	22.2 m
Beam	6.9 m
Draught, hullborne	2.06 m
Draught, on-cushion	1.22 m

Type 7203 fast ferry   **1987**

Weight, maximum	35 t
Passengers	81-100
Propulsive power	2 × 335 kW
Maximum speed	30 knots
Operational speed	26 knots
Range	180 nm

Structure: The skirt is a loop and segment type in bonded natural rubber coated fabric.
Propulsion: A multi-fan system improves seakeeping performance. There are three centrifugal fans of different diameters fitted separately in the bow, amidships and stern. Each feeds air to the bow

and stern skirts and the air cushion at different volumes and pressures. Diameters of the bow, amidships and stern fans are 800 mm, 1200 mm and 450 mm respectively. The lift system is powered by a single 12150C high-speed diesel rated at 226 kW at 1500 rpm. The lift engine directly drives the amidships and stern fans. The bow fan is driven via a hydraulic pump and motor. Total lift power is about 188 kW. Disengaging the bow fan reduces lift power consumption to about 76 kW in calm waters. When operating in waves the bow fan is required since it affects the craft's trim. Propulsive power is supplied by two 12150CZ water-cooled, turbocharged, high-speed marine diesels, each rated at 335 kW at 1450 rpm. Each drives a three-bladed propeller via a V-type transmission.

Control: Craft direction controlled by twin rudders and by differential use of water propellers.

Outfit: In standard configuration the passenger cabin seats 81 passengers. If required, seating capacity can be increased to 100. There are two aisles between the seats, 800 mm wide.

Jinxiang

Jinxiang, a Type 7203, is a joint project of the Marine Design and Research Institute of China and the Dagu Shipyard, Tianjin. In 1983 it successfully completed a 128 km maiden voyage along the Yangtze, from Shanghai to Vantong, in under three hours.

VERIFIED

DONG FENG SHIPYARD

Jiuxi, Hangzhou, Zhejiang, People's Republic of China

Telephone: +86 (571) 791695/791694
Telefax: +86 (571) 554163

Li Leng-Xing, *Director*

TYPE 7210

Two fully amphibious utility hovercraft Type 7210 were completed in May 1985. They were designed by MARIC and constructed by Dong Feng Shipyard, Hangzhou.

Principal Particulars

Length overall	9.85 m
Beam	3.40 m
Weight, maximum	4.7 t
Payload	0.8 t
Maximum speed	24 knots
Range	135 nm

Structure: Built in medium strength seawater resistant aluminium alloy of riveted construction. The skirt is of the bag and finger type in rubberised fabric, low temperature resistant down to −20°C. The total skirt height is 500 mm.

Propulsion: The craft is powered by air-cooled marine diesels. Lift is provided by a Deutz BF6L 912 diesel engine driving via a gearbox a centrifugal aluminium fan in a gearbox. Thrust is supplied by another diesel, a Deutz BF6L 913 driving via a transmission shaft and elastic coupling, a 1.8 m, five-blade, ducted air propeller built in GRP.

The first two craft were delivered to units of the oil industry for transporting people and equipment in offshore areas and marshes.

TYPE 717 II

This craft is a water-jet-propelled, rigid sidewall air cushion vehicle, designed by MARIC as a high-speed inland water passenger ferry for use on shallow water and is a development of the 717 design. The Type 717 II *Ming Jiang* passenger ferry hovercraft was completed in October 1984 and was delivered to the Chongqing Ship Transportation Company as a high-speed passenger ferry. The Type 717 *Chongqing* sidewall hovercraft was also completed in Dong Feng Shipyard, in September 1984, and was delivered to Chongqing Ferry Boat Company as a high-speed passenger craft operating on the rapids of the Yangtze river. A further Type 717 III was delivered in September 1989.

Structure: The sidewalls are built in GRP, but other parts of the hull and superstructure are built in riveted, high strength aluminium alloy.

Principal Particulars

	717 II	717 III
Length overall	20.4 m	21.4 m
Beam	4.54 m	4.54 m
Weight, maximum	21.2 t	23 t
Passengers	54-60	70
Propulsive power	2 × 224 kW	2 × 224 kW
Maximum speed	24 knots	23 knots
Range	220 nm	135 nm

Propulsion: Integrated system powered by two 12 V 150C marine diesels rated at 224 kW continuous. Two engines are mounted aft and each drives a 600 mm diameter centrifugal fan, Type 4-72 for lift and, via an elastic coupling, universal joint and transmission shaft, a mixed flow water-jet pump. Another bow fan is driven via a hydraulic pump and motor by the integrated power system. The Type 717 III is powered by two Cummins high-speed diesel NTA-855-M engines 298 kW (maximum) each.

MARIC-designed Type 7210 built by Dong Feng Shipyard   1986

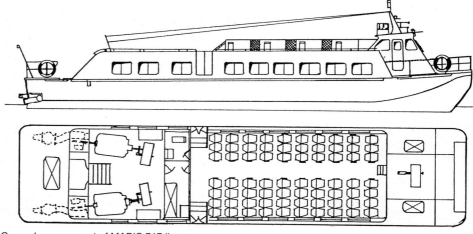

General arrangement of MARIC 717 II

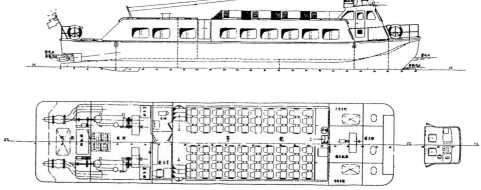

21m water-jet sidewall hovercraft, MARIC Type 717 III

TYPE 717 IIIC *Yu Xiang*

This new SES vessel was delivered to Chongqing Ferry Boat Company in September 1989.

The transverse structure is stronger than the previous Type 717 III in order to resist large stern waves.

Principal Particulars

Length overall	21.4 m
Beam	4.54 m
Draught, hullborne	0.95 m
Draught, on-cushion	0.7 m
Weight, maximum	23.5 t
Crew	4
Maximum speed	22.7 knots
Range	220 nm

Propulsion: 2 × Cummins NTA-855-M322 diesel engines manufactured by Sichuan Chongqing Automobile Motor Factory.

TYPE 7215

This craft was designed by MARIC and was completed in March 1993. The craft will be operated on the upper reaches of the Yangtze River in Shi Chua Province from Chongqing to Fuling and Wan Xian.

Principal Particulars

Length overall	28.0 m
Beam overall	6.84 m
Height overall	6.7 m
Draught, hullborne	1.67 m
Draught, on-cushion	1.44 m
Passengers	126-135
Operational speed	27 knots
Range	243 nm

Propulsion: Engines: 2 × Cummins KTA19-M diesels, 274 kW each, 2034 rpm.
Thrust device: 2 × directly driven marine propellers.
Lift engine: Cummins NT14-M diesel, 179 kW, 2000 rpm.
Fans: 2 × directly driven centrifugal fans, 0.85 m diameter.

TYPE 7218

This craft is a derivative of Type 716 II and was due to be completed in 1994. Both the hull and machinery are the same as for Type 716 II.

Principal Particulars

Length overall	20.5 m
Beam overall	8 m
Maximum speed	36 knots

TYPE 7224

This craft was designed by MARIC and three were completed by December 1992, one for Zhenzhou City as a touring boat operating on the Yellow River and two for personnel transportation at the Lieu River oil-field.

Principal Particulars

Length overall	12.4 m
Beam	4.5 m
Passengers	15
Operational speed	24.3 knots

Structure: Hull material: medium strength aluminium alloy.
Hull construction: riveted.
Propulsion: Engines: 2 × Deutz BF6L 913C air-cooled diesel (lift and propulsion, mechanically integrated arrangement).

VERIFIED

MARIC Type 717 IIIC on its delivery trip *1991*

MARIC Type 7215 *1994*

MARIC Type 7218 under construction *1994*

MARIC Type 7224 *1994*

HUANGPU SHIPYARD

PO Box 510336, Guangzhou, People's Republic of China

Telephone: +86 (20) 201345/201526
Telex: 44433 HPSPY CN
Telefax: +86 (20) 201387

Gao Feng, *Director*

TYPE 7211

A contract for designing and building a new 162 passenger SES ferry was signed on 15 April 1990 in Guangzhou. Ordered by China Merchants Development Company Ltd in Hong Kong, this Type 7211 passenger ferry was designed by MARIC and delivered in November 1992 to operate between Shekou and Hong Kong, a route operated by two Hovermarine International HM218s.

Principal Particulars

Length overall	29.95 m
Beam	7.6 m
Draught, hullborne	1.81 m
Draught, on-cushion	1.5 m

MARIC Type 7211 SES   *1993*

Passengers	162-171
Maximum speed	30 knots
Range	180 nm

Classification: This Type 7211 SES ferry is designed and built to ZC rules.
Structure: The craft has a welded aluminium main structure and a riveted aluminium superstructure.
Propulsion: The craft is powered by two MWM 12V TBD 234 diesel engines, each coupled to a propeller, and one MWM 6V TBD 234 diesel driving the lift fans.

VERIFIED

HUDONG SHIPYARD

Bahaoqiao, Pudong Dadao, Shanghai, People's Republic of China

Telephone: +86 (21) 840951
Telex: 33025 SHDSY CN
Telefax: +86 (21) 1675

TYPE 716 II

Designed by MARIC, the amphibious hovercraft Type 716 II was completed at Hudong Shipyard in 1985. The craft underwent evaluation by the China Air Cushion Technology Development Corporation (CACTEC) and now operates in offshore areas, shallow water and marshes where it is used to transport people and equipment.

MARIC Type 716 II 32 passenger ACV   *1986*

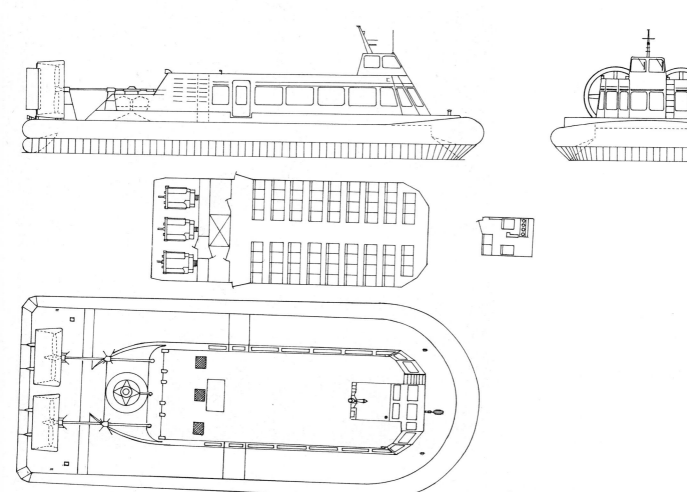

General arrangement of Type 716 III design

Principal Particulars

Length overall	18.44 m
Beam	7.72 m
Weight, maximum	19.4 t
Payload	4 t (no passengers)
Passengers	32 (no cargo)
Propulsive power	319 kW
Maximum speed	39 knots
Range	120 nm

Structure: Riveted skin and stringer structure employing high strength aluminium alloy sheet. Main hull forms a buoyancy raft based on a grid of longitudinal and transverse frames which form a number of flotation compartments.
Propulsion: One Deutz BF12L 413FC air-cooled marine diesel, 319 kW at 2300 rpm, via a gearbox and transmission shaft drives a 2 m diameter centrifugal fan. Two identical engines, via transmission shafts, drive directly two four-blade 2.3 m diameter ducted air propellers.
Control: Directional control is by two sets of twin vertical aerodynamic rudders mounted on the rear of the propeller ducts.

VERIFIED

MARIC

MARINE DESIGN AND RESEARCH INSTITUTE OF CHINA

346 Sichuan Road, Central, PO Box 3053, Shanghai, People's Republic of China

Telephone: +86 (21) 321 5044
Telex: 33029 MARIC CN
Telefax: +86 (21) 377 9744

Sun Songhe, *Director*
Yun Liang, *Deputy Chief Naval Architect*

The Marine Design and Research Institute of China (MARIC) has been responsible for much of the ACV research, development and design programmes on both amphibious and sidewall (SES) hovercraft built in China. The table summarises the more recent developments in ACVs in China.

TYPE 716 III

News of this design was given at the International High Performance Vehicle Conference given in Shanghai, 2-5 November 1988. This vessel is now under construction.

Principal Particulars

Length overall	20.5 m
Beam	8 m
Weight, maximum	26 t
Payload	6 t (no passengers)
Passengers	70 (no cargo)
Operational speed	40 knots

Propulsion: Three Deutz BF12L 413C air-cooled diesel engines provide lift and propulsion.

Summary of craft built

Builder and craft	Designer	Seats/payload	Launched
Bai Hai Shipyard			
Type 7217	MARIC	260 seats	December 1993
Dagu Shipyard			
Type 722 (Amphibious)	MARIC	15 t payload	August 1979
Type 7203 (Sidewall) *Jinxiang*	MARIC	81 seats	September 1983
Type 7212	MARIC	33 seats	1992
Type 7224 II	MARIC	15 seats	Under construction
MARIC			
Shanghai			
Jing-Sah (Amphibious)	MARIC	0.84 t payload	
Three-engined craft (Amphibious)	MARIC	(development craft, details in *Jane's Surface Skimmers 1985* and earlier editions) 2.8 t payload	
Shipbuilding and Marine Engineering Establishment			
Shanghai (Amphibious)			
Dong Feng Shipyard			
Type 717 II (Sidewall) *Ming Jiang*	MARIC	54-60 seats	October 1984
Type 717 III (Sidewall) *Chongqing*	MARIC	70 seats	September 1984
Type 717 IIIC (Sidewall) *Yu Xiang*	MARIC	—	September 1989
Type 7210 (Amphibious) two built	MARIC	0.8 t	May 1985
Type 7218 (Amphibious)	MARIC	70 seats	Under construction
Type 7224 (Amphibious)	MARIC	15-28 seats	April 1993
Type 7224 (Amphibious)	MARIC	15-28 seats	April 1993
Type 7224 (Amphibious)	MARIC	15-28 seats	April 1993
Type 7215 (Sidewall)	MARIC	126 seats	September 1993
Type 7226 (Amphibious)	MARIC	40-50 seats	Under construction
Chaohu Shipyard			
Anhui Province			
Type WR 901 (Sidewall), four built	Shanghai Ship and Shipping Research Institute	40 seats	December 1980 (pre-production prototype)
Huang Pu Shipyard			
Type 7211 (Sidewall)	MARIC	162 seats	December 1992
Hudong Shipyard			
Type 716 II (Amphibious)	MARIC	32 seats or 2.5 t	1985
Type 716 III (Amphibious)	MARIC	70 seats or 6 t	1988 (not completed)
Shanghai Aircraft Factory			
Type 7212 *Zhengzhou*	MARIC	33 seats	1989
Type 7228	MARIC	40 seats	Under construction
Zhong Hua Shipyard			
Type 719 II *Hong Xiang*	MARIC	257 seats	1988
Quog Hua Shipyard			
Type 719111	MARIC	257 seats	August 1988
Ming Jian Shipyard			
Type 717 V	MARIC	400 seats	August 1993

VERIFIED

SHANGHAI AIRCRAFT FACTORY

346 Sichuan Road Central, PO Box 3053, Shanghai, People's Republic of China

Telephone: +86 (21) 321 5044
Telefax: +86 (21) 377 9744

TYPE 7212 *Zhengzhou*

This amphibious hovercraft, completed in June 1989, was designed to operate on inland rivers, sea beaches and shallow water areas for short-range passenger transportation or touring. *Zhengzhou* is currently operating as a tour vessel on the Yellow River, while the second craft of this type is being built at Dagu Shipyard.

MARIC Type 7212 Zhengzhou *on the Yellow River*
1993

Principal Particulars

Length overall	13.2 m
Beam	5.5 m
Weight, maximum	10.33 t
Passengers	33
Maximum speed	28.1 knots
Operational limitation	Beaufort 6

Structure: Built in medium strength seawater-resistant aluminium alloy, riveted construction.
Propulsion: The main engines are two Deutz BF6L 913C air-cooled diesels. These drive two fixed-pitch ducted propellers, 1.80 m diameter, driven via a flexible coupling and clutch.

The lift engine is a Deutz BF6L 913C air-cooled diesel, driving a lift fan of centrifugal type, 1.5 m diameter, via a flexible coupling and gearbox.

VERIFIED

ZHONG HUA SHIPYARD

Shanghai, People's Republic of China

Builder of MARIC 719 II SES *Hong Xiang* operating between the Shanghai Municipality and Chong Ming Island.

TYPE 719 II

This 719 II sidewall hovercraft is the second such craft to be built with a steel hull.

The vessel can carry 257 passengers and meets the requirements for ships operating in the Yangtze River Class A area.

The control of engines is by remote-control systems produced by HDW-Elektronik of Germany with manual backup. The lift engine is directly connected to three double-intake centrifugal lift fans via a clutch system and there is no speed reduction device between them. The propulsion engines drive the propellers through a German speed reduction device Type WVS 642. The engine room also contains an auxiliary engine and an electric generator.

There are two double intake centrifugal fans in the fan room, arranged along the centreline of the ship.

Principal Particulars

Length overall	40 m
Beam	8.28 m
Draught, hullborne	2.45 m
Draught, on-cushion	1.85 m
Displacement, maximum	123.5 t
Payload	22 t
Passengers	257
Maximum speed	27.54 knots
Operational speed	24 knots
Range	370 km
Operational limitation	Beaufort force 7
	wave height 1.5 m

The MARIC 719 II steel-hull SES — 1989

Structure: The main structure of this vessel is welded from steel type ZCA. The superstructure is riveted from aluminium type LY12CZ.

The bow seal is a bag and finger skirt and the stern seal a two-lobe bag.
Propulsion: The vessel is powered by three MWM TBD 234 V16 high-speed diesel engines. One engine drives three centrifugal fans with double-sided air inlets for cushion lift, and each of the others drives a 1 m diameter marine propeller.
Control: There are two rudders with aerofoil section profiles fitted at the stern behind the propellers. They are interconnected and move synchronously by hydraulic actuation. A stand-by hydraulic system is provided as well as a hand pump for emergency use.
Safety equipment: To meet the lifesaving requirements, six lifebuoys, 257 lifejackets, 25 child life-

jackets and seven working lifejackets for crew are provided under passenger seats and in the storerooms.

There are eight fire extinguishers, Type 1211 (MY6) installed in the ship.
Outfit: Cabins of this ship are on two decks: the upper cabin is on the wheelhouse deck and the lower cabin is on the main deck.

The upper deck carries the wheelhouse, first class passenger cabin (48 seats), two high class cabins (with six seats each) and two storerooms. On the lower deck there is a front passenger cabin (second class, 154 seats), an aft passenger cabin (second class, 43 seats), an engine room, a crew cabin and a kitchen. There is a toilet near the aft passenger cabin and in the centre of the main deck there is a small shop and a toilet.

VERIFIED

COMMONWEALTH OF INDEPENDENT STATES

ALMAZ SHIPYARD

CENTRAL MARINE DESIGN BUREAU

19 Uralskaya Street, 199161 St Petersburg, Russia, CIS

Telephone: +7 (812) 350 2983
Telefax: +7 (812) 350 0925

Alexander V Shliakhtenko, *Chief Designer*

The ALMAZ central marine design bureau was established in 1940 and specialises in the design and construction of high-speed commercial and military craft (hydrofoils, hovercraft, SES and Swath).

BOBYOR AMPHIBIOUS CARGO CRAFT

The Bobyor is designed to transfer general cargoes of cars, tractors, construction plant or passengers over rivers or swampy ground. The first of these craft is under construction.

Principal Particulars

Length overall	30.2 m
Beam	11.5 m
Draught	0.9 m
Payload	25 t
Propulsive power	2 × 680 kW
Lift power	680 kW
Operational speed	38 knots
Range	240 nm

Structure: Welded aluminium hull and superstructure.
Propulsion: The main engines are two air-cooled diesels.

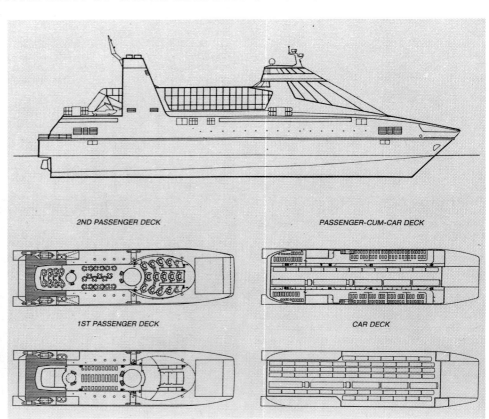

2ND PASSENGER DECK

PASSENGER-CUM-CAR DECK

1ST PASSENGER DECK

CAR DECK

General arrangement of RSES-500 — 1994

The lift system comprises two centrifugal fans driven by one diesel.

MISTRAL (DESIGN)

This SES craft is based on the military SES *Dergach* which was built in Russia and has operated on the Black Sea for many years. Much of the specified equipment for this craft is produced in Western Europe or the USA.

Principal Particulars

Length overall	65 m
Beam	18 m
Draught, hullborne	3.3 m
Passengers	353
Vehicles	67 cars
Operational speed	42 knots
Range	400 nm

Structure: Welded aluminium hull and super-structure.

Propulsion: Main engines: 2 × LM1600 gas-turbines and 2 × MTU 16V 595 TE 60 diesels. Lift engines: 2 × MTU 12V 538 TB 82.

RSES-500 (DESIGN)

The company has also developed an extensive range of SES craft designs from 200 to 2000 tonnes displacement. These are known as the RSES series. Brief details of the RSES-500 have been provided:

Principal Particulars

Length overall	93 m
Beam	23.5 m
Draught, hullborne	4.3 m
Draught, on-cushion	1.7 m
Passengers	450-700
Propulsive power	76 000 kW
Maximum speed	50 knots

UPDATED

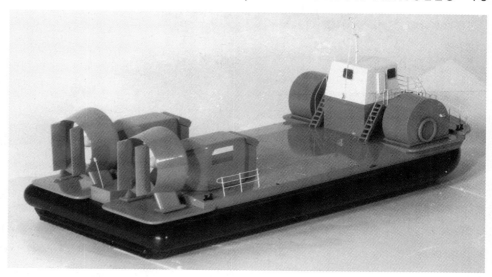

Model of Bobyor amphibious cargo craft

1994

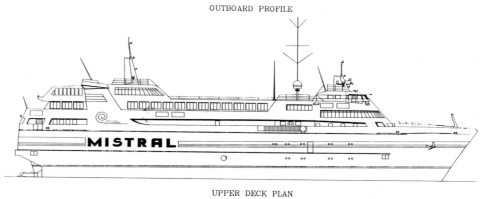

OUTBOARD PROFILE

UPPER DECK PLAN

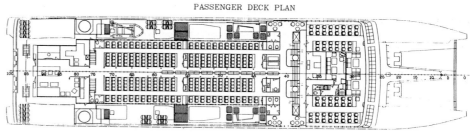

PASSENGER DECK PLAN

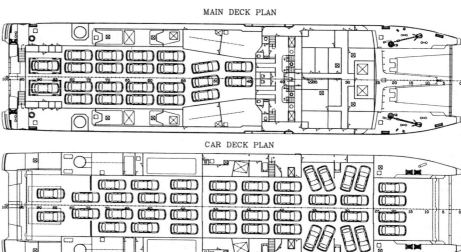

MAIN DECK PLAN

CAR DECK PLAN

General arrangement of Mistral
1994

ASTRAKHAN SHIPYARD

LUCH-1

A sidewall ACV for river use was completed at the Astrakhan Shipyard and underwent State trials in September 1983. Production of the ACV Luch-1 then began at the Moscow Shipyard. Designed to replace the 12 year old Zarnitsa, the Luch, Design No 14351, carries two crew and up to 66 passengers, 15 standing. Of all-welded aluminium construction, it has a maximum operating weight of 22.6 tonnes and a top speed of 24 knots. The shallow on-cushion draught of just over 0.5 m allows it to run bow-on to flat sloping river banks to embark and disembark passengers.

New design features permit operation on large rivers such as the Don, Kama, Oka and Volga, where higher waves are encountered.

Compared with the Zarnitsa, Luch has a more powerful diesel, the 382 kW 3KD12H-520, and uses a lighter form of construction. The overall dimensions of the craft permit rail transport to distant rivers and canals.

During trials before the commissioning of the first of the class, it was demonstrated that its operating and technical performance is significantly superior to that of the Zarnitsa. The craft is built to the requirements of the 'R' class of the CIS's River Craft Registry and has been produced in quantity.

Luch   1993

Principal Particulars

Length overall	22.81 m
Beam	3.85 m
Draught, on-cushion	0.5 m
Draught, hullborne	0.65 m
Weight, minimum	15.4 t
Weight, maximum	22.6 t
Crew	2
Passengers	66
Propulsive power	382 kW
Maximum speed	23.75 knots
Range	162 nm

Structure: The buoyancy structure is built in welded marine grade aluminium alloy. The superstructure is built in D16 alloy. Superstructure and bulkheads are riveted together. Pressed panels are employed throughout the hull to improve the external appearance and reduce the volume of assembly work necessary during construction.

The skirt is a fingered-type at bow, bag-type aft. Bow segments attached to an easily replaceable module.

Propulsion: The engine is a type 81H12A diesel with a maximum power of 380 kW or a type 3KD12H-520, 382 kW. Normal operating power: 346 kW.

The engine is mounted aft and drives, via a transmission shaft, a centrifugal fan for lift and a water-jet rotor for propulsion. The water-jet rotor and its bearing can be replaced while the craft is in displace-

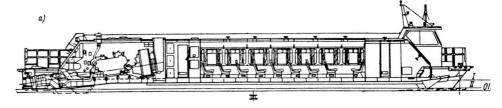

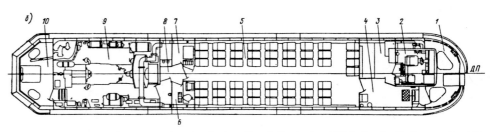

Inboard profile and plan of Luch: **a** *Longitudinal section;* **b** *Deck plan;* **I** *Waterline in displacement mode;* **II** *Waterline when cushionborne;* **1** *Fore deck;* **2** *Wheelhouse;* **3** *Duty compartment;* **4** *Vestibule;* **5** *Passenger saloon;* **6** *Toilet;* **7** *Storeroom;* **8** *Vestibule;* **9** *Engine room;* **10** *Aft deck*

ment condition without having to lift it out of the water.

Electrical system: One 1.2 kW 24 V DC engine-operated generator and batteries. During prolonged night stops power can be supplied by a shore-based

220 V, 50 Hz electrical supply.

Control: Twin rudder vanes in the water-jet stream control craft heading. Thrust reversal achieved by water-flow deflectors.

UPDATED

GORKOVSKI PHILIAL CNII im akad. A N Krylova

Krylov Specialised Shipbuilding Centre, Chkalovsk, Novgorod, Russia 606429, CIS

Telephone: +7 (83160) 25236
Telefax: +7 (83260) 25233

Sergei Usoltsev, *Director*

SIBIR

The shipyard developed and built the cargo-carrying ACV Sibir in 1990 with ACV Typhoon as a prototype. The craft is designed for year round fast delivery of tracked or wheeled vehicles and containerised cargo on the local and main river, lakes and reservoir.

Sibir in operation   1995

Principal Particulars

Length overall	25.2 m
Beam	11.7 m
Weight, maximum	55 t
Payload	20 t
Propulsive power	1874 kW
Maximum speed	43 knots
Obstacle clearance	1.25 m

Hull: The hull is built in 1561 weldable marine aluminium alloy with port and starboard superstructures. Each side structure contains an integrated

axial turbine fan installation. The bow ramp provides roll-on, roll-off loading and unloading.

The skirt is a bag and finger tapered skirt 1.2 m deep at the bow and 1.4 m at the stern. Longitudinal and transverse flexible keels divide the cushion into four compartments for stability.

Propulsion: Aerodynamically integrated system, powered by twin Ivchenko AI-24 gas turbines, maximum 1874 kW and continuous 1310 kW each. Each turbine drives a 2.5 m axial fan mounted on the tur-

bine shaft. This pumps the air downwards into the cushion and backwards through the duct for propulsion.

Control: Rudders fitted in the duct provide directional control. The air flow is deflected for braking by horizontal vanes, hydraulically controlled from the wheelhouse.

Outfit: All controls are in a raised port wheelhouse.

UPDATED

KRASNOYE SORMOVO SHIPYARD
A A Zhdanov

Nizhni Novgorod, Russia, CIS

M Yuriev, *Shipyard Director*
Ivan Yerlykin, *Chief Hydrofoil Designer*

ZARNITSA

Evolved from Gorkovchanin, the Zarnitsa is a 48 to 50 seat water-jet-propelled rigid sidewall ferry designed to operate on shallow rivers, some less than 0.7 m (2 ft 3 in) deep. Series production is established and large numbers have been delivered.

The prototype was put into trial service on the Vyatka river, in the Kirov region, in the Summer of 1972, and the first production models began operating on shallow, secondary rivers later in the year. During 1973-74, Zarnitsas entered service on tributaries of the Kama, Lena and Volga. More than 100 are employed on almost all the river navigation lines of the Russian Republic as well as on the rivers of Ukraine, Moldova, Belarus and Kazakhstan.

Principal Particulars

Length overall	22.3 m
Beam	3.85 m
Weight, minimum	9 t
Weight, maximum	15 t
Operational speed	19 knots

Structure, Propulsion, Control: Arrangements almost identical to those of the Gorkovchanin.

Outfit: Seats are provided for two crew members, accommodated in the raised wheelhouse forward, and 48 to 50 passengers. Access to the passenger saloon is via a single door at the bow in the centre of the wheelhouse. The craft runs bow-on to flat sloping banks to embark and disembark passengers.

VERIFIED

Passenger saloon in Zarnitsa looking aft   **1986**   Zarnitsa   **1986**

MARIJSKI POLYTECHNICAL INSTITUTE

3 Lenin Square, Yoshkar-Ola, Mari, Russia, CIS

The student design group at the Marijsky Institute of Technology has been involved in ACV development since 1971. It specialises in designing amphibious hovercraft for operation in the less accessible areas of the CIS and has successfully built and tested craft commissioned by the oil, gas and fisheries authorities. It has also adapted hovercraft for forestry and agricultural roles and for use in establishing communication networks.

SAV SERIES
SAVR-1M

In 1977 the Institute was awarded a contract by the Soviet gas industry for a small snowmobile/hovercraft to carry a driver and two passengers, plus 500 kg of cargo, over snow, ice and water. It also was required to travel over mud to ensure year round operation on rivers. The first stage of the programme was the design and construction of an experimental model, designated SAVR-1.

Principal Particulars

Weight, maximum	1.8 t
Payload	0.5 t
Crew	1
Passengers	2
Propulsive power	72 kW
Lift power	30 kW
Maximum speed	22 knots

Propulsion: Separate lift and propulsion systems enable the craft to be operated at its maximum clearance height and speed depending on the surface and weather conditions. There are two engines fitted, the propulsion engine which develops 72 kW, and the lift engine developing 30 kW. The propulsion engine drives a two-bladed airscrew and the lift engine an axial fan ahead of the cockpit.

SAVR-1 (CABP-1)

Built in 1980, this production version of the SAVR-1M is intended for high-speed ferrying of personnel and urgent cargoes up to 1.3 tonnes, over areas without roads and all year round access.

SAVR-1M (CABP-1M)   **1986**

Principal Particulars

Length	7.5 m
Beam	3.8 m
Weight, maximum	2.9 t
Payload	1.3 t
Propulsive power	118 kW
Lift power	73 kW
Operational speed	32 knots

Structure: Built in duralumin sheet. Buoyancy chamber of honeycomb construction.

Propulsion: Cushion air is supplied by a 73 kW car engine driving two standard centrifugal fans. A clutch between the engine and fans allows the fans to be disconnected during engine start up and idling. Thrust is supplied by a 118 kW (158 hp) engine, aft, which drives a 2 m diameter propeller. Distribution of power between cushion and thrust is varied according to terrain conditions.

Control: Directional control is by two air rudders operating in the slipstream.

SAVR-2 (CABP-2)

SAVR-2 made its appearance in 1982. It was designed and built to a specification prepared by the Soviet Ministry of Fisheries for a craft to serve the inaccessible water regions of North and West Siberia.

Principal Particulars

Length overall	9.8 m
Beam	4.5 m
Weight, maximum	5.9 t
Payload	2 t
Passengers	2
Crew	1
Fuel capacity	800 l
Propulsive power	294 kW
Maximum speed	27 knots
Range	108 nm

Structure: Believed to be a composite light alloy and glass fibre structure. Flotation compartments and basic raft structure filled with plastic foam make the hull unsinkable.

The skirts are segmented fore and aft, with bag-type skirts at the sides. An experimental model of the SAVR-2 has two flexible side skids replacing the conventional skirt. The skids consist of a number of right-angled plates, hinged together and fitted with removable stainless steel or polyethylene soles. The plates are fixed to the hull by lever suspension and spring shock absorbers. The area between skid and hull is covered with rubberised fabric. Flexible skids reduce to a minimum the air escaping from the cushion when travelling over rough ground, so reducing the power required from the lift system, as the skids follow the ground contours more accurately. When the craft is supported by the skids the pressure of the air cushion can be reduced considerably. Flexible skids provide lateral stability when the craft is stationary and when travelling over snow, ice, mud and surfaces covered in a thin layer of water.

Propulsion: Lift is provided by a single petrol engine aft of the crew cabin driving, via a split transverse shaft, two centrifugal fans. Thrust is supplied by a single 294 kW Ivchenko AI-14ChR air-cooled radial piston engine driving an AV-14 three-blade variable-pitch propeller. Fuel is carried in two 400 litre tanks, one for each engine. Fuel employed is standard automotive petrol.

The least cushion pressure is required over damp, muddy terrain or land covered with a thin layer of water. To cross open water the pressure must be increased from 1000 to 1200 Pa (70 to 80 per cent maximum) and over dry soil and ploughed land it has to be increased to the maximum, 1400 Pa.

Control: Craft heading is controlled by twin vertical aerodynamic rudders aft operating in the propeller slipstream. Reverse propeller pitch is employed for braking and reversing. A horizontal stabiliser is mounted between the twin rudders to adjust pitch trim. By altering its incidence angle the centre of gravity can be moved along the longitudinal axis should an uneven load distribution cause it to move.

Outfit: The cabin seats a driver with a passenger on each side. The interior is lined with a layer of poly-

SAVR-1 (CABP-1) *1992*

SAVR-2 (CABP-2) *1986*

urethane and PVC for thermal insulation. A passenger module seating 14 to 16 can be fitted on cargo platform aft of lift fan system.

SAVR-3

In 1981 the Ministry of Oil and Gas approved a programme for the construction of trackless modes of transport, building machines and pipe-laying equipment for muddy soils. Within this programme, spanning the period 1981 to 1985, the Institute was constructing three new transport hovercraft with the following load capacities: SAVR-3, 2 tonnes; SAVR-5, 5 tonnes and SAVR-40, 40 tonnes.

Principal Particulars

Payload	3 t
Propulsive power	380 kW
Maximum speed	27 knots

At the end of 1986 a decision was taken to build a working batch of SAVR-3 craft. In the Spring of 1985

and 1986, early top-dressing of Winter crops with granulated fertilisers and sowing of wheat and barley in damp soil were undertaken with the first SAVR-3.

SAVR-5

Developed by the Institute in 1983 for freight transport of year round construction of pipelines on swamps. Road tests began in the first half of 1987.

The SAVR-5 is propelled by caterpillar tracks from T54B tractors, driven by a series-produced diesel as is the fan for the air cushion system. Maximum vehicle weight is 10 tonnes.

SAVR-40

A 40 tonne load capacity air cushion vehicle for similar duties to the SAVR-5.

VERIFIED

SAVR-3 (CABP-3) *1990*

NEPTUN CDB CORP

25 Stanislavski St, Moscow, 103009 Russia, CIS

Telephone: +7 (095) 229 5862
Telex: 411700
Telefax: +7 (095) 292 6511

V S Sokolov, *President*
G E Andreyev, *Vice President*

The CDB (short for Central Design Bureau) Neptun Corp originally specialised in designing various types of small displacement motor boats and ships, but recently hovercraft design and production have become its main option. Having its own shipyard near Moscow the CBD is co-operating with other shipyards for serial production of hovercraft. Over 200 hovercraft of various types have been built from Neptun's designs over the last 15 years.

GEPARD (CHEETAH)

A multi-role five-seater introduced in 1981, Gepard has been designed to provide convenient, reliable and inexpensive transport in more remote areas of the CIS. Specialist professions in those areas were questioned about their transport needs before finalising the design. Early in 1983 a Gepard successfully underwent trials at Andreyevskoye Lake, near the centre of the Tyumen Oblast. About sixty Gepards had entered service by the end of 1990.

The craft is designed to operate in an ambient air temperature range from −40 to +40°C.

The following service life trials have been carried out:

Moscow to Lake Seleger and back: about 1000 km

Along small rivers to the city of Vyshnii Volochek and back: about 1000 km

Moscow by the Volga-Baltic route to St Petersburg: about 2000 km

Moscow to Volgograd on the lower Volga River: about 3500 km

Nearly 150 units have been built up to now and operate in various areas in the European and Asian parts of Russia. Its remarkable duties include anti-pollution patrol in the city of Moscow and auxiliary sevice with a hydrological expedition on the Yamal Peninsula in the Arctic. Examples of the Gepard series are also operated out of Russia by ship owners in the USA, Mexico and Canada.

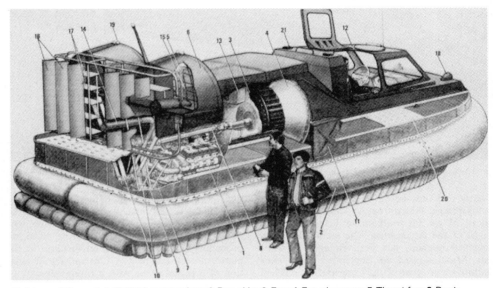

Cutaway of Gepard: **1** *ZMZ-53 power-plant;* **2** *Bag skirt;* **3** *Fan;* **4** *Fan air scoop;* **5** *Thrust fan;* **6** *Duct;* **7** *Main (cardan) shaft;* **8** *Fan drive (cardan) shaft;* **9** *Fan transmission belts;* **10** *Airscrew transmission belts;* **11** *Fuel tank;* **12** *Deck cabin;* **13** *Water and oil radiators;* **14** *Exhaust pipe (manifold);* **15** *Fan duct;* **16** *Vertical rudders;* **17** *Elevators;* **18** *Headlights;* **19** *Navigation and landing lights;* **20** *Drainage plate;* **21** *Ventilator heads* 1986

Principal Particulars

Length overall	6.63 m
Beam	3.3 m
Weight, maximum	1.86 t
Crew	5
Propulsive power	86 kW
Maximum speed	32 knots
Operational speed	24 knots
Operational limitation	−40°C to +40°C

Structure: Corrosion-resistant light alloy hull. Moulded pigmented glass fibre cabin superstructure.

Propulsion: Integrated system, powered by a ZMZ-53 lorry engine (a widely used engine), aft of the cabin. Output is transmitted to a centrifugal lift fan (0.97 m diameter with GRP blades) and a duct-mounted, multi-bladed 0.95 m diameter glass fibre propeller for thrust, the blade leading edges being protected with stainless steel sheaths. Power transmission is by toothed-belt drives and a clutch is provided between the engine and propeller and fan drives.

Control: Directional control by interconnected rudder vanes hinged to the rear of the thrust fan ducts and operated by a wheel. Horizontal vane surfaces are also provided.

PUMA

Design and building of this craft was completed in less than a year. The first three variants underwent comprehensive trials in 1988. As an ambulance the Puma is equipped with an operating table and related medical apparatus including oxygen bottles, making it possible to provide urgent medical aid on board, including simple operations. The passenger variant is fitted with 16 aircraft-type seats, while the passenger/cargo variant has 10 folding seats.

Pumas are engaged in passenger transportation services in Siberia, on the Caspian Sea and in the Far East of Russia. One craft is to be delivered to

The five-seat, 42 knot Gepard powered by a single 115 hp ZMZ-53 petrol engine

1991

Puma twin petrol engine hovercraft designed by the Neptun Central Design Bureau, Moscow

Mexico. The total number of craft built since 1985 is ten.

Principal Particulars

Length overall	12.2 m
Beam	4.5 m
Weight, minimum	3.6 t
Weight, maximum	5 t
Payload	1.45 t
Passengers	16
Propulsive power	2 × 90 kW
Maximum speed	35 knots
Operational speed	22 knots
Obstacle clearance	0.3 m

Propulsion: Two ZMZ-53 90 kW petrol engines driving two centrifugal fans and two reversible-pitch propellers with toothed-belt drives.

IRBIS

A twin-engine amphibious hovercraft designed to carry up to 32 passengers. Intended applications for this type include the transport of geologists and oil industry workers and their associated equipment, cargo shipment up to 2.5 tonnes and support for geophysical exploration. The craft is designed to operate in a wide range of operating conditions: in ambient temperatures from −40°C with maximum wind speeds of 29 knots, up to 30 miles from base; in significant wave heights up to 0.7 m when cushionborne, across deep or shallow water; on snow and compact ice and on broken and sludge ice. The craft has folding sidebodies for ease of transport.

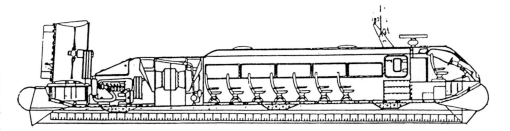

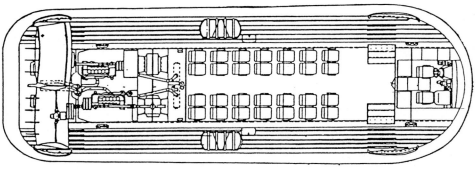

General arrangement of Irbis

Irbis

From their first appearance in 1989 these craft participated in many trials and commercial services in various areas of Russia, including inland water-ways routes Moscow - St. Petersburg - Astrakhan, sea routes in the Finnish bay of the Baltic sea and on the Caspian Sea as well as a scheduled passenger service on the North Dvina River and on the Amur River as a ferry across the Russian-Chinese border.

One Irbis of three in operation is based in Olcott, New York, USA, and after completing the demonstration program on Lake Ontario is passing a certification procedure to be assessed for operation in this area.

Classification: The craft is classed KM*1 SVPA Register of CIS.
Propulsion: The engines are two Deutz BF6L 913C air-cooled diesels, driving two 4-blade, variable-pitch (forward and reverse thrust) ducted propellers.
Electrical system: Two 1 kW generators.
Voltage: 24 DC.
Auxiliary systems: Trim (fuel transfer), hydraulic power provision, heating and special cold starting system (down to −40°C).
Principal Particulars

Length overall	16.5 m
Beam	6.2 m
Draught	0.27 m
Weight, minimum	7.4 t, passenger version
	6.5 t, freight version
Weight, maximum	10.7 t
Passengers	32
Fuel capacity	0.56 t
Propulsive power	2 × 141 kW
Maximum speed	30 knots
Operational speed	24.3 knots
Range	250 nm
Operational limitation	Sea State 3,
	Wind speed 8 knots
Obstacle clearance	0.4 m

UPDATED

St PETERSBERG SHIPYARD

St Petersberg, Russia, CIS

ORION-01

Design of the Orion, a rigid sidewall ACV with seats for 80 passengers, was approved in Moscow in Autumn 1970. The prototype, built in Leningrad, began trials in October 1973 and arrived at its port of registry, Kalinin, in late 1974, bearing the serial number 01.

The craft is used for passenger ferry services along shallow rivers, tributaries and reservoirs and can land and take on passengers bow-on from any flat sloping bank. It is faster than the Zarnitsa and its comfort and performance are less affected by choppy conditions. The cruising speed of the vessel, which is propelled by water-jets, is 28 knots. It belongs to the 'R' class of the Soviet River Register.

Series production of this vessel is being undertaken at the Sosnovskaya Shipbuilding Yard in Kirovskaya Oblast.

Summary of principal civil air cushion vehicle types built

Craft	Payload	No built	Year built	Designed by	Builders
Neva amphibious ACV	38 passengers	1			
Briz (Breeze)	6 passengers		1968		
Skate	50 passengers		1969		
Raduga amphibious ACV	5 passengers	1	1962		Krasnoye Sormovo Shipyard, Gorki
Sormovich amphibious ACV	50 passengers	1	1965		Krasnoye Sormovo Shipyard, Gorki
Gorkovchanin sidewall ACV	48 passengers	1	1969-70	CKB Vympel	Krasnoye Sormovo Shipyard, Gorki
Zarnitsa sidewall ACV (based on Gorkovchanin)	48 passengers	over 100	1972	CKB Vympel	Krasnoye Sormovo Shipyard, Gorki
Orion sidewall ACV	80 passengers		1973* 1975	CKB Vympel	Leningrad Shipyard
Chayka sidewall ACV	80 passengers	1		CKB Vympel	Sosnovskaya Shipyard
Rassvet sidewall ACV	80 passengers	1		CKB Vympel	Sosnovskaya Shipyard
Plamya sidewall ACV (based on Orion hull)	fire-fighting craft	1		Central Design Bureau, Gorki	
Raduga-2 amphibious ACV	0.65 t	n/a		Krasnoye Sormovo Shipyard, Gorki	
SAVR-1M amphibious ACV		1	1978		
SAVR-1 (CABP-1) amphibious ACV	1.3 t	production version of the 1M	1980	Mariski A M Gorki Memorial Polytechnical Institute	
SAVR-2 (CABP-2) amphibious ACV	2 t		1982	Mariski A M Gorki Memorial Polytechnical Institute	
SAVR-3 (CABP-3) amphibious ACV	2 t		1981	Mariski A M Gorki Memorial Polytechnical Institute	
SAVR-5GD (CABP-5GD) amphibious ACV	5 t		1981 onwards	Mariski A M Gorki Memorial Polytechnical Institute	
SAVR-40 (CABP-40) amphibious ACV	50 t		1987	Mariski A M Gorki Memorial Polytechnical Institute	
MPI-18 amphibious ACV	0.6 t				
MPI-20 amphibious ACV	2 and 5 t versions				
Neptun AKVPR-001 amphibious ACV	research craft		1977	Neptun Central Design Bureau, Moscow	
Barrs-1 (Snow Leopard) amphibious ACV	0.65 t or 7 passengers	30	1981	Neptun Central Design Bureau, Moscow	
Gepard (Cheetah) amphibious ACV	5 passengers	40+, in production	1981 onwards	Neptun Central Design Bureau, Moscow UFA Aviation Institute, Tyumen	
Taifun	20 passengers or 3 t				
Klest amphibious ACV	4 seats		1981	Vostok Central Design Bureau, Leningrad	
Luch sidewall ACV	66 passengers	reported in series production	1983 onwards	Astrakhan Shipyard	
Puma	16 passengers	2 prototypes	1985	Neptun Central Design Bureau, Moscow	
Typhoon	cargo	1	1987	Gorkovski Philial	
-	32 passengers	1 1989	1988-89	Neptun Central Design Bureau, Moscow	
Bargusin	130 passengers		1989	CKB Vympel	
Sibir	cargo	1	1990	Neptun Central Design Bureau, Moscow	
Tapir	seismic equipment	12	1990	Neptun Central Design Bureau, Moscow	Rybinsk Shipyard

*trials

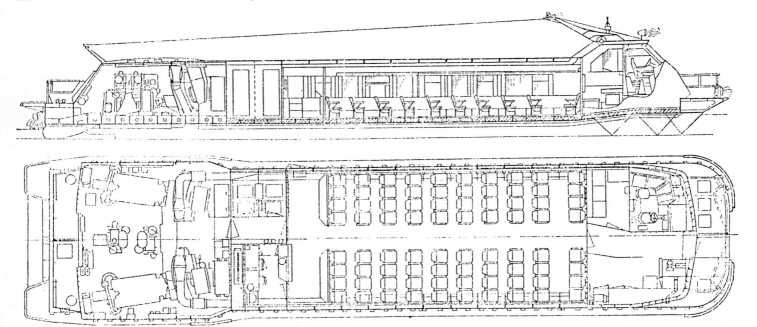

General arrangement of Orion

Principal Particulars

Length overall	25.8 m
Beam	6.5 m
Draught, hullborne	0.84 m
Draught, on-cushion	0.5 m
Weight, maximum	34.7 t
Weight, minimum	20.7 t
Crew	3
Passengers	80
Propulsive power	2 × 452 kW
Maximum speed	32 knots
Operational speed	28.6 knots
Range	216 nm
Operational limitation	1.2 m wave height

Structure: The hull is similar in overall appearance to Zarya and Zarnitsa types. All-welded structure in aluminium-magnesium alloy. Lateral framing throughout the hull with the exception of the bow and stern decks, where longitudinal frames have been fitted. The superstructure and wheelhouse are of welded and riveted duralumin construction on longitudinal framing.

GORKOVCHANIN Stopping and starting characteristics

Distance run by vessel from Full Ahead to Stop	
metres	100
Time in seconds	35
Distance run by vessel from Full Ahead to Full Astern	
metres	60
Time in seconds	14
Distance necessary for attainment of Full Speed from Stop	
metres	200
Time in seconds	52

Propulsion: Integrated system powered by two 3D12N-520 diesels mounted in an engine room aft. Each engine drives a Type Ts 39-13 centrifugal fan for lift and via a cardan shaft, a semi-submerged single stage water-jet rotor for propulsion. Fan air is fed via ducts to the bow skirt, a transverse stability slot and to the bag and finger skirt aft. Casing of the water-jet system, which is removable, forms the stern section of the vessel. The water-jets are mounted on shock absorbers to reduce vibration.

Electrical system: Two G-73Z engine-driven generators, linked with two sets of 6STK-180M batteries, provide 28 V, 1200 W. One battery set is employed for engine starting, the other for supplying current for the ship's systems.

VERIFIED

SOSNOVSKAYA SHIPYARD

Kirovskaya, Oblast, Russia, CIS

RASSVET (DAWN)
CHAYKA (GULL)

A water-jet-propelled sidewall passenger ferry, Rassvet is designed for local sea routes of limited water depth. It is an offshore counterpart to the Orion sidewall ACV. The Rassvet serves resort routes in the Crimea, on the Caspian and Baltic Seas as well as on large lakes and reservoirs. Like the Orion and Zarnitsa, its two predecessors, it can run bow-on to flat, sloping beaches to embark and disembark passengers. Landing on a beach is facilitated by an articulated gangway with a hydraulic drive.

Rassvet's features include shallow draught, good manoeuvrability and a relatively simple construction.

The water-jet reversing/steering system is specially protected to enable the craft to moor alongside existing berths built originally for small conventional displacement ferries.

Rassvet is designed to carry 80 passengers during daylight hours on coastal routes in conditions up to force 4. It complies with CIS Registration classification KM*II Passenger ACV Class.

Principal Particulars

Length overall	26.7 m
Beam	7.1 m
Draught, hullborne	1.27 m
Draught, on-cushion	0.8 m
Weight, maximum	47.5 t
Passengers	80
Propulsive power	2 × 383 kW
Lift power	110 kW
Maximum speed	29 knots
Operational speed	23 knots
Range	190 nm

Structure: The hull and superstructure are built in aluminium-magnesium alloy. The hull is of all-welded construction in AlMg-61 and the decks, superstructure, pilot-house and partitions are in AlMg-5 alloy. The hull, superstructure and pilot-house have longitudinal frames. Single piece pressed panels are employed for the lower sections of the sidewalls. Corrugated sheets are used for the hull bottom. Below the passenger deck the hull is subdivided by transverse bulkheads into seven watertight compartments, access to which is via hatches in the passenger deck. The craft will remain afloat in the event of any one compartment flooding.

The skirt is a double-row segmented type at bow; two-tier bag type skirt aft. Repair or replacement of sections of the bow skirt can be undertaken with the bow run on to a flat, gently sloping beach. The stern skirt is secured to special hinged sections which permit inspection and maintenance while still afloat.

Propulsion: Power for the water-jet system is provided by two 3D12N-520 lightweight (3.54 kg/kW) irreversible, high-speed four-cycle V-type marine diesels each with a gas-turbine supercharger and a rated power of 383 kW at 1500 rpm. Each powers a two-stage water-jet impeller. Water inlet scoops are arranged in the sidewalls and the pump ports, each comprising two rotors and two straightening devices, are installed in the sidewalls behind the transoms. Cushion air is generated by a single 110 kW PD6S-150A diesel driving an NTs6 centrifugal fan via a universal joint and a torque-limited coupling.

Electrical system: Power supply requirements are met by a 28 V, 29 kW generator driven by a power take-off shaft from the main engine and three 28 V, 12 kW G-732 charging generators mounted on the main engine. There are two banks of storage batteries installed. The first, comprising two Type 6STK-180M storage batteries, supplies DC power when the craft is operating. The second bank, comprising four batteries of the same type, is employed for engine starting and powering the diesel engine control circuits and emergency alarm systems. An inverter is installed for navigation and other equipment requiring AC supplies. An auxiliary circuit can be connected to shore systems for a 220 V single-phase 50 Hz AC supply.

Control: Craft direction is controlled by twin balanced rudders operating in the water discharged by each of the two water-jets. Reversal is achieved by applying rotatable deflectors to reverse the water-flow.

PLAMYA (FLAME) ACV RIVER FIRETENDER

The Central Design Bureau at Nizhni Novgorod has developed a river-going firetender. The craft is based on the hull of the Orion sidewall-type passenger ferry, but the passenger cabin superstructure has been replaced by an open deck forward to accommodate a tracked or wheeled fire-fighting vehicle and its crew. Plamya is designed for the fast delivery of an off the road fire-fighting vehicle and its

Plamya   1986

crew to points on lakes, reservoirs and major rivers near forest fires. The craft can be beached bow-on on the river bank and the fire-fighting vehicle or bulldozer offloaded across the bow ramp.

Principal Particulars

Length overall	26.1 m
Beam	6.5 m
Draught, hullborne	0.88 m
Draught, on-cushion	0.7 m
Weight, maximum	34.5 t
Payload	7.3 t
Crew	3
Propulsive power	2 × 452 kW
Maximum speed	27 knots

Classification: Plamya meets the requirements of the Register of Shipping of the CIS and is constructed to 'R' Class in the RSFSR Inland Waterways Register. It is in service on the River Kama.

Structure: All-welded structure in AlMg-61 aluminium-magnesium alloy. Frames, plates, partitions and roof of superstructure in D16 alloy.

The bow skirt is a triple-row, fully segmented type; stern, bag and finger type.

Propulsion: Integrated system powered by two 3D12N-520 marine diesels. Each engine drives a Type Ts 39-13 centrifugal fan for lift and, via a cardan shaft, a semi-submerged single stage water-jet rotor for propulsion.

Control: Rudders aft of the water-jet inlets and two water-jet deflectors control craft direction.

RADUGA-2

Little is known about this amphibious ACV, which was first reported in the Soviet press in late Spring 1981. Designed at the Krasnoye Sormovo ship and ACV building facility at Nizhni Novgorod, Raduga-2,

in common with the Gepard and Klest, is powered by an automotive engine, the Chayka. The 1962 Raduga was described in *Jane's Surface Skimmers 1985* and earlier editions.

BARGUSIN

The first production sidewall hovercraft (SES), Bargusin, was built in 1989 under the design developed by CKB "Vympel". The owner of the vessel is the Vostochno-Sibirskaya River Steamship Line.

The craft has a good seaworthiness and is intended for passenger ferry services along lakes, reservoirs and rivers. Having small draught it can land and take on passengers bow-on from any sloping bank.

The initial run of the Bargusin was organised in 1989 along the European waterways from Sosnovka to Belomorsk and then after transportation via motor-ship Kola by the North Sea Line from Tiksi to Yakutsk along the river Lena.

Bargusin's successful sea and strength trials took place at Baikal lake in Autumn 1990. Series production of this vessel started in 1991.

Principal Particulars

Length overall	32.4 m
Beam	6.4 m
Draught, hullborne	1.4 m
Draught, on-cushion	0.8 m
Weight, maximum	70.8 t
Weight, minimum	54.5 t
Passengers	130
Propulsive power	2 × 590 kW
Lift power	220 kW
Operational speed	27 knots
Range	325 nm
Operational limitation	1.2 m wave height

Classification: M standards of the River Register of the Russian Soviet Federal Republic.

Structure: The hull and superstructure are built in AlMg-61 aluminium-magnesium alloy and are of all-welded construction. There is lateral framing throughout the hull. Casing, floors and bulkheads are of pressed panels and framing is mainly of pressed profiles.

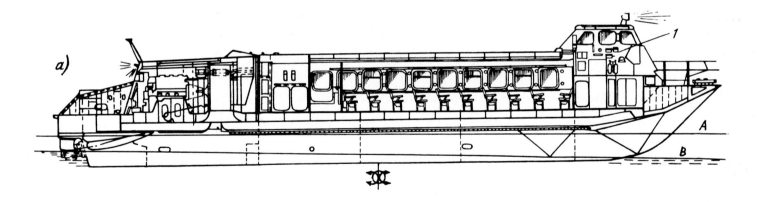

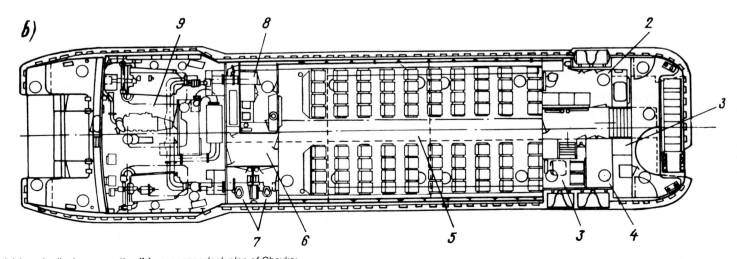

(a) *Longitudinal cross-section* **(b)** *passenger deck plan of Chayka;*
A *Water-line in displacement condition;* **B** *Water-line underway on air cushion;* **1** *Pilot-house;* **2** *Crew's off-duty cabin;* **3** *Storeroom;* **4** *Baggage compartment;*
5 *Passenger lounge;* **6** *Companionway;* **7** *Toilets;* **8** *Buffet;* **9** *Machinery space*

Propulsion: Main engine: two M 401A-1 (12 CHSN 18/20) diesels, driving propellers via standard reverse-coupling.

A special centrifugal fan designed and manufactured by NPO Vint generates the air cushion. A 7D 12A (12 CHN 15/18) diesel is used for driving the fan. Pressure and air supply which are necessary for the craft's stable motion both in calm water and in waves are provided at 160 kW and 1350 to 1400 fan rpm. The five-blade propellers are within the draught of the sidewalls.

Electrical system: Power supply requirements are met by a 24 V generator mounted on the main engine or by the accumulator battery.

Control: Two single-plate rudders behind each propeller. The rudders can be turned by hydraulic drive together or separately.

VERIFIED

Bargusin   1993

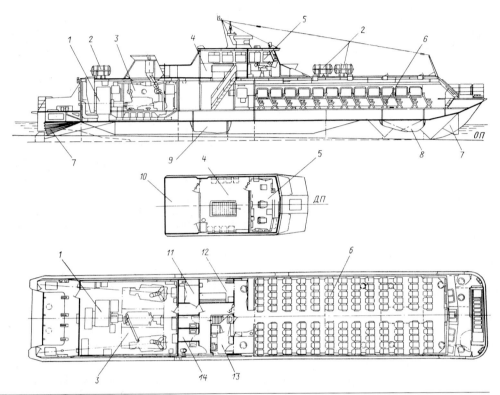

Bargusin. Key: **1** Fan; **2** Liferaft; **3** Engine room;
4 Veranda; **5** Rudder room; **6** Passenger saloon;
7 Flexible seal; **8** Ballast tank; **9** Transverse cushion
divider; **10** Observation platform; **11** Storeroom;
12 Crew rest area; **13** Snack bar; **14** Lavatories

VYMPEL CENTRAL DESIGN BUREAU

3 Kostin St, 603000 Nizhni Novgorod, Russia, CIS

Telephone: +7 (831) 234 2585
Telex: 151158 Trap SU
Telefax: +7 (831) 234 2096

Viacheslav V Shatalov, Director
Vladimir K Zoroastrov, Chief Designer

This Design Bureau has been responsible for the design of the following sidewall hovercraft: Zarnitsa, Orion, Chayka, Plamya, Luch, Luch-2, Altair, Olkhon and Bargusin, these craft having been built by the Sosnovskaya, Astrakhan and Moscow shipyards.

LUCH-2 PASSENGER SIDEWALL SES
Principal Particulars

Length overall	23.31 m
Beam	3.85 m
Draught, hullborne	0.67 m
Draught, on-cushion	0.6 m
Weight, minimum	17.63 t
Passengers	57
Propulsive power	382 kW
Operational speed	22 knots
Range	173 nm

ALTAIR PASSENGER SIDEWALL SES
Principal Particulars

Length overall	31.81 m
Beam	6 m
Draught, hullborne	1.4 m
Draught, on-cushion	0.8 m
Weight, minimum	58.6 t
Passengers	122
Propulsive power	2 × 735 kW
Lift power	220 kW
Operational speed	27 knots
Range	320 nm

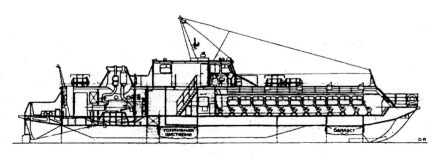

MAIN DECK

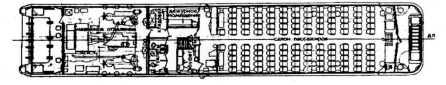

General arrangement of Altair
1994

OLKHON PASSENGER SIDEWALL SES

This is a double-deck, twin-screw vessel with passenger saloons in the fore and middle portions of the ship. The craft has a bow platform to embark/disembark passengers at an unequipped bank.

Principal Particulars

Length overall	32.4 m
Beam	6.4 m
Draught, hullborne	1.46 m
Draught, on-cushion	0.8 m
Weight, minimum	62.5 t
Passengers	130
Propulsive power	2 × 735 kW
Lift power	220 kW
Operational speed	27 knots
Range	540 nm

VERIFIED

UPPER DECK

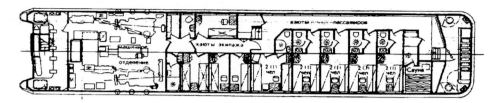

MAIN DECK

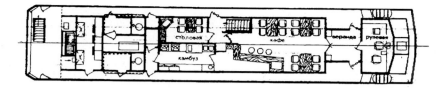

General arrangement of Olkhon
1994

FRANCE

ACKERMAN INDUSTRIE

Creux Redon de Cantadou, F-34400 Lunel, France

Telephone: +33 (1) 67 71 65 97
Telefax: +33 (1) 67 71 92 24

Guy Ackerman, *Technical Director*

Ackerman Industrie has over the past few years developed a range of light air cushion vehicles for sport and pleasure use which have led to a larger type, the ADOC 12, a 1.25 tonne payload utility craft supported in part by IFREMER.

ADOC 12

The ADOC 12 concept originally employed four very lightweight propulsion systems previously developed for much lighter craft. The same basic components are in use for Aeroplast 1-, 2-, 3- and 14-seat craft allowing considerable flexibility in manufacture and reduced stocks of spare parts.

The two lift fans supply the air cushion, of the same Multi-wing type as the four air propellers.

Principal Particulars

Length overall	8.4 m
Beam	4.4 m
Weight, maximum	3500 kg
Payload	1250-1500 kg
Crew	1 or 2
Passengers	12
Fuel capacity	300 l
Propulsive power	150 kW
Lift power	75 kW

ADOC 12   **1995**

Maximum speed	40 knots
Operational speed	30 knots
Range	210 nm
Operational limitation	wave height 1 m
Obstacle clearance	0.5 m

Classification: Bureau Veritas.
Structure: GRP frame.

Propulsion: In 1988 the craft was improved with a diesel engine, (225 kW Deutz diesel for both lift and propulsion), and a new propulsion system for better manoevrability, replacing the two petrol engines previously used. The propeller diameters were increased from 800 to 920 mm.

UPDATED

DCN

DIRECTION DES CONSTRUCTIONS NAVALES

2 rue Royale, F-75008 Paris, France

Telephone: +33 (1) 40 59 16 06
Telex: 202 184F
Telefax: +33 (1) 45 54 06 89

DCN INTERNATIONAL

19-21 rue du Colonel Pierre Avia, F-75015 Paris, France

Telephone: +33 (1) 41 08 71 71
Telefax: +33 (1) 41 08 00 27

and

DRET

DIRECTION DES RECHERCHES, ETUDES ET TECHNIQUES

26 boulevard Victor, F-75015 Paris Armées, France

Telephone: +33 (1) 45 52 49 24
Telex: 204 648 F

and

ACH

SOCIETE NOUVELLE DES ATELIERS ET CHANTIERS DU HAVRE

PO Box 1390, F-76066 Le Havre Cedex, France

Telephone: +33 35 26 81 77
Telefax: +33 35 25 09 70

and

CMN

CONSTRUCTION MECANIQUES DE NORMANDIE

PO Box 539, F-50105 Cherbourg Cedex, France

Telephone: +33 33 20 12 50
Telex: 170507F
Telefax: +33 33 44 01 09

AGNES 200 (ex NES 200)

The AGNES 200 has been developed within the framework of an inter-ministry programme, in which the following are participating: The Ministry of Defence, the Ministry of Research and the Ministry of Industry. The vessel was delivered at the end of 1990.

Involved in conducting the programme is Direction des Recherches, Etudes et Techniques (DRET). Industrial concerns involved are DCN, in respect of the project design, and ACH and CMN shipyards, in construction.

Agnes 200 is designed in the form of a basic air cushion platform for both civil and military versions and with an aft deck area of 208 m² is able to support a four tonne helicopter.

The major components (propulsion system, lift fans and so on) all use existing technology, and have therefore required only a limited degree of development. The evaluation prototype, named Agnes 200, has been built at Constructions Mécaniques de Normandie (CMN) and was launched on 2 July 1990. Maximum speed achieved during French Navy trials was 45 knots. The vessel is also fitted with a Codod propulsion system allowing the lift engines to drive the water-jets. The maximum speed in this mode is 15 knots.

During low speed transits it is possible to lift the bow and stern seals to the wet-deck and operate as a catamaran. Supplied by Zodiac Espace, the bow seal consists of a double loop and six segments, the stern seal is a more conventional triple loop design.

After 18 months with the French Navy the vessel entered passenger service on a 68 nm route between Dieppe and Brighton Marina, operated by Advanced Channel Express. The main modifications to prepare the vessel for its ferry role were the refitting of the existing bow saloon and the installation of a passenger saloon on the helicopter deck. Configured for 78 passengers in the bow saloon and 93 in the aft saloon, there was also a lounge on the upper deck with 12 first class seats for guests of the operator.

While on the English Channel the vessel had a crew of 12 comprising captain, mate, chief engineer, three sailors and six cabin crew.

Principal Particulars

Length overall	51 m
Beam overall	13 m
Draught, hullborne	2.3 m
Draught, on-cushion	1 m
Displacement, maximum	250 t
Propulsive power	2 × 2983 kW
Lift power	2 × 746 kW
Maximum speed	over 40 knots
Range	750 nm (25 knots)

AGNES 200 (in Brighton to Dieppe route, Summer 1992) entering Dieppe harbour (Roger Fayolle, STCAN)
1993

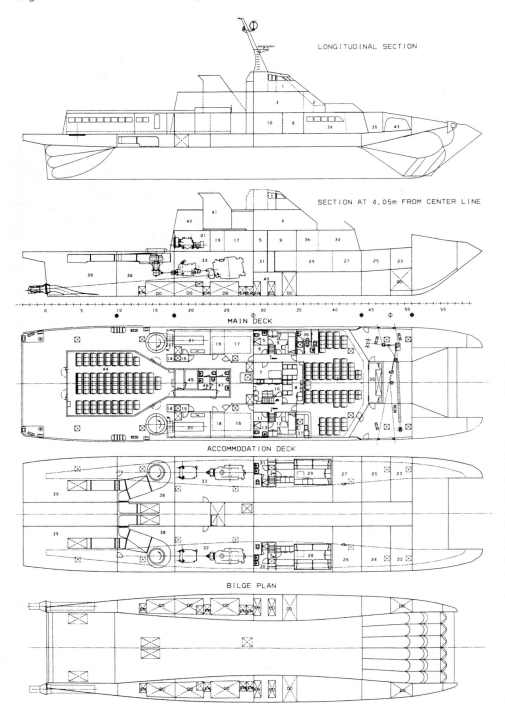

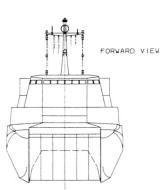

Agnes 200 key

1 *Wheelhouse/Radio room;* 2 *Storeroom;*
3 *Lounge;* 4 *Ventilation;* 5 *Toilet;* 6 *Fire cabinet;*
7 *Technical room;* 8 *Cafeteria;* 9 *Two berth cabin;*
10 *Pantry;* 11 *Storeroom;* 12 *Captain's cabin;*
13 *Toilet;* 14 *Fire cabinet;* 15 *Alleyway;*
16 *Storeroom;* 17 *Storeroom;* 18 *Engine casing starboard;* 19 *Engine casing port;* 20 *Generator set room starboard;* 21 *Generator set room port;*
22 *Void;* 23 *Void;* 24 *Storeroom starboard;*
25 *Storeroom port;* 26 *Void;* 27 *Void;* 28 *Six + two berth cabin;* 29 *Six + two berth cabin;* 30 *Toilet;*
31 *Toilet;* 32 *Engine room starboard;* 33 *Engine room port;* 34 *Forward saloon;* 35 *Boarding gate;*
36 *Men's toilet;* 37 *Bar;* 38 *Ventilators—Starboard and port;* 39 *Water-jets—Starboard and port;*
40 *Cofferdam;* 41 *Funnels;* 42 *Ventilation casing;*
43 *Covered deck;* 44 *Aft saloon;* 45 *Duty free kiosk;* 46 *Women's toilet;* 47 *Men's toilet*

AGNES 200 in passenger ferry configuration

Propulsion: Main propulsion: 2 × 2983 kW MTU 16V 538 TB 93 diesels driving 2 × KaMeWa 71 S II water-jet units.
Lift: 2 × 746 kW MTU 8V 396 TB 83 diesels each driving 1 × NEU centrifugal fan via a Renk 2-stage reduction gearbox, 180 000 m³/h at 600 kg/m². Off-cushion, power transferable to the 2 × KaMeWa water-jet units.

1200 TONNE ASW SES (DESIGN)

The Délégation Générale pour l'Armement (DGA) is engaged in a research and development pro-gramme on surface effect ships. So as to be able to fulfil perceived naval requirements for 1995, DCN is studying an SES project of approximately 1200 tonnes for Anti-Submarine Warfare (ASW) on the high seas. These studies are being conducted by the Service Technique des Constructions et Armes Navales (STCAN) under the aegis of a technical-operational working group, within the framework of a project named EOLES (light oceanic surface effect escort craft). The task lays down a requirement for an off-cushion speed of 18 knots but with speeds in the order of 50 knots on-cushion. Apart from its ASW armaments, the craft will be equipped with self-defence systems against air attack and surface ships.

Several stages of technology have to be passed through before this craft reaches the production phase. The experimental model, code-named MOLENES, has now finished its trials. In addition, DCN is involved in an inter-ministry programme aimed at developing the 200 tonne craft designed by STCAN. The experience from the AGNES 200 will give guidance to the operational and technological options arising from the EOLES project.

MOLENES (Modèle Libre Expérimental de Navire à Effet de Surface)

In 1980, DCN built under contract from DRET a five tonne craft, which had its trials in 1981 in the Toulon area. MOLENES is a dynamic manned model capable of proving the NES (Navire à Effet de Surface) concept of a high length-to-beam ratio, and confirmed results obtained in the experimental tank. It has provided data on seaworthiness, performance and manoeuvrability, as well as acceleration levels and their effects on the structure, equipment and fittings.

Principal Particulars

Length overall	12.1 m
Beam	3.43 m
Displacement, maximum	5.5 t

Propulsion: Propulsion is provided by two 55 hp water-jet units. The air cushion is effected by two centrifugal fans on vertical axes, giving a pressure of 1800 Pa (37.6 lb/ft²) and a flow of 4 m³/s (141 ft³/s).
Structure: The timber side keels are joined together by a tubular pyramid structure of light aluminium alloy 7020.

VERIFIED

GERMANY

BLOHM+VOSS AG

PO Box 100720, D-20005 Hamburg, Germany

Telephone: +49 (40) 3119 1803
Telex: 2 11 047-0 BV D
Telefax: +49 (40) 3113 3355

Blohm+Voss has built the SES prototype Corsair and since 1989 extensive test programmes and trials have been carried out to gain comprehensive technical data and experience for civil as well as mili-tary operations.

Blohm+Voss is entering the market with SES designs for passenger ferries and fast patrol craft, both based upon the operational experience of the prototype Corsair.

The original *Corsair* was modified for research purposes and now operates as *Mekat* for navy trials.

Mekat
Principal Particulars

Length overall	36 m
Beam	13 m
Draught, hullborne	2.2 m
Draught, on-cushion	0.8 m
Displacement	160 t
Payload	20 t
Propulsive power	2 × 2560 kW
Maximum speed	52 knots

Structure: The skirts are manufactured by Avon Rubber.
Propulsion: The main engines are two MTU 16V 396 TB 94, driving two Escher-Wyss surface-piercing CP propellers, 7-blade; through Maag MG-57 RO 2000/950 gearboxes.

The lift engines: 2 × MTU 6V 396 diesels driving 2 × centrifugal lift fans, through ZF gearboxes.

SES Mekat

CORSAIR 300 PASSENGER FERRY
(DESIGN)

Principal Particulars

Length overall	36.8 m
Beam	12.7 m
Draught, hullborne	1.8 m
Draught, on-cushion	0.6 m
Propulsive power	2 × 2000 kW diesel
Lift power	1 × 800 kW diesel
Fuel capacity	12 000 l
Water capacity	2000 l
Operational speed	approx 42 knots
Range	450 nm

Classification: GL or DnV
GL: GL +100 A4 High-Speed Air Cushion Vehicle, MC AUT.
DnV: DnV +1 A1 R45, Light Craft, SF-LC, EO.
IMO (Resolution A. 373 (X)) and national regulations.
Propulsion: 2 × KaMeWa (or equivalent) water-jets or 2 × Sulzer-Escher Wyss surface-piercing CPP.
Auxiliary systems: 2 × 70 kVA generators.
Control: Maritime Dynamics ride control system or equivalent.

CORSAIR 600 PASSENGER/CAR FERRY
(DESIGN)

Through co-operation between Blohm+Voss and Cirrus A/S of Norway, Blohm+Voss has extended the development programme for a combined car and passenger SES ferry, the Corsair 600, based upon the CIRR 200 design.

Principal Particulars

Length overall	61.4 m
Beam	16.4 m
Draught, hullborne	2.8 m
Draught, on-cushion	1.2 m
Passengers	360
Vehicles	36 cars
	4 coaches
Fuel capacity	29 000 l
Water capacity	5 000 l
Maximum speed	46 knots
Range	370 nm

Classification: The vessel is designed for classification by Det Norske Veritas or Germanischer Lloyd
DnV: 1A1 HSLC Passenger Car Ferry, R2, EO with notifications: 3 dk, 7 WTB, Surface Effect Ship.
GL: 100 A4 High-Speed Air Cushion Vehicle, MC AUT.
Regulations: IMO (Resolution A. 373 (X)), SOLAS, Marpol 73.
National Regulations as applicable. Provisions are made to later incorporate requirements expected from updated IMO regulations.
Structure: Hull material: Aluminium and FRP sandwich.
Propulsion: The vessel will be powered by four gas-turbines running water-jets through reduction gear-boxes. Lift fans and generators will be powered by separate diesel engines. Total installed power will be about 12 500 kW.

CORSAIR 900 PASSENGER/CAR FERRY
(DESIGN)

This new design from Blohm+Voss will have a total installed power of approximately 28 000 kW.

Principal Particulars

Length overall	90 m
Beam	23 m
Draught, hullborne	2.8 m
Draught, on-cushion	1.2 m
Passengers	770
Vehicles	140 cars
	10 coaches
Fuel capacity	95 000 l
Water capacity	8 000 l
Maximum speed	45 knots
Range	500 nm

SES MULTIPURPOSE CRAFT (DESIGN)

Blohm+Voss has also developed an SES multi-purpose craft applying the established MEKO technology for naval purposes in four versions: Surface warfare, Mine warfare, Anti-Submarine warfare and a Helicopter version.

UPDATED

Passenger/car ferry Corsair 600 design   **1993**

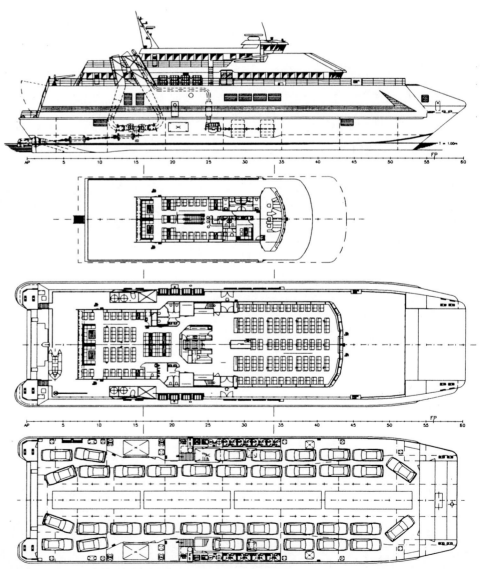

Passenger/car ferry Corsair 600 design

ITALY

FINCANTIERI CANTIERI NAVALI ITALIANI SpA

Via Genova 1, I-34121 Trieste, Italy
Naval Shipbuilding Division: Via Cipro 11, I-16129 Genoa, Italy

Telephone: +39 (10) 59951
Telex: 270168 FINCGE I
Telefax: +39 (10) 599 5272

Mario de Negri, *Naval Shipbuilding Division General Manager*

Fincantieri Naval Division has completed the detail design stage of three SES projects: the SES 250, a 450 passenger vessel; the SES 500, a 350 to 450 passenger plus 80 car vessel; and the SES 1000, a 450 to 600-passenger plus 118 to 180 car vessel. These designs were developed by applying the technology acquired in the naval field (Sparviero class hydrofoils and fast craft) to solve problems of high speed, noise reduction and accommodation comfort. Extensive model testing has been carried out to optimise the hull shapes, lift systems (cushion seals, fans and ducts) and the propulsion system in relation to hull resistance and sea-keeping in rough waters.

The structural design and drawings were presented for approval by the classification societies RINa and DnV, as well as the fire-fighting insulation and evacuation plans.

Cost analyses, both capital and operating, were developed for the most important Mediterranean routes for passenger and accompanied car services, and these considerations have considerably influenced the design aspects.

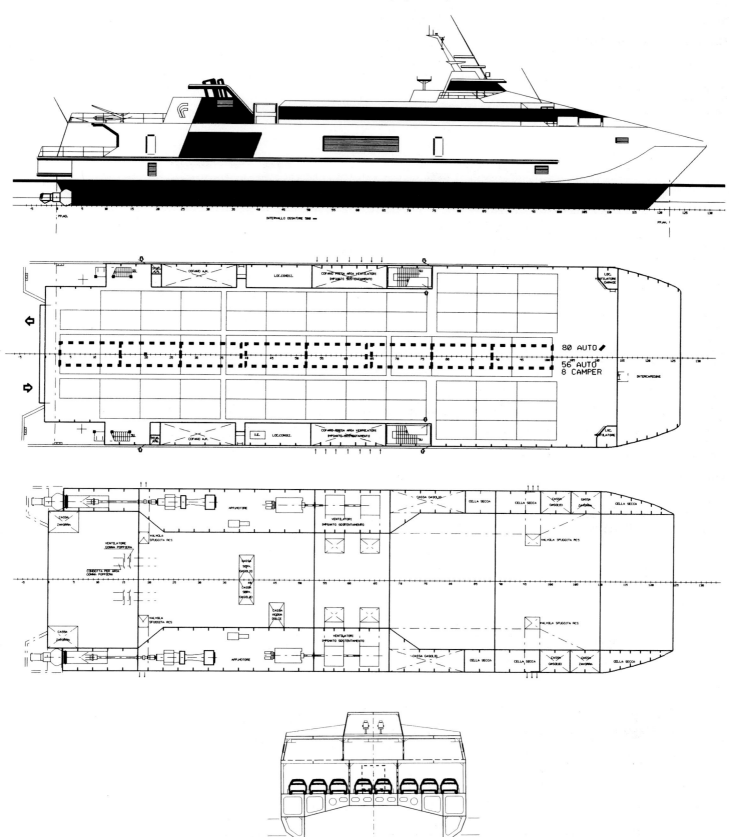

General arrangement of Fincantieri SES 500 design

SES 250 (DESIGN)
Principal Particulars

Length overall	42 m
Beam	14.5 m
Draught, hullborne	2.5 m
Draught, on-cushion	0.8 m
Passengers	450
Maximum speed	44 knots
Range	350 nm

Propulsion: 2 × MTU 16V 396 TB 84 engines.

The SES 250 has also been developed in two different naval configurations and was presented at the Italian Naval Exhibition in 1992.

SES 500 (DESIGN)
Principal Particulars

Length overall	66 m
Beam	18.4 m
Draught, hullborne	2.5 m
Draught, on-cushion	1.1 m
Passengers	350-450
Vehicles	80 cars
Maximum speed	46 knots (Allison 571KF)
	42 knots (MTU 20V 1163)
Range	550 nm

Propulsion: Choice of 2 × Allison 571KF or MTU 20V 1163 engines.

SES 1000 (DESIGN)
Principal Particulars

Length overall	84 m
Beam	23.2 m
Draught, hullborne	3.1 m
Draught, on-cushion	1.2 m
Passengers	450-600
Vehicles	118-180 cars
Operational speed	52 knots, 118 cars
	48 knots, 180 cars
Range	550 nm

Propulsion: 2 × GE LM 1600 gas-turbines.

UPDATED

SEC
SOCIETA ESERCIZIO CANTIERI SpA

Via dei Pescatori 56, Viareggio, Italy

Telephone: +39 (584) 3801
Telex: 500369 SEC I
Telefax: +39 (584) 384559

Registered Office:
Largo Toniolo 10, Rome, Italy

Dr Renzo Pozzo, *Managing Director*
Dr Ing Claudio Pesce, *Sales*
Dr Ing Leonardo Auoiarri, *Technical*

Società Esercizio Cantieri SpA (SEC) is the largest private shipbuilding company in Italy. In the 1980s a new project department became fully engaged on a study for determining the best configuration for new types of ferry suitable for the transport of up to 750 passengers and up to 200 vehicles, at maximum

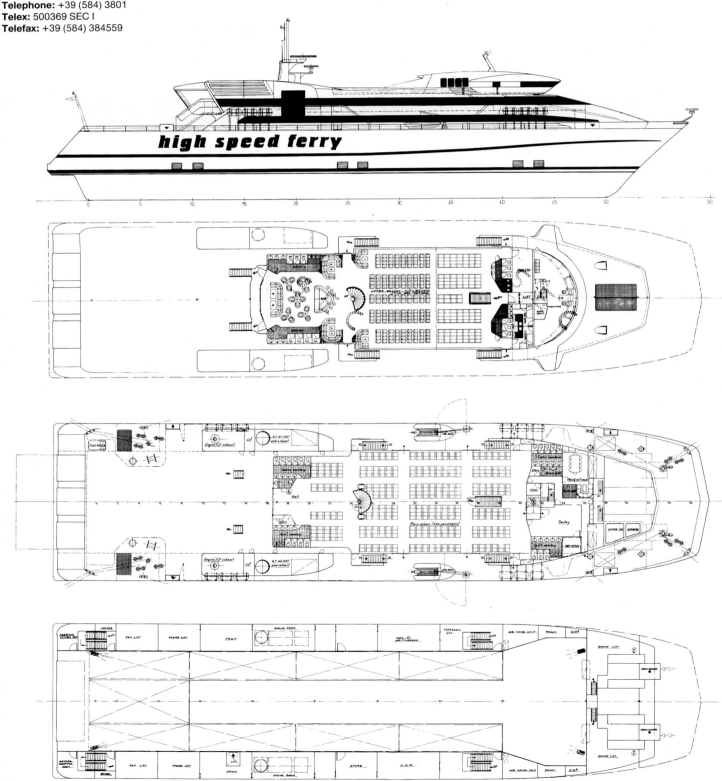

SEC 750 (design)

speeds above 50 knots. The choice fell on SES because of its high development potential.

By the middle of 1991 three vessel designs had been formulated and were designated SEC 450, SEC 550 and SEC 750. The following paragraphs detail the design philosophy.

Safety: Great attention has been paid to the safety of the passengers and the crew at sea. SEC has projected a vessel fully in compliance with the latest SOLAS requirements improving the safety of evacuation with the use of the latest chute and liferaft system.

In order to achieve this result the choices described in the following paragraphs have been made.

Steel structure: As far as the safety of the construction was concerned, the first aim was to comply with the SOLAS requirements to enclose the vehicle deck within A60 boundary against all other working and passenger areas of the vessel. This led to the choice of high tensile steel in order to reduce the structural weight. Nevertheless, this choice was confirmed only after having compared different materials and structures like FRP sandwich and aluminium alloy in respect to strength, fatigue and weight.

Stability: The maximum heeling angle with two flooded adjacent compartments is 5° (the engine room being one of the flooded compartments) instead of the limit of 7° required by SOLAS. An analysis concerning the on-cushion stability both in waves and high-speed manoeuvres has shown acceptable behaviour.

Life-saving equipment: The installation of the evacuation system, providing boarding platforms, chute and liferafts instead of the traditional lifeboats will be the only difference from SOLAS requirements for the Safety Equipment Certificate.

Redundancy: Throughout the designs, consideration has been given to maintaining a high degree of redundancy for the major systems even beyond the Regulations.

For example, the high speeds projected of 50 knots and above are achieved with only 75 per cent of the gas-turbine MCR. With one engine out of service and the remaining engines at 75 per cent MCR speeds will still be kept in the range of 38 to 40 knots. In addition a further power margin is built-in to the lift system where only 55 per cent of total lift power available is required in calm seas.

The air cushion seals (skirts) are composed of several interchangeable elements which allow the vessel to run on-cushion at full speed even when 30 per cent of the set of seals is worn.

Propulsion: The higher weight due to the construction material choice and to the high cargo capacity, along with the need to provide the highest possible speed, made gas-turbines the obvious choice. The

Model of SEC 750 (design)   *1993*

probable higher specific fuel consumption of the gas-turbine is largely compensated by weight saving and low maintenance cost.

SEC 750

Construction of the SEC 750 began in early 1992 but was suspended later that year due to a cut in the Italian Subsidy Law. Sea-keeping model trials were performed for SEC 750 at SSPA Maritime Consulting, Sweden. The design is aimed at providing the following features:

(1) high speed at full load compared to other high-speed vessels
(2) low vertical acceleration, comparable to a car travelling at 120 km/h on a motorway
(3) low internal noise levels, comparable to a conventional passenger ferry (55 dBA)
(4) a large number of passenger facilities
(5) a high level of acoustic isolation between different areas
(6) a low external noise level of 70 dBA
(7) a hull designed to minimise wave creation
(8) a very short crash stop distance
(9) a very high manoeuvrability
(10) a computerised anti-collision system
(11) infra-red night vision
(12) a very high capacity with respect to speed

(13) a shallow water sailing capability.

Principal Particulars

Length overall	93 m
Beam	23 m
Draught, hullborne	4.45 m
Draught, on-cushion	0.95 m
Passengers	750
Vehicles	200 cars
	or 80 cars and 10 coaches
Propulsive power	2 × 18 643 kW
Maximum speed	42 knots
Range	600 nm

Classification: RINa: *100. A.1.1. (UL) NAV. S (Mediterraneo) IAQ1.
ABS: +A.1. +AMS +ACCU (E) FERRY SERVICE.
Regulations: SOLAS 74, protocol 78, amended up to 1990.
Structure: Hull material: high tensile steel.
Superstructure material: aluminium alloy.
Skirt system: stern lobes, bow fingers.
Propulsion: The engines are two GE LM 2500 gas-turbines, driving two KaMeWa 180 SII water-jet units. The lift engines are four diesels.

VERIFIED

JAPAN

MITSUBISHI HEAVY INDUSTRIES

5-1, Marunouchi 2-chome, Chiyoda-ku, Tokyo, Japan

Telephone: +81 (3) 3212
Telex: 22443 J

Mitsubishi Heavy Industries is a joint partner in the technological research association of Techno-

Superliner. The company developed its own SES technology with the construction of an 18.5 m SES in 1989.

18.5 m SURFACE EFFECT SHIP

In August 1989 Mitsubishi completed the construction of an 18.5 m SES for the Japanese Defence Agency.

In mid-April 1989 a joint research and development programme was announced by the Japanese

Defence Agency and Mitsubishi Heavy Industries for a 50 knot SES designed to operate safely in rough coastal waters. The interest of the Defence Agency is in applying the technology to mine-sweepers, torpedo boats and patrol ships and stems from work started in 1983.

UPDATED

MITSUI ENGINEERING & SHIPBUILDING COMPANY LTD

6-4 Tsukiji 5-chome, Chuo-ku, Tokyo 104, Japan

Telephone: +81 (3) 3544 3462
Telex: 22821 J, 22924 MITZOSEN J
Telefax: +81 (3) 3544 3031

Hiroshi Kitashima, *Director and General Manager, Ship and Ocean Projects Division*
Yutaka Ikeda, *General Manager, Marine Department*

Mitsui's Hovercraft Department was formed in May 1964, following the signing of a licensing agreement in 1963 with Hovercraft Development Ltd and Vickers Ltd, whose ACV interests were later merged

with those of British Hovercraft Corporation. The company has been developing Mitsui hovercraft independently after terminating the licensing agreement in March 1986. The Mitsui ACVAS and

MV-PP5 Craft built	Seats	Launched	Operator
Hakuchyo No 3	75*	June 1970	Oita Hoverferry Co Ltd
Hobby No 1	75*	May 1971	Oita Hoverferry Co Ltd
Hobby No 6	75*	October 1974	Oita Hoverferry Co Ltd
Angel No 5	75*	April 1975	Oita Hoverferry Co Ltd
plus 15 others			

*Converted to Mk II configuration.

MV-PP10 represent such developments. The company has built 19 MV-PP5s, four MV-PP15s, two MV-PP05s, two ACVASs and two MV-PP10s. Details of the earlier hovercraft are given in the 1992-93 edition of this book.

ACVAS (ACV with Aft Skegs)

A new form of hovercraft was developed by the Mitsui company in the early 1980s with trials of the 10 m prototype *Eaglet* started in early 1986. The craft employs water-jet propulsion and is not therefore amphibious. The inlets for the two water-jet units are positioned in the underside of the two skegs which extend either side of the craft for approximately one-third of overall craft length. Over this length immersed areas of the skegs seal the air cushion; for the remainder of the cushion periphery a conventional loop and segment type skirt is employed. Unlike the sidewall hovercraft or surface effect ships the craft is almost totally supported by its air cushion at cruising speed. The craft is provided with a Mitsui motion control system exerting control over cushion air pressure variation and is fitted with fin stabilisers. The skirt/skeg combination is also found to give good ride comfort over waves through its soft response.

The Mitsui ACVAS concept is aimed principally towards applications in shallow rivers, lakes and other smooth waters and for ultra-fast ferries for operation in coastal and inland sea routes.

Eaglet
Principal Particulars
Length overall	10.9 m
Beam	5.1 m
Propulsive power	2 × 75 kW
Lift power	16 kW
Maximum speed	27 knots

Structure: Glass reinforced plastic.
Propulsion: Main engines: 2 × Nissan HA 120 (petrol).
Lift engine: 2 × Robin petrol.
Water-jet: 2 × Hamilton 771 units.

Sumidagawa

In August 1988, Mitsui received an order from the Tokyo Metropolitan Government Bureau of Construction for a river observation craft that can be used for observation and inspection of rivers in the Metropolis. The craft is fitted out in a manner suitable for international conferences to be held on board. This ACVAS vessel, named *Sumidagawa*, was delivered in March 1989.

Principal Particulars
Length overall	19.95 m
Beam	7.9 m
Draught, hullborne	1.5 m
Draught, on-cushion	0.5 m
Passengers	52-80
Propulsive power	2 × 346 kW
Lift power	2 × 272 kW
Maximum speed	30.4 knots
Operational speed	28.5 knots

MV-PP5 Mk II   1986

The Mitsui Sumidagawa *in operation with the Tokyo Metropolitan Government Bureau of Construction*   1990

Mitsui's ACVAS experimental craft Eaglet *fitted with HamiltonJet water-jet units*   1988

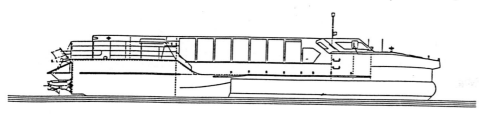

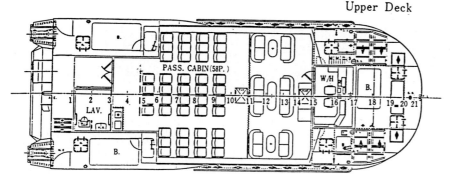

Upper Deck

Layout of Sumidagawa

MV-PP10 Dream No 2

1993

Structure: The vessel structure is made of anti-corrosive aluminium alloy with the hull longitudinally stiffened. Extruded sections are used extensively. The upper structure is of plate construction consisting of welded and riveted antiflexure material.

A flexible skirt made of rubberised nylon cloth is provided around the vessel excepting the skegs at the aft. The front part of the skirt system consists of a bag and fingers and the rear part has lobe seal construction. Air is supplied to the lobe seal from the bag at the front through a duct. The forward skirt is designed to minimise water spray for ease of navigation in rivers.

Propulsion: Two high-speed diesel engines are used for propulsion. The power is transmitted to two water-jet units through reduction gears. One high-speed diesel engine drives two lift fans, DC generator and cooler compressors through clutch and flexible joint.

Outfit: The layout of the passenger room can be changed by setting 80 seats for observation of rivers, 58 seats for observation of rivers and meetings and 52 seats for conferences.

MV-PP10

The most recent hovercraft developed by Mitsui is the MV-PP10, which can accommodate 84 to 100 passengers and has a maximum speed of 50 knots. This hovercraft embodies the technological progress of the hovercraft developed by MES over the years and has been designed for low cost, easy maintenance and a comfortable ride.

The main hull of the craft is constructed of marine grade aluminium alloy as for other MES high-speed craft. The MV-PP10 is fitted with a flexible skirt of improved durability and is powered by air-cooled, high-speed diesel engines, which are both inexpensive and easy to maintain and repair. The use of ducted propellers reduces the external noise.

Passenger accommodation is arranged on a single deck to allow the widest possible view. Seating arrangements are designed to allow many options such as increasing the capacity with auxiliary seats or making the accommodation more luxurious by expanding the legroom between rows of seats.

The MV-PP10 can also be fitted out for such purposes as surveying and rescue operations.

Two MV-PP10 type craft, *Dream No 1* and *Dream No 2*, were delivered in March 1990 and March 1991 respectively to the Oita Hoverferry Company Ltd.

In June 1994 Mitsui contracted for the construction of a third MV-PP10 hovercraft scheduled to be delivered to the same company in October 1995.

Principal Particulars

Length overall	23.1 m
Beam	11 m
Weight, maximum	40 t
Payload	9 t

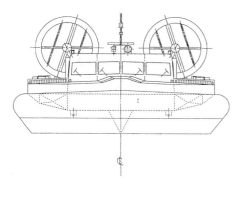

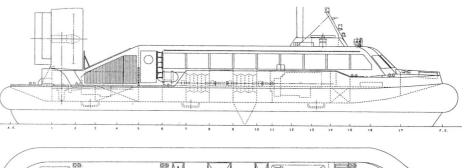

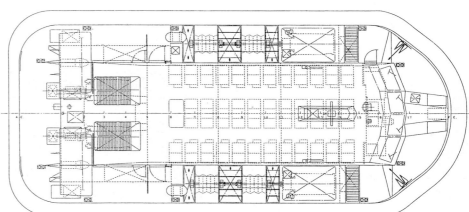

MV-PP10 general arrangement

Crew	3
Passengers	125
Propulsive power	2 × 441 kW
Maximum speed	50 knots
Operational speed	45 knots

Structure: The main hull of the craft is built in weldable anti-corrosive aluminium alloy, and the superstructure is of riveted construction.

The skirt is of bag and finger type and cushion depth is about 1.2 m. The lower side parts of fingers,

particularly susceptible to wear, are replaceable in sections.

Propulsion: The MV-PP10 is powered by four Deutz BF12L 513CP air-cooled turbocharged diesels, each rated at 441 kW (600 hp) at 2300 rpm maximum and 383 kW (520 hp) continuous. On each side of the craft, one engine drives two double-entry mixed flow fans for lift and two engines aft drive two ducted variable-pitch propellers.

Control: Twin aerodynamic rudders mounted on the

rear of the propeller ducts and differential thrust of the propellers provide directional control. Air bleed thruster ports are installed (one at the forward end and two at the aft end of the craft). Each thruster has an opening and shutting vane.

UPDATED

TECHNOLOGICAL RESEARCH ASSOCIATION OF TECHNO-SUPERLINER

Japan Research Centre Building, 1-3-8 Mejiro, Toshima Ku, Tokyo 171, Japan

Telephone: +81 (3) 3985 3841
Telefax: +81 (3) 3985 3740

Tokashi Nakaso, *President*
Kazuo Sugai, *Managing Director*

The programme of research and development of a super high-speed vessel named 'Techno-Superliner 93' is being undertaken in Japan. A target of the programme is to accomplish the technological foundation for developing and building a high-speed ocean-going cargo vessel with a speed of 50 knots, a payload of 1000 tonnes and a range of 500 nm. In addition, seaworthiness adequate to meet schedules in rough seas is desired.

In order to accomplish the Research and Development programme, Technological Research Association of Techno-Superliner was established in 1989 by seven leading shipbuilders in Japan.

This Research and Development programme ran from 1989 to 1994, throughout which the technological foundation for Techno-Superliner will be established through analysis, experiments and tests. The last year of the programme will be directed towards consolidating these technologies by scale model tests in actual seas. Debut of the actual ships is expected to be made in the latter half of the 1990s.

The Research and Development programme has a total budget of about ¥10 billion, over two-thirds of which will be raised privately.

As members of the association, Mitsubishi Heavy Industries Ltd and Mitsui Engineering and Shipbuilding Company Ltd are jointly investigating an SES type of novel super high-speed cargo ship (called TSL-A).

The concept of buoyancy/air cushion combination has three hull components: twin side hulls, an air cushion chamber and fully submerged foils. A 13 m test model (TSL-A12) was built in 1991 in order to confirm the basic performance of TSL-A in calm water. The model is controlled by the motion control systems operating on both air pressure and fins. A larger model, the TSL-A70, is now also under evaluation.

TSL-A70

The large scaled sea model named TSL-A70 was constructed separately at two major shipyards. The fore part was constructed at Mitsui Tamano Shipyard and the aft one at Mitsubishi Nagasaki. These two blocks were connected at Nagasaki and the vessel was launched in June 1994. A maximum speed of 54.4 knots was achieved at the official speed trial. The vessel is currently on evaluation trials.

Principal Particulars

Length overall	70 m
Beam	18.6 m
Draught, hullborne	3.5 m
Draught, on-cushion	1.1 m
Propulsive power	2 × 12 000 kW
Lift power	4 × 1500 kW
Maximum speed	54.4 knots
Range	500 nm

Structure: The hull material is aluminium.

Propulsion: There are two propulsion engines, driving a water-jet each.

The lift engines are three 1500 kW diesels and a 1500 kW gas-turbine, driving eight centrifugal lift fans.

The skirt system is: full finger (bow), lobe (stern).

The TSL-A70 design   1995

Manned test craft model TSL-A12   1993

The TSL-A design   1992

PROFILE

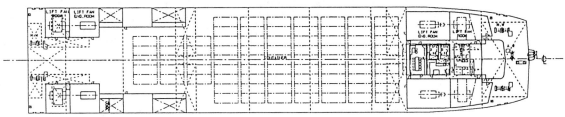

General arrangement of TSL-A127 (design)

1995

TSL-A127 (DESIGN)
At this stage of the design (1994) the following figures are approximate.
Principal Particulars

Length overall	127 m
Beam	27.2 m
Draught, hullborne	5 m
Draught, on-cushion	1.4 m
Payload	1000 t
Propulsive power	4 × 18 640 kW
Lift power	4 × 3200 kW
Maximum speed	50 knots
Range	500 nm
Operational limitation	4-6 m wave height

Structure: The hull material is aluminium.
Propulsion: The propulsion engines are four gasturbines, each driving a water-jet.

The lift engines are four gas-turbines, each driving a centrifugal lift fan.

The skirt system is: full finger (bow), lobe (stern).

UPDATED

KOREA, SOUTH

KOREA TACOMA MARINE INDUSTRIES LTD

(Hanjin Group)

PO Box 339, 974-15 Yangduck-dong, Masan, South Korea

Telephone: +82 (551) 551181/551188
Telex: 53662 KOTAMAN K
Telefax: +82 (551) 949449/949903

Choong-Hoon Cho, *Chairman*
Yi-Taek Chim, *President*
Chul-Kyu Chun, *Vice President*
Shin-Doo Kang, *Executive Managing Director*

Seoul office: PO Box 4296, 118, 2-Ga, Namdaemun-Ro, Chung-Ku, Seoul, South Korea

Telephone: +82 (2) 728 5446/8
Telefax: +82 (2) 757 0884

Since its founding in 1971, Korea Tacoma Marine Industries Ltd (KTMI) has built a variety of fast patrol boats and high-speed passenger boats, and has concentrated its efforts on the development of high-speed SES and amphibious hovercraft for civil and paramilitary applications.

In 1977 KTMI began an ACV development programme, and the company designed and constructed a test surface effect ship in 1978.

KTMI named its first surface effect ship Turt II. This had a length of 8.2 m, weight of 3.8 tonnes, and capacity for seven passengers. To date KTMI has developed and constructed five 18 m SES (90 passenger), one 11 m SES (56 passenger), one 17 m SES (72 passenger), two 26 m SES (158 passenger), one 28 m SES (200 passenger, modified 26 m SES), a manned test amphibious hovercraft, a 12 m diesel-powered prototype hovercraft and a 14 m diesel-powered sea ambulance hovercraft.

The company has now developed a 40 m SES design.

TURT III
18 m SES
The 18 m (59 ft) design has buoyant catamaran-type sidewalls almost identical in shape to those of the smaller craft.

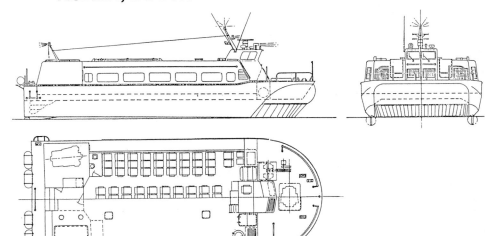

KTMI 18 m SES

Craft built (18 m SES)	Delivered to	Route
Air Ferry	Seo-Kyung Ferry Co	Pusan to Geoje Island
Cosmos	Geo-Je Ferry Co	Masan to Geoje Island
Phinex	Geo-Je Development Co	Pusan to Geoje Island
Sun Star	Kumsan Hungup	Yeosu to Near Island

Principal Particulars

Length overall	18.1 m
Beam	9 m
Draught, hullborne	1.74 m
Draught, on-cushion	1.08 m
Weight, maximum	36 t
Passengers	maximum 90
Propulsive power	2 × 485 kW, 596 kW or 970 kW
Maximum speed	35, 40 or 50 knots

Propulsion: Power for the lift system is provided by a single marine diesel in the 298 to 373 kW range. Power for the propulsion system is provided by twin diesels of 485, 596 or 970 kW, each driving a water propeller via a reversing gearbox and an inclined shaft.
Control: Twin water rudders aft, one on each side-hull. Differential propeller thrust for slow-speed manoeuvring.
Structure: Main structure built in welded marine aluminium alloy. Segmented skirt at the bow and stern.

26 m SES
Principal Particulars

Length overall	25.7 m
Beam	10.2 m
Draught, hullborne	2.45 m
Draught, on-cushion	1.45 m
Displacement, maximum	65 t
Payload	16.5 t
Crew	10
Passengers	158
Propulsive power	2 × 755 kW

KTMI 26 m SES   *1986*

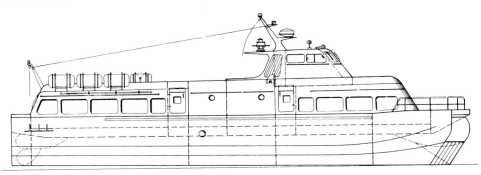

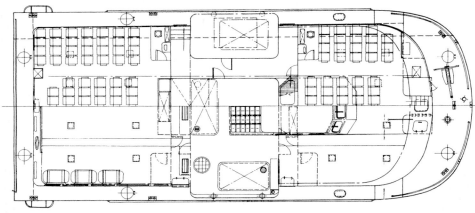

KTMI 26 m SES

Craft built (26 m SES)	Seats	Delivered to	Route
Duridoong Sil (ex *Young-Kwang I*)	158	Semo Co Ltd	Pusan to Geoje Island
Dudoong Sil (ex *Young-Kwang II**)	200	Semo Co Ltd	Pusan to Geoje Island
Soon Poong (ex *Tacoma III*)	158	Semo Co Ltd	Yeosu to Geomoon Island

*Modified to 28 m

Lift power	380 kW
Maximum speed	35 knots
Range	250 nm

Structure: The main structure is built in welded marine aluminium alloy and the superstructure is constructed in riveted marine aluminium alloy.

The bow skirt consists of single-bag and multi-segments. The stern skirt is a multi-bag type, consisting of three bag sections, inflated to a pressure slightly above that of the cushion by two 0.61 m fans on the deckhouse of the engine rooms.

Propulsion: The lift system is powered by a single General Motors Detroit Diesel Allison 12V-71TI. This engine directly drives a dual 1.075 m diameter lift fan, to provide cushion air to the plenum chamber and, via toothed belts and a hydraulic system, two secondary 0.61 m diameter fans for stern skirt inflation. Propulsive power is supplied by two MTU 8V 396 TB 83 diesels, each driving a water propeller via a reversing gearbox and an inclined shaft.

Electrical system: One GM 2-71 diesel generator, rated at 30 kW 60 Hz, 220 V, is provided.

Control: Craft heading is controlled by twin balanced stainless steel rudders operated hydraulically by a steering wheel. Additional control is provided by differential use of the water propellers.

Outfit: Air-conditioning, audio system and airliner-type seating is provided for 10 crew members and

158 passengers. The bridge accommodates the commander, navigator and engineer.

TURT IV

Builder of the first amphibious hovercraft in Korea, the Turt III type, a manned test craft launched in February 1981, KTMI followed it in December

1984 by the development of an amphibious utility hovercraft Turt IV type, the first diesel-powered amphibious hovercraft in Asia.

Principal Particulars

Length overall	12.65 m
Beam	7.04 m
Weight, minimum	8.1 t
Payload	1.5 t
Propulsive power	315 kW
Lift power	240 kW
Maximum speed	55 knots
Operational speed	40 knots
Range	200 nm
Operational limitation	2 m wave height

Structure: The main hull is built in welded aluminium alloy 5086-H116 (plate) and 6061-T6 (extrusion), and the deckhouse is riveted.

The skirt is an open loop and segment type and anti-bouncing ties are built into the loop.

Propulsion: The lift system comprises two single 1.075 m fans driven by a Deutz air-cooled diesel engine. Thrust is supplied by a Deutz air-cooled diesel engine driving a 2.75 m ducted propeller.

Control: One rudder and one elevator positioned in the ducted propeller slipstream provide directional control and trim control respectively. Additional control in low speed is provided by two puff ports which are designed specially for turning and reversing and are supplied by cushion air.

TURT IV Mk 1

As a sea ambulance version, Turt IV Mk 1 is intended for quick transportation of patients from islands to land. The distinctive features of the craft, compared with Turt IV, are the twin propulsion units for increased manoeuvrability and the reduced lift power due to the developed skirt. Turt IV Mk 1 was constructed in 1987 and was delivered in April 1988.

Principal Particulars

Length overall	13.35 m
Beam	7.44 m
Weight, minimum	11 t
Payload	2 kg
Propulsive power	2 × 203 kW
Lift power	203 kW
Maximum speed	50 knots
Operational speed	40 knots
Range	150 nm
Operational limitation	2 m wave height

Structure: The main hull is built in welded aluminium alloy 5086-H116 (plate) and 6061-T6 (extrusion), and the deckhouse is riveted.

The skirt is an open loop and segment type and anti-bouncing ties are built into the loop.

Propulsion: The lift system consists of two single 1.07 m diameter fans driven by a Deutz air-cooled diesel engine rated at 203 kW at 2300 rpm. Thrust is supplied by two 205 kW Deutz air-cooled diesel engines at 2300 rpm driving two 2.0 m diameter ducted propellers.

Control: Two rudders and two elevators positioned in each of the ducted propeller slipstreams provide directional control and trim control respectively. Additional control is provided by the differential thrust of the propellers. Directional control in low speed is provided by two puff ports which are designed specially for reversing and turning and are supplied by cushion air.

Craft built (TURT IV Mk 1)	Seats	Delivered to	Route
Jun-Nam 540	9	The Ministry of Health and Social Affairs	Coastal service

KTMI Turt IV type hovercraft Eagle II   *1986*

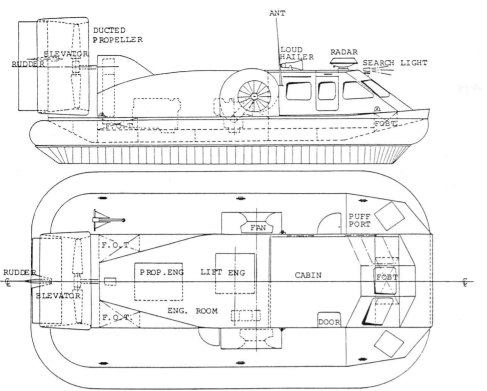

Layout of Turt IV

Weight, minimum	15 t
Payload	1.3 t
Propulsive power	2 × 254 kW
Lift power	203 kW
Maximum speed	40 knots
Operational speed	35 knots
Range	150 nm
Operational limitation	2 m wave height

TURT V

The prototype of the Turt V was developed at the end of 1989. Design was started from the end of 1985 and related model test (tank test, wind tunnel test, radio control test and so on) was conducted in 1986.

Turt V is a multipurpose amphibious vehicle capable of operating in open sea and confined shallow waterways including swamps, scrubland, sandbanks and mudflats.

A variety of payloads including wheeled vehicle, general cargo and removable cabin for passengers can be carried in the cargo deck and the bow ramp allows vehicles to be driven on and off the craft. Military versions are also available for fast attack and logistic support.

Principal Particulars

Length overall	26.5 m
Beam	13.8 m
Weight, maximum	95 t
Payload	30 t
Propulsive power	2 × 1864 kW
Lift power	2 × 1864 kW
Maximum speed	60 knots
Operational speed	50 knots
Range	300 nm

Structure: The main hull and the supersturcture are built in welded aluminium alloy 5086-H116 (plate) and 6061-t6 (extrusion).

The skirt is an open loop and segment type and anti-bouncing webs are built into the loop.

Propulsion: The lift system consists of six double inlet 1.07 m diameter fans driven by two gas-turbines rated at 1211 kW each. Thrust is supplied by two 1864 kW gas-turbines driving two 3.6 m diameter ducted controllable pitch air propellers.

TURT IV Mk 2

This craft, of which three have been built, is a stretched version of the Turt IV Mk 1. Lift and propulsion systems are identical to those of the Turt IV Mk 1, but the hull has been lengthened by 1.75 m and propulsion engines are upgraded from 203 kW (Deutz) to 254 kW to improve the performance in rough seas.

Control: Three rudders positioned in each of the propeller ducts provide directional control at high speed, and directional control at low speed is provided by four puff ports which are designed specially for reversing and turning.

Principal Particulars

Length overall	15.3 m
Beam	7.64 m

Turt IV Mk 2   1992

KTMI 28 m SES (Modified 26 m SES)   1992

Turt IV Mk 1   1989

KTMI 17 m SES Que-Ryong II   1989

Control: Two rudders on each side of propeller duct and rotating bow thrusters provide the directional control. Additional control is provided by the differential thrust of the propeller.

17 m SES

The first 17 m craft *Que-Ryong II* is a high-speed waterbus which was delivered and entered service on So-Yang man-made lake near Seoul in September 1988. The 17 m SES is designed as a very reliable, cost-effective, high-speed waterbus with good transportation efficiency for operating on inland waters such as lakes, rivers and inland waterways. Good ride quietness and comfortable passenger space enhance this craft.

Principal Particulars

Length overall	17.3 m
Beam	5 m
Crew	3
Passengers	72
Propulsive power	2 × 217 kW
Lift power	127 kW
Weight, maximum	21.5 t
Maximum speed	30.0 knots

Structure: The hull is built in welded marine grade aluminium alloy and the deckhouse is constructed in riveted marine grade aluminium alloy.

The bow and stern skirt consists of single-bag and multi-segments which are attached to the bag and connected to the underside of the hull by straps.

Propulsion: Power for the lift fan is supplied by a single VOLVO PENTA TAMD 41A marine diesel engine. Propulsion engines are two VOLVO PENTA TAMD 71A marine diesels.

Control: Twin rudders, one on each side of the hull, provide directional control. Additional control is provided by the differential thrust of the propellers.

Outfit: Audio system and airline-type seating is provided for 72 passengers and 3 crew members.

40 m SES (DESIGN)

KTMI's 40 m SES was designed as a high performance passenger craft.
Hull material is marine aluminium alloy rather than GRP for higher reliability and easier maintenance. Noise and vibration levels have been minimised and a ride control system is adopted on this craft.

Principal Particulars

Length overall	40 m
Beam	12 m
Draught, hullborne	2.5 m
Draught, on-cushion	0.9 m
Passengers	336
Propulsive power	2 × 2000 kW
Lift power	2 × 410 kW
Maximum speed	50 knots
Range	300 nm

Control: Remote-control and monitoring system, ride control system, autopilot system.

UPDATED

Craft built (17 m SES)	Seats	Delivered to	Route
Que-Ryong II	72	Dong-Bu Co Ltd	So-Yang river to In-Je

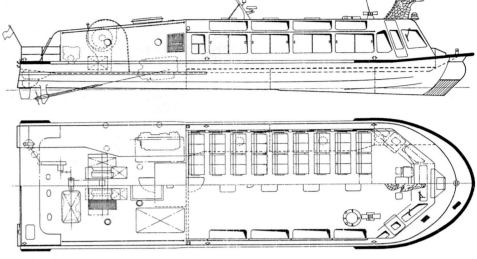

KTMI 17 m SES

Model of 40 m SES 1995

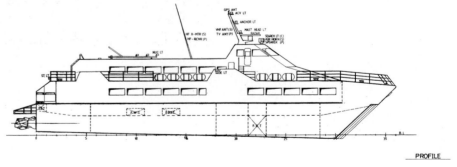

PROFILE

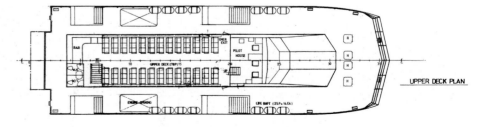

UPPER DECK PLAN

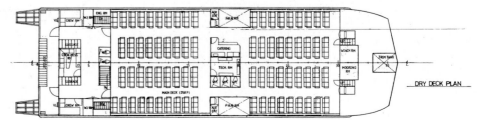

DRY DECK PLAN

General arrangement of 40 m SES
1994

SAMSUNG HEAVY INDUSTRIES COMPANY LTD

Headquarters: Namdaemun Building, 25 1-Ka, Bongrae-Dong, Chung-Ku, Seoul, Korea

Telephone: +82 (2) 728-6570
Telefax: +82 (2) 728-6789

Shipyard: 530 Jangpyung-ri, Sinhyun-up, Koje-Kun, Kyongnam, Korea

Telephone: +82 (558) 303015
Telefax: +82 (558) 322160

Hae Kyu Lee, *President*
Sung Ki Kim, *Marketing Director*
Young Ryeal Joo, *Principal Researcher*
Byung Lee, *Director Passenger Ship Construction*

Samsung Heavy Industries Co Ltd was established in 1974 and operates three very large production facilities in Korea.

The Koje shipyard builds various types of ships and offshore structures, large scale processing facilities and industrial machinery.

Since the shipbuilding business commenced in 1977, SHI has successfully built various types of vessels such as VLCCs, tankers, product carriers, full container vessels and bulk carriers.

In the area of high-speed craft, SHI has been performing research and development since 1991. The SES project was started in 1992 and its first passenger vessel, *Dong Yang Gold*, was delivered to the domestic owner in May 1994.

In addition to conventional catamarans and monohull vessels, SHI has also developed and designed an SES type high-speed passenger car ferry.

Dong Yang Gold

Ordered by Dong Yang Express Co Ltd, the 37 m SES vessel *Dong Yang Gold* was delivered in May 1994 and entered service on a route off the west coast of the country linking Mokpo with the islands of Heuksan-do and Hong-Do.

Principal Particulars

Length overall	36.5 m
Beam	12 m
Draught, hullborne	2 m
Draught, on-cushion	0.8 m
Crew	7
Passengers	352
Fuel capacity	7.2 t
Water capacity	0.8 t
Propulsive power	2 × 2000 kW
Lift power	2 × 405 kW
Maximum speed	50 knots
Operational speed	45 knots
Range	250 nm

Classification: Korea Register of Shipping.
Structure: FRP single skin in main hull, FRP sandwich in deck and superstructure.
Propulsion: Main engines: 2 × MTU 16V 396 TE74L diesel engines, each driving a Kamewa 63SII water-jet.
Lift engine: 2 × MTU 8V 183 TE 72 diesels.
Navigation and communications: Two radars, one gyro compass and magnetic compass, autopilot, Global Positioning System (GPS) navigator. Two VHF radio telephones, MF/HF radio telephone, satellite E. P. I. R. B.
Control: A microprocessor-controlled Ride Control System (RCS) for damping the vertical acceleration of the vessel by means of venting the overpressure in the main cushion chamber.

80 m SES Passenger Car Ferry (DESIGN)

SHI's 80 m SES was developed as a high-speed passenger car ferry in January 1994. A decision was made to select an SES, primarily because of the proven savings in power and cost, and its high development potential. The vessel is designed to carry a total of 500 passengers and 75 cars, and is capable of a fully loaded maximum speed at 100% MCR in calm water of 50 knots.

Principal Particulars

Length overall	79.84 m
Beam	20.18 m
Draught, hullborne	2.83 m
Draught, on-cushion	0.95 m

Dong Yang Gold   1995

PROFILE

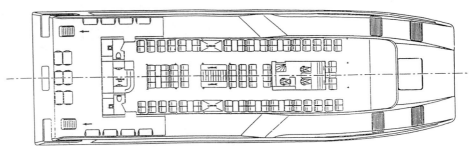

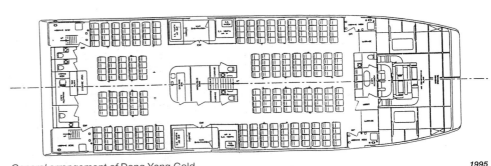

General arrangement of Dong Yang Gold   1995

Crew	16
Passengers	500
Vehicles	75
Propulsive power	2 × 13 500 kW
Lift power	3 × 1700 kW
Maximum speed	50 knots
Operational speed	45 knots
Range	600 nm
Operational limitation	Sea State 3

Classification: DnV +1A1 HSLC Passenger car ferry R2.

Structure: The hull is constructed in alluminium alloy.
Propulsion: Main engines: 2 × gas-turbines, each driving a water-jet.
Lift engine: 3 × diesels, driving 3 × 2 × (1.3 M DWDIs).
Control: A microprocessor-controlled RCS for damping the vertical acceleration of the vessel by means of venting the overpressure in the main cushion chamber.

NEW ENTRY

SEMO COMPANY LTD

Shipbuilding Division, 1 Jangiri Donghaemyun, Kosungkun, Kyungnam, South Korea

Telephone: +82 (556) 723535
Telefax: +82 (556) 723570

Bok-Hoon Lee, *Vice President*

Known for their ferry operating division which includes, in a fleet of 30 ferries, three hydrofoils, three amphibious hovercraft and now two SESs. Semo Company Ltd delivered in 1992 from their Kosungkun Shipyard the 36.4 m SES *Democracy* which began service in December 1992 in their fleet, operating between Inchon and Baknyung Island. Journey time for the route is approximately 3½ hours.

The Semo Company yard had delivered a further three 40 m SESs by the end of 1994.

36.4 m SES *Democracy*
Principal Particulars

Length overall	36.4 m
Beam	11.3 m
Draught, hullborne	2.15 m
Draught, on-cushion	0.7 m
Crew	10
Passengers	340
Fuel capacity	14 000 l
Water capacity	2000 l
Propulsive power	2 × 1680 kW
Lift power	2 × 373 kW
Maximum speed	50 knots
Operational speed	45 knots

Propulsion: Main engines: 2 × MWM TBD 604B V16 diesels, 1680 kW each at 1800 rpm.
Lift engines: 2 × DDC GM8V-92 TA diesels, 373 kW each at 2100 rpm.

40 m SES *Democracy II, III & IV*

These 40 m craft are developments of the 36.4 m vessel built in 1992. *Democracy II* entered service in April 1994 followed by *Democracy III* in August and *Democracy IV* in November 1994.

Principal Particulars

Length overall	40 m
Length waterline	33.8 m
Beam	11.6 m
Draught, hullborne	1.9 m
Draught, on-cushion	0.6 m
Crew	10
Passengers	390
Propulsive power	1970 kW
Lift power	529 kW
Maximum speed	50 knots
Operational speed	45 knots

Propulsion: Main engines: 2 × MTU 16V 396 TE 74L rated at 1970 kW each at 1920 rpm.
Lift engine: 2 × DDC 12V-92 TA rated at 529 kW each at 2100 rpm.

UPDATED

Democracy *built by Semo Company*   *1993*

Democracy III   *1995*

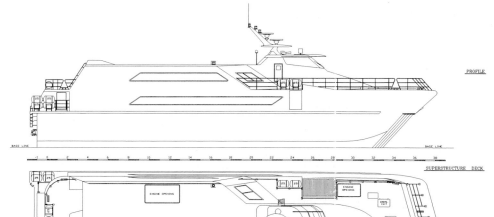

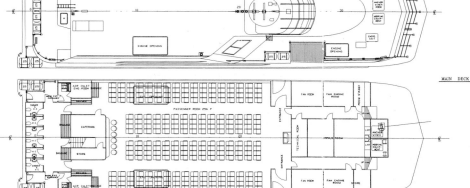

General arrangement of Democracy II
1995

NETHERLANDS

HOVERTRANS BV

Keizersveer 9, 4273 LD Hank, Netherlands

Telephone: +31 (1622) 3062/3089
Telefax: +31 (1622) 3075

R J Lubbers, *General Manager*
A M Koevoets, *Design Manager*

Hovertrans BV designs and builds special products applying state-of-the-art composite and metal bonding techniques. The production programme includes a single-engined hovercraft, the Colibrie, a twin-engined hovercraft, the Polar Bear, and a small four-seat rescue craft. Feasibility studies are currently also being made for a 30- to 50-seat high-speed craft. Incorporated in the design of these craft are the standards of the CAA, IMO, Bureau Veritas and Canadian Coast Guard.

Colibrie

The Hovertrans Colibrie amphibious hovercraft is an FRP single engine powered multiple role craft. The application of standard mechanical parts and easy access to vital parts of the craft ease and reduce maintenance and associated costs.

The most significant feature of Hovertrans hovercraft is the low noise production. The Colibrie craft produces, under cruising conditions, 75 dB(A) at 25 m.

The design of the Colibrie is based on safe life as well as on fail-safe principles. The safe life of mechanical parts extends well over the inspection and maintenance schedule period interval.

The combined hull and sideboards supply the craft with over 10 tonnes of floating capacity. The damage stability is in accordance with international rules and regulations. The propeller is protected by an FRP duct, placed well above the deck. The craft is controlled using three FRP rudders placed directly in the slipstream of the propeller. A skirt shift system is optional.

The Colibrie was tested by the Dutch Agency for Transport and Public Works in the Zeeland Delta area, fulfilling hydrographic surveying and supply tasks. This led to the frequent use of Hovertrans' own hovercraft, *Tuchone Princess*, by the agency on a lease basis. A second Colibrie hovercraft is currently employed at a holiday resort in the Indonesian Arcipel.

Colibrie is powered by a standard truck diesel engine, has a maximum speed of 37 knots and a cruising speed of 30 knots.

In 1994 a craft was successfully used in a round the clock evacuation and relief action when an abnormally high water level in the Dutch rivers caused the flooding of a large area in the south-east

Hovertrans Colibrie **1995**

of Holland. The craft evacuated inhabitants and transported medical equipment, fire-fighters, policemen, and the supplies for two villages.

Principal Particulars

Length overall	11.5 m
Beam	5.7 m
Weight, minimum	3.3 t
Payload	2.2 kg
Passengers	12 (Business class)
Passengers	16 (Tourist class)
Passengers	19 (High density)
Fuel capacity	600 l
Propulsive power	200 kW
Maximum speed	40 knots
Operational speed	30 knots
Operational limitation	1 m wave height
Obstacle clearance	0.4 m

Classification: CAA, IMO, Bureau Veritas and Canadian Coast Guard.
Structure: The hull is of semi-monocoque sandwich construction, selectively combining glass and aramid fibres with polyester resin, using PVC foam as a core material.
Propulsion: The propulsion and lift engine is a single MAN Rollo water-cooled diesel D 0826, which produces 199 kW at 2500 rpm. This drives a three-blade Hoffmann adjustable-pitch air propeller, 1.5 m diameter, through a toothed belt transmission.

The lift fan is an Asselberg & Nachenlue axial flow fan, or a centrifugal flow fan.
Electrical system: 24 V, 4 batteries, 2 × 80 Ah, 2 × 135 Ah.
Auxiliary systems: The hydraulic system runs on an engine-driven pump with an electrically driven backup system.

Outfit: On customer request the craft is fitted with an additional heating or air-conditioning system. Interior design is on request, as are a pantry, special equipment racks, hydrographic equipment and a high definition radar.

Polar Bear
Principal Particulars

Length overall	8.0 m
Beam	4.7 m
Weight, minimum	2.1 t
Payload	1000 kg
Passengers	10 max
Fuel capacity	600 l
Propulsive power	2 × 68 kW or 1 × 140 kW
Maximum speed	35 knots
Operational speed	27 knots
Range	270 nm
Operational limitation	-40°C

Classification: CAA, IMO, Bureau Veritas and Canadian Coast Guard.
Propulsion: The main engine can be either an automotive diesel, or an industrial engine, driving a Hoffmann four bladed wooden fixed-pitch propeller.

The lift fan is a centrifugal Asselburg & Nanchenius type.
Electrical system: 12-24 V. 1 set of batteries, standard 2 × 120 Ah. Alternator: 2 × 55 Ah.
Outfit: Storage benches with artificial leather covered cushions and soft interior finish.
Operations equipment: If the craft is to be operated in extreme cold conditions (-40°C), it would be fitted with heated windscreens, heated fuel tanks, heated fuel valves, and special air intakes.

UPDATED

ROYAL SCHELDE BV
KONINKLIJKE MAATSCHAPPIJ DE SCHELDE

PO Box 16, 165 Glacisstraat, NL-4380 AA Vlissingen, Netherlands

Telephone: +31 (1184) 83911
Telex: 37815 KMS NL
Telefax: +31 (1184) 82686

D M de Muijnck, *Managing Director Shipbuilding*
H Keers/A van der Knaap, *Marketing and Sales Fast Ferries*

The Royal Schelde Seaswift series of surface effect ships covers a range of vessels consisting of the Seaswift 26, Seaswift 34 and Seaswift 60 designs. As Royal Schelde has extensive expertise in both civil and naval shipbuilding, the vessels can be designed as a commuter/passenger ferry, a car/passenger ferry (Seaswift 60), a coastguard vessel, an offshore crew/utility vessel, or for other applications within the dimensions and limitations of the standard designs.

The development of these vessels covered design, training and operational stage aspects including the testing and trials of an 8 m scale model and a 23 m vessel, the Seaswift 23. This latter vessel was also tested for an extensive period by the Netherlands coastguard (Kustwacht).

SEASWIFT 23

The Seaswift 23 is a prototype/demonstrator vessel, used for demonstrating and testing the design of Royal Schelde's Seaswift series and has been used for demonstration purposes for prospective clients as well as having formed the basis of the further designs. In August 1991 the vessel entered service with Cowes Express, operating a passenger ferry service between Southampton and the Isle of Wight in the UK for a period of 12 months.

Principal Particulars

Length overall	24.25 m
Length waterline	20 m
Beam	7.7 m
Beam overall	approx 7.94 m
Draught, hullborne	1.45 m
Draught, on-cushion	0.8 m
Crew	3
Passengers	132
Fuel capacity	3.6 m³
Water capacity	0.5 m³
Propulsive power	2 × 520 kW
Maximum speed	31 knots
Operational speed	26 knots

Classification: DnV+1A1 R30 Light Craft, ECO.
Structure: Welded marine grade aluminium alloy; scantling dimensions assume a maximum amidships vertical acceleration of 1 g.
Propulsion: Three centrifugal lift fans, resiliently mounted, the forward two being driven directly by the lift system diesel engine and the aft one being driven hydraulically by the same engine. Propulsion is provided by two MWM TBD 234 12V diesels, 520 kW each at 2200 rpm MCR, driving KaMeWa 40S water-jet units.
Auxiliary systems: Fire prevention, detection and extinguishing equipment, including Halon 1301 flooding systems for the engine rooms. Normal fuel, seawater cooling, hydraulic oil and bilge systems.
Outfit: 132 passenger seats on main deck. Passenger cabin and wheelhouse ventilated by two-speed ventilation system which incorporates heating elements.

Royal Schelde Seaswift 23 1993

SEASWIFT 26 (DESIGN)

The Seaswift 26 is the smallest available vessel in the Seaswift range. The design is derived from the extensive tests with the Seaswift 23 with an adapted power rating and seating for a larger number of passengers. The vessel is ideally suited for commuter traffic in inter-harbour areas such as those encountered in large coastal cities worldwide, inter-island traffic, and river traffic on large rivers.

There are two options available, either a 40 knot version or a 50 knot version. Details below are for the 40 knot version.

Principal Particulars

Length overall	27.25 m
Length waterline	24.65 m
Beam	8.9 m
Draught, hullborne	1.45 m
Draught, on-cushion	0.75 m
Passengers	156
Maximum speed	42.5 knots
Operational speed	40 knots
Range	280 nm.

Classification: DnV +1A1 R30HS LC passenger ECO.

Structure: Welded marine grade aluminium alloy.

Propulsion: One main lift fan supplying cushion air is installed in the forward lift fan room. One booster fan supplies the aft seal air. The forward fan is driven by one intercooled, supercharged marine diesel engine and the aft fan is driven by an electric motor, electrically connected to the lift fan diesel-driven booster fan generator. Propulsion is provided by two Deutz MWM TBD 604B V8 diesels, or two MTU 8V 396 TE 74 diesels, driving two KaMeWa 45 S62 water-jets.

Auxiliary systems: An RCS is fitted for damping the vertical acceleration of the vessel by means of venting the overpressure in the main cushion and the aft seal.

Outfit: Seating is provided on the main deck for 156 passengers, arranged in 3-6-3 rows with a minimum pitch of 83 cm.

SEASWIFT 34 (DESIGN)

This vessel is designed for coastal traffic in moderate seas and operation within 50 nm of an established harbour.

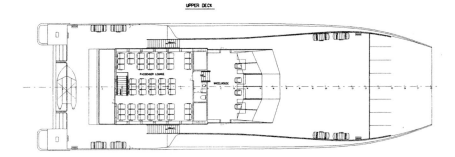

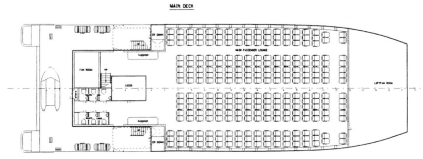

General arrangement of Seaswift 34 (design)

The design is also the basis for the paramilitary version which can be used by coastguards for policing, customs, fishery inspection and other duties.

Principal Particulars

Length overall	36 m
Length waterline	31.6 m
Beam	12 m
Draught, hullborne	1.7 m
Draught, on-cushion	0.8 m
Passengers	330
Maximum speed	47.5 knots
Operational speed	45 knots
Range	270 nm.

Classification: DnV + 1A1 R50 HS LC passenger EO.

Structure: Welded marine grade aluminium alloy.

Propulsion: Propulsion is provided by two MTU 16V 396 TE 74L diesels, or alternatively by two Deutz MWM, TBD 604B V16 diesels, driving two KaMeWa 63 S62 water-jets.

Two main lift fans supplying cushion air are installed in the forward lift fan room. These fans are driven by two intercooled supercharged marine diesel engines. The aft seal air is provided by two booster fans, driven by electric motors, electrically connected to the lift fan diesel-driven booster fan generators.

Auxiliary systems: A Ride Control System (RCS) is fitted for damping the vertical acceleration of the vessel by means of venting the overpressure in the main cushion and the aft seal.

Outfit: Seating is provided for a total of 330 passengers, 274 of which are situated in the main passenger lounge on the main deck and 56 in the second passenger lounge on the upper deck.

Seating in the main passenger lounge is arranged in rows of 3-5-5-3 with a pitch of 88 cm and in the second passenger lounge in rows of 3-3-3 with a pitch of 90 cm.

SEASWIFT 34, FAST COASTAL SECURITY CRAFT (DESIGN)

Basic data as per standard Seaswift 34, with elimination of passenger spaces and a proposed layout as shown in the general arrangement plan. With the application of Royal Schelde's naval technology and expertise, the vessel is ideally suited as paramilitary craft for police or coastguard tasks in confined waters and archipelagos. In addition, offshore duties such as anti-smuggling operations, protection within the EEZ area and environmental control can be carried out, as well as search and rescue missions. To perform these tasks, the vessel is fitted out with a complete communication package and a 20 mm gun. Other configurations to match a user's requirements can be considered and provided within the parameters of the design.

SEASWIFT 60 (DESIGN)

At present the largest SES vessel in the Royal Schelde Seaswift range, this passenger/car ferry is available in both diesel and gas-turbine versions. The vessel is designed to carry 434 passengers and 62 cars.

Principal Particulars

Length overall	59.5 m
Length waterline	53 m
Beam	17.5 m
Draught, hullborne	2.8 m
Draught, on-cushion	1.2 m
Payload	154.6 t
Crew	12
Passengers	434
Vehicles	62 cars

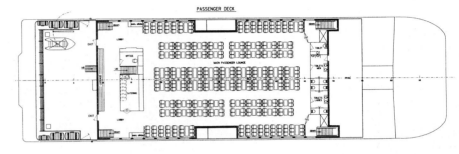

Royal Schelde Seaswift 60 (design)

Fuel capacity	36 500 kg
Water capacity	4000 kg
Propulsive power	2 × 6470 kW
Lift power	2 × 848 kW
Maximum speed	45 knots
Operational speed	42.5 knots
Range	550 nm

Classification: DnV + 1A1 R1 HS, EO.

Structure: Welded marine grade aluminium alloy, asymmetric V-shaped hulls with spray-rails on outer and inner sides.

Propulsion: Cushion air is provided by two lift fans, one in each hull, powered by two Deutz MWM TBD 604B V8 diesels, 848 kW each at 1800 rpm. Propulsion is provided by two SEMT Pielstick 20 PA6 V280 MPC diesels each having a maximum continuous rating of 6470 kW at 1050 rpm and each driving one KaMeWa 112 SII water-jet.

Auxiliary systems: An RCS is fitted for damping the

vertical acceleration of the vessel by means of venting the overpressure in the main cushion and the aft seal.

Outfit: Seating is provided for a total of 434 passengers at a seat pitch of 90 cm and arranged so that the main passenger lounge provides seating for 338 passengers and the first class passenger lounge for 96 passengers.

Doors at the forward and aft end of the car compartment avoid the necessity of vehicles turning when on board. Six straight car lanes are provided with a width of 2.35 m. The two centre lanes are designed for a maximum axle load of 1950 kg, the four side lanes for a maximum axle load of 840 kg. The free deck height is at least 2.6 m, so that passenger cars, caravans, vans and small campers can be loaded.

VERIFIED

TILLE SHIPYARDS BV

Tille Scheepsbovw Kootstertille BV, Baikwar 10, NL-9288 XH Kootstertille, Netherlands

Telephone: +31 (0) 5121 2300
Telefax: +31 (0) 5121 2395

Rein Amels, *Commercial Director*
A D (Bert) de Jonge, *Manager, High-Speed Craft*

SES 2000 (DESIGN)

Announced by Tille Shipyards BV towards the end

of 1991, the SES 2000 is a 25 m vessel with the hull to be built in either aluminium or GRP foam sandwich and incorporating a number of features deemed essential for commuter and longer range high-speed passenger transport. Special attention has been paid to the provision of easy access to all machinery for inspection and maintenance. No corrosive materials are used in the design of the craft, noise and vibration levels have been minimised and one particularly interesting feature is the use of fibreglass shafts, developed by Karlskronavarvet. On short commuter runs the bow loading/unloading configuration facilitates operation by one person.

Principal Particulars

Length overall	25 m
Length waterline	23 m
Beam	10.6 m
Passengers	153-220
Propulsive power	2 × 764 kW
Lift power	402 kW
Maximum speed	45 knots
Operational speed	35 knots

Classification: ABS or Lloyd's Register for harbour and sheltered waters operation.

Structure: Superstructure: GRP foam sandwich.

Propulsion: The propulsion engines are two Caterpillar diesels, driving 2 × KaMeWa 45 water-jets.

The lift engine is a Caterpillar diesel, driving 2 × 1.0 m lift fans, 1800 rpm.

Gearboxes: 2 × Nico MGN 332X 850 rpm output
Electrical system: 12/24 V from 2 battery banks.

AC power is provided from a diesel alternator.

VERIFIED

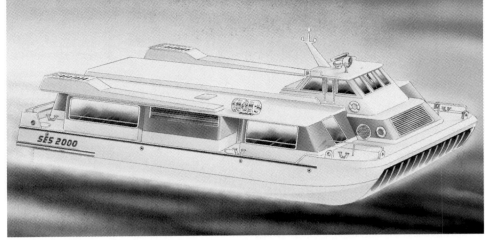

Tille Shipyards SES 2000 (design)   *1992*

NORWAY

KVÆRNER A/S FAST FERRIES

PO Box 303, Skøyen, N-0212 Oslo, Norway

Telephone: +47 (2) 296 7400
Telefax: +47 (2) 296 7410

Bent Hammel, *President*

KVÆRNER MANDAL A/S

Gismerøya, PO Box 283, N-4501 Mandal, Norway

Telephone: +47 (3) 827 9200
Telefax: +47 (3) 826 0388

Roger Sprimont, *Managing Director*

SES MINE COUNTERMEASURES VESSEL

'OKSØY' Class and 'ALTA' Class

A series consisting of four mine-hunters and five mine-sweepers (with an option on a sixth) is now under production at Kværner Mandal A/S for the Royal Norwegian Navy. The mine-hunters have the designation 'Oksøy' class and the mine-sweepers 'Alta' class. The design of the vessels is based on the Surface Effect Ship (SES) principle. The special characteristics of the SES concept are utilised to obtain advantages both with respect to operational capability and economy. Delivered between 1993 and 1996 these craft will replace the present class of eight US-built 1950s MSC-60 coastal mine-sweepers/hunters. The Kværner Group will provide engineering support, quality assurance services and financial assistance.

Kværner Mandal moved into new production facilities in 1991, the yard is located at Gismerøya Island near Mandal. The production hall has been built for the particular purpose of building high-speed military and civil vessels in composite materials and to the highest quality standards.

Based on the existing design of the MCMVs, Kværner Mandal has further developed and modified the vessel design in order to meet international demands. The first vessel, 'Oksøy', undertook sea trials in 1993 and was commissioned in August 1994. The fourth craft is now on sea trials and the sixth vessel is under construction.

Principal Particulars

Length overall	55.2 m
Beam	13.3 m
Draught, hullborne	2.15 m
Draught, on-cushion	0.87 m
Weight, maximum	370 t
Crew	29 (+12 extra capacity)
Water capacity	5000 l
Propulsive power	2 × 1400 kW
Lift power	2 × 700 kW
Operational speed	20+ knots (transit)
	5+ knots (mine-hunting)
	12+ knots (mine-sweeping)
Range	1200 nm

Kværner Mandal 12 m manned test craft   *1993*

'Oksøy' during harbour acceptance trials   *1994*

Propulsion: The propulsion engines are two MTU 12V 396 TE 84, driving two Kværner Eureka water-jets.

Engines, lift: 2 × MTU 8V 396 TE 54, 700 kW each.

12 m MANNED SES TEST CRAFT

On the 20 January 1993, Kværner Mandal launched a one-third scale prototype of a new air cushion catamaran high-speed patrol vessel. The

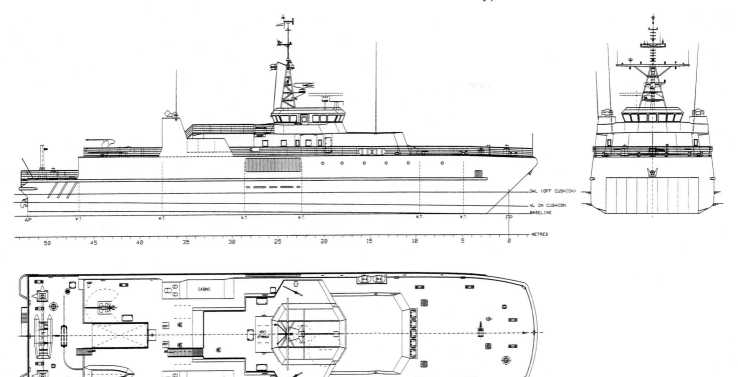

General arrangement of Kværner Mandal mine countermeasures SES

first of nine mine countermeasure vessels was launched two months later. The vessel is based on the air cushion catamaran principle (SES) and built of composite materials.

The favourable properties of air cushion catamarans are further enhanced in this vessel by a new single-skin hull construction of fibre-reinforced polymer, and by a novel hull geometry, developed by Kværner Mandal and their project partners.

To study materials, design and performance, Kværner Mandal has gone to the rather unusual step of building a 12 m, 40 knot manned model.

The Kværner Mandal new form of hull construction gives a reduction of 25 per cent in the hull structural weight over conventional GRP hull structures and even more when compared to aluminium hulls. This low weight allows a higher payload, longer range and higher speed to be offered. For a given payload it can mean smaller craft and lower engine power, and thus reduced investment, fuel consumption and operating and maintenance costs.

The 12 m model is part of an international research project called 'Advanced FRP Composite Hull Structures for High Speed Craft'. The study programme includes sea-going performance, speed and acceleration in calm and rough seas, dynamic stability in high waves, reactions to wave-induced slamming loads on the hull materials and improvement in air cushion design.

The other project participants are Du Pont, Conoco, Det norske Veritas, Veritas Research, the Marine Consulting Group, Devold AMT, Jotun Polymer, the Norwegian Defence Research Establishment, the Norwegian Industry Fund and the Royal Norwegian Research Council.

Kværner Mandal has patented a new production method for series building under controlled conditions. The production hall allows indoor building of large air cushion catamarans side by side.

UPDATED

ULSTEIN INTERNATIONAL A/S

N-6065 Ulsteinvik, Norway

Telephone: +47 (70) 014000
Telefax: +47 (70) 014002

Steinar Sivertsen Kulen, *Managing Director*

Harald Nordal, *General Manager High-Speed Craft*
Arne Mortensen, *Technical Manager High-Speed Craft*

The Ulstein group designs and builds air cushion catamarans in addition to conventional catamarans and monohull vessels.

The group has delivered 18 air cushion catamarans in FRP sandwich construction. The UT 904 Air Cushion Catamaran (ACC) is the latest design from the group, two having been launched in 1992.

A licence/technology transfer agreement was signed with International Shipyards of Australia in 1993 for the production of a series of UT 928 craft.

Air Cushion Catamarans from Ulstein/Brødrene Aa/Ulstein Eikefjord yards

Yard No	Type	Year delivered	Name	No of seats	Operation area	Operator	Flag
170	CIRR 105P	1984	Fjordkongen (ex Norcat)	264	North Norway	Troms Fylkes D/S	Norway
184	CIRR 115P	1986	Santa Lucia (ex Ekwata)	290	Mexico	Marítima Turística del Mar de Cortés	NIS
190	CIRR 120P	1988	Wight Queen (ex Virgin Butterfly ex Ekwata II)	280			UK
198	CIRR 60P	1988	Harpoon	85	(Test vessel)		Norway
199	CIRR 120P	1988	Express La Paz (ex San Pawl)*	315	Mexico	Marítima Turística del Mar de Cortés	NIS
200	CIRR 120P	1989	Santa Maria	330	Brazil	Tidewater	NIS
201	CIRR 120P	1989	Wight King (ex Sant' Agata)	280			NIS
202	CIRR 120P	1989	San Pietro	330	North Norway	Finnmark Fylkesrederi og Ruteselskap	Norway
210	CIRR 120P	1989	San Frangisk	330	Sicily-Malta	Virtu Ferries	NIS
211	CIRR 120P	1990	Catamaran II (ex Golden Olympics)**	330	Greece	Piraiki Naftiliaki SA	Greece
212	CIRR 120P	1990	La Vikinga	330	Cuba	KS Pantheon	NIS
213	CIRR 120P	1990	Perestroika	368	South Korea	Semo Marine Craft	South Korea
218	CIRR 120P	1990	Nissho	320	Japan	Yasuda Ocean Line	Japan
219	CIRR 120P	1990	Fjordkongen	320	North Norway	Troms Fylkes D/S	Norway
204	CIRR 120P	1991	Sea Flower	349	South Korea	Dae-A Kwaesok Ferry	South Korea
226	CIRR 120P	1991	Catamaran I	330	Greece	Piraiki Naftiliaki SA	Greece
208	UT 904	1991	Ocean Flower	360	South Korea	Dae-A Kwaesok Ferry	South Korea
205	UT 904	1992	Santa Eleonora	342	Italy-Corfu	Misano Alta Velocita	Italy

NIS=Norwegian International Shipping Register   * constructive total loss, Feb 1993   ** constructive total loss, 1992   *UPDATED*

UT 904

The UT 904 is designated an Air Cushion Catamaran by Ulstein International, a design in the category of surface effect ships and air cushion vehicles in general.

Construction of the first UT 904 started in September 1990. The vessel has accommodation for 320 passengers.

The lift fan engines power double-sided stainless steel centrifugal fans and in addition drive (hydraulically) two centrifugal booster fans which provide pressurising for the aft seal bag.

A hydraulically operated ride control system is fitted, employing louvre valves, pressure sensors and a microprocessor control unit. This system is designed to reduce vertical accelerations.

Principal Particulars

Length overall	39 m
Beam	12 m
Draught, hullborne	2.6 m
Draught, on-cushion	1 m
Passengers	320
Fuel capacity	13 800 l
Water capacity	2000 l
Propulsive power	2 × 2000 kW
Lift power	3 × 380 kW
Maximum speed	50 knots
Operational speed	46 knots

Classification: +1A1 R90 Light Craft EO.
Additional class:
SF-LC, stability and subdivision
F-LC, fire protection.
Regulations: National Flag Authorities.
Structure: The hulls are built in FRP/PVC foam sandwich or aluminium.
Propulsion: 2 × water-jet units.
The two lift fans are double-sided, stainless steel.
Auxiliary systems: The ride control system operates hydraulically controlled louvres, microprocessor-controlled, that vent the air chamber.

Ulstein UT 904 Ocean Flower   *1993*

Ulstein UT 904 Santa Eleonora
1993

WESTAMARIN WEST A/S

PO Box 143, N-4501 Mandal, Norway

Telephone: +47 (38) 262222
Telex: 21514 WRIN N
Telefax: +47 (38) 262302

Svein Berntsen, *Technical Manager*
Gowart Askildsen, *Purchasing Manager*
John Ihme, *Production Manager*

Westamarin West A/S (Mandal, Norway) entered SES work in 1986 when the company concluded a licence agreement with Karlskronavarvet AB of Sweden for the fitting out of two GRP hull SES 3400 Jet Rider vessels designed by Karlskronavarvet under which entry details of these craft are given. Following this development Westamarin embarked on the design of a larger SES, designated SES 4000, and built in aluminium. These craft employ air cushion systems licensed from Karlskronavarvet AB. There have been two Westamarin SES 4000 vessels built.

Westamarin SES 4000 Super Mexico (*ex* Super Dane)   *1990*

SES 4000
Super USA & Super Mexico
(ex Super Dane & Super Swede)
Principal Particulars

Length overall	40 m
Beam	12.6 m
Draught	2.21 m
Passengers	309
Fuel capacity	22 800 l
Water capacity	1500 l

Propulsive power	2 × 2720 kW
Lift power	4 × 270 kW
Operational speed	46 knots
Maximum speed	52 knots
Range	780 nm

Classification: DnV + 1A1 R45 EO, Light Craft Passenger Vessel.
Propulsion: 2 × SACM M7 UD 33 V16 main engines, each 2720 kW at 1600 rpm, driving 2 × Liaaen Speed-Z type CPZ 60/42-125 Mk II propeller units.

Lift: 4 × GM V6-92 TA, each 270 kW.
Navigation and communication: 2 × radars, 1 × gyro compass/magnetic compass, log, navigator echo-sounder.

2 × VHF transceivers, radiotelephones, mobile telephone, intercom, TV, radio and PA facility.
Auxiliary systems: 2 × GM V6-71T generators, each 201 kW.

UPDATED

SINGAPORE

SINGAPORE SHIPBUILDING AND ENGINEERING LTD

7 Benoi Road, Singapore 2262
PO Box 138, Jurong Town Post Office, Singapore 9161

Telephone: +65 861 2244
Telex: 21206 SINGA RS
Telefax: +65 861 3028/1601

Boon Swan Foo, *Managing Director*
See Leong Teck, *Deputy General Manager*
Wong Kin Hoong, *Assistant General Manager, Commercial*
Tan Pheng Hock, *Assistant General Manager, Yard*
Teh Yew Shyan, *Senior Manager, Quality Assurance*

TIGER 40

This Air Vehicles Tiger 40 was built by Singapore Shipbuilding and Engineering Ltd for a leasing company in Singapore, SAL Leasing, which owns the craft. In 1987 this craft was leased to the Singapore Navy. Tiger 40 craft are marketed in the Far East by Singapore Shipbuilding and Engineering Ltd.

VERIFIED

Air Vehicles Tiger 40 Hovercraft built by Singapore Shipbuilding and Engineering Ltd 1989

SPAIN

CHACONSA SA

COMPANIA HISPANO AMERICANA DE CONSTRUCCIONES CONSERVERAS SA
Mayor 57, 30006 Puente Tocinos, Apartado 419, E-30080 Murcia, Spain

Telephone: +34 (68) 230200/238512/230604
Telex: 67248 ABRO E
Telefax: +34 (68) 238508

Carlos Ruiz Valero, *ACV Programme Manager*

CHACONSA launched its air cushion vehicle research programme in 1973. In 1976 it received a contract for the development of the VCA-36 from the Spanish Ministry of Defence. Design of the lift and propulsion system was aided by experiments with laboratory models. Two manned research models, the 750 kg VCA-2 and the five tonne VCA-3, were later built to evaluate and refine the system. Details of these two craft are given in the 1992-93 edition of this book.

In addition to its military programme, CHACONSA has also examined industrial and agricultural applications of air cushion technology.

VCA-36

Designed to improve the rapid lift capability of the Spanish armed forces, the VCA-36 carries a 14 tonne payload, equivalent to three Land Rovers and 70 fully armed marines or infantrymen, to a beach landing zone at a speed of 60 knots. It can also be used for lighter-over-the-shore applications. Its dimensions allow it to operate from the docking wells of a number of LSDs and from ro/ro vessels with sufficient headroom and suitable ramps. Lifting eyes in the hull enable it to be hoisted on and off the decks of cargo ships. A removable roof above the cargo deck permits the craft to be loaded alongside supply ships.

CHACONSA VCA-36 during anti-submarine sea trials 1989

Principal Particulars

Length overall	25.5 m
Beam	11.04 m
Weight, maximum	36 t
Payload	14 t
Propulsive power	2 × 2500 kW
Maximum speed	60 knots

Structure: Riveted aluminium structure based on a grid of longitudinal and transverse frames which form a number of watertight buoyancy compartments. Fuel, ballast tanks and bilge systems are contained within these compartments. Access to the cargo deck is via hydraulically operated bow and stern ramps or the removable cargo deck roof. The central cargo deck is 18.65 m long, 2.6 m wide and 2.25 m high. Two main longitudinal vertically stiffened bulkheads run the length of the hull. These separate the central vehicle/cargo deck from the sidestructures which contain the gas-turbines, lift fans, transmissions, auxiliary power systems and cabins. Marines or assault troops are accommodated in two 35-seat cabins, 7.4 m long by 2.35 m wide, one in the forward section of each sidestructure. There are four landing pads fitted to the hull base. Four lifting eyes are provided for hoisting the craft.

The skirt is 1.4 m deep, bag and finger type of CHACONSA design in nylon fabric coated with synthetic rubber.

Propulsion: Integrated system powered by two Textron Lycoming TF25 gas-turbines, each with a maximum output of 1860 kW. Each drives two centrifugal fans and a 4 m diameter, five-bladed, variable-pitch propeller. Power is transmitted via two gearboxes with auxiliary outputs for lubrication, hydraulic pumps and generators. The combined epicyclic and bevel (splitter) gearbox (lower unit) transmits 620 kW from 14 500 rpm to 1080 rpm for the lift fans and 1400 kW from 14 500 rpm to 1988 rpm for the pylon propulsion gearbox (upper unit). The pylon bevel gearbox reduces the speed from 1988 rpm to the 1011 rpm of the propulsion propeller.

Electrical system: 2 × 15 kVA generators driven by the main engines provide three-phase 50 Hz at 380 V for AC and DC supplies.

BES (BUQUE DE EFECTO SUPERFICIE)

Early in 1987 it was announced that CHACONSA SA had teamed up with the Bazan yard (builder of fast naval craft) to develop a new surface effect ship, BES (Buque de Efecto Superfice).

CHACONSA BES-16   1990

BES-16

At the end of 1987 CHACONSA established a 50/50 joint programme with Empresa Nacional Bazan for the study, analysis and development of SES craft technology in order to design and build these craft in the range of 50 to 500 tonnes, full load displacement.

The first craft to be built was the BES-16 research craft, launched in 1988.

Principal Particulars

Length overall	16.78 m
Beam	5.4 m
Draught	0.75 m
Displacement	14 t
Propulsive power	2 × 335 kW
Lift power	2 × 82 kW

Structure: The hull is welded Al-Mg 4, 5 alloy.

Propulsion: Two Isotta Fraschini diesel engines, driving two Castoldi 06 water-jet units.

The lift engines are two VM-HRI 492 diesel engines, six centrifugal lift fans.

VERIFIED

FM-AERODESLIZADORES

Urb Nuevos Horizontes No 8, E-28971 Grinon, Madrid, Spain

Julian Martin, *Project Manager*
P Nogeroles, *Composite Manager*

Luis Moya, *Designer*
J V Lozano, *Production*

This company designs and builds small hovercraft for commercial use. Three main production craft have been built up to 7 m in length with payload capacities of up to just under 1 tonne. Speeds of up to 50 knots have been achieved. The production craft FMHC-001X, 002 and 004X are described in the 1989 and 1993 edition of this book. It is understood that the company is currently developing further craft although no details were available at publication.

UPDATED

SWEDEN

KARLSKRONAVARVET AB

S-371 82 Karlskrona, Sweden

Telephone: +46 (455) 19440
Telex: 8395018 KKRV S
Telefax: +46 (455) 17934

Hans Hedman, *Managing Director*

Karlskronavarvet is a subsidiary of Kockums AB, Malmø. It is a dockyard for construction, maintenance and modernisation activities mainly for the Royal Swedish Navy.

Extensive design and development work has been carried out to develop a surface effect ship for naval use as well as passenger transportation.

SES 3400 JET RIDER
Jet Cruise 2 (ex *Jet Prince*, ex *Sleipner*, Yard No 427)
Jet Cruise 3 (ex *Jet Princess*, ex *Draupner*, Yard No 428)

These two surface effect ships were built as a result of a co-operative agreement between Karlskronavarvet AB of Sweden and Westamarin A/S of Norway for the supply of two SESs for the Stavanger to Bergen 'Flaggruten' service. This contract was cancelled when the craft failed to meet the required performance, but they were subsequently bought (23 March 1988) by JKL Shipping for service between Copenhagen (Kastrup) and Helsingborg. The craft were then leased to Interscandic Line which operated them under the name Fast Ferry Siam from June 1989 till 24 August 1989 when Interscandic went into liquidation. In mid-1991 the two craft were sold to an operator in Thailand.

Karlskronavarvet obtained air cushion and skirt technology from Textron Marine Systems, USA in

Karlskronavarvet SES 3400 Jet Princess *(ex* Draupner*) sister vessel to* Jet Prince *(ex* Sleipner*)*   1989

exchange for their fibre-reinforced plastics. Design of the Karlskronavarvet surface effect ships was supported by extensive model testing at the SSPA in Gothenburg.

Principal Particulars

Length overall	33.4 m
Length waterline	28.2 m
Beam	10.5 m
Draught, hullborne	1.75 m
Draught, on-cushion	0.25 m
Crew	6
Passengers	244
Fuel capacity	10 000 l
Maximum speed	39 knots
Range	200 nm

Classification: DnV + 1A1 R15 EO.

Structure: Fibre-Reinforced Plastics (FRP) construction. Divinylcell PVC cellular plastic core, 40 to 60 mm thick, density 60 to 100 kg/m³. Facing of sandwich construction: glass-reinforced polyester resin, E grade glass, 800 g/m² woven roving and 100 or 300 g/m² chopped strand mat.

The skirt is made from rubber-coated nylon, the bow skirt has eight open segments, the rear skirt or seal has three lobes, bolted to each other; air is fed into the upper lobe and via feed holes into the lower lobes. Skirt design and manufacture by Karlskronavarvet AB.

Propulsion: Two KaMeWa 63562/6 water-jet units driven through ZF BU 750 reduction gearboxes.

The lift fans are four 0.76 m diameter double-inlet, centrifugal type, welded aluminium (designed and made by Karlskronavarvet AB) and driven via hydraulic transmission. Two fans in bow and two in stern.

Outfit: Initially 244 passengers and six crew (upper deck overnight cabins for crew), later modified to carry 292 passengers by removing overnight crew cabins, allowing a 48-seat 'Royal class' saloon to be provided.

Auxiliary systems: Heave damping, pressure monitoring system with electronic feedback.

Generators: 2 × Stamford MSC 334A.

SMYGE

This 30 m SES test craft was delivered to the Swedish Defence Materiel Administration (FMV) in the Spring of 1991, the contract having been received in June 1989.

The vessel has been built principally in order to develop 'stealth' technology and to gather operational SES experience.

One of the purposes of SMYGE is to test newly developed systems such as missile foundations, anti-submarine and mine-hunting equipment, various sensor systems and gun and antenna systems in realistic conditions.

Smaller vessels cannot carry all the weapons systems simultaneously. In Swedish conditions with relatively few units and limited space, flexibility is a precondition for obtaining the required objectives. Missiles and torpedoes and anti-submarine equipment are designed so that they can be placed on any ship and the ships in their turn are designed to carry these various pieces of equipment. It is anticipated that it will be possible to carry out this development work very efficiently on board SMYGE.

One advantage of SMYGE's hull construction is that there is an open work shaft from the hold down to the water, a 'moon pool'. The shaft is located at the ship's centre of gravity thus reducing movement forces on the equipment located there while at sea.

Examples of such equipment are hydrophones and other anti-submarine and mine-hunting equipment.

Principal Particulars

Length	30.4 m
Length waterline	27 m
Beam	11.4 m
Draught, hullborne	1.9 m
Draught, on-cushion	0.7 m
Displacement	140 t
Crew	14
Propulsive power	2 × 2040 kW
Lift power	2 × 460 kW
Maximum speed	>40 knots

Structure: The hull is of sandwich construction in Kevlar and fibreglass-reinforced plastic.

Propulsion: The main engines are two MTU 16V 396 TB 94 diesel motors, driving a pair of KaMeWa water-jet 63s.

Lift engines: Scania DS1 14, 460 kW.
Lift fans: 1.14 m intake diameter.

Electrical system: Mains: 440 V, 60 Hz, 3-phase.
Secondary supply: 220 V, 60 Hz, 3-phase.
Low voltage net: 24 V DC.
Generator: 72 kW.

UPDATED

SMYGE   *1992*

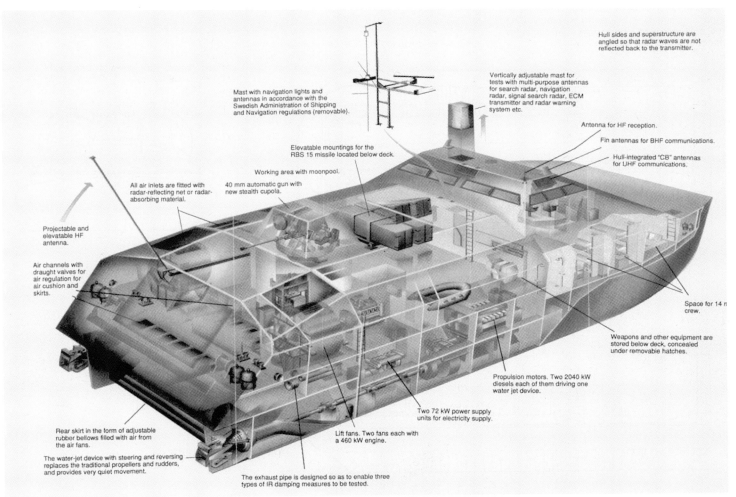

Major components and installed systems of SMYGE

1992

UNITED KINGDOM

ABS HOVERCRAFT LTD

PO Box 34, Totton, Southampton, Hampshire SO40 4LL, UK

Telephone: +44 (1703) 663533
Telefax: +44 (1703) 666438

K Blum, *Director*
W Sommer, *Director*
A F White, *Chief Designer*
E Southby-Tailyour, *Director*
A Byrne, *Operations Manager*

ABS Hovercraft Ltd has exclusive marketing and productions rights for the ABS range of hovercraft. The first craft in the series, the M-10, was launched in 1994 and has undergone extensive trials on the south coast of England. Highlights of the trials are the craft's high-speed capability, comfortably exceeding 50 knots fully laden at a continuous rating, and in rough weather trials coping on-cushion in waves of over 2 m in gale force winds. The design incorporates the latest composite technology providing the lowest operating costs yet achieved by this size of craft.

ABS M-10 on trials — *1995*

ABS P-80

One vessel is scheduled to be built in the USA for Hovertek Inc, Missouri, in 1995-96.

Principal Particulars

Length overall	19.8 m
Beam	7.8 m
Weight	29 t
Passengers	77
Propulsive power	2 × 390 kW
Operational speed	40 knots
Obstacle clearance	1 m

Propulsion: 2 × Deutz BF12L 513C 390 kW at 2300 intermittent, driving twin ducted, low noise CP propellers
Electrical system: Twin 24 V alternator system

ABS M-10

One vessel has been completed in the UK, built under subcontract to Vosper Thornycroft (UK) Ltd. The craft underwent trials and performance demonstration in November 1994.

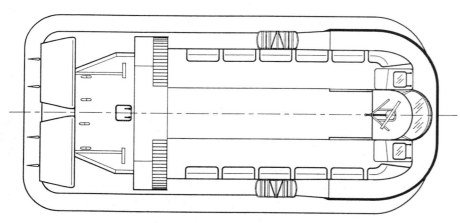

Artist's impression of ABS P-80 hovercraft — *1994*

PLAN VIEW.

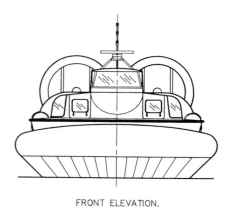

FRONT ELEVATION.

PROFILE VIEW.

General arrangement of ABS P-80 hovercraft
1994

Principal Particulars

Length overall	18.84 m
Beam	8.80 m
Payload	10 t
Crew	4
Fuel capacity	4600 l
Propulsive power	386 kW
Maximum speed	50 knots

Operational speed	40 knots
Range	600 nm
Obstacle clearance	1 m

Classification: Hull survey to Lloyds Register Certification.

Structure: Single-skin FRP hull, FRP foam sandwich deck.

Propulsion: Main engines: 2 × Deutz BF12L 513C air cooled diesels, driving twin 4-bladed controllable pitch, low noise propellers.

Electrical system: 24 V DC via transmission driven alternators charging 2 battery banks.

UPDATED

AIR VEHICLES LTD

Unit 4, Three Gates Road, Cowes, Isle of Wight PO31 7UT, UK

Telephone: +44 (1983) 293194
Telex: 86513 HVWORK G
Telefax: +44 (1983) 291987

C B Eden, *Director*

Air Vehicles Limited was founded in 1968 and has concentrated on the design and development of rugged fully amphibious hovercraft using welded marine aluminium hulls, simple systems and conventional piston engines. The company offers craft from four seats with designs of up to 200 seats and customers include the British, French and Canadian Ministries of Defence, the People's Republic of China, Nigerian Police, Bahrain Ministry of the Interior and the Republic of Singapore Navy.

Air Vehicles Limited is approved by the Civil Aviation Authority and undertakes modifications to larger craft. These have included flat-deck freight conversions of the BHC SR. N5 and SR. N6 hovercraft, power-assisted rudder packs for both types, and the conversion of an SR. N6 Mk 1S for high-speed hydrographic surveying.

Air Vehicles produced a conceptual feasibility study for a four-engined diesel-powered hovercraft to meet the requirements of Hovertravel Ltd. The eventual requirement of Hovertravel led to the design of the BHC AP1-88 for which Air Vehicles undertook much of the detail design work.

TIGER 12

The standard production craft has 12 seats (including the driver's) and the non-structural cabin top can be removed to suit various requirements. Fully amphibious, the craft can operate over a variety of surfaces such as mud, ice, sand and shallow water.

Principal Particulars

Length	8.0 m
Beam	3.85 m
Weight, minimum	1.9 t
Weight, maximum	2.7 t
Payload	0.9 t

Tiger 12 with high-speed, hydrographic 'fish' deployed in the water 1986

Crew	1
Passengers	11
Fuel capacity	213 l
Propulsive power	134 kW
Maximum speed	35 knots
Operational speed	25 knots
Operational limitation	25 knot wind
	1.25 m wave height

Structure: Superstructure and all bulkheads are of marine grade aluminium sheet welded to form a strong rigid box structure. Side members are inflatable, giving additional buoyancy and protection for the craft when mooring. By deflating the side members the vehicle can be trailed behind any large car or small truck. A built-in jacking system provides for loading and maintenance.

The skirt is a pressurised bag type with separate segments. The inflatable sides and skirt are attached to the craft with quick-release piano hinges.

Propulsion: Motive power for the integrated lift/propulsion system is provided by a single AMC 5900 cc petrol engine delivering 134 kW at 3600 rpm. The engine output is transferred to a 12-blade centrifugal lift fan and a 1.37 m diameter, four-blade, ducted propeller through a toothed belt system.

Electrical system: 12 V DC, negative earth, with an engine-driven 35 A alternator and a 60 Ah battery.

Control: Multiple rudders hinged at the aft end of the propeller duct provide directional control. Elev-

ators provide trim and, when raised fully, assist braking by reducing thrust. A water ballast system is used to adjust trim in pitch for varying load states.

Outfit: Enclosed cabin for the driver and up to 11 passengers. Access is via sliding doors, one port, one starboard. Driver's seat is forward right; navigator's forward left. There is adequate space for radar, radios and navigation equipment ahead of these positions.

TIGER 16

The Tiger 16 is a fully amphibious hovercraft capable of carrying 16 people over a variety of terrain including shallow water, sand, mud and ice. The first craft was completed at the end of 1985.

Principal Particulars

Length	11.27 m
Beam	4.1 m
Weight, minimum	2.5 t
Payload	1.5 t
Fuel capacity	790 l
Propulsive power	141 kW or 270 kW
Maximum speed	33 knots
Operational speed	25 knots
Operational limitation	25 knot wind
	1.25 m wave height

Structure: The hull is a fully welded, light but robust aluminium structure and offers a variety of options in the cabin layout. Seat mounting/load tie-down rails allow easy conversion of the cabin for passenger or

Tiger 16 with forward cabin and open well-deck 1989

load-carrying duties. The cabin options give any combination from fully trimmed and enclosed to a simple open workboat.

Rigid sidebodies provide a convenient work platform when surveying and a carrying area for long loads. For transportation the side decks are easily removed.

An inflatable ring around the periphery of the craft provides for coming alongside and a 'soft edge' when working off the side decks.

An open loop and segment skirt is fitted. The skirt assembly is attached to the craft using an aluminium piano hinge. Segments are individually and easily replaced. A skirt shift system is fitted.

Propulsion: Various engine options are available according to duty and include the Deutz BF6L 913C air-cooled diesel rated at 141 kW at 2500 rpm, and the Deutz BF8L 513 rated at 270 kW at 2300 rpm. The engine power is transmitted via a toothed belt drive system to a 12-blade centrifugal lift fan and a 1.5 m diameter, Robert Trillo Ltd designed four-blade ducted propeller. The propeller duct is designed to give efficient air entry and the outlet is shaped to provide for larger control surfaces. The propeller is designed to give high thrust per horse-power with low noise and is fitted with full length stainless steel leading edge protection.

Electrical system: 24 V DC negative earth with an engine-driven 45 A alternator and 90 Ah batteries.

Control: Four large rudders fitted at the propeller duct outlet provide directional control. Five elevators control pitch trim and when fully raised shut off the thrust. A skirt shift system provides rapid control of trim in pitch and roll.

Auxiliary systems: A fuel ballast system adjusts the craft trim in pitch, transferring fuel to the bow or stern of the craft. The main engine fuel tank is positioned amidships and is linked to the ballast system via a manually operated valve so that ballast fuel can be used to increase duration.

VERIFIED

ALUMINIUM SHIPBUILDERS LTD

Katana House, Fort Fareham Industrial Estate, Fareham, Hampshire PO14 1AH, UK

Telephone: +44 (1329) 826316
Telefax: +44 (1329) 825235

John Davies, *Managing Director*

Aluminium Shipbuilders is mainly known for its building of catamarans to the designs of International Catamaran Designs Pty Ltd, Australia. The company has however engaged in considerable hovercraft fabrication work. In particular contracts have been received from Griffon Hovercraft Ltd and Westland Aerospace. By the end of 1991 ASL had completed 12 hulls covering the current range of Griffon Hovercraft. For Westland Aerospace, ASL was involved in the total fabrication, fit out, and trials of a BHC AP1-88 hovercraft for operation by The Northern Shipping Company in the White Sea area of Russia.

VERIFIED

BRITISH HOVERCRAFT CORPORATION

(Division of Westland Aerospace)

East Cowes, Isle of Wight PO32 6RH, UK

Telephone: +44 (1983) 294101
Telex: 86761 WAD G
Telefax: +44 (1983) 298872

C C Gustar, *Managing Director, Westland Aerospace*
J M George, *Commercial Director*

The roots of the Corporation extend back to the world's first hovercraft, the SR. N1, which was built by Saunders Roe Limited in 1959, just prior to its being taken over by Westland.

BHC was formed in 1966, uniting the hovercraft interests of Westland and Vickers and also involving NRDC.

The world's first full-scale hovercraft production line was established at East Cowes in 1964. Since then BHC has produced 10 to 17 tonne SR. N6 craft, 50 tonne BH.7 craft and 200 to 300 tonne SR. N4

craft. The 39 tonne AP1-88 is the current production craft.

One BH.7 has been in service with the Royal Navy and six with the Iranian Navy. There have been four Iranian BH.7s refurbished by BHC at Cowes.

Military and general duty variants of the SR. N6 hovercraft are in service in the Middle East and Canada. This design is also used for general-purpose roles including hydrographic and seismic survey, freighting and search and rescue duties.

The current production AP1-88 diesel-powered, general-purpose hovercraft is built in welded aluminium alloy. Employing shipbuilding techniques, it combines a 10 to 12 tonne payload with a performance equal to that of the SR. N6. Full cabin versions of the AP1-88 operate regular passenger services and the type has also built up extensive charter experience. There are two craft in service with the US Navy as trainers under the LCAC programme, a half-well-deck variant is operated by the Canadian Coast Guard and an open-top freighter built by NQEA Australia Pty Ltd works in the gold mining industry in north-west Canada.

SR. N4 Mk 1 modified to Mk 3

Craft built	No of Seats	No of Cars	Yard No	Operator	Route
BHC SR. N4 Mk 1 *The Princess Margaret* (GH 2006) in service 1968, modified to Mk 3 in 1979	424	60	001	Hoverspeed Ltd	Dover to Calais
BHC SR. N4 Mk 1 *The Princess Anne* (GH 2007) in service 1969, modified to Mk 3 in 1978	424	60	004	Hoverspeed Ltd	Dover to Calais

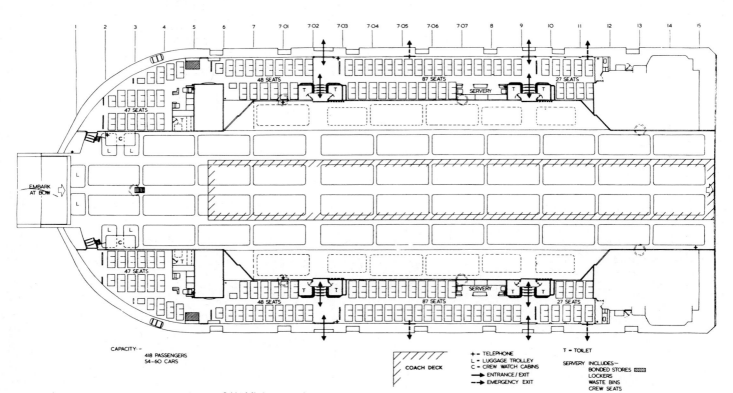

Layout of vehicle deck and passenger cabins on SR. N4 Mk 3 (Super 4)

In early 1993 the company was awarded a hovercraft design study contract by the Canadian Coast Guard for a new hovercraft to meet its expanding operational requirements.

The new craft is an enlarged version of the AP1-88, with a payload capability twice that of the current design in service with the Canadian Coast Guard and able to handle much larger buoys and other navigational aids.

SR. N4 Mk 3

This type has a payload of 418 passengers and 60 vehicles, a laden weight of 300 tonnes and a top speed in excess of 65 knots.

Principal Particulars

Length overall	56.38 m
Beam	23.16 m
Weight, maximum	300 t
Payload	112 t
Passengers	424
Vehicles	60
Fuel capacity	23 500 l
Propulsive power	2 × 2834 kW
Maximum speed	65 knots
Operational speed	50 knots
Operational limitation	2.5 m wave height
	Beaufort force 6

Propulsion: Motive power is supplied by four Rolls-Royce Marine Proteus Type 15M/529 free-turbine turboshaft engines, located in pairs at the rear of the craft on either side of the vehicle deck. Each engine is rated at 2834 kW and is connected to one of four identical propeller/fan units, two forward and two aft. The propellers are of four-bladed, controllable-pitch type. The lift fans are of 12-bladed centrifugal type, 3.5 m in diameter. Maximum fuel tankage, 28.45 tonnes; normal fuel allowing for ballast transfer, 18.29 tonnes.

Electrical system: Two Lucas turboshaft engines driving 55 kVA 200 V, 400 Hz Lucas alternators.

SR. N6 Mk 1

Designed primarily as a fast ferry for operation in sheltered waters, the SR. N6 Mk 1 can accommodate either 38 passengers or three tonnes of freight.

Fully amphibious, it can operate from bases above the high water mark, irrespective of tidal state.

Directional control is achieved by twin rudders and skirt lift, with a thrust port system to assist in low-speed manoeuvring. Two manually actuated elevators provide pitch trim at cruising speed.

SR. N6s have been in regular civil operations since 1965. Operators include the Canadian Coast Guard and Eurosense in Belgium. Military variants are in service in the Middle East.

Principal Particulars

Length overall	14.8 m
Beam	7.7 m
Weight, maximum	10 t
Payload	3 t
Passengers	38
Fuel capacity	1205 l
Propulsive power	671 kW
Maximum speed	52 knots
Operational speed	35 knots
Range	186 nm

Propulsion: Power for the integrated lift/propulsion system is provided by a Rolls-Royce Marine Gnome gas-turbine with a maximum continuous rating at 15°C of 671 kW. This drives a BHC 12-blade centrifugal 2.13 m diameter lift fan and a Dowty Rotol four-blade controllable-pitch 2.74 m diameter propeller for propulsion.

Outfit: Cabin size (length × width): 6.62 × 2.34 m. Cabin headroom centreline: 1.83 m.

SR. N6 Mk 6 GENERAL-PURPOSE

The SR. N6 Mk 6 represents a significant step forward in terms of all-weather performance and increased manoeuvrability, especially in high winds and at low speeds. There is also a significant reduction in the external noise level.

These advances have been achieved by the introduction of twin propellers and a redesigned skirt.

Principal Particulars

Length overall	18.8 m
Beam	7.92 m
Weight, maximum	17 t
Propulsive power	840 kW
Maximum speed	60 knots

SR. N4 Mk 3 (Super 4), The Princess Anne　　　　　　　　1986

Operational limitation	3.04 m wave height
	Beaufort force 8

Propulsion: Originally motive power was supplied by a single 840 kW Rolls-Royce Marine Gnome GN 1301 but the craft has been modified for hydrographic survey work and is now fitted with a Gnome GN 1051/1. Two 3.05 m diameter Dowty Rotol controllable-pitch propellers are fitted.

SR. N6 Craft built

SR. N6 Mks 1 to 5	42
SR. N6 Mk 6	7
SR. N6 Mk 8	8

SR. N6 Mk 8

The Mk 8 is the last military variant of the single propeller SR. N6.

In the logistic support role the Mk 8 can carry up to 55 fully equipped troops or loads reaching six tonnes. Access to the cabin, which measures 9.5 × 2.3 m, is via a bow door. Loads up to 500 kg which are too long for the cabin may be carried externally on the side decks.

Principal Particulars

Length overall	17.78 m
Beam	7.97 m
Payload	6 t
Passengers	55

SR. N6 operated by Canadian Coast Guard hovercraft units　　　　　　　　1986

SR. N6 Mk 6 general-purpose hovercraft fitted out for survey work　　　　　　　　1991

Fuel capacity	3022 l
Propulsive power	805 kW
Maximum speed	50 knots

Propulsion: Single Rolls-Royce GN 1451 marine gas-turbine rated at 805 kW at 15°C.

Auxiliary systems: Lucas SS923 gas-turbine driving a three-phase alternator.

BH.7

BH.7 is a 55 tonne hovercraft which was designed specifically for naval and military roles.

Principal Particulars

Length overall	23.9 m
Beam	13.8 m
Weight, maximum	56 t
Payload	18.3 t
Crew	3
Passengers	170 troops
Fuel capacity	13635 l
Propulsive power	3169 kW
Maximum speed	58 knots

Structure: Construction is of corrosion-resistant light alloy. Extensive use is made of components which were designed for the N4.

The fan delivers air to the cushion via a continuous peripheral bag and finger skirt made in neoprene-coated nylon fabric. The skirt provides an air cushion depth of 1.68 m. The cushion is divided into four compartments by a full length longitudinal keel and by two transverse keels located slightly forward of amidships.

Propulsion: Power for the integrated lift and propulsion system on the Mk 4 is provided by a Rolls-Royce Marine Proteus 15M/541 gas-turbine. On the Mk 5A, a 15M/549 is installed. In both types the engine drives a BHC 12-blade, centrifugal 3.5 m diameter lift fan and a four-blade, controllable-pitch pylon-mounted propeller. Propeller diameter on the Mk 4 is 5.79 m and 6.4 m on the Mk 5A.

Electrical system: Two Lucas Aerospace IS/90 APUs provide, via two 55 kVA generators, three-phase 400 Hz AC at 200 V for AC and DC supplies.

Control: Craft direction is controlled by swivelling the propeller pylon angle by a foot pedal. Thrust ports are fitted at each quarter to assist directional control at low speed, and a hydraulically operated skirt-lift system helps to bank the craft into turns, thereby reducing drift.

Fuel is transferred between forward and aft tanks via a ring main to adjust fore and aft trim.

Outfit: In this role, the main hold floor area of 56 m² (600 sq ft) of the Mk 4 provides an unobstructed space suitable for loading wheeled vehicles, guns and military stores.

Two side cabins, filled with paratroop-type seats, can accommodate up to 60 troops and their equipment.

BH.7 Mk 5A combat/logistics craft   1992

Access at the bow is through a 'clamshell' door.

Machine guns can be fitted in gun rings on the roof on either side of the cabin and provision can be made for armour plating to protect personnel, the engine and vital electrical components.

A typical military load would be 170 fully equipped troops or three field cars and trailers plus 60 troops or two armoured scout cars, or up to 20 NATO pallets.

BH.7 Mk 5A COMBAT/LOGISTICS VERSION

There were four BH.7 Mk 5As built for the Iranian Navy.

Designed for coastal defence operations, the BH.7 Mk 5A carries medium-range surface-to-surface missiles, such as Exocet, on its side decks. Secondary armament consists of two roof-mounted 20 mm guns.

The main central cabin, employed on the BH.7 Mk 4 for load-carrying, is equipped as an operations and fire-control room. The bow door is retained providing a dual missile/logistic capability. Since it is fully amphibious, the BH.7 can be operated from relatively unprepared bases on beaches and can head directly towards its target on interception missions

regardless of the tidal state and marginal terrain. Also, since none of its solid structure is immersed, it is invulnerable to underwater defences such as acoustic, magnetic and pressure mines or to attack by torpedoes.

A full range of electronic navigational aids permits the craft to operate by day or night.

AP1-88

Major advances in hovercraft technology enabled British Hovercraft Corporation to offer a 10 tonne payload craft with a performance equal to that of the well proven SR. N6. Built in welded aluminium alloy, AP1-88 is powered by air-cooled diesels. This craft design has low crew and maintenance requirements, footprint pressure and noise levels.

The craft can be employed in a wide variety of commercial, military and paramilitary roles including:

Passenger ferrying
Search and rescue
Hydrographic surveying
Ice-breaking
Anti-smuggling
Fire-fighting
Logistic support
Counter-insurgency
Mine countermeasures
Anti-submarine warfare
Mine-laying

The AP1-88 in a civil passenger configuration can seat up to 101 passengers. In a logistics role the AP1-88 will carry two Land Rovers, a BV202 tracked vehicle and trailer unit or approximately 10 000 kg of stores.

The first two AP1-88s *Tenacity* and *Resolution* began operating with Hovertravel between Ryde and Southsea in 1983. A similar craft, *Perseverance,* was built in 1985. These three craft are built to the 2.4 m shorter/80 configuration with Deutz 278 kW BF10L 413F lift engines and Deutz 367 kW BF12L 413FC propulsion engines.

During 1984 two of the production standard craft entered service with A/S Dämpskibsselskabet Øresund (DSØ) of Denmark on a route linking Copenhagen's Kastrup airport and Malmø. A third AP1-88 joined the route in 1988.

Two new production standard craft, fitted out to carry 95 passengers, entered service on the Hovertravel Ryde to Southsea route in 1989 and 1990.

In 1991 a further craft was completed for Northern Shipping to operate in Russia on the White Sea. This craft is fitted out for 68 passengers and incorporates sleeping accommodation for the crew, a galley forward and two marine lavatories aft.

AP1-88 building in Australia is licensed to NQEA Australia Pty Ltd at Cairns, and in the USA to Avondale Boat Division, Westwego, Louisiana.

A half-well-deck variant, designated AP1-88-200,

Northern Shipping AP1-88 Siverko   1992

Craft built (in UK)	Reg No	No of seats	Name	Launched	Delivered to
AP1-88-80	GH 2087	80	*Tenacity*	1983	Hoverwork Ltd
AP1-88-80	GH 2088	80	*Resolution*	1983	US Navy
AP1-88-80	GH 2100	80	*Perseverance*	1985	US Navy
AP1-88-100	GH 9029	81	*Idun Viking,* (ex *Expo Spirit*)	1984	A/S DSØ
API-88-100	GH 9030	81	*Freja Viking*	1984	A/S DSØ
AP1-88-100	GH 9031	81	*Liv Viking*	1984	A/S DSØ
AP1-88-200	CH-C-CG	12	*Waban-Aki*	1987	Canadian Coast Guard
AP1-88-100	GH 2107	95	*Double-O-Seven*	1989	Hovertravel Ltd
AP1-88-100	GH 2114	95	*Freedom 90*	1990	Hovertravel Ltd
AP1-88-100	099808	71	*Siverko*	1991	Northern Shipping, CIS

is in service with the Canadian Coast Guard undertaking search and rescue, navaid maintenance and ice-breaking tasks on the St Lawrence River and its tributaries.

The craft is of a half-well-deck configuration with accommodation for up to 12 crew members or technicians and up to 12 tonnes of cargo. This AP1-88 is equipped with a hydraulic crane, a capstan and winch to facilitate the conduct of a variety of specialised coastguard tasks.

Principal Particulars

Length overall	24.4 m
Beam	11 m
Weight, minimum	29.48 t
Weight, maximum	40.82 t
Payload	11.34 t
Passengers	101
Fuel capacity	1800 l
Propulsive power	2 × 336 kW
Lift power	2 × 336 kW
Maximum speed	50 knots

Operational limitation	2.4 m wave height windspeed 30 knots

Classification: BHSR, IMO, and DnV.

Structure: The basic hull is formed by a buoyancy tank made almost entirely of very wide aluminium alloy extrusions, one extrusion being used for the I-beams forming the transverse frames and a second for the integrally stiffened planking used for the bottom and deck. The remainder of the rigid structure is built from smaller welded extrusions and plating, with the exception of the roof, made from riveted light gauge corrugated panels. The propeller ducts are a composite structure of light alloy and Kevlar reinforced plastic. Marine alloys are used, including N8 plate and HE30 extrusions. In general, plate thicknesses are 2 or 3 mm except for the light gauge roof plating. The structure is welded throughout to eliminate mechanical fastenings which can be sources of corrosion. Detachable panels give easy access for engine and fan removal and facilitate the inspection of ventilation ducting and tail control

cable runs. Lifting, for the inspection of the craft underside and skirts, is achieved by three jacks which are fitted and operated from inside the craft. However, for general maintenance, the craft is put down on flyover blocks.

The skirt is low pressure ratio tapered skirt based on that of the Super 4. Mean cushion depth 1.37 m.

Propulsion: The AP1-88-100 craft is powered by four Deutz BF12L 513FC 12-cylinder air-cooled diesels. Two 2.74 m diameter four-blade Hoffmann ducted propellers are each driven by one of the diesels via a toothed belt. On craft as standard the propellers are of fixed-pitch type, but ground adjustable through ±5°. The two US Navy craft have controllable-pitch propellers, Type HOV-254P2DFR/D275. The belt-drive reduction ratio is 1:0.6.

Two of the engines, housed in the side box structures, power the lift and bow thruster systems. On each side of the craft one engine drives three 0.84 m diameter double-entry centrifugal fans, two of which supply air to the cushion via the skirt system and the third supplies air to the rotatable bow thruster. The well-deck version for the Canadian Coast Guard has four 0.885 m diameter fans for the lift system with two 0.84 m fans for the bow thrusters.

Navigation and communications: Remote reading gyro compass; a Lambda T.12 spherical compass. Optional range of automatic and semi-automatic navigational aids.

The communications are provided by a Sailor RT 145 VHF international marine band radio or similar equipment.

The radar systems installed are the Racal-Decca 914C, with the antenna turning unit and transceiver on the control cabin roof. The display unit is mounted in the control cabin on the port side and is north-up stabilised by gyro compass.

Control: Directional control is provided by two sets of triple aerodynamic rudder vanes mounted on the rear of the propeller ducts, differential propeller thrust and by swivelling bow thrusters. In the straight-aft position, the bow thrusters contribute to forward thrust. Trim is controlled by fuel ballast transfer.

Outfit: The superstructure is divided into four main components: a large central accommodation area forward of a propulsion machinery bay and two side-bodies containing the lift system machinery. A control cabin is mounted on top of the main cabin. In addition to the full cabin and half-well-deck versions, full well-deck variants are available. The commercial full cabin version seats a maximum of 101 passengers with the seats arranged in rows of seven across the cabin. The rows are divided by two gangways 600 mm wide which separate the seats into a 2-3-2 configuration. There are two doors, one port and one starboard, at the aft end of the cabin. Doorways are 1.75 × 0.9 m. An emergency door 1.06 × 0.9 m is at the forward end of the passenger cabin. Craft built to standard include a cabin heating and ventilation system adequate for operation in temperate climates; more elaborate systems are available as options. There are two sets of four luggage panniers on the side decks aft of the cabin doors. Total volume of the eight panniers is approximately 6.6 m³.

AP1-88-200
Waban-Aki

This craft entered service with the Canadian Coast Guard in 1987.

Principal Particulars

Length overall	24.5 m
Beam	11.2 m
Weight, maximum	47.15 t
Payload	12.45 t
Fuel capacity	5912 l
Propulsive power	4 × 441 kW
Maximum speed	50 knots

Propulsion: Four Deutz BF12L 513CP air-cooled turbocharged diesels, 441 kW each, at 2300 rpm. Two Hoffmann 2.75 m diameter controllable-pitch propellers Type HOV-254P2DFR/D275, ducted. Four centrifugal lift fans 0.885 m diameter. Two bow thrusters, centrifugal fans 0.840 m diameter.

The following details are specifically applicable to *Waban-Aki.*

Electrical system: Main system 28 V DC; auxiliary system 240/120 V AC 60 Hz single phase. DC supply: four Bosch Type T1, 28 V, 120A-17 generation. AC supply: diesel engine auxiliary power unit, 12 kW

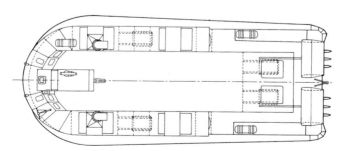

The Canadian Coast Guard Waban Aki *breaking ice*   1992

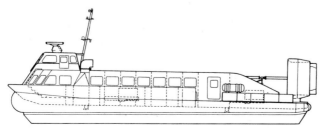

General arrangement of AP1-88-100 hovercraft

output. Batteries: start/service S1 two 12 V, 143 Ah; start/service S2 two 12 V, 143 Ah; essential service two 12 V; 143 Ah.
Navigation and communications: VHF radio FM Wulfsberg RT 7200, VHF radio AM King KY 196 Silver Crown, HF King KHF 990.
Radar: Decca RM 914C, VHF (FM/AM) ADF: OAR Type ADFS-347EH, HF ADF Sitex 511 AADF Navigator.
Plotter: Loran 'C' with RS 200 Shipmate colour track plotter. Gyromagnetic compass: AIM system.
Auxiliary systems: Power assistance to rudders; control of variable-pitch propellers; auxiliary hydraulic components.

AP1-88-300

This type is an open-top freighter developed from the standard AP1-88-100 design and sharing the same external dimensions and mechanical installation. AP1-88-300 was produced by Australian licensees NQEA Australia, Cairns, Queensland, under BHC design supervision.

One craft has been built to this design and is in service between the Snip gold mine, north-west Canada and Wrangell, Alaska.

AP1-88-400 (DESIGN)

The new craft is an enlarged version of the AP1-88, with a prolonged payload capacity twice that of the current design in service with the Canadian Coast Guard and able to handle much larger buoys and other navigational aids.

UPDATED

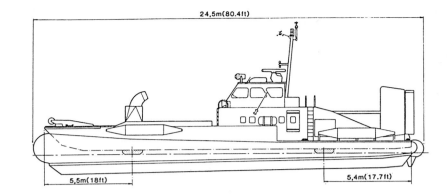

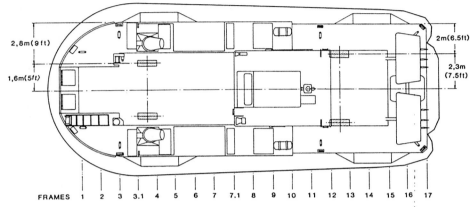

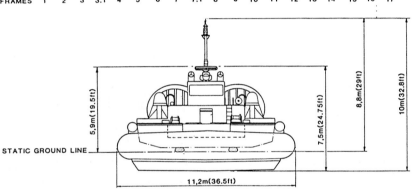

General arrangement of AP1-88-200 as delivered to the Canadian Coast Guard, 1987

GRIFFON HOVERCRAFT LTD

Head Office: Carlton House, Ringwood Road, Woodlands, Southampton, Hampshire SO4 2HT, UK

Telephone: +44 (1703) 814022
Telefax: +44 (1703) 813698

Dr E W H Gifford, *Chairman*
J H Gifford, *Managing Director*
G A Gifford, *Sales Director*

Founded in 1976, Griffon Hovercraft has concentrated on the design and development of small amphibious hovercraft.

The company's first design, Griffon, used a four-blade ducted propeller for propulsion with a centrifugal fan for lift, both driven by a Jaguar automobile engine. This craft was subsequently put into production as the Skima 12, built by Pindair Ltd under licence from Griffon Hovercraft Ltd. Many of this type of craft have been in service throughout the world in a variety of roles.

The initial choice of a petrol engine was due to its superior power-to-weight ratio, although the advantages of the diesel engine were recognised. The development of the turbocharged air-cooled diesel led to the company's decision, early in 1982, that a small commercial diesel-powered hovercraft would be feasible and would carry a useful payload.

Construction of the diesel-engined Griffon 1000 TD prototype began in June 1982. Performance trials began in May 1983 and exceeded expectations. There have been three craft of this type sup-

1000 TD for WAPDA, Pakistan

1995

plied to Geophysical Surveys Inc of Dallas, USA, for use in an oil-field survey on the Yellow River, China. Due to the intensive nature of these operations, thousands of operating hours have been accumulated with minimal maintenance, proving the inherently rugged nature of the design. In 1987, a 1000 TD was supplied to the Water and Power Development Authority of Pakistan (WAPDA) for survey work. There were three Griffon 1000 TDs supplied to the Royal Thai Navy in 1990, used for search and rescue, flood control, logistics and VIP transportation. A second 1000 TD was delivered to WAPDA Pakistan in 1993.

The success of the 1000 TD has led to a range of craft being developed with one to four tonne payloads, using similar machinery units and control systems. The company intends to concentrate on the requirements for a low-cost easily maintained craft for use in workboat, navy, paramilitary and ferry applications.

In January 1989 an improved and modified range of Griffon hovercraft was introduced. A six-seat hovercraft, the Mini 500, powered by a VW/Audi automotive diesel engine, and constructed in composite sandwich with Kevlar, was designed and built for a specific customer. In 1994 a new rigid inflatable five-seat hovercraft with a Land Rover diesel engine was produced for the fire department of Venice, Italy.

Of the larger craft, the Griffon 1000 TD continues to attract survey users and the new Griffon 2000 TD and 2000 TDX have replaced the 1500 TD and 1500 TDX respectively (the numerals in the name/title of these craft reflect their payload in kilogrammes). The 2500 TD and 2500 TDX have been replaced by the 37-seat 3000 TD, while the 4000 TD carries 48 to 60 passengers or a four tonne payload, and the larger engined Griffon 4000 TDX carries 60 to 72 passengers or six tonnes of payload. Fitted with either 10- or 12-cylinder engines, the craft is proving increasingly attractive to coastguards and navies. All craft in the Griffon range have commonality of design, systems and spare parts, and are designed to comply with the requirements of IMO, the UK CAA and Lloyd's Register.

375 TD

The 375 TD is the smallest craft in the Griffon range and is built on rigid inflatable boat lines. Powered by a 75 kW water-cooled diesel engine this craft carries a payload of 375 kg or five passengers.

MINI 500

The Mini 500 is a covered six-seat craft with an automotive water-cooled diesel engine. Please see the 1992-93 edition of this book for further details.

1000 TD

The smallest craft in the TD (Turbocharged Diesel) range, the 1000 TD carries a payload of 1000 kg or 10 passengers. The craft is powered by a single diesel engine and is available with a variety of superstructures. Folding side decks enable it to be loaded onto its purpose-built trailer and towed behind a small truck. It can also be fitted into a 20 ft container, after removal of bow and stern sections.

Please see the 1992-93 edition of this book for further details of this type.

The Water And Power Development Authority (WAPDA) of Pakistan ordered a second Griffon 1000 TD hovercraft in 1992.

Equipped with a special hatch (or 'moon pool') in the base of the craft through which a water sampling 'fish' will be trawled at depths of 100 m, the craft operates on the Tarbela Dam (and on the rivers that feed it) in north-western Pakistan. The hovercraft is required to maintain a stationary position, hovering over fast water flows of over five knots whilst carrying out water sampling. The 1000 TD carries six engineers plus half a tonne of specialised equipment and is used as a hydrographic survey vessel in shallow waters and for high-speed transportation along the 60 nm (110 km) length of the dam.

Craft built 1000 TD

001	Hover Systems Inc
002	Geophysical Surveys Inc, USA for Yellow River, China, 1984
003	Geophysical Surveys Inc, USA for Yellow River, China, 1984
004	Geophysical Surveys Inc, USA for Yellow River, China, 1984
008	Water And Power Development Authority, (WAPDA), Pakistan (GH 8456)
012	Royal Thai Navy, 1990
014	Royal Thai Navy, 1990
015	Royal Thai Navy, 1990
023	Water And Power Development Authority, (WAPDA), Pakistan, 1993

Griffon 2000 TD (GH 2110)   *1990*

Griffon 2000 TDX with the Frontier Guard of Finland   *1995*

1500 TD

This variant is 1.8 m longer than the 1000 TD, but with identical machinery. Capacity is increased to 1.5 tonnes or 16 persons. Bow and stern sections are not removable but folding side decks allow transportation within a 40 ft container.

Craft built 1500 TD

001	Griffon 1500 TD, Clements, Solomon Islands (GH 9452), 1987
002	Chiriqui Hovercraft, Panama, November 1985 to 1987
003	Griffon Hovercraft charter craft (GH 2102)

These craft have been sold for tourism, survey work and pilot duties and have now been replaced by the Griffon 2000 TD.

Details of the 1500 TD are as for the 1000 TD with the following exceptions:

Principal Particulars

Length overall	10.15 m
Weight, minimum	2.3 t
Payload	1.5 t
Maximum speed	33 knots
Operational speed	27 knots

2000 TD

The Griffon 2000 TD has now replaced the 1500 TD. Whereas the basic design, the engine and the systems remain the same, the 2000 TD has a larger propeller, a larger fan, and an improved design of skirt. These modifications enable the 2000 TD to carry a 33 per cent larger payload but still retain exactly the same performance as its predecessor. The cabin has also been slightly enlarged enabling the 2000 TD to carry a total of 20 to 24 persons.

Principal Particulars

Length overall	10.6 m
Beam	4.5 m
Weight, minimum	2.6 t
Payload	2 t
Crew	2
Passengers	22
Propulsive power	140 kW
Maximum speed	31 knots
Operational speed	27 knots

Classification: IMO, the UK CAA and Lloyd's Register.

Propulsion: Integrated lift and propulsion system powered by a single Deutz BF6L 913C air-cooled six-cylinder, in-line, turbocharged and intercooled diesel rated at 190 hp (140 kW) at 2500 rpm. A 0.91 m diameter centrifugal lift fan is driven from the front of the crankshaft via an HTD toothed belt. Power for the 1.8 m diameter four-blade Robert Trillo designed ducted propeller is transmitted from the back of the engine via an automotive clutch to another HTD toothed belt transmission running inside the propeller support pylon.

The engine, transmission, duct and pylon are mounted on a welded aluminium alloy subframe attached to the hull via resilient mounts.

Cooling air for the engine passes through a Knitmesh filter to remove spray and is drawn into the front of the engine by the engine cooling fan before passing over the cylinders and being drawn out from the rear of the engine bay by the propeller.

Structure: Main hull is of welded riveted and bonded marine grade aluminium.

Sidebodies made from composite materials fold upward for transport and are locked into the running position by use of struts either side. Forward and aft ballast tanks are fabricated from aluminium.

The skirts are a tapered HDL open loop type with similar segments at bow and sides. Cones are fitted at the stern. Segments are fitted to the loop with stainless steel bolts and inner ends are attached using plastic shackles. All skirt maintenance can be done without lifting the craft.

Electrical system: 24 V standard with 12 V option. 35 A alternator, two 75 A/h 12 V batteries fitted.

Control: Triple rudders in the GRP duct provide directional control. Elevators within the duct provide a degree of fore and aft trim augmented by a fuel ballast system. The craft is fitted with a skirt shift system operated by a small electrohydraulic ram which provides responsive control on roll trim, offsets crosswind effects and banks the craft into the turn.

Outfit: Two or three persons (including the driver) can be carried in the wheelhouse and a further 18 to 22 passengers can be carried in inward-facing bench-type seats in the cabin.

2000 TDX

This craft is virtually the same as the 2000 TD but is powered by the more powerful 239 kW V8 Deutz BF8L 513 engine, which gives it a superior into-wave and into-wind performance. A 2000 TDX was ordered by the Swedish Coast Guard in 1991 and, having operated the craft for nine months, an order for a further two was signed in January 1993.

In 1994 the Frontier Guard of Finland took delivery of two Griffon 2000 TDX craft and two further similar craft were delivered to Brazil as crash rescue craft at Rio de Janiero airport.

The British Ministry of Defence ordered four Griffon 2000 TDX(M) hovercraft. Designed to carry a crew of two, driver and commander, plus 16 fully equipped Marine Commandos, each craft is equipped with a 7.62 mm GPMG (General-Purpose Machine Gun), HF and VHF radios, radar, GPS and a variety of specialised equipment. Capable of speeds of over 35 knots, these craft are for 539 Assault Squadron (an integral part of three Commando Brigade) and are used worldwide for high-speed coastal insertion/amphibious assault, logistics support and other Commando-type applications. Each craft carries a payload of two tonnes which can be quickly converted from the all-troop to the all-cargo configuration, or to a variable combination of both.

Details for the 2000 TDX are very similar to the 2000 TD except for the propulsion and the following:

Principal Particulars

Maximum speed	40 knots
Operational speed	35 knots

2500 TD

This craft has now been superseded by the Griffon 3000 TD. One craft of this type was built by Griffon Hovercraft Ltd and the other was built by a licensee in the USA. Both are in operation in North America.

3000 TD

The Griffon 3000 TD design supersedes the original 2500 TD and the 2500 TDX. Seating up to 37 passengers, the 3000 TD uses two Deutz BF8L 513 engines and incorporates the very latest in skirt design and technology. The hover height is also increased over its predecessors and with its larger propellers and fans it now has a significantly improved rough weather capability.

Griffon 2000 TDX (Paul Rapson) 1992

Four Griffon 2000 TDXs in service with the British Royal Marines 1995

Craft built 2500 TD		Name	In service	Owner
001	Griffon Hovercraft 2500 TD	*Rain Dance*	November 1985	Hover Systems Inc, USA, (1986 Canadian registration CH-FHI)

Principal Particulars

Length overall	15 m
Beam	7 m
Weight, minimum	8.2 t
Payload	3000 kg
Passengers	27
Propulsive power	2 × 239 kW
Maximum speed	48 knots
Operational speed	35 knots

Classification: IMO, the UK CAA and Lloyd's Register.

Structure: The main hull is of welded marine grade aluminium alloy providing a very cost-effective light and durable structure. It consists of a number of fore and aft spars linked by the cabin floors and the craft bottom. This provides an immensely stiff structure.

Sidebodies, made of composite materials, fold upwards reducing width for road and sea transportation.

The skirt is of a tapered HDL open loop type.

Propulsion: The 3000 TD uses two identical machinery units from the 2000 TDX, fitted next to each other.

Electrical system: The electrical system is 24 V. Main and emergency supplies are provided. Each engine has a 35 A alternator.

Control: Similar controls to the single engine craft are fitted except no elevators are used.

Three rudders mounted in each duct are operated by a steering yoke via stainless steel cables to

Griffon 3000 TD (Paul Rapson) 1992

Griffon 4000 TD 1994

Two Griffon 3000 TDs and three Griffon 2000 TDXs (Paul Rapson) 1992

Griffon 375 TD Rigid Inflatable Hovercraft 1995

Craft built 4000 TD	Name	Seats	Delivered	Owner
4000 TD	*Shri Bajarangdasbapa*	51	1992	New India Business House Ltd
4000 TD (GH 9462)	*Shri Saibaba*	51	1992	New India Business House Ltd

provide directional control. Fore and aft trim is achieved by an electrically operated skirt shift system. Twin engine throttles are mounted near to the driver's left hand whilst clutch pedals (operated by the driver's feet) are provided for the propellers. By using only one propeller at low speed, together with the rudder and skirt shift, the craft can turn in its own length. Control systems are powerful enough to allow the craft to be operated and controlled on only one engine, although at a much reduced speed.

Outfit: The superstructure can be designed to suit the customer's specification. The standard passen-ger cabin is constructed in light alloy with GRP mouldings at the front and back. Great emphasis has been placed on giving the passengers clear uninterrupted views through the large windows, and narrow pillars are featured. A portion of the roof can be transparent if required and air-conditioning and heating systems can be installed. Aircraft-type seating is arranged in up to six rows of six seats, three either side of a central aisle. Luggage racks, toilets and a galley may also be provided to suit customers' specific requirements.

4000 TD

The 4000 TD is a stretched version of the 3000 TD (and the proven 2500 TD). It can carry up to 60 passengers at a cruising speed of 35 knots. There are two of these craft in India operating a 45 nm route across the bay of Cambay, between Surat and Bhavnagar.

Principal particulars

Length overall	17.85 m
Beam	7.3 m
Weight, maximum	15.85 t
Payload	4.05 kg
Passengers	60
Propulsive power	2 × 298 kW
Maximum speed	38 knots
Operational speed	35 knots

Classification: IMO, the UK CAA and Lloyd's Register.

Structure: Exactly the same cross-section and construction method as the 3000 TD but 2.85 m longer.

A tapered HDL open loop type skirt is fitted.

Propulsion: The same twin engine system as the 3000 TD but Deutz engines BF10L 513 V10 (298 kW each) are fitted.

Transmission details are similar to the smaller craft.

Electrical system: As the 3000 TD.

Control: As for the 3000 TD.

Outfit: The accommodation is normally arranged in up to nine rows of six seats, similar to those of the Griffon 3000 TD. Customers can specify their freight/passenger requirements and versions of this craft, like the 3000 TD, can include ro/ro facilities, with a bow ramp.

4000 TDX

The 4000 TDX is a stretched version of the 4000 TD carrying 60 to 72 passengers or 6 tonnes of payload. It has two of the larger BF12L 513C, 386 kW engines installed and is two metres longer than the 4000 TD.

12000 TD (DESIGN)

A proposed 120- to 150-seat (12 tonne payload) craft designated the 12000 TD has been designed in outline and is currently under negotiation with potential clients.

UPDATED

HOVERMARINE INTERNATIONAL LTD

Spitfire Quay, Hazel Road, Woolston, Southampton, Hampshire SO2 7GB, UK

Telephone: +44 (1703) 443122
Telefax: +44 (1703) 444429

P J Hill, *Managing Director*
E G Tattersall, *Technical Consultant*

Since its formation in 1966, Hovermarine has sold 106 Surface Effect Ships (SESs) to 33 countries and is one of the most experienced designers and builders of these craft. Hovermarine has its yard at Woolston, Southampton with an undercover area of more than 2300 m².

Production designs are the 200, 400 and 500 series craft. The 200 series comprises the HM 218 (18 m, 84- to 103-seat) passenger ferries, 29 of which have been delivered to The Hong Kong and Yaumati Ferry Company; the HM 218 multi-role harbour craft, four of which have been delivered to the Port of Rotterdam Authority; the HM 218 crewboat for the oil industry, five of which have been delivered to Shell Eastern Petroleum; the HM 221 (21 m) fireboat; the HM 221 (21 m) 112- to 135-seat passenger ferry and the HM 221 (21 m) crewboat. Other variants of the 200 series craft are offered for hydrographic survey, coastguard and patrol duties. The HM 500 series includes the Series 2 (27 m, 256-seat) and the Series 3 (27 m, 300-seat) passenger ferry design. The new HM 424 design is larger than the HM 200 series but smaller than the HM 500 series. Incorporating all the well proven systems (the results of 25 years' experience in design, manufacture and operation of SES) the HM 424 can be specified with DDC or Deutz MWM engines, giving cruising speeds of 40 and 50 knots respectively, with full payloads. Other designs are available for the following roles: naval fast strike and patrol craft, crewboat, hydrographic survey and coastguard patrol. All craft are type-approved in the UK by the Civil Aviation Authority, with Passenger and Safety Certificates issued by the Department of Transport. The craft have also been certified by Lloyd's Register of Shipping, Bureau Veritas and USCG.

HM 216 FERRY

About ten of this early 16 m HM2 type are still with operators. Full details of these craft are given in the 1978 edition of *Jane's Surface Skimmers*.

HM 218 FERRY

The HM 218 ferry provides a 40 per cent improvement in payload over the earlier HM 216 ferry for only a 15 per cent increase in operating costs. It can carry 84 to 103 passengers at cruising speeds up to 35 knots. An extended bow skirt permits passenger operations in up to 1.5 m (5 ft) waves.

The first HM 218 ferry went into service in 1976. A major operator of the type is The Hong Kong and Yaumati Ferry Company, which has 22 in commuter service within Hong Kong and on a 100 nm international route to Guangzhou (Canton) in China. Other HM 218 ferries operate in Brazil, Indonesia, Iraq, Japan, Malaysia, Singapore and Venezuela.

HM 218 Klassis *operating on the Sea of Marmara in Turkey* **1990**

Structure: Built in GRP mouldings the outer shell of the hull, including the bottom between the sidewalls and under the bow, is moulded in one piece, gunwale to gunwale. The hull moulding incorporates local thickening of the laminate to meet the design load requirements and to facilitate the incorporation of fittings and apertures. Frames and bulkheads are manufactured from sandwich panels of expanded PVC foam covered with GRP. All frames and bulkheads are laminated into the hull.

The extended bow skirt consists of a single loop extending from the bow chine to a line just below the base of the main hull. There are 32 segments attached to the main loop and connected to the underside of the hull by terylene ropes. An inner loop overlaps the fan volute outlet and causes the bow skirt to inflate.

The rear seal consists of a membrane and loop which is suspended front and rear by transverse continuous sheets of material. It is inflated, to a pressure slightly above that of the cushion, by the rear fan in the starboard propulsion engine room.

Principal Particulars

Length overall	18.29 m
Beam	6.1 m
Draught, hullborne	1.72 m
Draught, on-cushion	1.07 m
Weight, maximum	27.9 t
Payload	7154 kg
Crew	2
Passengers	84-103
Fuel capacity	1455 l
Propulsive power	2 × 347 kW

Lift power	154 kW
Operational speed	34 knots
Range	200 nm
Operational limitation	1.5 m wave height

Propulsion: Two Detroit Diesel Corporation 8V-92TI V, eight-cylinder marine diesels, each developing 347 kW at 2300 rpm, provide propulsive power. A single Caterpillar 3208 90° V, eight-cylinder marine diesel rated at 154 kW at 2800 rpm, drives the 0.6 m diameter centrifugal lift fans.

The lift engine drives two pairs of forward fans through toothed belts and one aft fan through a hydraulic system. Air for the forward fans is drawn through inlets at each forward cabin quarter and in the base of the wheelhouse structure. For the aft fan air is drawn through an inlet in the rear companionway.

The two propulsion engines each drive a 0.45 m diameter aluminium-bronze three-blade propeller through a reversing gearbox and 1:1 ratio vee box.
Control: Craft direction is by twin balanced stainless steel rudders operated hydraulically by a steering-wheel. Additional control is by differential use of the water propellers.

Outfit: The HM 218 ferry can be operated by a crew of two. Controls are in an elevated wheelhouse, with a 360° view, at the forward end of the passenger saloon. The saloon can be fitted-out with up to 84 aircraft-type seats or 92 to 103 utility seats. These are normally arranged three abreast in banks of three. Toilet and baggage compartments are located aft. Up to six luggage containers, able to hold a total of 1500 kg, may be carried on the saloon roof.

Craft built HM 216 (16 m SES) (list not complete)

Type	Name	No of seats	Yard No	Original delivery date	Owner/Operator	Country of operation
HM 216	(ex *HYF 101*)	60	326	1974	Associated Marine Sdn Bhd	Malaysia
HM 216	*Sea Express 101*	-	-	1976		Philippines (laid up)
HM 216	*Sea Express 102*	-	-	1976		Philippines (laid up)
HM 216	*Sea Express 103*	-	-	1976		Philippines (laid up)
HM 216	*Gavea*	65	321	1976	TRANSTUR	Brazil*
HM 216	*Gragoata*	65	322	1976	TRANSTUR	Brazil*
HM 216	*Suratiba*	65	323	1976	TRANSTUR	Brazil*
HM 216	*HYF 103*	74	328	1975	The Hong Kong Yaumati Ferry Company	Hong Kong (laid up)
HM 216	*HYF 104*	60	329	1975	The Hong Kong Yaumati Ferry Company	Hong Kong (laid up)
HM 216 (USA built)	*American Skimmer*	62	-	1974		USA (laid up)

* none operating

Craft built HM 218 (18 m SES)

Type	Name	No of seats	Yard No	Original delivery date	Delivered to	Country of operation
HM 218	*HYF 105*	100	435	1976	Hong Kong Yaumati Ferry Co	Hong Kong
HM 218	*HYF 106*	100	443	1976	Hong Kong Yaumati Ferry Co	Hong Kong
HM 218	*HYF 107*	100	445	1976	Hong Kong Yaumati Ferry Co	Hong Kong
HM 218	*HYF 111*	100	457	1979	Hong Kong Yaumati Ferry Co	Hong Kong
HM 218	*HYF 112*	100	458	1979	Hong Kong Yaumati Ferry Co	Hong Kong
HM 218	*HYF 113*	100	459	1980	Hong Kong Yaumati Ferry Co	Hong Kong
HM 218	*HYF 114*	74	462	1980	Hong Kong Yaumati Ferry Co	Hong Kong
HM 218	*HYF 115*	100	463	1980	Hong Kong Yaumati Ferry Co	Hong Kong
HM 218	*HYF 116*	84	464	1980	Hong Kong Yaumati Ferry Co	Hong Kong
HM 218	*HYF 117*	100	469	1980	Hong Kong Yaumati Ferry Co	Hong Kong
HM 218	*HYF 118*	74	470	1980	Hong Kong Yaumati Ferry Co	Hong Kong
HM 218	*HYF 119*	74	473	1980	Hong Kong Yaumati Ferry Co	Hong Kong
HM 218	*HYF 120*	100	474	1980	Hong Kong Yaumati Ferry Co	Hong Kong
HM 218	*HYF 121*	74	475	1980	Hong Kong Yaumati Ferry Co	Hong Kong
HM 218	*HYF 122*	100	476	1980	Hong Kong Yaumati Ferry Co	Hong Kong
HM 218	*HYF 123*	74	477	1980	Hong Kong Yaumati Ferry Co	Hong Kong
HM 218	*HYF 124*	74	478	1980	Hong Kong Yaumati Ferry Co	Hong Kong
HM 218	*HYF 125*	100	479	1980	Hong Kong Yaumati Ferry Co	Hong Kong
HM 218	*HYF 126*	100	480	1980	Hong Kong Yaumati Ferry Co	Hong Kong
HM 218	*HYF 127*	100	481	1980	Hong Kong Yaumati Ferry Co	Hong Kong
HM 218	(ex *HYF 129*)	-	-	1983	Changjiang Shipping	China, PR
HM 218	(ex *HYF 130*)	74	484	1980	Changjiang Shipping	China, PR
HM 218	(ex *RTS 101*)	100	466	1986	Discovery Bay Transportation Services	Hong Kong
HM 218	(ex *RTS 102*)	100	468	1987	Discovery Bay Transportation Services	Hong Kong
HM 218	(ex *RTS 103*)	100	471	1986	Discovery Bay Transportation Services	Hong Kong
HM 218	(ex *HYF 108*)	100	446	1976	Discovery Bay Transportation Services	Hong Kong
HM 218	(ex *HYF 109*)	100	447	1979	Discovery Bay Transportation Services	Hong Kong
HM 218	(ex *HYF 110*)	100	448	1979	Discovery Bay Transportation Services	Hong Kong
HM 218	(ex *HYF 129*)	-	-	1983	Changjiang Shipping	China, PR
HM 218	(ex *HYF 130*)	74	484	1982	Changjiang Shipping	China, PR
HM 218	*Kijang Mas*	-	-	1984	Kedah & Perlis Ferry Service Sdn Bhd	Malaysia
HM 218	*Rey del Titikaka*	-	-		Hovermarine Titikaka Transport (not in service)	Bolivia
HM 218	*Reina del Titikaka*	-	-		Hovermarine Titikaka Transport (not in use)	Bolivia
HM 218	-	-	-		Shenzou Transport Company	China, PR
HM 218	*Semandera Satu*	78	-	1986	PT Hover Maritim Semandera	Indonesia
HM 218	*Semandera Desu*	78	-	1986	PT Hover Maritim Semandera	Indonesia
HM 218	*Havendienst 7*	n/a	-	1979		Netherlands (laid up)
HM 218	*Havendienst 10*	n/a	452	1979		Netherlands (laid up)
HM 218	*Havendienst 9*	n/a	451	1980		Netherlands (laid up)
HM 218	*Havendienst 8*	n/a	-	1980		Netherlands
HM 218	*Innovator I*	-	-	1977		Nigeria (laid up)
HM 218	*Innovator II*	-	440	1977		Nigeria (laid up)
HM 218	*Innovator III*	-	439	1977		Nigeria (laid up)
HM 218	*Auto Batam 1*	78	472	1982	Yang Passenger Ferry Service	Singapore
HM 218	*Auto Batam 2*	-	-	-	Yang Passenger Ferry Service	Singapore
HM 218	*Zumbador*	70	454	1979	Maraven SA	Venezuela
HM 218	*Zumaya*	70	455	1980	Maraven SA	Venezuela
HM 218	*Barroso*	70	471	1980	Maraven SA	Venezuela
HM 218	*Auhah*	82	-	Feb 1983		Kuwait
HM 218	*Umn Al Maradam*	82	-	1983		Kuwait
HM 218	*J/Kubbar*	82	-	1984		Kuwait
HM 218	*Yin Bin 1*	-	-	1986	China Merchants	China, PR
HM 218	*Pomas No 1*	95	-	1986	Pomas Sdn Bhd	Malaysia
HM 218	*Calypso*	84		May 1988	Gozo Line	Malta
HM 218	*Klassis*	82		1989	Naviga Line	Turkey
HM 218	*Hover Express*	84				Norway
HM 218	*Bukom Deras*	90		1983	Shell Eastern Petroleum	Singapore
HM 218	*Bukom Pantas*	90		1983	Shell Eastern Petroleum	Singapore
HM 218	*Bukom Lekas*	90		1983	Shell Eastern Petroleum	Singapore
HM 218	*Bukom Maju*	90		1983	Shell Eastern Petroleum	Singapore
HM 218	*Bukom Jaya*	90		1983	Shell Eastern Petroleum	Singapore

HM 218 CREWBOAT

Since 1979 three HM 218 crewboats have been operating in Venezuela with Maraven, transporting crew to and from oil rigs on Lake Maracaibo. Five more have been delivered to Shell Eastern Petroleum in Singapore. The crewboat is based on the HM 218 passenger ferry but has a substantially reinforced hull.

A bow-loading technique has been developed; rollers are fitted to the bow allowing the craft to approach installations and transfer crew over the bow. This is safer than the conventional stern transfer system as the captain can view the whole operation.

Principal Particulars

Length overall	18.29 m
Beam	6.1 m
Draught, hullborne	1.72 m
Draught, on-cushion	1.07 m
Passengers	99
Propulsive power	2 × 347 kW
Lift power	154 kW
Maximum speed	34 knots
Range	200 nm
Operational limitation	1.5 m wave height

Classification: Construction is to Lloyd's Register survey requirements.

Structure: Shell mouldings, submouldings, frames, bulkheads and major attachments in GRP, using polyester resins and PVC foam.

Propulsion: Two DDC 8V-92TI marine diesels driving fixed-pitch propellers through Capitol reversing gearboxes and BPM V-drive gearboxes. Lift is by one Caterpillar 3280 V8 marine diesel driving two pairs of forward fans through toothed belts and one aft fan through a hydraulic system.

Outfit: Air-conditioned accommodation for up to 99 passengers in airline-type seats. Toilet compartment in stern.

HM 218 MULTI-ROLE HARBOURCRAFT

A total of four HM 218 multi-role harbour craft

were delivered to the Port of Rotterdam Authority in 1979-80. The design retains the standard HM 218 passenger ferry hull fitted with two superstructure modules to house port-monitoring and emergency service equipment.

Details are given in the 1988 edition, page 84.

HM 221 FIREBOAT

In November 1991 Hovermarine International Ltd announced a major technology transfer deal with Textron Marine Systems Inc. This agreement between the two companies follows the 1990 order by the City of New York for two HM 221 fire and rescue vessels, (a US$6.5 million package) and will allow Textron to build the HM 221 fireboat within the USA.

Details of these vessels are given under the Textron Marine Systems entry. Delivery of the fireboats was made in 1992. The hulls will be built by Hovermarine International Ltd, UK, together with various kits of parts. Engineering design and technical assistance has also been provided.

There were two HM 221 fire-fighting craft ordered by the city of Tacoma, Washington, USA in 1978. The first of these was delivered in May 1982 and the second late in 1982. They are fitted with a comprehensive range of fire-fighting, rescue, navigation and communications equipment.

Principal Particulars

Length overall	20.9 m
Beam	6.1 m
Draught, hullborne	1.55 m
Draught, on-cushion	1.1 m
Crew	2
Fuel capacity	2950 l
Water capacity	90 l
Maximum speed	33 knots
Range: 120 nm.	

Propulsion: Two DDC 8V-92TI marine diesels drive fixed-pitch propellers via direct-drive reversing gearboxes and V-drive gearboxes. Lift power is from one DDC 6V-92TI marine diesel which is also used as a pump engine. A second pump engine is provided by a DDC 8V-92TI marine diesel. Propulsion, lift and pumping machinery is controlled from the wheelhouse. All engines are started electrically.

Outfit: Utility-standard crew accommodation comprises a six-berth cabin with cooker, sink and toilet compartment. The normal crew consists of two persons.

Operations equipment: Two remotely controlled bow-mounted monitors each of 9400 l/min waterflow rate; one wheelhouse-mounted monitor of 20 800 l/min water-flow rate; two under-wharf monitors of 9400 l/min water-flow rate and one remotely controlled 5600 l/min foam/water monitor fitted to the telescopic end of a high-level (10.5 m) ladder which doubles as a crane. The monitors are remotely controlled for rotation and elevation from a console in the wheelhouse. The ladder is controlled from its base. All fire monitors, except the wheelhouse monitor, can be controlled from a straight stream to 90° fog.

HM 221 PASSENGER FERRY

Based on the HM 221 (21 m) hull, this variant seats 112 to 135 passengers depending on route requirements and has a continuous speed in excess of 34 knots in calm conditions and a range of 140 nm.

Principal Particulars

Length overall	21.19 m
Beam	5.91 m
Draught, hullborne	1.76 m
Draught, on-cushion	1.21 m
Payload	8.4 t
Crew	3
Passengers	112-135
Fuel capacity	1610 l
Propulsive power	2 × 365 kW
Lift power	201 kW
Operational speed	33 knots
Range	140 nm

Classification: Lloyd's Register + Class ACV, Group 2, +LMC, CCS.

Structure: Single shell GRP mouldings, with submouldings, frames, bulkheads and other attachments bonded together.

Propulsion: Power for the lift system is provided by a single Caterpillar 3280T V8 marine diesel with a

The first HM 221 Fireboat hull completed by Hovermarine International for the City of New York **1992**

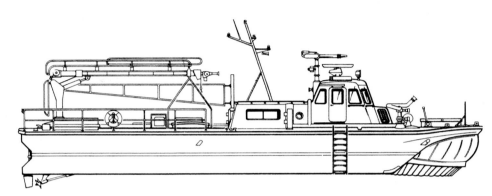

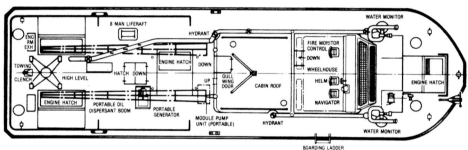

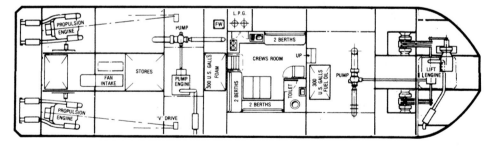

HM 221 fire-fighting craft

HM 221 FIREBOAT

Craft built HM 221	In service	Delivered to
HM 221 *Defiance* (Fireboat No 5)	December 1982	City of Tacoma Fire Department
HM 221 *Commencement* (Fireboat No 15)	February 1983	City of Tacoma Fire Department
HM 221	mid-1992	City of New York
HM 221 *John P Devaney*	mid-1992	City of New York

HM 221 CREWBOAT

Craft built	In service	Delivered to
HM 221 Grayspear	1982-1985	-

Details are given in the 1988 edition, page 85

HM 221 PASSENGER FERRY

Craft built	Seats	Built	Delivered to
HM 221	112	1985	Donau Dampfschiffahrts-Gesellschaft (DDSG)

continuous rating of 201 kW at 2800 rpm. Propulsive power is supplied by two DDC 8V-92TI marine diesels, each rated at 365 kW at 2300 rpm continuous.

Electrical system: Electrical voltage: 24 V DC nominal negative earth.

Generation/charging equipment: Two propulsion engine-driven AC/DC alternators rated at 27.5 V, 100 A. One lift engine-driven AC/DC alternator rated at 27.5 V, 100 A.

Two 24 V lead acid batteries, each with sufficient capacity to provide six starts for each engine.

Control: Power-assisted manual/hydraulic system operating twin rudders with a hard over angle of ±30° when set with a zero rudder divergence. A hydraulic pump is mechanically operated from the lift engines.

Outfit: Within the saloon of the 112-seat variant there are two toilet compartments. Seats have a depth of 420 mm, breadth of 430 mm and a seat pitch of 460 mm. Aisle width is a minimum of 470 mm. The saloon and wheelhouse are air-conditioned. The air-conditioning plant is belt-driven off the lift engine.

HM 424 (DESIGN)

Hovermarines HM 424 Cushion-Jet will transport 165-200 passengers in extreme comfort on an all year round basis on short sea routes. The craft will cruise at full load at 44 knots with machinery at 85% Maximum Continuous Rating (MCR) and will have a continuous speed capability of 48 knots at maximum engine rating. Other engines can be fitted to customer choice to give cruising speeds in the range 40-57 knots.

All machinery has been chosen for ease of maintenance. The primary choice is for either two MTU propulsion diesels or two MWM diesels and one MTU and MWM lift diesel. Each engine is directly coupled to the water-jet or lift fan via a short cardan shaft.

Principal Particulars

Length overall	26 m
Beam	10 m
Draught, hullborne	1.6 m
Draught, on-cushion	0.8 m
Payload	16.3 t
Passengers	199
Maximum speed	48 knots
Operational speed	44 knots
Range	300 nm

Classification: IMO Code of safety for Dynamically Supported Craft; Lloyd's Register - Class + A1 Air Cushion Vehicles, Group 2, with +LMC; United Kingdom Civil Aviation Authority (CAA).

HM 527

The first HM 527 was launched in January 1982. It has been designed to operate on coastal and inland waters. A computerised roll stabilisation system is fitted as standard. The first of four craft, ordered by Sealink Ferries Ltd, was delivered before the end of 1983.

Other designs based on the HM 527 hull include a hydrographic survey vessel and all passenger crewboats and mixed payload supply boats for the offshore oil industry.

Principal Particulars

Length overall	27.2 m
Beam	10.2 m
Draught, hullborne	2.55 m
Draught, on-cushion	1.7 m
Weight, maximum	87 t
Payload	21 t
Passengers	200
Fuel capacity	4940 l
Propulsive power	2 × 1050 kW
Lift power	550 kW
Operational speed	36 knots
Range	200 nm
Operational limitation	3 m wave height

Structure: Single shell GRP moulding with sub-moulding, frames, bulkheads and cabin sole panels bonded together. Materials used include expanded PVC foam, glass fibre, polyester resins, wood and aluminium alloy.

The bow skirt is made up of two tailored neoprene/nylon loops suspended in 180° arcs sidewall to sidewall and joined at their lower edges to form an

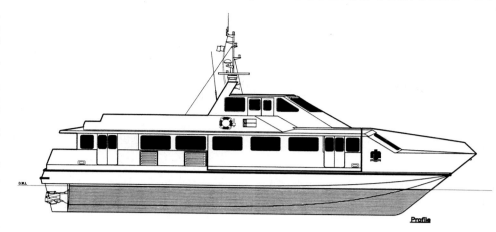

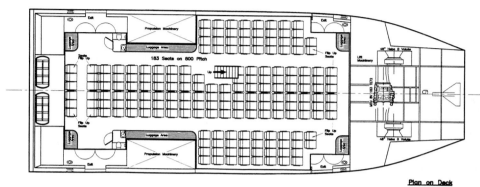

General arrangement of the HM 424 Cushion-Jet design   1995

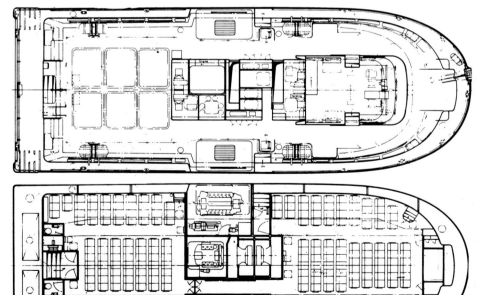

HM 527 Series 2 passenger ferry

irregularly shaped inflatable compartment. When inflated, the loops support 20 single fabric segments, attached at the loop joint line, and absorb wave impact shock to a degree. Four additional corner segments are attached on each side by ropes and shackles.

HM 527

Craft built HM 527	No of seats	In service	Delivered to
HM 527 *Tejo*	200	1983	Sealink Ferries Ltd, Hong Kong
HM 527 *Douro*	200	1984	Sealink Ferries Ltd, Hong Kong
HM 527 *Sado*	200	1984	Sealink Ferries Ltd, Hong Kong
HM 527 *Mondego*	200	1984	Sealink Ferries Ltd, Hong Kong

Propulsion: The marine diesels are in two amidships engine rooms, both accommodating one propulsion engine and one auxiliary power unit. The lift engine is an MTU 6V 396 TB 83 rated at 550 kW at 2300 rpm which drives lift fans via a gearbox, to provide cushion air and drives, via a hydraulic pump and hydraulic motors, two secondary fans for skirt inflation. The propulsion engines are MTU 12V 396 TB 83 diesels rated at 1050 kW at 1800 rpm. Each incorporates a ZF BW 455 reverse-reduction gearbox and drives a single three-bladed propeller via transmission shafting inclined at 13°. The outward rotating propellers operate at up to 900 rpm.

The main plenum chamber receives air from the two lift fans via ducts located amidships port and starboard. Bow and stern skirts receive air from port and starboard fans, driven hydraulically by lift engine gearbox pumps, via ducts forming part of the superstructure.

Electrical system: The two Perkins 4.236M marine diesels rated at 27.2 kW, 50 Hz, 220 V drive the AC alternators and compressors for the air-conditioning system.

Control: Vessel heading is controlled by power-operated twin water rudders. Additional control is provided by differential use of the propellers. An automatic roll stabilisation system operates through inclined independant rudders.

Outfit: Passenger access is via doors port and starboard in the forward saloon and rearward double door for aft saloon. Emergency exits are located in both saloons. There are four WC/wash basin units provided plus luggage space.

HM 780 CAR FERRY (DESIGN)

The HM 780 is designed to carry a payload of 650 passengers in one large saloon and a vehicle mix of typically 74 cars, 6 coaches and 8 light vans. The construction of hull, deck and superstructure can be in marine grade aluminium or composite materials, subject to customer requirements.

The craft is designed to operate at 48 knots in Sea State 5, on typical cross-channel routes these conditions are only exceeded for about 10 per cent of the year. Onboard motion levels in Sea State 5 will be low with vertical acceleration levels less than 0.15 g rms.

Principal Particulars

Length overall	80 m
Beam	25 m
Draught, hullborne	4.2 m
Draught, on-cushion	2 m
Weight	975 t
Payload	243.25 t
Passengers	650
Vehicles	74 cars
	8 vans
	6 coaches
Fuel capacity	48 000 l
Propulsive power	2 × 12 000 kW or 4 × 5400 kW
Lift power	2 × 3000 kW
Maximum speed	64 knots (Gas-turbines)
Maximum speed	58.5 knots (Diesels)
Operational speed	48 knots
Operational limitation	Sea State 5

Classification Lloyd's Register ✠A1, Air Cushion Vehicle, Group 1 ✠LMC.

Propulsion: The main engines are 2 × LM 1600 gas-turbines, 12 000 kW each or 4 × MTU 20V 1163 TB 73 diesels, 5400 kW each.

Thrust devices: 2 × KaMeWa 125 S2.

The lift power is provided by 2 × MTU 12V 1163 TB 73, 3000 kW each; and the aft skirt power by 1 × MTU 8V 396 TE74, 840 kW.

Auxiliary systems: Powered by 2 × 300 kW diesels.

General arrangement of the HM 780 (design)

PROFILE

WATER JET | FUEL | UP | PROPULSION | FAN | FAN | LIFT ENG | VOID

CARS×74 | VANS×8 | COACHES×6

WATER JET | FUEL | UP | PROPULSION | FAN | FAN | LIFT ENG | VOID

CAR DECK PLAN

ENG VENT | STORES & AIR CON. | W.C.s | EXIT

SHOPS & CATERING | 650 PASSENGERS | UP | CREW ACCOMMODATION

PROMENADE | EXIT | EXIT

W.C.s | STORES & AIRCON | ON | ENG VENT | EXIT

PASSENGER DECK PLAN

UPDATED

INGLES HOVERCRAFT ASSOCIATES LTD

101A High Street, Gosport, Hampshire PO12 1DS, UK

Telephone: +44 (1705) 510593
Telefax: +44 (1705) 502302

N A H Pool, *Director*
J W Wilson, *Director*
T J R Longley, *Design Consultant*
N J Smith, *Design Consultant*

Ingles Hovercraft Associates Ltd holds the patent rights relating to the 'Elevon' system of control. Under a manufacturing agreement, production of the River Rover Mk 4 hovercraft is currently carried out by the HoverAid Trust. HoverAid is a registered charity, established to design and build appropriate technology hovercraft primarily for use in developing countries. Sales are made to missions and aid agencies on a non-profit basis.

The River Rover series has been developed over the last two decades to create a vehicle capable of reliably coping with the most arduous of river and delta conditions. The patented Elevon control system was first proven on a British joint services expedition to conquer the rapids of the Nepalese Kali Gandaki in 1978. Similar expeditions to the

River Rover Mk 4 using its elevon controls to complete a tight turn above hump speed

River Rover Mk 4 craft operating in Papua New Guinea **1995**

Amazonian headwaters in Peru, and to the snow-bound source of the Yangtze, on the Tibetan plateau, have shown the River Rover to be unparalleled in terms of manoeuvrability.

The first River Rover Mk 4 was completed in April 1992. Several craft are at present in service with medical aid programmes.

RIVER ROVER Mk 4

The River Rover Mk 4 is a natural development of the River Rover series, however the concept has been significantly advanced in the Mk 4 by the extensive use of computer modelling. Using finite element optimisation techniques, the rugged and robust construction required has been achieved using a modular bolt-together system. A stronger, lighter and inherently simpler design has been developed, increasing payload and capacity, whilst remaining inexpensive and easy to maintain and repair when operating in primitive conditions. The River Rover Mk 4 is available with either a Volkswagen or Land Rover turbocharged and intercooled engine, providing greater economy, reliability, and global parts availability with either installation.

The River Rover has been designed from a unique background of experience, and has several features which set it apart from similar craft.

Principal Particulars

Length overall	6.83 m
Beam	2.77 m
Weight, minimum	0.95 t
Weight, maximum	1.55 t
Crew	1
Passengers	8
Fuel capacity	180 l
Propulsive power	97 kW
Maximum speed	32 knots
Operational speed	24 knots
Range	190 nm

Structure: To fulfil its intended operational parameters, the River Rover Mk 4 has been designed for simple maintenance and repair. The hull consists of a bolted aluminium spaceframe with repeated glass fibre box structures attached; the removable side decks are built from two sets of identical deck panels. The outer set can be lowered for containerisation or road transportation. In the event of damage no complicated aluminium welding or

composite construction is required, the entire craft being of a modular design. The overall appearance of the craft is essentially sleek and streamlined, contributing to increased fuel efficiency.

Propulsion: The operator has the choice of either a Volkswagen or Land Rover 2.4 litre turbocharged engine, developing 97 kW at 4000 rpm. The engine bay is fully accessible from all sides, and equipped with automatic fire detection and suppression systems. Two thrust fans and an axial flow pressure fan for lift, are driven directly from the engine via a clutch and a torsionally resilient coupling. The bearings and drive shafts employ a high quality, sealed for life, maintenance-free system.

All fuel is filtered twice and passed through a sedimentation and water separation system to ensure engine safety when available fuel composition is less than ideal.

Electrical system: Voltage is nominally 12 V DC. Two maintenance-free, sealed for life batteries are supplied as standard.

Navigation and communications: The craft can be supplied with any necessary instrumentation, such as flux gate compass, global positioning system, satellite-linked weather map receiver, and so on. The option of marine radar is available, and can be positioned for use by the co-driver.

VHF marine band type radio for short range communication can be supplied, for longer range either HF or Satcom standard satellite systems can be fitted.

Control: The unique twin cascade Elevon system allows precise positional control. Pitch and roll are actively adjusted by vertical thrust vectoring, this effect is enhanced by the wide separation of the thrust fans. When combined with the conventional rudders a high degree of lateral control is achieved, allowing, for example, operation in crosswinds without side-slip. High-speed power turns can be performed without tail breakaway, an undesirable characteristic of many conventional hovercraft; this allows River Rover to negotiate intricate river systems well above hump speed. Over rapids and on higher sea states, a steadier and more efficient ride is obtained, and when fully deployed the system acts as a brake allowing safe progress over dangerous or confined terrain.

The control systems are aerodynamically balanced to give excellent driver 'feel', providing sensitive and easy operation, essential on long journeys. Flight attitude is easily altered by using Elevon trim presets; in addition, a high-speed pump can rapidly transfer fuel forward or aft to balance the craft as required.

Outfit: The River Rover Mk 4 is intended as a multi-role utility hovercraft, and as such the cabin specifications allow a great deal of flexibility. The standard seating arrangement is for a driver and seven passengers. All seats can be folded flat to create a flat cargo area; folding back the front passenger seats as well converts it into a stretcher bay with space for two attendants. The gull wing side doors allow the entire side of the passenger compartment to be lifted creating ideal access for use as a river ambulance, or for carrying freight. If further cargo space is required all the seating can be removed.

Safety equipment: The River Rover Mk 4 contains sufficient closed cell protective foam to ensure against sinking, even when ruptured. Fire extinguishers are supplied in both passenger and engine compartments.

Operations equipment: External baggage pods can be supplied for extra cargo space, or for storing emergency equipment.

UPDATED

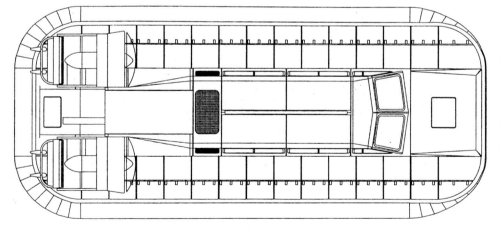

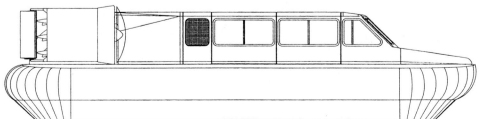

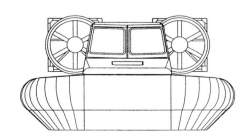

River Rover Mk 4

OSPREY HOVERCRAFT UK LTD

No 1 Work Base, The Historic Dockyard, Chatham, Kent ME4 4TZ, UK

Telephone: +44 (1634) 844573
Telefax: +44 (1634) 819153
East Grinstead Office
Telephone: +44 (1342) 314833
Telefax: +44 (1342) 317477

Kip McCollum, *Managing Director*
Tony Old, *Chairman and Marketing Director*

Osprey build a range of small hovercraft, ranging from single to five-seat capacity, with designs for larger craft.

OSPREY 5-SEATER
Principal Particulars

Length overall	4.87 m
Beam	2.13 m
Weight, minimum	0.5 t
Payload	0.4 t
Crew	1
Passengers	4
Propulsive power	64 kW
Operational speed	48 knots

Structure: Reinforced glass fibre.
Propulsion: Engine: 1360 cc, 63 kW 4-cylinder, 4-stroke, Citroen, liquid-cooled, with key start and charging.
Fuel: gasoline/petrol.

OSPREY 3-SEATER
Principal Particulars

Length	3.96 m
Beam	2.13 m
Weight, minimum	0.32 t
Payload	0.23 t
Crew	1
Passengers	2
Propulsive power	40 kW

Osprey single seater hovercraft 1994

Operational speed	21.7 knots

Structure: Reinforced glass fibre.
Propulsion: Engine: 1124 cc, 40 kW 4-cylinder, 4-stroke, Citroen, liquid-cooled with key start and charging.
Fuel: gasoline/petrol.

OSPREY SINGLE SEATER
Principal Particulars

Length	2.9 m
Beam	1.82 m
Weight, minimum	0.15 t
Payload	0.1 t
Crew	1
Propulsive power	13 kW
Operational speed	17 knots

Structure: Reinforced glass fibre with built-in buoyancy.
Propulsion: Engine: 13 kW air-cooled, twin cylinder 4-stroke, electric and recoil start.
Fuel: gasoline/petrol.
Control: Twin rudders.

VERIFIED

SLINGSBY AMPHIBIOUS HOVERCRAFT LTD

Kirkbymoorside, Yorkshire YO6 6EZ, UK

Telephone: +44 (1751) 432474
Telex: 57597 SLINAV G
Telefax: +44 (1751) 431173

Michael D Jones, *Group Chief Executive*
Russell D Haworth, *Managing Director*
Simon A Cooper, *Contracts Director*
Stephen B Boulton, *Marine Sales Manager*

Since its formation in the 1930s as Slingsby Sailplanes, building gliders, the Slingsby Group of Companies has grown in size and greatly expanded its capabilities. The development into composite materials design and manufacturing, has led into building aircraft, airships, submersibles and hovercraft.

In 1984 the hovercraft development commenced and this has resulted in the SAH 2200 amphibious hovercraft, of which more than 25 are in service around the world, both in military and commercial applications.

SAH 2200

The SAH 2200 is a single diesel-engined hovercraft manufactured in a composite of glass and Kevlar fibre, epoxy resin and PVC foam. This combination produces an exceptionally strong, lightweight structure with excellent fatigue life and resistance to corrosion from salt water. These characteristics give the hovercraft a very good payload and performance for the engine horsepower used, making it easy and inexpensive to maintain. With a maximum payload of 2200 kg the craft is certificated to carry up to 22 passengers and can hold sufficient fuel for more than 12 hours of operations.

Current operations include coastal patrol work in areas ranging from Scandinavia, where winter use is over ice and snow, to the Arabian Gulf, as a safety patrol craft on firing ranges, around coastal airports

SAH 2200 on exercises with the Royal Marines in Norway 1992

and as a training craft for crews on large military hovercraft.

Commercial and passenger-carrying operations have been established in the UK and other parts of Europe, South-east Asia, the Caribbean and the Indian subcontinent. In these operations the craft has been used for transporting people and equipment, carrying out survey work and acting as a safety craft around shallow water drilling operations.

Operational areas have included large tidal ranges with associated sand and mud flats, inland waters with large areas of shallow, weed infested water, mangrove swamp coastal waters and major

river complexes with conditions ranging from low water level sand banks to flood conditions with strong currents and a lot of debris in the water.

The hovercraft can be airlifted, trailed or shipped within a 40 ft flat rack. Packed dimensions with duct removed:
Length: 12 m
Height: 2 m
Beam: 2.4 m
Weight: 3 t

Principal Particulars

Length overall	10.6 m
Beam	4.2 m

Payload	2.2 t
Passengers	22
Fuel capacity	510 l
Propulsion power	142 kW
Maximum speed	40 knots
Range	500 nm
Obstacle clearance	0.5 m

Structure: Heavy-duty composite plastics structure strengthened with Kevlar in high load areas. Heavy-duty landing skids are provided. Four marine bollards on the deck form lifting rig attachments and guides for the integral jacking system. Side decks are rigid and enable large, bulky items to be carried outside the main load space. The side decks fold to allow transport of the craft by road vehicles or shipping within a 40 ft flat rack container.

The skirt is of a loop and segment type.

Propulsion: Integrated propulsion and lift system. The standard SAH 2200 is powered by a single Deutz BF6L 913C turbocharged air-cooled diesel, rated at 142 kW at 2500 rpm, driving a centrifugal lift fan and a Hoffmann variable-pitch ducted propeller. Alternatively, a Deutz BF8L 513 turbocharged air-cooled diesel, rated at 223 kW at 2300 rpm, or a Cummins 6CTA3M-1 turbocharged water-cooled diesel rated at 223 kW at 2500 rpm have been used to suit customer requirements. A deeper open loop skirt with increased lift height is also used with the higher powered engines as required.

Electrical system: 24 V electrical supply is standard. Provision is made for optional extras such as radar, air-conditioning, heating and searchlights.

Control: Rudders mounted in the propeller slipstream provide directional control; similarly mounted elevators provide fore and aft trim. Fuel ballast and roll control systems are incorporated to counteract adverse loading and to improve craft performance in high wind and sea states. A controllable pitch propeller allows variable thrust both in forward and reverse giving enhanced control particularly over land and in difficult downwind sea conditions.

Outfit: Seats forward for commander and passenger/navigator are in a self-contained wheelhouse. The load space is flexible in layout and two quick-release composite canopies allow conversion to three versions:

Passenger Version: Bench seating running fore and aft providing a total of 22 passenger seats. Access is port and starboard through gull wing doors mounted in canopies.

Supply Boat Version: Covered accommodation for eight passengers with open load space with a capacity for up to 1400 kg of cargo.

Logistic Support Version: With canopies and seats removed, integral cargo lashing rails are provided to enable a disposable load of up to 2200 kg to be carried.

In addition to the above, purpose-designed pods to fit the load space are manufactured to carry specialist equipment.

UPDATED

SAH 2200 operating with the Finnish Coast Guard **1995**

SAH 2200 operating between Bombay and Vashi (New Bombay) **1995**

SAH 2200 operating with the UK Ministry of Defence
1995

UNITED STATES OF AMERICA

AVONDALE BOAT DIVISION, Avondale Industries Inc

620 Labauve Road, Westwego, Louisiana 70094, USA

Telephone: +1 (504) 436 3322
Telefax: +1 (504) 436 3363

BHC AP1-88

In 1990 Avondale was appointed the United States licensee for AP1-88 amphibious hovercraft.

AIR RIDE 109

In late 1988 Avondale Boat Division announced the building under licence from Air Ride Craft Inc of Air Ride Craft 109 (400-passenger) surface effect ships for Tri-State Marine Transport Inc to operate between John F Kennedy Airport and lower Manhattan. The Air Ride Craft concept developed by Don Burg represents a unique form of surface effect ship, in that a flexible seal or skirt is only used at the bow to contain the air cushion. The Avondale craft are built in marine grade aluminium alloy and form part of the diversified range of ship and boat building, conversion, repair, foundry and propeller work undertaken by the company.

Two Air Ride 109 SESs have been delivered by Avondale Boat Division.

Principal Particulars

Length	33.23 m
Beam	10.37 m
Draught, on-cushion	0.91 m
Displacement	140 t (½ load)
Passengers	360-400

Air Ride 109 400-passenger ferry

1990

Fuel capacity	9463 l
Water capacity	1514 l
Propulsive power	2 × 1603 kW
Lift power	336 kW
Operational speed	44 knots

Classification: USCG + ABS.
Structure: Hull: aluminium

Propulsion: The main engines are two Deutz MWM TBD 604B V16, driving KaMeWa water-jet units. The lift engine is a Deutz MWM TBD 234 V12.
Auxiliary systems: Ride control system: standard

UPDATED

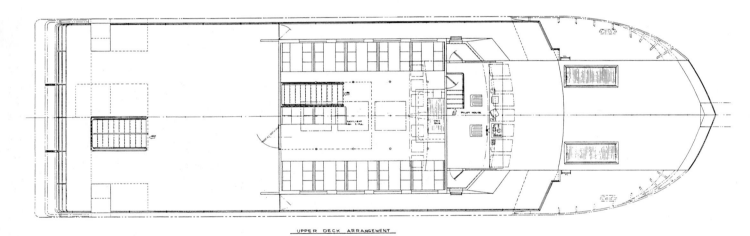

UPPER DECK ARRANGEMENT
68 PASSENGER SEATS

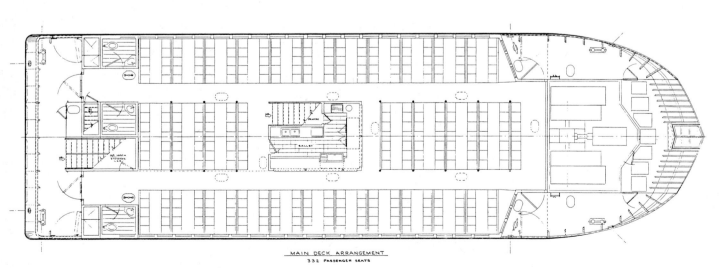

MAIN DECK ARRANGEMENT
332 PASSENGER SEATS

Air Ride 109 passenger ferry

NEOTERIC HOVERCRAFT INC

1649 Tippecanoe Street, Terre Haute, Indiana 47807-2394, USA

Telephone: +1 (812) 234 1120
Telefax: +1 (812) 234 3217

J Christopher Fitzgerald, *President*
Kathy Mains, *Accountant*

Neoteric Hovercraft Inc was formed in 1975 by three of the founders of Neoteric Engineering Affiliates Pty Ltd, Melbourne, Australia. The Neova range of two-seat ACVs, which is now being manufactured and marketed by Neoteric USA, was first introduced by the Australian associate. The fully amphibious Neova is available in kit or ready-built form. Other businesses may manufacture the Neoteric range under licence.

In 1992 Neoteric introduced its largest craft in the range, the eight-seat, 6.17 m Neova 8. The Neova 6 and Neova 4 are slightly smaller six- and four-seat craft.

NEOVA 8

This is a heavy-duty eight-seat hovercraft employing the proven skirt and control systems of the Neova II and Neova 4 machines. The use of a heavy-duty V8 automotive truck engine adds to the high levels of reliability, durability and economy. It has received US Coast Guard approval and is now a US Coast Guard certified vessel. The selling price is US$137 000 with all features.

Neova 8   1994

Principal Particulars

Length overall	6.17 m	Propulsive power	115 kW
Beam	2.97 m	Maximum speed	43 knots
Weight, maximum	1.75 t	Range	173 nm
Payload	0.635 t		
Passengers	8		*VERIFIED*

TEXTRON MARINE & LAND SYSTEMS
Division of Textron Inc

6600 Plaza Drive, New Orleans, Louisiana 70127-2584, USA

Telephone: +1 (504) 245 6600
Telefax: +1 (504) 245 6634

John J Kelly, *President*
James W Kratzer, *Executive Vice President*
Leonard E Caley, *Vice President, Materiel*
H J Smedley, *Vice President, Engineering*
Thomas A Corcoran, *Executive Director, Human Resources*
Irwin F Edenzon, *Vice President, Business Development and Marketing (Marine)*
Joseph J Halisky, *Vice President, Government Programs*
Frank P Higgins, *Vice President, Logistics and Customer Support*
Robert G Moore, *Director of Technology*
Robert E Peno, *Director, Product Assurance*
Robert J Rotundo, *Vice President, Commercial and Combat Vehicle Programs*
John P Schneider, *Vice President, Manufacturing*

Textron Marine & Land Systems (TM&LS), a new division of Textron Inc, began in 1969 as the New Orleans operations of Bell Aerospace Textron, which had been pursuing air cushion vehicle development programmes since 1958. It was renamed Textron Marine Systems in 1986 and acquired its manufacturing facility in 1988. In April 1994, TMS operations were joined with those of Cadillac Gage Textron under the name of Textron Marine & Land Systems. Cadillac Gage products include combat vehicles; weapon stations; and control, stabilisation and suspension systems for military vehicles.

The Textron Marine Systems Shipyard Operations, formerly Bell Halter Inc, was acquired in 1988 when TMS purchased it from Halter Marine Inc. Prior to that, the shipyard was operated as a joint venture of Bell Aerospace Textron and Halter Marine.

The TM&LS facility is located on a 10.1 ha (25 acre) site in eastern New Orleans, Louisiana, and has direct access to the Intra-coastal Waterway, the Mississippi River and the Gulf of Mexico. Vessels built at the facilty are in service with the US Army, the US Army Corps of Engineers, the US Navy, the US Coast Guard and the commercial sector, and have accumulated many thousands of hours of service.

LCAC-39 undergoing trials near New Orleans, Louisiana   1993

TM&LS also maintains a 1115 m² advanced suspension lab (for military and commercial vehicles) in eastern New Orleans and a 5202 m² storage facility in Slidell, Louisiana (32 km from the manufacturing facility).

The company has rights to manufacture and sell in the USA, machines employing the hovercraft principle, through a licensing arrangement with the British Hovercraft Corporation and Hovercraft Development Ltd. TM&LS produces Air Cushion Vehicle (ACV) products using aluminium and/or composite materials.

Craft built by TM&LS range in size from the 7.32 m Utility Air Cushion Vehicle (UACV 1200), to the 26.8 m Landing Craft, Air Cushion (LCAC) currently in production for the US Navy, to the 48.7 m SES-200 which has undergone modification for the US Navy.

TM&LS had delivered a total of 58 LCACs to the US Navy by September 1994.

There were 17 LCACs deployed to the Persian Gulf during the Gulf War.

LCACs provided relief to the outer islands of Bangladesh during the devastating cyclone of 1991. A total of 34 sorties was carried out in 14 days delivering 900 tonnes of desperately needed relief cargo.

Beginning in 1992, LCACs also played a vital role during Operation Restore Hope in Somalia.

Earlier work on air cushion vehicles, that has led to current TM&LS developments, is summarised in the 1991 and earlier editions of this book.

Principal craft built

SESs		
SES-100B	surface effect ship test craft (see *Jane's Surface Skimmers 1984* and earlier editions)	on trials February 1972
Model 210A (**110 Mk I**)	demonstration SES, became USCG *Dorado* (WSES-1)	launched 1978 June 1981
Model 730A	became Model 730A, US Navy SES-200, with 15.24 m extension	re-powered and water jets fitted 1990
Model 720A	*Rodolf*-hydrographic survey boat for US Army Corps of Engineers	delivered 1980
Model 212A (**110 Mk II**)	crewboats: *Speed Command* *Swift Command*	delivered February 1981 delivered July 1981
Model 522A (**110 Mk II**)	'Seabird' class: *Sea Hawk* (WSES-2) US Coast Guard *Shearwater* (WSES-3) Key West, Florida *Petrel* (WSES-4)	October 1982 June 1983
Model 212B	Model 212A *Speed Command* and *Swift Command* converted to become Model 212B crewboats: *Margaret Jill* (chartered by Tidewater Inc) *Speed Tide* (chartered by Tidewater Inc)	1984 1985
HM 221	Fire and rescue vessel. Two craft	delivered July and October 1992

AMPHIBIOUS AIR CUSHION VEHICLES

AALC JEFF(B) Amphibious Assault Landing Craft	completed March 1977	
LACV-30	Lighter, Air Cushion Vehicle. 24 completed by 1986 for US Army Troop Support Command	first ones delivered 1981
LCAC	Landing Craft, Air Cushion	58 delivered by November 1994
UACV	Utility Air Cushion Vehicle Demonstrator	1988
UACV 1200	Delivered to Shell Offshore Inc, *Hover 1*	June 1989
Model C-7 Hovercraft	High-speed ACV passenger/ cargo ferry, executive transporter configuration delivered to Freeport Indonesia	1994
Model FR-7	Fire/rescue vessel delivered to Singapore CAAS	1994

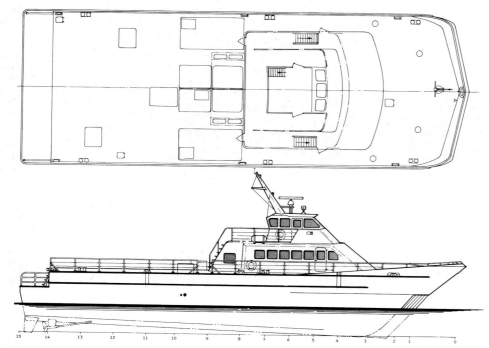

Original outboard profile and plan of Model 110 Mk I demonstration SES

LCAC
LANDING CRAFT, AIR CUSHION

On 5 June 1981 TM&LS signed a US$40 million contract with the US Navy for the detail design and long-lead materials for an amphibious assault landing craft, designated by the Navy as the LCAC (Landing Craft, Air Cushion). The LCAC is the production version of the JEFF(B) craft. The contract contained two options for the later construction of six craft. In February 1982 the US Navy exercised the first option for the production of three lead craft and in October 1982 ordered a further three craft.

In March 1984 TM&LS was awarded a contract to build six LCACs. By December 1986 a further contract had been awarded, to build two more LCACs bringing the total to 14 craft. On 1 July 1987, the US Navy awarded a $187 million contract to TM&LS to construct another 10 LCACs. This marked the start of full production for the LCAC programme.

On 15 December 1988 a second full production contract for 12 LCACs was awarded to TM&LS, along with central procurement activities for long-lead time materials. This was valued at $228 million. An option to this contract was exercised on 22

LCAC
LANDING CRAFT, AIR CUSHION

Craft built	Delivered to US Navy
LCAC-1	December 1984
LCAC-2	February 1986
LCAC-3	June 1986
LCAC-4	August 1986
LCAC-5	November 1986
LCAC-6	December 1986
LCAC-7	March 1987
LCAC-8	June 1987
LCAC-9	June 1987
LCAC-10	September 1987
LCAC-11	December 1987
LCAC-12	December 1987
LCAC-13	September 1988
LCAC-14	November 1988
LCAC-24	March 1990
LCAC-25	June 1990
LCAC-26	June 1990
LCAC-27	August 1990
LCAC-28	October 1990
LCAC-29	December 1990
LCAC-30	December 1990
LCAC-31	February 1991
LCAC-32	May 1991
LCAC-33	June 1991
LCAC-37	July 1991
LCAC-38	September 1991
LCAC-39	September 1991
LCAC-40	November 1991
LCAC-41	November 1991
LCAC-42	December 1991
LCAC-43	February 1992
LCAC-44	February 1992
LCAC-45	March 1992
LCAC-46	May 1992
LCAC-47	June 1992
LCAC-48	July 1992
LCAC-52	September 1992
LCAC-53	October 1992
LCAC-54	October 1992
LCAC-55	December 1992
LCAC-56	January 1993
LCAC-57	February 1993
LCAC-58	March 1993
LCAC-59	April 1993
LCAC-60	June 1993
LCAC-61	July 1993
LCAC-62	August 1993
LCAC-63	September 1993
LCAC-64	October 1993
LCAC-65	November 1993
LCAC-66	December 1993
LCAC-67	February 1994
LCAC-68	March 1994
LCAC-69	April 1994
LCAC-70	May 1994
LCAC-71	June 1994
LCAC-72	July 1994
LCAC-73	September 1994
LCAC-74	October 1994
LCAC-75	December 1994
LCAC-76	January 1995

December 1989, for an additional nine LCACs. On 24 April 1991, another full production contract, valued at $139 million, for 12 LCACs was awarded to TM&LS with additional central procurement activities for long-lead time materials. A $181 million option to this contract, for 12 LCACs, was exercised 22 May 1992.

Since March 1992, TM&LS has won all seven contracts in support of the LCAC midlife overhaul and refurbishment program aimed at upgrading the US Navy LCAC fleet and maintaining it in operational readiness. LCACs -1, -2, -3, -4, and -6 have been overhauled at TM&LS West Coast Operations, and LCAC-8 has been overhauled on the east coast.

In January 1993, TM&LS was awarded a $117 million contract for the production of seven LCACs. This award made TMS the sole LCAC producer for the US Government's FY92 acquisition.

In April 1994, the Japan Defence Agency awarded TM&LS a contract to build and deliver a large air cushion vehicle based on the US Navy LCAC. Valued at $50 million, the contract includes delivery of

USCG Dorado *(WSES-1), formerly the Model 110 Mk I demonstrator before conversion by lengthening to become the SES-200*   **1988**

Bow ramp of LCAC   **1987**

engineering documentation, training manuals, reserve subsystems, spare parts, and support and test equipment. The ACV is scheduled for delivery in 1997.

The LCAC is a high-speed, ship-to-shore and over-the-beach amphibious landing craft, capable of carrying a 60 tonne payload. It can transport equipment, personnel and weapons systems (including the main battle tank) from ships located at increased stand-off distances, through the surf zone, and across the beach to hard landing points beyond the waterline. The craft is supported on a pressurised cushion of air and travels at much higher speeds than are presently possible with current conventional landing craft. Over-the-horizon assaults are made possible by the high transit speeds of the LCAC.

The LCAC is capable of travelling over land, water, marshes and mud flats. Compared to conventional landing craft, the percentage of the world's shorelines suitable for landing is increased from 17 to 80 per cent. The LCACs will operate from well-deck equipped amphibious ships.

LCAC's multimission capability has led to the designation of Multipurpose Craft, Air Cushion (MCAC). Personnel transport modules can be fitted to the deck of the LCAC to carry up to 80 personnel or to convert the LCAC to a medical evacuation or mobile field hospital role. A mine countermeasures modular sweep deck, installable in 12 hours or less includes a winch and crane for sweep gear. Other potential roles for the MCAC include patrol, civil emergency, lighterage, and coastal anti-submarine warfare.

Principal Particulars

Length overall	26.82 m
Beam	14.33 m
Draught, hullborne	0.91 m
Weight, maximum	153.5 t
Payload	54.3 t
Propulsive power	4 × 3955 kW
Maximum speed	50 knots

Propulsion: Four Textron Lycoming TF40B gas-turbines are installed, driving two Dowty Rotol

3.582 m diameter 4-blade variable, reversible-pitch propellers; and four double-entry centrifugal type lift fans of 1.6 m diameter.

MODEL 210A (110 Mk I) DEMONSTRATION SES

Launched in late 1978, the Model 110 demonstration boat has undergone extensive successful testing by both commercial operators and the US Coast Guard. The basic hull and machinery layout permits modification of the deckhouse and arrangement of the deck space for a number of alternative applications, from crewboat and 275-seat passenger ferry to fast patrol boat.

In September 1980 the US Navy purchased the Demonstration SES (110 Mk I) to be used in a joint US Navy/US Coast Guard programme. The US

Coast Guard, designating the boat the USCG Dorado (WSES-1), conducted an operational evaluation of the craft for the first six months of the programme. The craft was modified to conform to US Coast Guard requirements for an operational evaluation vessel. On completion of its USCG evaluation a 15.24 m hull extension was added to the boat for the US Navy to assess the performance of a higher length-to-beam vessel. The craft has been designated the SES-200 by the US Navy (see later sub-entry for Model 730A and SES-200 conversion).

MODEL 522A US COAST GUARD SES

In June 1981 the US Coast Guard awarded a contract for the purchase of three Model 522A (110 Mk II) high-speed cutters, the first two of which were delivered in October 1982.

The craft, known as the 'Seabird' class, are designated *Sea Hawk* (WSES-2), *Shearwater* (WSES-3) and *Petrel* (WSES-4). *Petrel* was delivered in June 1983. These vessels, now decommissioned, were based at Key West, Florida, at a Coast Guard facility, where they were highly successful at intercepting drug runners operating in the Gulf of Mexico and the Caribbean Sea.

Principal Particulars

Length overall	33.52 m
Beam	11.88 m
Draught, hullborne	2.51 m
Draught, on-cushion	1.67 m
Displacement, maximum	152 t
Crew	12
Fuel capacity	34 050 l
Propulsive power	2 × 1800 kW
Lift power	260 kW
Maximum speed	30 knots
Range	1550 nm

Structure: Primary structure is built in welded marine aluminium alloy 5086. The structure is of catamaran configuration and consists of two side hulls separated by decks and transverse bulkheads. The side hull shell plating varies between ¼ and ½ in depending on local pressures and is stiffened by T-section longitudinals. The spacing of the longitudinals is 457 mm on the bottom plating and 381 mm on the side plating. Side hull shape is maintained by bulkheads spaced generally at 2.44 m which support the hull longitudinals. Bulkheads have ¼ in webs with T-section and flat bar stiffening and flat bar caps sized appropriately for each bulkhead.

Six of the bulkheads in each side hull and across the centre section between the hulls are watertight. There are two in the accommodation area and one forward of the deckhouse. The latter also forms a collision bulkhead. The bulkheads provide the transverse bending and torsional continuity to the hull structure.

The cabin superstructure consists of T-section frames fabricated from flat bars and spaced as the frames on the hull. T-stiffened plate is welded to the framing.

The bow seal consists of eight equally spaced fingers, each of which is attached to the underside of the centre hull. The stern seal, which has a constant

Sea Hawk *and* Shearwater, *the first two Model 522A cutters to be delivered to the US Coast Guard*   **1988**

cross-section, consists of two inflated horizontal lobes of coated-fabric material.

Propulsion: Motive power for the propulsion system is furnished by two DDA 16V-149TIB marine diesels. Each drives a 1.06 m diameter, 1.17 m pitch, three-bladed, fixed-pitch NiBrAl propeller Gawn-Burrill Series type.

Cushion lift is provided by two Detroit Diesel Allison 8V-92N marine diesels each driving a double-inlet centrifugal fan.

Control: Craft direction is controlled by twin rudders, one aft on each side hull. Differential propeller thrust is employed for slow-speed manoeuvring. The steering system is electrohydraulic and can be operated from any of the control stations in the pilot-house and the wing bridges.

Outfit: Deckhouse superstructure contains pilothouse at 01 level with communications and navigation equipment. Auxiliary control stations are provided plus additional controls on each wing bridge. Main deckhouse contains the ship's office, armoury, captain's stateroom, quarters for three officers and three crew. Second deck accommodation includes galley and additional quarters for 12 crew.

MODEL 212B (110 Mk II)

The Model 212B is a conversion of the Model 212A. The two craft converted are the *Margaret Jill* (ex *Speed Command*) and *Speed Tide* (ex *Swift Command*).

Principal Particulars

Length overall	33.25 m
Beam	11.89 m
Draught, hullborne	2.52 m
Draught, on-cushion	1.68 m
Crew	6
Passengers	119
Fuel capacity	20 212 l
Water capacity	3181 l
Propulsive power	2 × 1230 kW
Lift power	2 × 260 kW
Operational speed	31 knots

Structure: 5086 aluminium.

Propulsion: Main engines: two Detroit Diesel Allison 16V-149TIB engines, diesel, turbocharged, intercooled, heat exchanger cooled, air start.

Lift engines: two GM 8V-92 engines, diesel, heat exchanger cooled, air start.

Gears: two ZF BW 455 reduction gears. Input shafts - identical rotation, output shafts - opposite rotation (2:1 ratio).

Lift fans: two TMS 42 in welded aluminium centrifugal fans.

Propeller shafts: 4 in diameter 17-4 PH stainless steel.

Bearings: 4 in BJ Byplex rubber bearings.

Propellers: 3-blade stainless.

Rudders: stainless steel built-up blades with 5 in diameter stainless rudder stocks.

Bearings: 5 in BJ Byplex rubber bearings.

Outfit: Passenger accommodation: 119 × 4 in thick cushioned bench seats on two deck levels. Two passenger heads provided.

Crew accommodation: six in two single and two two-person cabins with hanging lockers. Two crew toilets with showers provided. Mess area for six adjoins galley.

Auxiliary systems: Two GM 3-71 65 kVA heat exchanger cooled generators, one air start, one hydraulic start.

Model 212B, Margaret Jill

1988

Textron Marine 48.78 m SES-200 before propulsion and hull structure change programme

1988

MODEL 730A (USN SES-200) HIGH LENGTH-TO-BEAM RATIO TEST CRAFT

The original 33.53 m SES demonstration boat is now owned by the US Navy. The boat was modified by adding a 15.24 m hull extension. The hull was cut amidships; the lift fans and engines remaining in the bow and the main engines remaining in the stern. Bow and stern sections were then moved apart and a 15.24 m plug section inserted between them. All major systems remained the same as they were in the original vessel, including the GM 16V-149TI engines.

In this configuration, the vessel had a 60 per cent greater disposable load than the demonstration boat, while its maximum speed was only reduced by three to four knots. At intermediate speeds, the power requirements were lower than for the shorter vessel, despite the greater displacement.

In 1986, the SES-200 successfully completed an eight-month series of joint technical and operational

HM-221 fire and rescue vessel John P Devaney

1993

trials. The trials, which were conducted in Canada, France, Germany, Norway, Spain, Sweden and the UK, provided each host nation opportunities for direct evaluation of the high length-to-beam SES in their own waters.

Principal Particulars

Length overall	48.7 m
Beam	11.88 m
Draught, hullborne	2.83 m
Draught, on-cushion	1.67 m
Displacement, maximum	207 t
Fuel capacity	80 128 l
Propulsive power	1230 kW
Lift power	325 kW
Maximum speed	28 knots
Operational speed	22 knots
Range	3850 nm

Propulsion: The main engines are two DDC 16V-149TI, each driving 1.016 m diameter fixed-pitch propellers. The lift engines are four DDC 8V-92TI, each driving 1.067 m diameter Bell centrifugal fans.

Electrical system: DDC diesel generator, 85 kW plus 55 kW backup driven off one lift engine.

Reference: *The United Kingdom Trials of the SES-200* by B J W Pingree, B J Russell and J B Wilcox. Paper given at the Fourth International Hovercraft Conference, 6-7 May 1987.

SES 200 after propulsion upgrading in 1990   1991

SES-200 CONVERSION

On 11 April 1990, Textron Marine & Land Systems announced the award of a $1 858 744 contract by the US Army Corps of Engineers for the conversion, modification and upgrading of the propulsion system and hull structure of the 48.78 m SES-200.

The conventional propellers and existing 16V 149 TI diesel engines and gearboxes have been replaced by two MTU 16V 396 TB 94 diesel engines, using two ZF BW 755 gearboxes driving KaMeWa 71 S62/6-SII water-jet systems. Following the conversion, which increases the propulsion power from 2386 to 4265 kW, the SES-200 achieved speeds in excess of 40 knots in calm water, had greater manoeuvrability, produced lower in-water noise emission and was able to operate in shallower waters.

To conduct the conversion/re-powering work, the SES-200 was lifted from the water at the Textron Marine & Land Systems shipyard, transported 160 m overland and brought into position in a high-bay construction building.

After successfully completing acceptance trials in the Gulf of Mexico, the SES-200 returned to its home port at the David Taylor Research Center (DTRC), located at the Naval Air Station, Patuxent River, Maryland on the Chesapeake Bay. The DTRC, the Navy's laboratory for advanced naval vehicle development, deploys the craft in evaluation programmes.

C-7 executive transporter   1995

HM 221
FIRE AND RESCUE VESSEL

In 1992, TM&LS delivered two SES fire and rescue vessels to the City of New York. The Hovermarine International HM 221 hulls are equipped for fire-fighting by TM&LS. Highly automated to allow operation by a crew of two, the vessels will provide the capability for fire-fighting, search and rescue, harbour patrol and pollution monitoring.

The Fire Department of the City of New York accepted delivery of the *John P Devaney*, the first of two SES fire and rescue vessels, on 17 July 1992. TM&LS delivered the second, the *Alfred E Ronaldson*, on 24 November 1992. The contract was valued at $6.5 million.

Principal Particulars

Length overall	21.23 m
Beam	5.88 m
Draught, hullborne	1.75 m
Weight, maximum	36.45 t
Crew	2
Fuel capacity	2460 l
Water capacity	76 l
Propulsive power	2 × 373 kW
Lift power	287 kW
Maximum speed	30 knots
Operational speed	20 knots
Range	60 nm

Structure: Shell mouldings, submouldings, frames, bulkheads and major attachments in glass-

C-7 fire/rescue craft (FR-7)   1995

C-7 Patrol craft (P-12), artist's impression   **1995**

reinforced plastic. Fendering is fitted to the gunwale.
Propulsion: The main engines are two Detroit Diesel
Corporation 8V 92TA diesels driving 48.26 cm,
three-blade propellers through direct-drive reversing
gearboxes (ZF IRM 310 PL) and V-drive gearboxes
(BPM VD/180; overdrive ratio 1.06:1).

Lift power is provided by a Detroit Diesel Corporation 6V 92TA which is also used as a pump engine.
A second pump engine is provided by a Detroit Diesel Corporation 8V 92TA diesel.
Controls: Hydraulic pump: Hobourn Eaton HE 3501
8014-34 driven from lift engine.

Steering unit: Danfoss OSPB 100, OSP 8100, NR
150 0027.

Hydraulic actuator: Adam Hydraulics 4.45 cm (1¾
in) bore × 30.5 cm (12 in) stroke.
Outfit: Utility-standard crew accommodation
includes a two-tiered bunk, cooking facilities, a sink
and a toilet compartment.
Operations equipment: Three fire pumps (port,
starboard, forward) with capacity for 6938 l/min
(1833 US gal/min) at 1427 KPa (207 lb.ft/in²). The
port and starboard pumps are driven by the fire
pump engine and the forward pump by the lift
engine. The fire-fighting equipment is remotely controlled for rotation and elevation from the wheelhouse: one 20 818 l/min (5500 US gal/min) master
monitor mounted on the wheelhouse; two 9629 l/
min (2500 US gal/min) monitors mounted on the
foredeck; and two 9629 l/min (2500 US gal/min)
monitors mounted on either side of the bow beneath
the foredeck. All fire monitors, except the wheelhouse monitor, can be controlled from a straight
stream to a 90° fog. There is a deck hydrant with
connections for four 7.62 cm (3 in) and one
11.43 cm (4 ½ in) fire hoses.

MODEL C-7

The C-7 Hovercraft is designed for minimum-cost
operation with high payloads and extreme environmental conditions. The 17.8 m craft combines a
lightweight composite superstructure with a welded
aluminium hull and is available in passenger ferry,
cargo and riverine military configurations.

The concept chosen for the entire superstructure,
propeller ducts and rudders is a Resin Transfer
Moulding (RTM) process employing primarily an
E-glass composition. The process uses resin injection under vacuum with a room temperature cure to
consistently achieve a glass content of over 60 per
cent. This compares to a conventional wet lay-up
process that typically produces a 40 per cent glass
content. Parts can be fabricated with virtually zero
void content and an exceptional surface finish ready
for paint.

The C-7 superstructure is composed of 12 basic
sections, plus hatches, doors and bulkheads. The
curved bow section, which is 139 by 247 in, is con-

sidered the largest production part ever fabricated
using this process: it weighs 450 lb without the windows installed. To obtain maximum stiffness at minimum weight, carbon fibre composite is used in
several transverse frames and in the centre ring section of the propeller shroud.

The basic C-7 hovercraft features a 40 plus knot
capacity, low noise levels, low operating costs, and

environmentally safe operations. It is available in
four configurations: fire and rescue craft (FR-7),
passenger ferry, executive transport and patrol craft
(P-12).

In 1994, TM&LS delivered an executive C-7 transporter for use by Freeport Indonesia. The *Kasuari*, as
it was named, features modern, quiet, first class
accommodation, windows forward and on both
sides, bar, kitchen, and an interior design tailored to
the customer.

An FR-7 configured for fire-fighting and rescue
was delivered to the Civil Aviation Authority of Singapore at Changi International airport. The FR-7 has a
bow ramp, a fire monitor that delivers preselected
concentrate strength foam at more than 1500 litres
per minute at least 30 feet from the craft, and accommodates 50 passengers/50 Stokes stretchers.

The P-12 patrol craft design, a stretched derivative
of the C-7, features 45 knot speed and 6 tonne payload; crew berthing and galley; bow ramp for roll-on/
roll-off capability; carrying capacity for a light vehicle
(HMMWV) and a 500 nm range.

Principal Particulars

Length overall	16 m
Beam	9.46 m
Weight, maximum	29.5 t
Payload	5.4 t
Crew	2
Passengers	46
Fuel capacity	3785 l
Water capacity	152 l
Propulsive power	2 × 386 kW
Lift power	235 kW
Maximum speed	40 knots
Range	500 nm

Classification: United States Coast Guard Sub-
chapter T Small Passenger Vessels (under 100
gross tons) and IMO Code of Safety for Dynamically
Supported Craft.
Structure: Hull material; welded 5456 aluminium.

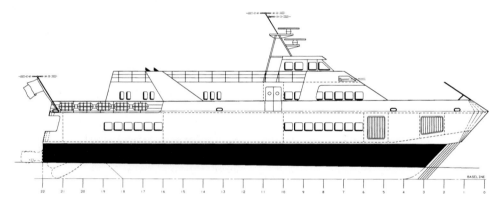

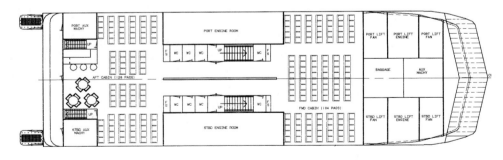

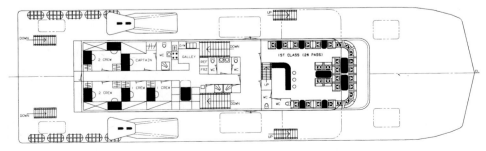

TM&LS 44 m SES ferry general arrangement (design)

Superstructure material: advanced marine composite.
Air cushion sealing: Bag and semi-closed finger, high stability skirt system with planing stern fingers. Bag material is neoprene-coated, open-weave, nylon fabric. Finger material is rubber-coated, open-weave, nylon fabric.
Propulsion: Two Dowty 2.44 m diameter, 4-bladed, ducted, controllable-pitch propellers driven by two Deutz BF12L 513C air-cooled diesel engines.

The lift system consists of two 0.92 m diameter double-width double-inlet centrifugal fans powered by one Deutz BF8L 51C air-cooled diesel engine.
Electrical system: 24 V DC. Four 24 V DC battery installations. 208 V AC, 100 A, 60 Hz, 3-phase shore power feed.
Auxiliary systems: One 25 kW air-cooled diesel generation set 120/208 V AC, 60 Hz, 3-phase.
Two 100 A 28 V DC alternators driven from the main engines.

44 m SES FAST FERRY (DESIGN)

The TM&LS 44 m SES fast ferry is a low-risk refinement of two service-proven SES craft: the US Navy SES-200 (52.5 m) and the BH 110 (36 m). A combination of wide beam and water-jet propulsion makes the craft highly manoeuvrable.

Principal Particulars

Length overall	40.84 m
Beam	12.5 m
Draught, on-cushion	1.22 m
Displacement, maximum	234.7 t
Payload	30.48 t
Crew	7
Passengers	236
Fuel capacity	15.95 t
Propulsive power	4 × 1500 kW
Lift power	2 × 746 kW
Maximum speed	49 knots
Operational speed	30 knots
Range	300 nm

Classification: United States Coast Guard Subchapter T; ABS load line by delegation to USCG; SOLAS equivalent SLE/SLC; IMO as required by gross tonnage.
Structure: Hull material: 5456 H-116 aluminium plates, 5456 H-111 aluminium shapes.
Propulsion: The main engines are four MTU 12V 396 TE 74L diesels.
Transmissions: two ZF BW 455 marine reduction gears, two ZF BW 755 offset/combining marine reduction gears. Thrust devices: two KaMeWa 071 SII water-jets.

The lift engines are two MTU 8V 396 TE 74 diesels each driving four TMS 1 067 mm double-width, double-entry centrifugal fans.
Electrical system: Two 100 kW diesel-driven 440 V AC, 60 Hz fully redundant generators.
Control: MTU/KaMeWa microprocessor-based integrated ship control and machinery monitoring system. Primary ship control is located in the pilot-house with port and starboard wing manoeuvring control stations.

A ride control system is available as an option.

UPDATED

HYDROFOILS

Company Listing by Country

Commonwealth of Independent States
Feodosia Shipbuilding Association (Morye)
Krasnoye Sormovo A A Zhdanov Shipyard
Sergo Ordzhonikidze Shipyard
Gomel Yard
Ś Ordzhonikidze Ship Building and Repair Yard

Indonesia
PT Pal Indonesia (Persero)

Italy
Fincantieri-Cantieri Navali Italiani SpA
Rodriquez Cantieri Navali SpA

Japan
Hitachi Zosen Corporation
Kawasaki Heavy Industries Ltd
Sumitomo Heavy Industries Ltd
Technological Research Association of Techno-
Superliner

United States of America
Boeing
Westfoil International

COMMONWEALTH OF INDEPENDENT STATES

FEODOSIA SHIPBUILDING ASSOCIATION (MORYE)

Feodosia 334871, Crimea, Ukraine, CIS

Telephone: +7 (6562) 69905
Telex: 187125 PTB SU KAFA
Telefax: +7 (6562) 32373

L Astakhov, *General Director*
Victor Oleinik, *Chief Engineer*
Gregory Klebanov, *Head of Foreign Economic Relations Department*

CYCLONE (*Liisa*)

Cyclone was built at the shipbuilding yard at Feodosia. The design is approved by certificate No 19931, 20 June 1985 and by the inventor's certificate dating from 1969 to 1984. Acceptance and pre-commissioning trials took place in 1986 and experimental operation of the vessel was first undertaken in 1987. This vessel is designed to Hydrofoil Passenger Class KM*2A2 of the Register of Shipping of the former Soviet Union. Cyclone is a gas-turbine powered hydrofoil designed for coastal routes and operations up to 100 miles from a port of refuge. It may operate foilborne in waves up to 3.5 m in height.

Liisa has been operating on the route Tallinn to Helsinki.

Principal Particulars

Length overall	44.2 m
Beam	7.3 m
Foil width	12.6 m
Draught, hullborne	4.3 m
Draught, foilborne	2.4 m
Displacement, maximum	137.1 t
Displacement, minimum	100.8 t
Payload	37 t
Crew	9
Passengers	250
Operational speed	7 knots hullborne
Operational speed	42 knots
Range	300 nm

Propulsion: 1 × M37 gas-turbine.
1 × 735 kW diesel (for slow running).

Cyclone   *1991*

The gas-turbine powered 250-seat Cyclone at sea   *1993*

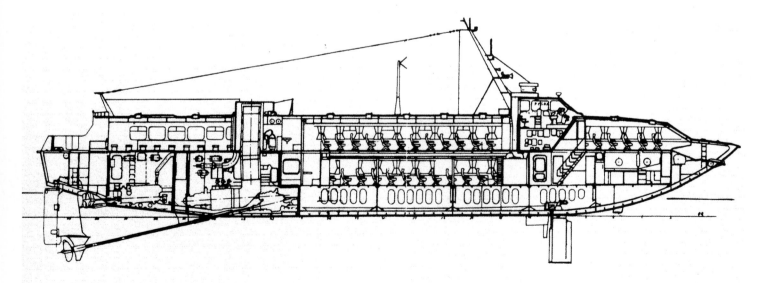

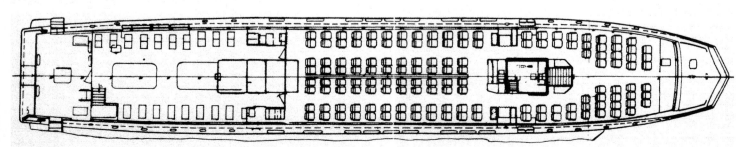

Layout of Cyclone

CYCLONE-M

Cyclone-M is an improved version of Cyclone and is powered by two gas-turbine engines. The vessel is designed to operate on sea routes of up to 100 miles from the port of refuge in countries with moderately cold climates; a tropical version of Cyclone is available. The production of Cyclone-M started in 1993-94.

Principal Particulars

Length overall	44.2 m
Beam	12.5 m
Draught, hullborne	4.3 m
Draught, foilborne	2.4 m
Displacement, maximum	146 t
Displacement, minimum	108 t
Passengers	210
Propulsive power	2 × 2960 kW
Operational speed	42 knots
Range	300 nm
Operational limitation	3 m wave height. Beaufort force 6

Structure: Hull material: aluminium.
Propulsion: Engines: 2 gas-turbines.
Thrust devices: propellers.

OLYMPIA

Olympia is a sea-going hydrofoil designed to operate on sea routes under tropical and temperate climatic conditions up to 50 miles from a port of refuge in open seas and up to 100 miles in inland seas and large lakes.

In a Sea State of 0 to 2 and in wind conditions up to Force 3 the speed of *Olympia* is 36 to 37 knots when foilborne and 10 to 12 knots when hullborne.

The first Olympia, *Laura*, was introduced on the Helsinki to Tallinn route in 1993 with the second craft delivered in September 1994.

Principal Particulars

Length overall	43.3 m
Beam	14 m
Draught, hullborne	4.6 m
Draught, foilborne	2 m
Displacement, maximum	135 t
Displacement, minimum	103 t
Crew	6
Passengers	250
Fuel capacity	6000 kg
Water capacity	2000 kg
Propulsive power	2 × 1905
Operational speed	37 knots
Range	300 nm
Operational limitation	3.5 m wave height Beaufort force 7

Structure: Hull material: aluminium.
Propulsion: Engines: 2 × MTU 16V 396 TE 74L diesels.
Thrust devices: propellers.

VOSKHOD-2

Designers of the Voskhod, which has been gradually replacing craft of the Raketa series, drew on engineering experience gained with the Raketa and

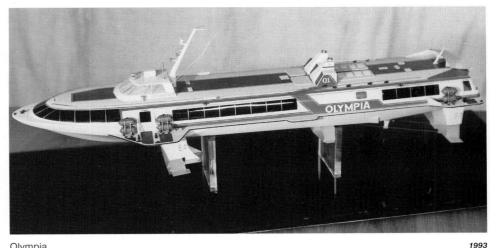
Olympia *1993*

also the more sophisticated Meteor and Kometa. Voskhod, in turn, was due to be succeeded by the new 50-seat Lastochka.

Among the basic requirements were that the Raketa's general characteristics should be preserved; foilborne operation should be possible in 1 m high waves, noise levels should be significantly reduced and the maximum use should be made of standard mechanical, electrical and other components and fittings proven on the Raketa. In fact, the end product bears little resemblance to its predecessor. Visually the Voskhod is more akin to a scaled-down Kometa with its engine room aft, replacing the rear passenger saloon.

Voskhod 14 was launched in June 1980 and delivered to the Amur Line for Summer services along the Amur river.

The vessel is designed for high-speed passenger ferry services during daylight hours on rivers, reservoirs, lakes and sheltered waters. It meets the requirements of Soviet River Register Class O with the following wave restrictions (three per cent safety margin): foilborne, 1.3 m; hullborne, 2 m.

The passenger saloons are heated and provided with natural and induced ventilation. Full air-conditioning can be installed in the craft required for service in tropical conditions. The crew comprises a captain, engineer, motorman and barman.

Principal Particulars

Length overall	27.6 m
Beam	6.2 m
Draught, hullborne	2 m
Draught, foilborne	1.1 m
Displacement, minimum	20 t
Displacement, maximum	28 t
Payload	5.9 t
Crew	4
Passengers	71
Fuel capacity	1647 l
Water capacity	138 l
Propulsive power	810 kW
Maximum speed	37.8 knots
Operational speed	32.4 knots
Range	270 nm
Operational limitation	1.3 m wave height

Structure: Similar in shape to the Kometa and earlier models of the Sormovo hydrofoil series, with a wedge-shaped bow, raked stem and spoon-shaped stern. A single step is provided to facilitate take off. In fabricating the basic structure, which is largely in AlMg-61 aluminium-magnesium alloy, extensive use has been made of arc and spot welding. The hull is framed on longitudinal and transverse formers. Below deck is divided into eight watertight compartments by transverse bulkheads. It will remain afloat with any one compartment or the machinery space flooded. Access to the forepeak, which houses the anchor capstan, is via the forward passenger saloon and then through a rectangular hatch on the forecastle. Aft of the main passenger saloon is an area split into three compartments by two longitudinal bulkheads. The lower central space contains the reduction gear and V-drive, the starboard compartment contains the sanitary tank and the port compartment forms part of the double bottom. Entrance to the engine compartment is via a door on the port side of the main deck. An emergency exit is provided starboard aft.

The craft has a fixed foil system, comprising one bow foil with a pitch stability sub-foil immediately behind, one aft foil, plus an amidships foil to facilitate take off. Bow and amidship foils appear to be of shallow V configuration and each has four vertical struts. The fully submerged stern foil has two side struts and is supported in the centre by the end bracket of the propeller shaft. The surface and lower parts of the foil struts and stabiliser are in Cr18Ni9Ti stainless steel, while the upper parts of the struts

Voskhod-2 *1988*

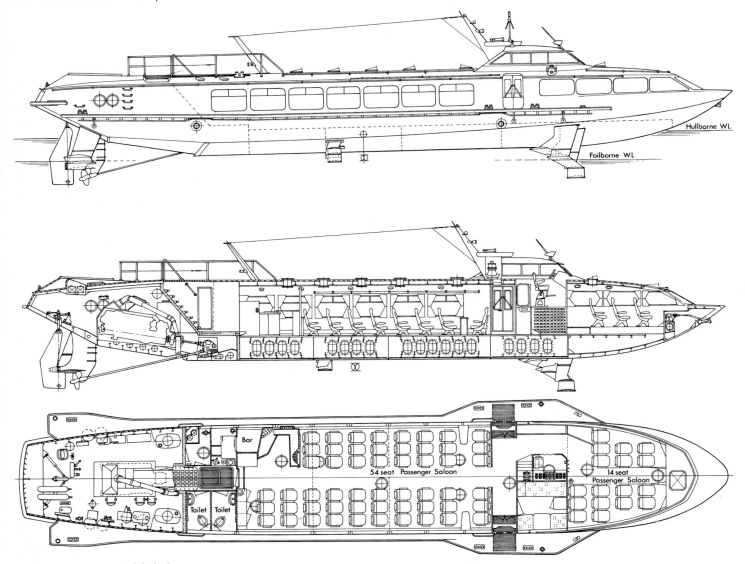

Voskhod-2, inboard profile and deck plan

and stabiliser and also the amidships foil are in AlMg-61 plate alloy.

Propulsion: Power is supplied by a single M-401A four-stroke water-cooled, supercharged 12-cylinder V-type diesel, delivering 810 kW at 1600 rpm maximum and 736 kW at 1550 rpm cruising. The engine, which has a variable-speed governor and a reversing clutch, is sited aft with its shaft inclined at 9°. Output is transferred via a flexible coupling to a single six-bladed variable-pitch propeller via an R-21 V-drive gearbox. Guaranteed service life of the engine before the first overhaul is 3000 hours. Specific oil consumption is not more than 8 g/kWh. The engine room is insulated with fire-retardant, heat and sound-insulating materials. Perforated aluminium alloy sheet is laid over the insulating materials.

Electrical systems: Power supply is 24 to 27 V DC. A 3 kW generator is attached to the engine and supplies 27.5 V while the craft is operating. Four 12 V storage batteries, each of 180 Ah capacity and connected in series-parallel to form a single bank, supply power during short stops. An auxiliary circuit can be connected to shore systems for 220 V, single-phase, 50 Hz AC supply.

Control: Single semi-balanced rudder in AlMg plate provides directional control. Operation of the engine, rudder, reverse gear and fuel supply is effected hydraulically from the wheelhouse.

Voskhod-2M   *1993*

VOSKHOD-2M

This version is a sea-going hydrofoil for daylight operation within 25 miles of a port of refuge. The dimensions are the same as Voskhod-2.

Production of the sea-going Voskhod-2M started in 1993.

Principal Particulars

Length overall	27.6 m		
Beam	4.4 m	Range	200 nm
Foil width	6.4 m	Operational limitation	1.25 m wave height
Draught	2 m		Beaufort force 4
Displacement, minimum	24.6 t	**Propulsion:** Engines: 1 × M419A diesel.	
Displacement, maximum	32.5 t	Thrust device: fixed-pitch 6-blade bronze propeller.	
Passengers	65		
Operational speed	30 knots		*UPDATED*

KRASNOYE SORMOVO
A A Zhdanov SHIPYARD

Head Office and Works: Nizhni Novgorod, Russia, CIS

M Yuriev, *Shipyard Director*
Ivan Yerlykin, *Chief Hydrofoil Designer*

Telephone: +7 (095) 255 1813
Telex: 411116 KURS SU

Krasnoye Sormovo is one of the oldest established shipyards in the CIS. In addition to building displacement craft of many kinds for the CIS River Fleet, the yard constructs the world's widest range of passenger hydrofoils, many of which are equipped with the Alexeyev shallow draught submerged foil system. The late Dr Alexeyev started work at the end of 1945 on the design of his foil system which had to be suitable for operation on smooth, but open and shallow rivers and canals. He succeeded in making use of the immersion depth effect, or surface effect, for stabilising the foil immersion in calm waters by the use of small lift coefficients.

The system comprises two main horizontal lifting surfaces, one forward and one aft, with little or no dihedral, each carrying approximately half the weight of the vessel. A submerged foil loses lift gradually as it approaches the surface from a submergence of about one chord. This effect prevents the submerged foils from rising completely to the surface. Means therefore had to be provided to assist take off and prevent the vessel from sinking back to the displacement condition. The answer lay in the provision of planing sub-foils of small aspect ratio in the vicinity of the forward struts arranged so that when they are touching the water surface the main foils are submerged approximately to a depth of one chord.

The approach embodies characteristics of the Grunberg principle of inherent angle of attack variation, comprising a 'wing' and a stabiliser system. When the Alexeyev foils drop below the shallow draught zone, the craft converts momentarily to the Grunberg mode of operation, duplicating its configuration. The otherwise inactive sub-foils, coming into contact with the water surface, become the Grunberg stabilisers and cause the foils to climb up into the shallow draught zone where they resume normal operation in the Alexeyev mode.

The foils have good riding characteristics on inland and sheltered waters.

The system was first tested on a small launch powered by a 77 bhp converted car engine. Three more small craft were built to prove the idea, then work began on the yard's first multi-seat passenger craft, the Raketa, the first of which was launched in June 1957 and completed more than 25 years of service.

The yard also co-operates with the Leningrad Water Transport Institute in the development of sea-going craft with fully submerged V-type and trapeze-type surface-piercing foils, similar in configuration to those of the Schertel-Sachsenberg system. Craft employing V or trapeze foils are generally described as being of the Strela-type, Strela being the first operational Soviet design to use trapeze foils. Seating 82 to 94 passengers, the vessel is powered by two M-50 diesels and in appearance is a cross between the PT 20 and the PT 50, though smaller than the latter.

Passenger hydrofoils in production at yards on the Baltic and Black Seas are the Zenit (designed to replace Meteor hydrofoils) and the Albatros and Kolkhida, which are Kometa replacements, with seats for 120 passengers. Smaller hydrofoils are also under development including the 50-seat Polesye at the river-craft shipyard at Gomel and Lastochka, which has been designed to supersede Voskhod.

Substantial numbers of hydrofoils have been exported, especially Kometas, Meteors, Raketas, Voskhods, Volgas and recently Kolkhidas which have been sold to Greek and Italian operators. Countries in which they are being or have been operated include Austria, Bulgaria, Cyprus, Czechoslovakia, Finland, France, East and West Germany, Greece, Iran, Italy, Morocco, the Philippines, Poland, Romania, Spain, the UK, the USA and Yugoslavia.

Principal civil hydrofoil craft built in the former Soviet Union

Type	Yard	No of seats	First launched
Raketa (produced in quantity and exported)		58	1957
Meteor (produced in quantity and exported)	Gorki	116	1960
Kometa (produced in quantity and exported)	Poti & Feodosia	100	
Sputnik	Gorki	300	1961
Mir		92	1961
Strela (two built)		94	1962
Vikhr (sea-going version of Sputnik)		268	1962
Burevestnik (one built)		130-150	1964
Chaika	Gomel		1965
Byelorus			1965
Kometa-ME		116-120	1968
Typhoon (one built)	Leningrad	98-105	1969
Voskhod (produced in quantity and exported)	Gorki	71	1969
Delphin (Strela derivative)			pre-1968
Nevka (in production 1969-70)	Leningrad		1969
Volga		6	1972
Voskhod-2			1974
Kolkhida (exported to Greece, Italy and Yugoslavia) & Albatros (replacement for Kometas)	Poti	120	1980
Polesye	Gomel	53	1985
Lastochka (replacement for Voskhod)		64	1986
Cyclone	Feodosia	250	1986

Principal military hydrofoil craft built in the former Soviet Union

Type	Number built	Weight	In service
P8-Class (wooden hull)		-	retired
Pchela	2	75 t	1968 or earlier
Turya	30	250 t	1973 or earlier
Matka	16	260 t	1977 or earlier
Sarancha (NATO code-name)	1	320 t	1977 or earlier
Babochka	1	400 t	1978 or earlier
Muravey	1+	230 t	1983

VERIFIED

Raketa M   *1986*

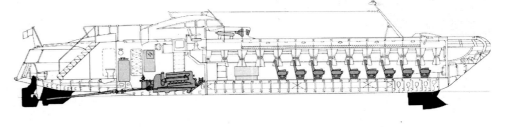

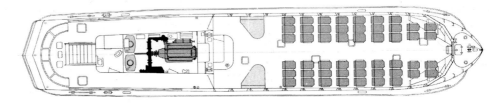

Inboard profile and plan view of standard 50-seat Raketa

RAKETA

The prototype Raketa was launched in 1957 and was the first multi-seat passenger hydrofoil to employ the Alexeyev shallow draught submerged foil system. Several hundred are now in service on all the major rivers of the CIS.

In August 1982 it was announced that the prototype was still in service and has carried more than two million passengers. The distance travelled by the craft during the period was stated to be equal to '52 voyages around the equator'.

A substantial number of Raketas has been exported. Examples are in service in Austria, Bulgaria, the Czech Republic, Germany, Hungary, Poland, Romania, Slovakia and the former Yugoslavia.

Production of the Raketa has now stopped and yards previously involved in their construction are building Voskhod and other designs.

The description that follows applies to the Raketa T, the standard export variant, powered by an M-401A diesel and with a cruising speed of about 58 km/h (32 knots).

The vessel is designed for high-speed passenger ferry services during daylight hours on rivers, reservoirs and sheltered waters in tropical climates. It meets the requirements of the Soviet River Register Class O with operation restricted to 0.8 m waves when foilborne and up to 1.5 m when hullborne.

The passenger saloon is provided with natural and induced ventilation and seats 58. The crew comprises a captain, engineer, deckhand and barman.

Principal Particulars

Length overall	26.96 m
Beam	5 m
Draught, hullborne	1.8 m
Draught, foilborne	1.1 m
Displacement, minimum	27.09 t
Displacement, maximum	20.31 t
Crew	4
Passengers	58
Fuel capacity	1647 l
Propulsive power	671 kW
Operational speed	31.32 knots
Operational limitation	0.8 m wave height

Structure: The hull is framed on longitudinal and transverse formers and all the main elements - plating, deck, partitions, bulkheads, platforms and wheelhouse - are in riveted duralumin. The stem is fabricated in interwelded steel strips. Below the freeboard deck the hull is divided into six watertight compartments employing web framing.

The foil system comprises one bow foil, one aft foil and two dart-like planing sub-foils, the tips of which are attached to the trailing edges of the outer bow foil struts. Foils, sub-foils and struts are in welded stainless steel. The bow foil, which incorporates sweepback, and the straight aft foil, are both supported by three vertical struts.

The base of the centre strut aft provides the end bearing for the propeller which is beneath the foil.

Propulsion: Power is supplied by a single M-401A water-cooled, supercharged 12-cylinder V-type diesel, with a normal service output of 671 kW. The engine drives, via a reverse gear and inclined stainless steel propeller shaft, a three-bladed cast bronze propeller. The fuel system comprises two fuel tanks with a total capacity of 1647 litres, a fuel priming unit and a hand fuel booster pump. A compressed air system, comprising a propeller shaft-driven air compressor and two 40 litre compressed air bottles, is provided for main engine starting, emergency stopping, operating the foghorn and scavenging the water intake.

Electrical system: A 3 kW generator, rated at 27.5 V and coupled to the main engine, is the main source of power while the vessel is underway. A 50 Hz, 230 V, 1500 rpm three-phase alternator supplies AC power. Four 12 V acid storage batteries, each with a 132 Ah capacity and connected in series to give 24 V, supply power during short stops.

The diesel generator unit comprises a Perkins P3.152 diesel engine employed in conjunction with a Stamford C20 alternator.

Control: The wheelhouse is equipped with a hydraulic remote-control system for the engine, reverse gear and fuel supply. The balanced rudder, made in aluminium-magnesium alloy, is controlled hydraulically by turning the wheel. A hand tiller is employed in an emergency. Employment of gas exhaust as a side-thruster to assist mooring is permitted at 850 rpm.

Safety equipment: The craft carries a full range of lifesaving and fire-fighting equipment. There are 62 lifejackets stowed in the passenger saloon and four for the crew in the wheelhouse and under the embarkation companionway. There are two lifebelts provided on the embarkation platform and two on the promenade deck. Fire-fighting equipment includes

Raketa operating as a fire tender in St Petersburg (J K Pemberton)   **1986**

Bow foil and planing stabiliser foils of Raketa   **1986**

four foam and four CO_2 fire extinguishers, two fire axes, two fire buckets and two felt cloths.

METEOR

Dr Alexeyev's Meteor made its maiden voyage from Gorki to Moscow in 1960, bringing high performance and unprecedented comfort to river boat fleets, and setting the pattern for a family of later designs.

The craft is intended for use in daylight hours on local and medium-range routes up to 600 km in length. It meets the requirements of Class O, experimental type, on the Register of River Shipping in the CIS.

Accommodation is provided for a crew of five and 116 passengers. Cruising speed at the full load displacement of 54.3 tonnes across calm water and in winds of up to Beaufort force 3 is about 65 km/h.

Outside the CIS Meteors have been operated in Bulgaria, Hungary, Poland and Yugoslavia.

Principal Particulars

Length overall	34.6 m
Foil width	9.5 m
Draught, hullborne	2.35 m
Draught, foilborne	1.2 m
Displacement, minimum	36.4 t
Displacement, maximum	53.4 t
Crew	5
Passengers	116
Fuel capacity	3000 l
Propulsive power	2 × 820 kW
Operational speed	35.1 knots
Range	324 nm
Operational limitation	Beaufort force 3

Structure: With the exception of the small exposed areas fore and aft, the Meteor's hull and superstructure are built as an integral unit. The hull is framed on longitudinal and transverse formers and both hull and superstructure are of riveted duralumin construction with welded steel members. Below the

Meteor operating in St Petersburg (J K Pemberton)   **1986**

Meteor 1988

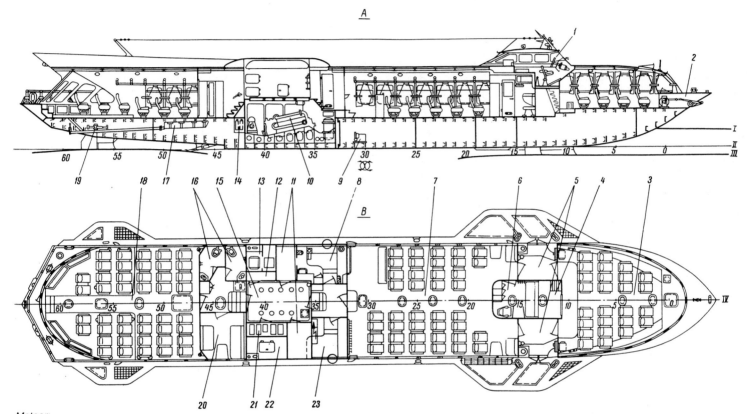

Meteor:

A *Inboard profile;* **B** *Main deck plan;* **I** *Water-line hullborne;* **II** *Hull base line;* **III** *Water-line foilborne;* **IV** *Longitudinal centreline;* **1** *Wheelhouse;* **2** *Anchor compartment;* **3** *Forward passenger saloon, 26 seats;* **4** *Luggage rack;* **5** *Embarkation companionway;* **6** *Crew duty room;* **7** *Midship passenger saloon, 42 seats;* **8** *Bar;* **9** *Refrigeration unit;* **10** *Engine room;* **11** *Pantry;* **12** *Boatswain's store;* **13** *Calorifier;* **14** *Fire-fighting equipment;* **15** *Promenade deck;* **16** *WCs;* **17** *Tank;* **18** *Aft passenger saloon, 44 seats;* **19** *Tiller gear;* **20** *Four-seat passenger cabin;* **21** *Storage batteries;* **22** *Hydraulic units;* **23** *Main switchboard*

main deck the hull is subdivided longitudinally into eight compartments by seven bulkheads. Access to the compartments is via hatches in the main deck. The craft will remain afloat in the event of any two adjacent compartments forward of amidships flooding or any one compartment aft of midship. Frame spacing in the hull is about 500 mm while that in the superstructure is 1000 mm.

The foil arrangement comprises a bow foil and a stern foil, with the struts of the bow system carrying two additional planing sub-foils. The foils are attached to the struts, which are of split type, by flanges and bolts. The foils are in stainless steel and the sub-foils in aluminium-magnesium alloy. The foil incidence can be adjusted when necessary by the insertion of wedges between the flanges and the foils when the vessel is in dock.

Propulsion: Power is supplied by two M-401A 12-cylinder, four-stroke, supercharged, water-cooled diesels with reversing clutches. Each engine has a normal service output of 745 kW at 1700 rpm and a maximum output of 820 kW at 1800 rpm. Specific consumption at rated output g/bhp/h is not more than 193, and oil, not more than six. Guaranteed overhaul life is 1000 hours. Each engine drives its own inclined propeller shaft through a reverse clutch. The propeller shafts are in steel and the propellers, which are five-bladed, are in brass. The drives are contrarotating.

Electrical system: 24 to 28.5 V DC from the vessel's power supply or 220 V AC, 50 Hz, from shore-to-ship supply sources.

Control: Control of the engines, reverse gear and fuel supply is effected remotely from the wheelhouse with the aid of a hydraulic system comprising transmitter cylinders in the wheelhouse, and actuators on the engine. The engines can also be controlled from the engine room.

Craft heading is controlled by two hydraulically controlled balanced rudders, the blades of which are in solid aluminium-magnesium alloy.

At low speed the craft can turn in its own length by pinwheeling - employing both engines with equal power in opposite directions - one ahead, the other astern.

Minimum diameter of the turning circle is approximately 250 m with the engines running at low speed (700 to 750 rpm) and with the rudder put through an angle of 35°. Turning circle diameter when operating foilborne with the rudder at an angle of 10° is approximately 750 m.

The vessel takes off for foilborne flight in 120 to 140 seconds, that is, within a distance of 25 to 28 lengths of its hull.

Landing run, with engines reversed, ranges from 1.5 to 2 hull lengths, while the braking distance without reversing the engines is within 3 to 4 lengths of the hull.

Auxiliary systems: 9 kW diesel for generating electrical power when the craft is at its moorings, warming the main engines in cold weather and operating drainage pump.

VERIFIED

SERGO ORDZHONIKIDZE SHIPYARD

KOMETA

Derived from the earlier Meteor, the Kometa was the first sea-going hydrofoil to be built in the Soviet Union. The prototype, seating 100 passengers, made its maiden voyage on the Black Sea in 1961, after which it was employed on various passenger routes on an experimental basis. Operating experience accumulated on these services led to the introduction of various modifications before the craft was put into series production.

Kometas are built mainly at the S Ordzhonikidze Shipbuilding and Repair Yard at Poti on the Black Sea and the Feodosia Yard.

Kometa operators outside the CIS have included Kompas Line, Yugoslavia; Alilauro SpA, Naples, Italy; and Transportes Touristiques Intercontinentaux, Morocco. Other vessels of this type have been supplied to Bulgaria, Cuba, the former German Democratic Republic, Greece, Iran, Poland, Romania and Turkey. More than 60 have been exported.

Export orders have been mainly for the Kometa-ME, designed for service in countries with a moderate climate, which was introduced in 1968. Two distinguishing features of this model are the employment of new diesel engines with increased operating hours between overhauls, and a completely revised surface-piercing foil system, with a trapeze bow foil instead of the former Alexeyev shallow draught submerged type.

A fully tropicalised and air-conditioned version is now in production and designated Kometa-MT.

The present standard production Kometa-ME seats 116 to 120. Due to the additional weight of the Kometa-MT's air-conditioning system and other refinements, the seating capacity is reduced in the interest of passenger comfort to 102.

Official designation of the Kometa in the CIS is Hydrofoil Type 342. The craft meets the requirements of the Rules of the Register of Shipping of the CIS and is constructed to Hydrofoil Class KM*211 Passenger Class under the Register's technical supervision. IMCO recommendations on fire safety are taken into account and non-flammable basalt fibres are employed for sound and heat insulation and the engine room is clad with titanium plating. The craft is designed to operate during daylight hours on coastal routes up to 44 nm from ports of refuge under moderate climatic conditions.

The standard craft has proved to be exceptionally robust and has a good, all-round performance. On one charter, a Kometa-ME covered 2867 nm by sea and river in 127 hours. It can operate foilborne in waves up to 1.7 m and travel hullborne in waves up to 3.6 m.

One of the features of the more recent models is the relocation of the engine room aft to reduce the noise in the passenger saloons and the employment of a V-drive instead of the existing inclined shaft. The revised deck configuration allows more seats to be fitted. These modifications are also incorporated in the Kometa derivative, the Kolkhida, which is fitted with two 1120 kW engines.

KOMETA-ME
Principal Particulars

Length overall	35.1 m
Foil width	11 m
Draught, hullborne	3.6 m
Draught, foilborne	1.7 m
Displacement, minimum	44.5 t
Displacement, maximum	60 t
Crew	6
Passengers	102
Propulsive power	2 × 820 kW
Maximum speed	36 knots
Operational speed	31 knots
Operational limitation	Sea state 4
	Beaufort force 5

Structure: The hull is similar in shape to that of the earlier Meteor, with a wedge-shaped bow, raked stem and a spoon-shaped stern. The hull and superstructure are built in AlMg-61 and AlMg-6 alloys. Hull and superstructure are of all-welded construction using contact and argon arc welding. The hull is framed on longitudinal and transverse formers, the spacing throughout the length of the hull is 500 mm and in the superstructure 1000 mm.

Kometa craft built to 1983

Type	Name	Yard	Built	Operator/area
Kometa	1	-	1962	Navigation Maritime Bulgare, Bulgaria
Kometa	2	Poti	1979	Navigation Maritime Bulgare, Bulgaria
Kometa	2	Poti	1965	
Kometa	3	-	1979	Navigation Maritime Bulgare, Bulgaria
Kometa	Daria (ex 4)	Poti	1967	Zegluga Szczecinska, Poland (ex Navigation Maritime Bulgare)
Kometa	5	Poti	1970	
Kometa	6	-	1972	
Kometa	7	Poti	1974	Navigation Maritime Bulgare, Bulgaria
Kometa	8	Poti	1974	Navigation Maritime Bulgare, Bulgaria
Kometa	9	-	1974	
Kometa	10	-	1975	
Kometa	11	-	1975	
Kometa	12	-	1976	Navigation Maritime Bulgare, Bulgaria
Kometa-MT	18	Poti	1973	Empresa Nacional de Cabotage, Cuba
Kometa-MT	Scheherazade (ex 37)	Feodosia		(ex Transtour SA, Morocco, ex Black Sea Shipping Co, Odessa)
Kometa-MT	Sindibad	-	1968	(ex Transtour SA, Morocco)
Kometa-MT	Aladin	-	1971	(ex Transtour SA, Morocco)
Kometa	Aliapollo 1984 (ex Alitunisi ex Alispan Secondo 1980, ex Atalanta, 1971)	Feodosia	1970	Alilauro SpA, Italy
Kometa	Alieros (ex Aliconamar 1984, ex Alibastea 1982)	Poti	1973	Alilauro SpA, Italy
Kometa	Alivenere (ex Aligiglio)	Poti	1972	Alilauro SpA, Italy
Kometa	Alisaturno (ex Alielba)	Poti	1972	Alivit Due
Kometa	Alisorrento	-	-	Alilauro SpA, Italy
Kometa	Alivesuvio	-	-	Alilauro SpA, Italy
Kometa	Alivulcano 1977 (ex Alipan Primo, 1977, ex Lepa Vida, 1970)	Poti	1970	Alilauro SpA, Italy
Kometa	Freccia Pontina (ex Wera)	Poti	1978	Societa di Navigazione Basso Lazio Srl, Gaeta, Italy
Kometa	Poseidon	-	1970	Intreprinderea de Exploatare a Floti Maritime NAVROM, Galatz, Romania
Kometa-M	Flying Dolphin I	Poti	1975	Ceres Flying Hydroways Ltd, Piraeus, Greece
Kometa-M	Flying Dolphin II	Poti	1975	Ceres Flying Hydroways Ltd, Piraeus, Greece
Kometa-M	Flying Dolphin III	Poti	1976	Ceres Flying Hydroways Ltd, Piraeus, Greece
Kometa-M	Flying Dolphin IV	Poti	1977	Ceres Flying Hydroways Ltd, Piraeus, Greece
Kometa-M	Flying Dolphin V	Poti	1976	Ceres Flying Hydroways Ltd, Piraeus, Greece
Kometa-M	Flying Dolphin VI	Poti	1976	Ceres Flying Hydroways Ltd, Piraeus, Greece
Kometa-M	Flying Dolphin VII	Poti	1976	Ceres Flying Hydroways Ltd, Piraeus, Greece
Kometa-M	Flying Dolphin VIII	Poti	1977	Ceres Flying Hydroways Ltd, Piraeus, Greece
Kometa-M	Flying Dolphin IX	Poti	1977	Ceres Flying Hydroways Ltd, Piraeus, Greece
Kometa-M	Flying Dolphin X	Poti	1978	Ceres Flying Hydroways Ltd, Piraeus, Greece
Kometa-M	Flying Dolphin XI	Poti	1979	Ceres Flying Hydroways Ltd, Piraeus, Greece
Kometa-M	Flying Dolphin XII	Poti	1979	Ceres Flying Hydroways Ltd, Piraeus, Greece
Kometa-M	Flying Dolphin XIV	Poti	1981	Ceres Flying Hydroways Ltd, Piraeus, Greece
Kometa-M	Flying Dolphin XV	Poti	1981	Ceres Flying Hydroways Ltd, Piraeus, Greece
Kometa-M	Flying Dolphin XVI	Poti	1981	Ceres Flying Hydroways Ltd, Piraeus, Greece
Kometa-M	Flying Dolphin XVII	Poti	1985	Ceres Flying Hydroways Ltd, Piraeus, Greece
Kometa-M	Flying Dolphin XVIII	Poti	1985	Ceres Flying Hydroways Ltd, Piraeus, Greece
Kometa-M	Flying Dolphin XIX	Poti	1986	Ceres Flying Hydroways Ltd, Piraeus, Greece
Kometa-M	Flying Dolphin XX	Poti	1975	Ceres Flying Hydroways Ltd, Piraeus, Greece
Kometa-M	Flying Dolphin XXI	Poti	1976	Ceres Flying Hydroways Ltd, Piraeus, Greece
Kometa-M	Flying Dolphin XXII	Poti	1977	Ceres Flying Hydroways Ltd, Piraeus, Greece
Kometa-M	Flying Dolphin XXIII	Poti	1980	Ceres Flying Hydroways Ltd, Piraeus, Greece
Kometa-M	Flying Dolphin XXIV	Poti	1973	Ceres Flying Hydroways Ltd, Piraeus, Greece

Kometa craft built to 1983 continued

Type	Name	Yard	Built	Operator/area
Kometa-M	*Flying Dolphin XXV*	Poti	1973	Ceres Flying Hydroways Ltd, Piraeus, Greece
Kometa-M	*Flying Dolphin XXVI*	Poti	1973	Ceres Flying Hydroways Ltd, Piraeus, Greece
Kometa	*Marilena*	-	1981	Nearchos Shipping Co, Greece
Kometa	*Gina*	-	1981	Nearchos Shipping Co, Greece
Kometa	*Poszum*	Poti	1973	Zegluga Gdanska, Gdansk, Poland
	Poweiw	Feodosia	1973	Zegluga Gdanska, Gdansk, Poland
	Poryw	Poti	1976	Zegluga Gdanska, Gdansk, Poland
	Poswist	Poti	1975	Zegluga Gdanska, Gdansk, Poland
	Pogwizd	Poti	1977	Zegluga Gdanska, Gdansk, Poland
	Polot	Poti	1977	Zegluga Gdanska, Gdansk, Poland
Kometa	*Flying Dolphin*, 1983 (ex *Podmuch*, 1973)	-	-	Motion Shipping Co Ltd, Limassol, Cyprus
Kometa	*Stoertebeker I*	-	1974	Fahrgastechiffahrt Staisund
Kometa	*Stoertebeker II*	-	1974	Fahrgastechiffahrt Staisund
Kometa	*Stoertebeker III*	-	1974	Fahrgastechiffahrt Staisund
Kometa	*Patmos* (ex *Alkyonis I*)	Poti	1978	
Kometa	*Rodos* (ex *Alkyonis II*)	Poti	1978	
Kometa	-	-	1966	-
Kometa	*Lida*	-	1971	Zegluga Szczecinska, Poland
Kometa	*Kalina*	-	1973	Zegluga Szczecinska, Poland
Kometa	-	-	1975	-
Kometa	*Liwia*	-	1978	Zegluga Szczecinska, Poland
Kometa	-	-	1970	Vedettes Armoricaines, Brest, France
Kometa	*Iran Resalat*, 1980 (ex *Arya Ram*)	Feodosia	1971	Islamic Republic of Iran Shipping Lines, Khorramshahr, Iran
Kometa	*Iran Taveeghat*, 1980 (ex *Arya Baz*, ex *Kometa S-26*)	Feodosia	1969	Islamic Republic of Iran Shipping Lines, Khorramshahr, Iran
Kometa	*Krila Kornata*	Poti	1980	Kompas-Jugoslavija, Koper, Yugoslavia
Kometa	*Krila Kvarnera*	Poti	1970	Kompas-Jugoslavija, Koper, Yugoslavia
Kometa	*Krila Pirana*	Poti	1979	Kompas-Jugoslavija, Koper, Yugoslavia
Kometa	*Krila Primorske*	Poti	1980	Kompas-Jugoslavija, Koper, Yugoslavia
Kometa	*Krila Slovenije*	Poti	1977	Kompas-Jugoslavija, Koper, Yugoslavia
Kometa	*Alischia*		1977	Alilauro SpA, Italy
Kometa	*Alicapri*		1983	Alilauro SpA, Italy

Below the freeboard deck, the hull is divided by watertight bulkheads into thirteen compartments which include the engine room, fuel compartments and those containing the fire-fighting system, tiller gear and fuel transfer pump.

Employment of a surface-piercing trapeze-type bow foil provides the Kometa-ME with improved seakeeping capability in waves. The foil system comprises a bow foil, aft foil and two auxiliaries, one (termed 'stabiliser') located above the bow foil for pitch stability, the other sited amidships near the longitudinal centre of gravity to assist take off. The foils are connected to the hull by struts and brackets; middle and side struts of the bow foil are of the split type, the lower and upper components of each strut are connected by flanges and bolts. The upper sections are connected to the hull by the same means.

The bow and stern foils are of hollow welded stainless steel construction. The midship and pitch stability foils and the upper components of the foil struts are in aluminium-magnesium alloy.

Propulsion: Power is supplied by two M-401A water-cooled, supercharged 12-cylinder V-type diesels, each with a normal service output of 745 kW at 1550 rpm and a maximum output of 820 kW at 1600 rpm. Guaranteed service life of each engine before first overhaul is 2500 hours. Each engine drives via a reverse gear its own inclined shaft and the twin propellers are contrarotating. The shafts are of steel and are parallel to the craft.

The propellers are of three-bladed design and made of brass.

Main engine controls and gauges are installed in both the wheelhouse and the engine room. A diesel-generator compressor-pump unit is provided for charging starter air bottles; supplying electric power when at rest; warming the main engines in cold weather and pumping warm air beneath the deck to dry the bilges.

Diesel oil tanks with a total capacity of 3530 l for the main engines and the auxiliary unit are located in the afterpeak. Two lubricating oil service tanks and one storage tank located at the fore bulkhead of the engine room have a total capacity of 250 kg. Diesel and lubricating oil capacity ensures a range of 200 nm.

Electrical system: Power supply is 24 V DC. A 1 kW DC generator is attached to each of the two engines and these supply power during operation. A 5.6 kW generator is included in the auxiliary unit and supplies power when the craft is at rest. It can also be used when underway for supplying the heating plant or when the 1 kW generators are inoperative. Four 12 V acid storage batteries of 180 Ah capacity, which are connected in series to provide 24 V, supply power during short stops.

Control: The wheelhouse is equipped with an electrohydraulic remote-control system for the engine reverse gear and fuel supply, fuel monitoring equipment, including electric speed counters, pressure gauges, lubricating and fuel oil gauges. The boat has a single, solid aluminium-magnesium alloy balanced rudder, which is controlled through a hydraulic steering system or a hand-operated hydraulic drive.

Kometa-ME
1986

A Kometa of Kompas Line, Yugoslavia, arriving at Venice, June 1986

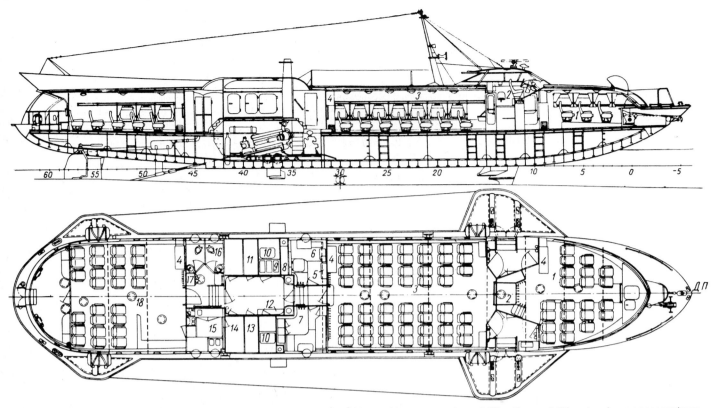

Internal arrangement of Kometa-MT, designed for tropical operation: **1** *22-seat forward passenger saloon;* **2** *Wheelhouse;* **3** *54-seat main passenger saloon;* **4** *Luggage rack;* **5** *Engine room door;* **6** *Control position;* **7** *Duty cabin;* **8** *Liquid fire extinguisher bay;* **9** *Battery room;* **10** *Engine room;* **11** *Boiler room;* **12** *Installation point for portable radio;* **13** *Store;* **14** *Provision store;* **15** *Bar;* **16** *Toilet wash basin units;* **17** *Boatswain's store;* **18** *26-seat aft passenger saloon*

Development of the Kometa is continuing. Current research is aimed at the introduction of a stability augmentation system employing either control flaps on the bow foil or air stabilisation on the stern foil and struts; the reduction of labour involved in construction; the introduction of design improvements through the use of GRP and sandwich construction; noise reduction in the saloons and the extension of the cruising range.

Lastochka
1990

Model of Lastochka showing foil configuration

1990

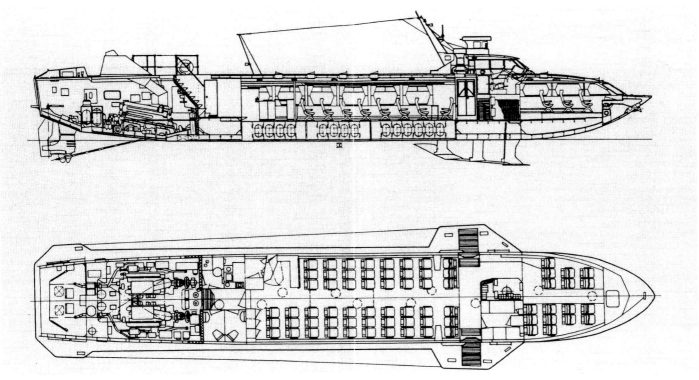

Layout of Lastochka

KOMETA-MT
Principal Particulars
Length overall	35.1 m
Foil width	11 m
Draught, hullborne	3.6 m
Draught, foilborne	1.7 m
Displacement, minimum	45 t
Displacement, maximum	58.9 t
Crew	6
Passengers	102
Propulsive power	2 × 820 kW
Maximum speed	33 knots

Operational speed	31 knots
Range	130 nm

LASTOCHKA

Successor to the 71-seat Voskhod, the first Lastochka was launched in 1986. The vessel is designed specifically for use over major rivers and reservoirs whose wave heights are unlikely to exceed 1.5 m in height. Loading conditions are optimised by means of a flap control on the bow foil arrangement.

Principal Particulars
Length overall	29 m
Beam	4.4 m
Foil width	7.2 m
Draught, foilborne	2.5 m
Displacement, minimum	28 t
Displacement, maximum	37.3 t
Propulsive power	2 × 994 kW
Maximum speed	48 knots
Range	270 nm

VERIFIED

GOMEL YARD

Belarus, CIS

BYELORUS

This craft was developed from the Raketa, via the Chaika, for fast passenger services on shallow winding rivers less than 1 m deep and too shallow for conventional vessels.

It was put into series production at the river shipyard at Gomel, Belarus in 1965. Byelorus was expected to be succeeded in service by the 53-seat Polesye.

Principal Particulars
Length overall	18.55 m
Beam	4.64 m
Draught hullborne	0.9 m
Draught foilborne	0.3 m
Displacement, minimum	9.6 t
Displacement, maximum	14.5 t
Passengers	40
Propulsive power	708 kW
Operational speed	34 knots

Structure: Hull and superstructure are built in aluminium-magnesium alloy. The hull is of all-welded construction and the superstructure is riveted and welded.

The shallow draught submerged foil system consists of one bow foil and one rear foil.

Propulsion: Power is supplied by an M-50 F-3 or M-400 diesel rated at 708 kW maximum and with a normal service output of 447 kW. The wheelhouse is fitted with an electrohydraulic remote-control system for the engine and fuel supply.

Outfit: Aircraft type seats for 40 passengers. The prototype seated only 30.

POLESYE

This shallow-draught hydrofoil craft (27 built by early 1989) is intended for the high-speed transpor-

Byelorus on Karakum Canal, Turkmenia 1986

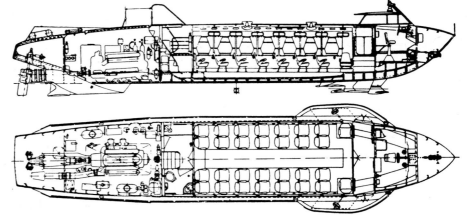

Profile and deck plan of Byelorus

Polesye   1988

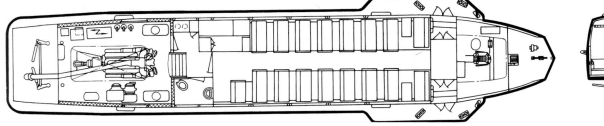

General arrangement of Polesye

tation of passengers and tourists during daylight hours in the upper reaches of major rivers, river tributaries and freshwater reservoirs in regions with temperate climate. Two Polesyes entered service in 1992 with MAHART on the Budapest to Vienna route. The craft is classified *R on the RSFSR Register of River Shipping and is suitable for use in conditions with a wave height of 0.5 m when running on the hydrofoils, and with a wave height of up to 1.2 m in the displacement mode.

The craft has capacity for a maximum of 53 passengers. The passengers are accommodated in a single lounge area in the mid-section of the vessel. In calm waters with wind conditions up to Force 3, the vessel is capable of a speed of 35.1 knots. The vessel is capable of running on the hydrofoils on river channels with a radius of turn up to 100 to 150 m.

The time to accelerate from the stationary condition to becoming fully foilborne does not exceed 1.5 minutes. The distance from service speed to stop, with the propeller in reverse, is five to six boat lengths.

The hull is divided into five compartments by means of watertight bulkheads. The foils and side fenders are removable to facilitate overland transport.

The vessel is powered by a 12-cylinder 'V' diesel engine with a maximum capacity of 810 kW at 1600 rpm. The engine is installed at an angle of 12.5° to the horizontal and transmits power to the propeller via a direct-coupled reversing gear unit.

Principal Particulars

Length overall	21.25 m
Beam	3.6 m
Foil width	5 m
Draught, hullborne	0.95 m
Draught, foilborne	0.4 m
Displacement, minimum	13.7 t
Displacement, maximum	20 t
Passengers	53
Propulsive power	810 kW
Operational speed	35 knots
Range	216 nm
Operational limitation	0.5 m wave height

MALAKHIT

A river ambulance hydrofoil designed for emergency medical calls for people living in remote regions and for passengers and crews of river-craft.

Malakhit is designed to take five patients. The project is based on the SPK Polesye series hydrofoil.

Principal Particulars

Length	22 m
Beam	3.6 m
Draught, hullborne	0.9 m
Draught, foilborne	0.4 m
Crew	2
Operational speed	35 knots
Range	216 nm

VERIFIED

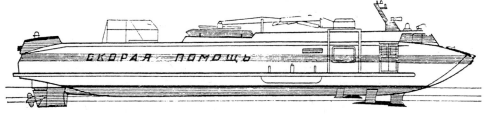

Malakhit river ambulance

Ś ORDZHONIKIDZE SHIP BUILDING AND REPAIR YARD

Head Office and Yard: Poti, Georgia, CIS

Z N Archaidze, *Yard Director*
I Ye Malechanov, *Chief Designer*
Yu Golubkin, *Deputy Chief Designer*
B Pavlyuk, *Chief Engineer*
G A Terentyeb, *Manager, Sea Trials*

KOLKHIDA

Designed to replace the 20 year old Kometa fast passenger ferry, Kolkhida is available in two versions: the Albatros, which operates on domestic services within the CIS, and the Kolkhida, intended for export.

Kolkhida is faster than Kometa, seats more passengers, uses less fuel and can operate foilborne in higher sea states. Among the various design innovations are a new foil system with automatic lift control, the use of new materials in the hull structure and a more rational cabin layout, permitting a substantial increase in seating capacity. The engine room is aft, as on the Voskhod, to reduce the noise level. Overall dimensions are almost identical to those of Kometa-M.

Trials of the Kolkhida prototype took place in the Baltic between March and June 1981 and the vessel has been in production since with sales being achieved in Greece, Italy and Yugoslavia.

Kolkhida is designed to operate under tropical and moderate climates up to 50 miles from a port of refuge in open seas and up to 100 miles from a port of refuge in inland seas and large lakes, with a permissible distance between two ports of refuge of not more than 200 miles.

Foilborne, the craft can operate in waves up to 2 m and winds up to Force 5; hullborne it can operate in waves up to 3 m and winds up to Force 6.

Principal Particulars

Length overall	34.5 m
Beam	5.8 m
Foil width	10.3 m
Draught, hullborne	3.5 m
Draught, foilborne	1.9 m
Displacement, minimum	56 t
Displacement, maximum	72 t
Crew	6
Passengers	155
Propulsive power	2 × 1050 kW
Operational speed	34 knots
Range	150 nm
Operational limitation	2 m wave height
	Beaufort force 5

Classification: The craft meets the requirements of the Register of Shipping of the CIS and is constructed to Hydrofoil Class KM* 2AS Passenger Class SPK under the Register's technical supervision. It complies fully with the IMO Code of Safety for Dynamically Supported Craft.

Kolkhida

Kolkhida   *1987*

Port double entrance doors on Kolkhida   *1987*

Kolkhida   *1991*

Kolkhida aft foil arrangement 1988

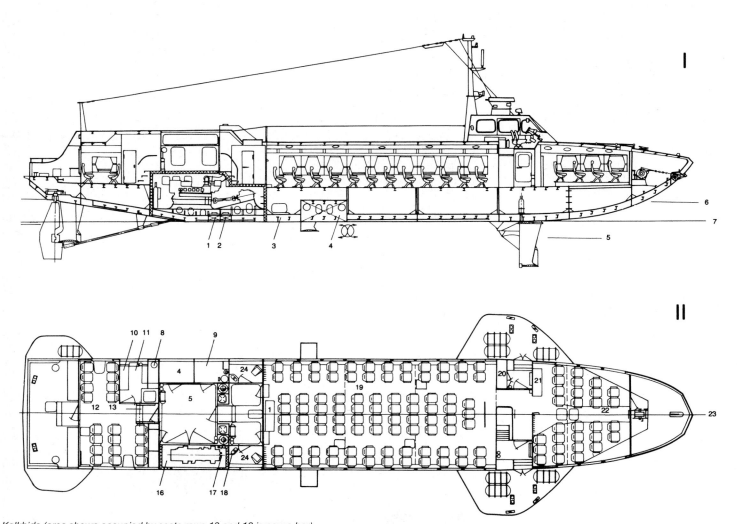

Kolkhida (area shown occupied by seats rows 12 and 13 is now a bar)
Longitudinal section: **1** *Waste oil collection tank;* **2** *Oil-containing water tank;* **3** *Sewage water tank;* **4** *Fuel tank;* **5** *Water-line when foilborne;* **6** *Water-line when hullborne;* **7** *Base-line main deck plan;* **8** *Hydraulic station;* **9** *Fuel and oil filling, waste water scavenging, fire-fighting station;* **10** *Conditioner;* **11** *Control post;* **12** *20-seat passenger saloon;* **13** *VP;* **14** *Luggage room;* **15** *Promenade platform;* **16** *Auxiliary unit room;* **17** *Gas exhaust trunk;* **18** *Air intake trunk;* **19** *91-seat passenger saloon;* **20** *Aggregate room;* **21** *Conditioner;* **22** *29-seat passenger saloon;* **23** *Central line;* **24** *Toilet*

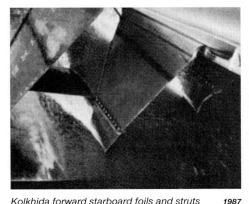

Kolkhida forward starboard foils and struts **1987**

Structure: Double-chine, V-bottom type, with raked stern and streamlined superstructure. The hull and superstructure are built in aluminium-magnesium alloys. Framing is based on T and T-angle web-frames. Frame spacing is 600 mm. Longitudinal framing of the sides, decks and hull bottom is based on stiffening ribs, keelson, stringers and deck girders. Below the main deck the hull is subdivided by watertight bulkheads into nine compartments. The craft will remain afloat with any two adjacent compartments flooded.

The foil system, which is similar to that of Kometa, comprises a trapeze-type bow foil, an aft and amidships foil, close to the longitudinal centre of gravity to assist take off. The foils are connected to the hull by struts and brackets. Bow and stern foil surfaces and the lower ends of the bow and stern foil struts are in steel alloy. The amidships foil, struts, upper sections of the bow and stern foil struts are in aluminium-magnesium alloy. A cast, balanced rudder in 40 mm thick aluminium-magnesium alloy is fitted. Total blade area is 2.75 m².

Propulsion: Power is supplied by two MTU 12V 396 TC 82 water-cooled, supercharged 12-cylinder V-type four-stroke marine diesels, each with a normal service output of 960 kW, 1745 rpm and 1050 kW, 1800 rpm maximum. Guaranteed service life of each engine before first major overhaul is 9000 hours; maximum service life is 12 years. Output is transferred to twin 740 mm diameter contrarotating fixed-pitch propellers through reversible gearboxes which are remotely controlled from the wheelhouse. The propeller shafts are inclined at 14° and supported by rubber and metal bearings.

Electrical system: Engine-driven generators supply power while the craft is operating. The 4.5 kW generator included in the auxiliary unit supplies power when the craft is at rest. Acid storage batteries connected in series supply power during short stops.

Control: A sonic/electronic autopilot controls lift by operating trailing edge flaps on the centre section of the bow foil and on the inner sections of the aft foil. The foil flaps are adjusted hydraulically to dampen heave, pitch, roll and yaw motions in heavy seas and provide co-ordinated turns.

Rudder movement is controlled hydraulically by any one of three systems: push-button, manual or via the autopilot.

UPDATED

Craft built to 1988

Type	Name	Built	Delivered to
Kolkhida		1983	Black Sea Shipping Co, Odessa, CIS
Kolkhida	*2*	1984	Black Sea Shipping Co, Odessa, CIS
Kolkhida	*3*	1984	Black Sea Shipping Co, Odessa, CIS
Kolkhida	*4*	1984	Black Sea Shipping Co, Odessa, CIS
Kolkhida	*5*	1984	Black Sea Shipping Co, Odessa, CIS
Kolkhida	*6*	1985	Black Sea Shipping Co, Odessa, CIS
Kolkhida	*Magnolija*	1986	Kvarner Express, Yugoslavia
Kolkhida	*Kamelija*	1986	Kvarner Express, Yugoslavia
Kolkhida	*Mirta*	1986	Kvarner Express, Yugoslavia
Kolkhida	*Mimosa*	1986	Kvarner Express, Yugoslavia
Kolkhida	*Aliatlante*	1986	Alilauro SpA, Italy
Kolkhida	*Alieolo*	1986	Alilauro SpA, Italy
Kolkhida	*Flying Dolphin XVII*	1986	Ceres Flying Hydroways Ltd, Piraeus, Greece
Kolkhida	*Flying Dolphin XVIII*	1986	Ceres Flying Hydroways Ltd, Piraeus, Greece
Kolkhida	*Flying Dolphin XIX*	1986	Ceres Flying Hydroways Ltd, Piraeus, Greece
Kolkhida	*Aligea*	1986	Alilauro SpA, Italy
Kolkhida	*Tiburon*	1988	Compania Naviera Mallorquina, Spain
Kolkhida	*Alikenia*	1986	Alilauro SpA, Italy
Kolkhida	*Aliflorida*	1988	Alilauro SpA, Italy

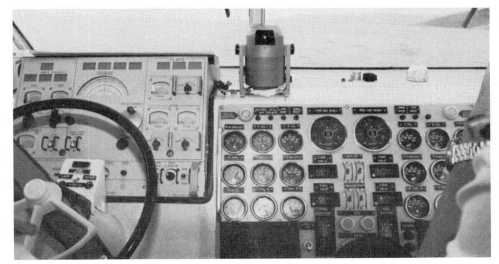

Controls and instruments in Kolkhida wheelhouse **1987**

Interior of Kolkhida cabin **1987**

Liferaft installation on Kolkhida **1987**

INDONESIA

PT PAL INDONESIA (PERSERO)

Head office: Arthaloka Building, 5th Floor, JL Jend Sudirman No 2, Jakarta 10220, Indonesia

Telephone: +62 (21) 570 3257/8, 570 5302/3
Telex: 65295 PAL JKT 1A
Telefax: +62 (21) 570 4275

Works: Ujung Surabaya, PO Box 134, Indonesia

Telephone: +62 (31) 291403, 333438/9
Telex: 31223 PAL SB
Telefax: +62 (31) 22516

With origins as a repair and maintenance facility for the navy in 1892, PT PAL now employs 6000 people, occupies an area of 150 hectares and has capacity for designing and building vessels from 60 to 30 000 tonnes.

Apart from the first Jetfoil 929-115 (*Bima Samudera I*) to be fitted out, no information has been received on any further Jetfoil fitting out or conversion by PT PAL but the company has two non-commercial versions of the Jetfoil for Indonesian Government use.

UPDATED

ITALY

FINCANTIERI-CANTIERI NAVALI ITALIANI SpA

Via Genova 1, I-34121 Trieste, Italy

Naval Shipbuilding Division: Via Cipro 11, I-16129 Genoa, Italy

Telephone: +39 (40) 59951
Telex: 270168FINCGE I
Telefax: +39 (40) 599 5272

Mario de Negri, *Naval Shipbuilding Division General Manager*
Franco Baracchini, *Naval Vessel Director*

The original Cantieri Navali Riuniti SpA took over the interests of Alinavi which was formed in 1964 to develop, manufacture and market advanced military marine systems.

Under the terms of a licensing agreement, Fincantieri had access to Boeing technology in the field of military fully submerged, foil hydrofoil craft.

In October 1970, the company was awarded a contract by the Italian Navy for the design and construction of the P420 Sparviero hydrofoil missile craft. This is an improved version of the Boeing PGH-2 Tucumcari. The vessel, given the design name Sparviero, was delivered to the Italian Navy in July 1974. An order for a further six of this type was placed by the Italian Navy in February 1976.

In 1991 Sumitomo Heavy Industries received an order for the building of two of a planned class of six Sparviero hydrofoils for the Japanese Defence Agency, successfully launched in July 1992. A third hydrofoil was launched in June 1994.

SPARVIERO

The Sparviero missile-launching hydrofoil gunboat displaces 60.5 tonnes and is designed for both offensive and defensive missions. Its combination of speed, fire-power and all-weather capability is unique in a ship of this class.

The vessel has fully submerged foils arranged in canard configuration and an automatic control system. A gas-turbine powered water-jet system provides foilborne propulsion and a diesel-driven propeller outdrive provides hullborne propulsion. A typical crew comprises two officers and eight enlisted men.

Sparviero's advanced automatic control system considerably reduces the vertical and transverse acceleration normally experienced in rough seas. In Sea State 4 the maximum vertical acceleration likely

Turning radius of Sparviero hydrofoils at 40 knots is under 125 m   **1986**

Craft built	Commissioned
P420 *Sparviero* (class type)	1974
P421 *Nibbio*	1981
P422 *Falcone*	1982
P423 *Astore*	1982
P424 *Grifone*	1982
P425 *Gheppio*	1983
P426 *Condor*	1983

to be found is in the order of 0.25 *g* (rms), while the maximum roll angle is not likely to be greater than ±2°.

In the lower Sea States Sparviero class hydrofoils have a maximum continuous speed of 44 knots, decreasing to 40 knots in Sea State 4.

The foils are in a fully submerged canard configuration, with approximately one-third of the dynamic lift provided by the bow foil and two-thirds by the two aft foils. Anhedral is incorporated in the aft foils to enhance the directional stability of the craft at shallow foil depths. In addition, the anhedral assures positive roll control by eliminating tip broaching during rough water manoeuvres.

Principal Particulars

Length overall	22.95 m
Beam	7 m
Foil width	10.8 m
Displacement, maximum	60.5 t
Crew	10
Propulsive power	3356 kW
Maximum speed	50 knots
Operational speed	44 knots
Range	1000 nm hullborne

Structure: The hull and superstructure are built in corrosion-resistant aluminium, the hull being welded and the superstructure riveted and welded.

Propulsion: Power for a water-jet is supplied by one 3356 kW Rolls-Royce Proteus 15M/553 gas turbine.

Engine output is transferred to a single double-volute, double-suction, two impeller centrifugal pump. Water is taken in through inlets on the nose of each aft foil at the foil/strut intersection and passes up through the hollow interiors of the struts to the hull, where it is ducted to the pump. From the pump, the water is discharged through twin, fixed-area nozzles located beneath the hull under the pump.

An Isotta Fraschini ID 38 6VN marine diesel drives via a toothed belt a steerable propeller outdrive unit, which is mounted on the centreline of the transom. The unit is retractable and rotates through 360°. Propeller is fixed-pitch. Continuous speed, hullborne, is eight knots.

UPDATED

RODRIQUEZ CANTIERI NAVALI SpA

Via S Raineri 22, I-98122 Messina, Italy

Telephone: +39 (90) 7765
Telex: 980030 RODRIK I
Telefax: +39 (90) 675294

Basbasso Gattuso, *President*
Giovanni Morace, *Managing Director*
Alcide Sculati, *Technical Manager*
Diego Mazzeo, *Sales and Marketing*

Rodriquez Cantieri Navali SpA, formerly known as Cantiere Navaltecnica SpA and as Leopoldo Rodriquez Shipyard, was the first company to produce hydrofoils in series, and is the biggest hydrofoil builder outside the CIS. On the initiative of the company's former president, Carlo Rodriquez, the Aliscafi Shipping Company was established in Sicily to operate the world's first scheduled sea-going hydrofoil service in August 1956 between Sicily and the Italian mainland.

The service was operated by the first Rodriquez-built Supramar PT 20, *Freccia del Sole*. Cutting down the port-to-port time from Messina to Reggio di Calabria to one-quarter of that of conventional

ferry boats, and completing 22 daily crossings, the craft soon proved its commercial viability. With a seating capacity of 72 passengers the PT 20 carried between 800 and 900 passengers a day and conveyed a record number of some 31 000 passengers in a single month.

Eight main types of hydrofoil have now been produced: the Supramar PT 20 and PT 50, the RHS 70, RHS 110, RHS 140, RHS 150, RHS 160 and RHS 200. Many of the early craft built are still operating. Please see earlier editions of *Jane's High-Speed Marine Craft* for details of PT 20 and PT 50 hydrofoils; the 1990 edition, pages 174 and 175 lists the PT 20s built by the Rodriquez yard.

RHS 70

This is a 32 tonne coastal passenger ferry with seats for 71 passengers. Power is supplied by a single 1066 kW MTU diesel and the cruising speed is 32.4 knots.

Principal Particulars

Length overall	22 m
Foil width	7.4 m
Draught, hullborne	2.7 m
Draught, foilborne	1.15 m

RHS 70 Shearwater 3, *sister vessel to three other RHS 70s delivered to Red Funnel Ferries* 1986

Craft built (RHS 70) 1972 to 1982

Type	Name	Yard No	No of seats	Operated in	Date built	Owner/Operator
RHS 70	Shearwater 3	150	67	UK	1972	Red Funnel Ferries
RHS 70	Shearwater 4	156	67	UK	1973	Red Funnel Ferries
RHS 70	Freccia delle Betulle	185	71	Italy	1974	Navigazione Lago di Como
RHS 70	Freccia delle Camelie	186	71	Italy	1974	Navigazione Lago Maggiore
RHS 70	Freccia del Benaco	187	71	Italy	1974	Navigazione Sul Lago di Garda
RHS 70	Freccia delle Magnolie	188	71	Italy	1975	Navigazione Lago Maggiore
RHS 70	Freccia delle Gardenie	189	71	Italy	1976	Navigazione Lago di Como
RHS 70	Freccia dei Gerani	196	71	Italy	1977	Navigazione Sul Lago di Garda
RHS 70	Shearwater 5	197	67	UK	1980	Red Funnel Ferries
RHS 70	Shearwater 6	221	67	UK	1982	Red Funnel Ferries

Displacement, maximum	31.5 t
Payload	6 t
Passengers	71
Propulsive power	1066 kW
Maximum speed	36.5 knots
Operational speed	32.4 knots

Structure: V-bottom hull of riveted light metal alloy construction. Watertight compartments are below the passenger decks and in other parts of the hull.

The foils are surface-piercing type in partly hollow welded steel.

Propulsion: A single MTU 12V 331 TC 82 diesel, developing 1066 kW at 2340 rpm, drives a three-bladed bronze-aluminium propeller through a Zahnradfabrik W 800 H 20 gearbox.

Electrical system: 24 V generator driven by the main engine; batteries with a capacity of 350 Ah.

Control: During operation the angle of the bow foil can be adjusted within narrow limits from the steering position by means of a hydraulic ram operating on a foil support across the hull.

Auxiliary systems: 120 kg/cm^3 pressure hydraulic system for rudder and bow foil incidence control.

Outfit: 44 passengers are accommodated in the forward cabin, 19 in the rear compartment and eight aft of the pilot's position, above the engine room, in the elevated wheelhouse. A WC/wash basin unit is provided in the aft passenger compartments. Emergency exits are provided in each passenger compartment. Cabin noise level is approximately 76 dBA.

RHS 110

A 54 tonne hydrofoil ferry, the RHS 110 was originally designed to carry a maximum of 110 passengers at a cruising speed of 37 knots.

Principal Particulars

Length overall	25.6 m
Beam	5.95 m
Foil width	9.2 m
Draught, hullborne	3.3 m
Draught, foilborne	1.25 m

Craft built (Supramar PT 50) 1959 to 1970

Type	Name	Yard No	No of seats	Operated in	Date built	Owner/Operator
Supramar PT 50	Freccia di Messina*	059	125	Italy	1959	-
Supramar PT 50	Freccia di Sorrento	062	125	Italy	1959	Ministero dei Mercantile Marine
Supramar PT 50	Freccia d'Oro	063	130	Italy	1959	Destroyed in storm 1992
Supramar PT 50	Freccia Atlantica	064	125	Italy	1960	Aliscafi SNAV SpA
Supramar PT 50	Freccia del Sud	065	50+ 7 t cargo	Italy	1960	Aliscafi SNAV SpA
Supramar PT 50	Pisanello	066	130	Italy	1961	SIREMAR
Supramar PT 50	Queenfoil (ex Sleipner)	076	125	-	1961	Transtour SA
Supramar PT 50	Freccia di Lipari	077	125	Italy	1961	Aliscafi SNAV SpA
Supramar PT 50	Flecha de Buenos Aires	078	125	Argentina	1962	Alimar SA
Supramar PT 50	Flecha de Colonia (ex Flecha de Montevideo)	079	125	Argentina	1962	Alimar SA
Supramar PT 50	Flecha del Litoral*	080	125	Argentina	1963	-
Supramar PT 50	Freccia del Mediterraneo	081	125	Italy	1963	Aliscafi SNAV SpA
Supramar PT 50	Freccia di Sicilia	088	125	Italy	1964	Aliscafi SNAV SpA
Supramar PT 50	Nibbio	089	125	Italy	1964	Adriatica di Navigazione SpA
Supramar PT 50	Flying Albatross	090	125	Hong Kong	1964	Hongkong Macao Hydrofoil Co Ltd
Supramar PT 50	Flying Skimmer	091	125	Hong Kong	1965	Hongkong Macao Hydrofoil Co Ltd
Supramar PT 50	Svalan*	092	125	-	1965	ex Tarnan Line, Limassol, Cyprus
Supramar PT 50	Flying Condor	093	125	Hong Kong	1966	Hongkong Macao Hydrofoil Co Ltd
Supramar PT 50	Freccia delle Isole	111	125	Italy	1966	Destroyed in storm 1992
Supramar PT 50	Tarnan	118	120	-	1966	ex Tarnan Line, Limassol, Cyprus
Supramar PT 50	Freccia Adriatica	119	125	Italy	1969	Aliscafi SNAV SpA
Supramar PT 50	Fairlight (scrapped 1988)	120	140	Australia	1966	-
Supramar PT 50	Flying Flamingo (scrapped)	121	125	-	1967	ex Hongkong Macao Hydrofoil Co Ltd
Supramar PT 50	Star Capricorn (ex Springeren)	122	117	Italy	1967	COVEMAR Eolie
Supramar PT 50	Stilprins (ex Teisten)	123	128		1970	
Supramar PT 50	Long Reef (laid up)	124	140	Australia	1969	NSW State Transit Authority
Supramar PT 50	Sun Arrow	125	125	Italy	1968	Aliscafi SNAV SpA
Supramar PT 50	Dee Why (scrapped 1988)	132	140	Australia	1970	-

*destroyed by fire 1986

Craft built (RHS 110) 1971 to 1973

Type	Name	Yard No	No of seats	Operated in	Date built	Owner/Operator
RHS 110	Cacilhas	147	110	Hong Kong	1971	-
RHS 110	Flecha de Angra (ex Flying Phoenix)	148	140	Brazil	1970	Laid up
RHS 110	Barca	157	122	Hong Kong	1972	-
RHS 110	Praia	158	111	Hong Kong	1973	-
RHS 110	Cerco	159	111	Hong Kong	1973	-

Displacement, maximum	54 t
Passengers	110
Fuel capacity	3600 l
Propulsive power	2 × 1006 kW
Maximum speed	40 knots
Operational speed	37 knots
Range	262 nm

Structure: V-bottom of high tensile riveted light metal alloy construction, using Peraluman plate and Anti-corrodal profiles. The upper deck plates are 3.5 mm thick Peraluman. Removable deck sections permit the lifting out and replacement of the main engines. The superstructure, which has a removable roof, is in 2 mm thick Peraluman plates, with L and C profile sections. Watertight compartments are below the passenger decks and other parts of the hull.

The foils are a surface-piercing type, in partly hollow welded steel.

Propulsion: Power is supplied by two 12-cylinder supercharged MTU MB 12V 493 Ty 71 diesels, each with a maximum output of 1006 kW at 1500 rpm. Engine output is transferred to two three-bladed bronze-aluminium propellers through Zahnradfabrik W 800 H 20 gearboxes. Each propeller shaft is 90 mm in diameter and supported at three points by seawater-lubricated rubber bearings. Steel fuel tanks with a total capacity of 3600 litres are aft of the engine room.

Electrical systems: Engine-driven generators supply 220 V, 50 Hz, three-phase AC. Two groups of batteries for 24 V DC circuit.

Control: Hydraulically operated flaps, attached to the trailing edges of the bow and rear foils, are adjusted automatically by a Hamilton Standard stability augmentation system for the damping of heave, pitch and roll motions. The rear foil is rigidly attached to the transom, its incidence angle being determined during tests.

Auxiliary systems: Steering, variation of the foil flaps and the anchor windlass operation are all accomplished hydraulically from the wheelhouse. Plant comprises two Bosch pumps installed on the main engines which convey oil from a 60 litre tank under pressure to the control cylinders of the rudder, foil flaps and anchor windlass.

Outfit: The wheelhouse observation deck saloon seats 58 and the lower aft saloon 39. Additional passengers are accommodated in the lower forward saloon, which contains a bar.

In the wheelhouse, the pilot's position is on the port side, together with the radar screen. A second seat is provided for the chief engineer. Passenger seats are of lightweight aircraft type, floors are covered with woollen carpets and the walls and ceilings are clad in vinyl. There are two toilets provided, one in each of the lower saloons.

Safety equipment: There is a fire-fighting fixed CO_2 plant for the main engine room, portable CO_2 and foam fire extinguishers of 3 kg and 10 litre capacity in the saloons, and one water fire-fighting plant.

RHS 140

This 65 tonne hydrofoil passenger ferry seats up to 150 passengers and has a cruising speed of 32.5 knots.

Principal Particulars

Length overall	28.7 m
Foil width	10.72 m
Draught, hullborne	3.5 m
Draught, foilborne	1.5 m
Displacement, maximum	65 t
Payload	12.5 t
Passengers	150
Propulsive power	2 × 1007 kW
Maximum speed	36 knots
Operational speed	32.5 knots
Range	297 nm

Structure: Riveted light metal alloy design framed on longitudinal and transverse formers.

The foils are surface-piercing V-foils of hollow welded steel construction.

Propulsion: Power is provided by two MTU 12V 493 Ty 71 12-cylinder supercharged engines, each developing 1007 kW at 1500 rpm. Engine output is transmitted to two, three-bladed 700 mm diameter bronze propellers through Zahnradfabrik gearboxes.

Electrical system: Two engine-driven generators supply 24 V DC. Two battery sets each with 350 Ah capacity.

Control: Lift of the bow foil can be modified by hydraulically operated trailing-edge flaps.

Auxiliary systems: Steering and variation of foil flap incidence is accomplished hydraulically from the wheelhouse. Plant comprises two Bosch pumps installed on the main engines and conveying oil from a 70 litre tank under pressure to the control cylinders of the rudder and foil flaps.

Outfit: Up to 150 passengers seated in three saloons. The belvedere saloon, on the main deck above the engine room, can be equipped with a bar. WC/wash basin units can be installed in the forward and aft saloons.

Safety equipment: Fixed CO_2 fire-fighting plant for the engine room; portable CO_2 and foam fire extinguishers in the saloons. Water intake connected to bilge pump for fire hose connection in emergency.

RHS 150

Combining features of both the RHS 140 and the RHS 160, the RHS 150 hydrofoil passenger ferry is powered by two 1066 kW MTU supercharged four-stroke diesels which give the craft a cruising speed of 32.5 knots and a cruising range of 130 nm.

Principal Particulars

Length overall	28.7 m
Foil width	11 m
Draught, hullborne	3.1 m
Draught, foilborne	1.4 m
Displacement, maximum	65.5 t
Passengers	150
Propulsive power	2 × 1066 kW

Rodriquez Supramar PT 50 Freccia di Sorrento *built in 1959 and now in use by the Ministero dei Mercantile Marine for anti-pollution work* **1988**

Forward foil arrangement of Rodriquez Supramar PT 50 Freccia del Mediterraneo **1988**

Craft built (RHS 140) 1971 to 1977

Type	Name	Yard No	No of seats	Operated in	Date built	Owner/Operator
RHS 140	Colonia del Sacramento (ex Condor)	133	140	Uruguay	1971	Belt SA
RHS 140	Flying Dragon	134	140	Hong Kong	1971	Hongkong Macao Hydrofoil Co Ltd
RHS 140	Flying Egret	152	125	Hong Kong	1972	Hongkong Macao Hydrofoil Co Ltd
RHS 140	Santa Maria del Buenos Aires (ex Tyrving)	153	116	Uruguay	1972	Belt SA
RHS 140	Farallón (ex Loberen)	154	111	Uruguay	1972	Belt SA
RHS 140	Curl-Curl	155	140	Australia	1972	NSW Transit Authority
RHS 140	Rapido de Ibiza (ex Viggen)	161	120	Spain	1973	Flebasa Lines
RHS 140	Flying Sandpiper (ex Flying Goldfinch)	180	125	Hong Kong	1972	Hongkong Macao Hydrofoil Co Ltd
RHS 140	Flying Swift	180	125	Hong Kong	1973	Hongkong Macao Hydrofoil Co Ltd
RHS 140	Flying Ibis	182	125	Hong Kong	1975	Hongkong Macao Hydrofoil Co Ltd
RHS 140	Condor 4	184	136	UK	1974	Condor Ltd
RHS 140	Duccio (ex Fabricia)	193	140	Italy	1977	TOREMAR SpA
RHS 140	Albireo	194	150	Italy	1977	CAREMAR SpA

Operational speed	32.5 knots
Range	130 nm

Structure: Riveted light metal alloy design framed on longitudinal and transverse formers.

Surface-piercing W-foils of hollow welded steel construction.

Propulsion: Motive power is furnished by two supercharged MTU MB 12V 331 TC 82 four-stroke diesels each developing 1066 kW at 2140 rpm continuous.

Engine output is transmitted to two bronze propellers via two Zahnradfabrik BW 255L gearboxes.

Electrical system: Two 1300 W engine-driven generators supply 24 V DC.

Control: Lift of the bow foil can be modified by hydraulically operated trailing edge flaps.

Outfit: The standard model seats 150 in three saloons. High density model design originally for services on the Italian lakes seats 180: 63 in the aft

Craft built (RHS 150) 1980

Type	Name	Yard No	No of seats	Operated in	Date built	Owner/Operator
RHS 150	Xel-Ha (laid up)	203	151	Mexico	1980	Secretaria de Turismo, Mexico

saloon, 45 in the forward saloon and 72 in the belvedere. The forward and stern saloons each have a toilet unit.

RHS 150 SL

This variant has been designed for inland navigation, particularly on the Great Lakes in Northern Italy. Due to the less severe conditions on such waters it has been possible to redesign the hull structure to allow for larger windows in the lower saloons and the superstructure, greatly increasing visibility for sightseeing. In addition, because the safety rules are less demanding than for open-water routes, there is a saving in weight in the design allowing an increase in passenger numbers, so that 200 may be carried, with lightweight seats fitted.

RHS 150F

This variant has a wider deck and the superstructure volume has been increased to give a more aesthetic shape as well as greater volume for passengers, giving greater comfort. Improvements have also been incorporated in this variant increasing performance and reducing maintenance costs.

RHS 160

A 95 tonne passenger ferry with seats for up to 180 passengers and a cruising speed of 32 knots.

In March and May 1986 two RHS 160s were used for oil spill clean-up trials.

Principal Particulars

Length overall	30.95 m
Beam	6.2 m
Foil width	12.6 m
Draught, hullborne	3.7 m
Draught, foilborne	1.35 m
Displacement, maximum	95 t
Payload	13.5 t
Passengers	180-200
Propulsive power	2 × 1400 kW
Maximum speed	36 knots
Operational speed	32 knots
Range	260 nm

Structure: Riveted light metal alloy longitudinal structure, welded in parts using inert gas. The hull shape of the RHS 160 is similar to the RHS 140

RHS 150FL Voloire delivered 1989 for service on Lake Como, Italy

RHS 150F Salina *operated by Aliscafi SNAV SpA*   **1995**

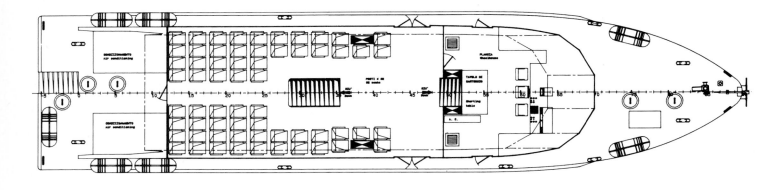

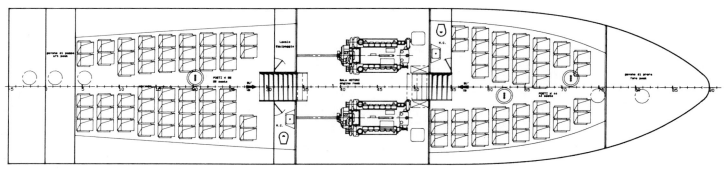

RHS 150F   **1995**

series. In the manufacture of the hull, plates of aluminium and magnesium alloy of 4.4 per cent are used while angle bars are of a high resistant aluminium, magnesium and silicon alloy.

The surface-piercing W-foils are of hollow welded steel construction.

Propulsion: Power is provided by two supercharged MTU MB 12V 652 TB 71 four-stroke diesel engines each with a maximum output of 1454 kW at 1460 rpm under normal operating conditions. Engine starting is accomplished by compressed air starters. Engine output is transmitted to two, three-bladed bronze propellers through two Zahnradfabrik 900 HS 15 gearboxes.

Electrical system: Two 35 kVA generating sets, 220 V, 60 Hz, three-phase. There are three insulated cables for ventilation, air-conditioning and power. Two insulated cables for lighting, sockets and other appliances, 24 V DC for emergency lighting, auxiliary engine starting and servo-control. A battery for radiotelephone supply is installed on the upper deck. Provision for battery recharge from AC line foreseen.

Control: Craft in this series feature a bow rudder for improved manoeuvrability in congested waters. The bow rudder works simultaneously with the aft rudders. Hydraulically operated flaps, attached to the

Craft built (RHS 150SL and FL) 1979 to 1989

Type	Name	Yard No	No of seats	Operated in	Date built	Owner/Operator
RHS 150SL	*Freccia del Giardini*	204	190	Italy	1980	Navigazione Lago Maggiore
RHS 150SL	*Freccia delle Valli*	199	190	Italy	1979	Navigazione Lago di Como
RHS 150SL	*Freccia dei Gerani*	196	190	Italy	1980	Navigazione Lago Maggiore
RHS 150SL	*Freccia delle Riviere*	206	190	Italy	1981	Navigazione Lago di Garda
RHS 150SL	*Galileo Galilei*	208	190	Italy	1982	Navigazione Lago di Garda
RHS 150SL	*Enrico Fermi*	220	190	Italy	1984	Navigazione Lago Maggiore
RHS 150SL	*Guglielmo Marconi*	207	190	Italy	1983	Navigazione Lago di Como
RHS 150FL	*Goethe*	232	200	Italy	1988	Navigazione Lago di Gardo
RHS 150FL	*Voloire*	237	200	Italy	1989	Navigazione Lago di Como
RHS 150FL	*Byron*	238	200	Italy	1990	Navigazione Lago Maggiore

Craft built (RHS 150F) 1984

Type	Name	Yard No	No of seats	Operated in	Date built	Owner/Operator
RHS 150F	*Dynasty*	210	161	Italy	1984	Aliscafi SNAV SpA
RHS 150F	*Salina*	233	161	Italy	1990	Aliscafi SNAV SpA
RHS 150F	*Panarea*	234	161	Italy	1990	Aliscafi SNAV SpA

Craft built (RHS 160) 1974 to 1986

Type	Name	Yard No	No of seats	Operated in	Date built	Owner/Operator
RHS 160	*Princess Zoe* (ex *Alijumbo Ustica*, ex *Lilau*)	181	160	Italy	1974	Aliscafi SNAV SpA
RHS 160	*Diomedea*	190	160	Italy	1975	Adriatica di Navigazione SpA
RHS 160	*Condor 5*	191	180	UK	1976	Condor Ltd
RHS 160	*Algol*	195	180	Italy	1978	CAREMAR
RHS 160	*May W Craig* (ex *Alijumbo*)	198	180	Italy	1979	Aliscafi SNAV SpA
RHS 160	*Alioth*	200	180	Italy	1979	CAREMAR
RHS 160	*Botticelli*	201	180	Italy	1980	SIREMAR
RHS 160	*Donatello*	202	180	Italy	1980	SIREMAR
RHS 160	*Nicte-Ha*	205	160	Mexico	1982	Secretaria de Turismo, Mexico

Craft built/being built (RHS 160F) 1984 to 1992

Type	Name	Yard No	No of seats	Operated in	Date built	Owner/Operator
RHS 160F	*Manly*	211	238	Australia	1984	NSW State Transit Authority
RHS 160F	*Sydney*	216	238	Australia	1985	NSW State Transit Authority
RHS 160F	*Condor 7*	217	200	UK	1985	Condor Ltd
RHS 160F	*Pez Volador* (ex *Alijumbo Eolie*)	218	220	Spain	1986	Compañia Naviera Mallorquina
RHS 160F	*Alnilam*	227	210	Italy	1986	CAREMAR
RHS 160F	*Fabricia*	228	210	Italy	1987	TOREMAR
RHS 160F	*Aldebaran*	229	210	Italy	1987	CAREMAR
RHS 160F	*Masaccio*	230	210	Italy	1988	SIREMAR
RHS 160F	*Mantegna*	231	210	Italy	1989	SIREMAR
RHS 160F	*Citti Ships*	236	210	Italy	1990	Alisafi SNAV SpA
RHS 160F	*Giorgione*	239	210	Italy	1989	SIREMAR
RHS 160F	*Monte Gargano*	240	210	Italy	1989	Adriatica SpA di Navigazione
RHS 160F	*Barracuda*	002/160	204	Spain	1989	Trasmediterranea SA
RHS 160F	*Marrajo*	003/160	204	Spain	1989	Trasmediterranea SA
RHS 160F	*Tintorera*	004/160	204	Spain	1990	Trasmediterranea SA
RHS 160F	*Alijumbo Zibibbo*	243	204	Italy	1991	Aliscafi SNAV SpA
RHS 160F	*Moretto I*	244	204	Italy	1991	Aliscafi SNAV SpA
RHS 160F	*Alijumbo Eolie*	245	204	Italy	1991	Aliscafi SNAV SpA
RHS 160F	-	246	-	-	1992	-
RHS 160F	*Alijumbo Messina*	248	204	Italy	1992	Aliscafi SNAV SpA
RHS 160F	*Alijumbo Stromboli*					

trailing edges of the bow and rear foils, are adjusted automatically by a Hamilton Standard electronic stability augmentation system, for the damping of heave, pitch and roll motions in heavy seas.

Auxiliary systems: Hydraulic steering from the wheelhouse. Plant comprises a Bosch pump installed on the main engines and conveying oil from a 45 litre (10 gallon) tank under pressure to the control cylinders of the rudder and anchor windlass, whilst a second hydraulic pump, which is also installed on the main engines, conveys oil under pressure to the flap control cylinders.

Outfit: 180 to 200 passengers seated in three saloons; 57 passengers are accommodated in the forward cabin, 63 in the rear compartment and 60 in the belvedere.

Safety equipment: Fixed CO_2 fire-fighting plant of four CO_2 bottles approximately 20 kg each for the engine room and fuel tank space; portable extinguishers in various parts of the craft. Water intake is connected to fire pump for fire connection in emergency.

RHS 160F

A further addition to the Rodriquez range is the RHS 160F, a 91.5 tonne passenger ferry with seats for up to 238 passengers and a cruising speed of 34.5 knots.

Principal Particulars

Length overall	31.2 m
Length waterline	26.25 m
Beam	6.7 m
Foil width	12.6 m
Draught, hullborne	3.76 m
Draught, foilborne	1.7 m
Displacement, maximum	91.5 t
Payload	17.8 t
Passengers	210-238
Propulsive power	2 × 1400 kW
Maximum speed	38 knots
Operational speed	34.5 knots
Range	100 nm

Structure: Riveted light metal alloy longitudinal structure, welded in parts using inert gas. The hull shape of the RHS 160F is similar to the RHS 140 series. In the manufacture of the hull, plates of aluminium and magnesium alloy of 4.4 per cent are used while angle bars are of a high resistant aluminium, magnesium and silicon alloy.

Surface-piercing W-foils of hollow welded steel construction.

Propulsion: Power is provided by two supercharged MTU 16V 396 TB 83 four-stroke diesel engines each with a maximum output of 1400 kW at 2000 rpm under normal operating conditions. Engine starting is accomplished by compressed air starters. Engine output is transmitted to two, three-bladed bronze propellers through two Zahnradfabrik BW 7505 gearboxes, or, alternatively, through two Reintjes WVS 1032U gearboxes as fitted to the RHS 160F craft supplied to the NSW State Transit Authority, Australia.

Electrical system: Two 35 kVA generating sets, 220 V, 60 Hz, three-phase. There are three insulated cables for ventilation, air-conditioning and power. Two insulated cables for lighting, sockets and other appliances, 24 V DC for emergency lighting, auxiliary engine starting and servo-control. A battery for radiotelephone supply is installed on the upper deck. Provision for battery recharge from AC line is foreseen.

Control: Craft in this series feature a bow rudder for improved manoeuvrability in congested waters. The bow rudder works simultaneously with the aft rudders. Hydraulically operated flaps, attached to the trailing edges of the bow and rear foils, are adjusted automatically by a Hamilton Standard electronic stability augmentation system, for the damping of heave, pitch and roll motions in heavy seas.

Auxiliary systems: Hydraulic steering from the wheelhouse. Plant comprises a Bosch pump installed on the main engines and conveying oil from a 45 litre (10 gallon) tank under pressure to the control cylinders of the rudder and anchor windlass, whilst a second hydraulic pump, which is also installed on the main engines, conveys oil under pressure to the flap control cylinders.

Outfit: 210 passengers seated in three saloons. 58 passengers are accommodated in the forward cabin, 63 in the rear compartment and 89 in the bel-

RHS 160F Barracuda (Dr Saro Armone)

1990

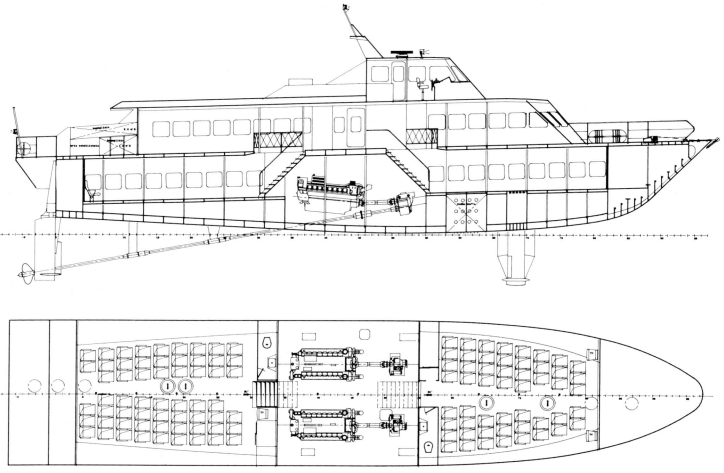

RHS 160F inboard profile and lower deck arrangement

1995

RHS 160F Citti Ships

1995

vedere. Forward and aft saloons and belvedere each have a toilet, wash basin units and toilet accessories.

Safety equipment: Fixed CO_2 fire-fighting plant of four CO_2 bottles approximately 20 kg each for the engine room and fuel tank space; portable extinguishers in various parts of the craft. Water intake connected to fire pump for connection in emergency.

RHS 200

Powered by two supercharged MTU MB 16V 652 TB 71 four-stroke diesel engines, the 254-seat RHS 200 has a cruising speed of 35 knots.

Principal Particulars

Length overall	35.8 m
Foil width	14.5 m
Draught, hullborne	4.55 m
Draught, foilborne	2.05 m
Displacement, maximum	130 t
Passengers	254
Propulsive power	2 × 1938 kW
Maximum speed	37 knots
Operational speed	35 knots
Range	200 nm

Structure: V-bottom hull of high tensile riveted light metal alloy construction, employing Peraluman plates and Anti-corrodal frames. The rake of the stem is in galvanised steel.

Surface-piercing W-foils of hollow welded steel construction.

Propulsion: Motive power is supplied by two super-charged MTU MB 16V 652 TB 71 four-stroke diesel engines, each with a maximum output of 1938 kW at 1460 rpm under normal operating conditions.

Engine output is transferred to two super cavitating, controllable-pitch propellers.

Electrical system: Two generating sets: one 220 V, three-phase AC, for all consumer services, the second for charging 24 V battery sets and operating fire-fighting and hydraulic pumps. Power distribution panel in wheelhouse for navigation light circuits, cabin lighting, radar, RDF, gyro compass and emergency circuits.

Control: Craft in this series feature a bow rudder for improved manoeuvrability in congested waters. This control operates simultaneously with the aft rudders. An advantage of the W configuration bow foil is its relatively shallow draught requirement in relation to the vessel's overall size. Hydraulically operated flaps are fitted to the trailing edge of the bow foil to balance out longitudinal load shifting, assist take off and adjust the flying height. The craft can also be equipped with the Hamilton Standard electronic stability augmentation system, which employs sensors and servo-mechanisms to position flaps automatically on the bow and stern foils for the damping of heave, pitch and roll motions in heavy seas.

Outfit: Seats for up to 400 passengers, according to the route served. In typical configuration there are three main passenger saloons and a bar. The standard seating arrangement allows for 116 in the main deck saloon, 58 in the aft lower saloon and 66 in the bow passenger saloon. Seating is normally four abreast in two lines with a central aisle. The bar, at the forward end of the wheelhouse belvedere superstructure, either has an eight-seat sofa or 19 seats.

The wheelhouse, which is raised to provide a 360° view, is reached from the main deck belvedere

saloon by a short companionway. Controls and instrumentation are attached to a panel on the forward bulkhead which extends the width of the wheelhouse. In the centre is the steering control and gyro compass, on the starboard side are controls for the two engines, gearboxes and controllable-pitch propellers, and on the port side is the radar. Seats are provided for the captain, chief engineer and first mate. In the wheelhouse are a radiotelephone and a chart table.

Safety equipment: Fixed CO_2 fire-fighting self-contained automatic systems for power-plant and fuel tank spaces, plus portable extinguishers for cabins and holds.

MEC 1
MAXIMUM EFFICIENCY CRAFT
Mec Ustica

Replacing the MEC 2 design previously reported, construction of MEC 1 started in July 1990. MEC 1 follows the same design principles and advances and is a new hydrofoil design developed in a joint effort with CETENA (the Italian Ship Research Institute) and incorporating Rexroth hydrostatic power transmission now continued by Hydromarine SA of Switzerland as the Power Shaft Concept. The design embodies a new Rodriquez surface-piercing foil system and hull form (fully automatic welding construction), with the rear foil unit carrying the maximum possible weight. It has been shown to be desirable to have a very stiff (in response to waves) front foil with low damping and a very soft rear foil with high damping. It is then convenient to carry the maximum possible weight on the rear foil, the Canard lift distribution allowing a finer hull bow form to be used.

The hull form has been derived from the well known 65 Series.

In comparison with comparable hydrofoils, a passenger capacity increase of about 25 per cent is anticipated, a speed increase of nine per cent, while displacement increases by less than five per cent. For equal passenger capacity, the installed power would be reduced by some 18 per cent with a conse-

Type	Name	Yard No	No of seats	Operated in	Date built	Owner/Operator
RHS 200	*Superjumbo Capri* (ex *Superjumbo*)	92	254	Italy	1981	Aliscafi SNAV SpA
RHS 200	*San Cristobal* (ex *Stretto di Messina*)	209	254	Italy	1984	Aliscafi SNAV SpA

Craft built (RHS 200) 1981 to 1984

RHS 160F Alijumbo Stromboli

1995

Craft built (MEC) 1991

Type	Name	Yard No	No of seats	Operated in	Date	Owner/Operator
MEC 1	*Mec Ustica*	242	146	-	1991	Aliscafi SNAV SpA
MEC 3						Yard No 260
MEC 4						Yard No 251, 1992

quent reduction in fuel consumption. Due to the aft location of the power-plant a passenger cabin noise reduction of 3 to 5 dBA is expected.

Principal Particulars

Length overall	25 m
Length waterline	20.8 m
Beam	6.7 m
Foil width	8.4 m
Draught, hullborne	2.8 m
Draught, foilborne	1.2 m
Displacement, maximum	55 t
Passengers	146
Operational speed	38 knots
Range	200 nm

Propulsion: Engines: 2 × Deutz MWM TBD 604B V8, driving hydrostatic power transmission.

Please see the Rexroth entry in the *Transmission* section of this book for discussion of the basic concept and for details of the system as applied to an early Rodriquez Supramar PT 20 hydrofoil craft, *Aligrado*.

FOILMASTER

The Foilmaster is an advanced variant of the RHS 160 surface-piercing hydrofoil. Improvements include resilient mounting of engines and gearboxes, exhaust gas silencers, the use of carbon fibre components in foil construction and more powerful

Belvedere cabin of RHS 200

1987

Rexroth hydrostatic power transmission with tandem propellers as applied to an early Rodriquez Supramar PT 20, Aligrado *for trial purposes* **1989**

Rodriquez MEC 1 Mec Ustica

1993

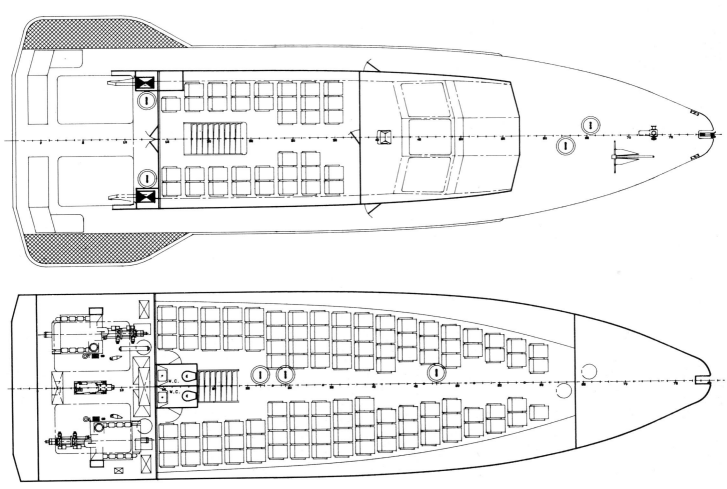

MEC 1

engines. Tandem configuration foils are fitted with trailing edge flaps. There are two sets of rudders provided, two flap rudders on the aft foil and a single flap rudder fitted to the fore foil. An air-conditioning system is installed in all passenger saloons as well as in the wheelhouse.

The first of a number of Foilmasters was delivered to SIREMAR in late 1994.

Principal Particulars

Length overall	31.4 m
Length waterline	26.4 m
Beam	6.7 m
Foil width	13.3 m
Draught, hullborne	3.76 m
Draught, foilborne	1.6 m
Displacement, maximum	107 t
Crew	7
Passengers	219
Fuel capacity	2.5 t
Water capacity	0.6 t
Propulsive power	2 × 1550 kW
Operational speed	38 knots
Range	150 nm

Propulsion: Engines: 2 × MTU 16V 396 TE 74.

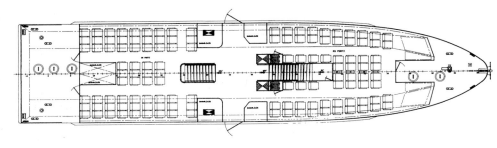

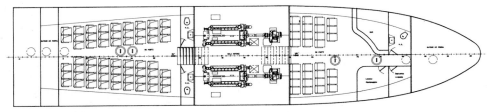

UPDATED Foilmaster deck layouts

Foilmaster Tiziano

1995

JAPAN

HITACHI ZOSEN CORPORATION

Head Office: 3-28 Nishikujo 5-chome, Konhana-ku, Osaka, 554 Japan

Telephone: +81 (6) 466 7546
Telex: 63376 J
Telefax: +81 (6) 466 7578

Works: 4-1 Mizue-cho, Kawasaki-ku, Kawasaki, Kanagawa Pref, Japan

Telephone: +81 (44) 288 1111
Telex: 3842524 J
Telefax: +81 (44) 276 0022

Yoshihiro Fujii, *President*
Shogo Furuta, *Executive Vice President*
Hirotaka Shirakami, *General Manager, Kanagawa Works*

Hitachi Zosen, the Supramar licensee in Japan, has been building Supramar PT 20, PT 32 and PT 50 hydrofoils since 1961. By 1970 some 32 hydrofoils had been built with another 10 by 1981. The majority of these have been built for fast passenger ferry

PT 20 Ryusei *operated by Ishizaki Kisen KK*

1987

services across the Japanese Inland Sea, cutting across deep bays which road vehicles might take two to three hours to drive round, and out to offshore islands. Other PT 20s and 50s have been exported to Hong Kong, Australia and South Korea for ferry services.

Specifications of the PT 32 (*Jane's Surface Skimmers 1967-68*), PT 20 and PT 50 will be found under Supramar (Switzerland) (*Jane's Surface Skimmers 1985*). The Hitachi Zosen craft are almost identical.

In 1974 the company completed the first PT 50 Mk II to be built at its Kawasaki yard. The vessel, *Hikari No 2*, is powered by two licence-built MTU MB 820Db diesels, carries 123 passengers plus a crew of seven and cruises at 33 knots. It was delivered to Setonaikai Kisen KK of Hiroshima in March 1975. Hitachi Zosen has constructed 25 PT 50s and 17 PT 20s.

In conjunction with Supramar, Hitachi Zosen has developed a new roll stabilisation system for the PT 50. The first to be equipped with this new system was completed in January 1983.

ROLL-STABILISED SUPRAMAR PTS 50 Mk II

Housho, a PTS 50 Mk II, was delivered to Hankyu Kisen KK on 19 January 1983 and is operating on the Kobe-Naruto route. The system, developed by Hitachi Zosen in conjunction with Supramar, reduces the PTS 50's rolling motion by between one-half and one-third.

The underside of the bow foil is fitted with two flapped fins to improve riding comfort. Operated by automatic sensors, the fins augment stability and provide side forces to dampen rolling and transverse motions.

Principal Particulars

Length overall	27.55 m
Beam	5.84 m
Foil width	10.8 m
Draught, hullborne	3.5 m
Draught, foilborne	1.4 m
Displacement, maximum	62 t
Passengers	123
Propulsive power	2 × 1029 kW
Maximum speed	38 knots

UPDATED

Hitachi hydrofoils believed to be currently in operation

Type	Name	Seats	Launched	Operator
Hitachi Supramar PT 20	*Hayate No 1*		April 1962	Showa Kaiun Co Ltd
Hitachi Supramar PT 20	*Kansei*		July 1962	Ishizaki Kisen KK
Hitachi Supramar PT 20	*Hibiki*		November 1966	Setonaikai Kisen KK*
Hitachi Supramar PT 20	*Hibiki No 3*	66	March 1968	Setonaikai Kisen KK*
Hitachi Supramar PT 20	*Shibuki No 2*		June 1969	Boyo Kisen Co Ltd
Hitachi Supramar PT 20	*Myojo*		June 1970	Ishizaki Kisen KK
Hitachi Supramar PT 20	*Kinsei*		July 1972	Ishizaki Kisen KK
Hitachi Supramar PT 20	*Ryusei*		March 1981	Ishizaki Kisen KK
Hitachi Supramar PT 50	*Ohtori*	113	January 1968	-
Hitachi Supramar PT 50	*Kosei*		February 1969	Ishizaki Kisen KK
Hitachi Supramar PT 50	*Ohtori No 2*	113	February 1970	Setonaikai Kisen KK
Hitachi Supramar PT 50	*Zuihoh*		December 1971	Hankyu Kisen KK
Hitachi Supramar PT 50	*Hoh'oh*		February 1972	Hankyu Kisen KK
Hitachi Supramar PT 50	*Condor*	121	June 1972	Setonaikai Kisen KK*
Hitachi Supramar PT 50	*Ohtori No 3*		October 1972	Setonaikai Kisen KK
Hitachi Supramar PT 50	*Ohtori No 5*		May 1973	Setonaikai Kisen KK
Hitachi Supramar PT 50	*Shibuki No 3*		October 1973	Boyo Kisen Co Ltd
Hitachi Supramar PT 50	*Saisei*		March 1974	Ishizaki Kisen KK
Hitachi Supramar PT 50	*Condor No 2*	121	April 1974	Setonaikai Kisen KK*
Hitachi Supramar PT 50	*Condor No 3*	100	August 1974	Setonaikai Kisen KK
Hitachi Supramar PT 50 Mk II	*Hikari No 2*	123	March 1975	Setonaikai Kisen KK
Hitachi Supramar PT 50 Mk II	*Shunsei* (ex *Kariyush I*)		June 1975	Ishizaki Kisen KK
Hitachi Supramar PTS 50 Mk II	*Housho*	123	January 1983	Hankyu Kisen KK

* no longer operational with Setonaikai Kisen

PTS 50 Mk II Housho

1986

KAWASAKI HEAVY INDUSTRIES LTD

Ship Group

Tokyo Head Office: World Trade Center Building, 4-1 Hamamatsu-cho 2-chome, Minato-ku, Tokyo 105, Japan

Telephone: +81 (3) 3435 2186
Telex: 242 4371 KAWAJU J
Telefax: +81 (3) 3436 3038 G3/G2

Kobe Works: 1-1 Higashi Kawasaki-cho 3-chome, Chuo-ku, Kobe 650-91, Japan

Telephone: +81 (78) 682 5120
Telex: 5623 931 KHIKOB J
Telefax: +81 (78) 682 5512

Ryúnosuke Kawazumi, *Managing Director and Senior General Manager of Ship Group*

JETFOIL 929-117

In January 1987, Kawasaki Heavy Industries Ltd acquired a licence for the design, manufacture, marketing, maintenance and repair of Jetfoil 929-117 hydrofoil craft. By June 1994 fourteen Kawasaki Jetfoils had been built. The majority of these craft have been built for fast passenger ferry services between mainland Japan and offshore islands. Two Jetfoils have been exported to Spain.

Principal Particulars

Length overall	27.4 m
Beam	9.1 m
Draught, hullborne	4.9 m
Maximum speed	45 knots

Kawasaki Crystal Wing

1995

Propulsion: Two Allison 501-KF gas-turbines, each rated at 2795 kW at 13 120 rpm. Each is connected to a Kawasaki Powerjet 20 axial flow water-jet propulsor through a gearbox drive train.

For details of the Jetfoil 929 series please see entry under Boeing Aerospace.

Craft built (Kawasaki Jetfoil 929-117 type)

Yard No	Name	Seats	Delivery	Operator
KJ01	*Tsubasa*	266	March 1989	Sado Kisen Kaisha
KJ02	*Toppy*	264	June 1989	Kagoshima Shosen Co Ltd
KJ03	*Pearl Wing* (ex *Nagasaki*)	230	September 1989	Kaijyo Access Co
KJ04	*Pegasus*	265	March 1990	Kyúshu Shósen Co Ltd
KJ05	*Sapphire Wing* (ex *Beetle*)	230	April 1990	Kaijyo Access Co
KJ06	*Princesa Dacil*	286	July 1990	Compania Trasmediterranea, SA
KJ07	*Unicorn*	233	October 1990	Higashi-Nihon Ferry Co Ltd
KJ08	*Beetle II*	232	February 1991	Kyushu Railway Co
KJ09	*Venus*	263	March 1991	Kyūshū Yusen Co Ltd
KJ10	*Suisei*	262	April 1991	Sado Kisen Kaisha
KJ11	*Princesa Teguise*	286	June 1991	Compania Trasmediterranea, SA
KJ12	*Toppy 2*	244	April 1992	Kagoshima Shosen Co Ltd
KJ14	*Crystal Wing*	230	June 1994	Kaijyo Access Co
KJ15	*Emerald Wing*	230	June 1994	Kaijyo Access Co

VERIFIED

SUMITOMO HEAVY INDUSTRIES LTD

5-9-11 Kitashinagawa, Shinagawa-Ku, Tokyo 141, Japan

Telephone: +81 (3) 5488 8181
Telefax: +81 (3) 5488 8178

Kenya Koseki, *General Manager*

PG Class

Sumitomo Industries are licensee of Sparviero Class hydrofoils, granted by Fincantieri (Italy).

Three PGs were constructed and delivered for the Japanese Defence Agency.

Principal Particulars

Length overall	21.8 m
Beam	7 m
Draught	1.4 m
Displacement	50 t
Crew	11
Maximum speed	46 knots

Propulsion: 2 × GE/IHI LM 500 gas-turbines, driving a water-jet pump; and an Isuzu diesel 180PS for hull-borne operations.

PG Class craft built

Name	Yard No	Delivered
PG01	821	17 June 1992
PG02	822	17 June 1992
PG03	823	15 June 1994

VERIFIED

TECHNOLOGICAL RESEARCH ASSOCIATION OF TECHNO-SUPERLINER

Japan Shipbuilding Research Centre Building, 1-3-8 Mejiro, Toshima Ku, Tokyo 171, Japan

Telephone: +81 (3) 3985 3841
Telefax: +81 (3) 3985 3740

Tokashi Nakaso, *President*
Kazuo Sugai, *Managing Director*

The Techno-Superliner Project in Japan involves seven leading shipbuilders, among them Kawasaki Heavy Industries Ltd, NKK Corporation, Ishikawajima-Harima Heavy Industries Company Ltd, Sumitomo Heavy Industries Ltd and Hitachi Zosen Corporation which are jointly investigating the concept of a novel super high-speed ship with all the load being borne by a fully submerged hull and fully submerged foils, so called TSL-F.

The TSL-F superliner has been designed to achieve the following performance targets:
Ship speed: 50 knots
Payload: approx 1000 t
Endurance range: >500 nm
Seaworthiness: regular service at Sea State 6

For this purpose, the speed liner must have a hull form which can reduce the influence of the wave as far as possible and minimise motion and speed reduction in rough seas, giving at least a 98 per cent yearly operation rate on the expected route.

To avoid the influence of the sea surface, the main hull containing the cargo, machinery and navigation systems is supported at a height well above the waves; a lower hull for buoyancy and the foils for dynamic lift are deeply submerged, and the struts to connect the main hull, the lower hull and foils are placed vertically as shown in the accompanying profile of the TSL-F concept. The planned TSL-F con-

Artist's impression of TSL-F design

1995

cept has been shown to have a high level of seaworthiness, with almost no speed reduction in high sea states through the extensive Research and Development programme.

TSL-F (DESIGN)
Principal Particulars

Length overall	85 m
Beam	37 m
Draught, hullborne	12 m
Draught, foilborne	8.1 m
Payload	1000 t
Maximum speed	50 knots
Range	500 nm
Operational limitation	6 m wave height

Propulsion: Engines: gas-turbines and water-jet propulsors.

A small prototype craft is currently under construction at Kawasaki Heavy Industries Ltd, Kobe Works to evaluate and verify the research findings.

The test craft is scheduled to be completed in mid-1994, at sea.

TSL-F PROTOTYPE CRAFT *Hayate*

A large scale model of a hydrofoil-type hybrid ship (TSL-F) named *Hayate* was completed in Kobe Works of Kawasaki Heavy Industries Ltd (KHI) at the beginning of July 1994.

Hayate, which is a ⅙ scale model of an R&D objective TSL-F ship, is composed of an upper hull, a fully submerged lower hull which bears buoyancy, fully submerged foils which generate dynamic lift, and struts which connect the upper hull and the lower hull or the foils. The main propulsion system of *Hayate* consists of a water-jet propulsor, a reduction gear and a gas-turbine.

Various at-sea tests of *Hayate* were conducted until November 1994 to acquire data unobtainable through laboratory tests and to evaluate and verify the overall performance of TSL-F as well as numerous elemental research findings.

Principal Particulars

Length overall	17.1 m
Beam	6.2 m
Draught, hullborne	3.1 m
Draught, foilborne	1.6 m
Propulsive power	2835 kW
Maximum speed	41 knots

Propulsion: 1 × gas-turbine, driving water-jet propulsor.

UPDATED   *Prototype TSL-F trials craft* Hayate   *1995*

UNITED STATES OF AMERICA

BOEING

Although this company is no longer engaged in the marketing of commercial or military hydrofoil vessels, details of the Boeing Jetfoil are included here since these craft represented a most significant step in high-speed marine craft technology.

The Boeing Company has licensed Kawasaki Heavy Industries Ltd for the design, manufacture, marketing, maintenance and repair of Boeing Jetfoil 929-117 hydrofoil craft. Boeing's entry into the hydrofoil field was announced in June 1960, when the company was awarded a US$2 million contract for the construction of the US Navy's 120 ton PCH-1

High Point, a canard design which was the outcome of experiments with a similar arrangement in the US Navy test craft, *Sea Legs*.

The history of Boeing hydrofoil development work is given in the 1990 and earlier editions of this book. As a result of Boeing's extensive hydrofoil programmes two principal vessel types evolved, the

The 1976-launched Acores *Jetfoil 929-100 in service on the Hong Kong to Macao route*   *1987*

235 ton NATO/PHM patrol boat (six built, 1977 to 1982) and the Jetfoil type of which, by January 1990, 39 had been built or ordered, including the Kawasaki vessels, almost entirely for ferry operations. Kawasaki has built 11 Jetfoil 929-117 craft.

Details of the NATO/PHM patrol boats are given in the 1992-93 edition of this book.

JETFOIL 929-100

This is a 110 ton water-jet propelled commercial hydrofoil for services in relatively rough waters. It employs a fully submerged, automatically controlled canard foil arrangement and is powered by two 2767 kW Allison 501-K20A gas-turbines. Normal foilborne cruising speed is 42 knots.

Typical interior arrangements include a commuter configuration with up to 350 seats and a tourist layout for 190 to 250 plus baggage.

Keel-laying of the first Jetfoil took place at the company's Renton, Washington, plant in January 1973 and the craft was launched in March 1974. After testing on Puget Sound and in the Pacific, the craft was delivered to Pacific Sea Transportation Ltd for inter-island services in Hawaii. High-speed foilborne tests began in Puget Sound in mid-July and it was reported that the vessel attained a speed of 48 knots during its runs.

During a rigorous testing programme to prove the boat's design and construction, Boeing No 001 operated for 470 hours, including 237 hours foilborne. The latter phase of testing was conducted in the rough waters of the straits of Juan de Fuca and the Pacific Ocean, where it encountered wave swells as high as 9.1 m, winds gusting up to 60 knots and wave chop averaging 1.8 m high.

The first operational Jetfoil service was successfully initiated in April 1975 by Far East Hydrofoil Company Ltd, Hong Kong, with Jetfoil 002, *Madeira*. Before this, the Jetfoil received its ABS classification, was certificated by the Hong Kong Marine Department and passed US Coast Guard certification trials. A US Coast Guard certificate was not completed as the craft would not be operating in US waters.

The first US service began in Hawaii in June 1975 and the tenth Jetfoil was launched in May 1977.

Principal Particulars

Length overall	27.4 m
Beam	9.5 m
Draught, hullborne	5 m
Displacement	110 t
Passengers	190-350
Fuel capacity	15 140 l
Propulsive power	2 × 2767 kW
Maximum speed	50 knots
Operational speed	42 knots
Operational limitation	3.65 m wave height

Structure: Hull and deckhouse in marine aluminium. Aircraft assembly techniques are used, including high-speed mechanised welding processes.

All structural components of the foil/strut system are in 15.5PH corrosion-resistant all-welded steel construction.

Propulsion: Power for the water-jet propulsion system is supplied by two Allison 501-K20A free-power gas-turbines, each rated at 2767 kW at 27°C at sea level. Each is connected to a Rocketdyne Powerjet 20 axial flow pump through a gearbox drive train. The system propels the craft in both foilborne and hullborne modes. When foilborne, water enters through the inlet at the forward lower end of the aft centre foil strut. At the top of the duct, the water is split into two paths and enters into each of the two axial flow pumps. It is then discharged at high pressure through nozzles in the hull bottom. The water path is the same during hullborne operations with the foils extended. When the foils are retracted, the water enters through a flush inlet located in the keel. Reversing and steering for hullborne operation only are accomplished by reverse-flow buckets located immediately aft of the water exit nozzles. A bow thruster is provided for positive steering control at low forward speeds.

A 15 140 litre integral fuel tank supplies the propulsion turbine and diesel engines. Coalescent-type water separating fuel filters and remote-controlled motor-operated fuel shut-off valves provide fire protection.

Electrical system: A 60 Hz, 440 V AC electrical system, supplied by two diesel-driven generators each rated at 62.5 kVA. Either is capable of supplying all vital electrical power. 90 kVA capacity shore connection facilities are provided and equipment can accept 50 Hz power. Transformer rectifier units for battery charging provide 28 V DC from the AC system.

Control: The foil system is a fully submerged canard arrangement with a single inverted T strut/foil forward and a three-strut, full-span foil aft. The forward foil assembly is rotated hydraulically through 7° in either direction for steering. All foils have trailing edge flaps for controlling pitch, roll and yaw and for take off and landing. Foils and struts retract hydraulically above the water-line, the bow foil forward, and the rear foil aft.

The craft is controlled by a three-axis automatic system while foilborne and during take off and

Craft built (Jetfoil 929-100)

Name	Launched	Current Operator
Flores (ex *Kalakoua*, 1978 Boeing No 001)	29 Mar 1974	Far East Hydrofoil Co Ltd, Hong Kong
Madeira (002)	Oct 1974	Far East Hydrofoil Co Ltd, Hong Kong
Corvo (ex *Kamehameha*) (003)	Feb 1975	Far East Hydrofoil Co Ltd, Hong Kong
Santa Maria (005)	Apr 1975	Far East Hydrofoil Co Ltd, Hong Kong
Pico (ex *Kuhio*) (004)	Jun 1975	Far East Hydrofoil Co Ltd, Hong Kong
São Jorge (ex *Jet Caribe I*) (006)	Dec 1975	Far East Hydrofoil Co Ltd, Hong Kong
Acores (ex *Jet Caribe II*, 1980, ex *Oriente*, 1978) (008)	Nov 1976	Far East Hydrofoil Co Ltd, Hong Kong
Urzela (ex *Flying Princess*) (007)	May 1976	Far East Hydrofoil Co Ltd, Hong Kong
Ponta Delgada (ex *Flying Princess II*) (010)	May 1977	Far East Hydrofoil Co Ltd, Hong Kong
Guia (ex *Okesa*)	Dec 1976	Far East Hydrofoil Co Ltd, Hong Kong

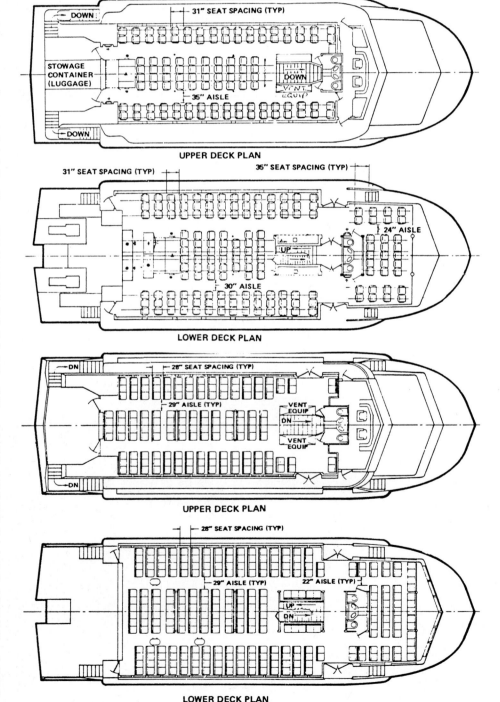

Jetfoil 929-100 interior arrangements

landing. The system senses the motion and position of the craft by gyros, accelerometers and height sensors, signals from which are combined in the control computer with manual commands from the helm. The resulting computer outputs provide control surface deflections through electrohydraulic servo actuators. Lift control is by full-span trailing edge flaps on each foil. Forward and aft flaps operate differentially to provide pitch variation and height control. Aft flaps operate differentially to provide roll control for changes of direction.

The vessel banks inwardly into all turns to ensure maximum passenger comfort. The ACS introduces the correct amount of bank and steering to co-ordinate the turn in full. Turn rates of up to 6°/s are attained within one second of providing a heading change command at the helm.

There are three basic controls required for foil-borne operation: the throttle is employed to set the speed, the height command lever to set the required foil depth, and the helm to set the required heading. If a constant course is required, a 'heading hold' circuit accomplishes this automatically.

For take off, the foil depth is set, the two throttles advanced and the hull clears the water in about 60 seconds. Acceleration continues until the craft automatically stabilises at the command depth and the speed dictated by the throttle setting. The throttle setting is reduced for landing, the craft settling as the speed drops. The speed normally diminishes from 45 knots (cruising speed) to 15 knots in approximately 30 seconds. In emergencies more rapid landings can be made by the use of the height command lever to provide hull contact within two seconds.

Quality of the ride in the craft is comparable with that of a Boeing 727 airliner. The vertical acceleration at the centre of gravity is very low and depends on sea state, for example, at 2 m significant wave height the vertical acceleration is only 0.05 g rms. Lateral acceleration is substantially less than vertical. Angles of pitch and roll are less than 1° rms. A structural fuse is provided which limits deceleration to less than 0.4 g longitudinally and 0.8 g vertically. In the event of the craft striking a major item of floating debris at full speed, the structural fuse, when actuated, allows the foil and strut to rotate backwards, preventing the system from sustaining significant damage.

Crew comprises a captain and first officer plus cabin attendants.

The last of the Jetfoil 929-100 series was the 010 *Flying Princess II*. The first of the improved 929-115 series, Jetfoil 011 *Mikado*, was launched at Renton, Washington in June 1978, and is operated by Sado Kisen in the Sea of Japan.

The improved model Jetfoil has a lighter structure allowing an increased payload and greater reliability, and is easier to maintain. Some of the modifications are listed below.

Principle Particulars

Length overall	27.4 m
Beam	9.5 m
Draught, hullborne	5.2 m
Displacement, maximum	117 t
Maximum speed	43 knots

Structure: The bow structure design has been simplified to provide equivalent strength with increased payload and bulkhead two has been revised for decreased stress levels. Based on a seven minute evacuation time in case of fire the following fire protection provisions have been made:

(1) Fibreglass is used for thermal insulation where required throughout the passenger accommodation areas

(2) Aluminium ceiling panels and air-conditioner sleeves are employed throughout, together with aluminium doors and frames

(3) One ½ in thick Marinite is employed in machinery spaces, with US Coast Guard-type felt added wherever required for insulation to comply with 30 minute fire test

(4) External stiffeners on the foil struts have been eliminated and the bow foil has been changed from constant section to tapered planform for improved performance. Stress levels have been reduced for extended life.

Propulsion: The propulsion system has been up-rated to operate at 2200 maximum intermittent

JETFOIL 929-115

Craft built (Jetfoil 929-115 type and conversions)

Name	Launched	Owner
Mikado (011)	Jun 1978	Sado Kisen Kaisha, Japan
Ginga (ex *Cu na Mara*)	Nov 1979	Sado Kisen Kaisha, Japan
Terceira (ex *Normandy Princess*)	Jan 1979	Far East Hydrofoil Co Ltd, Hong Kong
Funchal (ex *Jetferry One*)	May 1979	Far East Hydrofoil Co Ltd, Hong Kong
Horta (ex *Jetferry Two*) (016)	Mar 1980	Far East Hydrofoil Co Ltd, Hong Kong
Calcilhas (ex *Princesa Guayarmina*)	Nov 1980	Far East Hydrofoil Co Ltd, Hong Kong
Taipa (ex *Princesa Guacimara*)	Jul 1981	Far East Hydrofoil Co Ltd, Hong Kong
Bima Samudera I (Boeing No 022)	Oct 1981	PT PAL, Indonesia
Princesse Clementine	Feb 1981	Regie des Transports Maritimes, Belgium
Prinses Stephanie	Apr 1981	Regie des Transports Maritimes, Belgium
Jet 7 (ex *Spirit of Friendship*, ex *Aries*, ex *Montevideo Jet*)	Aug 1980	Kato Kisen Co Ltd/Kansai Kisen Co Ltd
Jet 8 (ex *Spirit of Discovery*)	Apr 1985	Kato Kisen Co Ltd/Kansai Kisen Co Ltd
- (modified to 929-119)	Aug 1984	Indonesian Government (Navy)
- (modified to 929-119)	Nov 1984	Indonesian Government
Lilau (ex *Speedy Princess 929-320*) (shipped 1986 to Hong Kong to be modified to type 929-320)	Jul 1979	Far East Hydrofoil Co Ltd, Hong Kong (*Speedy Princess* (ex British Royal Navy, *HMS Speedy*) was purchased in September 1986 by FEH (departed UK, 16 Oct 1986) and converted to a commercial passenger vessel)
- (modified to 929-120)	Jan 1986	Indonesian Government
- (modified to 929-120)	June 1986	Indonesian Government

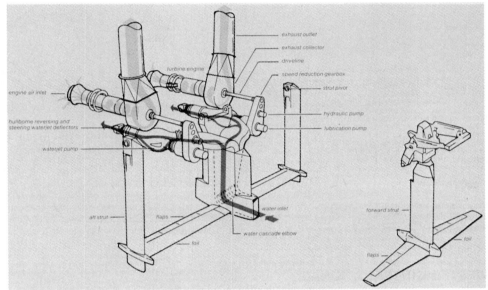

Principal elements of the Jetfoil propulsion and foil system   **1992**

Boeing Jetfoil 929-115 Cu na Mara *renamed* Ginga *and in service with Sado Kisen Kaisha*   **1987**

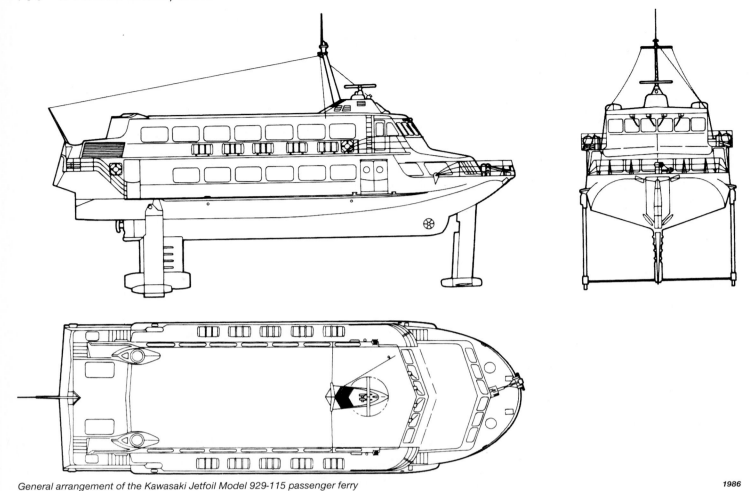

General arrangement of the Kawasaki Jetfoil Model 929-115 passenger ferry   1986

pump rpm with an increase of three tons in maximum gross weight.

JETFOIL 929-117

Since 1985 Boeing has not manufactured any model of the Jetfoil. The 929-117 model, an updated version, has been licensed for production outside the USA, with Kawasaki Heavy Industries Ltd, Kobe, Japan and PT PAL Indonesia. See Kawasaki entry for further details.

JETFOIL 929-320
Lilau (ex *Speedy Princess*, ex *HMS Speedy*)

The Jetfoil 929-320 was delivered to the Royal Navy in June 1980 for use in fisheries patrol in the North Sea. Named *HMS Speedy*, the craft was a modified Model 929-115 commercial Jetfoil and was built on the commercial Jetfoil production line. The craft was decommissioned by the Royal Navy in April 1982 and eventually sold to the Far East Hydrofoil Company Ltd (FEH) in the Autumn of 1986. The craft has been converted to passenger configuration and operates on their Hong Kong to Macao route.

UPDATED

WESTFOIL INTERNATIONAL

PO Box 1757, Westport, Washington 98595, USA

Telephone: +1 (206) 268 0117
Telefax: +1 (206) 268 0119

Randy Rust, *Representative*

WESTFOIL 25 m

Design started on the Westfoil 25 m fully submerged hydrofoil in the Autumn of 1986 and construction started during the Summer of 1987. The hull lines come from Westport Shipyard's latest mould, for a boat designed to meet the rigours of year round commercial service. The submerged foil and automatic control system are based on 25 years of hydrofoil experience by the designers using the latest proven technology to provide a ride which should be better than existing hydrofoils. The ducted air propellers provide thrust at low tip speed while the ducts have acoustical treatment to further reduce noise. Some parts of the design have now been patented.

Trials of the Westfoil 25 m hydrofoil started in the Summer of 1991.

Principal Particulars

Length overall	24.39 m
Beam	7.16 m
Draught, hullborne	4.88 m
Displacement	71.11 t
Passengers	149
Fuel capacity	5677 l
Water capacity	378 l
Propulsive power	4 × 805 kW
Maximum speed	42 knots

Westfoil 25 m hydrofoil   1992

Structure: The foils are Nitronic 50 stainless steel and composite structure.

Propulsion: Four DDC 12V-92 TA diesels with 145 type injectors, each 805 kW max, at 2300 rpm. Engine rpm is limited to 2100, driving two ducted air propellers by Pacific Propeller Inc with low tip speed variable-pitch propellers.

Control: The foils are arranged in a canard arrangement. The front and aft foil and strut systems can be retracted independently.

An Automatic Control System (ACS) includes the flaps located at the trailing edges of both the fore and aft foils, the front strut rudder, the foil flap actuation system and the automatic stabilisation and control system. The foil flaps provide control of the craft in pitch, roll and yaw to provide a smooth ride in all seas up to design sea conditions and for take off and landing. The foil flap actuators use input from the automatic stabilisation and control system to select the angle of the foil flaps so that the wave motions are counteracted. Flaps are moved in response to helm control to turn the boat in a banked attitude. The automatic stabilisation and control system employs a computer, motion sensors, a height sensor and gyroscopes to generate the commands sent to the actuators so that the foil flaps move to maintain the desired stable attitude and foil depth.

Foilborne steering is accomplished by actuating the aft flaps differentially (in response to helm commands) to roll the boat into a turn with appropriate front strut rudder setting to maintain a co-ordinated turn. The flaps and front strut rudder settings will be maintained by the ACS in response to helm commands and motion and height sensor feedback.

Hullborne steering utilises an Arneson drive system for hullborne steering and reversing. A bow thruster is installed.

The start, idle, power management and shut down, propeller pitch, boat direction, foilborne or hullborne mode selection and strut extension/retraction controls are located for one-man operation in the wheelhouse. In addition, hullborne controls are located on each bridge wing. Engine instrumentation is located in the wheelhouse.

Auxiliary systems: Air-conditioning and heating is installed.

VERIFIED

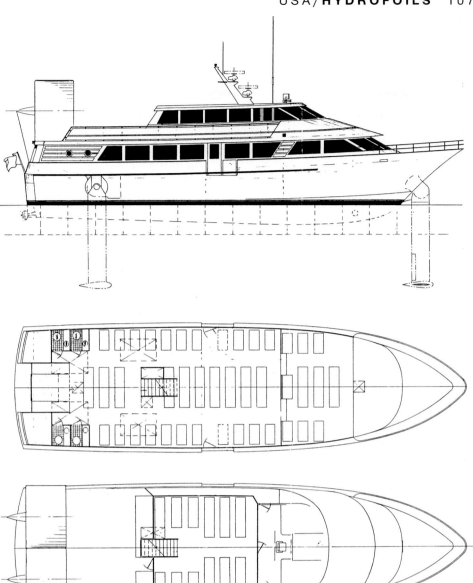

Provisional general arrangement of Westfoil 25 m

HIGH-SPEED MULTIHULL VESSELS

Company Listing by Country

Australia
Alufast International Pty Ltd
Astra Bay Enterprises
Atlay Catamarans Australia Pty Ltd (Cougar Catamarans)
Austal Ships Pty Ltd
Ferries Australia
Incat Australia Pty Ltd
Lloyd's Ships Holdings Pty Ltd
NQEA Australia Pty Ltd
Oceanfast Pty Ltd
Sabre Catamarans Pty Ltd
SBF Engineering
Wavemaster International Pty Ltd

China, People's Republic
Hang Tong High Speed Ship Development Co Ltd

Commonwealth of Independent States
Almaz Shipyard Central Marine Design Bureau
Sudoexport

Chile
Asenav MR

Denmark
Danyard A/S

Finland
Finnyards Ltd

France
CMN
Constructions Aluminium Navales Sarl

Germany
HDW
Ultimar GmbH & Co KG

Hong Kong
A Fai Engineers and Shiprepairers Ltd

Italy
Moschini
Rodriquez Cantieri Navali SpA

Japan
Hitachi Zosen Corporation
IHI
Kawasaki Heavy Industries Ltd Ship Group
Mitsubishi Heavy Industries Ltd
Mitsui Engineering & Shipbuilding Company Ltd
NKK Corporation
Yamaha Motor Company Ltd

Korea, South
Daewoo Shipbuilding and Heavy Machinery Ltd
Hyundai Heavy Industries Company Ltd
Korea Tacoma Marine Industries Ltd

Netherlands
Royal Schelde BV
Tille Shipyards
Van Der Giessen-de Noord

Norway
Båtservice Holding A/S
CPS Production A/S
CPS Drive A/S

Holen Mek Verksted A/S
Hydrocat Techno A/S
Kværner a.s. Fast Ferries
Kværner Fjellstrand A/S
Lindstøls Skips- & Båtbyggeri A/S
Rosendal Verft A/S
Westamarin A/S
Westamarin West A/S

Singapore
Aluminium Craft (88) Pte Ltd
Kværner Fjellstrand (S) Pte Ltd
Marinteknik Shipbuilders (S) Pte Ltd
Singapore Shipbuilding and Engineering Ltd

South Africa
Teknicraft Design

Sweden
Oskarshamns Varv AB

Thailand
Italthai Marine Ltd

United Kingdom
Aluminium Shipbuilders Ltd
FBM Marine Group

United States of America
Allen Marine, Inc
Gladding-Hearn Shipbuilding
Nichols Brothers Boat Builders Inc
Peterson Builders Inc
USA Catamarans Inc

AUSTRALIA

ALUFAST INTERNATIONAL PTY LTD

Lot 5, Clarence Beach Road, Coogee, Western Australia, 6166

Telephone: +61 (9) 437 3033
Telefax: +61 (9) 437 3110

John Mason, *Managing Director*
Simon Thornton, *Production Technical Director*

Alufast International is a builder of high-speed welder aluminium ferries. The company specialises in the construction of total vessels or complete hulls with final assembly and componentry fabrication carried out in overseas shipyards. It also provides a refurbishment refit service for ferries throughout the world with the work carried out in its shipyards in Australia and China.

They currently have two vessels under construction:

Nansha 38
Nansha 68

These two vessels are 42 m aluminium ferries which will achieve full load speeds of over 43 knots and lightship speeds of approximately 48 knots. They were designed to provide a high quality and fast transportation link between Hong Kong and the city of Nansha which is 48 nautical miles from Hong Kong, in just over an hour.

Principle Particulars

Length overall	42.0 m
Length waterline	36.0 m
Beam	12.0 m
Draught	1.5 m
Crew	12
Passengers	280
Fuel capacity	12 000 l
Water capacity	1250 l
Maximum speed	48 knots
Operational speed	43.5 knots

Classification: China Classification Society (CCS), in accordance with IMO res A373X, 1978.
Structure: Marine grade aluminium (MIG welded).
Propulsion: The main engines are 4 × MTU 16V 396 TE 74L diesels; driving 4 × KaMeWa 63 S62.6 waterjets; via 4 × Reintjes VLJ 930 gearboxes.

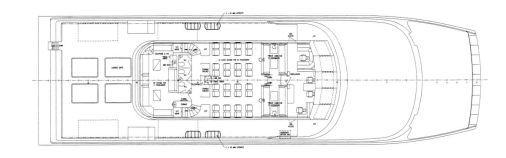

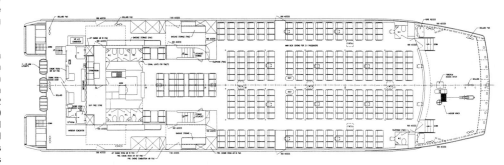

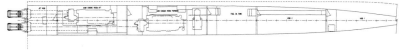

NEW ENTRY   *General arrangement of* Nansha 38 and 68   *1995*

ASTRA BAY ENTERPRISES

4 Sultan Way, Rous Head, North Fremantle, Western Australia

Telephone: +61 (430) 6336
Telefax: +61 (430) 6338

Ian Mcintosh, *Managing Director*
Simon Clifford, *Manager*
Arthur Broere, *Project Manager*

Astra Bay Enterprises was formed by Condor marine as a seperate company to build the designs of Advanced Multihull Designs (AMD), under a licensing agreement.

An AMD 350 wave piercing catamaran is being constructed at present, for delivery in March 1995.

AMD350 under construction at the Astra Bay facilities
1995

AMD 350 wave-piercing catamaran
Principle Particulars

Length overall	42.5 m
Beam	12.2 m
Draught	1.4 m
Passengers	250-400
Propulsive power	2 × 1960 kW
Maximum speed	32 knots
Operational speed	32 knots

Classification: Det Norske Veritas +1A1 HSLC R2 EO.

Propulsion: The main engines are 2 × MTU V16 396, each driving a KaMeWa 71SII water-jet.

NEW ENTRY

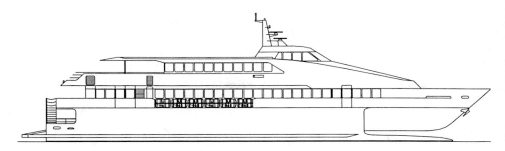

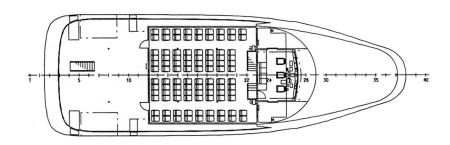

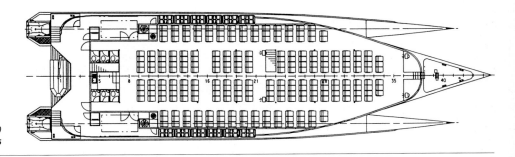

General arrangement of AMD 350
1995

ATLAY CATAMARANS AUSTRALIA PTY LTD (COUGAR CATAMARANS)

39-41 Activity Crescent, Ernest Junction, Southport 4214, Australia

Telephone: +61 (75) 392244/392482
Telex: 43470 AA
Telefax: +61 (75) 971075

Harry Roberts, *Managing Director*
Elizabeth Hay, *Export Manager*

Cougar Catamarans has been in continuous operation for some 24 years and has designs available for boats between 7.5 and 39 m in length. Speeds are typically in the range of 20 to 35 knots.

Whitsunday Freedom
A 14.6 m, 27 knot catamaran ferry delivered in 1988 to the Whitsunday Water Taxis company. Six Cougar Catamaran boats have been delivered to this operator.

Principal Particulars

Length overall	14.6 m
Crew	3
Passengers	60
Propulsive power	2 × 304 kW
Maximum speed	27 knots
Operational speed	22-23 knots

Propulsion: Engines: 2 × MAN 2866 LE diesels.

Encore
A 16.15 m catamaran servicing South Strabroke Island on the Gold Coast, Queensland.

Principal Particulars

Length	16.15 m
Beam	5.18 m
Crew	57+ (inshore)
	23 (offshore)

Propulsion: Engines: 2 × 266 kW Volvo diesels.
Auxiliary power: 8.5 kVA.

San Bei
A 27.2 m catamaran ferry delivered in 1994 to Shanghai, China.

San Bei   *1995*

Principal Particulars

Length overall	27.2 m
Passengers	220
Crew	5
Maximum speed	31 knots
Operational speed	27 knots

Propulsion: Engines: 2 × 820 kW Detroit Diesel 16V 9TA.
Auxilliary systems: 2 × 50 kVA Perkins generators.

Yun Tong
A 32 m catamaran ferry delivered in 1994 to Shanghai, China.

Principal Particulars

Length overall	32 m
Beam	8.38 m
Passengers	266
Crew	5
Propulsive power	2 × 1342 kW
Maximum speed	32 knots
Operational speed	28 knots

Propulsion: Engines: 2 × 1342 kW Detroit Diesel 16V 149TI.
Auxilliary systems: 2 × 67 kVA Perkins generators.

Ying Bin 5

A 25 m catamaran ferry delivered in 1993 to Hong Kong.

Principal Particulars

Length overall	25 m
Beam	8.38 m
Passengers	200
Crew	5
Maximum speed	28 knots
Operational speed	25 knots

Propulsion: Engines: 2 × 820 kW Detroit Diesel 16V 92TA.

Auxilliary systems: 2 × 37 kVA Isuzu generators.

UPDATED

Yun Tong
1995

AUSTAL SHIPS PTY LTD

100 Clarence Beach Road, Henderson, Perth, Western Australia, Australia 6166

Telephone: +61 (9) 410 1111
Telefax: +61 (9) 410 2564

John Rothwell, *Managing Director*
Christopher Norman, *Director, Marketing and Sales*
Garry Heys, *Director and General Manager*
Kevin Stanley, *Director and General Manager*

Since commencing operation in 1988, Austal has earned an international reputation as the world's leading manufacturer of custom designed, high-performance aluminium passenger catamarans and cruise ships. With delivery of their 22nd high-speed catamaran to China (including three revolutionary 40 m gas-turbine vessels) and an $18 million ship-yard expansion project, 1994 has been a year of achievement for aluminium shipbuilder Austal Ships.

34 m CATAMARAN
Bali Hai

Delivered in March 1990 to run day cruises from Bali to the islands of Nusa Penida and Lembongan. *Bali Hai* is constructed in aluminium and designed to carry 300 passengers at 20 knots.

Principal Particulars

Length overall	33.6 m
Length waterline	30.7 m
Beam	10.8 m
Draught	1.95 m
Crew	8
Passengers	300
Fuel capacity	16 000 l
Water capacity	4000 l
Propulsive power	2 × 735 kW
Operational speed	20 knots

Classification: DnV.
Structure: Hull, superstructure and deck construction material: marine grade aluminium alloy.

Vessel	Engines	Hull No	Length	Seats	Delivery date	Operating country
Bali Hai	2 × MAN D2842 LYE 735 kW each	3	33.6 m	300	March 1990	Indonesia
Tong Zhou	2 × MTU 16V 396 TB 83 1470 kW each	8	38.0 m	430	November 1990	China
Shun Shui	2 × MWM TBD 604B V16 1680 kW each	18	40.1 m	354	January 1991	China
Equator Triangle	2 × Caterpillar 3516 TA 1430 kW each	14	40.1 m	216	July 1991	Singapore
Shun De	2 × MWM TBD 604B V16 1680 kW each	28	40.1 m	354	February 1992	China
Xin Duan Zhou	2 × MTU 16V396 TE 74L 1825 kW each	38	40.1 m	338	February 1992	China
Zhuhai	2 × MWM TBD 604B V16 1680 kW each	288	40.1 m	338	May 1992	China
Nan Gui	2 × MTU 16V 396 TE 74L 1825 kW each	48	40.1 m	338	August 1992	China
Kai Ping	2 × MWM 16V 396 TE 74L 1920 kW each	68	39.9 m	318	September 1992	China
Cui Heng Hu		78	39.9 m	354	November 1992	China
Lian Shan Hu		88	39.9 m	354	November 1992	China
Nan Xing		98	39.9 m	338	March 1993	China
Hai Chang		99	39.9 m	338	March 1993	China
Hui Yang*		100	39.9 m	368	July 1993	China
Tai Shan*		101	39.9 m	354	July 1993	China
Gang Zhou		102	39.9 m	318	September 1993	China
Gao Ming		103	39.9 m	338	September 1993	China
Gui Feng		109	39.9 m	318	December 1993	China
San Bu		110	39.9 m	338	December 1993	China
Bali Hai II*	2 × MTU 12V 396 TE 74L 1470 kW each	15	35.7 m	337	April 1994	Singapore
Shun Jing	2 × Textron Lycoming gas-turbines	105	39.9 m	354	March 1994	China
Lian Gang Hu	2 × Textron Lycoming gas-turbines	106	39.9 m	354	March 1994	China
Yi Xian Hu	2 × Textron Lycoming gas-turbines	108	39.9 m	354	March 1994	China
Free Flying*	2 × MTU 12V 396 TE 74L 1960 kW each	168	40.1 m	450	April 1994	China
Xin He Shan	2 × MTU 12V 396 TE 74L 1940 kW each	111	40.1 m	300	August 1994	China
Zhong Shan	2 × Textron Lycoming gas-turbines	115	40.1 m	354	December 1994	China
	4 × MTU 16V 396 TE 74L 1960 kW	39	43.0 m	331	May 1995	Japan

*Fitted with Austal 'Ocean Leveller' ride control system.

Propulsion: Engines: 2 × MAN D284 2LYE diesels developing 735 kW each at 2300 rpm.

36 m CATAMARAN
Bali Hai II

Bali Hai II is the second catamaran to be built for Tropic Charterers Pte Ltd to run day cruises from Bali to the islands of Nusa Penida and Lembongan. This vessel was delivered in April 1994.

Principal Particulars

Length overall	35.7 m
Beam	10.5 m
Draught	1.2 m
Crew	8
Passengers	322
Fuel capacity	12 000 l
Water capacity	6000 l
Propulsive power	2 × 1470 kW
Operational speed	29 knots

Structure: Hull, superstructure and deck construction material: aluminium alloy.
Propulsion: Main engines: 2 × MTU 12V 396 TE 74L diesels rated at 1470 kW each at 1940 rpm, driving 2 × MJP J650R DD water-jets.

38 m CATAMARAN
Tong Zhou

In June 1987, Austal Ships secured a contract for the construction of a 38 m, 430 passenger catamaran ferry for the Nantong High-Speed Passenger Ship Company in China. Valued at A$5.5 million, the delivery was in November 1990. The vessel is fitted with two MJP water-jet units.

Principal Particulars

Length overall	38 m
Length waterline	32.4 m
Beam	11.8 m
Draught	1.3 m
Displacement, maximum	145 t
Fuel capacity	2 × 7500 l tanks
Water capacity	1200 l
Crew	12
Passengers	430
Maximum speed	30 knots

Bali Hai II   *1995*

Structure: Hull, superstructure and deck construction material: marine grade aluminium alloy.
Propulsion: Main engines: 2 × MTU 16V 396 TB83 marine diesels developing 1470 kW each at 1940 rpm. 2 × MJP J650R water-jet units.

40 m CATAMARAN
Shun Shui

Shun Gang Passenger Transportation Company operates this vessel between Hong Kong Harbour and Shun De in mainland China.
Principal Particulars

Length overall	40.1 m
Beam	13.3 m
Displacement, maximum	162 t
Crew	8
Passengers	354
Fuel capacity	10 000 l
Water capacity	1500 l
Propulsive power	2 × 1680 kW
Maximum speed	31.4 knots

Structure: Hull, superstructure and deck construction material: marine grade aluminium alloy.
Propulsion: Main engines: 2 × MWM TBD 604B V16 diesels 1680 kW each at 1800 rpm, driving 2 × KaMeWa 71S water-jets.

Shun Shui   *1994*

Tong Zhou   *1994*

Equator Triangle   *1994*

Xin Duan Zhou   *1993*

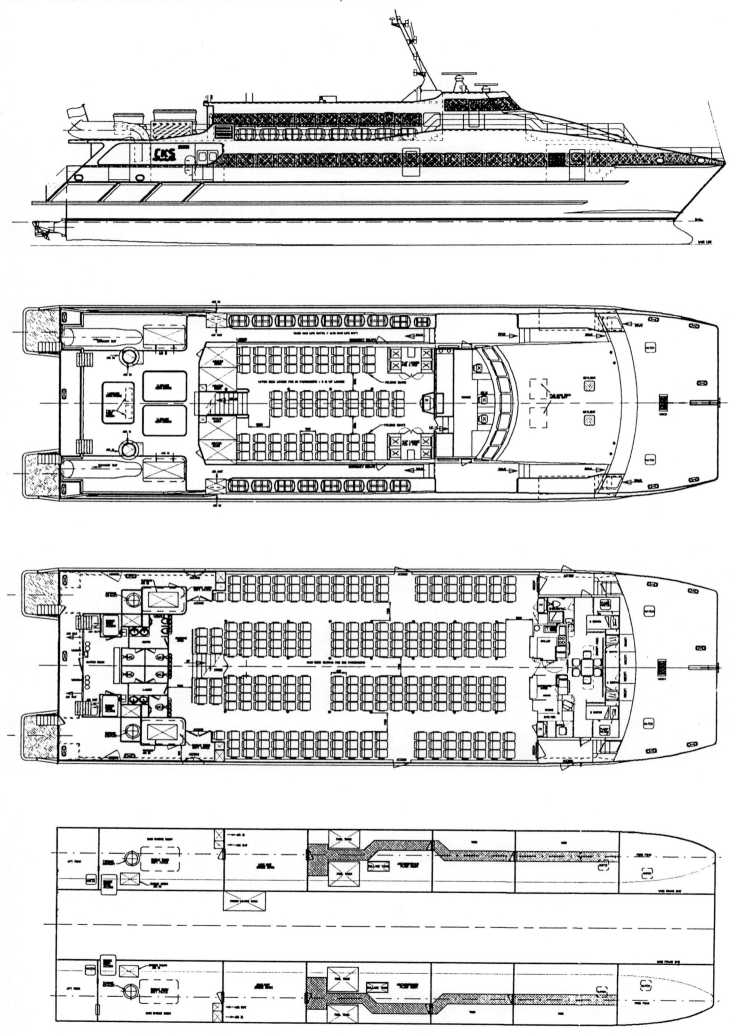

Austal 40 m gas-turbine catamaran general arrangement

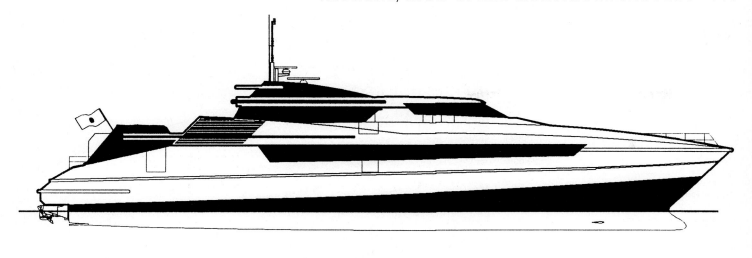

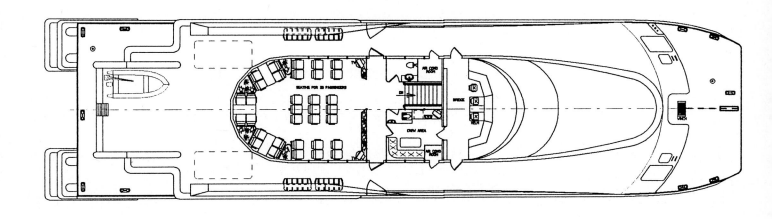

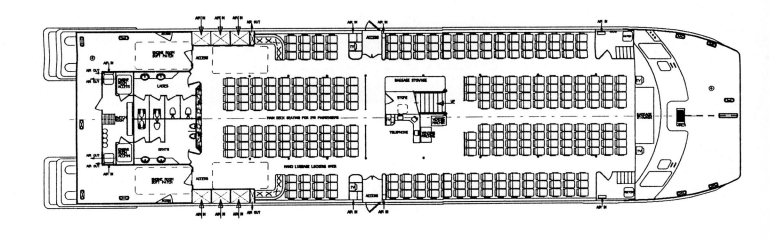

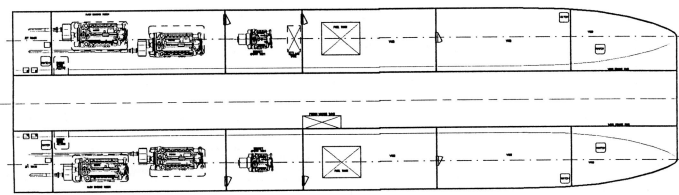

Austal 43 m catamaran general arrangement

1995

40 m CATAMARAN
Equator Triangle
Principal Particulars

Length overall	40.1 m
Beam	13.3 m
Draught	2.4 m
Displacement, maximum	176 t
Crew	34
Passengers	216
Fuel capacity	4 × 5000 l
Water capacity	2 × 5000 l
Propulsive power	2 × 1430 kW
Maximum speed	25.5 knots

Structure: Hull, superstructure and deck construction material: marine grade aluminium alloy.

Propulsion: Main engines: 2 × Caterpillar 3516 TA diesels, 1430 kW each at 1800 rpm, driving fixed-pitch propellers.

40 m CATAMARAN
Xin Duan Zhou
Owned by Zhao Gang Steamer Navigation Company, this vessel operates from Zhao Qing port, China.

Principal Particulars

Length overall	40.1 m
Length waterline	35.4 m
Beam	11.5 m
Draught	1.4 m
Crew	12
Passengers	338
Fuel	10 000 l
Water capacity	1500 l
Propulsive power	2 × 1825 kW
Maximum speed	32 knots

Structure: Hull material: aluminium alloy. Superstructure material: aluminium alloy.

Propulsion: Engines: 2 × MTU 16V 396 TE 74L diesels, 1825 kW each.

Transmissions: 2 × Reintjes VLJ930 gearboxes.

Thrust devices: 2 × KaMeWa 71S water-jets.

Auxiliary systems: Engines: 2 × MTU 6V 183 AA51 diesels, 98 kW each.

40 m CATAMARAN
Shun De
Owned by Shun Gang Passenger Transportation Corporation, this vessel operates from Rong Qi port, China.

Principal Particulars

Length overall	40.1 m
Length waterline	35.4 m
Beam	12.9 m
Draught	1.4 m
Crew	12
Passengers	354
Fuel capacity	10 000 l
Water capacity	1500 l
Propulsive power	2 × 1680 kW
Maximum speed	31.5 knots

Structure: Hull material: aluminium alloy. Superstructure material: aluminium alloy.

Propulsion: Engines: 2 × MWM TBD 604B V16 diesels, 1680 kW each.

Transmissions: 2 × ZF BU755 2.235:1 reduction gearboxes.

Thrust devices: 2 × KaMeWa 71S water-jets.

Auxiliary systems: Engines: 2 × MTU 6V 183 AA51 diesels, 98 kW each.

40 m CATAMARAN
Nan Gui
Owned by Ping Gang Passenger Transportation Corporation, this vessel operates from Fu Shan port, China.

Principal Particulars

Length overall	40.1 m
Length waterline	35.4 m
Beam	11.5 m
Draught	1.4 m
Crew	12 (8 berths)
Passengers	338
Fuel capacity	9000 l
Water capacity	1500 l
Propulsive power	2 × 1825 kW
Maximum speed	34 knots
Operational speed	32 knots
Range	300 nm

Structure: Hull material: aluminium alloy.

Xin He Shan   *1995*

Free Flying   *1995*

Superstructure material: aluminium alloy.

Propulsion: Engines: 2 × MTU 16V 396 TE 74L diesels.

Transmissions: 2 × ZF BU755 gearboxes.

Thrust devices: 2 × KaMeWa 71SII water-jets.

Auxiliary systems: Engines: 2 × MTU 6V 183 AA51 diesels, 98 kW each

Electrical systems: 380 V/220 V 50 Hz AC, 24 V DC

40 m CATAMARAN
Zhuhai
Owned by Jiuzhou Port Administration Group, this vessel operates from Zhuhai port, China.

Principal Particulars

Length overall	40.1 m
Length waterline	35.4 m
Beam	11.5 m
Draught	1.46 m
Crew	12
Passengers	338
Fuel capacity	9000 l
Water capacity	1500 l
Propulsive power	2 × 1680 kW
Operational speed	32
Range	265 nm

Structure: Hull material: aluminium alloy. Superstructure material: aluminium alloy.

Propulsion: Engines: 2 × MWM TBD 604B V16 diesels.

Transmissions: 2 × ZF BU755 gearboxes.

Thrust devices: 2 × KaMeWa 71S II water-jets.

Auxiliary systems: Engines: 2 × MTU 6V 183 AA51 diesels, 98 kW each.

40 m CATAMARAN
Kai Ping Class
Eleven of these craft have been delivered to various owners in China.

Principal Particulars

Length overall	39.9 m
Length waterline	35 m
Beam	10 m
Draught	1.4 m
Crew	12
Passengers	318-368
Fuel capacity	10 000 l
Water capacity	1500 l
Propulsive power	2 × 1580 kW
Operational speed	32 knots

Structure: Hull material: aluminium alloy. Superstructure material: aluminium alloy.

Propulsion: Engines: 2 × MTU 16V 396 TE 74 diesels, 1580 kW each.

Transmissions: 2 × Reintjes VLJ930 gearboxes.

Thrust devices: 2 × KaMeWa 71S water-jets.

Auxiliary systems: Engines: 2 × MTU 6V 183 AA51 diesels, 98 kW each.

Electrical system: 380 V/220 V 50 Hz AC, 24 V DC.

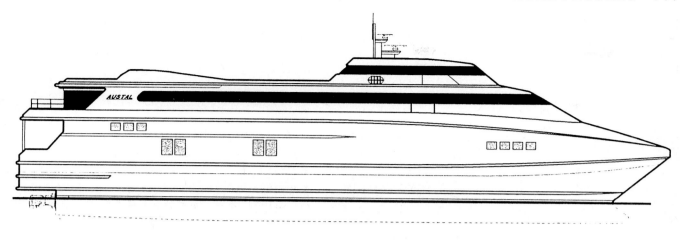

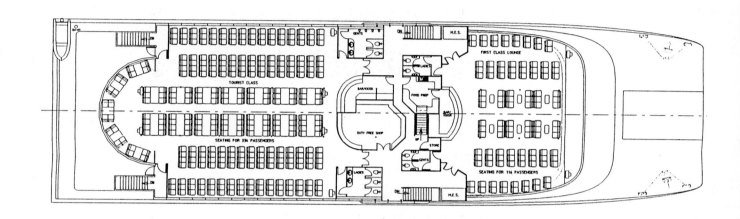

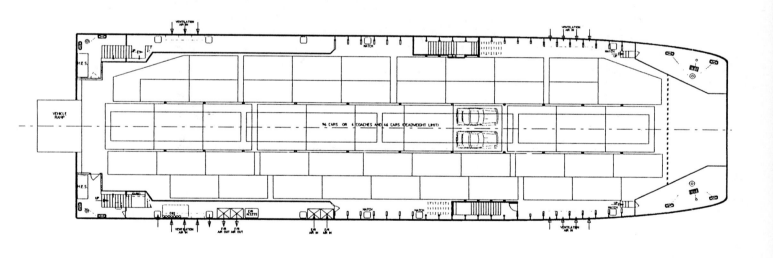

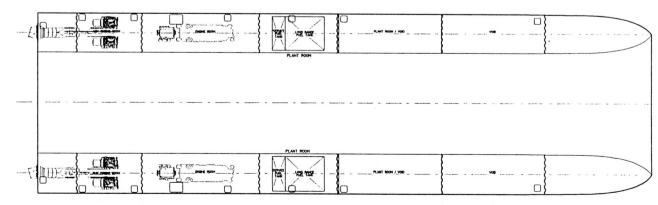

General arrangement of the 59 m Vehicle Passenger catamaran

1995

Nan Gui   *1994*

Kai Ping   *1994*

40 m GAS-TURBINE CATAMARAN CLASS

Four of these vessels have been constructed, *Shun Jing, Lian Gang Hu, Yi Xian Hu,* and *Zhong Shan,* all for Chinese owners.

Principal Particulars

Length overall	40.0 m
Length waterline	35.0 m
Beam	11.5 m
Draught	1.4 m
Crew	12
Passengers	354
Fuel capacity	10 000 l
Water capacity	1500 l
Propulsive power	2 × 2570 kW
Maximum speed	39.5 knots

Propulsion: These vessels are powered by two Textron Lycoming TF40 gas-turbines rated at 2570 kW at 15400 rpm. Each turbine drives through a MAAG MPG-80 gearbox to a KaMeWa 71S water-jet. (For Zhong Shan the gearbox is a Cincinnati Gear MA-107 model).

Auxiliary systems: Two MTU 6V 183 AA51 diesel generators rated at 98 kW at 1500 rpm.

43 m CATAMARAN

This craft is the largest passenger only catamaran under construction at Austal Ships and is scheduled to be delivered to the Diamond Ferry Company in Japan in mid-1995.

Principal Particulars

Length overall	43.0 m
Length waterline	37.7 m
Beam	11.2 m
Draught	1.3 m
Crew	6
Passengers	331
Fuel capacity	14 000 l
Water capacity	1500 l
Propulsive power	7840 kW
Maximum speed	42.5 knots

Propulsion: The vessel is powered by four MTU 16V 396 TE 74L diesels each driving through a ZF BU755-D reduction gearbox to a KaMeWa 63S11 water-jet.

Gas-turbine propelled *Shun Jing, Lian Gang Hu* and *Yi Xian Hu*   *1995*

59 m VEHICLE/PASSENGER CATAMARAN

This vessel was ordered by Hebrides Ships Limited of Vanuator in November 1994 and will be chartered to EMINRE AS, an Estonian Joint Venture Company for operation in the Baltic Sea. The vessel design is based on the Ferries Australia 79 m catamaran and is scheduled to be delivered in November 1995.

Principal Particulars

Length overall	59.9 m
Length waterline	55.0 m
Beam	17 m
Draught	2.0 m
Crew	12
Passengers	450
Vehicles	96 cars
Fuel capacity	20 000 l
Water capacity	2000 l
Propulsive power	13 000 kW
Operational speed	37 knots

Classification: Det Norske Veritas.

Propulsion: Main Engines: 2 × MTU V20 1163 diesel engines driving. 2 KaMeWa water-jets.

UPDATED

FERRIES AUSTRALIA

100 Clarence Beach Road, Henderson, Perth, Western Australia, Australia 6166

Telephone: +61 (9) 410 1111
Telefax: +61 (9) 410 2564

Chris Norman, *Managing Director*

Ferries Australia is a joint venture between Austal Ships and Oceanfast, both of Western Australia, and was formed to serve the growing demand for lightweight, large capacity vehicle and passenger carrying vessels, particularly those over 60 m in length.

The joint venture was formed in early 1994 on the basis of a contract to build the first in a new series of 79 m Super Seacat for Sea Containers Ltd. The craft

is being built at the Austal Ships yard where the new facilities will include two 100 m × 65 m building sheds, a 2000 tonne slipway and a 150 m commissioning dock.

79 m SUPER SEACAT

The design of this vessel is based on the Austal semi-Swath round bilge hull and incorporates the use of the company's 'Ocean Leveller' stabilisation system. With the main structure built entirely of aluminium, the outfit of the vessel incorporates many advanced material components such as ceramic fibre fire protection insulation and carbon fibre propulsion shafting. The first vessel is scheduled for delivery in mid-1995 and is expected to operate on the cross-channel, Folkestone to Boulogne route between the UK and France. Contracts for another four vessels are expected to follow this first delivery.

Principal Particulars

Length overall	78.68 m
Length waterline	68.50 m
Beam	23 m
Draught	2.4 m
Crew	24
Passengers	600
Vehicles	184 cars or
	64 cars + 10 coaches
Fuel capacity	60 000 l
Water capacity	4000 l
Operational speed	38 knots
Range	360 nm

Propulsion: The main propulsion consists of quadruple Ruston 16 RK270 diesel engines each driving a KMW water-jet via Reintjes VLJ 4430 reduction gearboxes.

Electrical system: Electrical power is provided by four Caterpillar 3406T/SR4 rated at 200 kW each.

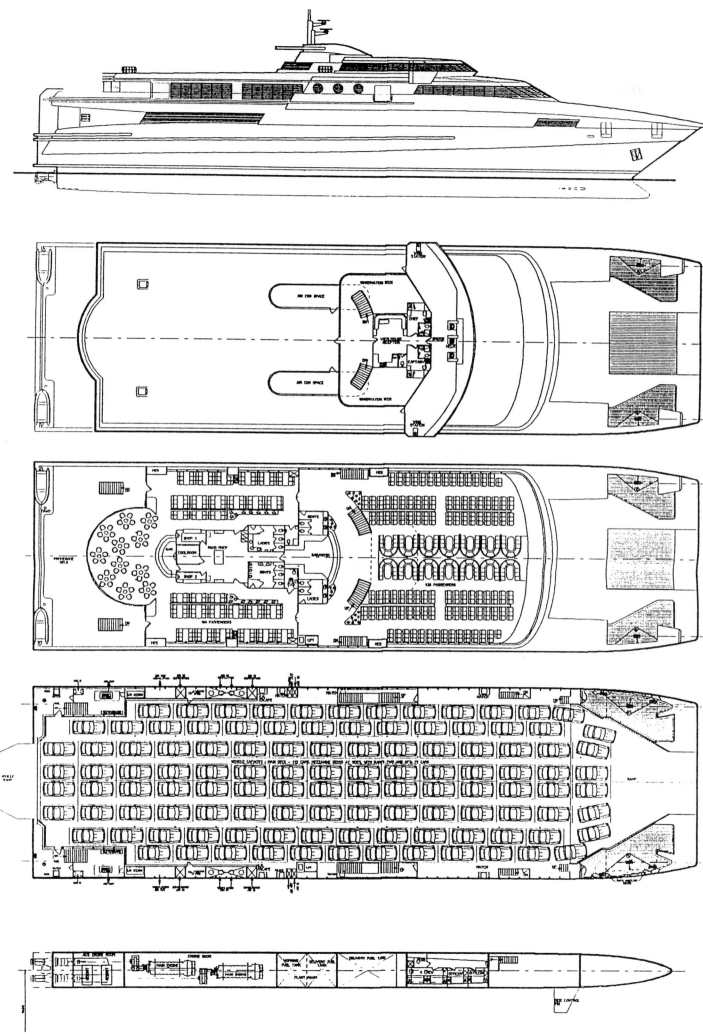

79 m Super Seacat, general arrangement

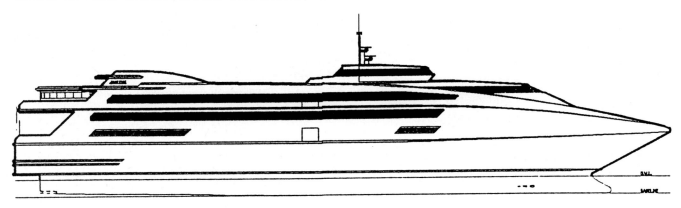

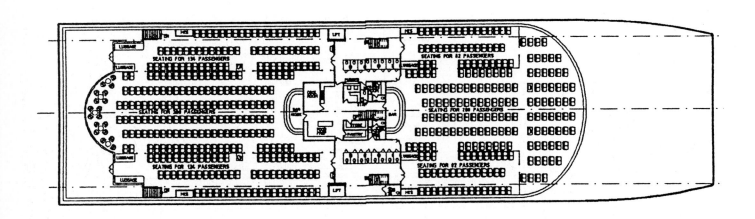

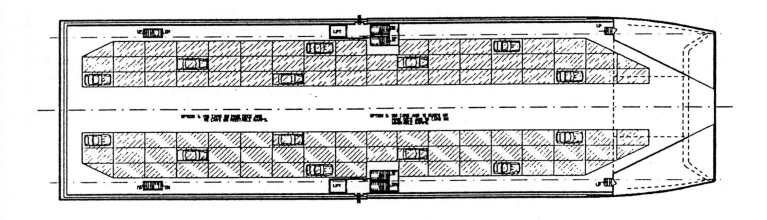

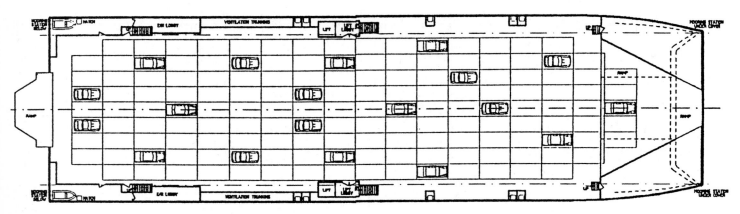

94 m vehicle/passenger ferry, general arrangement (design)

1995

79 m Super Seacat, artist's impression

1995

79 m Super Seacat, under construction at Austal Ships

1995

94 m VEHICLE PASSENGER FERRY
(DESIGN)

This large vehicle/passenger ferry design is based on the smaller 79 m craft currently under construction. The design has a substantial carrying capacity with a similar maximum speed.

Principal Particulars

Length overall	93.6 m
Length waterline	78.8 m
Beam	27 m
Draught	2.5 m
Passengers	1000
Vehicles	252 cars or
	198 cars + 12 buses

NEW ENTRY

INCAT AUSTRALIA PTY LTD

18 Bender Drive, Moonah, Tasmania 7009, Australia

Telephone: +61 (02) 730677
Telefax: +61 (02) 730932

Robert Clifford, *Chairman and Managing Director*

The building of InCat designs has been proceeding for over 18 years. As well as craft being built at the Hobart facilities, builders have been licensed in Australia, Hong Kong, the UK and the USA. There were 15 conventional high-speed catamarans and 15 wave-piercing catamarans built at Hobart in the years 1977 to 1995 for ferry services worldwide.

In 1983 InCat Designs conceived a design for a wave-piercing catamaran and an 8.7 m test craft was built. This craft, *Little Devil*, first underwent trials in 1984 and the results obtained allowed InCat to proceed with a 28 m wave-piercing catamaran, the *Spirit of Victoria*, which has been in commercial operation since mid-1985. This craft was followed by *Tassie Devil 2001* launched in December 1986, a 31 m wave-piercing catamaran of similar construction to its predecessor but with enclosed side supports and improved appearance. It operated in the rough waters off Perth during the America's Cup races. Continuing catamaran development has been concentrated by International Catamaran Designs Pty Ltd on the passenger/vehicle market and nine 74 m passenger/vehicle ferries have now been delivered by InCat Australia Pty Ltd. The first of these, *Hoverspeed Great Britain,* became a holder of the Hales Trophy for the Blue Riband of the Atlantic, achieved in June 1990 during its delivery from Hobart, Tasmania to Portsmouth, UK. Since that time two larger 78 m versions have been delivered. Two further car-carrying catamarans of over 70 m in length and with speeds well in excess of 50 knots, have also been built making InCat Australia the most prolific builder of large fast catamarans in the world.

78 m WAVE-PIERCING CATAMARAN

Direct developments of the 74 m design, three of these vessels are currently under construction.

Principal Particulars

Length overall	77.76 m
Length water-line	64.05 m
Beam	26 m
Hull beam	4.33 m
Draught	3.1 m
Displacement	900 t
Passengers	600

InCat 74 m Condor 10 at the InCat shipyard in Hobart.   **1995**

Vehicles	150
Propulsive power	4 × 4320 kW
Maximum speed	43 knots
Operational speed	35 knots
Fuel consumption	3400 l/h

Classification: The vessels are built to Det Norske Veritas Class +1A1 HSLC which generally comply with SOLAS 83 and IMO Dynamically Supported Craft Code as appropriate.

Structure: The vessel is constructed from marine grade aluminium alloys. Each waterborne hull is sub-divided into seven watertight compartments. These are connected by an arched bridging structure with a central forward hull above the smooth water loaded waterline.

An aluminium superstructure supported on vibration damping mounts provides seating for up to 600 passengers and crew. A full width wheelhouse is provided with central and wing positions for docking.

Propulsion: The vessel is powered by 2 × 2 conventional high-speed diesel engines. Ruston 16 RK270 or Caterpillar 3616 engines are standard. Each engine directly drives a transom-mounted water-jet (Lips IR115DX is standard) providing an arrangement for thrust vectoring and jet reverse and steering.

Electrical system: Two generators in each hull (4 × 145 kW total) feed associated independent main switchboards which are capable of disconnection in an emergency. The built-in redundancy provides a high level of security for operation of safety services. The standard AC supply and distribution system is a 415/240 V three-phase wire neutral earth system without hull return. Under normal operating con-

ditions the two main switchboards are linked by a bus tie which allows variable sequencing of all switchboards. In the event of the loss of one side, the bus tie can be tripped to provide complete isolation of the main switchboards.

74 m WAVE-PIERCING CATAMARAN

In January 1991, five of these vessels were ordered, four for Hoverspeed Ltd, a subsidiary of Sea Containers Ltd, and one for Tasmanian Ferry Services for the Bass Strait crossing. The first two were ordered by Sea Containers on 18 September 1988 and the next two on 26 January 1990. The vessels had an approximate price of A$20 million each. Of exceptional interest is the decision to employ relatively heavy, medium-speed diesel engines in an advanced lightweight aluminium vessel structure. The aim was to exploit the low fuel consumption and long time between overhaul of these engines as well as avoiding the use of gearboxes. The nominal dry weight, with flywheel, of the 16 RK270 Ruston engine to be used, is 25.82 tonnes.

By January 1995 a further nine 74 m wave-piercing catamarans had been delivered. A considerable number of design changes has been made in the recent vessels including the fitting of ride control systems (an active trim tab is fitted as standard and a forward foil system is optional) and in the sixth craft the use of Caterpillar 3616 medium-speed diesels instead of the Ruston 16 RK 270 diesels. In addition large superstructure and accommodation changes have been made in the vessels built for Buquebus, Argentina, Condor Ltd and Stena, UK. This has allowed passenger numbers to increase to 600 and vehicle numbers to over 100.

Principal Particulars

Length overall	73.65 m
Beam	26 m
Hull beam	4.4 m
Draught	2.4 m
Displacement, maximum	650 t
Payload	171 t
Passengers	383
Vehicles	80
Fuel capacity	20 000 l
Water capacity	3000 l
Propulsive power	4 × 3760 kW
Operational speed	35 knots

Classification: DnV + 1A1 Light Craft Catamaran + MV R280, passenger ship, EO, car ferry A.

Structure: All-welded construction, most plating thicknesses 6 mm to 20 mm and up to 50 mm in the transom/water-jet areas. Superstructure (65 t) is built as a separate unit and fitted to the hulls with resilient mountings.

Propulsion: Four Ruston 16 RK 270 medium-speed diesels, each 3760 kW (5042 hp) at 720 rpm; specific fuel consumption at 90 per cent full engine load: 201.5 g/kWh at 720 to 750 rpm, tolerance + five per cent. At 1000 rpm these engines can deliver 4600 kW (6169 hp) with an sfc of 208.5 g/kWh at 90 per cent full engine load.

These directly drive four Riva Calzoni (now Lips Jet) IRC 115 DX water-jet units, with only one on each side being equipped with steering and reversing systems.

Controls: The manoeuvring of the ship is controlled by a Lips Ancos 2000/joystick system called LIPS-STICK. The control system is split up in individual controls for each water-jet (two steerable and two

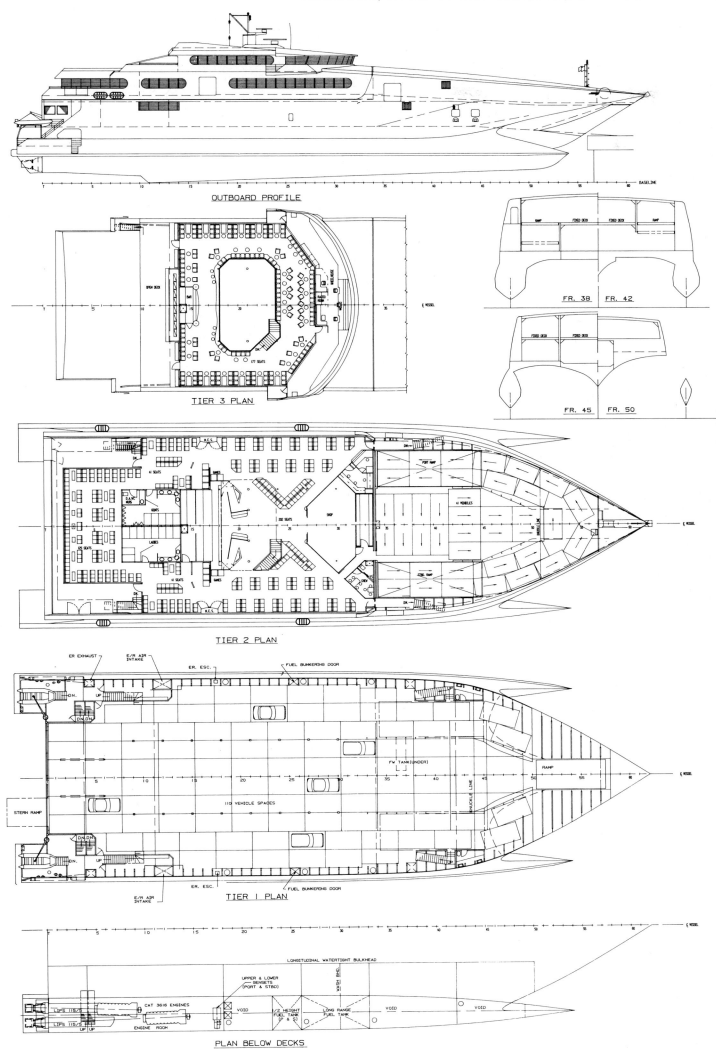

OUTBOARD PROFILE

TIER 3 PLAN

FR. 38   FR. 42

FR. 45   FR. 50

TIER 2 PLAN

TIER 1 PLAN

PLAN BELOW DECKS

InCat 78 m passenger/vehicle ferry

1994

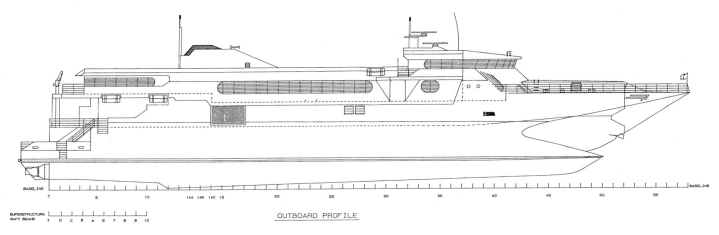

OUTBOARD PROFILE

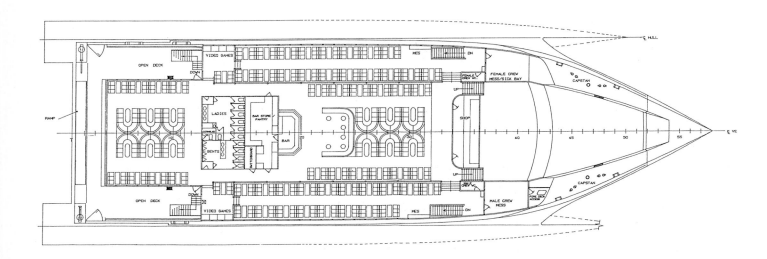

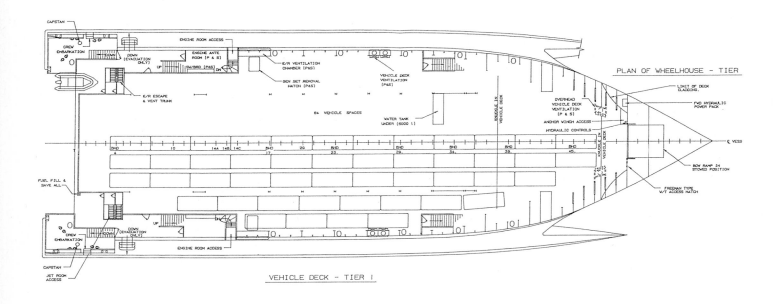

VEHICLE DECK - TIER I

PLAN OF WHEELHOUSE - TIER

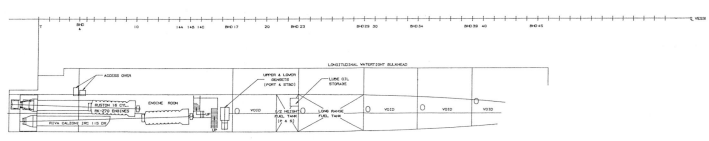

PLAN BELOW DECKS

General arrangement of InCat 74 m as delivered to Sea Containers

Craft built and ordered	Yard No	Completed	Max speed	Seats	Engines	Delivered to
18 m *Derwent Explorer* (ex *Jeremiah Ryan*)		September 1977	26 knots	145	2 × Cummins V8	
18 m *Tropic Princess*, (ex *James Kelly I*)	002	June 1979	28 knots	100	-	Ecrolight
20 m *Fitzroy Flyer* (ex *Fitzroy*)	004	June 1981	28 knots	-	-	Great Adventures
20 m *Tangalooma*		December 1981	28 knots	200	-	Tangalooma Island Resort
15 m *Amaroo*		December 1981	12 knots	120	-	
20 m *Islander*, (ex *Green Islander*)	007	June 1982	28 knots	220	-	
20 m *Low Isles Reef Express* (ex *Quicksilver*)		August 1982	28 knots	100	-	Outer Barrier Reef Cruises
29 m *Spirit of Roylen*		December 1982	27 knots	250	-	McLeans Roylen Cruises Pty Ltd (ex Barrier Reef Holdings)
20 m *Magnetic Northerner* (ex *Keppel Cat 2*, ex *Trojan*)		1983		200	-	Hydrofoil Seaflight Services Pty Ltd
20 m *Keppel Cat I*		September 1984		195	-	Hydrofoil Seaflight Services Pty Ltd
27.4 m WPC *Spirit of Paradise*, (ex *Spirit of Victoria*)	016	June 1985	28 knots	-	2 × DDC GM 12V 92 TA	(Indonesia)
30 m *Our Lady Patricia*		March 1986	31 knots	452	2 × MTU 16V 396 TC 83	Wightlink Ferries Ltd
30 m *Our Lady Pamela*		July 1986	31 knots	452	2 × MTU 16V 396 TC 83	Wightlink Ferries Ltd
31 m WPC *2001* (ex *Tassie Devil 2001*)	017	December 1986	30 knots	196	2 × MWM TBD 234 V16	InCat Charters
22.8 m (*Starship Genesis*), (ex *Genesis*)	018	July 1987	36 knots	200	2 × DDC GM 16V 92 TA	In NSW
31 m WPC *2000*	019	1988		231	-	Hamilton Island Cruises
37.2 m WPC *Seaflight*	022	1988	30 knots	-	2 × DDC GM 16V 149 TIB	Seaflight Ltd, New Zealand
74 m WPC *Hoverspeed Great Britain* (ex *Christopher Columbus*)	025	1990	35 knots	600 + 90 vehicles	4 × Ruston 16 RK 270	Sea Containers, Hoverspeed Ltd
74 m WPC *SeaCat Boulogne* (ex *SeaCat Denmark*, ex *Sardegna Express* ex *Hoverspeed France*)	027	1990	35 knots	483 + 80 vehicles	4 × Ruston 16 RK 270	Sea Containers, Hoverspeed Ltd
74 m WPC *Patricia Olivia*	024	mid-1992	37 knots	450 + 84 vehicles	4 × Caterpillar 3616	Los Cipreses SA Buquebus
74 m WPC *Condor 10*	030	January 1993	37 knots	584 + 84 vehicles	4 × Ruston 16 RK 270	Condor Ltd
74 m WPC *Stena Sea Lynx*	031	June 1993	37 knots	450 + 84 vehicles	4 × Ruston 16 RK 270	Buquebus under charter to Stena Sealink Line
74 m WPC *SeaCat Calais* ex *SeaCat Tasmania*	023	1990	35 knots	350 + 84 vehicles	4 × Ruston 16 RK 270	Sea Containers, Hoverspeed Ltd
74 m WPC *Seacatamaran Denmark* (ex *Hoverspeed Boulogne*) ex *Hoverspeed Belgium*	029	mid-1991	35 knots	420 + 85 vehicles	4 × Ruston 16 RK 270	Sea Containers, Hoverspeed Ltd
74 m WPC *SeaCat Scotland*	028	mid-1991	35 knots	450 + 80 vehicles	4 × Ruston 16 RK 270	Sea Containers, Hoverspeed Ltd
74 m WPC *Juan L*	032	October 1993	37 knots	600 + 110 vehicles	4 × Caterpillar 3616	Los Cipreses SA Buquebus
78 m WPC *Stena Sea Lynx II*	033	February 1994	37 knots	640 + 150 vehicles	4 × Ruston 16 RK 270	Stena Sealink Line
78 m WPC *Condor II*	034	October 1994	37 knots	600 + 150 vehicles	4 × Ruston 16RK 270	Condor Int
78 m WPC *Spaekhuggeren*	035	May 1995	37 knots	640 + 150 vehicles	4 × Caterpillar 3616	Holyman, Sydney
70 m CAT *K55*	036	November 1994	55 knots	450 + 63 vehicles	4 × Caterpillar 3616	Los Cipreses SA Buquebus
78 m CAT *K50*	037	-	51 knots	720 + 32 vehicles	4 × Caterpillar 3616	Dae A Gosok, Korea

boosters) through which rpm, angle of thrust and reversing of thrust are controlled. The LIPS-STICK system combines all individual controls in one single lever.

30 m CATAMARAN
Our Lady Patricia
Our Lady Pamela

The first of these vessels entered service with Sea-link British Ferries (now Wightlink Ferries) on 29 March 1986 and the second arrived on 30 July 1986.

Principal Particulars

Length overall	29.6 m
Length water-line	25.5 m
Beam	11.2 m
Hull beam	3.2 m
Draught	2.2 m
Displacement, minimum	80 t
Displacement, maximum	125 t
Payload	45 t
Passengers	452
Fuel capacity	4800 l
Water capacity	1000 l
Propulsive power	2 × 1430 kW
Maximum speed	31 knots

Classification: Det Norske Veritas + 1A1 Light Craft (CAT) R45 Passenger Ship, EO UK DOT Class IV Category D Water Limits Passenger Vessel.

Structure: Welded aluminium alloy construction (5083-H321 plating 6061-T6 sections) with the superstructure on anti-vibration mountings. There are large gangway doors on the upper deck for embarkation and disembarkation at the existing Portsmouth and Ryde Pier berthing facilities.

Propulsion: Two MTU 16V 396 TC83 diesels of 1430 kW each at 1845 rpm continuous rating. Gearboxes are ZF BW 750 ratio 2.548:1.

These drive two five-blade aluminium-bronze fixed-pitch propellers.

Electrical system: Two Perkins 4108 diesels driving 26 kVA alternators.

Navigation and communications: Two radars, gyro compass, two VHF radios, one echo-sounder.

Control: International Catamarans patented hydraulically operated lifting rudders.

Spirit of Paradise (ex Spirit of Victoria)

This unusual 28 m craft, Yard No 016, was launched in June 1985. The object of the design was to minimise the wave-following tendency as experienced by conventional semi-planing and planing hull craft; for this to be achieved a hull form that would cut through waves was envisaged. To explore the possibilities of this concept an 8.6 m manned model, *Little Devil*, was constructed capable of car-

rying six people and powered by a 25 hp outboard motor; extremely encouraging results were achieved, a speed of 16 knots being obtained at a scale displacement of 1.1 tonnes. This led to the decision to build a 28 m version, *Spirit of Victoria*, with the backing of MBM Management Pty Ltd which was prepared to operate the boat under long-term charter from the owner Incat Charters.

Principal Particulars

Length overall	27.4 m
Length water-line	25 m
Beam	13.02 m
Hull beam	2.22 m
Draught	1.74 m
Passengers	219
Fuel capacity	7000 l
Water capacity	300 l
Propulsive power	485 kW
Maximum speed	28 knots
Operational speed	26 knots

Classification: DnV +1A 2K Light Craft R15. Marine Board of Victoria, Class 1C.

Structure: Welded marine grade aluminium. Materials: 5083 H321, and 6061 T6 alloys, 5086 H32.

Propulsion: Two DDC GM 12V-92 TA, 650 bhp each, at 1980 rpm continuous rating.

The two five-blade, 1000 mm diameter Wagenin-

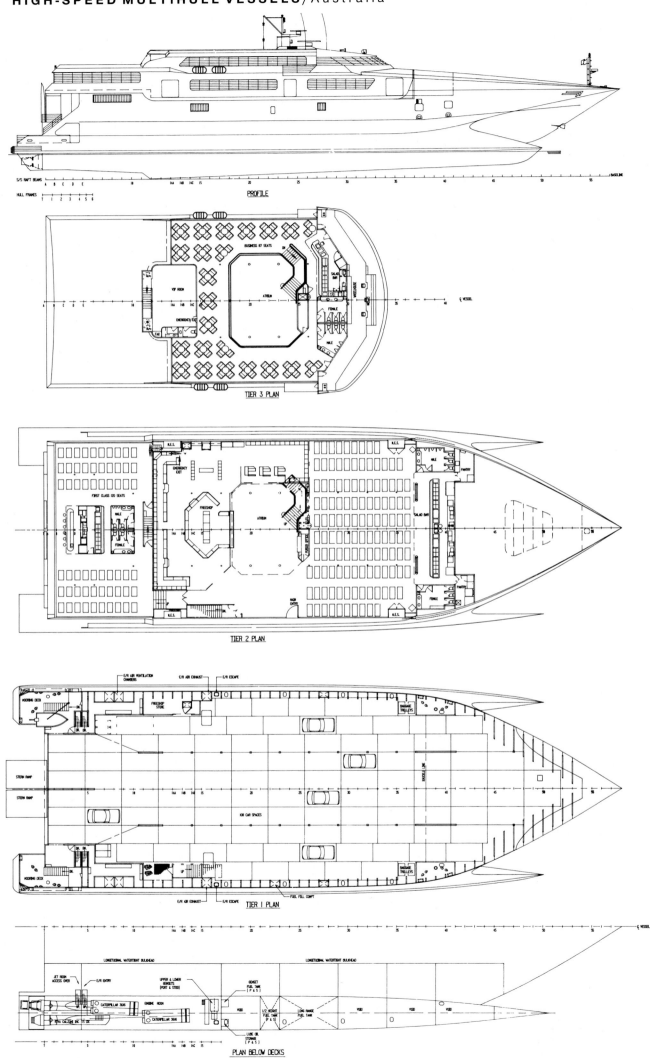

General arrangement of Juan L

InCat 78 m Stena Sea Lynx II

1995

gen B series propellers are driven through a pair of Reintjes WVS 532 gearboxes, ratio 2.452:1.

Electrical system: Deutz S2L912 diesel-driven 17.5 kVA alternator 415 V, 3-phase, 50 Hz AC or 240 V, single-phase, 50 Hz AC.

Navigation and communications: 24 nm JRC radar; Wagner Mk II autopilot.

Communication is provided by the following: Codan 8121 SSB, GME VHF, Clarion PA.

Outfit: 219 seats; 115 in main cabin, 40 in upper cabin, 22 open main deck, 42 open upper deck.

Tassie Devil 2001

A developed version of *Spirit of Victoria* and the third wave-piercing catamaran to be built.

Principal Particulars

Length overall	30.45 m
Length waterline	25 m
Beam	13 m
Draught	2 m

Passengers	196
Propulsive power	2 × 830 kW
Maximum speed	31 knots

Classification: Det Norske Veritas Class + 1A1 Light Craft (CAT) R45. In addition the vessel is under survey by The Navigation and Survey Authority of Tasmania, Class ID, Partially Smooth Water Limits Passenger Vessel.

Propulsion: Two MWM 234 16V engines, producing 830 kW each at 2265 rpm (overload rating), 755 kW each at 2200 rpm (continuous light duty rating). The gearboxes are ZF type BW 250, reduction ratio 3:1. Flexible couplings: Vulcan Rato S.

The propellers are five-blade modified Troost 'B' type, aluminium bronze, 1383 mm pitch, 1150 mm diameter, blade area ratio: 0.89.

Navigation and communications: Furuno 1700 radar, Mariner log.

The communications are provided by: Codan 8121 HF, President Sea Eagle 55 VHF.

Genesis Starship

An InCat development vessel launched in August 1987 for development with water-jet systems, surface-drive systems and InCat transom drive.

Principal Particulars

Length overall	22.8 m
Length waterline	18.5 m
Beam	8.2 m
Draught	0.88 m
Propulsive power	2 × 930 kW
Maximum speed	35 knots

Propulsion: Two GM DDA 16V-92 TA engines are installed, 930 kW each at 2300 rpm. Gearboxes: Niigata MGN 332X, ratio: 2.50:1.

The propellers are aluminium-bronze surface-piercing types under development.

K55

InCat Australia, the industry's leading builder of high-speed ferries, commissioned Advanced Multi-

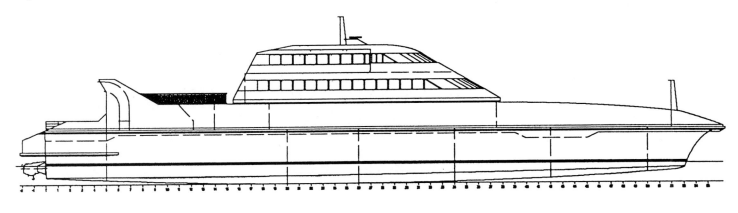

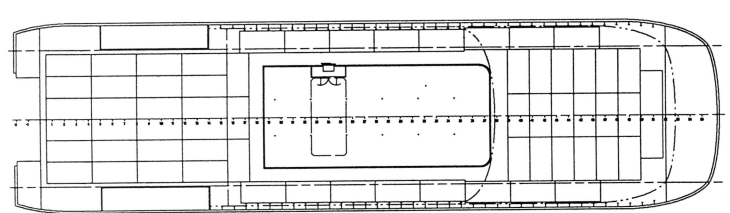

K55 general arrangement

1995

hull Designs Pty Ltd to design their fifth newbuilding for Argentine-based Buquebus International. The vessel, known as the K55, is the world's fastest car carrying catamaran ferry with a maximum speed of about 55 knots.

The K55 vessel is a 71 m conventional catamaran designed for operation across the Rio del Plata between Uruguay and Argentina. The vessel has a capacity of 450 passengers and 63 cars or a mix of cars with light trucks on the aft open deck.

Construction of the vessel commenced in May 1994 and was delivered to Argentina in early 1995.

Principal Particulars

Length overall	70.36 m
Beam	19.46 m
Draught	2.15 m
Passengers	450
Vehicles	63 cars
Propulsive power	4 × 5310 kW
Maximum speed	55 knots
Operational speed	49 knots

Classification: +1A1 HSLC R3 Car Ferry "B" EO.

Propulsion: The vessel will be powered by four Caterpillar 3616 medium-speed diesel engines, which will directly drive KaMeWa 80 size water-jets. Two of the jets will be steerable and two will be boosters.

Control: A Maritime Dynamics ride control system will be fitted to the vessel, consisting of a pair of active trim tabs mounted at the transom.

K50 Car & Passenger Ferry

In August 1994 InCat Australia received an order from the Dae A. Gosok Ferry Company of South Korea for a 78 m conventional catamaran vessel. InCat Australia commissioned Advanced Multihull designs Pty Ltd to design this vessel which is to be known as the K50.

The K50 vessel is designed for operation on a 117 nautical mile route between Pohang on the Korean mainland and the island of Ullung-do in the Japan Sea. The vessel will ferry tourists to a resort on this extinct volcanic island. Construction of the vessel commenced in late September 1994 with the vessel scheduled for delivery in late 1995.

Principal Particulars

Length overall	78 m
Beam	19.46 m
Draught	2.1 m
Passengers	750
Vehicles	32 cars
Propulsive power	4 × 5310 kW
Maximum speed	51 knots
Operational speed	47 knots

Classification: +1A1 HSLC R3 Car Ferry 'A' EO.

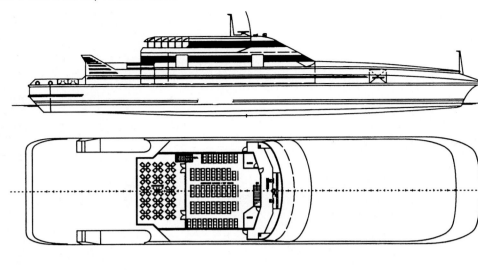

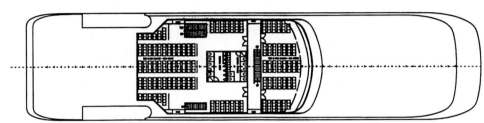

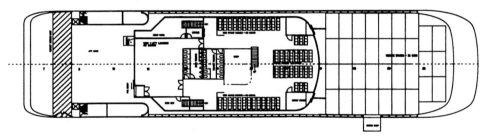

K50 general arrangement 1995

Propulsion: The vessel will be powered by four Caterpillar 3616 medium-speed diesel engines, which will directly drive KaMeWa 80 size water-jets. Two of the jets will be steerable and two will be boosters.

Control: A Maritime Dynamics ride control system will be fitted to the vessel, consisting of a pair of active trim tabs mounted at the transom.

UPDATED

LLOYD'S SHIPS HOLDINGS PTY LTD

41 Oxford Street, Bulimba, Queensland 4171, Australia

Telephone: +61 (7) 399 6866
Telex: +61 (7) 395 5000

John Hardie, *General Manager*

Lloyd's Ships design and construct a range of luxury motor yachts and large catamaran ferry vessels. All Lloyd's ships are constructed to 'Class' and are of the highest standard.

The company has as its major shareholder, Daikyo Australia Pty Ltd, with over 130 people directly employed and a turnover in excess of A$25 million per annum.

The first catamaran to be built by Lloyd's Ships was *Equator Dream*, a 35.6 m vessel with a maximum speed of 24 knots and accommodation for 260 passengers.

Reef Queen
Reef Prince

These fast catamaran ferries to complement the existing Great Adventures fleet were launched in March 1993 and May 1995 respectively and are being used to transport passengers around the islands in the North Queensland region. The vessels were designed by Lock Crowther/Lloyd's Ships.

Lloyd's Ships Reef Queen 1994

Principal Particulars

Length overall	37.39 m	Propulsive power	2 × 1470 kW
Length waterline	34 m	Maximum speed	31 knots
Beam	12.25 m	**Classification:** DnV + 1A1 light ship R3 EO Class 1C (DOT Marine Ports Qld).	
Displacement	120 t		
Crew	25	Yard No V104.	
Passengers	384	**Structure:** All-welded aluminium alloy.	
Fuel capacity	10 500 l	**Propulsion:** 2 × MTU 16V 396 TE 74L engines, 1470 kW each.	
Fresh water	4000 l		

UPDATED

NQEA AUSTRALIA PTY LTD

60-92 Cook Street, PO Box 1105, Cairns, Queensland 4870, Australia

Telephone: +61 (70) 527222
Telex: 48087 AA
Telefax: +61 (70) 352812/352520

D G Fry, *Chairman*
E W Graham, *General Manager*
R Bannah, *Marketing Manager*
R D Rookwood, *Senior Design Engineer*
M Richards, *Chief Naval Architect*

NQEA started services in 1948 from the residence of its founder with a staff of three, the principal activity being the operation of general engineering agencies, leading to general engineering manufacture. In 1964 it entered the shipbuilding industry with the construction of dumb barges. This was followed by work on many types of vessel, including Australian Navy patrol boats until in 1975 the first construction of vessels was undertaken. In 1977 NQEA was the successful tenderer for 14 'Freemantle' 42 m class patrol craft for the Australian Navy, the first having been built by Brooke Marine in England.

Throughout the 1980s, NQEA built large numbers of high-speed ferry craft for the international marketplace as well as some special purpose vessels. Search and rescue vessels, luxury motor yachts, dredge and barge units (capable of being linked using an NQEA designed Autodock system), hovercraft and patrol boats have all been produced at the Cairns Australia NQEA facilities. However, the majority of vessels produced in recent years have been high-speed passenger ferries of the International Catamaran designs.

After delivery of the 34.8 m catamarans (Yard Nos 163, 172 and 173) to the New South Wales State Transit Authority as hydrofoil replacements, NQEA was awarded a contract to build six low-wash catamaran passenger ferries for the same operator, which were delivered in 1993.

The shipyard currently has a 45 m wave-piercing catarmaran under construction, scheduled for delivery to Quicksilver Connections in mid-1995.

Quicksilver V   *1991*

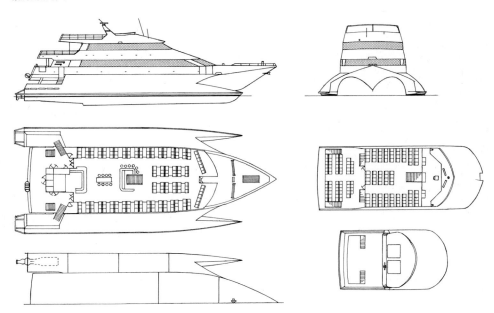

General arrangement of 38.6 m InCat wave-piercing catamaran for Quicksilver Connections Ltd

Craft built	Yard No	Delivered	Class 1D	Engines	Delivered to
23 m *Green Island Express*	106	June 1982	230	2 × DDC 12V 92TA	Great Adventures
23 m *South Molle Reef* (ex *Telford Reef*)	107	October 1982	204	2 × DDC 12V 92TA	Fantasea Cruises
23 m *Magnetic Express*	108	March 1983	240	2 × DDC 12V 92TA	Great Adventures
29.2 m *South Molle Capricorn* (ex *Telford Capricorn*)	111	November 1983	326	2 × DDC 16V 92TA	Fantasea Cruises
23 m *Cougar*	113	1984	200	2 × DDC 12V 92TA	Great Adventures
23 m *Reef Link*	109	1984	200	2 × MTU 8V 396 TC 82	Magnetic Link Townsville
24 m *Quickcat I*	115	August 1984	145-200	2 × DDC 16V 92TA	-
24 m *Quickcat II*	123	1985	195	2 × DDC 16V 92TA	Fantaesea Cruises
30 m *Reef Cat*	126	May 1986	345	2 × DDC 16V 92TA	Great Adventures
30 m *Quicksilver III*	127	October 1986	308	2 × MWM TBD 604 V12	Philippines
24 m *Auto Battam III* (ex *Supercat II*)	138	October 1988	205	2 × MWM TBD 234 V12	Singapore
30 m *Reef Link II*	147	February 1987	403	2 × MWM TBD 604B V12	Fullers NZ
24 m *Taupo Cat*	148	March 1987	205	2 × MWM TBD 234 V16	Fullers NZ
30 m *Quicksilver IV*	130	May 1987	300	2 × MWM TBD 604 V12	Philippines
30 m *Supercat III*	125	August 1987	390	2 × MWM TBD 604 V12	IGSA Shipping
24 m *Roylen Sunbird*	151	August 1987	245	2 × MWM TBD 234 V16	Roylen Cruises Pty Ltd
30 m *Reef King*	152	December 1988	390	2 × MWM TBD 604B V12	Great Adventures
25.3 m *Wauri*	129	1988		2 × MWM TBD 234 V12	Queensland Fisheries
26.9 m *Adaire*	156	August 1988	150	2 × MWM TBD 234 V16	Kuwait Public Transport Co
26.9 m *Na'Aye*	157	September 1988	150	2 × MWM TBD 234 V16	Kuwait Public Transport Co
38.6 m WPC *Quicksilver V*	158	November 1988	252 + 66 externally	2 × DDC 16V 149 TIB	Quicksilver Connections
38.6 m WPC *Quicksilver VI*	159	February 1989	350	2 × DDC 16V 149 TIB	Quicksilver Connections
38.6 m WPC *Quicksilver VII*	161	September 1989	350	2 × DDC 16V 149 TIB	Quicksilver Connections
39.6 m WPC *Prince of Venice*	160	6 June 1989	303	2 × DDC 16V 149 TIB	Kompas Touristik
34.8 m *Blue Fin*	163	March 1990	250	2 × MWM TBD 604B V16	NSW State Transit Authority
39 m WPC *Seacom I*	170	July 1990	300	2 × DDC 16V 149 TIB	SeaCom Corporation
34.8 m *Sir David Martin*	172	December 1990	250	2 × MWM TBD 604B V16	NSW State Transit Authority
34.8 m *Sea Eagle*	173	March 1991	250	2 × MWM TBD 604B V16	NSW State Transit Authority
34 m *Dawn Fraser*	180	February 1992	200	2 × DDC 8V 92TA	NSW State Transit Authority
34 m *Betty Cuthbert*	181	February 1992	200	2 × DDC 8V 92TA	NSW State Transit Authority
34 m *Shane Gould*	184	January 1993	200	2 × DDC 8V 92TA	NSW State Transit Authority
34 m *Marlene Mathews*	185	January 1993	200	2 × DDC 8V 92TA	NSW State Transit Authority
34 m *Evonne Goolagong*	186	September 1993	200	2 × DDC 8V 92TA	NSW State Transit Authority
34 m *Marjorie Jackson*	187	September 1993	200	2 × DDC 8V 92TA	NSW State Transit Authority

Blue Fin

1991

28 m CATAMARAN

InCat design with an all-welded aluminium hull and a resiliently mounted superstructure to minimise noise and vibration.

Principal Particulars

Length overall	29.2 m
Length waterline	25 m
Beam	11.2 m
Draught	1.76 m
Fuel capacity	2 × 5000 l tanks
Propulsive power	2 × 1200 shp
Maximum speed	29 knots
Operational speed	26 knots

Classification: Queensland Marine Board, Class 1C, November 1983.

Propulsion: Two 1200 shp GM 16V-92 TA high-speed diesels with ZF reverse/reduction gearbox 2.4:1; driving a 5 blade aluminium-bronze propeller.

Electrical systems: 415 V AC from shore power, or 80 kVA GM diesel alternator set 24 V DC.

38.6 m CATAMARAN
Quicksilver V

The first of these vessels *Quicksilver V* was completed by NQEA in November 1988 for Quicksilver Connections with a further two identical craft delivered in February and September 1989 for the same operator and a fourth vessel delivered to Yugoslavia, also in June 1989.

A 39 m variation of the Quicksilver style was constructed for Kompas Touristik International, underwent an 11 000 mile delivery voyage from the builder's yards to Piran in Yugoslavia, and immediately went into operation, plying between the Istrian ports and Venice. This vessel is fitted with KaMeWa water-jet units driven by DDC 16V 149 TA diesel engines.

Principal Particulars

Length overall	38.6 m
Length waterline	31.4 m
Beam	15.6 m
Hull beam	2.6 m
Draught	1.6 m
Passengers	340
Fuel capacity	2 × 2000 l tanks
Water capacity	3000 l
Propulsive power	2 × 1230 kW
Maximum speed	30 knots

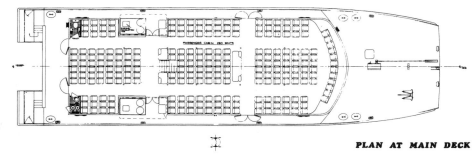

PROFILE

PLAN AT MAIN DECK

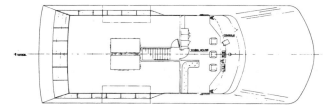

PLAN AT WHEELHOUSE DECK

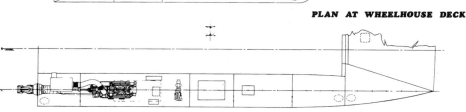

General arrangement of Blue Fin

Operational speed 27 knots

Structure: All-welded aluminium generally using alloys 5083 H321 and 6061 T6. Some light plates are 5086 H32.

Classification: DnV +1A1 R45 Queensland Department of Harbours and Marine, Class 1G.

Propulsion: Two GM diesel engines model 16V-149 TIB, each coupled to ZF gearbox model BU 460. Each engine is rated at 1230 kW at 1800 rpm, and drives two KaMeWa water-jets model 63S 62/6.

Electrical system: Main services are supplied by either of two diesel engine (Cummins 6BT5) driven 100 kVA Stamford alternator sets. These supply 415 V three-phase and 415 V, single phase 50 Hz power. Engine starting, auxiliary and emergency services are supplied from 24 V DC battery banks.

Outfit: 350 passengers. Interior seats are individual armchairs with woollen upholstery. Exterior seats are moulded polypropylene shells. A food service area is fitted at the aft end of the lower cabin and a drinks bar in the middle of the lower cabin. Passenger spaces are air-conditioned.

40.17 m WAVE-PIERCER
Seacom I

SeaCom Corporation of Japan (formerly known as the Nisshin Steamship Company) took delivery of this vessel in Cairns in July 1990. The ferry sailed to Japan under its own power and is operating as a ferry south of Tokyo Bay between Izu and Bohsoh Peninsula.

Principal Particulars

Length overall	40.17 m
Length waterline	31.4 m
Beam	15.6 m
Hull beam	2.5 m
Draught	1.6 m
Crew	5
Passengers	302
Fuel capacity	2 × 4500 l
Water capacity	3500 l
Propulsive power	2 × 1435 kW
Operational speed	29 knots
Maximum speed	32 knots

Classification: Nippon Kaiki Kyokai NS (restricted coastal service/aluminium catamaran/passenger ship).

Propulsion: Two GM Detroit diesel engines model 16V-149 TIB, each coupled to ZF BU460 gearboxes. The engines are each rated at 1435 kW at 2000 rpm. Propulsion is delivered through two KaMeWa 63 water-jets.

Electrical system: Provided by two Hino WO6/DTI engines driving Stamford 100 kVA UCM274D marine alternators.

CHEETAH PATROL BOAT

NQEA has designed a patrol boat variant of the 23 m commercial catamaran design. These boats will be identified as the 'Cheetah' class. One has been constructed for the Queensland Fisheries department and will be used for surveillance work in northern Australian waters. Normally operated by a six-man crew, the craft has facilities to carry an additional 12-man landing party and has extended range cruising capabilities.

Principal Particulars

Length overall	25.3 m
Beam	8.7 m
Hull beam	2.5 m
Draught	2 m
Crew	6
Propulsive power	2 × 605 kW
Operational speed	25 knots
Range	1000 miles at 20 knots

Propulsion: 2 × Deutz MWM TBD 234 V12 engines, 605 kW each at 2200 rpm; driving 2 × ZF BW195 gearboxes, ratio 2.46:1; to 2 × 5-blade, 1 m diameter, aluminium-bronze propellers.

34.8 m CATAMARAN
Blue Fin

One of three InCat catamarans ordered by the State Transit Authority of New South Wales.

Survey: Maritime Services Board of NSW class 1D.

Principal Particulars

Length overall	34.8 m
Length waterline	28.4 m
Beam	9.75 m
Hull beam	2.80 m
Draught	1.0 m
Passengers	250
Fuel capacity	8830 l
Water capacity	500 l
Propulsive power	2 × 1675 kW
Operational speed	35 knots
Maximum speed	41 knots

Classification: Lloyd's Register of Shipping + 100 A1 Catamaran Passenger Vessel + LMC.

Propulsion: Engines: 2 × MWM TBD 604B V16, 1675 kW each, driving 2 × KaMeWa 63 S11 water-jets.

LOW-WASH CATAMARAN

The NSW State Transit Authority, in June 1991, placed an order with NQEA to build two 36.8 m low-wash catamaran ferries to link the city of Parramatta with Sydney's Circular Quay. In 1992 the same client placed an order for a further four vessels with NQEA after the successful operation of the first Rivercats. All six were completed by September 1993.

Designed by Grahame Parker construction is light aluminium with foam FRP coring in the deck/cabin structure.

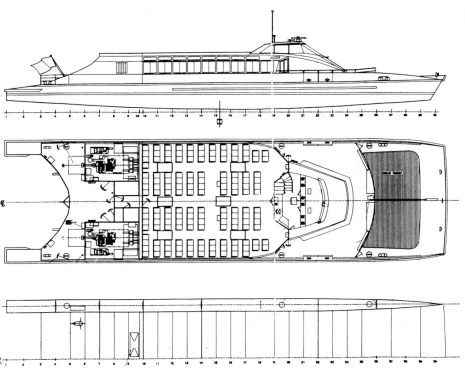

General arrangement of 150-seat low-wash ferry for NSW State Transit Authority

NQEA low-wash catamarans

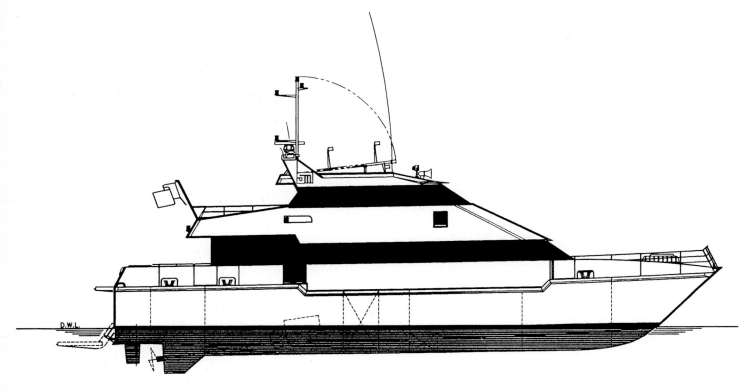

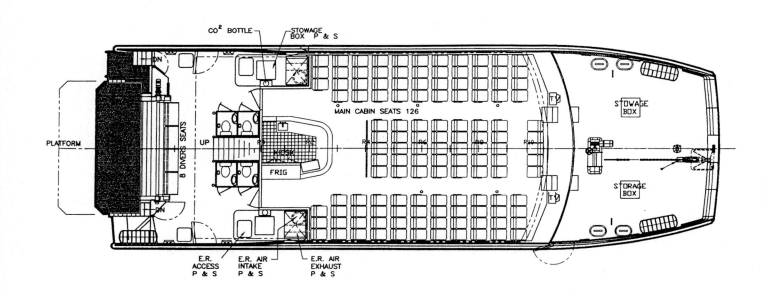

CO² BOTTLE

STOWAGE
BOX P & S

DN

PLATFORM

8 DIVERS SEATS

UP

KIOSK

FRIG

MAIN CABIN SEATS 126

R9

R4

R6

R10

STOWAGE
BOX

STORAGE
BOX

DN

E.R.
ACCESS
P & S

E.R. AIR
INTAKE
P & S

E.R. AIR
EXHAUST
P & S

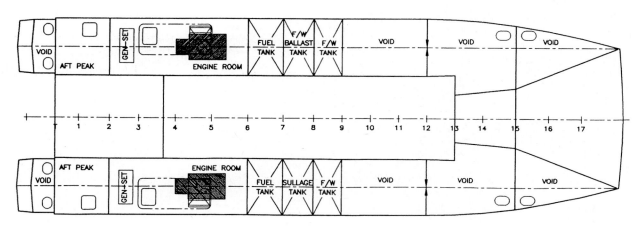

VOID

AFT PEAK

GEN-SET

ENGINE ROOM

FUEL
TANK

F/W
BALLAST
TANK

F/W
TANK

VOID

VOID

VOID

1   2   3   4   5   6   7   8   9   10   11   12   13   14   15   16   17

VOID

AFT PEAK

GEN-SET

ENGINE ROOM

FUEL
TANK

SULLAGE
TANK

F/W
TANK

VOID

VOID

VOID

General arrangement of Payar

1995

The propulsion system for these vessels is unusual. The designers chose Schottel Rudderpropellers, an uprated system based on the Schottel SRP 132/131 type. The modifications of this unit enable power input to be raised to about 367 kW. The position of these thrust and steering devices is also unusual in that they are positioned beneath the bridging structure of the catamaran towards its aft end with the propellers facing forward.

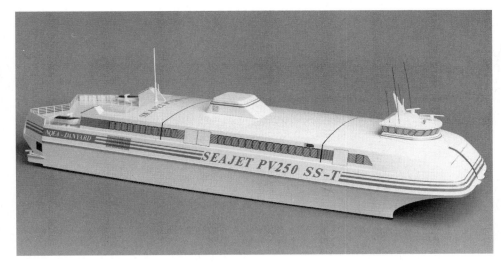

The NQEA Danyard Seajet PV 250 SS. T (design) **1993**

Principal Particulars

Length overall	36.8 m
Length waterline	35 m
Beam	10.5 m
Draught	1.35 m
Displacement, minimum	45 t
Passengers	200
Fuel capacity	5500 l
Water capacity	600 l
Propulsive power	2 × 373 kW
Operational speed	22.5 knots
Maximum speed	23.7 knots
Range	660 nm

Propulsion: 2 × DDC 8V 92TA engines, 373 kW each at 2100 rpm; driving 2 × Schottel steerable propeller units SRP 132/131.

SEAJET PV 250 SS. T

The Seajet PV 250 SS. T is a joint venture between NQEA Australia and Danyard of Frederikshavn, Denmark. Two of these vessels are currently under construction at the Danyard Shipyard and are scheduled for delivery in mid-1996.

The semi-Swath hull form was developed with the Swedish Marine Research Institution, SSPA. The resultant hull form experiences relatively low vertical accelerations compared to a conventional catamaran for a given sea state without the use of a ride control system.

The four loading lanes at the bow and twin side exit lanes aft would allow for very fast turnaround times.

Principal Particulars

Length overall	76.10 m
Beam	23.4 m
Draught	3.4 m
Passengers	450
Vehicles	120 cars
Propulsive power	2 × 12400 kW
Operational speed	40 knots
Range	240 nm

Classification: DnV +1A1 HSLC R2 Passenger Car Ferry A EO ICS NAUT.

Propulsion: Engines: 2 × GE LM1600 gas-turbines each rated at 12 400 kW and 2 × MTU 1163 diesel engines each rated at 6000 kW. This CODOG arrangement drives four KaMeWa water-jets.

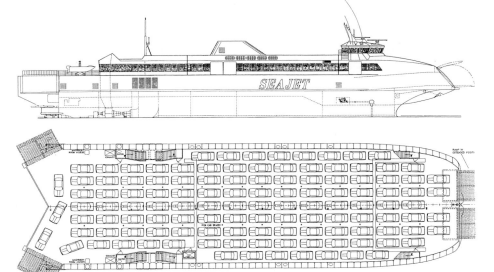

The NQEA Danyard Seajet PV 250 SS. T (design)

Payar

This is a 25 m catamaran built for Sriwani Tours and Travel Snd Bhd, for transporting tourists from Langkawi, Malaysia, to a small island called Pulau Payar.

Principal Particulars

Length overall	26.5 m
Length waterline	23 m
Beam	8.70 m
Draught	2.00 m
Passengers	210
Fuel capacity	4800 l
Water capacity	2500 l
Propulsive power	2 × 736 kW
Maximum speed	27.2 knots

Classification: DnV +1A1 HSLC R4 Passenger EO.

Propulsion: The main engines are 2 × MAN D2842 LE402 diesels; driving 2 × Veem 5-bladed series "B" 1000 mm × 1015 mm; via ZF BW 255 Rev Red gearboxes.

UPDATED

Payar **1995**

OCEANFAST PTY LTD

26 St George's Terrace, Perth, PO Box X2256, Western Australia, Australia

Telephone: +61 (9) 325 8599
Telex: 94598 IAL AA
Telefax: +61 (9) 325 6484/221 1813

Boat Factory: 15 Egmont Road, Hendersen, Western Australia 6166, Australia

Telephone: +61 (9) 410 1900
Telefax: +61 (9) 410 2095

John Farrell, *Managing Director*

Oceanfast specialises in high performance motor yachts and luxury cruisers. The company's naval architect is Phil Curran and yacht design is by Jon Bannenberg Ltd. The company is a wholly owned subsidiary of the Western Australia-based International Assets Ltd group, with over 250 people directly employed and a turnover in excess of A$30 million per annum.

Current new projects include a 53 m, 20 knot, propeller-driven semi-displacement yacht. This craft, which is a departure from Oceanfast's normal range, is due for delivery in Europe in early 1994.

Oceanfast is also part of Ferries Australia, the joint venture company formed in 1994 with Austal Ships.

Moecca

Delivered in December 1992, this vessel is the world's first catamaran megayacht.

Principal Particulars

Length overall	45 m
Beam	13 m
Draught	2 m
Displacement, minimum	250 t

Oceanfast Moecca *the world's first catamaran megayacht*   **1993**

Fuel capacity	82 000 l
Water capacity	10 000 l
Maximum speed	25 knots
Operational speed	20 knots

Propulsion: The main engines are 2 × MTU 12V 396 TB 94 diesels, driving 2 × KaMeWa 80 water-jets.

Auxiliary systems: Engines: 2 × MTU 10V 183 AA51 diesels, 172 kW each.
Outfit: Owner's suite and 6 guest cabins; Captain's cabin and 6 crew cabins.

UPDATED

SABRE CATAMARANS PTY LTD

156 Barrington Road, Spearwood, Western Australia 6163, Australia

Telephone: +61 (9) 418 3000
Telefax: +61 (9) 434 1457

Bill Harry, *Principal*

Builder of a number of aluminium fast catamaran fishing and passenger vessels. The most recent is *Aremiti II*, a 29 m 30 knot catamaran ferry built for Aremiti Pacific Cruises. The two earlier catamarans *Aremiti* and *Saladin Sabre* were operated by Stirling Marine Services during the construction of the Saladin oil-field off the coast of Western Australia. *Saladin Sabre* is now working as a Tahiti-Moorea ferry. Two smaller high-speed catamarans have also been built, the *OT Manu* and *Paia*. These 16.7 m catamarans each have accommodation for 73 passengers and a maximum speed of 25 knots. They operate in Bora Bora lagoon in French Polynesia.

SABRE 55
Aremiti
Saladin Sabre
Principal Particulars

Length overall	16.76 m
Length waterline	14.95 m
Beam	7.2 m
Draught	0.72 m
Passengers	100
Fuel capacity	2 × 1000 l tanks
Water capacity	500 l
Maximum speed	34.6 knots
Operational speed	28 knots

Propulsion: The main engines are 2 × DDC 8V 92T diesels, driving 2 × Levi 800 series surface-piercing drive units.

Auxiliary systems: The auxiliary generator is an Isuzu 17 kVA model.

Saladin Sprint
Built for the same purpose as *Saladin Sabre*.
Principal Particulars

Length overall	13.19 m
Length waterline	11.6 m

Beam	5.4 m
Draught	0.6 m
Passenger	40
Fuel capacity	1800 l
Water capacity	500 l
Propulsive power	2 × 266 kW
Maximum speed	28 knots
Operational speed	24 knots
Range	350 nm

Propulsion: The main engines are 2 × Volvo Penta 266 kW, TAMD 71A turbocharged, after-cooled diesels, driving Levi 400 series surface-piercing drive units.

Aremiti II
Owned by Aremiti Pacific Cruises, this vessel operates from Papeete, Tahiti. Delivered June 1992.
Principal Particulars

Length overall	29.95 m
Length waterline	26.95 m
Beam	9.3 m
Draught	1.5 m
Passengers	288
Fuel capacity	2000 l

The Sabre 55 Aremiti   **1994**

Aremiti II. *The fourth high-speed commuter ferry delivered to Tahiti by Sabre Catamarans*   **1994**

Propulsive power   2 × 1360 kW
Maximum speed   32 knots
Propulsion: 2 × Detroit Diesel 12V 149TIB diesels rated at 1360 kW each.

OT Manu and Paia
Owned by Bora Bora Navettes, these vessels were delivered in 1991.
Principal Particulars
Length overall   16.7 m
Length waterline   13.25 m
Beam   6.51 m
Draught   0.9 m
Passengers   73
Fuel capacity   3000 l
Operational speed   25 knots

Foveaux Express
Owned by Stewart Island Marine Services and delivered in 1991.
Principal Particulars
Length overall   19.9 m
Length waterline   17.6 m
Beam   7.2 m
Draught   1.5 m
Passengers   67
Fuel capacity   8000 l
Operational speed   30 knots

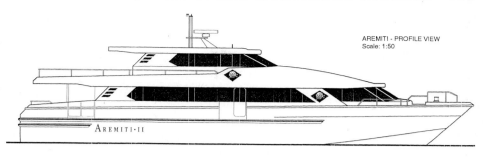

AREMITI - PROFILE VIEW
Scale: 1:50

AREMITI·II

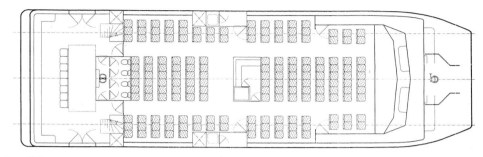

VERIFIED Aremiti II

OT Manu and Paia   1994

Foveaux Express   1994

SBF ENGINEERING

Waters Edge, Lot 33 Cockburn Road, South Coogee, Western Australia 6166, Australia

Telephone: +61 (9) 410 2244
Telex: +61 (9) 410 1807

Don Dunbar, *Managing Director*
Alan McCombie, *Director, Finance*
Don Johnston, *General Manager*
Capt Kim Cleggett, *Director, Technical Sales*

Victory III
Passenger ferry.
Designer: Lock Crowther, Sydney.
Owner: Great Keppel Island Tourist Services Pty Ltd, Rockhampton, Queensland, Australia.
Legislating authority: Queensland Marine and Harbours Department.
Principal Particulars
Length overall   33 m
Beam   10 m
Draught   1.4 m
Passenger capacity   448
Propulsive power   2 × 807 kW
Maximum speed   28 knots
Operational speed   24 knots
Structure: The catamaran hull and superstructure are constructed in all-welded marine grade aluminium alloy. Each bow has a streamlined bulb on the forefoot which increases water-line length and performance. Draught of hulls forward is slightly over 1 m and the craft is designed to be beached by the bow to allow passengers to embark and disembark using an SBF-designed telescopic ramp lowered from the foredeck.
Propulsion: Two MWM 16-cylinder marine diesels, each producing 807 kW (1082 bhp); driving two right-handed 970 mm × 1760 mm propellers.
Electrical systems: Electrical generator: 1 × MWM 3-cylinder generator producing 33 kVA.
Navigation and communications: JRC JMA 3425 colour radar; NWU 51 colour plotter; JAX2 Weatherfox; JLE 3850 satellite navigator; JFX 80 colour sounder.
Codan 8121 SSB radio; Icom IC M80 VHF radio.
Safety equipment: Lifesaving: 450 coastal lifejackets; 450 flotation rafts.
Fire-fighting: Halon gas fire extinguishers.

High-speed catamaran craft built	Seats	Delivered to	Route
33 m *Victory III*	448	Tourist Services Pty Ltd	Great Keppel Island
33.37 m *Tropic Sunbird*	500+	Sunseeker Cruises, Queensland, Australia	Cairns-Townsville-Dunk Island
33.37 m *Quickcat*	500+	Waiheke Shipping, Auckland, New Zealand	Auckland-Waiheke
31.7 m *Lada Satu*	250	Lada Langkawi, Malaysia	Lada Langkawi
31.7 m *Lada Dua*	250	Lada Langkawi, Malaysia	Lada Langkawi
31.7 m *Lada Tiga*	250	Lada Langkawi, Malaysia	Lada Langkawi
31.7 m *Lada Empat*	250	Lada Langkawi, Malaysia	Lada Langkawi
19.9 m *Seabreeze*	116	Mackenzies Marine, Esperance Western Australia	—
22 m *Lada Lima*	106	Lada Langkawi, Malaysia	Lada Langkawi

Tropic Sunbird
Passenger ferry, but first employed as a top press and spectator boat at the 1987 Americas Cup.
Designer: Lock Crowther, Sydney.
Owner: Sunseeker Cruises, Cairns, Queensland.
Legislation authority: Department of Marine and Harbours, Western Australia.
Principal Particulars
Length overall   33.37 m
Length waterline   30.01 m
Beam   13 m
Draught   1.36 m
Passengers   600
Maximum speed   32 knots
Operational speed   27 knots

Structure: The catamaran hull and superstructure are constructed in all-welded marine grade aluminium alloy. The hulls incorporate bulbous bows which reduce pitching through their extra buoyancy.
Propulsion: The main engines are 2 × Deutz-MWM TBD 604B V12, driving through 2 × ZF BW 455 gearboxes.
Navigation and communications: Koden MDC 4105 colour radar; Koen CVS 88 Colour echosounder; Robertson AP-40 autopilot; Codan P121 12 V radio

Quickcat
Passenger ferry.
Designer: Lock Crowther, Turramurra, NSW, Australia.
Owner: Waiheke Shipping Company Ltd, Auckland, New Zealand.
Legislation authority: New Zealand Ministry of Transport.
Principal Particulars
As for *Tropic Sunbird* except that the passenger cabin behind the wheelhouse for *Quickcat* extends to the full width of the craft over its whole length.
Navigation and communications: Koden 410 colour radar; Raytheon echo-sounder; Wagner SE autopilot; Codan 8121 24 V radio.

31.7 m CATAMARANS
Lada Satu
Lada Dua
Lada Tiga
Lada Empat
By the end of 1994 SBF Engineering had delivered all four 250-passenger catamarans under construction following contracts signed in 1992 and 1993 with Lada Langkawi in Malaysia
Principal Particulars

Length overall	31.7 m
Length waterline	27 m
Draught	1 m
Beam	9.6 m
Passengers	250
Fuel capacity	5000 l
	(12 000 l for *Lada Empat*)
Water capacity	1000 l
Propulsive power	2 × 1435 kW
Operational speed	35 knots

Propulsion: The main engines are 2 × MTU 12V 396 TE 74L, 1435 kW each at 2000 rpm; driving 2 × KaMeWa 56 water-jets, via 2 × ZF BUK455-1 gearboxes

SBF 31.7 m catamaran Lada Satu   *1994*

Seabreeze in service   *1995*

Seabreeze
This vessel was delivered to Western Australian operator Mackenzies Marine in mid-1994.
Principal Particulars

Length overall	19.9 m	Length waterline	18 m
		Beam	7 m
		Draught	1.4 m
		Passengers	116
		Fuel capacity	3000 l

General arrangement of Lada Empat   *1995*

Water capacity	1000 l
Propulsive power	2 × 550 kW
Maximum speed	25 knots

Structure: Marine grade aluminium.
Propulsion: The main engines are 2 × MTU 12V 183 TE62 diesels, each producing 550 kW at 2000 rpm; driving 2 × 5 blade Stone Marine propellers; via 2 × Twin Disc MG 5141 gearboxes.

Lada Lima
This vessel was delivered to Lada Langawi Holdings in Malaysia in late 1994.

Principal Particulars

Length overall	19.9 m
Length waterline	17.95 m
Beam	6.6 m
Draught	0.8 m
Passengers	106
Fuel capacity	7000 l
Water capacity	1000 l
Propulsive power	2 × 610 kW
Maximum speed	28 knots

Classification: Bureau Veritas.
Structure: Marine grade aluminium.
Propulsion: The main engines are 2 × MTU 12V 183 TE 72 diesels, each producing 610 kW at 2100 rpm; driving 2 × Castoldi 07 series waterjets.

UPDATED

Lada Empat
1995

Lada Lima on trials
1995

WAVEMASTER INTERNATIONAL PTY LTD

Lot 500, Cockburn Road, Henderson, Western Australia 6166, Australia

Telephone: +61 (9) 410 1422
Telex: 93356 AA
Telefax: +61 (9) 410 2089

Glen Williams, *Director*

Designer and builder of over 20 high-speed monohull ferries, WaveMaster International in 1989 delivered *Yin Shan Hu,* its first high-speed catamaran. Built in welded aluminium alloy, this is a 32 m fully planing vessel for the People's Republic of China.

By early 1995 Wavemaster had delivered twelve more catamarans, mainly for Chinese and Hong Kong owners.

Yin Shan Hu
Yard Number: 020
Principal Particulars

Length overall	32 m
Beam	9.5 m
Draught	1.2 m
Payload	30 t
Crew	6-8
Passengers	252
Propulsive power	2 × 1089 kW
Maximum speed	32 knots
Operational speed	28 knots

Classification: Z C China Classification Society, DnV + 1A1 R45 EO.
Propulsion: Engines: 2 × MTU 12V 396 TB 83, 1089 kW each (32°C air, 32°C water) MCR 1940 rpm; driving 2 × KaMeWa 63 S water-jet units

WaveMaster International 310-seat Zhen Xing Hu
1991

WaveMaster International 380-seat Nansha 28   **1995**

Electrical system: Power for this is supplied by 2 × Mercedes-Benz/Stamford alternator sets, 92 kW each.

Navigation and communications: 72 and 48 mile colour radars, gyro compass, echo-sounder, SSB and VHF radios.

Zhen Xing
Principal Particulars

Length overall	34.5 m
Beam	9.8 m
Draught	1.3 m
Payload	38 t
Crew	8
Passengers	310
Propulsive power	2 × 1458 kW
Operational speed	30 knots
Maximum speed	35 knots

Classification: Z C China Classification Society, DnV + 1A1 R45 EO.

Propulsion: Engines: 2 × MTU 16V 396 TB 83, 1458 kW each (32°C air, 32°C water) MCR 1940 rpm; driving 2 × KaMeWa 63 S62.60 water-jet units.

Electrical system: 2 × Mercedes-Benz/Stamford alternator sets, 92 kW each.

Navigation and communications: 72- and 48- mile colour radars, gyro compass, echo-sounder, SSB and VHF radios.

44 m PASSENGER/CARGO CATAMARAN
Negeen

A symmetrical hull catamaran for a Middle East customer, Valfajre & Shipping Co, delivered in late 1993.

Principal Particulars

Length overall	44 m
Length waterline	37.6 m
Beam	12.4 m
Hull beam	2.7 m
Draught	1.4 m
Displacement	169 t
Payload	36.15 t
Crew	8 (9 berths)
Passengers	244
Fuel capacity	14 000 l
Water capacity	4000 l
Propulsive power	2 × 1940 kW
Operational speed	30.6 knots continuous
Range	400 nm

Classification: DnV +1A1 R3 HSLC, Passenger, EO.

Structure: Hull material: welded aluminium.

Propulsion: Engines: 2 × MTU 16V 396 TE 74L, 1940 kW each at 2000 rpm.

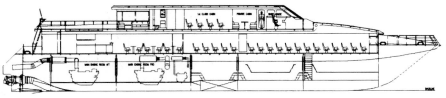

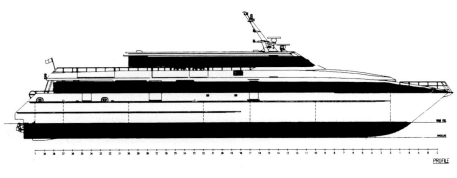

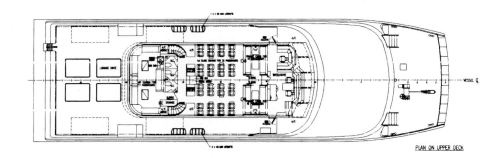

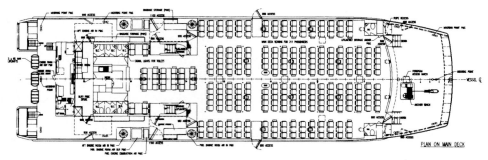

General arrangement of Nansha No 28   **1995**

WaveMaster 44 m catamaran Negeen   *1993*

Craft built	Yard No	Delivered	Seats	Engines	Delivered to
Yin Shan Hu	020	July 1989	252	2 × MTU 12V 396R TB 83	Sanfu
Zhen Xing Hu	022	March 1990	310	2 × MTU 12V 396R TB 83	Jiangmen
Mystique	027	August 1991	150	2 × Perkins T 63544	Boat Torque Cruises
Wu Yi Hu	028	November 1991	354	2 × MTU 16V 396 TE 74	Jiangmen Hong Kong Macao
Peng Lai Hu	037	December 1992	354	2 × MTU 16V 396 TE 74	Jiangmen Hong Kong Macao
Nansha 11	046	December 1992	300	2 × MTU 8V 396 TE 74L	Panyu Nansha Port Passenger Transportation Co
Peng Jiang	035	July 1993	193	2 × MTU 8V 396 TE 74L	Jiangmen Hong Kong Macao
Nansha 18	047	August 1993	386	2 × MTU 8V 396 TE 74L	Panyu Nansha Port Passenger Transportation Co
Negeen	032	November 1993	244	2 × MTU 8V 396 TE 74L	Valfajre 8 Shipping Co
Fei Long	048	March 1994	485	2 × MTU 12V 183 TE 72	Yick Fung Ship & Enterprises Co Ltd
Fast Craft	049	November 1993	218	2 × MTU 12V 183 TE 72	Fastcraft Pty Ltd
Seaflyte	051	December 1993	160	2 × MTU 8V 183 TE 72	Fullers Ferries
Nansha 28	068	June 1994	380	4 × MTU 16V 396 TE 74L	Panyu Nansha Port Passenger Transportation Co
White dolphin II	052	(February 1996)	320	2 ×Wartsila UD23	Boat Torque Cruises
Catamaran Andromeda	126	July 1995	380	4 × MWN TBD 620 V16	-
Rivercat 7	130	(August 1995)	230	2 × Detroit 8V92TA	Sydney Ferries
Not named	117	(May 1996)	450 + 46 cars	4 × MWM TBD 620 V16	-
Not named	137	(June 1996)	450 + 46 cars	4 × MWM TBD 620 V16	-

Transmissions: 2 × Reintjes VLJ 930 gearboxes.
Thrust devices: 2 × water-jets KaMeWa 71S.
Electrical system: Engines: 2 × MTU 6V 183 TA51; generators: 2 × Stamford UC 1274 135 kVA.

Peng Lai Hu

A catamaran delivered early in 1993 to a Chinese operator.

Principal Particulars

Length overall	39 m
Beam	11.4 m
Draught	1.35 m
Crew	14
Passengers	354
Fuel capacity	8800 l
Water capacity	1500 l
Propulsive power	2 × 1580 kW
Operational speed	30 knots

Classification: China Classification Society, ZC or DnV.
Propulsion: Engines: 2 × MTU 16V 396 TE 74 diesels, 1580 kW each at 1975 rpm; driving 2 × KaMeWa 71S water-jets.

Nansha 18
Nansha 28

Delivered in August 1993 and June 1994 respectively, these are the fastest passenger catamarans delivered by Wavemaster to date. Full load speeds of over 43 knots were achieved with a lightship speed of approximately 48 knots.

Principal Particulars

Length overall	42 m
Length waterline	36 m
Beam	12 m
Draught	1.5 m
Displacement	175 t
Crew	8
Passengers	378
Propulsive power	4 × 1960 kW
Operational speed	43.5 knots
Range	185 nm

Classification: ZC, DnV +1A1 HSLC Pass Cat R3.
Propulsion: Engines: 4 × MTU 16V 396 TE 74L at 1960 kW at 1950 rpm; driving 4 × KMW 63SII water-jets.

Peng Jiang

Delivered in August 1993, this vessel has been designed to meet restrictive low wash requirements imposed by the operator.

Principal Particulars

Length overall	34.6 m
Length waterline	29.5 m
Beam	9.8 m
Draught	1.4 m
Crew	12
Passengers	193

Propulsive power	2 × 1960 kW
Operational speed	40 knots
Range	250 nm

Classification: ZC, DnV +1A1 HSLC Pass Cat R3.
Propulsion: Main engines: 2 × MTU 16V 396 TE 74L at 1960 kW at 1950 rpm.
Water-jets: 4 × KaMeWa 63SII.

Fei Long

Delivered in March 1994, *Fei Long* is the largest catamaran ferry built by Wavemaster to date. The craft operates with other catamarans on the Bohai Sea in northern China on a route linking Dalian and Yantai.

Principal Particulars

Length overall	49 m
Length waterline	41 m
Beam	13.6 m
Draught	1.5 m
Passengers	485
Operational speed	40.5 knots
Range	390 nm

Classification: DnV +1A1 HSLC R3 passenger.
Propulsion: Engines are two MTU 16V 396 TE 74L, driving reduction gearboxes to KaMeWa 71S water-jets.

UPDATED

CHILE

ASENAV MR

Fidel Oteiza 1956 P 13, Santiago 9, Chile

Telephone: +56 (2) 274 1515
Telex: 240841 EKOS CL
Telefax: +56 (2) 204 9118

ASENAV (Astilleros y Servicios Navales) delivered a second fast catamaran in late 1994 based on the Båtservice Sea Lord 28. The first craft, *Patagonia Express,* was delivered in 1993 for service with the Patagonia Travelling Service as a fast passenger ferry. The second vessel, *Pacifico Express,* is designed as a live fish carrier and can carry six removable fish tanks on deck.

The company has a third catamaran under construction, also based on the Båtservice Sea Lord 28 design, which is designed to carry 150 passengers through the Beagle canal at the southern tip of South America. Named the *Luciano Beta,* the vessel is due for delivery in late 1995.

Pacifico Express
Principal Particulars

Length overall	29.8 m
Beam	8.3 m
Draught	1.65 m
Payload	54 t
Crew	12
Maximum Speed	30 knots
Operational Speed	22 knots

Propulsion: The vessel is powered by two Detroit Diesel 12V 149TI engines each rated at 1150 kW at 1900 rpm. Each engine drives a KaMeWa controllable pitch propeller via a Reintjes WVS 430 gearbox.

UPDATED

CHINA, PEOPLE'S REPUBLIC

HANG TONG HIGH SPEED SHIP DEVELOPMENT CO LTD

Fenjiang Road, Xinhui City, Guangdong Province, People's Republic of China 529100

Telephone: +86 (0750) 661 0966 / 663 2967
Telefax: +86 (0750) 666 6547 / 661 0966

Hang Tong, a joint venture company, is specialised in the development of aluminium alloy high-speed craft. At present they are developing hydrofoils, catamarans and other high-speed ships, co-operating with partners in Australia and Russia. They are also producing sophisticated hovercraft backed by advanced technology and the research of the aerospace industry in China.

The repair of high-speed ships and welding of aluminium alloy and stainless steel structures are undertaken also.

The yard are licensed builders of AMD catamaran designs, and are currently building a AMD 150.

AMD 150 Wave-Piercing Catamaran Ferry

Construction of this vessel commenced in September 1994 with delivery scheduled for mid-1995.
Principal Particulars

Length overall	25 m
Beam	10.65 m
Draught	1.8 m
Passengers	170
Operational speed	28 knots

Classification: Chinese Classification Society.
Propulsion: The main engines are 2 × Isotta ID36SS V12 high-speed diesels.

NEW ENTRY

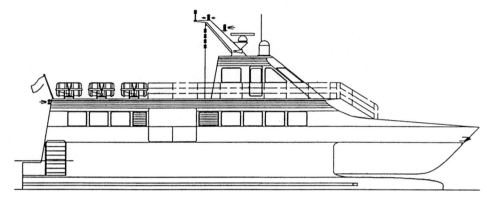

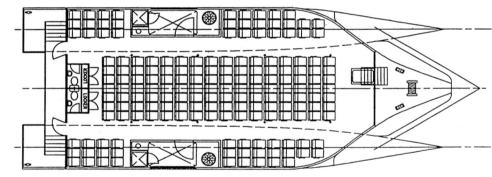

General arrangement of AMD150

1995

COMMONWEALTH OF INDEPENDENT STATES

ALMAZ SHIPYARD CENTRAL MARINE DESIGN BUREAU

19 Uralskaya Street, St Petersburg 199161, Russia, CIS

Telephone: +7 (812) 350 2983
Telefax: +7 (812) 350 0925

Alexander V Shliakhtenko, *Chief Designer*

The Almaz central marine design bureau was established in 1940 and specialises in the design and construction of high-speed commercial and military craft (hydrofoils, hovercraft, catamarans, SES and Swath).

In 1993 a catamaran design was announced by Almaz Shipyard aimed at the river and coastal route markets.

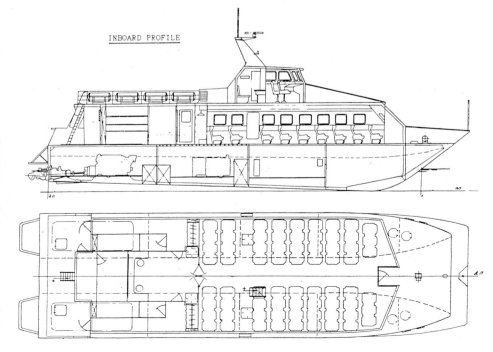

General arrangement of Almaz Fast Passenger Ferry
1994

FAST PASSENGER FERRY (DESIGN)
Principal Particulars

Length overall	21.5 m
Beam	7 m
Draught	1.6 m
Passengers	70

Propulsive power	2 × 1044 kW
Maximum speed	30 knots
Range	300 nm

Propulsion: 2 × DDEC 16V 92 TA diesels, 1044 kW each driving one Hamilton 422 water-jet.

UPDATED

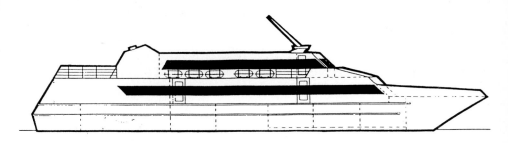

SUDOEXPORT

11 Sadovaya Kudrinskaya, Moscow 123231, Russia, CIS

Telephone: +7 (095) 252 4401
Telex: 411116 KURS
Telefax: +7 (095) 200 2250

Vladimir A Chmyr, *General Director*
Vjacheslav V Yanchenko, *Director of Imports*
Yuri I Fomichev, *Director of Exports*

In 1994 three catamaran designs were being marketed by Sudoexport in the range of 31.8 to 49.3 m, and aimed at the river and coastal route markets.

ANDROMEDA (DESIGN)
Principal Particulars

Length overall	31.8 m
Beam	10 m
Draught	1.8 m
Passengers	180
Propulsive power	2 × 809 kW
Maximum speed	30 knots
Operational speed	27 knots
Range	300 nm

Propulsion: The main engines are 2 × Zvezda M4O1 A-2 diesels, 809 kW max each, at 1550 rpm.

IMPULSE (DESIGN)
Principal Particulars

Length overall	35 m
Beam	12.5 m
Draught	2.6 m
Passengers	400
Maximum speed	36 knots
Operational speed	33 knots
Range	300 nm

Propulsion: The main engines are 2 × MTU 16V 396 TB 84.

PERSEUS (DESIGN)
Principal Particulars

Length overall	49.3 m
Beam	10 m
Draught	2 m
Passengers	140
Propulsive power	2 × 3675 kW
Maximum speed	40 knots
Operational speed	37 knots
Range	250 nm

Propulsion: The main engines are 2 × Zvezda M5O4B-3 diesels, 3675 kW each at 2000 rpm.

VERIFIED

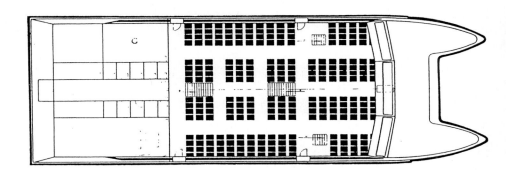

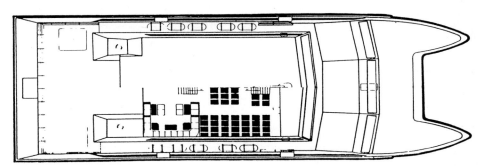

General arrangement of Impulse

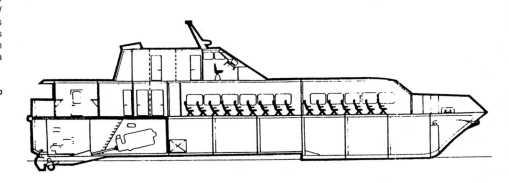

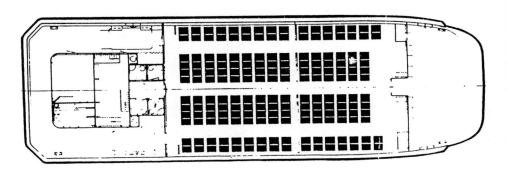

General arrangement of Andromeda

DENMARK

DANYARD A/S

Kragholmen 4, PO Box 719, DK-9900 Frederikshavn, Denmark

Telephone: +45 (98) 422299
Telefax: +45 (98) 432930

Jens Viskinge Jensen, *President and CEO*
Gunnar Lage, *Executive President*
Christian Rodin-Nielson, *Vice President, Sales*
Niels Knudsen, *Vice President, Project Design*

SEAJET 250

The Seajet 250 is a fast ferry Developed by Danyard A/S in cooperation with NQEA Australia Pty Ltd. Two of these craft were ordered by the Danish owners Mols-Linen in late 1994 for delivery in mid-1996. The 76 m passenger/vehicle semi-Swath catamaran ferry has a hull form which has been developed with the Swedish Maritime Research Institution, SSPA.

The Seajet combines the good sea-keeping qualities of a Swath with the good resistance qualities of catamarans. Through this design approach it has been possible to minimise the heave and pitch movements, and to lower the acceleration forces imposed on the passengers. The four loading lanes at the bow and twin side exit lanes allow for fast turn-around times.

Principal Particulars

Length overall	76 m
Beam	23.4 m
Draught	3.4 m
Passengers	450-600
Vehicles	120
Operational speed	40.8 knots

Classification: DnV R3 EO.
Propulsion: The main engines are 2 × LM 1600 gas-turbines; driving 4 × water-jets.
Control: Ride control: optional, recommended above significant 2.5 m wave height.

UPDATED

Artist's impression of Seajet 250   *1994*

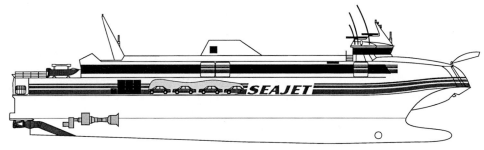

Seajet 250 side elevation

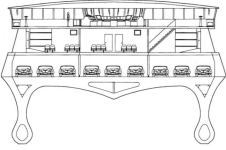

Seajet 250 transverse section

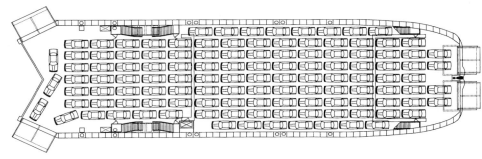

Seajet 250 car deck arrangement   *1994*

FINLAND

FINNYARDS LTD

PO Box 139, SF-261 01 Rauma, Finland

Telephone: +358 (38) 83611
Telex: 65117 FYARD SF
Telefax: +358 (38) 836 2366

Aarno Mannonen, *President*
Sten Segerqvist, *Vice President, Shipbuilding*

Finnyards Ltd was incorporated and became operational in January 1992, combining the total resources and facilities of Rauma Yards and Hollming Ltd, two leading shipyards located adjacent to one another in the city of Rauma, Finland. Since 1992 the company has invested heavily in new dry-dock and aluminium production facilities.

In July 1993 Finnyards received an order for two of the largest high-speed catamaran ferries to date. Ordered by Stena AB, the contract was worth in

Artist's impression of the Stena HSS   *1994*

excess of $200 million. The design of the vessel was undertaken by Stena Rederi and is codenamed Stena HSS (High-speed Sea Service). A third craft was ordered in 1994 with an option for a further vessel.

Stena HSS

There have been three vessels ordered by Stena AB for operation in the UK. The first vessel to be delivered in late 1995 is scheduled to operate on the Holyhead-Dun Laoghaire route. The second vessel is scheduled to be delivered in April 1996 for operation between Stranraer and Belfast and the third vessel is currently scheduled to be delivered in January 1997.

The hull design is of a patented narrow hulled catamaran semi-Swath form designed to DnV certification with a service speed of 40 knots in a significant wave height of 5 m.

Principal Particulars

Length overall	124 m
Beam	40 m
Passengers	1500
Vehicles	375 cars or
	50 lorries + 100 cars
Operational speed	40 knots

Propulsion: The vessel is fitted with four gas-turbines, one General Electric/Kværner LM 1600 and one LM 2500 turbine in each hull. The turbines will drive through a MAAG gearbox to two KaMeWa 760 SII water-jets. This arrangement of the gas-turbines allows the vessel to cruise at 24 knots on the two LM 1600s, at 32 knots on the two LM 2500s and at 40 knots on all four.

102 m FAST FERRY (DESIGN)

Finnyards is currently marketing a new range of catamaran ferries from 100 to 170 m in length with speeds of between 30 and 45 knots. Besides its own research and development work, Finnyards is actively taking part in two development programmes, the Shipyard 2000 Ultralight vessel study in Finland and the Nordic dynamically loaded light construction programme.

The 102 m vessel is one variant of their design study and is capable of carrying 920 passengers and 266 cars at speeds of up to 40 knots with a power requirement of 33 MW.

UPDATED

Lower hulls of the Stena HSS under construction　　　　　　**1995**

Artist's impression of the 102 m Finnyards design (design)
1995

FRANCE

CMN

CONSTRUCTIONS MECANIQUES DE NORMANDIE

51 rue de la Bretonnière, PO Box 539, F-50105 Cherbourg, France

Telephone: +33 33 20 12 50
Telex: 170507 F
Telefax: +33 33 44 01 09

This company has been licensed by Advanced Multi-Hull Designs Pty Ltd of Sydney, Australia, to build their catamaran designs.

VERIFIED

CONSTRUCTIONS ALUMINIUM NAVALES SARL

Quatali de la Cabaude, F-85100 les Sables d'Olonne, France

Telephone: +33 93 47 30 30
Telex: 710 775 F
Telefax: +33 51 21 20 06

Fabrice Epaud, *Commercial Director*

Ville de Toulon III

A 200-passenger, 20 knot vessel (length 25 m, beam 8 m) launched in 1987. The superstructure is of interest in that it is built up with tubular frames. Principal material of construction is aluminium AG 4 MC 5086. The craft is classified by Bureau Veritas.

VERIFIED

Ville de Toulon III, *one of three catamaran ferries built to a design by Constructions Aluminium Navales sarl*
1992

GERMANY

HDW

HOWALDTSWERKE-DEUTSCHE WERFT AG

PO Box 6309 Werftstrasse 112-114, D-24143 Kiel, Germany

Telephone: +49 (431) 700 2799/2314
Telex: 292288-0 HDW D
Telefax: +49 (431) 700 3374/3388

Howaldtswerke-Deutsche Werft AG is a member of the Preussag Group and one of the largest ship-building companies in Germany. The production programme covers all types of merchant ships especially large container ships, ferries and cruise liners, LPG and LNG carriers and crude oil tankers. As well as conversions and repairs the naval construction covers the production of submarines, frigates and corvettes. The yard participates in substantial research and development projects in which it has gained a thorough knowledge of advanced marine technologies. It is currently participating in the European research program 'Eurofast' for flexible advanced sea transportation.

CARGO CAT (DESIGN)

The Cargo Cat project was launched at the beginning of 1991 as part of a three-year research project on fast multihull vessels. This joint industry project is supported by the German Ministry of Research and Development and HDW is focusing on cargo and combined passenger cargo transport. The basic design features symmetrical hard-chined hulls, built in aluminium; the use of steel is being examined. Propulsion will be achieved by gas-turbine or diesel-

Artist's impression of HDW Cargo Cat (design)   *1992*

driven water-jet installations. The engine room will be fully automated.

The deck will give enough space for ro-ro or lo-lo cargo, with a payload capacity of about 400 tonnes, depending on service speed and route distance. The basic design can be easily adapted for passenger/car ferry service.

Principal Particulars

Length overall	78 m
Beam overall	26 m
Draught	2.5 m
Payload	400 t
Operational speed	36 knots

VERIFIED

ULTIMAR GmbH & Co KG

Am Seedeich 39, D-27572 Bremerhaven, Germany

Telephone: +49 (471) 799833
Telefax: +49 (471) 75011

ULTIMAR 62

The Ultimar 62 is a fast catamaran in a pleasure craft configuration with a range of 600 nm and a service speed of 35 knots. In June the vessel completed the trip from London to Monte Carlo in the record time of 89 hours total and a running time of 75 hours, averaging 29 knots.

The Ultimar is a deep V catamaran with excellent sea-keeping and outstanding economy due to its hydrofoil system.

The hull deck and superstructure are built in carbonfibre honeycomb composite at a total hull weight of only 7.5 tonnes.

Propulsion consists of 2 MAN diesel engines connected directly via propshafts to Hamilton water-jets.

Principal Particulars

Length overall	19.6 m
Beam	6 m
Draught	1 m
Draught, foilborne	0.5 m
Displacement, maximum	27 t
Maximum speed	40 knots

Hysucat Offshore
Nordblitz

This fast ferry was launched in 1994 and is of a similar design to the Ultimar 62, and uses the same patented hydrofoil system. These foils are arranged to carry 50 per cent of the ship's weight, and have no controllable flaps or other such moveable surfaces. The foils increase the hull's efficiency and also improve the seakeeping of the craft.

Principal Particulars

Length overall	21.55 m
Length waterline	18.80 m
Beam	7.50 m
Draught	1.35 m
Passengers	118
Propulsive power	2 × 750 kW
Maximum speed	40 knots
Operational speed	36 knots

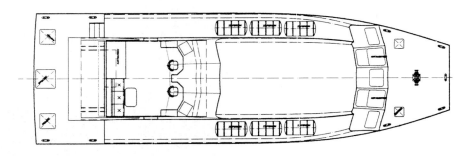

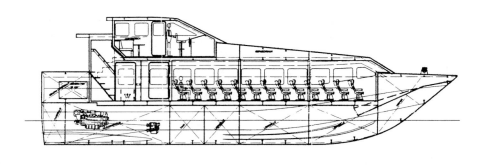

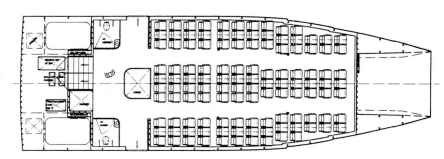

Layout of the Nordblitz   *1995*

Classification: The craft is designed to the IMO code for high speed craft.

Propulsion: The main engines are 2 × high-speed diesels each producing 700 kW at 2000 rpm, driving 2 × controllable pitch propellers. The propellers operate in tunnels in the hull's underside, which increases the propulsion efficiency and allows a shallower draught, (the draught was limited to 1.5 m at the design stage).

Hysucat River
Rheinjet

This 70 passenger fast ferry was launched in 1994 and also uses the Hysucat patented foil system, although simplified for river operations.

Principal Particulars

Length overall	17.80 m
Length waterline	15.00 m
Beam	6.00 m
Draught	1.30 m
Passengers	60
Propulsive power	2 × 450 kW
Maximum speed	40 knots
Operational speed	38 knots

Propulsion: The main engines are 2 × high speed diesels each producing 450 kW, driving 2 × controllable pitch propellers operating in tunnels.

UPDATED *The Ultimar 62* *1993*

HONG KONG

A FAI ENGINEERS AND SHIPREPAIRERS LTD

NKML31 Po Lun Street, Lai Chi Kok, Kowloon, Hong Kong

Telephone: +852 (2307) 6268
Telex: 45517 AFES HX
Telefax: +852 (2307) 5170

Vitus Szeto, *General Manager*

A Fai Engineers and Shiprepairers Ltd has been an InCat licensee since the early 1980s and has built 13 catamarans to their design. Since 1990 the company has concentrated on fast catamaran vessels designed by Advanced Multihull Designs Pty Ltd (AMD).

CA3 AIRPORT RESCUE BOAT

A Fai Engineers and Shiprepairers delivered an InCat 23 m airport rescue catamaran to the Hong Kong Government's Civil Aviation Department in July 1990. In addition to providing rescue services at Kai Tak airport, the vessel is also equipped for firefighting duties. Standard crewing is seven men.

Intended to be normally operated only within

Civil Aviation 3 airport rescue boat *1991*

Craft built	Completed	Seats	Speed	Delivered to	Route
21 m *Mingzhu Hu*	January 1982	150	29 knots	Ning Bo Hua Gang Co Ltd, Zhe Jiang Province, China	Hong Kong to Inland River
21 m *Yin Zhou Hu*	March 1982	150	29 knots	Ning Bo Hua Gang Co Ltd, Zhe Jiang Province, China	Hong Kong to Inland River
21 m *Liuhua Hu*	September 1982	150	29 knots	Guangdong Province, Hong Kong, Macao Navigation, China	Hong Kong to Taiping
21 m *Li Jiang*	June 1983	150	29 knots	Kwai Kong Shipping Co Ltd, Hong Kong	Hong Kong to Wuzhou
16 m *Kwong Fai*	June 1984	40	21 knots	Castle Peak Power Co Ltd, Hong Kong	Hong Kong
21 m *Yue Hai Chun*	October 1984	169	29 knots	Shen Zhen Shipping, China	Shekou to Zhu Hai
21 m *Shen Zhen Chun*	July 1985	169	29 knots	Shen Zhen Shipping, China	Shekou to Zhu Hai
21 m *Zhu Hai Chun*	December 1986	169	29 knots	Shen Zhen Shipping, China	Shekou to Zhu Hai/Macau
22 m *Gong Bian 153*	August 1988	-	33 knots	Guang Zhou Custom Dept, China	Whampo and Pearl River Area (Patrol Boat)
22 m *Ling Nan Chun*	November 1988	187	28 knots	Shen Zhen Shipping, China	Shekou to Zhu Hai
22 m *Nan Hai Chun*	March 1989	187	28 knots	Shen Zhen Shipping, China	Shekou to Zhu Hai
23 m *CA3*	June 1990	250 rescue places	28 knots	Civil Aviation Department, Government (Airport Rescue Boat)	Hong Kong Class 1 and 2 Limit Area Hong Kong
23 m *Dong Fang Chun*	April 1991	197	28 knots	Shen Zhen Shipping, China	Shekou to Zhu Hai
28 m AMD 200 *Jian Xing*	Early 1993	235	28 knots	Shen Zhen Shipping, China	Shekou to Zhu Hai
24 m AMD 170 *Wuzhou*	Mid-1994	150	29 knots	Wuzhou Guangxi Navigation	
17 m AMD 60	Early 1995	72	27.5 knots	Fei Dong Shipping, China	

class I and II waters, it is designed to withstand minimum wave heights of 1.2 m at speeds of at least 25 knots. Forward there is a wheelhouse with a floor 1 m above the main deck level to give the crew a good all-round view. A fire-fighting monitor is mounted on the roof of the wheelhouse.

An emergency recess with two stairways is provided on each side of the vessel, the length of the rescue recess platforms being at least 2.5 m to facilitate the easy handling of stretchers. Aluminium fold-up panels with non-skid steps are fitted at each side of the recesses to allow survivors in the water to climb on board.

An awning aft of the wheelhouse is high enough to provide ample headroom for two tiers of stretchers and not restrict rearward visibility from the wheelhouse. Below the awning, there are three floodlights on each side to illuminate the deck area after dark.

Six rows of seats located port and starboard adjacent the outer awning supports are used as weathertight lockers for rescue equipment. Total rescue capability of the design is 32 people on stretchers, 64 on the seats and at least 154 standing. With the two diesels operating at their continuous rating of 550 kW at 2000 rpm and leaving base with 2400 litres of fuel on board, endurance is 4.5 hours.

The vessel is the 13th InCat design built by A Fai at its Hong Kong yard since 1982.

AMD200 *Jin Xing*

Constructed by A Fai Engineers to an AMD design for a Chinese customer, this 28 m AMD design was delivered in June 1993.

Principal Particulars

Length overall	28 m
Beam	10.3 m
Draught	1.8 m
Passengers	242
Fuel capacity	8000 l
Water capacity	1000 l
Operational speed	25 knots

Classification: Chinese ZC(CCS).

Propulsion: Engines: two Deutz MWM TBD 604B V8, 840 kW each at 1800 rpm (other engine options available).

Li Jiang, one of nine International Catamarans 21 m craft operated by Kwai Kong Shipping Company **1988**

AMD200 Jin Xing **1994**

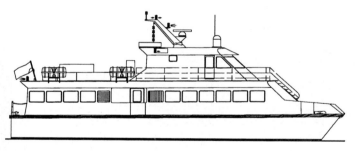

AMD170 PROFILE

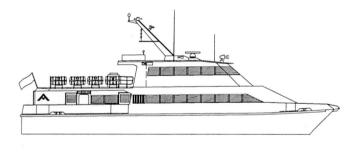

AMD200 PROFILE

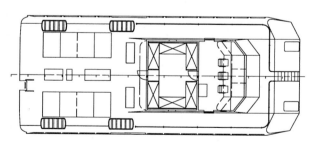

UPPER DECK

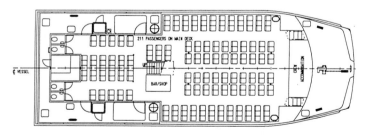

MAIN PASSENGER DECK : 211 PASSENGERS

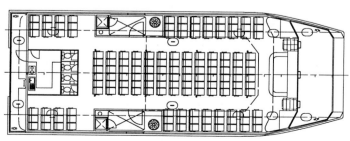

MAIN DECK : 150 PASSENGERS

Layout of AMD170 conventional catamaran **1994**

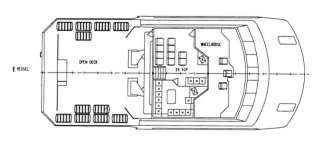

VIP LOUNGE AND UPPER DECK : 24 PASSENGERS

AMD200 built by A Fai Engineers, Hong Kong **1994**

Transmissions: two Reintjes WVS 430 gearboxes.
Thrust devices: two FP Propellers.
Electrical system: 380 V AC 3-phase, 220 V AC single phase, 24 V DC.
Generators: two 75 kVA.

AMD170 *Wuzhou*

Constructed by A Fai Engineers to an AMD design for the Wuzhou Guangxi Navigation Co, this vessel was delivered in mid-1994.

Principal Particulars

Length overall	24 m
Beam	8.9 m
Draught	1.8 m
Passengers	150
Fuel capacity	8000 l
Operational speed	29 knots

Classification: Chinese ZC(CCS).
Propulsion: 2 × Issotta Fraschini ID 36SS12 diesels each driving a fixed-pitch propeller via a ZF BW460 reverse reduction gearbox.

UPDATED

AMD170 Wuzhou
1995

ITALY

MOSCHINI

CANTIERI ING MOSCHINI SpA

Via De Nicola, 5, I-61032 Fano (PS), Italy

Telephone: +39 (721) 854236/854484
Telefax: +39 (721) 854934

Moschini are builders of high-speed mono-hull and catamaran vessels in Kevlar fibre and GRP structures.

21 m PASSENGER CATAMARAN (DESIGN)
Principal Particulars

Length overall	21.2 m
Beam	7 m

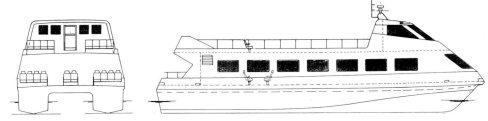

Moschini 21 m passenger catamaran (design)

Displacement, maximum	58 t
Passengers	200
Operational speed	23 knots

VERIFIED

RODRIQUEZ CANTIERI NAVALI SpA

Via S Raineri 22, I-98122 Messina, Italy

Telephone: +39 (90) 7765
Telex: 980030 RODRIK I
Telefax: +39 (90) 675294

Barbasso Gattuso, *President*
Giovanni Morace, *Managing Director*
Alcide Sculati, *Technical Manager*
Diego Mazzeo, *Sales and Marketing*

SEAGULL 400

The Seagull 400 catamaran is based on extensive Rodriquez background in high-speed vessels and a study carried out since 1978. The vessel is built in light alloy, mostly welded but riveting is used wherever possible. The hulls are of symmetrical form.

The first vessel of this type was ordered by CAREMAR SpA and delivered to this Naples based operator in February 1993. The vessel is operated on the company's route from Naples to Capri.

Principal Particulars

Length overall	43.25 m
Length waterline	36.4 m
Beam	10.9 m
Draught	1.45 m
Displacement, minimum	115 t
Displacement, maximum	150 t
Passengers	354
Propulsive power	2 × 2000 kW
Maximum speed	34 knots
Range	200 nm

Propulsion: Engines: 2 × MTU 16V 396 TE 74L, 2000 kW each at 2000 rpm, driving 2 × KaMeWa 71 SII water-jets.

UPDATED

Seagull 400
1994

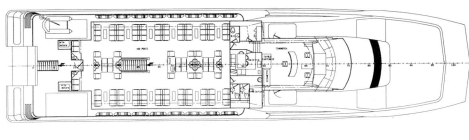

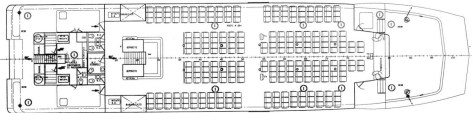

Seagull 400 deck layouts
1994

JAPAN

HITACHI ZOSEN CORPORATION

Head Office: 3-28 Nishi Kujo 5-chome, Konohana-ku, Osaka, 554 Japan

Telephone: +81 (6) 466 7500
Telex: 63376 SHIPYARD J
Telefax: +81 (6) 466 7572

Superjet-30

Superjet-30 is a foil-assisted catamaran with a maximum speed of 40 knots. The hull is a hybrid design consisting of a catamaran and fully submerged foils. The lift of hydrofoils supports more than 80 per cent of the ship's weight. The control system of flaps and ailerons on the hydrofoils offers high sea-keeping capability.

Seven Superjet-30s were constructed at Hitachi Zosen Kanagawa Works.

Principal Particulars

Length overall	31.5 m
Beam	9.8 m
Draught	1.9 m
Draught, hullborne	2.8 m (including foils)
Displacement	190 GRT
Passengers	200
Propulsive power	2 × 3729 kW
Maximum speed	40 knots

Propulsion: The main engines are two high-speed diesel engines driving two water-jets.
Control: Motion control system provided.

UPDATED

Craft built (Superjet-30)	Yard No	Delivered	Seats	Operator
Trident Ace	7306	September 1993	160	Airport Awaji Aqualine Co Ltd
Artemis	7307	November 1993	160	Airport Awaji Aqualine Co Ltd
Apollon	7308	August 1994	160	Airport Awaji Aqualine Co Ltd
Dogo	7310	December 1993	156	Setonaikai Kisen Co Ltd
Miyajima	7312	April 1994	156	Setonaikai Kisen Co Ltd
Zuiko	7309	November 1993	156	Isizaki kisen Co Ltd
Shoko	7311	March 1994	156	Isizaki kisen Co Ltd

UPDATED

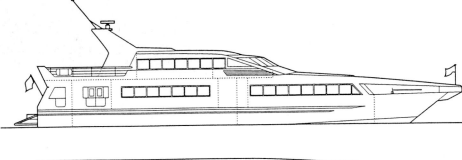

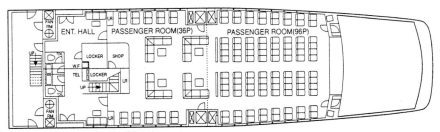

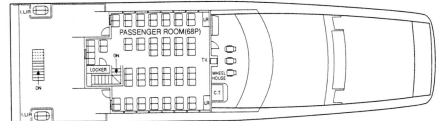

General arrangement of the Superjet-30

1994

Superjet-30 Miyajima

1995

IHI

ISHIKAWAJIMA-HARIMA HEAVY INDUSTRIES COMPANY LTD

Tokyo Chuo Building, 6-2 Marunouchi 1-chome, Chiyoda-ku, Tokyo 100, Japan

Telephone: +81 (3) 3286 2353
Telex: 24104 IHISEN J
Telefax: +81 (3) 3286 2435

Mikuni Komatsu, *General Manager*
Kenichiro Kondo, *Assistant Manager*

SSTH (Super Slender Twin Hull)

The SSTH concept has been developed by IHI over the past five years. In 1991 the first SSTH project was launched called the SSTH 30. The concept has the benefits of displacement hulls, large loading deck space and, apart from the very high length-to-beam ratio of the hulls the design incorporates a double stage bow and a motion damping foil

SSTH 30   *1993*

SSTH 30

This craft experiences vertical accelerations less than 0.1 *g* measured in head sea of 40 m wave length and 1 m significant wave height.

Principal Particulars

Length overall	30.4 m
Beam	5.6 m
Passengers	68
Propulsive power	2 × 440 kW
Maximum speed	28.2 knots
Operational speed	21 knots

Propulsion: Engines: 2 × MTU 8V 183 TE 92 diesels, 440 kW (MCR) each.

SSTH 50 (DESIGN)

Principal Particulars

Length overall	49.9 m
Beam	8 m
Draught	1.2 m
Passengers	320
Propulsive power	2 × 1820 kW
Maximum speed	35 knots
Range	150 nm

Structure: Hull material: welded aluminium.
Propulsion: Engines: 2 × 1820 kW (MCR) diesels, driving 2 × water-jets.

SSTH 90 (DESIGN)

Principal Particulars

Length overall	92.4 m
Beam	19.4 m
Draught	2.1 m
Payload	170 t
Passengers	400
Vehicles	80 cars
Propulsive power	4 × 5150 kW
Maximum speed	42 knots
Range	200 nm

SSTH 90 (design)   *1995*

Structure: Hull material: welded aluminium.
Propulsion: Engines: 4 × 5150 kW high-speed diesels, driving water-jets.

SSTH 150 (DESIGN)

Passenger/car carrying high-speed ferry designed with steel hull and aluminium superstructure.

Principal Particulars

Length overall	153.5 m
Beam	27.5 m
Draught	3.5 m
Passengers	1000
Cars	300
Propulsive power	2 × 20 600 kW
Maximum speed	37 knots
Range	400 nm

Propulsion: 2 × gas-turbine engines each driving a water-jet unit.

SSTH 200 (DESIGN)

The SSTH 200 is a new all-steel design arranged for cargo and passenger operations.

Principal Particulars

Length overall	199.9 m
Beam	29.8 m
Draught	4.9 m
Passengers	500
Propulsive power	2 × 20 600 kW
Maximum speed	32 knots
Range	600 nm

Propulsion: 2 × LM 2500 19 800 kW gas-turbine engines each driving a water-jet propulsor.

UPDATED

KAWASAKI HEAVY INDUSTRIES LTD SHIP GROUP

Tokyo Head Office: World Trade Center Building, 4-1 Hamamatsu-cho 2-chome, Minato-ku, Tokyo 105, Japan

Telephone: +81 (3) 3435 2186
Telex: 2424371 KAWAJU J
Telefax: +81 (3) 3436 3038

Kobe Works: 1-1 Higashi Kawasaki-cho 3-chome, Chou-ku, Kobe 650-19, Japan

Telephone: +81 (78) 682 5120
Telex: 5623931 KHIKOB J
Telefax: +81 (78) 682 5512

Ryunosuke Kawazumi, *Managing Director and Senior General Manager of Ship Group*

The concept design of wave-piercing catamarans was introduced from Advanced Multi-Hull Designs Pty Ltd in 1990. Since then Kawasaki has been developing the design by conducting a wide range of tank tests, structural analysis and fire tests of

AMD1500 Kawasaki Jet Piercer, Hayabusa   *1995*

aluminium structures. Kawasaki Heavy Industries Ltd executed a construction contract between Maritime Credit Corporation of Japan and Kyushi Ferry Boat Co Ltd for a Kawasaki Jet Piercer AMD1500 in March 1994. The keel of the vessel was laid at KHI's Kobe yard on 2 April 1994. The vessel, *Hayabusa*, was on trials by November 1994 and was delivered in December 1994. The vessel will be introduced on the route between Yawatahama, on the west coast of Shikoku, and Usuki, on the east coast of Kyushi by Kyushi Ferry Boat Company. The trip time will be reduced from 130 minutes to 90 minutes.

The design of the AMD1500 allows for two modes of operation. In car/passenger mode the vessel will carry 460 passengers and 94 cars at a maximum speed of 35 knots. In Freight mode the single vehicle deck can accomodate up to 24 twelve tonne freight trucks or 32 eight tonne freight trucks. This freight capacity results in a maximum deadweight of 570 tonnes. Such capacity provides flexibility for the operator allowing low season or night freight services for additional revenue.

AMD1500 KAWASAKI JET PIERCER
Hayabusa
Principal Particulars

Length overall	100 m
Beam	19.98 m
Draught	3.1 m
Passengers	460
Vehicles	94 cars
Maximum speed	35.5 knots

Propulsion: 2 × Caterpillar 3616 and 2 × Caterpillar 3612 engines, driving 4 × Kawasaki KPJ-169A water-jets.

UPDATED

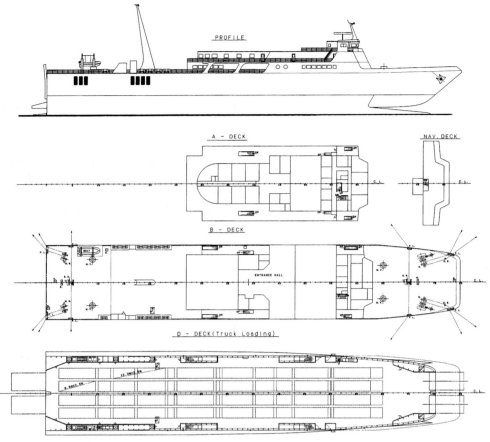

AMD1500 Kawasaki Jet Piercer   *1995*

MITSUBISHI HEAVY INDUSTRIES LTD

5-1 Maranouchi 2-chome, Chiyoda-ku, Tokyo, Japan

Telephone: +81 (3) 3212 3111
Telex: 22443J
Telefax: +81 (3) 3212 9822

HI-STABLE CABIN CRAFT (HSCC)
Ukishiro

Completed by Mitsubishi in the Autumn of 1987 this prototype catamaran craft features a passenger cabin mounted on hydraulically actuated autostabilising rams. The cabin is centrally mounted on top of a 200 mm diameter central hydraulic jack having a stroke of 1 m. This supporting member is attached by a ball and socket joint to the hulls and positions the cabin completely clear of the hulls. Four other 85 mm hydraulic rams, attached with shock absorbers, support the cabin's four corners.

When motion of the basic catamaran craft occurs in heave, yaw, surge or sway, all hydraulic rams are activated simultaneously by an onboard computer (a 16 bit personal computer) with a rapid response capability to monitoring sensors, thereby almost eliminating or minimising cabin motion. Trials have demonstrated reductions of cabin motion to one-third of the motion of the basic supporting catamaran structure.

The catamaran type was chosen as the basic vehicle because of its good stability characteristics and cabin width advantages. It is reported that the computer software required for the system was developed in a five-year study programme initiated by MHI and supported by the semi-governmental Japan Foundation for Shipbuilding Advancement.

Principal Particulars

Length	12.7 m
Beam	5.4 m
Displacement	17 t (GRT)
Maximum speed	20 knots

Propulsion: 2 × Mitsubishi 239 kW diesels.
Operator: Higashi Chugoku Ryoju Kosan.

HI-STABLE CABIN CRAFT (HSCC)
Voyager

Following the prototype HSCC *Ukishiro* completed in 1987, Mitsubishi, in July 1990, completed a

Voyager   *1992*

Super Shuttle 400 Rainbow   *1993*

The Mitsubishi HSCC at sea   **1989**

200-passenger HSCC delivered to Nishi-Nippon Kaiun Kaisha Ltd.

Principal Particulars

Length overall	26.5 m
Beam	9 m
Draught	1.4 m
Displacement	132 (GRT)
Passengers	200

Maximum speed	18 knots

Propulsion: 2 × DDC 16V 92TA engines, 843 kW each.

SUPER SHUTTLE 400
Rainbow

Mitsubishi Supershuttle 400 *Rainbow* is the world's first diesel-driven hydrofoil catamaran. It was delivered to Oki Shinko Ltd in March 1993 and entered service in April 1993. Main engines, water-jets, foils and computerised ride control system were newly developed and manufactured by Mitsubishi Heavy Industries Ltd for this project.

Principal Particulars

Length overall	33.3 m
Beam overall	13.2 m
Foil width	12.8 m
Displacement	302 t (GRT)
Passengers	341
Maximum speed	45.4 knots

Propulsion: 4 × Mitsubishi S16R-MTK-S diesel engines, 2125 kW each, driving 2 × Mitsubish MWJ-5000A water-jets

Operator: Oki Kisen Ltd

VERIFIED

MITSUI ENGINEERING & SHIPBUILDING COMPANY LTD

6-4 Tsukiji 5-chome, Chuo-ku, Tokyo 104, Japan

Telephone: +81 (3) 3544 3462
Telex: 22821 J, 22924 MITZOSEN J
Telefax: +81 (3) 3544 3031

Hiroshi Kitashima, *Director and General Manager, Ship and Ocean Project Division*
Yutaka Ikeda, *General Manager, Marine Department*

In 1978 Mitsui, employing its own design team, developed the Supermaran CP20HF, seating 195 passengers and with a cruising speed of about 30 knots. This craft has been redesigned for better sea-worthiness and to operate in a maximum wave height of 2.5 m when comfortable service can be provided with no loss of speed. There were two delivered in March and June 1979.

The Supermaran CP30 was delivered to the Nankai Ferry Company Limited in Japan in July 1983. It carries 280 passengers at a cruising speed of 28 knots. The maximum operable wave height is 3 m and comfortable service is assured at a wave height of 2.5 m. The Supermaran CP30 Mk II, *Marine Shuttle*, was introduced into service by the Tokushima Shuttle Line Company Ltd in February

Mitsui Supermaran CP15 Aquajet III   **1990**

1986. The vessel has a higher service speed than its predecessor the CP30, 32 knots against 28.1 knots.

A new type, the Supermaran CP10, *Marine Queen*, was delivered to the Sanzo Kigyo Company Ltd in April 1987, for cruising service in the Seto Inland Sea.

The two 280-seat Supermaran CP30 Mk IIIs, *Blue Star* and *Sun Rise*, entered service in 1987 with Tokushima, and a Supermaran CP30 Mk III, *Coral*, entered service in 1988 on the coastal route of the Shikoku Island facing to the Pacific Ocean.

They have a service speed of 32 knots and the improved seaworthiness and superior propulsive

Craft built (CP types)	Yard No	Completed	Seats	Delivered to
26.46 m CP20 Super Westamaran (ex *Blue Hawk*)	-	1975	162	
26.46 m CP20 Super Westamaran (ex *Marine Star*)	-	1976	180	
26.4 m CP20 Super Westamaran (ex *Sun Beam*)	-	1978	188	
32.8 m CP20HF Supermaran *Sun Shine*	1600	March 1979	195	Tokushima Kosokusen Co Ltd
32.8 m CP20HF Supermaran *Blue Sky*	1601	June 1979	195	Tokushima Kosokusen Co Ltd
40.9 m CP30 Supermaran *Marine Hawk*	1603	July 1983	280	Nankai Ferry Co Ltd
41 m CP30 Mk II Supermaran *Marine Shuttle*	1604	February 1986	280	Tokushima Shuttle Line Co Ltd
21.67 m CP10 Supermaran *Marine Queen*	1607	April 1987	88	Kyowa Kisen KK
41 m CP30 Mk III Supermaran *Blue Star*	1605	June 1987	280	Tokushima Kosokusen Co Ltd
41 m CP30 Mk III Supermaran *Sun Rise*	1606	July 1987	280	Tokushima Kosokusen Co Ltd
41 m CP30 Mk III Supermaran *Coral*	1608	July 1988	250	
33.2 m CP25 Supermaran *Queen Rokko*	1609	June 1988	250	Awaji Ferry Boat Co Ltd
19.9 m CP5 Supermaran *Mon Cheri*	1610	July 1988	53	Tenmaya Marine Corporation
39 m CP25 Supermaran *New Tobishima*	1611	May 1989	300	Sakata City
33.2 m CP20 Supermaran *Wakashio*	1612	March 1989	96	Chiba Prefecture
34.2 m CP15 Supermaran *Aquajet I*	1613	March 1989	198	Kyodo Kisen Co Ltd
34.2 m CP15 Supermaran *Aquajet II*	1614	June 1989	198	Kyodo Kisen Co Ltd
34.2 m CP15 Supermaran *Aquajet III*	1616	November 1990	190	Kyodo Kisen Co Ltd
34.2 m CP15 Supermaran *Aquajet IV*	1617	January 1991	190	Kyodo Kisen Co Ltd
43.2 m Mightycat 40 *Sun Shine*	1618	June 1991	300	Tokushima Kosokusen Co Ltd
43.2 m Mightycat 40 *Soleil*	1619	September 1991	300	Tokushima Kosokusen Co Ltd
21.7 m CP10 Supermaran *Fusanami*	1620	February 1991	-	Chiba Prefecture
34.2 m CP20 Supermaran *Yumesaki*	1621	March 1992	83	Osaka City
43.2 m Mightycat 40 *Argo*	1622	December 1992	300	Nankai Ferry Co Ltd
43.2 m Mightycat 40 *Polar Star*	1623	March 1993	300	Tokushima Kosokusen Co Ltd
43.2 m Mightycat 40 *Venus*	1624	July 1993	300	Tokushima Kosokusen Co Ltd
43.2 m Mightycat 40 (on order)	1625	June 1995	300	Tokushima Kosokusen Co Ltd
30.3 m CP15 Supermaran (on order)	1626	March 1995	235	Bantan Renraku Kisen Co. Ltd.

CATAMARANS	Supermaran CP5	Supermaran CP10	Supermaran CP15	Supermaran CP20 Mk II
Dimensions				
Length overall	19.9 m	21.67 m	34.2 m	33.2 m
Breadth	6 m	7.2 m	8 m	9 m
Draught	1.1 m	1.23 m	1.2 m	1.5 m
GRT, approx	50	80	154	—
Passengers	58	88	198	250
Crew	4	3	5	5
Main engines		2	2	2
	GM 6V-92 TA	GM 12V-92 TA	MTU 16V 396 TB 83	MWM 604B V12
Max continuous rating, each	332 kW at 2170 rpm	615 kW at 2170 rpm	1469 kW at 1940 rpm	1278 kW at 1800 rpm
Continuous rating, each	—	492 kW	1320 kW at 1870 rpm	—
Max speed, approx	21 knots	26.6 knots	35 knots	30 knots
Service speed, approx	17 knots	21.8 knots	31 knots	25 knots
Endurance, approx	8 h	20 h	9 h	9 h

CATAMARANS	Supermaran CP30	Supermaran CP30 Mk II	Supermaran CP30 Mk III	Mightycat 40
Dimensions				
Length overall	40.9 m	41.9 m	41 m	43.2 m
Breadth	10.8 m	10.8 m	10.8 m	10.8 m
Draught	1.37 m full load	1.39 m full load	1.39 m full load	1.3 m
GRT, approx	283	268	270	300
Passengers	280	280	280	300
Crew	4	4	4	4
Main engines	2 × Ikegai 16PA4V185-VG	2 × Fuji Pielstick 16V 190 ATC	2 × Fuji Pielstick 12 PA4V 200 VGA	2 × Niigata 16 PA4V 200 VGA
Max continuous rating, each	1801 kW at 1475 rpm	2050 kWs at 1450 rpm	1961 kW at 1475 rpm	2685 kW at 1475 rpm
Continuous rating, each	1700 kW at 1475 rpm	1700 kW at 1425 rpm	1845 kW at 1400 rpm	2550 kW at 1450 rpm
Max speed, approx	31.1 knots	34 knots	35.1 knots	41 knots
Service speed, approx	28.1 knots	32 knots	32 knots	37 knots
Endurance, approx	10 h	8 h	8 h	5 h

performance over the earlier CP20HF resulting from the improved hull form and their greater size.

Mitsui has, in addition, completed other high-speed catamarans, the Supermaran CP25 *Queen Rokko*, the Supermaran CP20 *Wakashio,* the Supermaran CP25 *New Tobishima*, the Supermaran CP5 *Mon Cheri* and the Supermaran CP15 *Aquajet I, II, III* and *IV* with water-jet propulsion. Five craft of the latest version Mightycat 40 with a maximum speed of over 40 knots have been completed, and a further CP15 and Mightycat 40 are currently under construction and scheduled to be delivered in March and June 1995 respectively.

SUPERMARAN CP15
Aquajet I, II, III and IV

These catamaran passenger ferries have water-jet propulsion and were built for Kyodo Kisen Company Ltd. They entered service in 1988 to ply the route between Osaka, Kobe and Awaji Island.

Principal Particulars

Length overall	34.2 m
Beam	8 m
Draught	1.2 m
Maximum speed	35 knots
Operational speed	31 knots

Propulsion: 2 × MTU 16V 396 TB 83, 1469 kW (1970 hp) each, at 1940 rpm. These drive 2 × KaMeWa water-jets S63

SUPERMARAN CP20 Mk II
Queen Rokko

This is the catamaran double-decker cabin cruiser built for Awaji Ferry Boat Company in 1988.

Principal Particulars

Length overall	33.2 m
Beam	9 m
Draught	1.5 m
Displacement	217 t
Passengers	250
Maximum speed	30 knots
Operational speed	25 knots

Propulsion: Two Deutz MWM 604B V12 engines, 1278 kW (1714 hp PS) each, at 1800 rpm. These drive two fixed-pitch propellers through Niigata Converter MGN 433 EW gearboxes with electric variable propeller speed control device (reduction ratio 2.06:1).

Mitsui Supermaran CP20 Mk II Queen Rokko   *1991*

Mitsui Mightycat 40 Sun Shine   *1992*

SUPERMARAN CP30 Mk III
Sun Rise

This is a catamaran passenger ferry and the fourth one of the CP30 series built for Tokushima Kosokusen Company Ltd in 1987.

Principal Particulars

Length overall	41 m
Beam	10.8 m
Depth	3.4 m
Draught	1.3 m
Passengers	280
Maximum speed	35 knots
Operational speed	32 knots

Propulsion: Two Fuji-Pielstick 12 PA4V 200 VGA engines, 1961 kW each, at 1475 rpm. The craft is propelled by two fixed-pitch propellers.

MIGHTYCAT 40

This is the latest catamaran passenger ferry of the CP30 series having the highest speed of all Japanese catamarans.

Five craft including *Sun Shine* and *Soleil* were built for Tokushima Kosokusen Company Ltd, Kyosho Kisen Company Ltd, Kobe Senpaku Company Ltd and Nankai Ferry Company Ltd.

Principal Particulars

Length overall	43.2 m
Beam	10.8 m
Passengers	300
Maximum speed	41 knots

Propulsion: Two Niigata 16 PA4V 200 VGA engines, driving KaMeWa 71S II water-jets.

UPDATED

Mitsui Supermaran CP30 Mk III Sun Rise

1993

NKK CORPORATION

Shipbuilding and Offshore Division:
1-1-2 Marunouchi, Chiyoda-Ku, Tokyo 100, Japan

Basic Ship Design Department:
2-1, Suehiro-Cho, Tsurumi-Ku, Yokohama 230, Japan

Telephone: +81 (45) 505 7522
Telefax: +81 (45) 505 7521

Kazuo Hayashi, *Product Development Manager*

In early 1991 the NKK Corporation announced the development of a high-speed catamaran project, the V-CAT. The company has built over 40 catamarans and has engaged in extensive research and development work on ultra-high-speed ships. Since July 1991 a 10 m sea-going test craft has been available for development trials.

The V-CAT is designed as a displacement vessel with special attention being given to the cross-sectional areas near the water surface, the upper side hull areas being particularly thin in order to reduce wave forces.

V-CAT vessels would be built in aluminium alloy, have water-jet propulsion and be powered with high-speed diesel engines; there are two versions proposed.

V-CAT (DESIGN)
200-passenger version
Principal Particulars

Length overall	42 m
Beam	10.8 m
Draught	1.4 m
Passengers	200
Operational speed	40 knots

Propulsion: Main engines: 2 × high-speed diesels, MCR 2386 kW.

V-CAT (DESIGN)
400-passenger version
Principal Particulars

Length overall	52 m
Beam	15 m
Draught	1.6 m
Passengers	400
Propulsive power	2 × 3878 kW
Maximum speed	40 knots

Propulsion: Main engines: 2 × high-speed diesels, MCR 3878 kW.

UPDATED

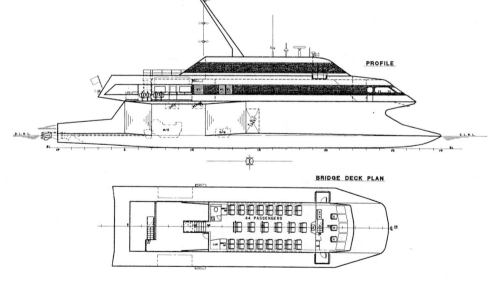

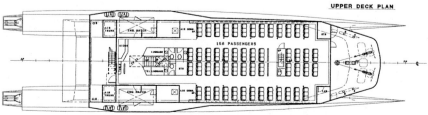

V-CAT 200-passenger ferry (design)

YAMAHA MOTOR COMPANY LTD

(Gamagori Shipyard) 2500 Shingai, Iwata, 438, Japan

Telephone: +81 (538) 321145
Telex: 59645 J
Telefax: +81 (538) 374250

29.1 m CATAMARAN TYPE 291

Two of these vessels were delivered in March 1989 to Tokyo Blue Cruises.

Built in GRP, they are powered by two DDC 16V 92TA 895 kW diesels driving five-blade propellers employing skew blades.

The most recent delivery of the Type 291, also to Tokyo Blue Cruises, was named *Bay Dream*.

Bay Dream
Yard No S-250.
Principal Particulars

Length overall	29.1 m
Beam	8.1 m
Draught	2.05 m
Displacement, minimum	98.2 t
Crew	5
Passengers	182
Fuel capacity	5000 l
Water capacity	2000 l
Propulsive power	2 × 895 kW
Maximum speed	30.7 knots
Operational speed	23 knots (95% MCR, 70% load)
Range	200 nm

Classification: J G certified for limited coastal water operation.
Propulsion: The main engines are 2 × DDC 16V 92TI, 895 kW each at 100% MCR.

Electrical system: Auxiliary engines: 4-stroke diesels, 1 × 48.5 kW at 1800 rpm, 1 × 61 kW at 1800 rpm; alternator: 3-phase AC, 1 × 50 kVA, 1 × 60 kVA.

Bay Bridge
Bay Frontier
Principal Particulars
Details as for *Bay Dream* except as follows:

Displacement, 70% load	82 t
Passengers	230
Maximum speed	33 knots
Operational speed	25 knots

Electrical system: The auxiliary engines are 4-stroke diesels, 1 × 37.5 kW at 1800 rpm, 1 × 35.2 kW at 1800 rpm.
Alternator: 3-phase AC, 1 × 34.1 kVA, 1 × 20 kVA.

VERIFIED

Yamaha Motor Company Ltd catamaran Type 291 Bay Bridge

1990

KOREA, SOUTH

DAEWOO SHIPBUILDING AND HEAVY MACHINERY LTD

1 Ajoori, Changseungpo, Koje-Kun, Kyungnam, Korea

Telephone: +82 (558) 680 5121
Telefax: +82 (558) 681 7407

Daewoo's Okpo shipyard has recently completed a 42 m 40 knot passenger catamaran for operation from Koje island to Pusan in South Korea. This is the first such craft constructed by Daewoo and the company is now marketing a range of vessels including a 37 m SES and an 80 m passenger/car ferry.

F-CAT 40 *Royal Ferry*

This all-aluminium vessel has been developed by Daewoo for Korea's domestic market. In order to achieve the high speed with acceptable sea-keeping qualities the design incorporates a foil extending between the two hulls. The vessel was delivered in late 1994.
Principal Particulars

Length overall	40.25 m
Length waterline	37 m
Beam	9.3 m

Royal Ferry

1995

Draught	1.48 m
Passengers	350
Vehicles	8
Fuel capacity	2 × 2500 l
Water capacity	1400 l
Propulsive power	2 × 2000 kW
Maximum speed	40 knots
Operational speed	36 knots
Range	400 nm

Classification: Korean Register.

Propulsion: 2 × MTU 16V 396 TE 74L diesels, producing 2000 kW each at 2000 rpm. Each drives a KaMeWa 63 SII water-jet

Electrical system: 2 × Cummins 6BT5.9G1(M) generators, 2 × Onan-Newage 75 kW alternators.

F-CAT 80 (DESIGN)

This 78 m catamaran design is based on the F-CAT 40 vessel but with the capability of transporting vehicles as well as passengers.

Principal Particulars

Length overall	78 m
Length waterline	70.0 m
Beam	16.40 m
Draught	2.30 m
Payload	113 t
Crew	12
Passengers	600
Vehicles	56 cars
Fuel capacity	4 × 14000 l
Water capacity	6350 l
Propulsive power	2 × 5257 kW
Maximum speed	36 knots
Operational speed	33 knots

Classification: DnV +1A1 HSLC, Car ferry A, R1, EO.

Propulsion: The main engines are 2 × Caterpillar CAT3616 DITA, each producing 5420 kW at 1000 rpm, driving 2 × LIPS, LJ 140 DL water-jets via a reduction gearbox.

Electrical system: A Ssangyong-Cummins NT-855-GC6(M) generator, 250 kW, 450 V AC, 60 Hz, 3PH.

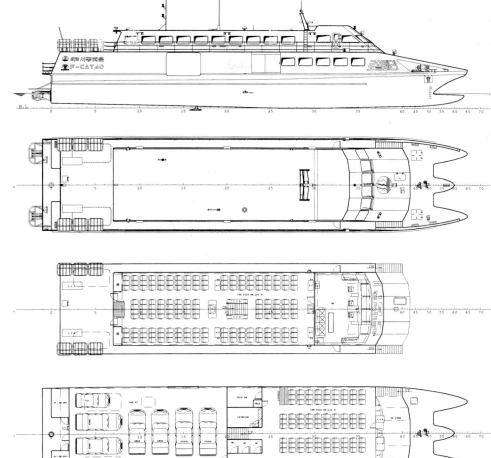

UPDATED *General arrangement of the F-CAT 40* 1995

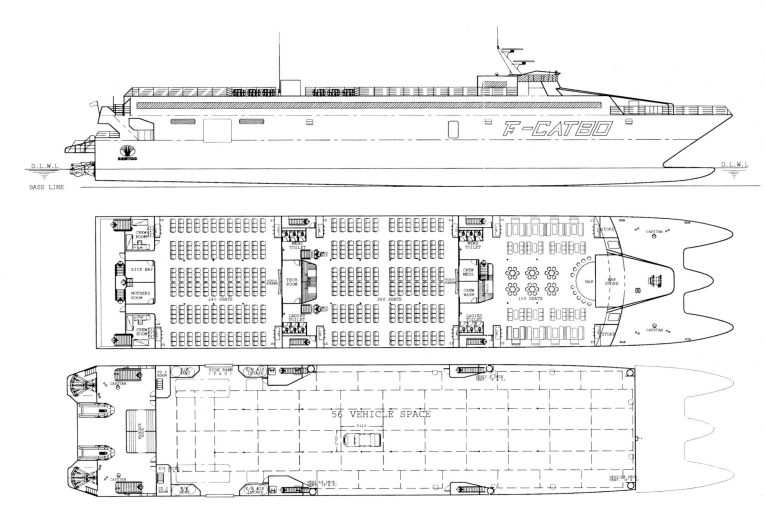

General arrangement of the F-CAT 80 1995

HYUNDAI HEAVY INDUSTRIES COMPANY LTD

Head Office and Ulsan Works: 1 Cheonha-Dong, Dong-Ku, Ulsan, South Korea

Telephone: +82 (522) 302841
Telex: 52452 HHIYARD K
Telefax: +82 (522) 330491

Seoul Office and Special and Naval Shipbuilding Division:
140-2 Kye-Dong, Chongro-Ku, Seoul, South Korea

Telephone: +82 (2) 746 4671/2
Telex: 28361/27496 HHIYARD K
Telefax: +82 (2) 741 1152

45.5 m CATAMARAN FERRY
Han Ma Um Ho

A demand from a domestic customer for a high-speed passenger vessel for a 700 nm round trip with more than 300 passengers was received in 1990. A comprehensive survey was undertaken of existing catamaran designs which motivated Hyundai to develop a design which could meet the long-range requirement and corresponding sea-keeping requirement. The sea-keeping capability has been met by incorporating a two-foil ride control system, the foils being positioned beneath the hulls at extreme forward and aft locations, and spanning the distance between the hulls. The company has previous experience of foil technology from their involvement in the building of an RHS 70 hydrofoil, Angel IX in 1985.

The design work began in August 1990 and was completed in mid-1991, supported by a large number of model tests both within and outside Hyundai

Hyundai 45.5 m catamaran on trials (without foils fitted)   **1994**

Heavy Industries. The vessel with and without foils fitted, underwent instrumented sea trials throughout 1994. Data from this vessel are understood to be the basis of a much larger craft being developed by Hyundai.

Principal Particulars

Length overall	45.5 m
Beam	11.4 m
Draught	1.6 m
Passengers	300
Propulsive power	3061 kW
Operational speed	35 knots
Range	600-700 nm

Classification: DnV +1A1 R170, EO, HSLC.
Propulsion: The main engines are 2 × Paxman Valenta 18RP 200CM, 3061 kW each at 1540 rpm, driving 2 × water-jets.

UPDATED

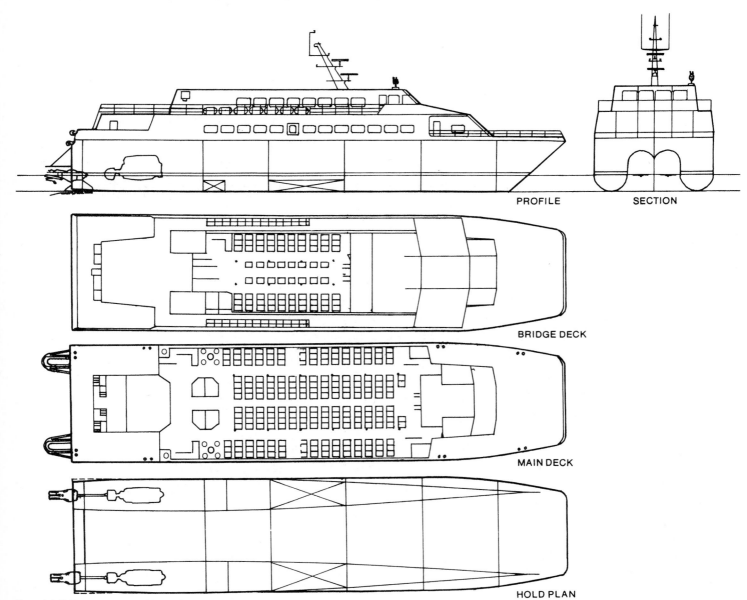

PROFILE   SECTION

BRIDGE DECK

MAIN DECK

HOLD PLAN

Hyundai 45.5 m catamaran with two-foil ride control system

KOREA TACOMA MARINE INDUSTRIES LIMITED
(Hanjin Group)

PO Box 339, 974-15 Yangduck-dong, Masan, South Korea

Telephone: +82 (551) 551181/551188
Telex: 53662 KOTAMAN K
Telefax: +82 (551) 949449/949903

Choong-Hoon Cho, *Chairman*
Yi-Taek Chim, *President*
Chul-Kyu Chun, *Vice President*
Shin-Doo Kang, *Executive Managing Director*

Seoul office: PO Box 4296, 118, 2-Ga, Namdaemun-Ro, Chung-Ku, Seoul, South Korea

Telephone: +82 (2) 728 5446/8
Telefax: +82 (2) 757 0884

KTMI entered the catamaran market in 1995 with two new designs, the Seacat 34 and 40. These are designed as fast passenger vessels and built of marine grade aluminium alloy.

Model of the Seacat 34   **1995**

SEACAT 34 (DESIGN)
Principal Particulars

Length overall	35 m
Length waterline	32 m
Beam	8.4 m
Draught	1.55 m
Passengers	200-250
Maximum speed	40 knots
Range	200 nm

SEACAT 40 (DESIGN)
Principal Particulars

Length overall	38.8 m
Length waterline	36 m
Beam	9.4 m
Draught	1.55 m
Passengers	300-350
Maximum speed	38 knots
Range	300 nm

UPDATED

NETHERLANDS

ROYAL SCHELDE BV

PO Box 16, 165 Glacisstraat, 4380 AA, Vlissingen, Netherlands.

Telephone: +31 (1184) 882973/82120/82118
Telex: 37815
Telefax: +31 (1184) 85010

Th P Winde, *Director of Shipbuilding*
A Van der Knapp, *Marketing and Sales of Fast Ferries*
H Keers, *Marketing and Sales of Fast Ferries*

Royal Schelde BV is well known for the naval frigates and patrol craft designed and constructed by the shipyard. The first fast ferry produced by Royal Schelde was the SES Seaswift 23 in 1990. The company is now offering a range of SES, catamaran and monohull craft for passenger and vehicle transportation.

Low Wash River Catamarans
The company is marketing its three low wash river catamarans; a 34.6 m, 116 passenger version; a 37.6 m, 144 passenger version and a 45 m, 200 passenger version. They all have speeds in the range of 30 to 40 knots with draughts of less than 1.0 m.

40 m CATAMARAN (DESIGN)
This all-aluminium vessel is designed for fast passenger transportation.
Principal Particulars

Length overall	42.20 m
Length waterline	37.00 m
Beam	10.20 m
Draught	1.50 m
Passengers	330
Fuel capacity	10 000 l
Maximum speed	34 knots
Operational speed	32.5 knots
Range	300 nm

Classification: DnV +1A1 R3 HS LC Passenger EO.
Propulsion: The main engines are 2 × MTU 16V 396 TE 74L diesels, each driving through a reduction gearbox to a KaMeWa 71 S11 water-jet.

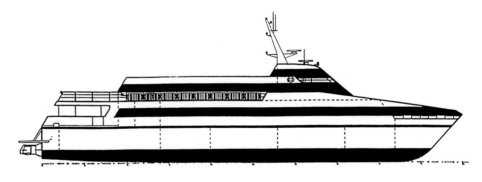

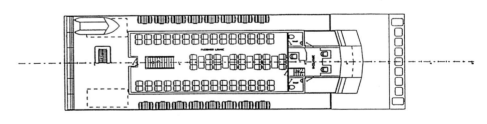

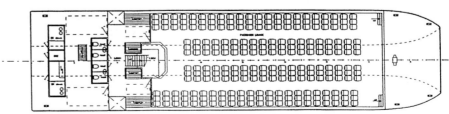

40 m Catamaran general arrangement   **1995**

70 m CATAMARAN - STANDARD (DESIGN)
This all-aluminium vessel is designed for car, bus, truck and passenger transportation. The standard version of the design can accommodate 432 passengers and 100 cars. The heavy lift (HL) version can accommodate 600 passengers and 196 cars or a combination of trucks, buses and cars.
Principal Particulars

Length overall	70.70 m
Length waterline	62.50 m

Beam	22.40 m
Draught	2.74 m
Passengers	432
Vehicles	100 cars
Maximum speed	43 knots
Operational speed	41 knots
Range	325 nm

Propulsion: Four Caterpillar 3616 engines each drive through reduction gearboxes to a KaMeWa 100 water-jet unit.

Outfit: The car deck is arranged to allow for rapid loading/unloading using a drive-through system with combined ramp and doors aft and independent ramp and doors forward. The width of the car lanes is 2.35 m with a free height of 3.30 m.

70 m CATAMARAN - HEAVY LIFT (HL)

This design is similar to the standard design but incorporates increased passenger and vehicle loads with a higher superstructure. One vessel is understood to be under construction for Catamaran Lines (Greece).

Principal Particulars

Length overall	70.70 m
Length waterline	63 m
Draught	3.30 m
Passengers	600
Vehicles	196 cars
Maximum speed	40 knots
Operational speed	38 knots
Range	300 nm

Propulsion: The main engines are 4 × MTU 20V 1163 TB 73 diesel engines each driving through reduction gearboxes to a KaMeWa 112 S11 water-jet.

Outfit: The car deck is arranged with a mezzanine side deck and hoistable centre portion. The free height of the main car deck is 2.5 m and for the mezzanine deck is 2.0 m. The bus lanes have a total of 118 m length with a free height of 4.5 m.

NEW ENTRY

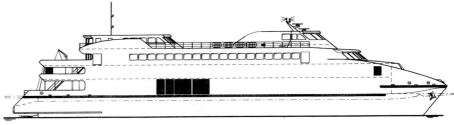

BRIDGE DECK

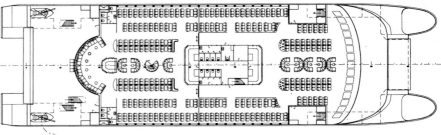

PASSENGER DECK

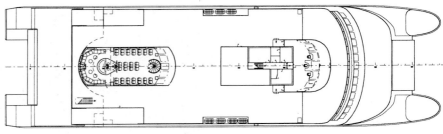

UPPER CAR DECK

CAR DECK

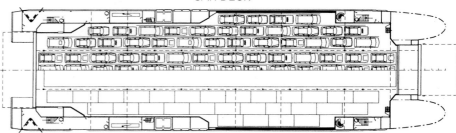

70 m (HL) Catamaran general arrangement
1995

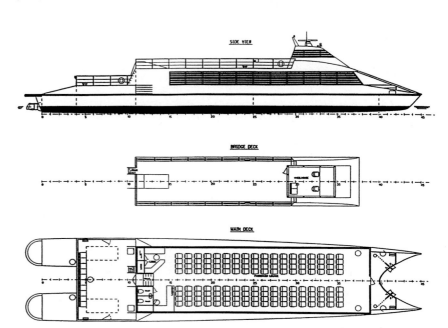

37.6 m, 144 passenger low-wash catamaran
general arrangement (design)
1995

TILLE SHIPYARDS

Tille Scheepsbovw Kootstertille BV, Baikwar 10, NL-9288 XH Kootstertille, Netherlands

Telephone: +31 (0) 5121 2300
Telefax: +31 (0) 5121 2395

Rein Amels, *Commercial Director*
A D (Bert) de Jonge, *Manager, High-Speed Craft*

Iles de Lerins

Delivered to Mr Coopamat, France.

Principal Particulars

Length overall	25 m
Beam	8.5 m
Draught	1.8 m
Passengers	220
Propulsive power	2 × 478 kW
Operational speed	20 knots

Propulsion: The main engines are 2 × DDC diesels, each 478 kW at 2300 rpm.

32 m CATAMARAN
Khadeeja Beevi
Hameedath Bee

(Yard Nos 276 and 277)

Based on the company's experience building the catamaran *Iles de Lerins*, the Joint Secretary (Shipping) Ministry of Surface Transport New Delhi, India, placed an order with the yard in 1989 for two 100-passenger high-speed catamarans for inter-island passenger services in the Lakshadweep area of South-west India. The vessels designed by Mulder Design of Gorinchem, are powered by two Deutz MWM diesels, 1242 kW each at 1800 rpm, driving through ZF gearboxes KaMeWa 63S II water-jet units.

Auxiliary power is provided by two Cummins 6B5.9G S 4 kW auxiliary engines with two Newage Stamford MHC-234 61 kVA generators.

Principal Particulars

Length overall	31.9 m
Beam	9.4 m
Draught	1.3 m
Crew	8
Passengers	100
Propulsive power	2 × 1242 kW

Propulsion: The main engines are 2 × Deutz MWM TBD 604B V12, 1242 kW each at 1800 rpm; driving 2 × KaMeWa 63 SII water-jets.

UPDATED

Hameedath Bee *built by Tille Shipyards*   1992

Iles de Lerins   1991

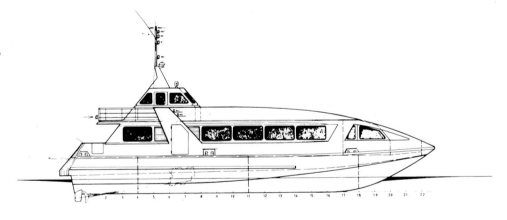

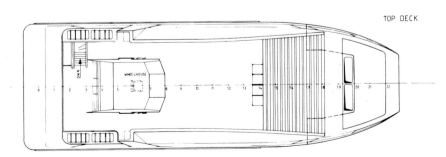

Iles de Lerins *general arrangement*

VAN DER GIESSEN-DE NOORD

Schaardijk 23, 2921 LG Krimpen aan den Ijssel, Rotterdam, Netherlands

Telephone: +31 (10) 8071 2144
Telefax: +31 (10) 8071 8180

This company has been licensed by Advanced Multi-Hull Designs Pty Ltd (AMD) of Sydney, Australia, to build their catamaran designs.

In the Autumn of 1992 it was announced that Van Der Giessen-de Noord had become a shareholder in the Advanced Multi-Hull Designs company and together with Kawasaki Heavy Industries have joined the international advisory board of AMD.

VERIFIED

NORWAY

BÅTSERVICE HOLDING A/S

Box 113, N-4501 Mandal, Norway

Telephone: +47 (38) 261011
Telex: 21862 YARD N
Telefax: +47 (38) 264580

Bjorn Fjellhaugen, *Managing Director*
Jarl Mydland, *Sales Manager*

SEA LORD CATAMARANS

In November 1990 Båtservice Holding A/S launched its first Sea Lord 28 high-speed catamaran. Two further vessels have now been delivered; all three are operated by Rogaland Trafikkselskap A/S. In addition, a 19 and 21 m rescue boat were delivered in 1991 to NSSR (the Norwegian Society for Seaman's Rescue), Oslo.

SEA LORD 28
Fjorddrott
Fjordbris
Fjordsol
Principal Particulars

Length overall	28 m
Beam	8.3 m
Draught	2.3 m
Passengers	150
Fuel capacity	6000 l
Water capacity	400 l
Propulsive power	2 × 1500 kW
Maximum speed	37 knots
Operational speed	35 knots

Classification: DnV + 1A1 R15 Light Craft - EO.
Propulsion: The main engines are 2 × MTU 12V 396 TE84, 1500 kW each at 2000 rpm (100% MCR), driving Servogear CP propellers, via ZF Type BW 465S gearboxes.
Auxiliary systems: 2 × MTU generators, 76 kW each.

SEA LORD 32
Delivered to Rutelaget Askoy, Bergen, in December 1992.
Principal Particulars

Length	32 m
Passengers	177
Operational speed	26 knots

Propulsion: The main engines are 2 × MTU 12V 183 TE92, 550 kW each.

Fjordrott, Fjordbris *and* Fjordsol *Sea Lord 28 catamarans* 1993

Sea Lord 36 pollution control vessels for Aramco, Ain Dar 7 *and* Ain Dar 8 1994

SEA LORD 36 POLLUTION CONTROL
Ain Dar 7
Ain Dar 8

Early in 1991 Båtservice Industrier signed a contract with the Saudi Arabian company Aramco for the building of two 36 m Pollution Control Catamarans for operation out of the oil terminal at Ra's Tanurah. The contract was valued at US$15 million and was handled by the Aramco Overseas Company BV of the Netherlands.

The two vessels are equipped with MARCO Pollution Control Oil Recovery Filter belt systems. Produced by MARCO in Seattle, USA, since 1972, these systems employ a continuous mesh belt that allows water to pass through it but retains the collected oil. Oil and debris are carried towards the drive roller and collected in separate containers, the heavier material being scraped off first by a scraper blade.

Principal Particulars

Length overall	36 m
Beam	11.8 m
Draught	1.85 m
Displacement, maximum	210 t
Crew	8
Fuel capacity	15.5 t
Water capacity	14.0 t
Propulsive power	2 × 1630 kW
Maximum speed	33 knots
Operational speed	27 knots
Range	450 nm

Structure: Hull material: aluminium.
Superstructure material: aluminium.
Propulsion: The main engines are 2 × Caterpillar 16V 3516 diesels, 1630 kW each, driving 2 × VD802A Servogear CP propellers, via ZF gearboxes.
Auxiliary systems: Engines: 2 × 185 kW.

SEA LORD 38

The first Sea Lord 38 is scheduled to be delivered to TROMS FYLKES DAMPSKIBSSELSKAP in mid-1995.

Principal Particulars

Length overall	38 m
Beam	11.8 m
Draught	1.6 m
Crew	4
Passengers	336
Fuel capacity	7000 l
Water capacity	1000 l
Operational speed	35 knots

Propulsion: The main engines are 4 × MTU 12V 183 TE 92 each rated at 735 kW at 2300 rpm. Two pairs of diesels through a servogear 250 gearbox to servo-gear controllable pitch propellers.

SEA LORD 42 (DESIGN)

A 42 m, 380-passenger vessel was also being marketed in 1994. This design is classed to DnV +1A1 HSLC-EO R4.

Principal Particulars

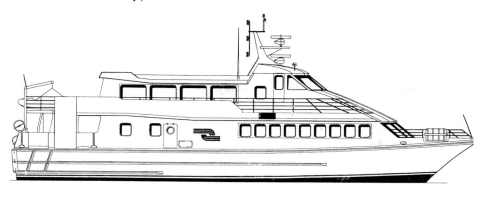

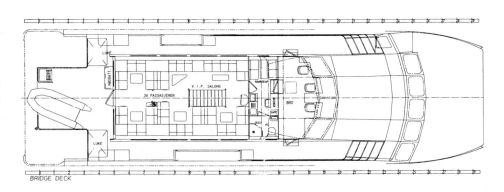

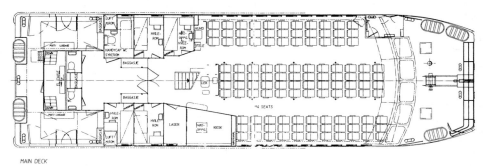

General arrangement of Sea Lord 28

Length overall	42 m	Operational speed	34 knots
Beam	11.8 m	Fuel capacity	6000 l
Draught	1.7 m	**Propulsion:** The main engines are 4 × GM92 V16.	
Crew	4		
Passengers	380		*UPDATED*

CPS PRODUCTION A/S

Støperi GT 7, PO Box 724 Tangen, N-3002J Drammen, Norway

CPS DRIVE A/S

Dr Natvigs vei 4, N-1315 Nesøya, Norway

Telephone: +47 (66) 982007
Telefax: +47 (66) 982085

Jørgen Selmer, *Chairman*
Ragnar T Zachariassen, *General Manager*

CPS Mk III
HIGH-SPEED CATAMARAN *Citius*

An innovative project completed in 1993, the CPS Mk III High-Speed Catamaran combines a number of unique features, particularly in relation to the machinery and propulsion system of the craft.

A large number of small engines (four in each hull) enables slender hulls to be used for this type of craft. An unusual transmission system is employed which permits for easy coupling and uncoupling of engines and rapid acceleration to cruise speed. An internal gantry crane arrangement allows for engine removal

Citius on trials

to be carried out without impinging on payload deck area. Engines may be engaged and disengaged depending on the output power required.

The basic version is a flat deck transporter but by adding various superstructures it is possible to configure the vessel for a wide range of applications.

Special attention has been paid to the aerodynamics of the superstructure and to crew visibility. Modular construction is employed for ease of manufacture and transport to an assembly area. Considerable care has been taken to provide a low weight, high strength structure, by the introduction of carbon fibre shafts, a pre-impregnated kevlar/epoxy superstructure and aluminium hull profiles.

Propulsion is provided by controllable-pitch surface-piercing propellers with a low drag drive and manoeuvring system.

Trials have taken place throughout 1994 and production of these craft is scheduled for mid-1995.

Principal Particulars

Length overall	20.8 m
Beam	5.7 m
Draught	0.9 m
Displacement, minimum	19 t (basic version)
	19.5 t (passengers)
Displacement, maximum	24 t (basic version)
	31.5 t (passengers)
Crew	2
Passengers	68
Fuel capacity	3-5 × 1200 l
Water capacity	500 l
Propulsive power	8 × 257 kW
Maximum speed	60 knots
Operational speed	50 knots

Propulsion: The main engines are 8 × Sabre 350C diesel, 257 kW each at 2600 rpm, driving 2 × CPS controllable-pitch surface drive units with Rolla propellers.

UPDATED

HOLEN MEK VERKSTED A/S

PO Box 20, N-6030 Langevaag, Norway

Telephone: +47 (701) 92578
Telefax: +47 (701) 93584

Capt. S Gudmundset, *Director*

Holen mek Verksted A/S specialises in the construction of high-speed vessels in welded aluminium, of up to 60 m in length. Comprehensive facilities for conversion and repair work on both aluminium and steel craft are also available at the yard, which is located close to Ålesund on Norway's west coast.

New buildings in aluminium include two 26 m catamaran passenger tenders carrying four hundred passengers.

MM 24 PC
Baronessa
Baronen

These are two identical high-speed catamarans which were delivered to Hardanger Sunnhordlandske Dampskipsselskap A/S on the west coast of Norway, in May and August 1994. They have been designed for operation at high speed in adverse weather conditions.

Principal Particulars

Length overall	24 m
Length waterline	22 m
Beam	8.25 m
Draught	1.23 m
Passengers	125
Fuel capacity	5000 l
Water capacity	1000 l
Propulsive power	2 × 735 kW
Maximum speed	32 knots

Classification: DnV +1A1 HSLC Passenger R3 EO, IMO Resolution A373(X), Norwegian Maritime Directorate.
Structure: The hull and superstructure are constructed from aluminium.
Propulsion: The main engines are 2 × MTU 12V 183 TE92 diesels; driving 2 × Servogear variable pitch propellers.

NEW ENTRY

Baronessa at speed
1995

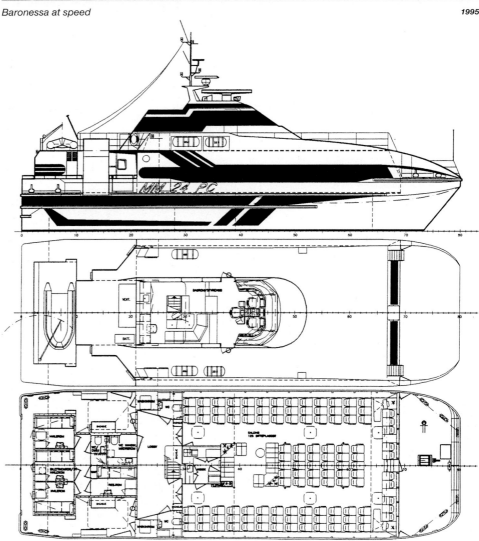

General arrangement of MM 24 PC
1995

HYDROCAT TECHNO A/S
HYDROCAT PRODUKSJON A/S

Wergelandsweien 2, N-6500 Kristiansund N, Norway

Telephone: +47 7167 3322
Telefax: +47 7167 3353

J Helseth, *Director*

HYDROCAT 2000 AC (DESIGN)

This project began in 1983 and since about 1986 has proceeded as a joint venture under Hydrocat Produksjon A/S with Mjosundet Båtbyggeri A/S, which delivered a 24 m, 72-seat, 20 knot catamaran ferry to Fosen Trafikklag A/S in 1991.

The Hydrocat 2000 AC concept is aimed at the provision of a craft of moderate size, having the capability of operating in rougher seas than would only normally be reasonable with a craft of larger size. With fixed surface-piercing foils it is seen by the Hydrocat company as a simple solution.

Due to the roll stability available in the catamaran configuration, the spanwise extent of the foil surfaces is relatively less than for a conventional surface-piercing hydrofoil vessel. This further contributes to a lower foil system weight than for the hydrofoil vessel.

The lines and materials of Hydrocat 2000 AC were established by late 1991. Propulsion will be by conventional propeller, and an all-hydraulic transmission system developed by Rexroth and Hydromarine may be used.

A quarter scale (6.6 m) manned model has been engaged in trials at speeds around 25 knots.

UPDATED

KVÆRNER a.s. Fast Ferries

PO Box 303 Skøyen, N-0212 Oslo, Norway

Telephone: +47 (22) 967400
Telefax: +47 (22) 967410

Bent Hammel, *President*

KVÆRNER FJELLSTRAND A/S

N-5632 Omastrand, Norway

Telephone: +47 (56) 554100
Telex: 42148 FBOAT N
Telefax: +47 (56) 554244/554268

Anders Jordal, *President*
Ragnat Bölstad, *Marketing Manager*
Alf Steine, *Financial Manager*

Fjellstrand was founded in 1928 in Omastrand, which is on the west coast of Norway. In January 1988 Fjellstrand merged with Kværner to form Kværner Fjellstrand AS. A Singapore yard, Kværner Fjellstrand Pte Ltd, was opened in November 1991. Since February 1992 Kværner's high-speed craft activities have operated as Kværner a.s. Fast Ferries.

Kværner Fjellstrand has achieved the most extensive and sustained export penetration of the world high-speed ferry market, both in terms of number of vessels sold and number of countries sold into. By 1995, Kværner Fjellstrand had delivered 81 high-speed catamarans to 21 different countries.

Following the delivery of nearly 400 aluminium vessels starting in 1952, Fjellstrand built its first catamaran (25.5 m) in 1976, the Alumaran 165 type. A further four vessels of this size followed up to 1981. The first 31.5 m passenger catamaran was delivered to a Norwegian operator. Between 1981 and 1985 a further twelve 31.5 m catamarans were delivered worldwide for passenger ferry work and crew/supply operations in the offshore oil industry. Design work on a larger 38.8 m type, the Advanced Slender Catamaran (ASC), started in 1983 and by June 1991, Fjellstrand had delivered 33 of this type. Please see earlier editions of this book for details of the 25.5, 31.5 and 38.8 m catamarans. The 40 m Flying Cat type is an extension of the 38.8 m ASC as well as putting emphasis on a very high standard of exterior and interior design.

Kværner Fjellstrand now offers three main types of advanced high-speed catamarans to the market, the 79 m Jumbo Cat, Foil Cat and 40 m Flying Cat.

79 m JUMBO CAT (DESIGN)

In 1992 Kværner Fjellstrand began design studies for the all-aluminium 79 m Jumbo Cat passenger/vehicle ferry. The vessel has two car decks with drive-through arrangements. This project incorporates the advanced slender hull design experience gained through the company's 38.8 m catamarans and 40 m Flying Cat vessels and their Clipper Motion Dampening System.

Principal Particulars

Length overall	78.8 m
Beam	18.75 m
Draught	3.1 m
Crew	12
Passengers	600
Vehicles	122 cars or
	4 buses + 91 cars
Fuel capacity	40 000 l
Water capacity	3000 l
Operational speed	35-40 knots

Artist's impression of 79 m Jumbo Cat   1995

Prototype of Foil Cat (Yard No 1604)   1994

40 m Flying Cat Craft built or on order to 1995

Yard No	Name	Completed	Seats	Operator
1597	*Kommandøren*	April 1990	252	Fylkesbaatane i Sogn og Fjordane, Norway
1602	*Flying Cat I*	November 1990	372	Ceres Hellenic Shipping Co, Greece
1603	*Jet Cat*	December 1990	272	Seatran Travel, Malaysia
1605	*Alicone*	June 1991	352	CAREMAR SpA, Naples, Italy
1607	*Royal Vancouver*	October 1991	302	Royal Sealink Express, Vancouver, Canada
1609	*Royal Victoria*	November 1991	302	Royal Sealink Express, Vancouver, Canada
1610	*Orca Spirit*	May 1992	296	Nanaimo Express, Vancouver, Canada
1611	*Søløven*	May 1992	296	KatExpress, Århus, Denmark
1612	*Xin Shi Ji*	May 1993	300	Yantai Marine Shipping Co, China
1613	*Søløven II*	May 1993	292	Dampskibsselskabet Øresund, Denmark
1614	*Hai Ou*	January 1993	400	Dalian Steamship Co, Dalian, China
1615	*Victoria Clipper IV*	February 1993	324	Clipper Navigation Inc, Seattle, USA
1618	*Hai Yan*	December 1993	447	Dalian Marine Transport (Group) Company
1620	*Kraka Viking*	June 1994	168	DSØ, Denmark
1621	*Sifka Viking*	June 1994	168	DSØ, Denmark
1623	*Vargøy*	June 1994	230	Fylkesrederi og Ruteselskap, Norway
1624	*Fjordkongen*	December 1994	320	Troms Fylkes Dampskibsselskap, Norway
1628	—	May 1994	—	Seo Kyung Shipping Co. Ltd, South Korea

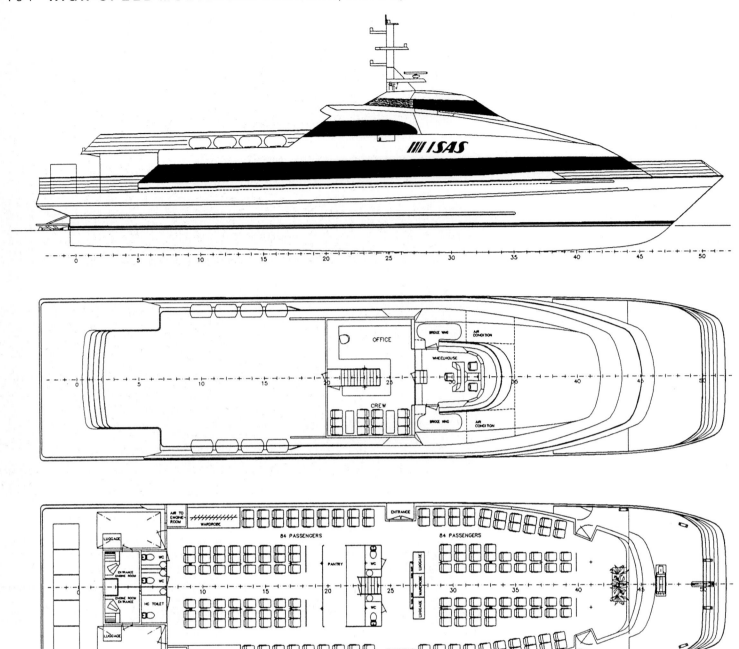

General arrangement of the 40 m Flying Cat as delivered to DSØ   *1995*

Flying Foil Cat main deck passenger accommodation   *1992*

Flying Foil Cat top deck bar, looking aft   *1992*

40 m Flying Cat Kraka Viking

1995

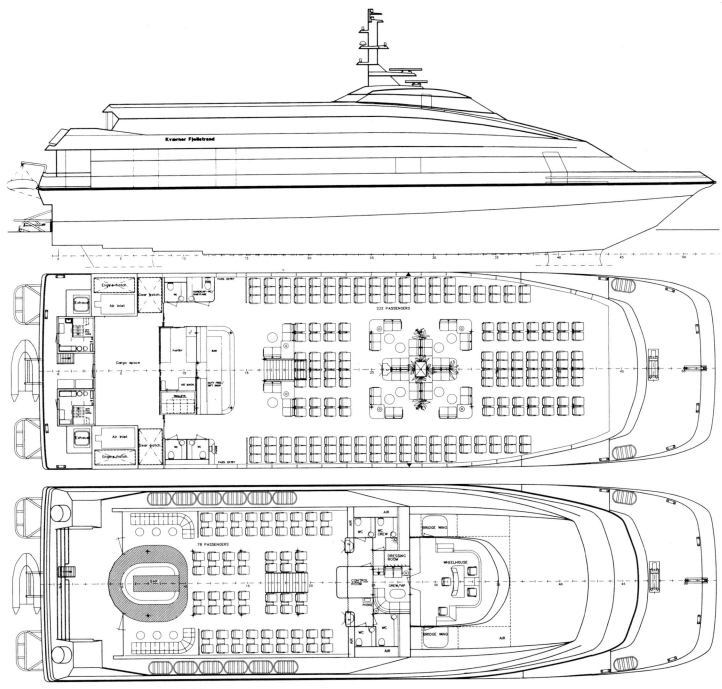

General arrangement of the first Flying Foil Cat

Classification: DnV + 1A1 HSLC R1, EO.

Propulsion: The main engines are 4 × high-speed diesel or 2 × gas-turbines driving water-jets.

There are also two bow thrusters for manoeuvring.

Electrical system: This is powered by 2 × 213 kW generators.

FOIL CAT

Development of this concept was undertaken with the assistance of a large scale manned test craft enabling full-scale service speeds up to 50 knots to be explored. While the simplicity of the catamaran construction is maintained in this new concept, the addition of the lifting and stabilising foil system enables considerably higher speeds at the level of 50 knots to be achieved economically and in rougher seas. In comparison with comparable vessels of other types the transport efficiency is significantly higher, leading to fuel consumption figures 50 per cent less than, for example, conventional high-speed catamarans. In addition, speed loss in waves is much reduced and vertical accelerations can be reduced to less than half those for comparable craft of other types.

After launching the 40 m prototype, comprehensive testing and improvements have been carried out. The next generation of the Foil Cat (Foil Cat 2/s) has been based on the wide experience gained from the prototype testing programme. Although the next model is shorter in length it has improved capacities and performance. Two of these improved craft were delivered in 1995 to Far East Hydrofoil for its Hong Kong to Macau route.

Principal Particulars

Length overall	35 m
Beam	12 m
Draught, hullborne	4.7 m (maximum)
Draught, foilborne	2.55 m (minimum)
Crew	4
Passengers	407
Fuel capacity	20 000 l
Water capacity	3000 l
Operational speed	40-50 knots
Range	300 nm

Classification: DnV+1A1 HSLC passenger, R2, EO.

Propulsion: The main engines are 2 × GE LM 500 gas-turbines, driving 2 × KaMeWa 80 SII/6, water-jets.

Navigation and communications: Arpa radars, gyro compass, log, autopilot, electronic map system, GPS, echo-sounder; VHF radiotelephones, PA/intercom, CCTV, mobile telephone.

Control: Foil system: fully submerged foil system, active flap control.

Automatic control system: Kværner Fjellstrand AFCS.

40 m FLYING CAT

This Kværner Fjellstrand design was launched in 1989. By 1995 34 craft had been built, 16 from the Omastrand yard and 18 from the Singapore yard.

Victoria Clipper IV, Yard No 1615

Delivered March 1993 to Clipper Navigation Inc of the USA, the vessel operates between Seattle in the USA and Victoria in Canada. With a capacity of 324 passengers, the vessel employs water-jets to give a service speed of 33 knots with a 25.42 tonne load. A Clipper MDS will be installed.

Clipper Navigation Inc has operated a 38.8 m ASC from Kværner Fjellstrand, Victoria Clipper, since 1986. In April 1992 a Clipper MDS was installed on this vessel.

Vargøy

Vargøy, a Kværner Fjellstrand 40 m Flying Cat, was delivered to Norwegian shipowner Finnmark Fylkesrederi og Ruteselskap (FFR) on 14 June 1994. It was ordered in December 1993 at a price of US$5.7 million, and operates cruises for FFR between Hammerfest and the North Cape during the Summer.

ADVANCED SLENDER CATAMARANS (38.8 m) Craft built or on order 1985 to December 1991

Yard No	Name	Completed	Seats	Operator
	Tian Lu Hu	September 1985	326	Zhen Hing Enterprises Co Ltd, China
1570	Yong Xing	November 1985	312	Ningbo Huagang Ltd, China
1571	Mexico (ex Can Cun)	January 1986	370	Cruceros Maritimos del Caribe SA, Mexico
1572	Victoria Clipper	May 1986	330*	Clipper Navigation Inc, USA
1573	Anne Lise**	July 1986	195	Hardanger Sunnhordlanske A/S, Norway
1574	Sevilla 92 (ex Caribbean Princess)	31 October 1986	310	Islena de Navegacion, Spain
1575	Rapido de Algeciros (ex Bahamian Princess)	February 1987	310	Islena de Navegacion, Spain
1576	Caka Bey	February 1987	449	Istanbul Great City Municipality, Turkey
1577	Fjordprins	September 1987	201	Fylkesbaatane i Sogn og Fjordane, Norway
1578	Umur Bey	May 1987	449	Istanbul Great City Municipality, Turkey
1579	Yeditepe	May 1987	449	Istanbul Great City Municipality, Turkey
1580	Sognekongen	December 1987	201	Fylkesbaatane i Sogn og Fjordane, Norway
1581	Sarica Bey	September 1987	449	Istanbul Great City Municipality, Turkey
1582	Ulbatli Hasan	October 1987	449	Istanbul Great City Municipality, Turkey
1583	Uluc Ali Reis	January 1988	449	Istanbul Great City Municipality, Turkey
1584	Nusret	March 1988	449	Istanbul Great City Municipality, Turkey
1585	Karamürsel Bey	March 1988	449	Istanbul Great City Municipality, Turkey
1586	Sea Cat/Blue Manta	April 1988	249	n/k
1587	Hezarifen Celebi	September 1988	449	Istanbul Great City Municipality, Turkey
1588	Cavli Bey	September 1988	449	Istanbul Great City Municipality, Turkey
1589	Sleipner	April 1989	243	Flaggruten, Norway
1590	Draupner	April 1989	243	Flaggruten, Norway
1591	Dae Won Catamaran	November 1988	396	Dae Won Ferry Co Ltd, South Korea
1592	Nordlicht	April 1989	272	AG EMS Emden, Germany
1593	Leopardo	June 1989	290	Cat Lines SA, Spain
1594	Jetcat	June 1988	213	n/k
1595	Eyra	August 1989	290	Cat Lines SA, Spain
1596	Nam Hae Star	October 1989	350	Nam Hae Express, South Korea
1598	Mercury	March 1990	288	AKP Sovcomflot, CIS
1599	Solovki	March 1990	246	AKP Sovcomflot, CIS
1600	Varangerfjord	June 1990	164	Finnmark Fylkesrederi og Ruteselskap, Norway
1601	Løberen	September 1990	256	Dampskibsselskabet Øresund, Denmark
1608	Springaren	June 1991	255	Svenska Rederi AB Øresund, a subsidiary of Dampskibsselskabet Øresund, Denmark

* of which 30 are external

** converted from freighter layout March 1991 having been bought from God Trans A/S, Norway in 1991.

The aft deck has been designed to carry two passenger cars and up to 16 Euro-pallets in a closed cargo hold. A Palfinger cargo handling crane is installed on the second deck. Freight earnings will provide an important supplement to passenger services.

Principal Particulars

Length overall	40 m
Beam	10.10 m
Draught	1.6 m
Passengers	230
Vehicles	2 cars
Propulsive power	2 × 2000 kW
Operational speed	33 knots

Propulsion: The main engines are 2 × diesels generating a total of 4000 kW at 100% MCR to drive 680 mm water-jets from Kværner Energy.

Navigation and communications: Racal Decca Bridgemaster 180C (3 cm) and 250 (10 dm) radars, a Robertson AP9 Mk2 autopilot and an electronic chart monitor.

Control: A Kværner motion dampening system is installed on the vessel to provide optimum seakeeping performance under demanding conditions.

40 m FLYING CAT - M2 VERSION

Kværner Fjellstrand after carefully studying the changes in the market, is continually developing its products. Alterations in the high-speed ferry market have influenced Kværner Fjellstrand to develop a new Flying Cat design. The new and more cost-effective version, Flying Cat M2, maintains the high quality of the original Flying Cat with regard to safety, seaworthiness and reliability.

UPDATED

LINDSTØLS SKIPS- & BÅTBYGGERI A/S

Solsiden 1, N-4950 Risør, Norway

Telephone: +47 3715 0344
Telefax: +47 3715 2060

Einar K Lindstøl, *Director*
Arne Lindstøl, *Manager*

Lindstøls Skips- & Båtbyggeri A/S was founded in 1870 by Erik K Lindstøl. Through the years Lindstøls Skips has acquired a broad experience in the construction of various types of vessels in the size range up to 60 m in length. A large number of sailing cargo vessels, rescue vessels, research, arctic, fishing and pleasure vessels were delivered to customers in several countries.

One of the most famous of these vessels was delivered in 1917 and named *Quest*; it travelled the oceans with Captain Shackleton on Antarctic expeditions for many years.

Erik K Lindstøl's son, Arne K Lindstøl, headed the yard for 40 years, up to 1952, when Einar K Lindstøl changed the building material from wood to steel. The company began using aluminium in construction in 1960.

LIGHT 22.5 m CATAMARAN

The first Light 22.5 m catamaran built by Lindstøl Skips A/S, *Namdalingen*, was delivered from the yard in August 1990. Ordered by A/S Namsos Trafikkselskap the vessel has entered the rough coastal service route between Namsos and Rorvik/Leka in mid-Norway, north of Trondheim.

The Light 22.5 m is a 100 per cent Lindstøl-designed concept based on the first Norwegian built slender catamarans with symmetric hulls developed and built by Lindstøl Skips A/S in 1983 to 1985.

Namdalingen is the latest design in a continuous line of deliveries since the first sailing ship was built in 1870.

Lindstøl Skips A/S has been in aluminium constructions since the beginning of the 1960s and is today equipped with the most advanced CAD/CAM systems available, in order to offer the customer the best service during the projecting and building period.

Consideration has been given to ensure the possibility of changing a main engine within eight hours. The reason for this is that *Namdalingen* is the only high-speed passenger vessel covering the Namsos -

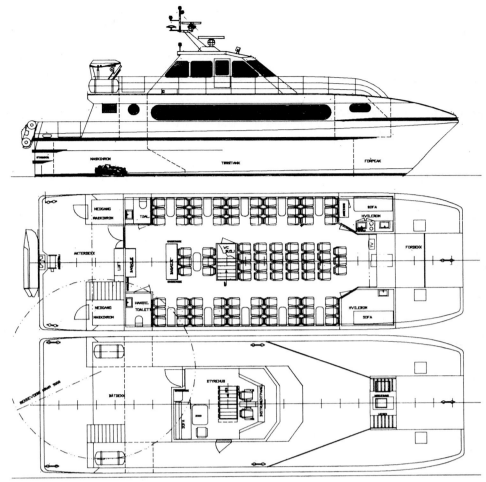

General arrangement of Lindstøl's Light 22.5 m catamaran

Rorvik and Leka area, and the vessel has to be in traffic 360 days a year. The owner, A/S Namsos Trafikkselskap, therefore has one spare engine in stock for replacing when routine overhauls are necessary.

Model tests indicated that when operating in 30 knots in a significant wave height of 1 m (maximum wave height of 2 m), accelerations in the passenger saloon will be 0.1 *g*. The wash at 30 knots is measured to 0.3 m, 30 m from the side of the vessel.

Special attention has been given to passenger and crew visibility, the wheelhouse has 360° visibility.

Namdalingen, Yard No 296
Principal Particulars

Length overall	22.5 m
Beam	7.6 m
Draught	1.1 m

Fosningen

Passengers	110
Crew	2
Fuel capacity	2 × 1700 l tanks
Water capacity	400 l
Propulsive power	2 × 672 kW
Operational speed	30 knots
Range	440 nm

Classification: DnV + 1A1 R5, EO Light-Craft Passenger Catamaran.
Structure: Aluminium alloy, decks and superstructure of Lindstøl aluminium alloy sandwich profile.

Propulsion: The main engines are 2 × MTU 12V 183 TE 92, 672 kW each, at 2300 rpm; driving Servogear CP propellers type 800 A, V drive gear VD 250 B.
Electrical system: Auxiliary engine: Mitsubishi/Mustang A 372-22, 16 kW, 20 kVA.

Fosningen, Yard No 298

This is the second light 22.5 m catamaran built by Lindstøls Skips and was delivered on 25 June 1991. This vessel has 118 seats and is in service with Fosen Trafikklag A/S of Trondheim on an 8.3 nm route between Skansen and Vanvikan. *Fosningen* is similar in many respects to *Namdalingen,* the main differences being large 1.1 m diameter four-bladed CP propellers to give good starting, stopping and manoeuvring qualities, and a change of saloon layout with the inclusion of a kiosk and office section. Some changes have also been made to the hull form below the waterline.

UPDATED

ROSENDAL VERFT A/S

PO Box 55, N-5470 Rosendal, Norway

Telephone: +47 53481322
Telefax: +47 53481934

Hallgeir Skjelnes, *Chairman*
Ќre Hjelmeland, *Marketing Director*
Ronold Hellenes, *Technical Manager*

Rosendal Verft A/S, situated in Hardanger on the west coast of Norway, was established in 1989. The history of the yard reaches back to 1855 and during the intervening years a great number and range of ships have been built and launched: fishing vessels, ferries, research vessels, inspection craft, naval vessels, chemical tankers, lifeboats, ice-breakers, tugs and mine-layers for the Royal Norwegian Navy, and high-speed catamarans. The yard employs 60 people.

With 30 years' experience in building with aluminium the yard started in 1986 with a subcontract for Fjellstrand A/S. The work included complete production of five 38.8 m passenger catamarans for delivery in Turkey.

The current range of Rosendal catamarans consists of two types, the Admiral 29 m, and the Admiral 36 m, both are designed for clearly defined operational areas.

Admiral 29 m

The Admiral 29 m passenger catamaran has been designed to operate on coastal routes. The recommended service speed is 32 to 40 knots. Passengers are seated in two compartments on two decks with restaurant and entertainment facilities provided.

Since 1989, Rosendal Verft has delivered eight 29 m catamarans to owners in Norway and Holland.

Principal Particulars

Length overall	29 m
Beam	8 m
Passengers	250
Propulsive power	4 × 550 kW
Maximum speed	35 knots
Operational speed	33 knots

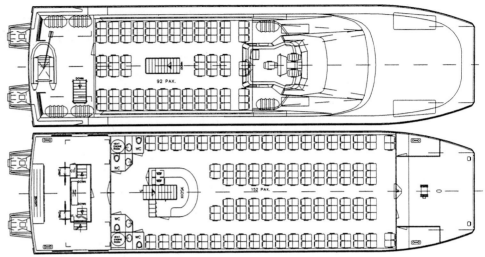

Admiral 29 m 250 passenger catamaran general arrangement

1995

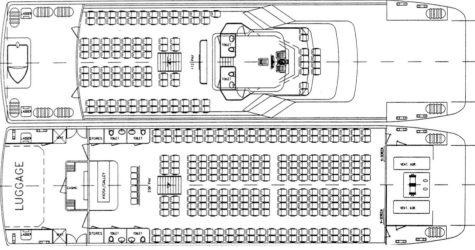

Admiral 36 m 400 passenger catamaran general arrangement

1995

Agdenes, an Admiral 29 m passenger catamaran delivered in July 1991 to Fosen Trafikklag, Norway

Propulsion: The main engines are 4 × MTU 12V 183 TE 62. There will be two engines in each engine room, connected to a common gearbox. This is the most economical installation regarding investment costs and safety. The installation will also implicate higher regularity, which will lead to substantial savings in maintenance, fuel consumption, spare parts, purchase price, and the vessel total operations economy.

Admiral 36 m

The Admiral 36 m passenger catamaran has been designed to operate on coastal and open water routes. The reccommended service speed is 32 to

Koegelwieck
1993

Recent Rosendal Verft 28 m and 29 m Catamarans (See 1992-93 edition for details of 28 m *Stuifdijk*)

Name	*Prinsessen*	*Skogøy*	*Agdenes*	*Tedno*
Built	1990	1991	1991	1992
Type	Slender-hull passenger catamaran	Slender-hull passenger/cargo catamaran	Slender-hull passenger catamaran	Slender-hull passenger catamaran
Owner/Operator	Nesodden Bundefjord, Norway	Salten Dampskipselskap, Norway	Fosen Trafikkselskap, Norway	Hardanger Sunnhordlandske, Norway
Classification	DnV+1A1 Light Craft Passenger Catamaran (R20, EO)	DnV+1A1 Light Craft Passenger Catamaran (R15, EO)	DnV+1A1 Light Craft Passenger Catamaran (R15, EO)	DnV+1A1 HSLC Passenger Catamaran (R2, EO)
Hull	Aluminium	Aluminium	Aluminium	Aluminium
Dimensions				
Length	28 m	28.75 m	28.75 m	29 m
Beam	9 m	8 m	8 m	8 m
Draught	1.9 m incl propeller	2.1 m incl propeller	2.1 m incl propeller	2.4 m
Capacities				
Fuel oil	2 × 3000 l	2 × 3000 l	2 × 2000 l	2 × 3000 l
Fresh water	500 l	500 l	500 l	1500 l
Lube oil	300 l	300 l	200 l	300 l
Accommodation				
Passenger seats	175	130	210	173
Facilities	Non-reclinable seats. Entertainment system: Television, radio, music. One toilet accessible for disabled persons.	Reclinable seats. Kiosk. Entertainment system: Television, video, radio, music. Hot and cold meals. Telephone. Three toilets, one for disabled persons.	Reclinable seats and sitting groups. Kiosk. entertainment system: 5 channels for CD, video music and radio. Hot and cold meals. Telephone. Three toilets, one for disabled persons.	Non-reclinable seats. Kiosk. Entertainment system: 5 channels for CD, video, music and radio. Hot and cold meals. Telephone. Four toilets, one for disabled persons.
Main engines	2 × Detroit Diesel 16V 92 TA; 566 kW each	2 × Detroit Diesel 16V 149 TIB; 1324 kW each	2 × Deutz MWM TBD 604 BV12; 1260 kW each	2 × MTU 12V 396 TE 74L 1500 kW each
Propulsion	Twin controllable-pitch propeller	Twin controllable-pitch propeller	Twin controllable-pitch propeller	Twin controllable-pitch propeller
Performance				
Speed max	28 knots	36.3 knots	36 knots	36.5 knots
Speed service	25 knots at 85% MCR	33.3 knots at 85% MCR	33 knots at 85% MCR	34 knots at 85% MCR
Fuel consumption	280 l/h	565 l/h	510 l/h	653 l/h

HIGH-SPEED CATAMARAN CRAFT BUILT 1987 TO THE PRESENT

Yard No	Type	Name	Delivered	Seats	Delivered to	Route
242* Fjellstrand	38.8 m	*Umur Bey*	May 1987	450	Istanbul Great City Municipality, Turkey	Istanbul, Bosphorus
243* Fjellstrand	38.8 m	*Ulbatli Hasan*	Nov 1987	450	Istanbul Great City Municipality, Turkey	Istanbul, Bosphorus
244* Fjellstrand	38.8 m	*Uluc Ali Reis*	Feb 1988	450	Istanbul Great City Municipality, Turkey	Istanbul, Bosphorus
245* Fjellstrand	38.8 m	*Karamursel Bey*	Apr 1988	450	Istanbul Great City Municipality, Turkey	Istanbul, Bosphorus
246* Fjellstrand	38.8 m	*Cavli Bey*	Sep 1988	450	Istanbul Great City Municipality, Turkey	Istanbul, Bosphorus
256 Admiral	26 m	*Havstril*	Jun 1989	150	PEMEX, Mexico	Mexico
257 Admiral	29 m	*Lauparen* (ex *Stuifdijk*)	Jun 1990	250	More og Romsdal, Norway	Keistiansuno - Trundheim
258 Admiral	29 m	*Prinsessen*	Nov 1990	175	Nesodden Bundefjord	Oslofjorden
259 Admiral	29 m	*Skogøy*	Apr 1991	130+ cargo	Salten Dampskipselskap, Norway	Svolvær - Narvik
260 Admiral	29 m	*Agdenes*	Jul 1991	210	Fosen Trafikklag, Norway	Trondheim - Sula
262 Admiral	35 m	*Koegelwieck*	Jun 1992	300	Rederij Doeksen, Holland	Terschelling - Harlingen
263 Admiral	29 m	*Tedno*	Nov 1992	173	Hardanger Sunnhordlanske, Norway	Bergen - Stavanger
264 Admiral	29 m		Dec 1994	100 + cargo	Torghatten Trafikk, Norway	North Norway
265 Admiral	29 m		Mar 1995	100 + cargo	Helgeland Trafikk, Norway	North Norway
266 Admiral	36 m		May 1995	350	Shenzhen Xunlong	China
267 Admiral	36 m		Aug 1995	350	Shenzhen Xunlong	China

*Subcontract for Fjellstrand A/S

40 knots. Passengers are seated in three compartments on two decks with restaurant and entertainment facilities provided.

Principal Particulars

Length overall	36 m
Beam	9.6 m
Passengers	350
Propulsive power	4 × 735 kW
Maximum speed	36 knots
Operational speed	34 knots

Propulsion: The main engines are 4 × MTU 12V 183 TE 92. There will be two engines in each engine room, connected to a common gearbox. This is the most economical installation regarding investment costs and safety. The installation will also implicate higher regularity, which will lead to substantial savings in maintenance, fuel consumption, spare parts, purchase price, and the vessel total operations economy.

Koegelwieck

In February 1991, Rosendal Verft started a development project for a 36 m catamaran. The hull is extremely slender to give the best possible speed characteristics and seaworthiness. The width-to-length ratio has been reduced compared with the 1:11 ratio of Rosendal 29 m catamarans. Beam overall is 9.6 m.

The first Rosendal 36 m was delivered to Rederij Doeksen for operation between the Dutch Frisland islands and the northern coast of the Netherlands. The company, which was also the launch customer for the Rosendal 29 m catamaran, specified a 300-seat variant of the twin deck design.

Admiral 29 m Tedno   1993

WESTAMARIN A/S

Andøyveten 23, PO Box 115, Vågsbygd, N-4602 Kristiansand, Norway

Telephone: +47 (38) 088200
Telex: 21514 WRIN N
Telefax: +47 (38) 085012

Westamarin A/S is a subsidiary of the Swedish company Addum AB. The shipyard was established in 1855 and has been associated with the design and production of ships and offshore structures since that time. With a prior association with Westamarin West A/S, the yard has been developing large fast catamaran craft since 1990. The company holds the ISO-9001 quality assurance standard.

WESTAMARAN 12000 OCEAN FLYER
(DESIGN)

The Westamaran 12000 was announced towards the end of 1990. Originally designed to carry up to 1200 passengers and 275 cars, the current design is for a vessel with a maximum vehicle capacity of 550 cars and seating for 1500 passengers. The design now allows for commercial traffic with various combinations of cars, trucks, trailers and buses to be carried.

Principal Particulars

Length overall	124.5 m
Beam	34 m
Draught	4.5 m
Payload	750-1000 t
Crew	20
Passengers	1500
Vehicles	520 cars
Propulsive power	40 000-50 000 kW
Operational speed	40 knots
Range	600 nm

Structure: Hull material: high tensile steel. Superstructure material: aluminium alloy.
Propulsion: Engines: 2 or 4 gas-turbines, 40 000-50 000 kW.

WESTAMARAN 12000 TC
(DESIGN)

Principal Particulars

Length overall	124.6 m
Length waterline	107.6 m
Beam	40 m
Draught	5.5 m
Crew	20
Fuel capacity	400 000 l

Water capacity	10 000 l
Maximum speed	30 knots
Operational speed	23-30 knots

Classification: DnV 1A1-HSLC, R1 A - EO NAUT.
Structure: High tensile steel and seawater-resistant aluminium.
Propulsion: The propulsion arrangement is configured with either two diesel or two gas-turbine engines, each driving CP propellers, depending on the operational speed requirements. Water-jets can also be accommodated for the higher speeds.

WESTAMARAN 9600 RORO FERRY
(DESIGN)

Principal Particulars

Length overall	95.8 m
Beam	34 m
Draught	4 m
Crew	12
Vehicles	730 lane metres
Fuel capacity	150 m³
Maximum speed	44 knots
Operational speed	35-44 knots
Range	600 nm

Westamarin-12000 TC (design) artist's impression   1995

Propulsion: The main engines are either diesels or gas-turbines.

WESTAMARAN 9500 OCEAN FLYER
(DESIGN)

Announced in the latter half of 1991 the Westamaran 9500 is another large high-speed passenger/car ferry being offered by Westamarin A/S. The two symmetrical hulls and bridging structure are to be made of high tensile steel with the rest of the construction in aluminium. A ride control system will be employed and the engine room will be fully automated.

Principal Particulars

Length overall	95 m
Beam	29 m
Draught	4.5 m
Payload	450-500 t
Crew	20
Passengers	1000
Vehicles	320
Propulsive power	40 000/50 000 kW
Operational speed	45 knots
Range	600 nm

Structure: Hull material: high tensile steel.
Superstructure material: aluminium alloy.
Propulsion: Engines: gas-turbine.

WESTAMARAN 8700 (DESIGN)
Principal Particulars

Length overall	87 m
Beam	26 m
Draught	3.4 m
Crew	115 max
Passengers	950
Fuel capacity	75 m³
Water capacity	10 m³
Propulsive power	24 000 kW
Operational speed	35 knots

Classification: DnV + 1A1, HSCL, R2 Passenger
vessel - EO NAUT or equivalent recognised classification society.

WESTAMARAN 7500 (DESIGN)
Principal Particulars

Length overall	75 m
Beam	25.5 m
Draught	3.4 m
Crew	15
Passengers	900
Vehicles	187 cars
Fuel capacity	40000 l
Water capacity	6000 l
Propulsive power	22-30 mw
Operational speed	35-40 knots

WESTAMARAN 7100 OCEAN FLYER
(DESIGN)

This design is offered in two versions; an all-
aluminium construction or high tensile steel hulls
with aluminium superstructure. Various stowage
arrangements for cars with fixed/hoistable tween
decks are offered to accommodate vehicles of
double-decker/commercial trailer size. A choice of
diesel or gas-turbine propulsion is available.

Principal Particulars

Length overall	72.53 m
Beam	22.6 m
Draught	3.44 m
Payload	230-250 t
Crew	12
Passengers	450
Vehicles	128-144
Operational speed	33-40 knots
(Depends on structural material)	
Range	350 nm

Structure: Hull material: aluminium or high tensile
steel.
Superstructure material: aluminium alloy.
Propulsion: Engines: gas-turbine or diesel.

NEW ENTRY

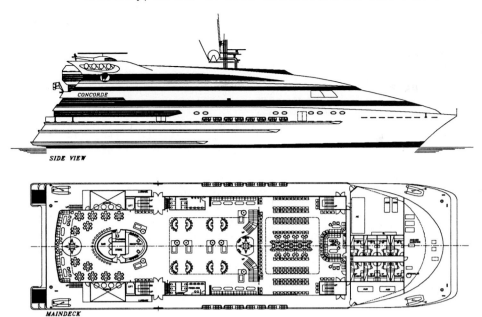

Westamaran 8700 (design) general arrangement

1995

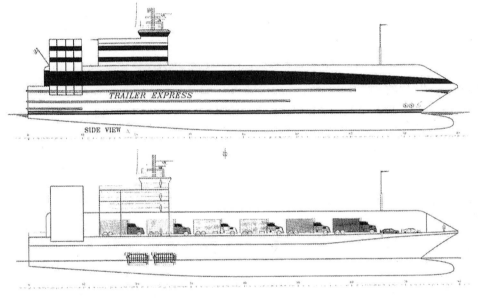

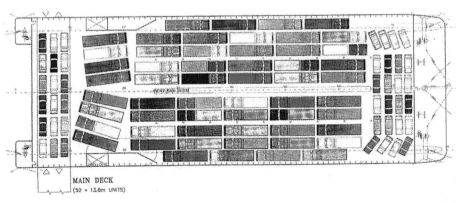

*Westamaran 9600 ro-ro ferry (design) general
arrangement*
1995

WESTAMARIN WEST A/S

PO Box 143, Vågsbygd, N-4501 Mandal, Norway,

Telephone: +47 (38) 262222
Telex: 21514 WRIN N
Telefax: +47 (38) 262302

Svein Berntsen, *Technical Manager*
Gowart Askildsen, *Purchasing Manager*
John Ihme, *Production Manager*

Westamarin West A/S in Mandal was established
in 1961, under the name of Westermoen Hydrofoil
A/S, to produce, develop, design and market high-

speed vessels for commercial and military purposes. A number of Supramar PT hydrofoil craft was
built in the 1960s.

In 1970-71 the first catamaran of an assymetric-
hull type, the Westamaran, was introduced. The
catamaran was based on a semi-planing hull form of
welded marine aluminium. This design was the first
high-speed catamaran to enter ferry operations.
Monohull vessels, type S75 and S80, have been
built, as well as Patrol boats for the Royal Norwegian
Navy and the Swedish Royal Navy. In 1988 the yard
delivered its first catamaran with symmetrical, slender hulls and increased speed compared to the
assymetric type. Westamarin West A/S departed
from pure catamaran development with its latest

vessels of type FOILCAT 2900 and FOILCAT 3000
which are foil-assisted catamarans. Recently a
South-east Asian owner placed an order for one
FOILCAT 3000 with options for two more.

Since 1986 Westamarin West A/S has been part
of the Swede Ship Invest AB group of companies
which includes Oskarshamns Varv AB, Swede Ship
Composite AB and an electrical contractor, Electro
Swede AB.

FOILCAT 2900 (Yard No 107)

Foilcat 2900 is a hydrofoil-assisted catamaran
initially developed by Hardanger Sunnhordlandske
Dampskibsselskap (HSD), operators of hydrofoils
and catamarans since 1961, and Westamarin A/S,

Catamaran craft built (W86) 1971 to 1979

Yard No	Name	Originally delivered	Seats
21	Fjordglytt	June 1971	140
22	Ar Vo (ex Trident 1, ex Belle de Dinard, ex Karmsund)	January 1972	
24	Fjordtroll	May 1972	140
25	Supercats (ex Sauda)	June 1972	148
26	Mayflower	October 1972	134
27	Kongsbussen	April 1973	
28	Hertugbussen	May 1973	
29	Tedno	June 1973	140
32	Flycat (ex Koegelwieck)	September 1973	135 + cargo
34	Olavsbussen	February 1974	
35	Tjelden (ex Haugesund)	November 1973	94 + cargo
41	Hilde (ex Fjordbris, ex Storesund)	September 1974	165
42	Stilbris (ex Carib Link, ex Fjordkongen II)	January 1975	140
44	Brynilen	June 1975	94 (+ 6 t freight)
45	Øygar	September 1975	140
46	Fjorddronningen	January 1976	174
47	Trident 2 (ex Highland Seabird)	May 1976	
48	Ternøy (ex Fjorddrott)	June 1976	167
49	Fjordprinsessen	March 1977	163
65	Bornholm Express (ex Steigtind)	June 1977	182
54	Mediteran	June 1978	
67	Marina I	July 1978	
66	Hornoy	October 1979	136

Catamaran craft built (W95) 1974 to 1982

Yard No	Name	Originally delivered	Seats
36	Trident 5 (ex Vingtor)	May 1974	240
37	Tranen (ex Sleipner)	June 1974	
38	Rapido de Formentera (ex Sunnhordland)	April 1975	180
	Nasstro Azzurro (ex Martini Bianco, ex Amarischia, ex Martini Bianco)	May 1975	
43	Alisur Azul (ex Westjet) (W95T)	December 1976	
51	Salem (ex Tryving) (ex Draupner)	April 1977	
52	Tunen	May 1977	180
50	Pegasus	June 1977	
53	Tranen	June 1978	180
68	Siken (ex Tumleren)	April 1979	180
79	Trident 6 (ex Azur Express, ex Alisur Amarillo (W95D))	April 1981	211
80	Tromsprinsen	July 1981	210
81	Trident 4 (ex Celestina)	June 1981	218
84	Trident 3 (ex Venture 84)	July 1982	205

Catamaran craft built (W88) 1981 to 1986

Yard No	Name	Delivered	Seats
78	Haugesund	March 1981	180
82	Midthordland	November 1981	170
88	Skøgoy	May 1985	132 + 10 t cargo
91	Fjordsol	June 1986	202

builder of hydrofoils since 1962 followed by catamarans from 1970. Extensive model testing has been carried out by the Norwegian Marine Technology Research Institute A/S (MARINTEK) and by the Institut fur Schiffs- und Meerestechnik, Technical University, Berlin.

The Foilcat 2900 combines the best properties of the super slender-hull catamarans with the speed capability of hydrofoil craft fitted with fully submerged foils. The foils are not surface-piercing and do not give self-stabilisation. When the hulls are clear of the water surface no stabilisation is provided by them.

At a certain combination of rudder control and speed, a banking angle will be introduced automatically during the turn thereby reducing the horizontal g forces on passengers and craft. During turns the outer hull is not raised thereby avoiding the harmful effects of propeller and foil aeration. Maximum rudder angles are ±25°, the rudders being the front foil struts.

The Foilcat 2900 entered service between Århus and Copenhagen (2.5 hour journey time) towards the end of November 1992 being chartered by DSØ and Difko Shipinvest A/S, and continued in operation to the end of March 1993. The vessel is currently operating in Indonesia.

Principal Particulars

Length overall	29.25 m
Length waterline	26.4 m
Beam	8.36 m
Draught, hullborne	3.65 m

Foilcat 2900   1994

Draught, foilborne	1.9 m
Displacement, minimum	104 t
Displacement, maximum	123 t
Passengers	140
Fuel capacity	5000 l
Water capacity	500 l
Propulsive power	2 × 2000 kW
Maximum speed	50 knots
Operational speed	45 knots

Classification: DnV 1A1 R90 light craft passenger catamaran EO.

Structure: Hull material: plates Al. AA 5083, profiles Al. AA 6082.

Superstructure material: aluminium alloy.

Foils: stainless steel.

Propulsion: The main engines are two MTU 16V 396 TE.74L, 2000 kW each at 2000 rpm.

These drive two propellers, Ulstein-Liaaen Speed-Z Type CPZ 60/42 -125C (1.25 m diameter,

Wheelhouse of Foilcat 2900   1993

Foilcat 2900 passenger lounge   1993

4-blade, Newton Rader blade sections, at 800 rpm).
Control: The vessel is fitted with three foils, two separate front foils (turntable-mounted) and a single
transverse rear foil. Spanwise variation of angle of
attack and camber have been incorporated to avoid
downwash induced cavitation on the rear foil. The
front foils are fitted with winglets to increase lift/drag
ratio and during development tests a speed increase
of approximately 7.5 knots was obtained.

At a speed of approximately 10 knots (at which the

hull is still providing stability) the FCS is activated,
the stabilisation is automatic and the trim is kept at
+1° and roll is damped by the lifting forces generated by the foils. The FCS has control of the stabilisation long before it is possible to enter the lifting
height at which insufficient hull stabilisation would
result; this would occur at approximately 28 knots.
The transition stability between the hullborne and
the foilborne condition is therefore fully controlled.

Auxiliary systems: The auxiliary systems are powered by: two Mitsubishi S6F-T diesels, 56 kW each at
1500 rpm; and two Newage Stamford UCM224G
generators, 65 kVA, 230 V 3-phase 50 Hz.

Active foil stabilisation system equipped with trailing edge flaps actuated hydraulically (Movator actuators) via electric control valves working through an
electronic control system named Flight Control System (FCS). Software for this system was provided by
Camo A/S, supported by MARINTEK A/S which
supplied the basis for this development.

FOILCAT 3000

This design is a direct development of the 2900
design and provides increased passenger capacity.

One vessel is currently under construction with two
further craft under negotiation.

Principal Particulars

Length overall	30 m
Length waterline	27 m
Beam	9.55 m
Draught, hullborne	3.8 m (including foils)
Payload	15 t
Passengers	200
Fuel capacity	5000 l
Water capacity	1000 l
Propulsive power	2 × 2000 kW
Maximum speed	47 knots
Operational speed	44 knots

Classification: DnV +1A1 HSLC R2 Passenger, EO;
IMO Code of Safety for Dynamically Supported
Craft.

General arrangement of Foilcat 3000

Structure: The hull is to be built in seawater-resistant aluminium. Alternately, deckhouse/wheelhouse to be built in plastic composites. The foils and struts built in steel of quality S165M. Three flap sets to be mounted on aft foil and one set on each of front foils. Flaps and similar parts can alternately be built in titanium or similar.

Propulsion: High-speed marine diesel engines (two), make 16V 396 TE 74L; driving two Ulstein Speed-Z CPZ-60/42-125L-HC units, with controllable-pitch propellers. Reduction gears are included.

Electrical system: 380 V AC, 50 Hz, 3 phase +N with supply from two motor aggregates.
220 V AC, 50 Hz, 1 phase.
24 V DC with supply from batteries.
The motor aggregates (2) are each 65 kVA.

Control: The forward foil struts are to be used as rudders. The struts/rudders are to be electrically synchronised.

WESTAMARAN 5000
Anne Lise

This vessel originally delivered as a thermo-cargo catamaran has been converted by Oskarshamns Varv to a passenger/car ferry; please see Oskarshamns entry for details. For details of the vessel in its original form please see the 1992-93 edition of this book.

WESTAMARAN W86

A total of 23 Westamarin W86s were built up to 1979 with speeds in the range of 24 to 28 knots. Details of these craft are given in earlier editions of this book.

WESTAMARAN W95

This longer version of the W86, of which 14 were delivered, can carry up to 248 passengers. Details of these craft are given in earlier editions of this book.

WESTAMARAN 3000 (ex W88)

A faster but slightly smaller capacity craft than the W86 or W95 and replacing the W86, four W88s were sold, the last, *Fjordsol*, being slightly longer at 29.4 m. Details of these craft are given in earlier editions of this book.

WESTAMARAN 3000
Fjordsol
Principal Particulars

Length overall	29.4 m
Length waterline	25.4 m
Beam	9 m
Draught	2.2 m
Payload	10 t (additional)
Passengers	202
Fuel capacity	2 × 2800 l tanks
Water capacity	600 l
Propulsive power	2 × 1150 kW
Operational speed	30 knots
Range	270 nm

Propulsion: 2 × MTU 12V 396 TB83, 1150 kW each at 1940 rpm, ZF BW 455S gearboxes. Auxiliary engines: 2 × Daimler Benz OM 352A driving Stamford MSC 234F generators, 3 × 230 V, 50 Hz.

Structure: aluminium AA 5083.

WESTAMARAN W100
Principal Particulars

Length overall	32.9 m
Beam	9.8 m
Draught	2.0 m
Passengers	300
Operational speed	28 knots

Propulsion: Main engines: 2 × MTU 16V 396 TB 83 or similar.

Catamaran craft built (W100) 1980 to 1982

Yard No	Name	Delivered
75	Gibline I (W100D) (ex Gimle Belle, ex Condor 6)	April 1980
76	Independencia (ex Gimle Bird)	September 1981
77	Porec (ex Gimle Bay)	January 1982
83	Nearchos (ex Venture 83)	May 1982

Westamaran 3700 S Maria   **1991**

WESTAMARAN 3700 SC
(Yard Nos 93 and 94)

In 1988 these craft were operated by Saltens Dampskibsselskap, and Ofotens Dampskibsselskap.

Principal Particulars

Length overall	36.5 m
Length waterline	31.1 m
Beam	9.5 m
Draught	1.47 m
Payload	15 t (additional cargo)
Passengers	195
Fuel capacity	2 × 4000 l tanks
Water capacity	600 l
Operational speed	35 knots
Range	280 nm

WESTAMARAN 3700 SC
Pilen (ex Vindile)
(Yard No 95)
Principal Particulars

Length overall	37 m
Length waterline	31.1 m
Beam	9.5 m
Draught	1.47 m
Passengers	322
Propulsive power	2 × 2040 kW

Classification: DnV + 1A1, R45, light craft passenger vessel.

Structure: Hulls, superstructure and deckhouse with wheelhouse built in seawater corrosion-resistant aluminium plates AA5083 (D54S 1/4H), profiles in AA 6081 WP (B 51 SWP).

Propulsion: 2 × MTU 16V 396 TB 84 engines, 2040 kW each, at 1940 rpm. These drive two KaMeWa 63S water-jet units.

Auxiliary systems: 2 × Mercedes OM 352 driving Stamford MSC 234 E70 kVA, 250 V, 50 Hz, 3-phase generators.

WESTAMARAN 3700 S
Maria
(Yard No WM 101- OV 527)
Principal Particulars

Length overall	37 m
Beam	9.5 m
Draught	1.7 m
Passengers	318
Fuel capacity	13 000 l
Water capacity	1200 l
Propulsive power	2 × 2000 kW
Maximum speed	41 knots
Operational speed	38 knots

Classification: DnV

Propulsion: Engines: 2 × MTU 16V 396 TE 74L, 2000 kW each at 1980 rpm. These drive two KaMeWa 63S II water-jet units.

Auxiliary systems: 2 × Mercedes-Benz OM 352A generators.

WESTAMARAN 3600 (ex W120)
Zi Liang
Principal Particulars

Length overall	36.2 m
Length waterline	32.26 m
Beam	9.77 m
Passengers	354
Fuel capacity	2 × 5000 l tanks
Water capacity	1200 l
Speed	25-27 knots
Range	270 nm

Classification: DnV + 1A1, R45.

Structure: aluminium AA5083.

Propulsion: Main engines: 2 × MTU 16V 396 TB 83, each 1540 kW at 1940 rpm.
Gearboxes: ZF BU 755S, ratio 3.07:1.
Auxiliary engines: 2 × Mercedes-Benz OM 352A.

Auxiliary systems: 2 × Stamford MSC 234F

Catamaran craft built (W3600, ex W120) 1987

Yard No	Name	Seats	Delivered	Operator
89	Zi Liang	354	January 1987	Nantong Hi-Speed Passenger Ship Co, China

Catamaran craft built (W3700 SC) 1988

Yard No	Name	Seats	Delivered	Owner
93	Salten	195 + 30 m² cargo hold	April 1988	Saltens Dampskibsselskap A/S
94	Ofoten	195 + 30 m² cargo hold	May 1988	Ofotens Dampskibsselskap A/S

Catamaran craft built (W3700 S) 1988

Yard No	Name	Seats	Delivered	Owner
95	Pilen (ex Vindile)	300	1988	
101	Maria	318	June 1990	Brudey Frères

WESTAMARAN 4100 S
Yard Nos:
Kyrmskaya Strela, 103
Golubaya Strela, 104
Irbis, 105
Sirius, 106

On 9 May 1989 Westamarin A/S announced an order from AKP Sovcomflot for two catamaran ferries of a new type, the Westamarin 4100 S, for delivery to the Soviet Union Black Sea Shipping Company together with an option for a further two. This option was taken up in June 1989. The value of the first order was given as approximately NOK80 million for the two vessels. Delivery of first two vessels was in August and September 1990.

Principal Particulars
Length overall	42.5 m
Length waterline	37.2 m
Beam	10 m
Draught	1.6 m
Passengers	292
Fuel capacity	13 260 l
Water capacity	2000 l
Maximum speed	38 knots
Operational speed	35 knots
Range	400 nm

Classification: USSR Register of Shipping (RS) KM 2 II A3 pass CAT.
Propulsion: Engines, main: 2 × MTU 16V 396 TB 84, 2040 kW each at 1940 rpm; driving 2 × KaMeWa 71 S water-jet units.
Auxiliary systems: 2 × Mercedes-Benz OM 366A.

WESTAMARIN 4200 S
Westamarin 4200 S

The first vessel of this type was delivered to Japan in June 1991 and named after the type. Two further vessels of this type were delivered to Japan in 1991 and 1992 and built by Oskarshamns Varv AB, Sweden.

Principal Particulars
Length overall	42.23 m
Beam	10 m
Draught	1.6 m
Crew	4
Passengers	230
Propulsive power	2 × 2000 kW
Maximum speed	38 knots
Operational speed	35 knots

Classification: NKK (NS * AI Catamaran Passenger Ship, MNS * Restricted Coastal Service)
Propulsion: Engines: 2 × MTU 396 V16 TE 74L, 2000 kW each; driving KaMeWa 71S II water-jets through 2 × ZF BU 755 gearboxes, ratio 2.333:1.
Auxiliary systems: 2 × Mitsubishi S6 FT diesels, 56 kW each driving Stamford Generators UCM 224 G23, 380 V AC, 50 Hz, 65 kVA.

Catamaran craft built (W4100 S) 1990
Yard No	Name	Seats	Delivered	Owner
103	*Kyrmskaya Strela*	292	1990	Black Sea Shipping Co
104	*Golubayaa Strela*	300	Mar 1990	Black Sea Shipping Co
105	*Irbis*	292	Aug 1990	Novorossiysk Shipping Co
106	*Sirius*	292	Sep 1990	Novorossiysk Shipping Co

Catamaran craft built or on order (W4200 S) 1990 onwards
Yard No	Name	Seats	Delivered	Owner
108	*Westamarin 4200 S*	230	June 1991	Mitsui Company, Japan
109	*Mahatani Express*	304	1992	PT Pelni, Indonesia

UPDATED

Westamaran 4200 S   *1992*

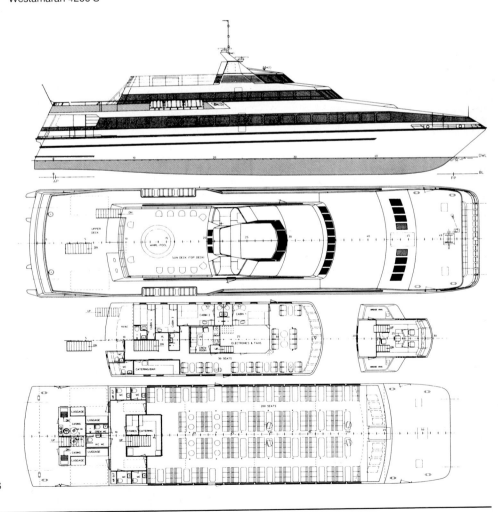

General arrangement of Westamaran 4200 S

SINGAPORE

ALUMINIUM CRAFT (88) PTE LTD

A division of Singmarine Industries Ltd
55 Gul Road, Singapore 2262

Telephone: +65 862 4800
Telefax: +65 862 4803

Chang Seak Foo, *Director and General Manager*
Fong Weng Meng, *Technical Manager*
Gabriel Tan, *Marketing Manager*

Singmarine's aluminium specialist, Aluminium Craft (88) Pte Ltd has accumulated over 24 years of experience in the building and repair of aluminium craft and industrial structures. Apart from its own proven monohull it also offers other hull designs such as the SWATH (Small Waterplane Area Twin Hull) and SES (Surface Effect Ship), Lock Crowther catamaran design, and construction of any designs of owners' choice.

SS23

The first of these vessels, the *Glory of Singapore*, was launched in July 1989; both are for service on the Singapore to Batam route and have seating for 130 passengers. They are powered by two 671 kW high-speed diesel engines, giving a service speed of 25 knots.

The hulls of these vessels are of asymmetrical form, backed up by research and development with support from the Singapore Economic Development Board which provided a grant for the design.

Island Pearl
Sea Pearl

These semi-displacement hull catamarans were delivered in 1991 for service between Singapore and Tioman Island. Air-conditioning is fitted.

Principal Particulars

Length overall	34.5 m
Beam	9.82 m
Draught	1.55 m
Crew	6
Passengers	228
Fuel capacity	9000 l
Water capacity	3000 l
Propulsive power	2 × 1260 kW
Speed	25 knots

Classification: GL + 100A4K.
Propulsion: Engines: 2 × Deutz MWM TBD 604B V12, MCR 1260 kW each, driving two nickel aluminium-bronze 5-blade fixed-pitch propellers, left- and right-handed.
Auxiliary systems: 2 × Perkins/Stamford 80 kVA.

Tai An
Dong Qu Er Hao

Ordered by Humen Lungwei Passenger Transportation of Guandong in mid-1992, *Tai An* was delivered in July 1993. The craft was designed by Lock Crowther of Australia.

Island Pearl 1993

Dong Qu Er Hao 1995

A repeat order was contracted in late 1993 and *Dong Qu Er Hao* was delivered in mid-1994.

Principal Particulars

Length overall	35 m
Beam	11 m
Draught	1.5 m
Maximum speed	29 knots
Crew	8
Passengers	270
Fuel capacity	10 000 l
Propulsive power	2 × 1260 kW

Propulsion: The main engines are two MTU 12V 396 TE 74L.
Auxiliary systems: Generators: 2 × 100 kVA MTU 6R 099 TE51.

38 m CATAMARAN

Ordered by Humen Transportation Co in 1994, this 360 passenger, 15 crew vessel is similar to *Tai An* and is scheduled for delivery in mid-1995.

UPDATED

KVÆRNER FJELLSTRAND (S) PTE LTD

29 Tuas Crescent, Singapore 2263

Telephone: +65 861 4180
Telefax: +65 861 4181

Are D Dahl, *President*
P P Wee, *Senior Marketing Manager*
Aage Christensen, *Senior Operations Manager*

With over 60 high-speed catamaran vessels sold to 21 countries, Kværner Fjellstrand began construction in 1990 of a building yard in Singapore. Centrally placed in the Asia-Pacific region, the

40 m Flying Cat Nam Hae Queen
1995

Singapore yard is engaged in building the same range of vessels as the Norwegian yard and provides immediate after sales services in the region for existing and future operators of their vessels.

UPDATED

Catamaran vessels built or under construction by Kvaerner Fjellstrand (S) Pte

Type	Name	Seats	Delivered	Owner
40 m Flying Cat	Perdana Ekspres	352	April 1992	Inlandpark Sdn Bhd, Malaysia
40 m Flying Cat	Mabua Express	248	November 1992	PT Mabua Intan Express, Indonesia
40 m Flying Cat	Universal Mk I	259	December 1992	Woolaston Holdings Ltd, Hong Kong
40 m Flying Cat	Universal Mk II	259	December 1992	Woolaston Holdings Ltd, Hong Kong
40 m Flying Cat	Universal Mk III	258	October 1993	Woolaston Holdings Ltd, Hong Kong
40 m Flying Cat	Universal Mk IV	266	February 1994	Universal Mk IV Ltd, Hong Kong
40 m Flying Cat	HKF I	449	September 1993	Hong Kong & Yaumati Ferry Co Ltd
40 m Flying Cat	HKF II	449	August 1993	Hong Kong & Yaumati Ferry Co Ltd
40 m Flying Cat	Universal Mk V	266	January 1994	Universal Mk IV Ltd, Hong Kong
40 m Flying Cat	Paradise	380	April 1994	Won Kwang Shipping Co Ltd, Korea
40 m Flying Cat	Nam Hae Queen	350	April 1994	Nam Hae Express Co, Korea
40 m Flying Cat	Indera Bupula	312	July 1994	Damania Shipping Ltd India
40 m Flying Cat	Damania	392	September 1994	Damania Shipping Ltd India
40 m Flying Cat	HKF III	433	December 1994	Hong Kong & Yaumati Ferry Co Ltd
40 m Flying Cat	Aria Bupula	270	January 1995	Bintan Resort Ferries Pte Ltd, Singapore
40 m Flying Cat	Aremiti	449	October 1994	Aremiti Pacific Cruises Tahiti
40 m Flying Cat	To be named		1995	Singapore
40 m Flying Cat	To be named		1995	Singapore

Kværner Fjellstrand (S) Pte Ltd Shipyard in Singapore 1995

MARINTEKNIK SHIPBUILDERS (S) PTE LTD

31 Tuas Road, Singapore 2263

Telephone: +65 861 1706
Telefax: +65 861 4244

Patrick Cheung, *Managing Director*
Priscilla Lim, *Financial Director*
Hans Erikson, *Director, Marketing and Sales*
Andrew Yeo, *Director, Project and Design*
Sölve Mårdh, *Director, Production*
Clas Norrstrand, *Director, Research and Development*

Marinteknik Shipbuilders (S) Pte Ltd was established in 1984 as FBM Marinteknik (S) Pte Ltd, for the building of high-speed vessels. To date, the yard has built more than 30 vessels for customers worldwide, of both monohull and catamaran type as passenger vessels and crew boats. Current craft under

Artist's impression of the 41 CPV 387 seat ferry currently under construction 1995

Selesa Ekspres *1993* Magellan *1993*

construction include passenger ferries with speeds of up to 50 knots and passenger capacities of up to 500.

An associated company, Marinteknik Verkstads AB of Sweden, ceased trading in 1994 and details of their craft are included in this entry in a separate table.

36 m CATAMARAN
Selesa Ekspres

Selesa Ekspres is a 36 m passenger catamaran vessel and was delivered to its owner in November 1990. Its route of operation is between Penang/Pulau Langkawi and Penang/Medan.

The vessel's hull form consists of two symmetrical hulls with low resistance and semi-planing characteristics. The complete craft was constructed of welded salt-resistant aluminium alloy plates and profiles. The craft is powered by two MTU 12V 396 TB 74L engines coupled to two KaMeWa 63 SII water-jets. The vessel attains a speed of 30 knots in loaded condition.

Selesa Ekspres has a total seating capacity of 350 passengers in an aircraft type seating arrangement. Operator: Kuala Perlis-Langkawi Ferry Service Sdn Bhd based in Pulau Langkawi.

Principal Particulars

Length overall	36.5 m
Beam	9.4 m
Draught	1.2 m
Displacement, maximum	109.2 t
Payload	26.8 t
Crew	6
Passengers	350
Fuel capacity	9000 l
Water capacity	1000 l
Propulsive power	2 × 1400 kW
Maximum speed	32 knots
Operational speed	30 knots
Range	300 nm

Classification: Det Norske Veritas + 1AZ1 R-30 EO, Catamaran Light Craft.

Propulsion: 2 × MTU 12V 396 TE 74L high-speed marine diesel engines, each giving 1400 kW at 2000 rpm coupled to 2 × KaMeWa 63-SII water-jets.

MARINJET 41 m CATAMARAN
Camoes

Camoes is one of a series of catamarans built by Marinteknik Shipbuilders (S) Pte Ltd. The Jumbocat Class as it is known, has proved to have good and efficient hull characteristics. The ride comfort for passengers is noted to be exceptional with the installation of a pitch damping system. To date, seven such craft owned by Hongkong Macau Hydrofoil Company Ltd have been put into service for the route between Hong Kong and Macau.

The 41 m vessel has a total seating capacity for 306 passengers in a single-deck seating arrangement. The passenger saloon is well furnished with a high standard of interior fittings and deluxe high-back aircraft type seats. A refreshment and snack kiosk is also incorporated.

The vessel is powered by two MTU 16V 396 TB 84 engines coupled to two Marine Jet Power (MJP) J650R-DD water-jets.

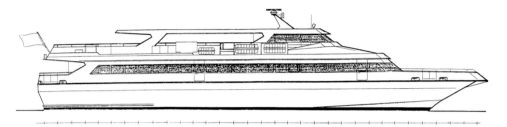

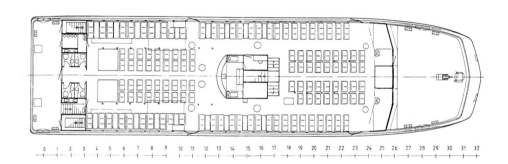

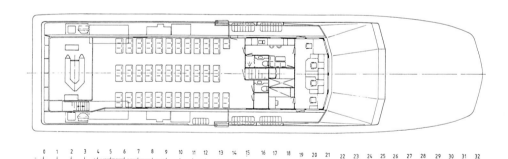

General arrangement of Marinteknik 41.5 CPV four-engine catamaran

Principal Particulars

Length overall	41.5 m	Water capacity	1000 l
Beam	11 m	Propulsive power	2 × 1940 kW
Draught	1.2 m	Operational speed	38 knots
Displacement, maximum	130 t	Range	240 nm
Payload	27.11 t	**Classification:** Det Norske Veritas + 1A1 R-25 EO,	
Crew	8	Catamaran Light Craft	
Passengers	306	**Propulsion:** 2 × MTU 16V 396 TB 84 high-speed	
Fuel capacity	7000 l	marine diesel engines, each giving 1940 kW at	
		1940 rpm coupled to 2 × MJP J650R-DD water-jets.	

Catamaran vessels built or under construction by Marinteknik Shipbuilders (S) Pte Ltd

Type	Yard No	Craft name	Owner/operator	Delivered	Engines	Classification	Payload	Speed
34 CCB	101	*Hakeem*	Ocean Tug Services	1985	2 × MTU 12V 396 TP 62 880 kW each	DnV R-60	50 passengers + 2.7 t cargo	27 knots
34 CCB	103	*Layar Sinar*	M I S C	1986	2 × MTU 12V 396 TB 83 1185 kW each	DnV R-150	70 passengers + 6 t cargo	29 knots
34 CCB	105	*Layar Sentosa*	M I S C	1987	2 × MTU 12V 396 TB 83 1185 kW each	DnV R-150	70 passengers + 6 t cargo	29 knots
36 CPV	111	*Airone Jet*	Med Mar srl, Naples	1988	2 × MTU 16V 396 TB 84 1940 kW each	RINA/DnV	318 passengers	35 knots
34 CPV	112	*Jiu Zhou* (ex *Shun de*)	Shun Gang	1987	2 × MTU 12V 396 TB 83 1180 kW each	Z C	250 passengers	27 knots
36 CPV	115	*Condor 8*	Condor Ltd	1988	2 × MTU 16V 396 TB 84 1940 kW each	DnV R-150	300 passengers	35 knots
36 CPV	117	*Selesa Ekspres*	Kuala Perlis-Langkawi Ferry Services Bhd	1990	2 × MTU 12V 396 TE 74L 1400 kW each	DnV R-30	350 passengers	30 knots
41 CPV	119	*Camoes*	Hongkong Macao Hydrofoil Co Ltd	1989	2 × MTU 16V 396 TB 84 1940 kW each	DnV R-25	306 passengers	38 knots
41 CPV	120	*Estrela do Mar*	Hongkong Macao Hydrofoil Co Ltd	1990	2 × MTU 15V 396 TB 84 1940 kW each	DnV R-25	306 passengers	38 knots
41 CPV	121	*Lusitano*	Hongkong Macao Hydrofoil Co Ltd	1990	2 × MTU 16V 396 TB 84 1940 kW each	DnV R-25	306 passengers	38 knots
41 CPV	123	*Vasco da Gama*	Hongkong Macao Hydrofoil Co Ltd	1991	2 × MTU 16V 396 TB 84 1940 kW each	DnV R-25	306 passengers	38 knots
27 CPV	126	*Marine Star II*	Samavest Sdn Bhd	1990	2 × MTU 12V 396 TB 83L 1180 kW each	DnV R-25	215 passengers	30 knots
41 CPV	127	*Santa Cruz*	Hongkong Macao Hydrofoil Co Ltd	1991	2 × MTU 16V 396 TB 74L 1940 kW each	DnV R-25	306 passengers	39 knots
41 CPV	128	*Magellan*	Hongkong Macao Hydrofoil Co Ltd	1991	2 × MTU 16V 396 TE 74L 1940 kW each	DnV R-25	306 passengers	38 knots
41 CPV	129	*St Malo*	—	1991	2 × MTU 16V 396 TE 74L 1940 kW each	Bureau Veritas	350 passengers	35 knots
41 CPV	130	*Saphir Express*	Antilles Trans-Express	1994	4 × MTU 12V 396 TE 74L	Bureau Veritas	387 passengers	39.5 knots
41 CPV	133	*Nam Hae Prince*	Nam Hae Express Co Ltd	1993	2 × MTU 16V 396 TE 74L 1940 kW each	DnV R-90	359 passengers	36.5 knots
35 CPV	118	Under construction	—	1995	2 × MTU 16V 396 TE 74L	DnV	300 passengers	37 knots
44 CPV	136	Under construction	—	1995	2 × Lycoming TF40 gas-turbines	DnV	390 passengers	50 knots
42 CPV	137	*Discovery Bay 1*	—	1995	2 × MWM 16V Diesels	DnV	500 passengers	33 knots
42 CPV	138	Under construction	—	1995	2 × MWM 16V Diesels	DnV	500 passengers	33 knots
42 CPV	139	Under construction	—	1995	2 × MWM 16V Diesels	DnV	500 passengers	33 knots
41 CPV	140	Under construction	—	1995	4 × MTU 12V 396 TE 74L	Bureau Veritas	387 passengers	40 knots

Fast catamaran craft built by Marinteknik Verkstads AB of Sweden which ceased trading in 1994

Yard No	Type	Marinteknik Designations Old	New	Engines	Craft name	Cruise speed, full load, knots	Delivered to	Originally delivered	Application	Seats	Loaded displacement, tonnes
42	29 m	JC-F1	—	2 × MTU 12V 396 TC 82, 1175 kW	*Formentera Jet* (ex *Jaguar*, ex *Jaguar Prince*, ex *Mavi Hali*, ex *Aliterreno 1*)	27	Spain	Nov 1980	Ferry	197	85
46	29 m	JC 3000	—	2 × MTU 12V 396 TB 83, 1225 kW	*Apollo Jet*	29	Hongkong Macao Hydrofoil Co Ltd	Jan 1982	Ferry	215	86
47	29 m	JC 3000	—	2 × MTU 12V 396 TB 83, 1225 kW	*Hercules Jet*	29	Hongkong Macao Hydrofoil Co Ltd	1982	Ferry	215	86
48	29 m	JC 3000	—	2 × MTU 12V 396 TB 83, 1225 kW	*Janus Jet*	29	Hongkong Macao Hydrofoil Co Ltd	Oct 1982	Ferry	215	86
50	29 m	JC 3000	—	2 × MTU 12V 396 TB 83, 1225 kW	*Duan Zhou Hu* (ex *Triton Jet*)	29	Zhao Gang Steamer Navigation Co of China	1983/ 23 Sep 1986	Ferry	215	86
51	33.71 m	PV 2400	Marinjet 33 CPV	2 × MTU 12V 396 TB 83, 1225 kW	*Alize Express* (ex *Nettuno Jet*)		SURF, Congo	May 1984	Ferry	218	86
54	33.71 m	PV 2400	Marinjet 33 CPV	2 × MTU 12V 396 TB 83, 1225 kW	*Jet Kat Express* (ex *Jetkat I*)		ATE	1984	Ferry	240	93.67
55	33.71 m	PV 2400	Marinjet 33 CPV	2 × MTU 12V 396 TB 83, 1225 kW	*Giove Jet*		Alilauro SpA	1985	Ferry	276	96
56	34 m	PV 3100 (Jumbo)	Marinjet 34 CPV-D	2 × MTU 16V 396 TB 83, 1540 kW	*Lommen*	32	Dampskibssellskabet Øresund A/S	Dec 1985	Ferry	235	97.58
59	34.1 m	PV 3100	Marinjet 34 CPV-D	2 × MTU 16V 396 TB 83, 1540 kW	*Ørnen*	32	Dampskibssellskabet Øresund A/S	Jul 1986	Ferry	235	97.68
60	34.1 m	CV 3400	Marinjet 34 CCB	2 × MTU 16V 396 TB 93, 1700 kW	*Emeraude Express*	40	Chambon (SURF)	Jan 1986	Crew boat	240	99.8
61*	34 m	—	Marinjet 34 CCB	2 × MTU 16V 396 TB 83, 1180 kW	*Layar Sentosa*	30	on charter to Shell Sarawak	1986	Crew boat	—	90
62	34 m	—	Marinjet 34 CPV-D	2 × MTU 16V 396 TB 84, 1935 kW	*Giunone Jet*		Alilauro SpA	—	Ferry	—	—
69	34 m	—	Marinjet 34 CPV PV-D	2 × MTU 16V 396 TB 84, 1935 kW	*Acapulco Jet*	34	Alilauro SpA	Apr 1989	Ferry	300	96
70	34 m	—	Marinjet 34 CPV	—	*Nettuno Jet*		Alilauro SpA	1988	Ferry	—	—
74	41.5 m	—	Marinjet 41 CPV-SD	2 × MTU 16V 396 TB 84, 1935 kW	*Öregrund*		Hongkong Macao Hydrofoil Co Ltd	28 Nov 1988	Ferry	306	130

Fast catamaran craft built by Marinteknik Verkstads AB of Sweden which ceased trading in 1994 (continued)

Yard No	Type	Marinteknik Designations Old	New	Engines	Craft name	Cruise speed, full load, knots	Delivered to	Originally delivered	Application	Seats	Loaded displacement, tonnes
73	34 m	—	—	2 × MTU 16V 396 TB84	*Saud*	32.5	Yasmine Line	Nov 1990	Ferry	255	—
82	41.5 m	—	CPV	4 × MTU 12V 396 TE 74L	*Jet Kat Express II*	40	Compagnie Maritime des Caraibes	1991	Ferry	380	—
86	34 m	—	CPV	2 × MTU 16V 396 TE 74L	*Antilles Express*	—	Antilles Trans-Express	1992	Ferry	297	—
88	41 m	—	CPV	—	*Saint Malo*	—	Channiland	1993	Ferry	350	—

CPV 41 CATAMARAN
Saphir Express

Saphir Express is a 42 m catamaran of Marinteknik standard and a sister vessel to *Jet Cat Express II*, earlier delivered from Marinteknik Verkstads in Sweden. *Saphir Express* was delivered to Antilles Trans-Express, Guadeloupe, in September 1994.

A further vessel of the same size but with different superstructure styling has been ordered by Antilles Trans-Express, and will be delivered in 1995.

Principal Particulars
Length overall	41.5 m
Beam	11 m
Draught	1.2 m
Crew	4
Passengers	387
Propulsive power	4 × 1415 kW
Operational speed	40 knots

Classification: Bureau Veritas
Propulsion: The main engines are 4 × MTU 12V 396 TE 74L diesel engines, each rated 1415 kW at 2000 rpm; each driving an MPJ J650R water-jet; via ZF 465 gearboxes.

CPV 42 Catamaran

The three new buildings, yard numbers 137, 138 and 139 ordered by Hong Kong Resort Co are all of the same type and have been designed to offer a 20 minute shuttle service from Discovery Bay to central Hong Kong. The first vessel *Discovery Bay 1* was delivered in January 1995.

Princpal Particulars
Length overall	42 m
Beam	11.5 m
Draught	1.3 m
Passengers	500
Operational speed	33 knots

UPDATED

Saphir Express *in service with Antilles Trans-Express*

1995

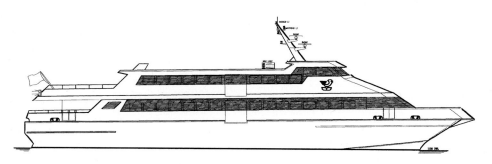

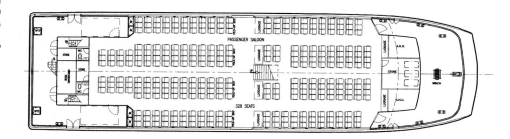

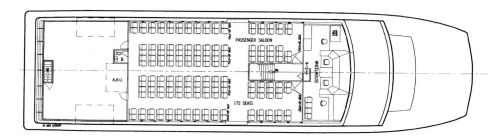

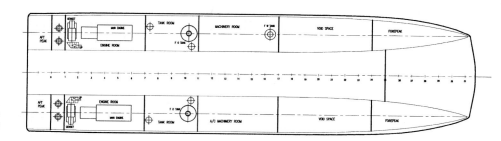

General arrangement of the CPV42 500 seat ferry, three of which are currently under construction
1995

SINGAPORE SHIPBUILDING & ENGINEERING LTD

7 Benoi Road, Singapore 2262
PO Box 138, Jurong Town Post Office, Singapore 9161

Boon Swan Foo, *Managing Director*
See Leong Teck, *Deputy General Manager*
Wong Kin Hoong, *Assistant General Manager, Commercial*
Tan Pheng Hock, *Assistant General Manager, Yard*
Teh Yew Shyan, *Senior Manager, Quality Assurance*

Telephone: +65 861 2244
Telex: 21206*SINGA RS
Telefax: +65 861 3028/ 1601

Singapore Shipbuilding & Engineering Ltd (SSE), a member of Singapore Technologies, announced in 1990 a contract to build a 282 passenger, 34.6 m high-speed catamaran ferry for operation between Hong Kong and the Pearl River Delta of Kwangtung Province, China.

Completely designed by SSE engineers, this vessel marks a significant move for SSE into the high-speed catamaran ferry business.

The company has, to date, built and on order, more than 100 aluminium high-speed vessels (with a length of 12 m or more) with speeds in excess of 20 knots.

34 m CATAMARAN
Tai Ping
Principal Particulars

Length overall	34.6 m
Beam	10.5 m
Draught	2.1 m
Crew	10
Passenger	282
Fuel capacity	7000 l
Water capacity	1000 l
Propulsive power	2 × 1412 kW
Maximum speed	29 knots
Operational speed	28 knots

Structure: Each hull is divided into seven separate watertight compartments by means of watertight bulkheads and has a forepeak, store void space, main engine room, auxiliary engine room and steering compartment. The accommodation cabin is sited above the main deck. The wheelhouse is arranged at the forward end of the upper deck.

Outfit: Immediately aft of the foredeck is the passenger saloon which also houses the toilets, a pantry and a kiosk.

The passenger saloon accommodates 272 passengers in aircraft style seats (non-reclinable type) with a fold-down plastic table. The VIP saloon, sited at the aft of wheelhouse on upper deck accommodates 10 VIPs in settee-seating. There are two cabins, provided on the upper deck, one for two officers and the other for eight crew.

All accommodation spaces are air-conditioned.

Propulsion: The main engines are 2 × MTU 12V 396 TE 74L diesels, each producing 1412 kW at 2000 rpm MCR; driving fixed-pitch propellers through stern tube and shaft bearings; via ZF BW 465 gearboxes.

Electrical system: The primary system is 2 × 100 kVA, 380 V, 50 Hz, 3-phase; the secondary system is 230 V, 50 Hz, single-phase by 380/230 V transformers.

The emergency and engine starting use 24 V DC battery banks.

VERIFIED

Tai Ping   *1993*

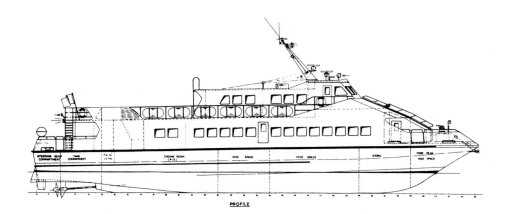

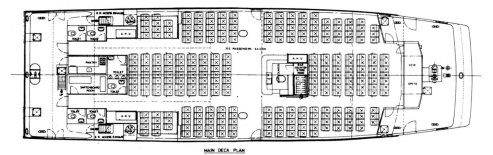
General arrangement of Tai Ping

SOUTH AFRICA

TEKNICRAFT DESIGN

PO Box 381, Paarden Eiland 7420, Cape Town, South Africa

Telephone: +27 (21) 790 1295
Telefax: +27 (21) 790 1295

N De Waal, *Managing Director*
R Kalley, *Marketing*

The company PINI (Pty) Ltd was established in 1984 and since 1992 has been trading as Teknicraft Design. The company specialises in the design of waterborne craft, in particular medium- and high-speed catamarans.

Teknicraft Design currently deals with clients in South Africa, the United Kingdom, Europe, the Middle East and Australia and is constantly expanding its client base.

The company also offers a technical consulting service as well as assisting boatyards in project management and the streamlining of manufacturing processes.

Teknicraft and a finance company Competitive Concepts (Europe) Ltd have jointly constructed the 22.5 m foil-assisted catamaran ferry called *Sea Shuttle* and are marketing this and other vessels worldwide.

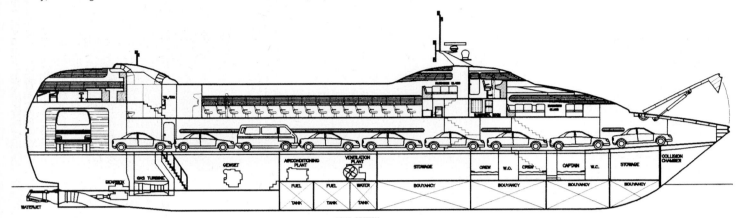

LONG SECTION

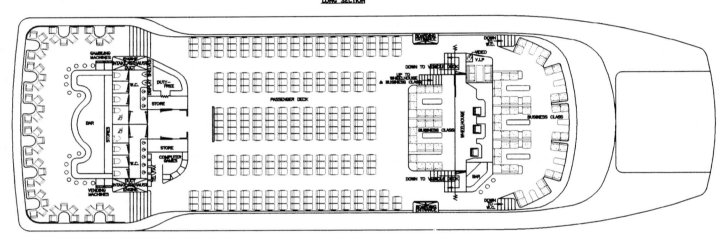

PLAN ON PASSENGER DECK

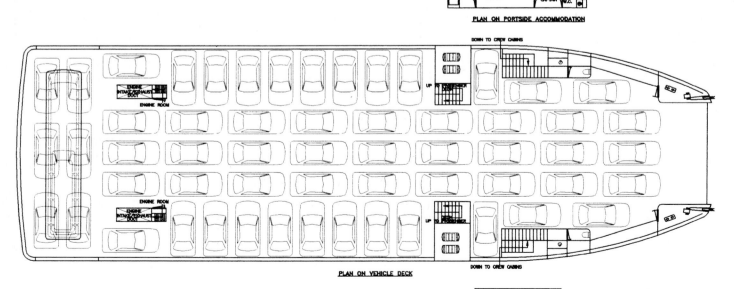

PLAN ON VEHICLE DECK

PLAN ON PORTSIDE ACCOMMODATION

PLAN ON STBDSIDE ACCOMMODATION

General arrangement of 50 m Super Shuttle ferry (design)

Sea Shuttle *during trials*

1994

Sea Shuttle

The vessel is constructed in GRP foam sandwich to Lloyd's Register HCC(SC) service group 2.

Length overall	22.5 m
Length waterline	19.6 m
Beam	7.2 m
Draught	1 m
Displacement	36 t
Payload	12 t
Crew	3
Passengers	117
Maximum speed	40 knots

Operational speed	30 knots
Range	250 nm

Propulsion: 2 × MWM Deutz 234 TBD V16 diesels, driving 2 × Hamilton 422 water-jets, through 2 × Reintjes reduction gearboxes.

50 m SUPER SHUTTLE FERRY (DESIGN)
Principal Particulars

Length overall	50 m
Length waterline	15.9 m
Displacement, minimum	185 t
Displacement, maximum	300 t

Passengers	360
Vehicles	57 cars
Fuel capacity	15 t
Water capacity	3t
Operational speed	35 knots
Range	270 nm

Structure: Aluminium alloy.
Propulsion: Main engine: 2 × LM 500 gas-turbines, driving water-jets.

UPDATED

SWEDEN

OSKARSHAMNS VARV AB

PO Box 704, S-572 28 Oskarshamn, Sweden

Telephone: +46 (491) 85500
Telefax: +46 (491) 15312

Curt Tappert, *Managing Director*
Olle Johansson, *Technical Manager*
Ronnie Petersson, *Repair and Production Manager*

Part of the Swede Ship Invest AB Group of Rönnäng, Sweden, Oskarshamns Varv AB has been involved in the building of Westamarin catamarans.

W-4200 S
Mirage

Oskarshamns Varv's NB 531 *Mirage* was delivered to Northwest Shipping Ltd on 25 June 1991 and is a sister vessel to the Westamarin A/S NB 108 *Westamarin 4200 S* delivered to Mitsui, Japan, in June 1991. *Mirage* was later sold to Japan leaving the yard in August 1991. The vessel is the result of a co-operation between the two sister yards in the Swede Ship Group, Oskarshamns Varv AB and Westamarin A/S.

Principal Particulars

Length overall	42.23 m
Beam	10 m
Draught	1.6 m
Passengers	408
Fuel capacity	13 200 l
Water capacity	2000 l
Propulsive power	2 × 2000 kW
Maximum speed	38 knots
Operational speed	35 knots

Classification: DnV + 1A1 R90 LC EO.
Propulsion: The main engines are 2 × MTU 396 V16

Mirage, *a Westamaran 4200 S built by Oskarshamns Varv AB*

1992

TE 74L, 2000 kW each, at 2000 rpm; driving 2 × KaMeWa 71S II water-jets; via 2 × ZF BU 755 gearboxes, ratio 2.333:1.
Electrical system: 2 × Mitubishi S6 FT 56 kW diesels driving Stamford UCM 224 G23 generators.

Pelni Ekspres Satu

Delivered in 1992 to Jakarta this Westamarin 4200 S is very similar to the *Mirage* except for different auxiliary engines, which are Volvo Penta TAMD 71A,

110 kW at 1500 rpm, and the main engines are rated at 1830 kW, 1940 rpm (tropical).

W-5000 CF
Madikera (Ex Anne Lise)

This vessel is a car ferry conversion of the original W-5000 *Anne Lise*, the 49.5 m thermo-cargo catamaran which was delivered in August 1987, Yard No 92. Details of the vessel in its old configuration are given in the 1992-93 edition of this book.

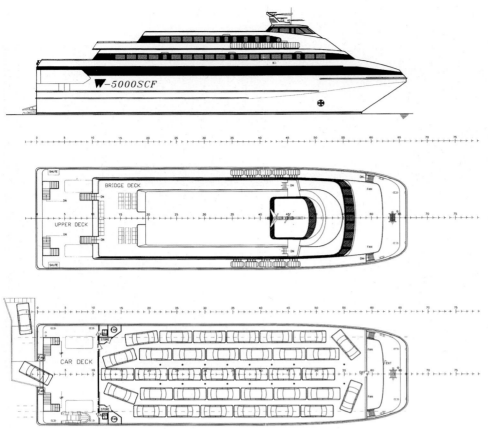

Proposed arrangement of the future W-5000 craft   **1995**

This car ferry conversion was ordered by Brudey Frères for operation on a Guadeloupe to Martinique route with a trip time of about three hours. She was delivered in May 1993.

The vessel is equipped with two MacGregor Navire hydraulically operated ramps, port and starboard on the aft car deck.

Principal Particulars

Length overall	49.45 m
Length waterline	43.6 m
Beam	14 m
Draught	2.6 m
Crew	8
Passengers	450
Vehicles	35 cars
Fuel capacity	40 000 l
Water capacity	2000 l
Propulsive power	4 × 2000 kW
Operational speed	30 knots

Classification: DnV + 1A1 R280 LC Car Ferry A-EO.
Structure: Hull material: aluminium alloy.
Superstructure material: aluminium alloy.
Propulsion: The main engines are 4 × MTU 396 16V TE 74L, 2000 kW each at 2000 rpm; driving 4 × four KaMeWa 63S II water-jets; via 4 × ZF BU 755 reduction gearboxes.
Electrical system: 2 × Volvo Penta/Stamford generators or similar, 130 kVA, 380 V 50 Hz 3-phase.

W-5600 CF

This design is based on the proven W-5000 CF design, again a Westamarin design.

Principal Particulars

Length overall	56 m
Beam	16 m
Draught	2.6 m
Payload	100 t
Passengers	450
Vehicles	50
Fuel capacity	2 × 26 000 l
Water capacity	1 × 2000 l
Propulsive power	2 × 5420 kW
Maximum speed	40 knots
Operational speed	36 knots

Classification: DnV *1A1, R2, HSLC, Car Ferry A, EO.
Structure: Seawater-resistant aluminium (marine grade).
Propulsion: The main engines are 2 × Caterpillar 3616 each producing 5420 kW at 1000 rpm; driving 2 × KaMeWa 100S II or 4 × KaMeWa 71S II water-jets.
Electrical system: 2 × Stamford/Volvo Penta or similar each 130 kVA, 3 × 380 V, 50 Hz or similar.
Control: One motion damping system with active flaps for damping of pitch, heave and roll. Regulation system type Robertson Tritech with software from Camo.

W-7500 (DESIGN)

Principal Particulars

Length overall	75 m
Beam	25.50 m
Draught	3.40 m
Payload	350 t
Passengers	900
Vehicles	190 cars or
	158 cars + 8 buses
Fuel capacity	40 000 l
Water capacity	6000 l
Propulsive power	4 × 5500 kW
Operational speed	36 knots

Classification: DnV *1A1, R1, HSLC, Car Ferry A, EO.
Structure: Seawater-resistant aluminium (marine grade).
Propulsion: The main engines are 4 × Ruston 16 RK270 diesels, each producing 5500 kW at 1000 rpm; driving 4 × KaMeWa 112SII or similar; via 4 × reduction gears.
Electrical system: 4 × generator sets each 150 kVA, 3 × 380 V 50 Hz or similar.

UPDATED

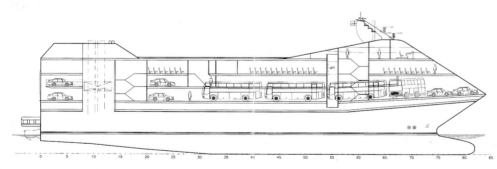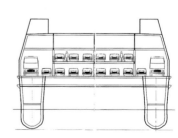

Car deck arrangement of the W-7500 (design)   **1995**

THAILAND

ITALTHAI MARINE LTD

Italthai House, 11th Floor, 2018 New Petchburi Road, Bangkok, Thailand

Telephone: +66 (2) 314 6101/7578/7246
Telex: 21225 ITELECT TH
Telefax: +66 (2) 314 6385

Dr Chaijudh Karnasuta, *Chairman*
Angelo Gualtieri, *Managing Director*

Dou Men (Yard No 78)
Zhong Shan Hu (Yard No 80)

Two catamaran ferries were delivered in June and July 1990 to Yuet Hing Marine Supplies, Hong Kong, for the Hong Kong to Tao Mun, China route. These vessels are powered by two MWM TBD 604B V12 1250 kW high-speed diesel engines driving KaMeWa 63 S water-jet units.

VERIFIED

Dou Men
1993

UNITED KINGDOM

ALUMINIUM SHIPBUILDERS LTD

Fishbourne Quay, Ashlake Copse Road, Fishbourne, Isle of Wight PO33 4EE, UK

Telephone: +44 (1983) 884719
Telefax: +44 (1983) 884720

J A Davies, *Managing Director*
M J Love, *Chairman*
P D P Kemp, *Deputy Chairman*
M J Peters, *Production Director*
P Owen, *Contracts Manager*

Aluminium Shipbuilders was formed in 1983 by the current Managing Director and principal shareholder, John Davies. Initially, ASL undertook a design contract for the Belgian Shipbuilders Corporation for a new Bridge Erection Boat (BEB).

In early 1985 ASL was instrumental in the sale of two Australian designed and built 30 m catamarans to Sealink (UK) Ltd for service on the Portsmouth to Isle of Wight route. These craft, designed by International Catamaran Designs Pty Ltd (InCat) were built at their yard in Hobart, Tasmania.

The first InCats built in Europe were the result of an initiative in late 1985 whereby, in association with McTay Marine Limited, the company responded to a Ministry of Defence (Navy) MoD(N) enquiry for the supply of Towed-Array Recovery/Deployment Vessels (TARVs). In December 1985 this joint venture resulted in the award of a contract for three TARVs and ASL undertook the fabrication and assembly of these vessels for fitting out by McTay Marine on Merseyside. The first hull was delivered to McTay Marine Ltd one month later, with subsequent hulls being delivered every two weeks and the first complete TARV delivered to the MoD(N) 15 weeks from receipt of order.

In 1986 ASL was awarded a contract for a 16 m Catamaran Riverbus from Thames Line plc. Subsequently, and after successful proving trials with the first craft named the *Daily Telegraph*, a further seven slightly larger 17.5 m craft were built in the succeeding two years, all for Thames Line.

Early in 1989 ASL obtained a £5 million contract from Condor Limited to build a 49 m wave-piercing catamaran of InCat design.

Condor 9 was delivered in August 1990 and operated a daily service from March to November on the arduous Western Channel route from St Malo to Weymouth and return, via the Channel Islands. This large vessel, which carries 450 passengers in two air-conditioned saloons at a service speed of 35 knots, meets the statutory safety requirements of the United Kingdom Department of Transport for a

Condor 9 *built by Aluminium Shipbuilders Ltd* *1992*

vessel operating on Short International Routes and was built to and classified to the classification requirements of Det Norske Veritas Light Craft rules.

During the last quarter of 1991 the company received a contract for the fabrication of a novel high-speed trimaran passenger ferry. The craft is the prototype of a 70-seat variant which with its inherent low wash characteristics and economical propulsion arrangement is intended as the next generation of smooth water fast river ferries.

In 1992 ASL expanded its high-speed craft repair facilities to cater for the increasing volume of specialised repair work associated with the entry into service of further SeaCats.

The company is currently in the process of acquiring construction facilities large enough to accommodate the next generation of SeaCat (of 78 m and above) for an ever growing marketplace.

RIVER 50

In August 1987, the first of a series of eight lightweight, high-speed passenger catamarans was delivered to Thames Line plc for operation between Charing Cross Pier and West India Dock on the River Thames. The vessel is powered by twin Volvo Penta TAMD 71A engines driving Riva Calzoni water-jets. Delivery was completed in 1988.

Principal Particulars

Length overall	16.35 m
Beam	5.4 m
Draught	0.6 m

Craft built		Seats	Date
InCat 17.5 m	*Barclays Bank*	51	1987
InCat 17.5 m	*London Docklands*	62	April 1988
InCat River 50	*Le Premier (ex Daily Telegraph)*	62	May 1988
InCat 17.5 m	*Chelsea Harbour*	62	May 1988
InCat 17.5 m	*Debenham Tewson and Chinnocks*	62	Aug 1988
InCat 17.5 m	*Harbour Exchange*	62	Aug 1988
InCat 17.5 m	*Daily Telegraph*	62	1988
InCat 17.5 m	*London Broadcasting Company*	62	1989
InCat WPC 49 m	*Condor 9*	450	1990

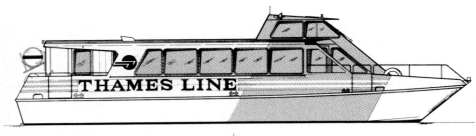

One of eight Aluminium Shipbuilders InCat 17.5 m catamarans **1992**

Fuel capacity	2 × 320 l
Water capacity	100 l
Propulsive power	2 × 228 kW
Operational speed	23-25 knots

Classification: UK DOT Class V smooth water limits.
Propulsion: The main engines are 2 × Volvo Penta TAMD 71A, 228 kW each at 2500 rpm; driving Riva Calzoni IRCL 39 D water-jets; via MPM IRM 301 PL-1 gearboxes.

17.5 m CATAMARAN

A total of seven vessels was ordered by Thames Line plc for delivery during 1988. The vessels are 17.5 m long and have revised interior arrangements which allow for a spacious cabin for 62 passengers.

Principal Particulars

Length overall	17.5 m
Beam	5.4 m
Draught	0.6 m
Passengers	50-70
Maximum speed	30 knots

Propulsion: water-jets.

Condor 9
49 m WAVE-PIERCING CATAMARAN

The order by Condor Ltd for a 49 m InCat wave-piercing catamaran was announced on 18 April 1989. Designed to carry 450 passengers, *Condor 9* replaced two hydrofoil vessels. The vessel was handed over in late August 1990.

Principal Particulars

Length overall	48.7 m
Length waterline	40.5 m
Beam	18.2 m
Hull beam	3.3 m
Draught	1.9 m
Crew	15
Passengers	450
Fuel capacity	2 × 7200 l
Water capacity	2 × 1000 l tanks
Operational speed	35 knots

Classification: DnV + 1A1 Light Craft (CAT) R45 Passenger Ship EO. Also surveyed under UK Department of Transport category Class 2, Short International Voyage vessel.
Structure: welded aluminium
Propulsion: The main engines are 4 × MWM TBD 604BV 16, 1682 kW each at 1800 rpm; driving 4 × MJP J650R-DD water-jet units.

If one engine should break down a speed of 30 knots can be maintained; each engine with its water-jet unit is entirely independent of the other three in its operation.

UPDATED

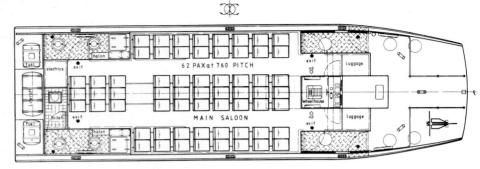

General arrangement of InCat-designed 17.5 m catamaran

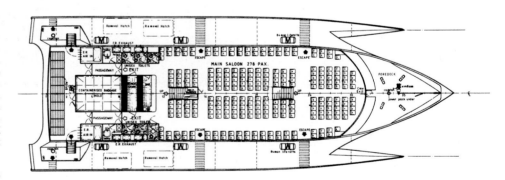

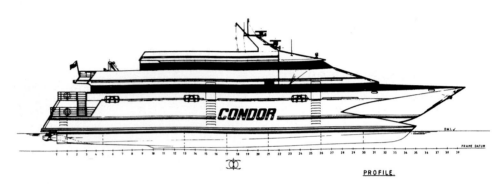

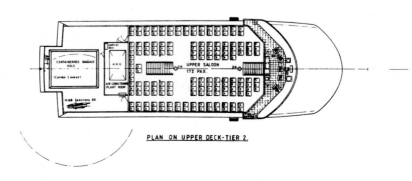

Condor 9

FBM MARINE GROUP

Cowes Shipyard, Cowes, Isle of Wight, UK

Telephone: +44 (183) 297111
Telex: 86466 FAMBRO G
Telefax: +44 (183) 299642

Michael Roberts, *Deputy Chairman*
John Warbey, *International Sales Director*
Malcolm Keith, *Managing Director*
Mike McSorley, *Sales Manager, Ferries*
Nigel Warren, *Chief Designer*
Heather Cox, *Marketing Manager*
Craig Moyes, *Sales Manager*

The FBM Marine Group, formerly Fairey Marinteknik and Fairey Marine, builds of a wide range of monohull and catamaran vessels for many applications. FBM Marine has also produced the first UK-built Swath, the Atlantic Class Fast Displacement Catamaran. Details of this 36.4 m vessel are given in the *Swath vessels* section of this book.

In October 1993 the company was awarded a £42 million order to build five (+ two) 45 m, 47 knot Tricat Class vessels.

THAMES CLASS CATAMARAN (RTL HYDROCAT)

There have been three of these 62-seat minimum-wash high-speed ferries delivered. The concept originated with Robert Trillo Ltd (RTL) and was introduced to Fairey Marine Ltd (now FBM Marine Ltd) in 1986. It combines a number of features specifically aimed at optimising a design of a relatively high-speed vessel for river use. Of particular importance in such applications is the minimisation of wash disturbance and noise. Both of these aspects are inherent in the RTL concept, coupled with minimum water and air draughts.

The remarkably low wash of the concept is of particular value in rivers such as the Thames where very shallow conditions occur at low tide in many areas. The Riverbus Partnership took delivery of three Thames Class catamarans from January 1992 onwards and operated them on the Thames as commuter ferries.

The hulls of the vessels are built in Fibre-Reinforced Composite plastics (FRC) and are bridged by an aluminium platform and superstructure. SP Systems of Cowes, Isle of Wight, UK has

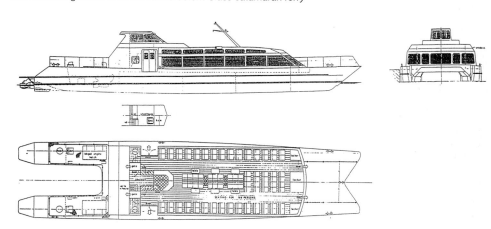

General arrangement of FBM Marine Solent Class catamaran ferry

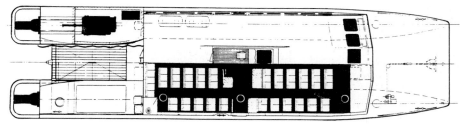

General arrangement of 29 m Thames Class catamaran (design)

FBM Marine Thames Class catamaran (RTL Hydrocat) in service on the Thames

FBM Marine Solent Class catamaran ferry Red Jet 1 *for Red Funnel Ferries*   *1991*

undertaken the FRC construction technology for these catamarans combining this with FBM's experience in the materials with their RNLI Mersey Class lifeboats.

Principal Particulars

Length overall	25 m
Length waterline	23 m
Beam	5.7 m
Draught	0.75 m
Crew	2
Passengers	62
Fuel capacity	1000 l
Maximum speed	25 knots

Structure: The hull structure is an FRC sandwich laminate with the bridge platform, box beams and salon constructed in low-maintenance marine grade aluminium alloy.

Propulsion: Two 6-cylinder in-line, turbocharged, heat exchange-cooled Scania DSI 11 marine diesel engines fitted with flanged-mounted MPM 320 reverse gearboxes drive the two Riva Calzoni IRC 390 water-jet units, via Aquadrive Cardan shafts.

Electrical system: 24 V DC insulated 2-wire system. Two 24 V battery banks (each bank of 200 Ah), one bank per engine, consisting of 12 V AC Delco-sealed lead acid batteries stowed in GRP boxes.

30 m CITY SLICKER CATAMARAN
(DESIGN)

The 30 m city slicker is an ultra low wash aluminium catamaran specifically designed for high-speed operation on riverine and harbour ferry routes.

Designed for medium- and high-speed passenger routes this variation of the 30 m City Slicker is capable of carrying 100-135 passengers at speeds up to 35 knots.

Principal Particulars

Length overall	32.4 m
Length waterline	30 m
Beam	8 m
Draught	1 m
Passengers	100-135
Operational speed	30 knots

Structure: Aluminium hull and superstructure.
Propulsion: Main engines: 2 × MWM TBD 234 V12, driving a pair of water-jets.

SUBMARINE SUPPORT VESSEL
Adamant

This new building for the Ministry of Defence delivered in early 1993 is based on the symmetrical hulls of the Solent Class range of passenger catamarans. The water-jet-propelled aluminium catamaran craft features a constant tension brow/gangway arrangement and large hydraulically operated fenders to facilitate 'at sea' transfers to and from submarines lying offshore.

The transfer system consists of an 8.1 m long aluminium brow pivoted at the inboard end to the base of an Effer Model 9600/3S hydraulic crane. A constant tension winch fitted on the crane supports the brow, allowing its outboard end, which is fitted with wheels and rubber tyres, to rest on the submarine. Relative movement between the two vessels is compensated by the automatic operation of the constant tension winch.

To prevent any possibility of damage to the submarine hull during such operations, two large foam filled fenders, each 2.5 m long × 1.25 m diameter, can be deployed on each side of the SSV. These fenders are normally stowed in deck cradles and are lowered and maintained in position by locally controlled hydraulic winches and an endless belt which passes through an eye located at water level.

Principal Particulars

Length	30.8 m
Beam	7.8 m
Draught	1.1 m
Propulsive power	2 × 507 kW
Maximum speed	23 knots
Range	250 nm

Propulsion: Engines: 2 × Cummins KTA19M diesels. Transmissions: 2 × ZF gearboxes. Thrust device: 2 × MJP water-jets.

SOLENT CLASS CATAMARAN
Red Jet 1 and *Red Jet 2*

Another low wash catamaran design, the 31.5 m Solent Class is in service with Red Funnel Ferries; the first of two was delivered in February 1991, following its launching on 4 December 1990.

The new Solent Class catamarans are specifically designed for operations on coastal routes, rivers and urban environments. Great attention has been paid to the comfort of the passengers and the reduction of wash and noise levels, factors important for operations in Southampton Water and Cowes Harbour.

During trials, *Red Jet 1* in full load condition, that is, 120 passengers, baggage, full fuel, water and three crew, achieved the following results:

MJP water-jet installation on Solent Class catamaran   *1992*

FBM 30.8 m submarine support vessel Adamant   *1993*

Speed, maximum (measured mile): 38.3 knots at 100% MCR
Speed, contract: 32.5 knots at 63% MCR
Speed, single engine: 24 knots
Acceleration: 35 knots in 47 s in 520 m
Fuel consumption: 375 l/h at 32.8 knots

The 30 m Solent Class Catamaran can maintain cruising speed of 38 knots in a 1 m head sea, and is well within the vertical acceleration limits prescribed for normal passenger comfort.

Principal Particulars

Length overall	31.5 m
Beam	8.4 m
Draught	1.1 m
Displacement, maximum	65 t
Passengers	120
Fuel capacity	1685 l
Water capacity	250 l
Propulsive power	2 × 1360 kW
Operational speed	32.5 knots

Classification: DnV + 1A1, R15, EO and UK Department of Transport Class IV for Solent use only.
Structure: Hull: marine grade aluminium, BS 1470 N8 plate, H30 TF extrusions.
Propulsion: Engines: 2 × MTU 12V 396 TE 84, 1360 kW each, at MCR, 1940 rpm; driving two MJP 650 water-jet units, driven via ZF gearboxes.
Control: The craft responds very quickly to the steering control at all speeds. The maximum rate of turn at 1800 rpm is 6.6°/s. The turning circle under full helm becomes progressively tighter and the speed falls away to about 20 knots after a full circle. The diameter of this circle is approximately 325 m.

The craft can rotate about its own axis at the rate of 7.5°/s.

By pushing the 'harbour mode' button and moving the power stick sideways, the craft will move slowly directly sideways through the water.

35 m TRICAT CLASS CATAMARAN

Delivered in January 1994 this development of the well proven Solent Class catamaran transports passengers on the increasingly popular route from Hong Kong to the new airport at Shenzhen on the Chinese mainland.

This 35 m catamaran is designed for use in coastal and sheltered waterways and is particularly suitable for operation in busy harbours due to its manoevrability, shallow draught and low wash characteristics.

Principal Particulars

Length overall	35.1 m
Length waterline	29.5 m
Beam	8.3 m
Draught	1.2 m
Passengers	160
Maximum speed	34 knots

Structure: Hull material: aluminium. Superstructure material: aluminium.
Propulsion: Engines: 2 × MTU 12V 396 TE74. Thrust devices: 2 × MJP water-jets.

45 m TRICAT CLASS CATAMARAN

FBM's 45 m Tricat Fast Passenger has been specifically designed in association with one of the world's leading designers of luxury yachts and mini cruise liners, Terry Disdale.

This 312-seat catamaran is the result of FBM's extensive research and development programme to build a passenger catamaran which can achieve very high speeds with good passenger comfort without recourse to foils or air cushioned systems.

This 45 m fast passenger catamaran is designed to meet the requirements of the Hong Kong Marine Department for short international voyages out of Hong Kong under a Hong Kong flag and DnV Classification R1 for High-Speed Light Craft.

Five of these Tricats have been ordered by CTS-Parkview Ferry services for the route between Hong Kong and Macau. Two Tricats will be built under licence by Babcock Rosyth (Fabricators) Ltd at the Rosyth Royal Dockyard. The first Tricat was launched on 8 September 1994. This craft was delivered to Hong Kong in January 1995.

Principal Particulars

Length overall	45 m
Length waterline	40 m
Beam	11.80 m
Draught	1.45 m
Payload	36.1 t

35 m Tricat Class catamaran during sea trials   *1994*

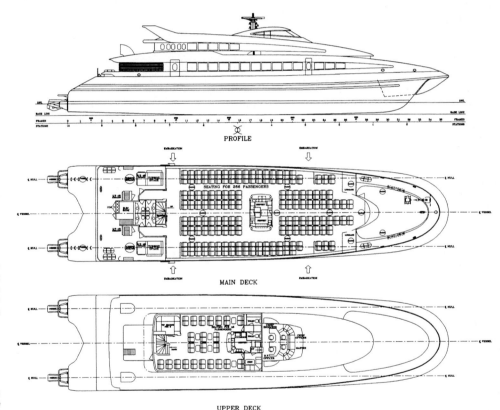

PROFILE

MAIN DECK

UPPER DECK

General arrangement of 45 m Tricat Class catamaran   *1995*

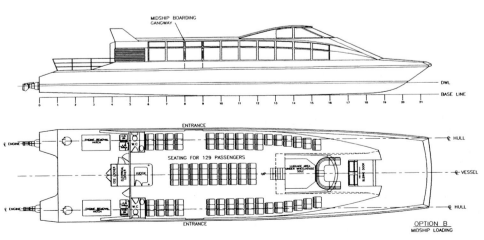

General arrangement of FBM's 30 m City Slicker catamaran (design)   *1995*

45 m Tricat Class catamaran on trials   1995

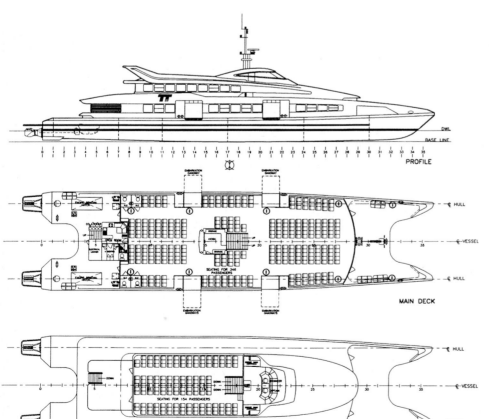

General arrangement of 45 m River Cat   1995

Passengers	312
Fuel capacity	7500 l
Propulsive power	2 × 4200 kW
Maximum speed	47 knots
Operational speed	44 knots
Range	125 nm

Classification: DnV Classification R1 for High-Speed Light Craft.

Structure: The hull is constructed with aluminium and the superstructure is aluminium with lightweight FRP cladding.

Propulsion: The Tricat is powered by two Caterpillar Solar Taurus gas-turbines each rated at 4200 kW at 13000 rpm. These engines drive via separate rigidly mounted reduction gearboxes to KaMeWa waterjets. The turbines and gearboxes are mounted on a raft rigidly bolted to the ship's structure.

FBM 45 m RIVER CAT

This passenger ferry is intended for intensive commuter passenger services within shallow harbours and sheltered routes. The FBM 450 River Cat specifically addresses the requirements for low fuel consumption and low wash. This catamaran incorporates the latest requirements of the IMO code for safety and incorporates the FBM TriCat unique futuristic styling.

Four of these craft are currently under construction for service on the River Tagus in Lisbon, Portugal. Two of these catamarans will be subcontracted to a Portugese yard. The first craft is scheduled to be delivered in July 1995.

Principal Particulars

Beam	11.8 m
Draught	1.38 m
Passengers	500
Fuel capacity	4000 l
Water capacity	1000 l
Operational speed	25 knots

Classification: IMO code for Safety of High-Speed Craft.

Structure: The hull is constructed of aluminium, and the superstructure is aluminium with lightweight FRP cladding.

Propulsion: The main engines are twin MWM TBD 616 V16s. These drive twin LIPS water-jets LJ76DL.

UPDATED

UNITED STATES OF AMERICA

ALLEN MARINE, INC

Sitka, Alaska, USA

Alaskan Dream

Built in five months in 1988 for transport of miners to an island off Juneau, Alaska.

Principal Particulars

Length overall	30 m
Displacement, maximum	72 t
Crew	3
Passengers	150
Operational speed	33 knots

Propulsion: Main engines: 4 × Caterpillar 3412 560 kW (750 hp) at 2100 rpm, driving 4 × Hamilton 422 water-jet units, driven via a pneumatic clutch.

Golden Spirit

This 23.8 m catamaran, built in 1987 and designed by E A Drake Ltd of Seattle, was given a 222 per cent increase in installed power in 1992 to give a speed of 25 knots. Two MAN D2842 diesels, 746 kW each, were installed forward of the original engines, two DDC 8V71 diesels. Each new engine drives a 1 m diameter propeller via a ZF VW 165 reduction gearbox. The propellers are 2.78 m forward of the Hamilton water-jet inlets of the original installation. The water-jet inlets have been modified to straighten out the rotational component of the propeller slipstream. The modifications were carried out by the Union Bay Shipbuilding Corporation of Seattle. The vessel is now operated by Alaska Travel Adventures for wildlife tours from Sitka, Alaska.

Golden Spirit powered by two MAN and two DDC diesel engines 1993

UPDATED

GLADDING-HEARN SHIPBUILDING

PO Box 300, One Riverside Avenue, Somerset, Massachusetts 02726-0300, USA

Telephone: +1 (508) 676 8596
Telefax: +1 (508) 672 1873

George R Duclos, *President*

This shipyard is a member of the Duclos Corporation and is well known for its range of commercial workboat and fast ferry craft. The yard has built a large number of small pilot craft as well as its well-known InCat catamaran ferries, (it is a licensed builder of International Catamarans Designs Pty Ltd, Australia).

24 m CATAMARAN
Mackinac Express
Island Express

Two InCat catamaran ferries were built for the Arnold Transit Company for service from Upper and Lower Peninsulas of Michigan to the resort island in the Mackinac Straits. The vessels are powered by two MWM TBD 604B V8 diesel engines.

Principal Particulars

Length overall	25.17 m
Length waterline	21.5 m
Beam	8.7 m
Hull beam	2.5 m
Draught	2.1 m
Passengers	365 (*Mackinac express*)
	300 (*Island Express*)
Operational speed	31 knots

25 m CATAMARAN
Express II,
(ex Vineyard Spray)

Delivered September 1988.

Principal Particulars

Length overall	25.17 m
Length waterline	21.51 m
Beam	8.7 m
Hull beam	2.5 m
Draught	2.1 m
Passengers	300
Fuel capacity	3974 l
Propulsive power	2 × 1290 kW
Operational speed	31 knots

Propulsion: The main engines are 2 × MWM 1290 kW diesels.
Electrical system: 2 × 35 kW Lister generators.

28 m CATAMARAN
Jet Cat Express

Delivered 15 April 1991 for service with *Catalina Channel Express*.

Principal Particulars

Length overall	31.25 m
Beam	8.69 m
Draught	1.01 m
Crew	4
Passengers	368
Fuel capacity	7570 l

Craft built (InCat) or on order		Originally delivered	Seats	Operator
24 m	*Makinac Express*	1987	365	Arnold Transit Co
24 m	*Island Express*	1988	300	Arnold Transit Co
25.17 m	*Express II* (ex *Vineyard Spray*)	September 1988	380	Express Navigation
25.17 m	*Express I*	February 1989	260	Express Navigation
28.2 m	*Jet Express*	May 1989	380	Put-in Bay Boat Line Co
31.1 m	*Victoria Clipper III* (ex *Audubon Express*)	1990	368	Clipper Navigation Inc
31.1 m	*Jet Cat Express*	1991	368	Doug Bombard Enterprises Catalina Channel Express
30 m	*Jet Express II*	May 1992	395	Put-in Bay Boat Line Co
28 m	*Friendship VI*	June 1993	149	Bar Harbor Whale Watch

Jet Cat Express 1992

Friendship IV 1995

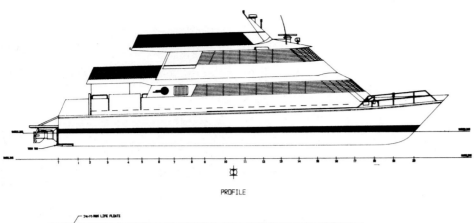

PROFILE

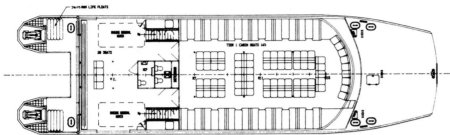

PLAN AT TIER 1

Jet Express II *general arrangement*

Water capacity	757 l
Propulsive power	2 × 1298 kW
Operational speed	31 knots

Propulsion: The main engines are 2 × DDC 16V 149TA, 1298 kW each; driving 2 × KaMeWa 63S2 water-jet units; via 2 × ZF BUK485 gearboxes.

30 m CATAMARAN
Jet Express II

This craft is powered by two 1298 kW MWM diesel engines driving KaMeWa water-jets and can reach 32 knots fully loaded. The draught is 1 m.

28 m CATAMARAN Z-Bow
Friendship IV

The vessel is designed and certified to carry up to 149 passengers for distances of up to 100 miles offshore. Operating from Bar Harbor, Maine, the vessel *Friendship IV*, carries passengers on whale watching/sightseeing excursions which last for approximately 3 hours. The craft was designed by InCat in 1993 and delivered by Gladding Hearn in June 1994.

Principal Particulars

Length overall	28 m
Beam	9.0 m
Draught	1.7 m
Passengers	149
Fuel capacity	6000 l
Propulsive power	2 × 607 kW
Maximum speed	28.6 knots
Operational speed	26 knots

UPDATED

The Put-in Bay Gladding Hearn InCat ferries
1993

NICHOLS BROTHERS BOAT BUILDERS INC

5400 S Cameron Road, Freeland, Whidbey Island, Washington 98249, USA

Telephone: +1 (360) 331 5500
Telefax: +1 (360) 331 7484

Matt Nichols, *President*
Archie Nichols, *Vice President*
Ken Schoonover, *Yard Supervisor*
Scott Murphy, *Financial Officer*
Bryan Nichols, *Marketing*

Licensed builder of International Catamaran Designs Pty Ltd, Australia.

22 m CATAMARAN
Klondike

Eight of these craft have been delivered since 1984, the main order coming in 1988 for six identical craft for the Port of Puerto Rico. These vessels operate on a five mile route between old San Juan and the newer metropolitan area of Puerto Rico city.

The 400 passenger, 26 m Dolphin

1989

Principal Particulars

Length overall	21.98 m
Beam	8.69 m
Passengers	210
Fuel capacity	1000 US gallons
Water capacity	1000 US gallons

Operational speed	26 knots

Propulsion: *Klondike* is powered by 2 × Caterpillar 3412 TA diesels, 522 kW each; *Spirit of Alderbrook* by 2 × 12V-92TA diesels; and the Puerto Rico boats by 2 × DDC GM 12V71 diesels.
Gearboxes: Niigata MGN-80.

The 37 m InCat wave-piercing catamaran Nantucket Spray, *renamed* SeaJet I

1991

Propellers: Coolidge 5-blade.
Electrical system: Northern Lights 40 kW generator.
Control: The rudders are the curved dipping InCat type.

26 m CATAMARAN
Catamarin
Dolphin
Gold Rush
Klondike II (ex *Victoria Clipper*, ex *Glacier Express*, ex *Baja Express*)
Principal Particulars

Length overall	26.14 m
Beam	9.45 m
Draught	2.39 m
Fuel capacity	20 440 l
Water capacity	1893 l (*Catamarin*)
	1515 l (*Klondike II*)
Propulsive power	2 × 1004 kW
Operational speed	28 knots

Propulsion: The main engines are 2 × Deutz BAM 16M 816C diesels, each 1004 kW continuous at 1800 rpm; driving Coolidge 5-blade, 1.169 m × 1.194 m propellers; via Reintjes WVS 832 gearboxes, ratio 1:2.29.
Electrical system: Generators: 2 × John Deere 4275 engines and Northern Lights 50 kW generators. *Glacier Express* has Pacific Diesel units.

36 m CATAMARAN
Catalina Flyer

The largest capacity high-speed catamaran to be built in the USA, the 500-seat *Catalina Flyer* (delivered May 1988) is in service between Newport Harbor and Catalina Island in Southern California with Catalina Passenger Service.
Principal Particulars

Length overall	36 m
Beam	12.2 m
Draught	2.44 m
Passengers	500
Fuel capacity	11 355 l
Water capacity	1514 l
Propulsive power	2 × 1490 kW
Maximum speed	30 knots
Operational speed	27 knots

Propulsion: The main engines are 2 × Caterpillar 3516 TA, 1490 kW each, specially lightened diesels; driving 3-blade CuNiAl Bronze, 1.3 m diameter

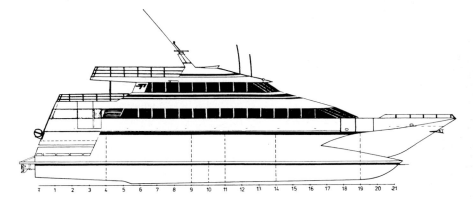

PROFILE

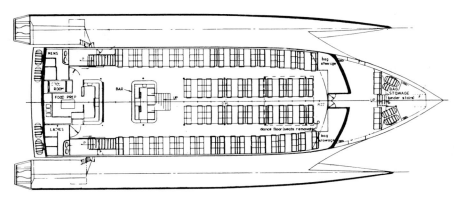

MAIN DECK
SEATS 198

General arrangement of the 37 m InCat wave-piercing catamaran SeaJet I, *ex* Metro Atlantic, *ex* Nantucket Spray

propellers; via 2 × Reintjes WS-1023, 2.538:1 gearboxes.
Electrical system: John Deere generators, 2 × 40 kW units.

Navigation and communications: Ross DR 600D flasher, 2 ICOM VHF radios, Furuno 1510D and 8030D radars, Sperry 8T autopilot, Furuno LC-90 Loran

Bow-loading ramp operation of Executive Explorer   1989

InCat Jelang K   1989

30 m CATAMARAN
Executive Explorer
A 31.7 m cruising catamaran, built in 1986 for Alaskan and Hawaiian islands cruising.

Principal Particulars

Length overall	30.03 m
Beam	11.2 m
Draught	2.51 m
Crew	20
Passengers	49
Fuel capacity	63 588 l
Water capacity	19 682 l
Propulsive power	2 × 1004 kW
Operational speed	22 knots

Propulsion: The main engines are 2 × Deutz BAM 816, 1004 kW continuous, each at 1800 rpm; driving ISO class 1, 5-blade, Nicel 1.346 m × 1.422 m Columbia Bronze propellers; via 2 × Reintjes 842, 2.96:1 gearboxes.
Electrical system: The generator is a 120 kW, PDC 120 MB Mercedes-Benz W/OM-421.

38.6 m InCat WPC
Seajet I (ex *Metro Atlantic,* ex *Nantucket Spray*)
This $4 million vessel was ordered in June 1988 and entered service with Bay State Cruises, Boston.

Principal Particulars

Length overall	38.6 m
Beam	15.6 m
Hull beam	2.6 m
Draught	1.3 m
Passengers	367
Fuel capacity	2 × 14 130 l
Water capacity	7570 l
Propulsive power	2 × 1768 kW
Maximum speed	36.4 knots
Operational speed	32 knots

Classification: USCG, SOLAS.
Propulsion: The main engines are 2 × MWM TBD 604 V16 1768 kW each, at 1800 rpm; driving 2 × KaMeWa 63 S62/6 water-jet units.
Electrical system: 2 × John Deere; 55 kW generators.

Jera FB-816
Jelang K FB-817
There were two 23.17 m InCat catamarans built in 1988 for ferry service at the US Army's missile test range in the Marshall Islands. *Jera* was handed over to the Nichols Brothers Boatyard on 9 April 1988 and *Jelang K* on 7 October 1988.

Principal Particulars

Length overall	23.17 m (*Jera*)
	21.95 m (*Jelang K*)
Beam	8.94 m (*Jera*)
	8.69 m (*Jelang K*)
Draught	1.8 m
Passengers	232
Fuel capacity	5300 l (*Jera*)
	4164 l (*Jelang K*)
Water capacity	946 l
Propulsive power	2 × 715 kW
Operational speed	31 knots

Propulsion: The main engines are 2 × DDC GM 16 V92 TA, 715 kW each; driving 5-blade Osborne bronze propellers, 940 mm × 927 mm; via 2 × ZF BW 250, 2.03:1 ratio gearboxes.
Electrical system: 2 × 50 kW Northern Lights generators, John Deere 4276 engines.

Bay Breeze
Designed by International Catamarans, this craft was delivered in April 1994.

Principal Particulars

Length overall	29 m
Beam	9 m
Draught	1.2 m
Passengers	250
Fuel capacity	4166 l
Water capacity	2840 l
Propulsive power	2 × 768 kW
Maximum speed	30 knots

Craft built (InCat)	Delivered	Seats	Operator	Owner
22 m InCat *Klondike*	June 1984	210	Yukon River Cruises, Inc	Brad Phillips
22 m InCat *Spirit of Alderbrook*	August 1984	240	Wes Johnson, Seattle Harbor Tours	
26 m InCat *Catamarin*	May 1985	400	Red and White Fleet	Crowley Maritime Corporation
26 m InCat *Gold Rush*	September 1985	400	Glacier Bay Yacht Tours	Robert Giersdorf
26 m InCat *Klondike II* (ex *Victoria Clipper*, ex *Glacier Express*, ex *Baja Express*)	1985			
26 m InCat *Dolphin*	January 1986	245*	Clipper Navigation Inc	
	August 1986	400	Red and White Fleet	Crowley Maritime Corporation
30 m InCat *Executive Explorer*	June 1986	49 passengers in 25 staterooms	Glacier Bay Yachts Tours, Inc Catamaran Cruise Lines, Hawaii	
23 m InCat *Jera FB-816*	April 1988	232	US Army	US Army
36 m InCat *Catalina Flyer*	May 1988	500	California Cruisin'	Catalina Passenger Service
23 m InCat *Jelang K FB-817*	October 1988	232	US Army	US Army
37 m InCat (WPC) *SeaJet I* (ex *Metro Atlantic*, (ex *Nantucket Spray*)	Spring 1989	400	Metro Marine Express	Metro Marine Express
22 m InCat *Martin Peña*	August 1989	167	Port of Puerto Rico	—
22 m InCat *Amelia*	November 1989	167	Port of Puerto Rico	—
22 m InCat *Covadonga*	December 1989	167	Port of Puerto Rico	—
22 m InCat *San Geronimo*	March 1989	167	Port of Puerto Rico	—
22 m InCat *Viejo San Juan*	May 1989	167	Port of Puerto Rico	—
22 m InCat *Cristobal Colón*	June 1989	167	Port of Puerto Rico	—
37 m InCat *Kona AggressorII*	December 1992	5 staterooms	Alaska Dive Boat, Inc	—
29 m InCat *Bay Breeze*	April 1994	250	City of Alameda	—
32 m Incat *Palau Aggressor III*	November 1994	49	Alaska Dive Boat, Inc	—
37 m Swath Int *Cloud X*	due March 1995	365	Party Line Cruises Ltd	Martin Automatic Inc

*400 total with outside seating

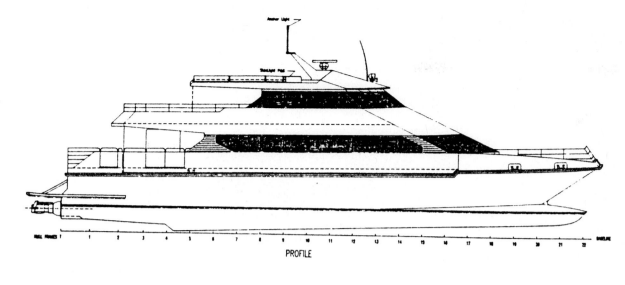

PROFILE

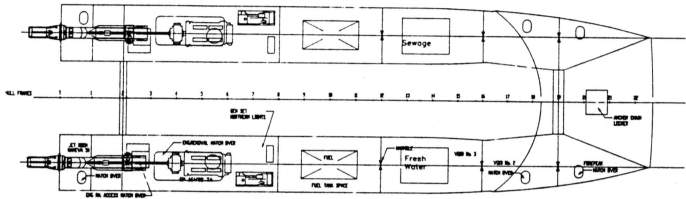

PLAN BELOW DECK

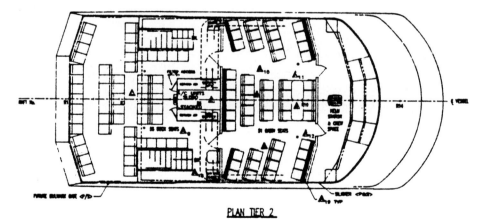

PLAN TIER 2

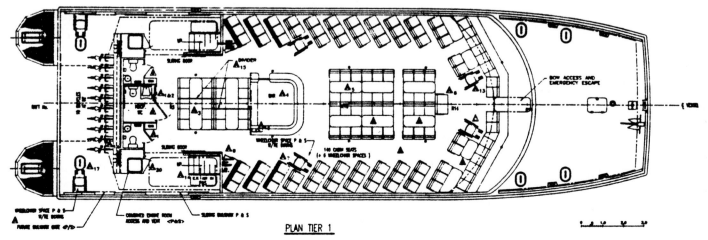

PLAN TIER 1

General arrangement of the 29 m Incat wave-piercing catamaran

1994

Bay Breeze   1995

Operational speed   28 knots
Propulsion: The main engines are 2 × Detroit Diesel 16V 92TA DDEC - 768 kW; driving 2 × KaMeWa 50 water-jet units.
Electrical system: 2 × John Deere 4276 50 kW generators.

Palau Aggressor II
This second vessel purchased by the Alaska Dive Boat Company carries 16 overnight passengers and 49 day passengers. It is designed by InCat Designs Pty Ltd using their Z-Bow hull form.

Principal Particulars

Length overall	32 m
Beam	9 m
Draught	1.3 m
Passengers	49
Fuel capacity	17000 l
Water capacity	7600 l
Propulsive power	1570 kW
Operational speed	23 knots

Propulsion: The main engines are 2 × Caterpillar 3412 diesels each rated at 785 kW; driving 2 × Hamilton water-jets model 5711.

                                               UPDATED

PETERSON BUILDERS INC

101 Pennsylvania Street, PO Box 650, Sturgeon Bay, Wisconsin 54235-0650, USA

Telephone: +1 (414) 743 5574
Telex: 263423
Telefax: +1 (414) 743 4784

Ellsworth L Peterson, *President and General Manager*
Allen A Powell, *Director Business Development*

Established builders of patrol boats and Mine CounterMeasure (MCM) ships, Peterson Builders has launched twelve 68 m MCM ships and one 20 m coastal patrol craft. It was announced in 1993 that Peterson had reached non-exclusive agreements with Royal Schelde Shipbuilding of the Netherlands and FBM Marine in the UK to market and produce under licence a wide range of high-speed passenger and passenger/car vessels. The designs to which Peterson now has access include a range of Surface Effect Ships (SESs), high-speed catamarans, low-wash catamarans, fast displacement (Swath type) catamarans, and high-speed monohulls.

SEA STALKER CLASS
In August 1993, PBI was awarded a contract by the United States Special Operations Command to construct the Sea Stalker. PBI's Sea Stalker Class patrol craft is an assymetric catamaran based on the Cougar Cat 2100 Dark Moon Class patrol craft developed by Cougar Marine Ltd of Hamble, England.
PBI has also developed several variations of this

Peterson Builders Inc Sea Stalker Class   1995

high-speed craft for diverse operational requirements, including a closed cockpit version with a flying bridge for coastal patrol and search and rescue.

Principal Particulars

Length overall	21.5 m
Propulsive power	2 × 2610 kW
Maximum speed	>50 knots

Classification: Det Norske Veritas.
Propulsion: 2 × MTU 16V 396 TE 94 diesel engines, driving Rolla surface-piercing propellers.
Loitering propulsion will be provided by a dedicated diesel engine driving a Hamilton water-jet.

                                               NEW ENTRY

USA CATAMARANS INC

Fort Lauderdale, Florida, USA

Builder of the first Air Ride Dual-Air Sea Coaster, a 20 m, 45 knot, 150 passenger ferry. See the Air Ride Craft Inc entry for details of the Dual-Air concept.
USA Catamarans Inc has also produced a 19.76 m, 140 seat catamaran ferry *Andromeda* powered by two MAN V-12 D2842 LYE 746 kW diesels, driving Rolla surface-piercing propellers.

                                               VERIFIED

SMALL-WATERPLANE-AREA TWIN-HULL (SWATH) VESSELS

Company Listing by Country

Commonwealth of Independent States
Almaz Shipyard Central Marine Design Bureau

Germany
Schichau Seebeckwerft AG

Japan
Mitsui Engineering & Shipbuilding Company Ltd

Korea, South
Hyundai Heavy Industries Company Ltd

Norway
Norsk Sisumaran KS/AS

United Kingdom
FBM Marine Group

United States of America
Navatek Ships Ltd
Nichols Brothers Boat Builders Inc
SSSCO
Swath Ocean Systems, Inc

COMMONWEALTH OF INDEPENDENT STATES

ALMAZ SHIPYARD CENTRAL MARINE DESIGN BUREAU

19 Uralskaya Street, 199161 St Petersburg, Russia, CIS

Telephone: +7 (812) 350 2983
Telefax: +7 (812) 350 0925

Alexander V Shliakhtenko, *Chief Designer*

The Almaz Central Design Bureau was established in 1940 specialising in the design and construction of high-speed commercial and military craft.

In 1993 Almaz Shipyard announced that a contract had been signed to construct two Swath craft designed by Marine Systems of Sukhoi. These were still under construction in 1994-95.

SUKHOI SWATH
Principal Particulars

Length overall	32 m
Beam	11 m
Draught	2.3 m
Passengers	198
Operational speed	27 knots
Range	250 nm

Propulsion: 2 × 1500 kW diesels driving 2 × water-jets.

UPDATED

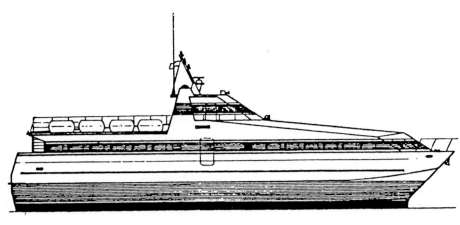

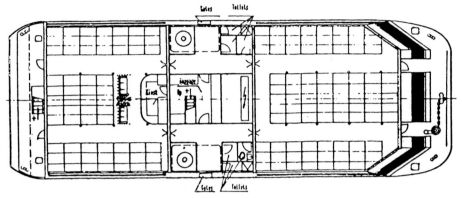

Sukhoi Swath profile and passenger deck layout
1994

GERMANY

SCHICHAU SEEBECKWERFT AG

PO Box 1240, Riedemannstrasse 1, D-27512 Bremerhaven, Germany

Telephone: +49 (471) 3920
Telex: 238651 SISEW D
Telefax: +49 (471) 392239

Josef Klar, *Chairman*
Dr Jürgen Gollenbeck, *Director*
Elmar Fritsche, *Director*
Hans Tempel, *Director*
Peter Güldensupp, *Director*

Schichau Seebeckwerft AG is a member of the Bremen Vulkan Group, the largest shipbuilder in reunited Germany. Schichau Seebeckwerft AG specialises in the construction of ro-ro ferries and other types of sophisticated craft.

SSW 320 A (DESIGN)

The SSW 320 A is the result of three years' effort in developing a high-speed Swath which is performance competitive with other types of craft in its class. Seating for over 600 passengers is provided with ample capacity to carry 100 cars or 75 cars and four large buses.

A high deadweight fraction has been achieved through the application of advanced technology. Power and speed are competitive with other craft types. The sea-keeping is excellent with test results indicating less than 0.01 *g* (rms) midships vertical acceleration in 3 m significant seas. No fins are required for stabilisation.

Safety arrangements comply with the proposed amendments to the IMO High-Speed Craft Code. Auxiliary machinery is centrally located on the main deck to reduce service costs. Gas-turbines driving conventional CP propellers offer high propulsion efficiency.

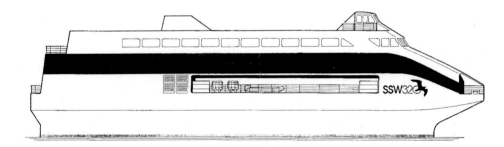

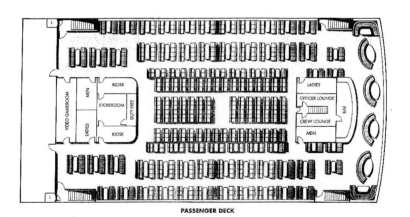

General arrangement of SSW 320 passenger vehicle ferry (design)
1994

Swath designs of other capacities and speeds are available.

Principal Particulars

Length overall	54.4 m
Beam	23 m
Draught	4.6 m
Passengers	600
Vehicles	100 cars
Fuel capacity	40 t
Operating speed	36 knots
Range	300 nm

Structure: The hull is constructed from aluminium alloy.

Propulsion: The main engines are 4 × Allison 571-KF diesels; driving a CP propeller 2 × reduction gearboxes each with two inputs.

UPDATED

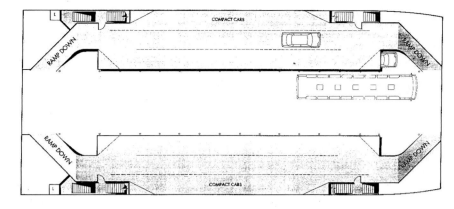

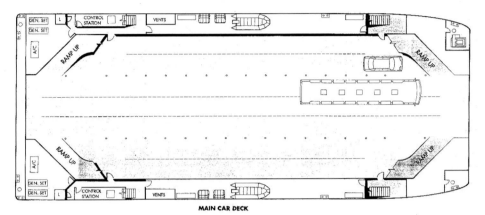

General arrangement of SSW 320 passenger vehicle ferry (design) continued
1994

JAPAN

MITSUI ENGINEERING & SHIPBUILDING COMPANY LTD

6-4 Tsukiji 5-chome, Chuo-ku, Tokyo 104, Japan

Telephone: +81 (3) 3544 3462
Telex: 22821 J, 22924 MITZOSEN J
Telefax: +81 (3) 3544 3031

Hiroshi Kitashima, *Director and General Manager, Ship and Ocean Project Division*
Yutaka Ikeda, *General Manager, Marine Department*

Mitsui began its high-speed Semi-Submerged Catamaran (SSC) development programme in 1970. Since 1976, the programme has been operated in conjunction with the Japanese Marine Machinery Development Association (JAMDA). In 1977 Mitsui built the experimental 18.37 tonne *Marine Ace* in order to obtain practical experience with this hull form. In 1979 the first SSC high-speed passenger vessel was launched under the provisional name *Mesa 80*. After extensive trials it was completed in 1981 and renamed *Seagull*. It has since been operated by Tokai Kisen Company Ltd on a passenger ferry service between Atami and Oshima island.

The company has also developed and built a SSC hydrographic survey vessel, *Kotozaki*, for the Fourth District Port Construction Bureau of the Japanese Ministry of Transport. This vessel was completed in 1981.

Marine Ace

Mitsui's first experimental SSC, *Marine Ace*, is built in marine grade aluminium alloy and can operate in Sea States 2 to 3.

Principal Particulars

Length overall	12.35 m
Beam	6.5 m
Draught	1.55 m
Displacement, maximum	18.37 t*
Fuel capacity	1.45 m³
Operational speed	18 knots

* after modification in 1978

Propulsion: The main engines are two V-type four-cycle petrol engines, each developing 150 kW at 3700 rpm. Each drives, via a vertical intermediate transmission shaft and bevel gear, a three-bladed fixed-pitch propeller.

Control: Four sets of fin stabilisers, driven by hydraulic servo motors, reduce ship motion in heavy seas.

Seagull

Developed jointly by Mitsui Engineering & Shipbuilding Company Ltd and the Japanese Marine Machinery Development Association (JAMDA), the 27 knot *Seagull* was the world's first commercial semi-submerged catamaran. Despite its small size, the overall length is just under 36 m, the vessel provides a stable ride in seas with 3.5 m waves.

During the first 10-month long commercial run in a service between Atami and Oshima, *Seagull* established an operating record of 97 per cent availability.

Principal Particulars

Length overall	35.9 m
Beam	17.1 m
Draught	3.15 m
Crew	7
Passengers	446
Maximum speed	27 knots

Structure: Marine grade aluminium alloy.

Propulsion: Main engines are two Fuji-SEMT marine diesels, each developing 3000 kW max continuous at 1475 rpm. Each drives, via a vertical transmission shaft and bevel gear, a four-blade fixed-pitch propeller.

Electrical system: Two 206.25 kVA generators provide electrical power.

Control: Four sets of fin stabilisers driven by hydraulic servo motors reduce ship motion in heavy seas.

SSC 15
Marine Wave

The first Semi-Submerged Catamaran SSC 15 type cruiser *Marine Wave* built by MES for Toray Industries Inc was delivered in July 1985.

Marine Wave, which is only about 15 m in length, is relatively free from rolling and pitching by virtue of its SSC design which also allows a spacious deck to be provided and facilitates comfortable cruising. One of its most interesting features is the

Mitsui SSC high tech cruiser SSC 15 type, Marine Wave, *built in glass- and carbon-reinforced plastic*
1986

Particulars of the high-speed SSC vessels built by Mitsui

Ship name	Marine Ace	Seagull	Kotozaki	Marine Wave	Sun Marina
Type	Experimental vessel	High-speed passenger ferry	Hydrographic survey vessel	Cabin type luxury boat	Saloon type luxury boat
Completion	1977	1979	1981	1985	1987
Length overall	12.35 m	35.9 m	27 m	15.1 m	15.05 m
Length waterline	11 m	31.5 m	25 m	11.95 m	11.9 m
Breadth	6.5 m	17.1 m	12.5 m	6.2 m	6.4 m
Depth	2.7 m	5.85 m	4.6 m	2.75 m	2.75 m
Draught	1.55 m	3.15 m	3.2 m	1.6 m	1.6 m
GRT	-	670	250	19	19
Payload/passengers	20 passengers	402-446 passengers	approx 36 t	17 passengers	33 passengers
Strut type	twin/single	single	single	single	single
Hull material	Aluminium	Aluminium	Steel/Aluminium	FRP	FRP
Maximum speed	17.3 knots	27.1 knots	20.5 knots	18.2 knots	20.5 knots
Main engines	2 × gasoline 147 kW	2 × diesel 2973 kW	2 × diesel 1395 kW	2 × diesel 200 kW	2 × diesel 220 kW
Propeller	FPP	FPP	CPP	FPP	FPP
Fin control	automatic	automatic	manual	automatic	automatic

Ship name	Bay Queen	Seagull 2	Diana	Bay Star	SSC 30
Type	Multipurpose boat	High-speed passenger ferry	Party boat	Multipurpose boat	Passenger ferry
Completion	Feb 1989	Dec 1989	Mar 1990	Nov 1991	1995
Length overall	18 m	39.3 m	20.7 m	19.45 m	29.2 m
Length waterline	15.9 m	33.7 m	15.9 m	15.9 m	24.3 m
Breadth	6.8 m	15.6 m	6.8 m	6.8 m	11.3 m
Depth	2.8 m	6.8 m	2.8 m	2.8 m	4.55 m
Draught	1.6 m	3.5 m	1.6 m	1.6 m	2.35 m
GRT	39	567	52	50	140
Payload/passengers	40 passengers	410 passengers	40 passengers	40 passengers	96 passengers
Strut type	single	single	single	single	single
Hull material	Aluminium	Aluminium	Aluminium	Aluminium	Aluminium
Maximum speed	20 knots	30.6 knots	19.2 knots	20 knots	24 knots
Main engines	2 × diesel 345 kW	4 × diesel 1967 kW	2 × diesel 272 kW	2 × diesel 345 kW	2 × diesel 1100 kW
Propeller	FPP	FPP	FPP	FPP	FPP
Fin control	automatic	automatic	automatic	automatic	automatic

combination of its unusual shape with Toray's newly developed hull material incorporating carbon fibre composites. The SSC 15 has two sets of computer-controlled stabilising fins and two fixed fins.

Marine Wave is certificated by the Japan Craft Inspection Organisation for use in coastal waters. By August 1986 *Marine Wave* had operated over 860 hours including a voyage to West Japan in which it experienced 4.5 m in height.

Principal Particulars

Length overall	15.1 m
Beam	6.2 m
Draught	1.6 m
Crew	2
Passengers	15
Fuel capacity	2000 l
Water capacity	300 l
Maximum speed	18 knots
Operational speed	16 knots

Structure: Glass-reinforced plastic and carbon-reinforced plastic.

Propulsion: Two high-speed marine diesel Ford Sabre 5950 cc engines, 200 kW each at 2500 rpm, driving fixed-pitch propellers via Twin Disc MG 506 gearboxes, ratio 2.03:1.

Electrical system: Onan MDJJF-18R diesel unit.

SSC 15
Sun Marina

The second of SSC 15 series, *Sun Marina* was built by Mitsui for San Marina Hotel, opened as a grand resort hotel in Okinawa in March 1987.

Sun Marina has a large luxurious party cabin which can accommodate 30 guests of the hotel, and sails round many coral reefs from the privately owned marina of the hotel.

Principal Particulars

Length overall	15.1 m
Beam	6.4 m
Draught	1.6 m
Crew	3
Passengers	30
Fuel capacity	2 × 900 l
Water capacity	400 l
Maximum speed	20.5 knots
Operational speed	17 knots

Propulsion: The propulsive power is provided by two 170 kW marine diesels.

Electrical system: 15 kW generator.

Bay Star   1993

Bay Queen   1993

SSC 20
Bay Queen

Bay Queen is the seventh SSC vessel built by Mitsui since 1977. It can carry a maximum of 40 passengers and has entered service for operation in inspection tours, sightseeing, crew transportation and many other purposes in Tokyo Bay.

Bay Queen is the first and smallest commercialised SSC vessel in the world, made of aluminium to a design based on the concept of *Marine Wave* which was made of FRP.

Principal Particulars

Crew	4
Passengers	40
Fuel capacity	2400 l
Water capacity	1000 l

Propulsion: 2 × high-speed marine diesel engines, 350 kW each at 2000 rpm.
Electrical system: Yanmar 4JHL-TN diesel generator unit.

SSC 20
Diana

Diana is the second vessel of Mitsui SSC-20 series and was completed in the middle of March 1990. It is operated for day and night cruises as a party boat in Osaka Bay, a good application of the Mitsui SSC type, which can provide spacious deck area and a comfortable ride in rough sea conditions. It has an automatic motion control system to minimise ship motion.

Principal Particulars

Length overall	20.7 m
Beam	6.8 m
Draught	1.6 m
Crew	3
Passengers	40
Maximum speed	19.22 knots

Structure: Marine grade aluminium alloy.
Propulsion: Main engines are two high-speed diesel engines, each developing 276 kW (370 hp) max continuous at 2250 rpm.
Control: Maintenance-free sensors and a sophisticated fin control system are applied. One pair of canard fin stabilisers is automatically controlled by an electric motor.

SSC 30

Mitsui currently has a contract with Japanese Shipping Company for the construction of one SSC 30. The first SSC 30 is scheduled to enter into service in Japan as a passenger/cargo ferry in August 1995.

The first SSC 30 has been newly developed as a medium sized standard SSC vessel. SSC 30 can give a comfortable ride in a 2 to 2.5 m wave height with a cruising speed of 20 knots.

Principal Particulars

Payload	5 t deck cargo
Crew	4
Passengers	96

Structure: Marine grade aluminium alloy.
Propulsion: The engines are two high-speed marine diesels, 1120 kW.
Control: One set of forward fin stabilisers driven by hydraulic servo motors, and one set of fixed fins aft.

SSC 20 Diana   *1991*

SSC 40 Seagull 2   *1991*

SSC 40
Seagull 2

Seagull 2 has a capability of running at 30.6 knots at maximum continuous rating and 27.5 knots service speed with 410 passengers. According to the analysis of log book records, *Seagull 2* has better speed sustainability than *Seagull* in wave heights of 2.5 m and higher.

Principal Particulars

Length overall	39.32 m
Beam	15.6 m
Draught	3.5 m
Crew	7
Passengers	410
Maximum speed	30.6 knots

Propulsion: Main engines are four MTU 16V 396 TB 84, each developing 2000 kW max continuous at 1940 rpm. Each pair of engines drives a four-blade fixed-pitch propeller, through a long straight tube shaft with two ZF reversible reduction gearboxes. A microcomputer-based remote-control system is applied.
Control: The ship control system is composed of a display of nautical information and ballast control. Nautical information includes draught, trim, heel, rudder angle, fin angle, ship speed, wind data, ship course and so on. A ballast control system displays ballast line layout and can operate ballast pumps and valves remotely.

Four fin stabilisers are automatically controlled by hydraulic rotary actuators.

UPDATED

KOREA, SOUTH

HYUNDAI HEAVY INDUSTRIES COMPANY LTD

1 Cheonha-Dong, Dong-Gu, Ulsan, Kyung-Nam, South Korea

Telephone: +82 (522) 321307/302841
Telex: 52220 HYARD K
Telefax: +82 (522) 324007

35 m Hyundai Swath vessel
1994

35 m SWATH VESSEL

Building of the 35 m Swath vessel started in 1991 and it was delivered in April 1993.

Principal Particulars

Length overall	34.5 m
Length waterline	32.5 m
Beam	15 m
Draught	3.5 m
Propulsive power	2 × 2000 kW
Operational speed	21.6 knots

Propulsion: The main engines are 2 × MTU 16V 396 TE84 2000 kW at 1940 rpm.

27.1 m (DESIGN)

For several years Hyundai Heavy Industries had been investigating coastal passenger Swath vessel designs, including eighth scale model testing before building the 35 m craft. However, among the variants investigated, a 27.1 m version was selected as satisfying the growing passenger accommodation requirements of the market.

Principal Particulars

Length overall	27.1 m
Beam	12.4 m
Draught	2.6 m
Displacement, maximum	132 t
Passengers	254
Maximum speed	25.3 knots
Operational speed	24.7 knots

Propulsion: The main engines are 2 × 1327 kW at 1650 rpm (MCR).

UPDATED

NORWAY

NORSK SISUMARAN KS/AS

Uno-Glaupa, PO Box 816, N-7001 Trondheim, Norway

Telephone: +47 735 20615/701 25660
Telefax: +47 735 35858/701 21595

Prof Arlid Rødland, *Director*
Per Kverndokk, *Director*

This company has produced a number of designs based on experience with an 11.4 m prototype. These designs include a 33 m 360 passenger Swath; a 28 m 250 passenger Swath, and a 30 m 304 passenger design.

STORMULK

This vessel is believed to be the first Norwegian Swath type and was launched on 20 June 1990. The STORMULK (Submerged Torpedo Multihull Craft) features an auxiliary bow hull which is designed to enhance static and dynamic behaviour of the Swath vessel concept without significant reductions in speed and economy.

STORMULK has completed successful testing off the mid-Norwegian coast at Froude numbers up to 1.202, corresponding to the anticipated service speed of 30 knots for a 20 m vessel.

Principal Particulars

Length overall	11.4 m
Beam	6.4 m
Displacement, minimum	6.5 t
Passengers	32
Fuel capacity	2400 l
Water capacity	1370 l

Structure: Hull structure in marine grade aluminium, deck and superstructure in GRP sandwich construction.
Propulsion: The main engines are 2 × Iveco 8061 SRM 27.

NORSK SWATH (DESIGN)

Based on the STORMULK prototype experience, a sequence of designs has now been made for modified Swath passenger ferries and/or combined passenger/cargo carriers in the LOA 23-33 m range with service speeds of 25 to 30 knots.

Principal Particulars

Length overall	33 m
Beam	12.6 m
Passengers	360
Propulsive power	2 × 1680 kW
Operational speed	25 knots

Propulsion: The main engines are 2 × MTU 16V 396 TE 74.

UPDATED

Norsk 33 m 360 passenger Swath (design)
1995

UNITED KINGDOM

FBM MARINE GROUP

Cowes Shipyard, Cowes, Isle of Wight, UK

Telephone: +44 (1983) 297111
Telex: 86466 FAMBRO G
Telefax: +44 (1983) 299642

Michael Roberts, *Deputy Chairman*
John Warbey, *International Sales Director*
Malcolm Keith, *Managing Director*
Mike McSorley, *Sales Manager, Ferries*
Nigel Warren, *Chief Designer*
Heather Cox, *Marketing Manager*
Craig Moyes, *Sales Manager*

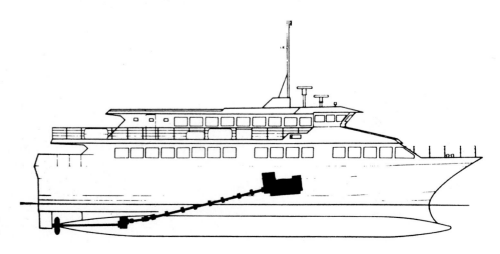

Transmission arrangement on 37 m
Atlantic class FDC
1990

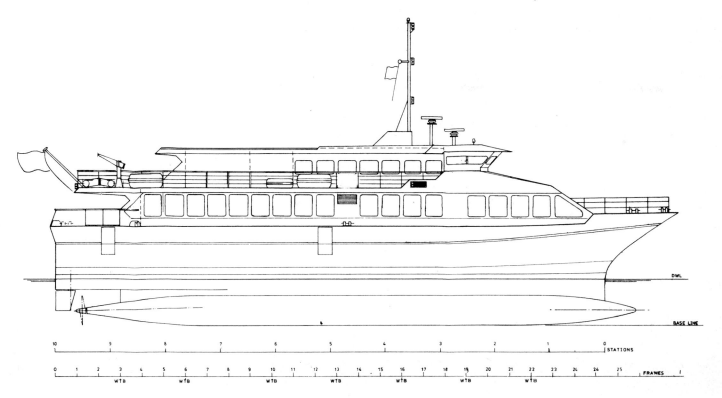

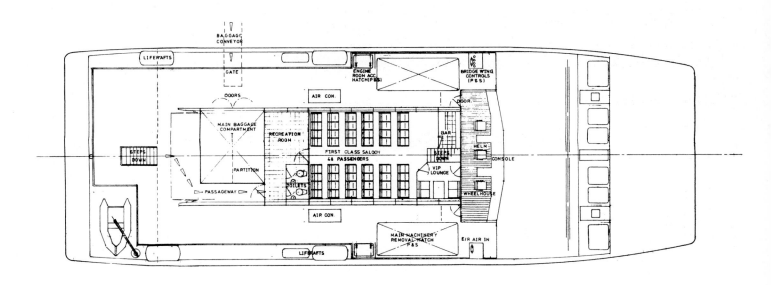

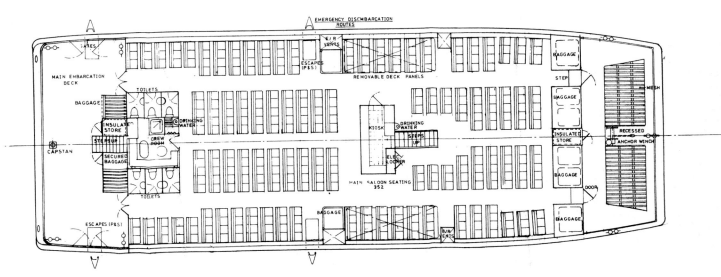

General arrangement of 37 m Atlantic class FDC

1990

37 m ATLANTIC CLASS
FAST DISPLACEMENT CATAMARAN (FDC)
Patria

In August 1988 Fairey Marinteknik, now FBM Marine, announced the award of a contract for the supply of a 400-seat fast displacement catamaran to the Regional Government of Madeira, Portugal. Valued at £4 million the craft was delivered in early 1990.

First trials started in October 1989. On 5 October 1989 the vessel achieved a speed of 32.1 knots at two-thirds load, some 4 to 5 knots higher than the previous maximum recorded speed for a Swath type, therefore establishing a record.

In late January 1990 Patria was on trials in storm conditions and spent a total of seven hours at sea averaging 28 knots in a fully loaded condition in wave heights of 2.5 to 3.5 m and wind speeds that seldom dropped below 70 knots and gusted, at times, above 90 knots. On Sunday 19 August 1990 Patria went into service.

Principal Particulars

Length overall	36.5 m
Beam	13 m

Draught	2.7 m
Displacement, maximum	approx 180 t
Crew	8-10
Passengers	400
Fuel capacity	17 750 l
Propulsive power	2 × 2040 kW
Operating speed	31.7 knots
Range	472 nm
Operational limitations	3.5 m wave height

Classification: DnV Passenger Ship Light Craft.

Propulsion: Main engines: 2 × MTU 16V 396 TB 84 rated at 2040 kW (25°C air, 25°C sea) 1940 rpm, driving twin shaft and 3-blade fixed-pitch Lips propellers via 3.23:1.0 ZF gearboxes.

Electrical system: 2 × AC generating sets.

Auxiliary systems: A ballast tank system is operated to adjust craft attitude: Pump: 50 m³/h, 1.5 kW, 380 V on each of four ballast tanks in the platform, each of 7.5 t capacity.

Mk 2 FDC (DESIGN)

A new fast displacement catamaran design was announced by FBM Marine Ltd in October 1990. This is a development of the Patria design which provides for water-jet propulsion.

Principal Particulars

Length overall	38.75 m
Length waterline	31.7 m
Beam	13 m
Draught	2.7 m
Displacement, maximum	200 t
Payload	40 t
Passengers	396
Fuel capacity	7000 l
Water capacity	1000 l
Propulsive power	2 × 2000 kW
Operational speed	30 knots
Range	222 nm

Classification: +1A1 R25 Light Craft EO.

Propulsion: Main engines: 2 × MTU 16V 396 TE 74L, 2000 kW each at 2000 rpm; driving a pair of water-jets.

Electrical system: 2 × Volvo diesels coupled to 2 × Stanforth 84 kW alternators (380 V 3-phase 50 Hz and 220 V single-phase 50 Hz).

UPDATED

Atlantic class FDC Patria *in service between Funchal and Porto Santo*

1991

UNITED STATES OF AMERICA

NAVATEK SHIPS LTD

A subsidiary of Pacific Marine

Suite 1880, 841 Bishop St, Honolulu, Hawaii 96813, USA

Telephone: +1 (808) 531 7001
Telefax: +1 (808) 523 7668

William Clifford, *President*

Technology for the development of the first Pacific Marine Swath came from Dr Ludwig Seidl, Chairman of Department of Ocean Engineering, University of Hawaii. In 1977 Pacific Marine and Dr Seidl formed the Pacific Marine Engineering Science Company. In 1979 the company was granted patent (US Patent 4174671) covering its Swath design.

Pacific Marine invested $4.5 million to build a prototype vessel, the hull construction being subcontracted to Thompson Metal Fabricators, Vancouver, Washington.

Navatek I

The hull was launched in February 1989. After being outfitted at Northwest Marine, Portland, Oregon with a partial superstructure and pilot-house, sea trials commenced in May 1989. During those trials, Navatek I sailed 600 miles from Portland to San Francisco, California, then 2100 miles across the Pacific to Honolulu, Hawaii. During the six day trip it averaged 15 knots, its design cruising speed, through seas of 1.8 to 3 m. It also demonstrated the ability to maintain 93 per cent of its speed through Sea State 5. Navatek I achieved a top speed of over 17 knots and its fuel consumption was 265 l/h at 1600 rpm cruising speed. Its reduced ships motions were extremely good; waves up to 2.4 m produced almost no motion.

In Hawaii, sea trials included extended runs in rough channel waters between all major islands. In July and August 1989 in the Molokai and Alenuihaha channels, Navatek I routinely ran all headings in average seas of 3.65 m, with occasional waves of just over 4.6 m. The largest wave it encountered

during its trials was a 5.5 to 6.1 m wave set off Makapuu, Oahu. During that encounter, beer glasses sitting on tables in the forward lounge remained in place without spilling a drop.

With the successful completion of sea trials in September 1989, Royal Hawaiian Cruises Ltd of Honolulu, Hawaii signed a long-term lease on the vessel for use as a day excursion/dinner cruise boat serving the Hawaiian tourist trade. In October 1989, Navatek I sailed 6500 miles via the Panama Canal to New Orleans, Louisiana where Trinity Marine installed the rest of the two-deck superstructure. Navatek Ships holds a US design patent on the superstructure design. The vessel completed the 13 000 mile round trip back to Hawaii in January 1990.

In early 1990, the US Coast Guard certified Navatek I to carry 400 passengers on an ocean route. It thus became the first Swath to receive US Coast Guard approval as a commercial, passenger-carrying vessel.

Navatek I began commercial service in March

Navatek I

1993

1990 and currently operates three scheduled cruises a day, seven days a week, in ocean waves ranging from 1.5 to 4.5 m. The cruises range from sightseeing in Pearl Harbor to a sunset dinner cruise, and during the Spring whale season a whale-watching cruise is available.

In September 1991, the Coast Guard increased the passenger certification of *Navatek I* to 430 persons.

Royal Hawaiian Cruises has been able to command premium prices for places on these cruises due to the excellent stability and radically reduced motions of the Swath vessel. Despite operating daily in waves as high as 4.5 m, passenger reaction to the ride has been exceptional. During the initial three months of operation, Royal Hawaiian Cruises had its cabin crew report any incidence of passenger seasickness. Out of 17 430 passengers carried during this period only six were seasick. Since the start of service, operating days lost due to mechanical failure have been zero. Royal Hawaiian Cruises is able to offer tour wholesalers exclusive routes no other Hawaiian vessel can operate.

Navatek Ships Ltd began commercial production of its 40 m class Swath with the lease of *Navatek I* in September 1989. It has licensed Kaiduan Offshore Sdn Bhd of Malaysia to build and market its Swath designs outside the USA on a non-exclusive basis.

Principal Particulars

Length overall	43 m
Beam	16 m
Draught	2.44-4.27 m
Passsengers	430
Propulsive power	2 × 1007 kW
Operational speed	15 knots
Maximum speed	18 knots

Propulsion: Main engines: twin Deutz MWM 16V-816CR diesels, continuous rating of 1007 kW each, driving Ulstein reduction gears and Ulstein controllable-pitch 4-blade propellers.

Electrical system: Twin Detroit Diesel 6-7 l generators rated at 99 kW each.

General arrangement of Navatek I
1990

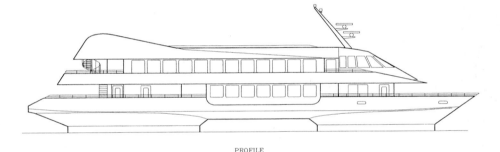

PROFILE

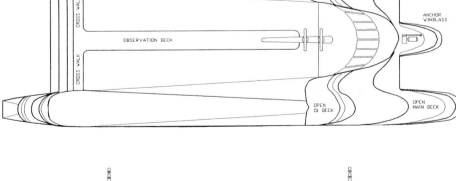

OPEN 01 DECK
OPEN MAIN DECK
ANCHOR WINDLASS
CROSS WALK
OBSERVATION DECK
CROSS WALK
OPEN 01 DECK
OPEN MAIN DECK

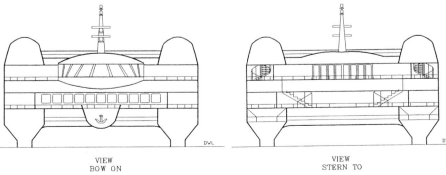

VIEW BOW ON

VIEW STERN TO

Navatek II

In 1991, Navatek Ships Ltd completed design, development and tank model testing in California of a proprietary, second-generation Swath design developed by engineers at Navatek Ships Ltd. In contrast to the original PAMESCO design, the new design features twin canted struts for which Navatek Ships Ltd itself holds patents pending.

Navatek's new, patented canted strut design offers several advantages over the vertical strut design employed in *Navatek I*. Inherent in any Swath design is the tendency of the bow to dive (monk moment), requiring fin stabilisation to overcome this phenomenon. But fin systems add resistance, requiring increased horsepower to move the vessel through the water. The twin, canted hull design of Navatek Ships Ltd produces a smaller bow down trimming moment, thus allowing smaller fins which results in less resistance and more speed per horse-power installed. Other advantages of canted struts include a larger damping effect in pitch, roll and heave, resulting in significantly better motion characteristics.

In November 1992, Navatek Ships Ltd began construction of its first twin, canted strut Swath, the *Navatek II,* at its Honolulu shipyard.

Navatek II was launched in January 1994 and began commercial service in April 1994 as a day cruise/adventure boat in the Hawaii tourist trade. Variations of this design for US Coast Guard duties have also been studied.

Principal Particulars

Length overall	25 m
Beam	11.6 m
Draught	1.7 m
Passengers	150
Operational speed	23 knots
Range	750 nm

Propulsion: Engines: 2 × MTU 12V 183. Transmissions: 2 × ZF BW 250 gearboxes. Thrust devices: 2 × 4-blade workboat style propellers.

Auxiliary systems: Generators: 2 × 45 kW Northern Lights.

PARTNERSHIP WITH LOCKHEED

In September 1993, Navatek Ships and the Marine Systems division of Lockheed Missiles & Space Company, Sunnyvale, California, announced that they had teamed up to commercialise Swath ship technology originally developed by Lockheed for the defence industry. Lockheed Missiles & Space Company, a leading defence contractor, has been involved in the development of many unique, high technology marine vehicles. In addition to the world-recognised Polaris/Poseidon/Trident missile pro-grammes, Lockheed developed one of the world's first deep diving manned vehicles, *Deep Quest,* followed by development of the Navy's submarine rescue submersibles, Deep Submergence Rescue Vehicles I and II. Lockheed's patented motion con-trol system has been installed in the US Navy's T-AGOS 19 and T-AGOS 23 Swath surveillance ships. The company's high technology Swath hull designs and computer-aided ship control systems continue to push the state of the art. In April 1993, the US Navy unveiled its Swath stealth ship *Sea Shadow,* designed and built by Lockheed. In addition to their collaboration on Swath design, Navatek and Lockheed are exploring other hull forms, first developed by Lockheed for the US de-fence industry, which may offer commercial poten-tial. One of these hull forms, called SLICE, is a

Navatek II *in operation*   *1995*

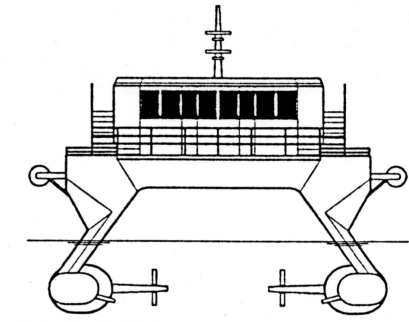

US Coast Guard patrol boat Swath (design)   *1993*

high-speed, 35 knot variant of Swath technology. By minimising wave-making resistance at high speeds, it produces significantly higher speeds for constant horsepower when compared to conventional Swath hull technology, yet it retains the sea-keeping of Swath technology. Navatek has negotiated world-wide rights to this technology, with Lockheed retain-ing military sales rights. In late 1993 the two companies received a $10 million advanced tech-nology development grant from the US Navy to design and build a 220 tonne, 37 m SLICE prototype.

Design and tank testing work on the SLICE proto-type is currently underway at Lockheed's California facilities. Construction of the prototype is expected to begin in early 1995 at Pacific Marine's shipyard in Hawaii. The first commercial application of the SLICE prototype is expected to be a ferry boat. In June 1994, Pacific Marine received a grant from the US government to do a global market study of the potential for SLICE fast ferries.

UPDATED

NICHOLS BROTHERS BOAT BUILDERS INC

5400 S Cameron Road, Freeland, Whidbey Island, Washington 98249, USA

Telephone: +1 (360) 331 5500
Telefax: +1 (360) 331 7484

Matt Nichols, *President*
Archie Nichols, *Vice President*
Ken Schoonover, *Yard Supervisor*
Scott Murphy, *Financial Officer*
Bryan Nichols, *Marketing*

Nichols Brothers received an order for a 37 m Swath vessel in late 1992, to be operated by Party Line Cruises of Miami. This vessel is currently under construction in the same facilities used for the ship-yard's catamaran ferries.

37 m SWATH FERRY *Cloud X*

Designed by Swath International Limited, this craft was launched in May 1995 and is scheduled to be delivered in July 1995. The craft is intended to operate from Miami to Key West in Florida as a pass-enger ferry with modern gambling facilities.

Principal Particulars

Length overall	37.2 m
Beam	18 m
Draught	3.4 m
Passengers	365
Fuel capacity	16 000 l
Water capacity	3000 l
Propulsive power	2 × 2870 kW
Maximum speed	30 knots
Operational speed	28 knots

Propulsion: The main engines are 2 × Textron Lycoming TF40 gas-turbines rated at 2870 kW each, driving 2 × KaMeWa CPP propellers.

NEW ENTRY
1994

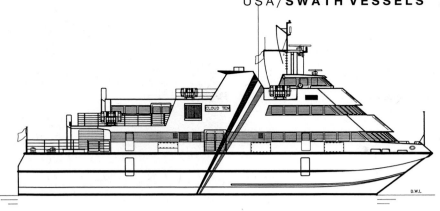

PROFILE

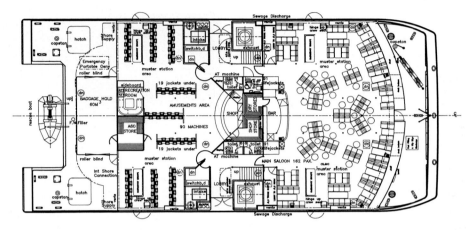

PLAN ON MAIN DECK

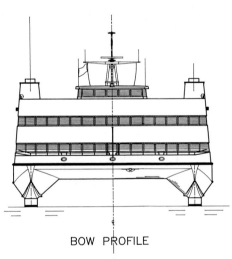

BOW PROFILE

Profiles and plans of the Swath Ferry Cloud X

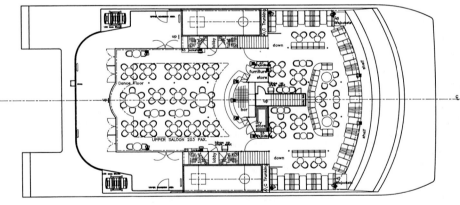

PLAN ON UPPER DECK

SSSCO
SEMI-SUBMERGED SHIP CORPORATION

417 Loma Larga Drive, Solana Beach, California 92075, USA

Telephone: +1 (619) 481 6417
Telefax: +1 (619) 481 7282

Dr Thomas G Lang, *President*

(PATENT HOLDING AND DEVELOPMENT)

SSSCO was founded by Dr Thomas G Lang, the inventor of the Semi-Submerged Ship (S³). The S³ consists of two parallel torpedo-like hulls attached to which are two or more streamlined struts which pierce the water surface and support an above-water platform. Stabilising fins are attached near the aft end of each hull and a pair of smaller fins are optionally located near their forward ends.

Semi-submerged ship technology (also known as Swath) has been proven over the past 20 years by the 190 ton SSP *Kaimalino*, a US Navy-developed range-support vessel which has been operating in the rough seas off the Hawaiian islands since 1975. Following private development, Dr Lang introduced the concept into the US Navy. He led the Navy's first research work and initiated and developed the hydrodynamic design for the SSP *Kaimalino*, the world's first high performance, open-ocean Swath ship.

The US Navy's present SWATH (Small-Waterplane-Area Twin-Hull) ship programme is based on the S³ concept. The performance features that distinguish S³s from conventional vessels are greatly reduced motions with sustained speed even in heavy seas, lower hydrodynamic drag and reduced power requirements at moderate to high speeds, and far superior course-keeping character-istics at all sea headings. S³s have excellent manoeuvrability at speed, when operating in con-fined harbours and when station-keeping.

A number of applications of the S³ principle has been proposed by Dr Lang and these were described in *Jane's Surface Skimmers 1985* and earlier editions. These design proposals have included an offshore crew change vessel, a high-speed ferry, a rapid intervention vessel, supply and diving support vessels. Fishing vessel and cruise ship applications are also suggested.

Kaimalino

Operated by the Naval Command Control and Ocean Surveillance Centre at San Diego, California, the SSP *Kaimalino* has operated from near calm conditions to beyond Sea State 6 at speeds up to 25 knots. Its motion is small relative to a conventional monohull of similar payload capacity, either when at rest or underway. The SSP has made smooth tran-sits in 4.57 m swells without any impacts; however, in short, steep 3.7 m waves occasional bow impacts have occurred. No structural damage has occurred, even during storm conditions when 7.6 to 9.2 m high waves were encountered.

In February 1985 ten Woods Hole Oceanographic Institution scientists participated in a series of two-and three-day cruises off Hawaii on the Swath vessel *Kaimalino* over a two week period; as a result they highly recommended the Swath design for oceanographic research. In 1993 the two gas-turbines used for propulsion were replaced by two 671 TA Detroit Diesel engines to provide greater economy.

Principal Particulars

Length	27 m
Beam	14 m
Height	9.7 m
Displacement	217 t
Payload	50 t
Maximum speed	25 knots
Operational speed	15 knots
Range	400 nm

VERIFIED

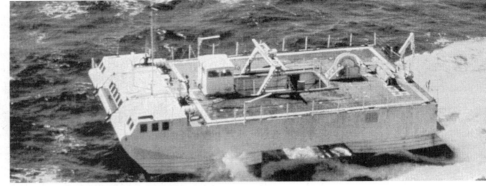

SSP Kaimalino (US Navy)   *1986*

SWATH OCEAN SYSTEMS, INC

1313 W 24th Street, National City, California 91950, USA

Telephone: +1 (619) 336 4615
Telefax: +1 (619) 336 4616

Swath Ocean Systems (SOS) moved to a larger premises in late 1993. A 35 m Oceanographic Swath *Western Flyer* is currently under construction in the new yard for delivery in 1995.

Chubasco

Chubasco was launched 28 March 1987 by James Betts Enterprises of San Diego for Leonard Friedman for drift fishing. The design and building are under patents of Dr Thomas G Lang of the Semi-Submerged Ship Corporation.

Chubasco is currently a demonstration vessel for Swath Ocean Systems. She served as the official committee boat for the judges for the 1988 America's Cup races held at San Diego.

Chubasco   *1989*

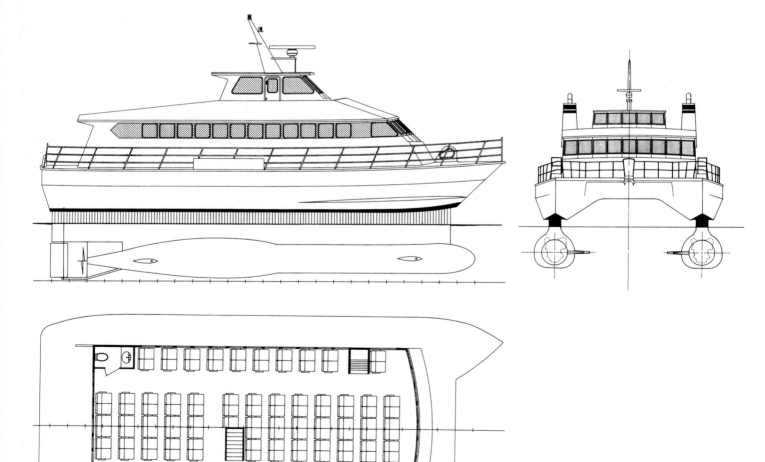

Swath Ocean 2000 class layout,
Frederick G Creed
1991

Principal Particulars

Length overall	21.95 m
Beam	9.45 m
Draught	3.05 m
Displacement, maximum	70 t
Fuel capacity	18920 l
Water capacity	1890 l
Propulsive power	2 × 559 kW
Maximum speed	21 knots
Operational speed	20 knots

Structure: Marine grade aluminium.

Propulsion: The main engines are 2 × DDC 8V 92 TI diesels, 559 kW (750 hp) each, turbocharged.

Electrical system: Two 50 kW Northern Lights, one 7.5 kW Northern Lights.

Control: Gyro-activated stabiliser fin system.

Steering station at stern, steering station at each wing outside pilot-house, bow thruster and controls at three stations.

Navigation and communications: One Magnavox Sat-Nav, one Furuno Loran unit, one Alden weather fax, two Furuno 72 mile daylight radars, two Data Marine 305 m fathometers, two Furuno colour fathometers, one Furuno 214 m sonar unit, two water speed indicators, one wind speed indicator, one wind direction indicator, one Sperry gyro compass and automatic pilot.

Three VHS transceivers with ADF, two SSB radios, one Citizens Band radio, one Magnavox Satcom telephone.

Outfit: Sleeping accommodation for nine passengers on main deck in master stateroom, two staterooms, two sofa berths in saloon, plus one bunk. Pilot-house berths three; all air-conditioned. Fully equipped galley.

Betsy (ex *Suave Lino*)

Completed in 1981 for Mr Friedman as a fishing boat, *Betsy* was used as a tender by the Sail America Syndicate during the America's Cup defence off Fremantle, Australia.

The vessel is contructed of aluminium with a single strut configuration for each hull. Two high-speed diesels of 425 hp each, mounted at deck level, drive fixed-pitch propellers through bevel gears. Automatic fin control fitted. Based in San Diego.

Principal Particulars

Length overall	19.2 m
Beam	9.1 m
Draught	2.13 m
Displacement, minimum	53 t
Payload	14 t
Maximum speed	18 knots

Propulsion: The main engines are 2 × DDC 8V 71, 317 kW (425 hp) each.

2000 CLASS
Frederick G Creed

A 20.4 m 80 tonne Swath vessel launched in November 1989 and made available for the Canadian Department of Fisheries and Oceans under a lease purchase contract for oceanographic and hydrographic service off the eastern coasts of Canada and the USA.

Principal Particulars

Length overall	20.4 m
Beam	9.75 m
Draught	2.6 m
Displacement, maximum	80.26 t
Displacement, minimum	57.9 t
Passengers	125
Propulsive power	2 × 805 kW
Maximum speed	29 knots
Operational speed	25 knots

Propulsion: The main engines are 2 × DDC 12V 92TA 805 kW diesels.

SD-60
Halcyon

RMI designed and built a 18.3 m Swath demonstrator boat, the *Halcyon,* which was launched in March 1985.

The SD-60 Swath offers advantages over conventional craft in transporting passengers and cargo. For example, pitch and roll motions are significantly less than those of comparable small monohulls over the full range of anticipated sea conditions, and this will give an improved ride. Its increased speed performance in heavy seas enables it to maintain headway at design speed through and beyond Sea

SD-60 Halcyon *operating in San Francisco Bay*

1986

Houston Pilot Cutter

1994

State 4; an important advantage in commercial service operations. The wide separation between its variable-pitch propellers allows precise manoeuvring within ports, channels and rivers, and positioning alongside ships or offshore oil platforms.

The deckhouse has a galley, head and berthing accommodation for the crew of three and space for 20 passengers. The passenger space can be converted to living quarters for nine additional crew members. The pilot-house accommodates a full range of commercial communications and marine navigation systems. Microprocessor ship control systems and vessel management systems are fitted. Oceangoing ships or Lighter-Aboard-Ship (LASH) barges will be able to carry the boat on deck.

Propulsion power is by twin Caterpillar 3408 DITA marine diesels each driving, via a reduction gear and Eaton V-belt drive, a 45 in diameter VPO FR-H Hundested variable-pitch propeller. The electric plant features twin Model 4.236M (25 kW) Perkins marine diesel electric generator sets. The design meets USCG safety requirements and certification as a commercial passenger boat under 100 tonnes displacement, fully loaded.

The operator is the US Army Corps of Engineers, Savannah, Georgia.

Principal Particulars

Length overall	18.28 m
Beam	9.14 m
Draught	2.29 m
Payload	8 t
Displacement, maximum	62 t
Displacement, minimum	52 t
Maximum speed	20 knots
Operational speed	18 knots
Range	800 nm

HOUSTON PILOT CUTTER

A 20.4 m 80 tonne Swath vessel, based on the SOS 2000 class craft was delivered to the Houston Pilots in early 1993.

Principal Particulars

Length overall	20.4 m
Beam	11.28 m
Draught	2.44 m
Displacement, maximum	78 t
Displacement, minimum	57 t
Propulsive power	2 × 750 kW
Operational speed	23 knots

Propulsion: The main engines are 2 × Cat 3412 diesels rated at 750 kW each.

VERIFIED

HIGH-SPEED MONOHULL CRAFT

Company Listing by Country

Australia
Austal Ships Pty Ltd
Geraldton Boat Builders
Lloyd's Ships Holdings Pty Ltd
Oceanfast International Pty Ltd
SBF Engineering Pty Ltd
Transfield Shipbuilding (WA)
Wavemaster International Pty Ltd

Chile
Asmar Shipbuilding and Docking Co

Commonwealth of Independent States
Central Hydrofoil Design Bureau

Finland
Kværner Masa-Yards Inc

France
Ateliers et Chantiers du Havre
Guy Couach Constructions Navales
Leroux and Lotz
Navysurf
SBCN

Germany
Abeking and Rasmussen Shipyard
Blohm+Voss AG
Lürssen Werft GmbH & Co

Greece
Hellenic Shipyards Company

Hong Kong
Cheoy Lee Shipyards Ltd
Chung Wah Shipbuilders Ltd

Italy
Azimut SpA
Cantieri Ing Moschini SpA
Cantieri Navali Italcraft Srl

Cantieri Navali Lavagna Srl
Cantieri Posillipo SpA
Cantieri Riva SpA
Crestitalia SpA
Fazioli Nautica Srl
Fincantieri Cantieri Navali Italiani SpA
Intermarine SpA
Rodriquez Cantieri Navali SpA
Tecnomarine SpA
Cantiere Nautico Versilcraft Srl
Sciomachen

Japan
Etoh Marine Corporation
Mitsubishi Heavy Industries Ltd
Shimonoseki Shipyard and Machinery Works
Mokubei Shipbuilding Company
Yamaha Motor Company Ltd

Korea, South
Semo Company Ltd

Malaysia
Chiong Brothers Shipyard
Wong's Shipbuilding Contractor & Designer

Netherlands
Kees Cornelissen Shipyard
Royal Schelde BV

Norway
Båtutrustning A/S
Mjellem & Karlsen Verft A/S

Singapore
Aluminium Craft (88) Pte Ltd
Marinteknik Shipbuilders (S) Pte Ltd
Singapore Shipbuilding and Engineering Ltd

Spain
Bazan, Empresa Nacional

Sweden
Boghammar International AB
Oskarshamns Varv AB

Thailand
Technautic Intertrading Company Ltd

United Kingdom
Ailsa-Perth Shipbuilders Ltd
Berthon Boat Company Ltd
FBM Marine Group
McTay Marine
Vosper Thornycroft (UK) Ltd

United States of America
Admiral Marine Works Inc
Aluminum Boats Inc
Blount Marine Corporation
Bollinger Machine Shop & Shipyard Inc
Breaux's Bay Craft Inc
Christensen Motor Yacht Corporation
Denison Marine Inc
Derecktor Shipyards
Derecktor-Gunnell
Robert E Derecktor, Inc
Equitable Shipyards Inc
Gladding-Hearn Shipbuilding
Gulf Craft Inc
Halter Marine Inc
Magnum Marine Corporation
Munson Manufacturing Inc
Peterson Builders Inc
Swiftships Inc
Tempest Yachts Inc
Trinity Marine Group
Trinity Yachts Inc
Westport Shipyard Inc

AUSTRALIA

AUSTAL SHIPS PTY LTD

100 Clarence Beach, Henderson, Perth, Western Australia 6166, Australia

Telephone: +61 (9) 410 1111
Telefax: +61 (9) 410 2564

John Rothwell, *Managing Director*
Christopher Norman, *Director, Marketing and Sales*
Garry Heys, *Director and General Manager*
Kevin Stanley, *Director and General Manager*

48 m HIGH-SPEED MONOHULL PASSENGER FERRY
Ono-Ono

In December 1993, Austal won a $5.8 million contract to build a 48 m high-speed monohull ferry. The vessel was delivered in June 1994 and is operated by SPI Maritime from Tahiti's main port Papeete to the neighbouring islands of Huahine, Raiatea, Bora Bora and Tahea.

During delivery the vessel sailed under its own power from Western Australia to Tahiti covering over 7000 nm.

Principal Particulars

Length overall	48 m
Length waterline	41.3 m
Beam	9 m
Draught	1.2 m
Crew	11
Passengers	450
Fuel capacity	20 000 l
Water capacity	2000 l
Propulsive power	3 × 1960 kW
Maximum speed	35 knots

Propulsion: The main engines are 3 × MTU 16V 396 TE 74L rated at 1960 kW at 1940 rpm, driving 3 × KaMeWa 63 water-jets via 3 × Reintjes VLJ930 gearboxes.

30 m MONOHULL FERRY

Austal delivered two 30 m monohull ferries in December 1994 to unspecified owners.

Principal Particulars

Length overall	30 m
Length waterline	25.8 m
Beam	7.05 m
Draught	1.2 m
Crew	4
Passengers	155
Fuel capacity	4000 l
Water capacity	400 l
Propulsive power	2 × 822 kW
Operational speed	25 knots

Propulsion: The vessel is powered by two MTU 8V 396 TE 74 diesels rated at 822 kW each. Each diesel drives through a ZF BU255 gearbox to an FFJet 550 water-jet.

UPDATED

Ono-Ono *on trials*   *1995*

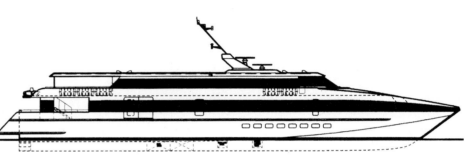

PROFILE

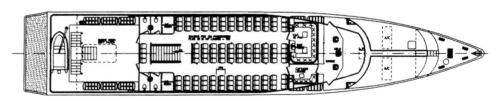

UPPER DECK

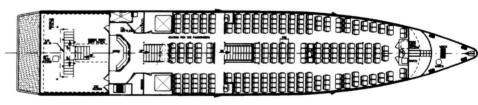

MAIN DECK

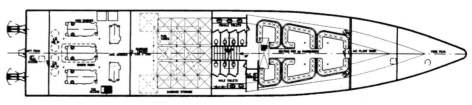

General arrangement of Ono-Ono
1995   **HULL**

GERALDTON BOAT BUILDERS

15 Larkin St, Geraldton, Western Australia 6530

Telephone: +61 (099) 211288
Telefax: +61 (099) 216404

Geraldton Boat Builders specialises in building small fast patrol craft and commercial vessels, offering a range of both monohull and catamaran designs, all of a high-speed planing type. Hulls are manufactured from aluminium or GRP.

22 m PATROL VESSEL

This vessel was delivered to the Victorian State Government in Australia in late 1993.

Principal Particulars

Length overall	22 m
Beam	6.6 m
Draught	1.6 m
Displacement, minimum	28 t
Displacement, maximum	43 t
Fuel capacity	14 000 l
Water capacity	200 l
	and 1500 l/day desalinator

Propulsive power	2 × 1500 kW
Maximum speed	28 knots
Operational speed	21.5 knots
Range	1000 nm

Propulsion: The vessel is powered by two MTU 12V 183 TF 92 diesel engines rated at 2300 rpm each driving a fixed-pitch propeller via a ZF 193 reverse reduction gearbox.

NEW ENTRY

LLOYD'S SHIPS HOLDINGS PTY LTD

41 Oxford Street, Bulimba, Queensland 4171, Australia

Telephone: +61 (7) 399 6866
Telefax: +61 (7) 395 5000

John Hardie, *General Manager*

Lloyd's Ships designs and constructs a range of luxury motor yachts and large catamaran ferry vessels with speeds up to 40 knots. All Lloyd's ships are constructed to 'Class'.

The company has Daikyo Australia Pty Ltd as its major shareholder, has over 130 people directly employed and a turnover in excess of A$25 million per annum.

29.5 m MOTOR YACHT V102

Launched in February 1993, construction of this all-aluminium yacht started in August 1991.

Principal Particulars

Length overall	29.5 m
Length waterline	23.1 m
Beam	8.5 m
Draught	1.7 m
Displacement	128 t
Crew	6
Passengers	6 guests
Fuel capacity	26 t
Water capacity	6 t

Lloyd's Ships 29.5 m motor yacht, V102   **1995**

Maximum speed	25 knots
Operational speed	16 knots

Classification: DnV + A1 High Speed Lightcraft (Winter R280).

Propulsion: 2 × MTU 12V 396 TE 94 engines, powering 2 × KaMeWa S71 water-jets.

UPDATED

OCEANFAST INTERNATIONAL PTY LTD

26 St George's Terrace, Perth, PO Box X2256, Western Australia, Australia

Telephone: +61 (9) 325 8599
Telex: 94598 IAL AA
Telefax: +61 (9) 325 6484/221 1813

Boat Factory: 15 Egmont Road, Henderson, Western Australia 6166, Australia

Telephone: +61 (9) 410 1900
Telefax: +61 (9) 410 2095

John Farrell, *Managing Director*

Oceanfast International is part of the Oceanfast Marine group which also includes International Shipyards, Motor Yacht International and Ferries Australia.

The Oceanfast Marine Group is one of Australia's largest shipbuilding operations, building a diverse range of craft from commercial fishing vessels and passenger ferries through to luxury motor yachts. The group operates under the ISO 9002 Quality Assurance code.

The most recent project, a 53 m, 20 knot propeller-driven semi-displacement luxury yacht, was delivered in mid-1994.

Opal C
Principal Particulars

Length overall	40.3 m
Beam	8.0 m
Draught	1.4 m
Displacement, minimum	140 t
Displacement, maximum	170 t

53 m high-speed displacement yacht   **1994**

Crew	7
Passengers	7
Fuel capacity	35 000 l
Water capacity	7000 l
Propulsive power	2 × 2595 kW
Maximum speed	35 knots
Operational speed	30 knots
Range	900 nm

Classification: Det Norske Veritas unlimited letter of compliance for hull construction and machinery installation.

Propulsion: The main engines are 2 × MTU 16V 396 TB 94 diesels each producing 2595 kW, driving 2 × KaMeWa type 80 S62/6 water-jets via 2 × ZF BU755 non-reversible gearboxes.

Electrical system: The generator sets are 1 × 98 kW MTU/Mercedes, and 1 × 65 kW MTU/Mercedes.

Control: One pair of Koopnautic roll stabilisers and hydraulically operated trim tabs are fitted.

Antipodean
Principal Particulars

Length overall	36 m
Beam	7.4 m
Draught	1 m
Displacement, minimum	95 t
Displacement, maximum	110 t
Fuel capacity	22 000 l
Water capacity	2400 l
Propulsive power	2 × 1461 kW
Maximum speed	30 knots
Operational speed	25 knots

Propulsion: The main engines are 2 × MTU 12 cylinder 396 TB 93 diesels, each producing 1461 kW at 2100 rpm, driving 2 × KaMeWa S62/6 water-jets.

Mystique
Principal Particulars

Length overall	50 m
Beam	8.96 m

Draught   1.5 m
Displacement, minimum   210 t
Fuel capacity   93 000 l
Water capacity   10 000 l
Maximum speed   35 knots
Operational speed   28 knots

Propulsion: The main engines are 2 × MTU 16V 396 TB 94, and 1 × MTU 12V 396 TB 93, driving 3 × KaMeWa type 80 S62/6 water-jets.

Electrical system: The power is supplied by 2 × 130 kVA Northern Lights generators.

Madiblue (ex Parts VI)
Principal Particulars
Length overall   46.69 m
Beam   8.36 m
Draught   1.25 m
Displacement, minimum   140 t
Crew   5
Fuel capacity   45 000 l
Water capacity   5700 l
Propulsive power   3896 kW
Maximum speed   30 knots

Propulsion: The main engines are 2 × MTU 12 cylinder 396 TB 93, and 1 × MTU 8 cylinder 396 TB 93 diesels, driving 3 × KaMeWa 63S62/6 water-jets.

Electrical system: The power is supplied by 2 × 68 kVA Mercedes-Benz OM 352 220/380 V generator sets.

Sounds of Pacific
A 37.6 m cruising monohull vessel built for Island Cruise Line Pacific Inc. Now operating in Guam after its promotional trip to Japan.

Principal Particulars
Length overall   37.6 m
Length waterline   31.4 m
Beam   7.5 m
Draught   1.05 m
Displacement, minimum   92 t
Crew   8
Passengers   100
Fuel capacity   6000 l
Water capacity   2500 l
Maximum speed   31 knots
Operational speed   27.5 knots

Propulsion: The main engines are 2 × MWM TBD 604B V16; driving 2 × KaMeWa 71S 62/6 water-jets.

Oceana
This all-aluminium motor yacht was launched in May 1991 for a European owner.

Principal Particulars
Length overall   55 m
Length waterline   43.5 m
Beam   9 m
Draught   1.45 m
Displacement, minimum   254 t
Fuel capacity   96 000 l
Water capacity   14 000 l
Propulsive power   7136 kW
Maximum speed   35 knots
Operational speed   29 knots
Range   3000 nm (one engine)

Propulsion: The main engines are 2 × MTU 16V 396 TB 94, 2595 kW each and 1 × MTU 12V 396 TB 94, 1946 kW.

Outfit: Owner's stateroom, 4 guest staterooms, 1 captain's stateroom, 4 crew cabins.

UPDATED

Oceanfast Oceana   1993

Oceanfast Opal C
1995

SBF ENGINEERING PTY LTD

Waters Edge, Lot 33 Cockburn Road, South Coogee, Western Australia 6166, Australia

Telephone: +61 (9) 410 2244
Telefax: +61 (9) 410 1807

Don Dunbar, *Managing Director, Designer*
Alan McCombie, *Director, Financial Controller*
Don Johnston, *General Manager*

SBF Engineering builds high-speed aluminium crew boats and passenger ferries, designed to meet the operational needs of individual shipping companies. Apart from the vessels detailed below, SBF Engineering has also built a 54 passenger, 35 knot, water-jet-propelled ferry, the *Fitzroy Reef Jet*.

Tung Hsin

The most recent building from SBF Engineering (Yard No TW27), this vessel is SBF's first export to Taiwan and was secured after about six months of negotiation with the client, Tung Hsin Steamship Company Ltd. Operating in the south of Taiwan from Ping Tung to Hsiao Liu Chiu Island, *Tung Hsin* was designed and built to suit the client's operation. Consideration had to be given to the transport of motorbikes on the aft deck, therefore passengers are loaded forward and aft. The vessel was launched in January 1993 and delivered in February.

Principal Particulars

Length overall	26.55 m
Length waterline	24.3 m
Beam	6.4 m
Draught	1.8 m
Displacement	53 t
Passengers	193
Fuel capacity	4000 l
Operational speed	29 knots

Classification: China Corporation Register of Shipping.
Safety standards: Taiwan Marine Authority.
Structure: Hull material: aluminium.
Superstructure material: aluminium.
Propulsion: The main engines are 3 × MTU 12V 183 TE 72 diesels, driving 3 × Stone Marine 5-blade propellers via 3 × Niigata MGN 232 gearboxes.
Electrical system: Engine: 1 × Perkins 4.236 diesel. Generator: 1 × Lister 19 kVA.

Auto Batam 7

This monohull ferry (Yard No KP07) was delivered in March 1991 for service with Kalpin Shipping and Trading Company of Singapore for the Singapore to Batam Island route. She is a sister vessel of *Auto Batam 6*, delivered in 1990.

Principal Particulars

Length overall	30 m
Length waterline	24.6 m
Beam	6.5 m
Draught	1.8 m
Displacement	54 t
Passengers	200
Fuel capacity	5500 l
Operational speed	27 knots

Classification: Bureau Veritas.
Structure: Hull material: aluminium.
Superstructure material: aluminium.
Propulsion: The main engines are 3 × MTU 12V 183 TE 62 diesels, driving 3 × 5-blade propellers via 3 × ZF BW755 gearboxes.
Electrical system: 1 × Cummins 4B3.9 37 kVA 50 Hz 415/250 V generator, 1 × Lister-Petter 19 kVA air-cooled generator.

Sea Dragon 2

A 23 m workboat for ship delivery and support work in Singapore harbour anchorage, delivered to Kalpin Shipping and Trading Company in late 1991.

Principal Particulars

Length	23 m
Beam	6.2 m
Draught	1.3 m
Operational speed	22 knots

Propulsion: The main engines are 2 × Cummins KT19, 380 kW at 2100 rpm.

Craft name	Payload	Engines	Delivery	Operating Country
Auto Batam 7	200 passengers	3 × MTU 12V 183 TE 62	March 1991	Singapore
Sea Dragon		2 × Cummins KT19	1991	Singapore
Satrya Express	62 passengers	2 × MTU 12V 396 TB 83		Indonesia
Sea Flyte	240 passengers	2 × MTU	1980	Singapore
Sundancer	160 passengers	3 × MWM TBD 234 V12		Singapore
James Kelly II	200 passengers	2 × GM 12V 92		Tasmania
Wilderness Seeker	100 passengers	2 × MWM TBD 234 V12	1985	Tasmania
Sing Batam 1	226 passengers	3 × MTU 12V 183 TE 62	December 1991	Singapore
Sea Dragon 3		2 × Cummins KT19-M	March 1992	Singapore
Tung Hsin	193 passengers	3 × MTU 12V 183 TE 72	February 1993	Taiwan

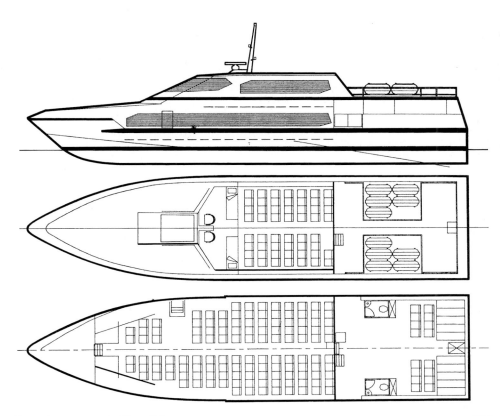

General arrangement of Tung Hsin

1995

Auto Batam 7

1993

Sea Dragon 3

This vessel was ordered when the owners, Sea Dragon Marine Services Pte Ltd, took delivery of its sister vessel *Sea Dragon 2*. Launched and delivered in March 1992, the vessel was delivered under its own power.

Principal Particulars

Length overall	22.55 m
Beam	6.2 m
Draught	1.3 m
Passengers	12
Propulsive power	2 × 3171 kW

Structure: Hull material: aluminium. Superstructure material: aluminium.

Propulsion: The main engines are 2 × Cummins KT19-M diesels, 317 kW each, driving 2 × 4-blade propellers, through 2 × Twin Disc 5111A gearboxes.

Sing Batam 1

This triple screw vessel (Yard No SB28) was ordered at the same time as *Sea Dragon 2* by the same owners but under the company name of Sing Batam Ferries Pte Ltd. This vessel is based upon *Auto Batam 7* delivered to Kalpin Shipping and Trading Company Pte Ltd earlier in 1991. The difference is that the upper deck is fully enclosed and air-conditioned with the same interior seating as the main deck. This vessel was launched in Fremantle in December 1991 and delivered the same month, it took seven days under its own power to arrive in Singapore.

Principal Particulars

Length overall	30 m
Length waterline	24.6 m
Beam	6.5 m
Draught	1.8 m
Displacement	54 t
Passengers	226
Fuel capacity	5500 l
Operational speed	27 knots

Classification: Bureau Veritas. Safety standards: Singapore Marine Department.

Structure: Hull material: aluminium. Superstructure material: aluminium.

Propulsion: The main engines are 3 × MTU 12V 183 TE 62 diesels, driving 3 × Stone Marine 5-blade propellers via 3 × Niigata MGN 232 gearboxes.

Electrical system: Engines: 2 × Cummins 4B3.9 37 kVA 50 Hz 415/250 V generators.

Osprey

This vessel was delivered in September 1994 to Rottnest Express Pty Ltd for operation from Perth to Rottnest Island.

Principal Particulars

Length overall	30 m
Length waterline	26.6 m
Beam	6.5 m
Draught	1.8 m
Passengers	257
Propulsive power	3 × 610 kW
Maximum speed	32 knots

Classification: Surveyed for Australian Department of Transport (Marine) 1D.

Structure: Marine grade aluminium.

Propulsion: The main engines are 3 × MTU 12V 183 TE 72 diesels, driving 3 × 5-blade Stone Marine propellers via 3 × Twin Disc MG 5141 reversing gearboxes.

UPDATED

Sea Dragon 2 *crew boat*   *1993*

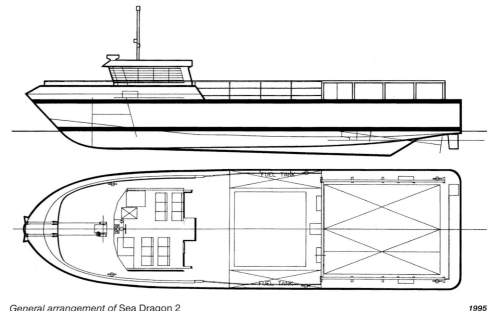

General arrangement of Sea Dragon 2   *1995*

MV Osprey V   *1995*

TRANSFIELD SHIPBUILDING (WA)

781 Cockburn Road, South Coogee, Western Australia 6166, Australia

Telephone: +61 (9) 437 0437
Telex: 93458AA
Telefax: +61 (9) 410 2065

Formerly known as Australian Shipbuilding Industries (WA) Pty Ltd, Transfield Shipbuilding is continuing to build high-speed craft based on the original ASI 35 m patrol boat.

Developments of this design have now been supplied to the Royal Hong Kong Police (a total of six) and Kuwait Coast Guard (a total of four).

ASI 31.5 m PATROL BOAT

Australian Shipbuilding Industries won the contract to build patrol boats for the Pacific Patrol Boat Project. Participating countries and number of boats purchased are Papua New Guinea (4), Vanuatu (1), Western Samoa (1), Solomon Islands (2), Cook Islands (1), Tonga (3), Marshall Islands (1), Fiji (3), Kiribati (1), Tuvalu (1) and the Federated States of Micronesia (2). The craft will undertake surveillance and enforcement of the Exclusive Economic Zones of the countries concerned. The craft listed in the accompanying table have been completed and handed over.

Principal Particulars

Length overall	31.5 m
Length waterline	28.6 m
Beam	8.21 m
Draught	2.12 m
Displacement, maximum	165 t
Maximum speed	23 knots
Operational speed	21 knots
Range	2500 nm (at 12 knots)

31.5 m COAST GUARD BOAT

Four of these craft have been delivered to the Kuwait Coast Guard.

Principal Particulars

Length overall	31.5 m
Length waterline	27.1 m
Beam	6.5 m
Draught	1.96 m
Displacement, maximum	150 t

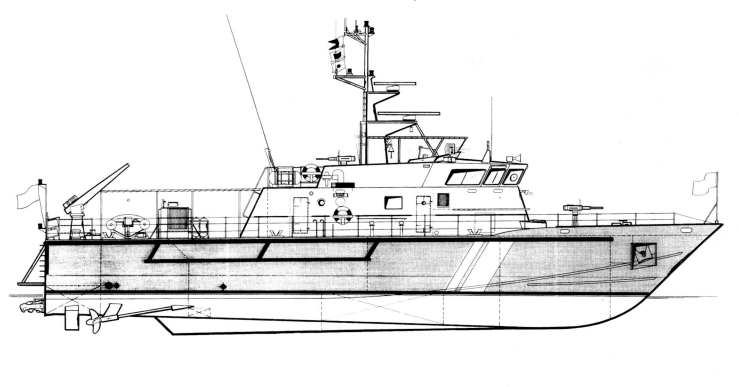

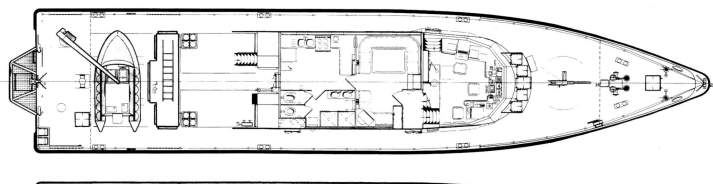

General arrangement of the Kuwait Coast Guard craft **1995**

33 m craft supplied to the Royal Hong Kong Police Force **1994**

31.5 m craft supplied to the Kuwait Coast Guard **1994**

Crew	11
Propulsive power	4325 kW
Operational speed	28 knots
Range	300 nm

Structure: Steel hulls, aluminium superstructure.

Propulsion: The main engines are 2 × MTU 16V 396 TB 94 diesels, driving propellers; and 1 × MTU 8V 183 TE 62 diesel, 550 kW, driving a Hamilton 422 water-jet. The third engine provides a loiter capability.

33 m POLICE BOAT

Six of these craft have been delivered to the Royal Hong Kong Police Force.

Principal Particulars

Length overall	32.02 m
Length waterline	28.6 m
Beam	8.21 m
Draught	1.6 m
Crew	19

UPDATED

High-speed vessels built by Transfield Shipbuilding (WA)

Name	Country	Date
HMPNGS *Tarangau*	Papua New Guinea	16 May 1987
RVS *Tukoro*	Vanuatu	13 June 1987
HMPNGS *Dredger*	Papua New Guinea	31 October 1987
MV *Nafanua*	Western Samoa	19 March 1988
RSIPV *Lata*	Solomon Islands	7 July 1988
HMPNGS *Seeadler*	Papua New Guinea	29 October 1988
CIPPB *Tekukupa*	Cook Islands	1 September 1989
HMPNGS *Basilisk*	Papua New Guinea	1 July 1989
VOEA *Neiafu*	Tonga	28 October 1989
FSS *Palikir*	Micronesia	24 March 1990
VOEA *Pangai*	Tonga	30 June 1990
FSS *Micronesia*	Micronesia	3 November 1990
VOEA *Savea*	Tonga	23 March 1991
RMIS *Lomor*	Marshall Islands	22 June 1991
RSIPV *Auki*	Solomon Islands	2 November 1991
RKS *Teanoai*	Kiribati	22 January 1994
RFNS *Kula*	Fiji	28 May 1994
	Tuvalu	8 October 1994
RFNS *Kikau*	Fiji	27 May 1994
RFNS *Ruve*	Fiji	7 October 1994
PL 51 *Protector*	Hong Kong	
PL 52 *Guardian*	Hong Kong	
PL 53 *Defender*	Hong Kong	
PL 54 *Preserver*	Hong Kong	
PL 55 *Rescuer*	Hong Kong	
PL 56 *Detector*	Hong Kong	
P 301 *Inttisar*	Kuwait	January 1993
P 302 *Aman*	Kuwait	January 1993
P 303 *Maimon*	Kuwait	June 1993
P 304 *Mobark*	Kuwait	June 1993

31.5 m ASI patrol boat HMPNGS Tarangau
1988

WAVEMASTER INTERNATIONAL PTY LTD

115 Egmont Road, Henderson, Western Australia 6166, Australia

Telephone: +61 (9) 410 1422
Telex: 93356 AA
Telefax: +61 (9) 410 2089

Trevor Kitcher, *Chairman*
John Mason, *Director*

WaveMaster International, a leading designer and manufacturer of fast ferries was taken over by the Penang Shipbuilding Corporation of Malaysia in 1994, providing a strong financial base for the planned expansion of their Western Australian yard. Formerly owned by Portmore Pty Ltd, WaveMaster was originally established in 1983 and has since delivered over 30 commercial craft in the range 30 m to 50 m.

Senang Ekspres
1990

Barbaros

Launched August 1987.

Principal Particulars

Length overall	34.05 m
Length waterline	28.7 m
Beam	7.1 m
Draught	1.75 m
Displacement, minimum	58 t
Displacement, maximum	84 t
Crew	4
Passengers	246
Fuel capacity	7000 l
Water capacity	500 l
Propulsive power	2 × 1075 kW
Maximum speed	30 knots
Operational speed	27 knots

Classification: Det Norske Veritas + IAI, R45, Light Craft, SF-LC, FLC, Naut C, Naut B, EO-LC.

Structure: Monohedron planing type constructed in aluminium. The main deck consists of forward lounge, main lounge and aft lounge with an aft upper deck lounge and wheelhouse deck.

Propulsion: The main engines are two MTU 12V 396 TB 83 series marine diesels rated at 1075 kW, driving custom-designed four-blade propellers via ZF 455 2:1 reverse reduction gearboxes.

Electrical system: MWM 226-TD4 4-cylinder marine diesel driving Stamford 47.5 kVA alternator.

Navigation and communications: Radar, Furuno 72 NM; VHF radio, Sailor 144C; HF radio, Sailor T124/R110; watch-keeping receiver, Sailor R501; autopilot, Wagner Mk IV.

Kita Ekspres

Launched November 1987.

Designed by WaveMaster to suit the demanding operational requirements in South-east Asian waters this vessel has triple water-jet units and air-conditioned accommodation for 152 passengers.

Principal Particulars

Length overall	30.4 m
Length waterline	27.5
Beam	6.1 m
Draught	0.8 m
Displacement, minimum	42 t
Displacement, maximum	60 t
Crew	8
Passengers	152
Fuel capacity	3750 l
Water capacity	500 l
Maximum speed	33 knots
Operational speed	32 knots

Classification: Australian Uniform Shipping Laws Code IC, restricted offshore service (IMO).

Structure: Monohedron planing form. Construction in aluminium. Wheelhouse forward on forward deck, lower main cabin with aft engine room.

Propulsion: The main engines are three MWM TBD 234 V12 marine diesels rated at 605 kW at 2200 rpm at 45°/32° ambient conditions driving Hamilton 402 water-jets via cardan shafts.

Electrical system: Two MWM D226-6 marine diesels driving Stamford 55 kVA alternators for 100 per cent redundancy.

Navigation and communications: Radar, Furuno 24 nm range; VHF radio, Uniden MC 610; HF radio, Cidan 8525S; autopilot, Wagner SE.

Star Flyte

A Glen Williams design, delivered in October 1988.

Principal Particulars

Length overall	41 m
Length waterline	35.2 m
Beam	8.5 m
Draught	2.05 m
Crew	5
Passengers	500
Fuel capacity	15 400 l
Water capacity	2600 l
Operational speed	26 knots
Maximum speed	30 knots

Classification: Det Norske Veritas + 1A1, R90 Light Craft. SF-LC, F-LC, Naut C, Naut B, ED-LG.

Propulsion: The main engines are two MTU 12V 396 TB 83 marine diesel engines driving custom-designed 4-blade propellers via ZF BW 465 2.025:1 reverse reduction gearboxes.

Electrical system: Two Perkins T6.3544 marine diesels driving 75 kW 415/240 V alternators.

Craft built in the last 10 years (high-speed monohulls)

Length overall	Vessel	Launched	Current owner/operator	Area of operation
32.4 m	Sea Raider I	1983	Boat Torque Cruises	Hillary's-Rottnest (Perth WA)
32.4 m	Gordon Explorer	1984	Morrison Tourist Services	Gordon River (Tasmania)
32.4 m	Sea Raider II	1984	Palayaran Bintan Baruna Sakti	Singapore-Batam Island
32.4 m	Sea Raider III (ex Sea Spirit)	1985	Palayaran Bintan Baruna Sakti	Singapore-Batam Island
34.05 m	Barbaros	August 1987	Kuala Perlis-Langkawi Ferry Services Sdn Bhd	Langkawi Island Malaysia
30.4 m	Kita Ekspres	November 1987	Kuala Perlis-Langkawi Ferry Services Sdn Bhd	Langkawi Island Malaysia
41 m	Star Flyte	October 1988	Boat Torque Cruises	Fremantle-Rottnest (Perth WA)
27 m	Suka Ekspres	November 1988	Kuala Perlis-Langkawi Ferry Services Sdn Bhd	Langkawi Island Malaysia
27 m	Senang Ekspres	March 1989	Kuala Perlis-Langkawi Ferry Services Sdn Bhd	Langkawi Island Malaysia
37 m	Jet Raider	June 1990	Gulf Ferries Ltd	New Zealand
37 m	Jet Raider II	November 1990	Boat Torque Cruises Ltd	Rottnest (Perth WA)
37 m	Jet Raider III	March 1991	Palayaran Bintan Baruna Sakti	Singapore-Indonesia
39 m	Ocean Raider	July 1992	Seaflyte Ferry Services	Singapore
44.6 m	Super Flyte	1993	Boat Torque Cruises Ltd	Fremantle-Rottnest (Perth WA)
33 m	Langkawi II	November 1994		
33 m	Langawi III	November 1994	Kuala Perlis-Langkawi Ferry Services Sdn Bhd	Langkawi Island Malaysia
31.5 m	Undisclosed	(Mid-1995)	Kuala Perlis-Langkawi Ferry Services Sdn Bhd	Langkawi Island Malaysia

Jet Raider   *1995*

Star Flyte, 26 knots with up to 500 passengers   *1995*

Super Flyte

1995

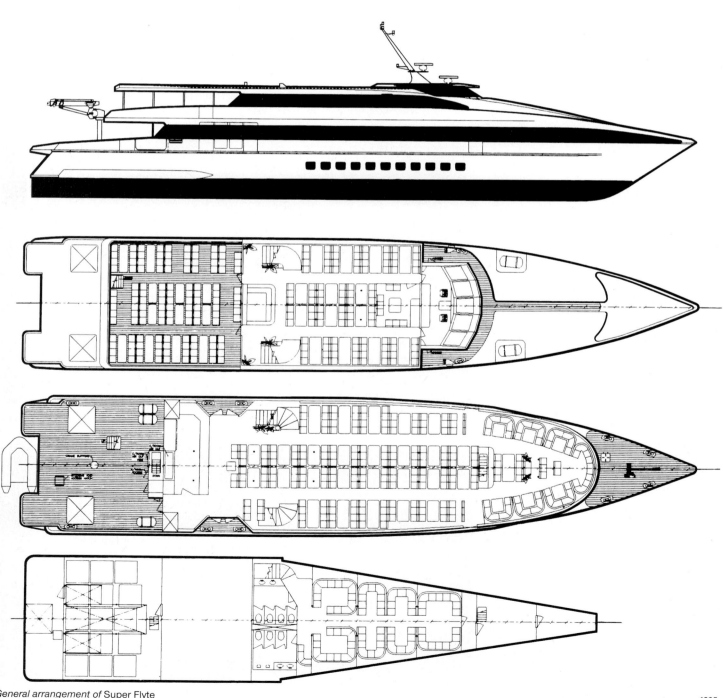

General arrangement of Super Flyte

1995

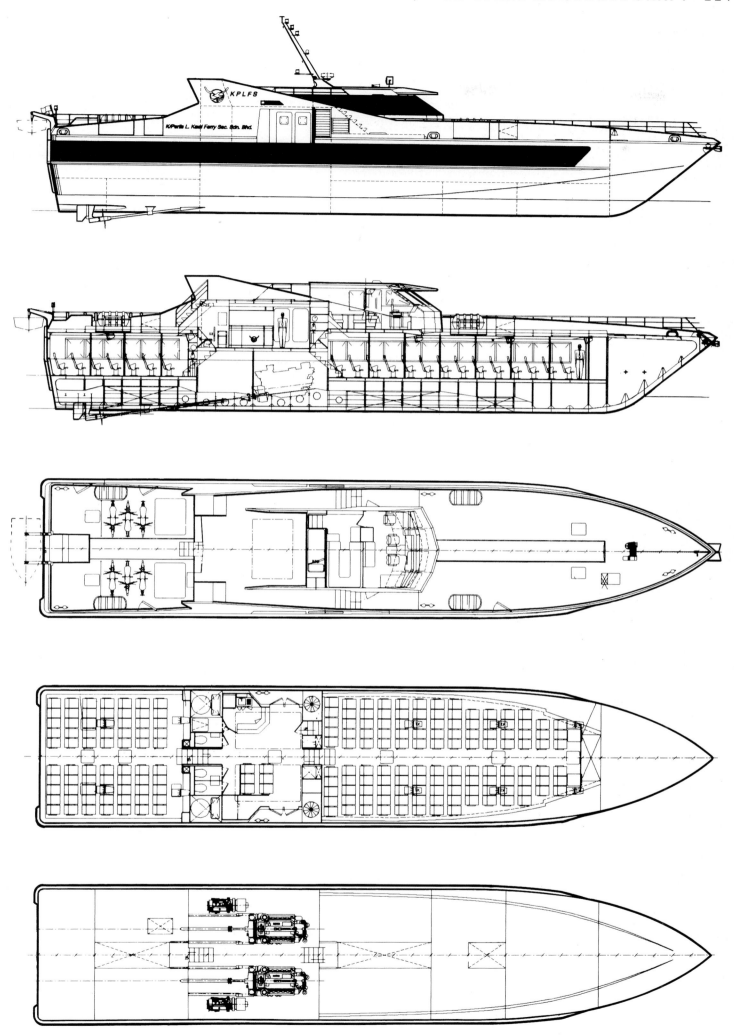

General arrangement of 33 m Langawi II *and* Langawi III

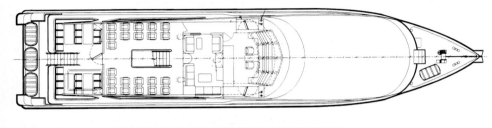

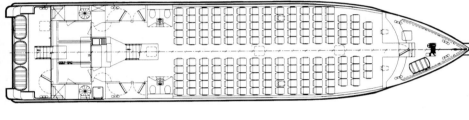

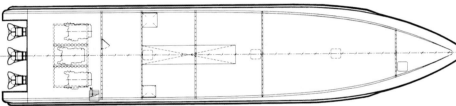

General arrangement of the 31.5 m monohull currently under construction

1995

Crew	5
Passengers	400
Fuel capacity	13000 l
Water capacity	2000 l
Propulsion	2 × 1260 kW
Maximum speed	31 knots
Operational speed	36 knots

Classification: DnV + 1A1 R45 LC.
Propulsion: 2 × MWM 12V TBD 604B, 1260 kW each, MCR, 1800 rpm, driving 2 × KaMeWa 56/S water-jet units.

Jet Raider III
This all aluminium high-speed monohull was launched in March 1991 for operation by Palayaran Bintan Baruna Sakti.

Principal Particulars

Length overall	36.5 m
Beam	7.2 m
Draught	1.1 m
Crew	6
Passengers	351
Fuel capacity	10 000 l
Water capacity	1000 l
Propulsive power	2 × 1180 kW
Operational speed	30 knots
Maximum speed	36 knots

Propulsion: The main engines are 2 × MTU 12V 396 TE 74, 1180 kW each at 2000 rpm, driving 2 × KaMeWa 56S water-jets.
Electrical system: 2 × MTU 6R009 generators.

Super Flyte
A monohull delivered early in 1993.

Principal Particulars

Length overall	44.6 m
Beam	9 m
Draught	2.3 m
Crew	5
Passengers	550
Fuel capacity	12 000 l
Water	2500 l
Propulsive power	2 × 1630 kW
Operational speed	27 knots

Classification: China Classification Society, ZC or DnV.
Propulsion: The main engines are 2 × MTU 16V 396 TE 74 diesels, 1630 kW each at 2000 rpm, driving 2 × propellers.

31.5 m MONOHULL FERRY
Principal Particulars

Length overall	30.8 m
Beam	6.5 m
Draught	0.95 m
Crew	5
Passengers	200
Fuel capacity	6000 l
Water capacity	1000 l
Propulsive power	3 × 610 kW
Maximum speed	29.5 knots
Range	360 nm

Structure: Marine grade aluminium (MIG welded).
Propulsion: The main engines are 3 × MTU 12V 183 TE 72, each producing 610 kW at 2100 rpm, driving Hamilton water-jets via ZF gearboxes.
Electrical system: The power is supplied by 2 × MTU 6RO99 TA51 generators.

Outfit: Passenger accommodation on three decks. The lower passenger cabin is forward with the engine room aft of midships and cargo hold aft of engine room. The main deck has a forward passenger cabin and main cabin with a bar for refreshments.

Suka Ekspres and Senang Ekspres
These 32 knot, 27 m high-speed ferries were delivered in November 1988 and March 1989 to Malaysia.

Principal Particulars

Length overall	27 m
Length waterline	23 m
Beam	6.6 m
Draught	1.65 m
Crew	4
Passengers	140
Fuel capacity	5500 l
Water capacity	750 l

Propulsion: The main engines are 2 × MWM 8V TBD 604B.
Electrical system: 1 × MWM D 226.6, 55 kW generator.

37 m JET RAIDER
A new project introduced in 1989, three of these craft have now been built. The first was delivered to New Zealand for operation by Fullers Gulf Ferries and the second completed towards the end of 1990 for Boat Torque Cruises, Rottnest (Perth WA).

Jet Raider II
Principal Particulars

Length overall	37 m
Beam	7.2 m
Draught	1 m

UPDATED

CHILE

ASMAR SHIPBUILDING AND DOCKING CO

Prat 856, Rapa Nui Building, Valparaiso, Chile

Telephone: +56 32 256373/259411
Telefax: +56 32 231297/214627

Sergio Garcia, *Managing Director*
Juan Chales De Beaulieu, *Commercial Director*

ASMAR Shipbuilding and Docking Company has three main facilities in Chile, one at Valparaiso and two at Punta Arenas. The company builds a range of military and commercial high-speed vessels and has recently delivered four 42.5 m patrol vessels to the Chilean Navy. The Protector class pilot launches built at the Valparaiso yard were delivered in 1989. The company currently has plans for a series of 75 m patrol vessels.

PROTECTOR CLASS PILOT LAUNCHES
Lep Hallef
Lep Alacalufe
Two 33 m 20 knot boats built under licence from FBM Marine Ltd entered service in September 1989. These vessels have a range in excess of 1000 nm and an endurance of up to 20 days and are powered by two MTU diesels. Both craft are permanently stationed in the Magellan Strait areas.

Principal Particulars

Length overall	32.7 m
Length waterline	29 m
Beam	6.7 m
Draught	2.1 m
Displacement, maximum	100 t
Crew	14
Fuel capacity	20 t
Water capacity	5000 l
Propulsive power	2 × 900 kW
Maximum speed	20 knots
Operational speed	18 knots
Range	1100 nm

UPDATED

One of two FBM Marine-designed Chilean pilotboats
1990

COMMONWEALTH OF INDEPENDENT STATES

CENTRAL HYDROFOIL DESIGN BUREAU

51 Svobody Street, Nizhny Novgorod 603003, Russia, CIS

B V Chubikov, *General Director*

In 1991 Sudoexport announced the availability of two high-speed monohull ferry designs, one for river use and one for open sea use. Since that time over 10 of the LINDA craft have been delivered.

In 1993 details of the 25 m landing craft Serna were released and it is understood that two of these craft have been constructed for operation on the Azov sea.

LINDA

Designed for passenger use on shallow rivers the vessel takes two basic forms: for long routes accommodation is provided for 50 passengers with a bar and baggage space of 5 m³; on shorter routes the vessel is equipped with 70 seats with no bar and the same 5 m³ baggage space. Ten of these craft have now been constructed with a continuing production planned for over 20 craft. The high calm water speed is achieved by a patented hull air lubrication system.

Principal Particulars

Length overall	24.1 m
Beam	4.6 m
Draught	1 m
Passengers	50-70
Propulsive power	800 kW
Maximum speed	38 knots
Operational speed	30 knots
Range	215 nm

Propulsion: The engine is a single M401A-2 rated at approximately 800 kW.

HERMES (DESIGN)

A design by the Central Hydrofoil Design Bureau.

Principal Particulars

Length overall	50.2 m
Beam overall	12.6 m
Draught	2.6 m
Passengers	456
Maximum speed	43 knots
Operational speed	40 knots
Range	400 nm

Propulsion: The main engines are 2 × MTU 20V 583 TB 91.

SERNA

Principal Particulars

Length overall	25.35 m
Beam	5.85 m
Draught	1.58 m
Operational speed	30 knots
Range	600 nm

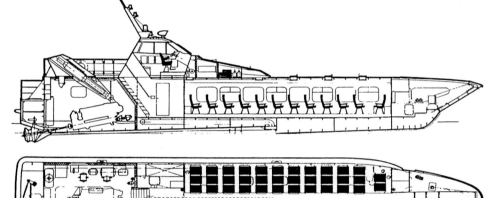

Linda
1993

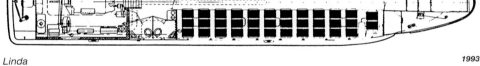

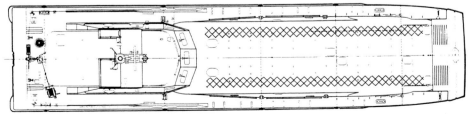

General arrangement of Serna
1994

Propulsion: Two M503A-Z Russian-built diesels drive two tunnelled surface propellers.

UPDATED

FINLAND

KVÆRNER MASA-YARDS INC

PO Box 152, FIN-00151 Helsinki, Finland

Telephone: +358 (0) 1941
Telex: 121246 MASAH SF
Telefax: +358 (0) 650051

Martin Saarikangas, *President, CEO*
Ulf Jernström, *Senior Vice President, Sales*
Kaj Liljestrand, *Senior Vice President, Sales*
Kai Levander, *Senior Vice President, Technology*

EUROEXPRESS
YARD 2000 PROJECT (DESIGN)

This project is included in a study programme funded 50:50 by the Finnish Government and the shipbuilding industry. Fast vessels and fast ships for operating in ice conditions are to be covered in the study, in particular, high-speed cargo ships linking Finland with the European market. A 40 knot Euroexpress concept has been designed around a deadweight capacity of approximately 4000 tonnes and would be capable of executing a Finland to Germany trip in 24 hours (18 at sea, 6 turnround in port), halving existing times. KMY is concentrating on monohull solutions for such operations.

Kværner Masa-Yards has developed the fast monohull hullform suitable for both propeller and water-jet propulsion. The wave-piercing "whale back" bow reduces the impact loads and can therefore maintain high speed in heavy sea conditions.

These ships can have diesel or gas-turbine machinery depending on the speed requirements. Electric drive has been used in some applications to give freedom in machinery location. The slender monohull technique can be supplied in both cargo vessels, ferries and cruise liners ranging from 150 to 300 m in length and 5000 to 50000 tonne displacement.

In particular the KMY slender monohull concept has been designed to be integrated with fast loading and unloading port facilities.

UPDATED

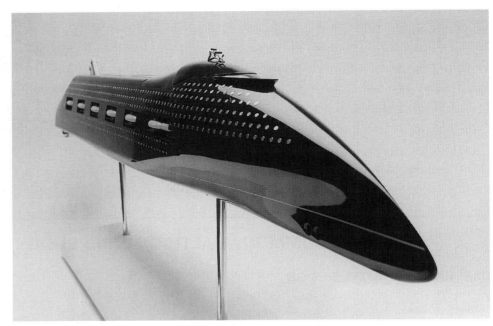

Kværner-Masa superliner concept for a 35 knot cruise vessel (design)   **1995**

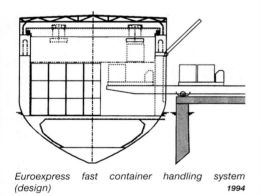

Euroexpress fast container handling system (design)   **1994**

Euroexpress fast Ro-Ro handling system (design)   **1995**

FRANCE

ATELIERS ET CHANTIERS DU HAVRE

30 rue J.-J.-Rousseau, BP 1390, F-76066 Le Havre Cedex, France

Telephone: +33 35 198000
Telex: 190 322 F
Telefax: +33 35 198040

Gilbert Fournier, *ACH Group Chairman*
Alain Tessandier, *General Secretary*
François Faury, *Shipbuilding Manager*
Antoine Castetz, *Sales and Design Manager*

As a holding company Ateliers et Chantiers du Havre manages the activities of Société Nouvelle des Ateliers et Chantiers du Havre (SNACH), and Société Nouvelle des Chantiers de Graville (SNCG), as well as other companies operating in ship repairs, industrial or other activities.

The company runs two shipyards in Le Havre, the Graville yard which creates and realises fabrication drawings and builds hulls; and the Harfleur yard which is responsible for all outfitting.

Both shipyards specialise in medium-size high technology ships, particularly prototypes, varying in length from 50 to 215 m.

Apart from shipbuilding, the company deals with marine, naval and offshore engineering, covering mechanics, hydraulics, robotics, electronics and computing, ship repair and mechanics, steel light and high alloy constructions, boiler construction and so on.

100 m PASSENGER/CAR FERRY (DESIGN)

In 1992 ACH released details of a high-speed stabilised monohull design concept. The principles are given in the following description.

The hull is made up of one long and highly streamlined main hull, with two lateral wings providing transverse stabilisation. The specially designed geometry and position of the wings are the result of an optimisation process carried out during multiple computer calculations and towing tank tests by both head and transverse seas. The slenderness of the main hull and the optimised shape of the lateral wings lead to highly advantageous propulsion characteristics over a wide speed range. The exceptional length of the main hull (which is more important than in other concepts of high-speed vessels) and the very slim bow shape allow the vessel to 'cut' through waves causing only a little pitching and virtually no 'slamming'. Within this concept, the lateral sea-keeping and stability are adjusted precisely to the values which allow safety and comfort depending solely on the position and the dimensions of the lateral wings and these independently of the general architecture of the vessel and of the position of its load.

The hydrodynamic performance of the hull, which is of displacement type, is less sensitive to load variation, a higher deadweight causing only a slight reduction in speed. This characteristic of the slender monohull allows the use of steel for the hull structure, in particular for the larger sized vessel. In addition, the very slim shape of the hull allows high speeds to be maintained in rough seas.

The concept does not require, in contrast with SES, SWATH and hydrofoil types, any lifting, stabilisation systems and therefore presents little risk to the construction, offers reliability in use and only requires limited maintenance in operation. It is envisaged that the vessel is to be integrated into a total system which consists of special harbour equipment adapted to high-speed passenger transport, such as dock ramps or special landing pontoons, encompassing the entire mooring, loading and supply functions of the vessel.

Principal Particulars

Length waterline	100 m
Beam	28 m
Draught	2.6 m
Passengers	450-600
Vehicles	150-180
Propulsive power	30 000 kW
Maximum speed	40 knots

Propulsion: Engines: 2 × gas-turbines, 15 000 kW each or 1 × gas-turbine 20 000 kW and 2 × diesel engines 5000 kW each driving 2 × water-jets.

UPDATED

Range of Vessel Characteristics

Model	Capacity Cars/Passengers	Speed Full Load
150	550 vehicles/2200 passengers	30-40 knots
120	300 vehicles/900 passengers	30-45 knots
100	180 vehicles/600 passengers	30-50 knots
76-400	80 vehicles/400 passengers	30-40 knots
76-300	60 vehicles/300 passengers	30-40 knots
45	300-400 passengers	20-35 knots
25	50-70 passengers	15-30 knots

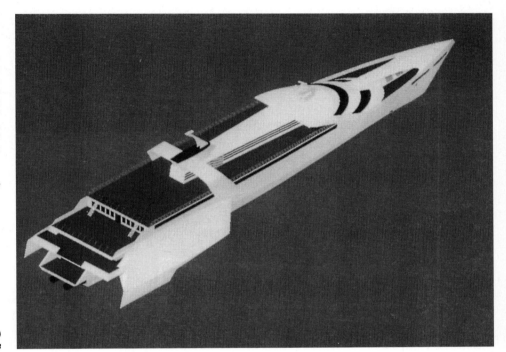

ACH 100 m passenger/car ferry (design)
1993

GUY COUACH CONSTRUCTIONS NAVALES

215 Avenue Francis Tonner, F-06150 Cannes La Bocca, France

Telephone: +33 93 47 11 22
Telex: 470737 F
Telefax: +33 93 48 03 66

Guy Couach is the successor to Couach Ltd which has been famous in yachting since 1897. It has been building motor yachts in glass fibre since 1962, and was the first to build a large motor yacht in Kevlar. The company now offers a range of 35 speed boats to luxury motor yachts of 6 to 30 m. Its shipyards currently build over 30 per cent of all French powerboat production with a turnover in 1994 of £18 million. The table below states models offered above 25 m.

UPDATED

Guy Couach 2501 class
1995

MODELS 2500 to 3100						
Type	**2501**		**2701**		**2901**	**3101**
Dimensions						
Length overall	25.5 m		27.77 m		29.8 m	31.2 m
Beam	6.3 m		6.34 m		6.3 m	7.0 m
Displacement, minimum	40 t		43 t		N/K	N/K
Main engines						
(largest installations)	2 × DDC	2 × DDC	2 × DGM	2 × DGM	2 × DDC	2 × MTU
	12V 71 TA	16V 92 TA	12V 71 TA	12V 92 TA	16V 92 TA	12V 96 TB 93
	1357 kW	2177 kW	1357 kW	2118 kW	2119 kW	1461 kW
	each	each	each	each	each	each
Maximum speed	24 knots	32 knots	20 knots	30 knots	29 knots	32/33 knots

* Kevlar + Levi Drive Units (LDU) can increaseperformance by approx 3/4 knots

LEROUX AND LOTZ

10 rue des Usines, F-44100 Nantes, France

Telephone: +33 40 959697
Telefax: +33 40 46 52 06

Michell Breheret, *Commercial Director*
J Ninet, *Marketing Manager*

With seven building and repair yards located along the Atlantic and Channel coasts, and design and engineering offices in Nantes and Paris, the marine division of the Leroux and Lotz Group is specialised in design and building of a wide range of medium sized civil and naval vessels.

The yard delivered its first fast ferry in 1994 and currently has one other under construction.

CORSAIRE 4500 (DESIGN)
Principal Particulars

Length overall	50 m
Beam	7.8 m
Draught	1.6 m
Passengers	450
Fuel capacity	17 t
Water capacity	4000 l
Propulsive power	6103 kW
Maximum speed	37 knots
Operational speed	35 knots
Range	165 nm

Propulsion: The main engines are 3 × Deutz-MWM 16V 620B diesels, each producing 2034 kW, driving 2 × KaMeWa S63 and 1 × KaMeWa B63 water-jets.
Electrical system: 2 × 180 kW generating sets.

Emeraude *on trials*
1995

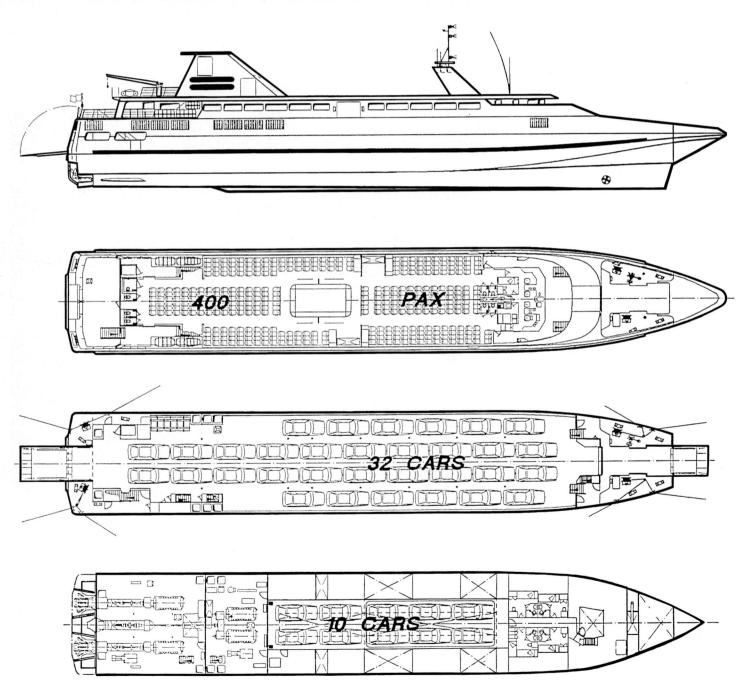

General arrangement of Emeraude

1995

CORSAIR 6000

The first vessel to this design, the *Emeraude*, was delivered to Emeraude Lines in Spring 1994 for service on the Saint Malo to Channel Island route.

Principal Particulars

Length overall	66 m
Length waterline	58 m
Beam	10.9 m
Draught	2 m
Passengers	400
Vehicles	42 cars
Fuel capacity	30 000 l
Water capacity	8000 l
Propulsive power	4 × 2245 kW
Maximum speed	34 knots
Operational speed	32 knots
Range	150 nm

Propulsion: The main engines are 4 × MWM 620B V16 diesels rated at 2245 kW each; 3 × KaMeWa water-jets, 2 × S80 and 1 × B90 units.

Control: The vessel is fitted with four roll stabilisation fins.

CORSAIRE 11000

Construction of this vessel commenced in mid-1994 for delivery in late 1995.

Principal Particulars

Length overall	102 m
Beam	15.4 m
Draught	2.4 m
Passengers	550
Vehicles	148 cars or
	108 cars + 4 coaches
Fuel capacity	84 t
Water capacity	8000 l
Propulsive power	4 × 6000 kW
Maximum speed	40 knots
Operational speed	37 knots
Range	300 nm

Classification: Bureau Veritas I 3/3 E.

Structure: All aluminium hull and superstructure.

Propulsion: The main engines are 4 × MTU 20V 1163 TB 73L diesels, each producing 6000 kW; driving 2 × KaMeWa S112 and 2 × KaMeWa B112 water-jets.

Electrical system: 3 × 400 kW generator sets.

Auxiliary systems: One 300 kW bow thruster.

UPDATED

Stern view of Emeraude *at speed* **1995**

Model of Corsaire 11000
1995

SBCN
SOCIETE BRETONNE DE CONSTRUCTION NAVALE

BP 20, Hent-Croas, F-29750 Loctudy, Brittany, France

Telephone: +33 98 87 42 71
Telex: 941356 SBCN F
Telefax: +33 98 87 91 40

Joel Ballu, *Principal*

SBCN specialises in high-speed craft built in cold moulded wood composite. The compound material is made up of very thin layers criss-crossed with hard mahogany fibres running in the same direction, vacuum-moulded in a matrix of epoxy resin. The resulting product is flexible, break-resistant and light, offers ease of maintenance and repair, good thermal and acoustic properties, avoidance of hull vibration and long-term maintenance of shape. The yard has a workshop area of 2500 m². The yard is now manufacturing its own water-jets in copper aluminium alloy and glass epoxy casing under the name Centaur Jet.

Atlante (1985)
Amiral de Joinville
Tourville

For details of these craft please see the 1992-93 edition of this book.

Nicolas Bouchard

32 m fast passenger ferry. Delivered in September 1987 to Société Anonyme Atlantic Armement for service between La Baule and Belle Ile.

Principal Particulars

Length overall	32 m
Beam	6.8 m
Passengers	270
Propulsive power	1790 kW
Maximum speed	37 knots
Operational speed	32 knots

Structure: Cold moulded wood composite.

Propulsion: 2 × MWM TBD 234 V16 marine diesels 895 kW each; driving 2 × MJP J550 water-jet units.

Patriote

38 m patrol boat. Launched in November 1987.

Owners: Benin Navy.

Principal Particulars

Length overall	38 m
Beam	6.9 m
Propulsive power	2685 kW
Operational speed	34 knots

Structure: Cold moulded wood composite.

Propulsion: 3 × Baudouin 12P15-2 SR7 marine diesels, 895 kW each, driving 3 × Centaur Jet CJ600.

Atlante

A new French fast passenger ferry incorporating several interesting design concepts completed its first short summer holiday season in 1990 serving the Iles de Glenan off the southern coast of Brittany. *Atlante* was conceived and built by the Société Bretonne de Construction Navale (SBCN). The introduction of the vessel has halved the previous fastest journey time to the Iles de Glenan some 15 km offshore, enabling the operator, Vedettes de l'Odet, to schedule an extra return trip each day on this busy seasonal route.

The lightweight hull uses construction techniques developed by SBCN originally for fast military craft. Thin veneers of hard mahogany are sandwiched together with the fibres of each alternate layer running in different directions. Each layer is soaked in resin and finally the whole is vacuum-moulded in an epoxy matrix producing a lightweight structure which is resilient and durable, resistant to rot, waterproof in both directions and possessing a remarkable strength to weight ratio. Eight years of experience by the builder also indicate that the material is easy to repair and maintain, has excellent thermal and acoustic properties, is less prone to vibration and holds its shape well. For military applications it benefits from a greatly reduced magnetic and radar profile.

The new Atlante *(Andrew N Smith)*   *1991*

Unladen, the craft weighs 37 tonnes which compares very favourably with a disposable load of 24 tonnes of passengers and full tanks.

Principal Particulars

Length overall	28 m
Beam	6.3 m
Draught	1.2 m
Displacement, minimum	37 t
Payload	24 t
Passengers	224
Propulsive power	1683 kW
Operational speed	29 knots

Propulsion: The main engines are 2 × MWM V12, 634 kW each; 1 × MWM V8, 425 kW; each driving a PP170 water-jet, all identical except that the central jet has a different impeller and nozzle to ensure maximum thrust from the lower horsepower. All 3 jets have steering nozzles.

Soleil Royal

This passenger ferry was delivered to its owners (SOTEL, Cayenne, French Guyana) in 1989 for service between Kourou and Iles du Salut.

Principal Particulars

Length overall	26.2 m
Beam	6.7 m
Passengers	105
Operational speed	21 knots

Structure: The hull material is cold moulded wood composite.

Propulsion: The main engines are 2 × MWM TBD 234 V12; driving 2 × Hamilton 402 water-jet units.

UPDATED

GERMANY

ABEKING AND RASMUSSEN SHIPYARD

An der Fahre 2, PO Box 1160, D-2874 Lemwerder, Germany

Telephone: +49 (421) 6733532
Telex: 245128 AR D
Telefax: +49 (421) 6733115

37 m MOTOR YACHT

Principal Particulars

Length overall	37 m
Displacement	200 t
Maximum speed	32 knots

Propulsion: Water-jet propulsion.

SAR 33 FAST PATROL BOAT

Fourteen craft have been built and are in service in Turkey.

Principal Particulars

Length overall	34.6 m
Beam	8.6 m
Displacement	160 t
Operational speed	40 knots

27 m MOTOR YACHT

Principal Particulars

Length overall	27 m
Displacement	95 t
Operational speed	46.4 knots

CGV 26 FAST PATROL BOAT

Principal Particulars

Length overall	26 m
Beam	5.8 m
Displacement	75 t
Operational speed	40 knots

Structure: Built in steel with an aluminium superstructure.

Abeking and Rasmussen 37 m motor yacht   *1989*

Abeking and Rasmussen 34.6 m Coast Guard patrol boat, SAR 33   *1989*

SAR 65/70 FAST PATROL CRAFT (DESIGN)

Principal Particulars

Length overall	65-71 m
Beam	9-10 m
Displacement, maximum	650-850 t
Maximum speed	40 knots

UPDATED

Back to Basics with M&K Fast Ferries

The M&K fast ferry concept is one of the most effective monohull designs on the market. The design has been chosen to provide a safe and predictable vessel. In addition to saving time by high speed, much emphasis has been given to car and passenger handling as well as a high degree of manoeuvrability, reducing turnaround time in ports. The ferry is equipped with a bow and a stern ramp system that will fit most conventional ferry terminals.

The ferry provides a high degree of passenger comfort with cafeterias and lounges for 600 passengers. Passenger access is separated from car access.

Principal Particulars

Length o.a.:	95.0 m
Beam mld:	17.4 m
Depth to Maindeck:	6.0 m
Draught:	3.7 m
Passengers:	600
Cars:	160
Busses/Lorries:	12 (+54 cars)
Main Engines:	4 x MTU 1163 TB63L
	4 x 5,800 kw MCR
Water Jets:	4 x KaMeWa 112 SII
Hull Material:	Aluminium
Speed:	35 knots

The basic solution – your best choice

Mjellem & Karlsen

P.O. Box 2713, N-5026 Bergen, Norway
Telephone +47 55 54 22 00 – Telefax +47 55 54 23 35

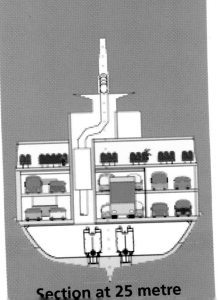

Section at 25 metre

weight for repairs or new buildings. There are three floating docks also of maximum length 251.7 m, capable of taking ships up to 37 000 tonnes deadweight. A lifting capacity of up to 30 000 tonnes is provided.

High-speed craft types delivered in recent years have included fast attack and patrol boats and luxury motor yachts.

25 m MOTOR YACHT

Four of these vessels have been built.

Principal Particulars

Length overall	25 m
Beam	5.72 m
Draught	1.09 m
Displacement, minimum	56.3 t
Displacement, maximum	60.6 t
Fuel capacity	9700 l
Water capacity	3350 l
Propulsive power	2 × 1134 kW
Maximum speed	32 knots
Operational speed	29 knots

Propulsion: The main engines are 2 × MTU diesels, 1134 kW each, sprint, 951 kW each, continuous.

HONG KONG

CHEOY LEE SHIPYARDS LTD

NKML 32-33, Lai Chi Kok, Po Lun Street, Kowloon, Hong Kong

Telephone: +852 307 6333
Telex: 56361 CLS HX
Telefax: +852 307 5577

Ken Lo, *Director*

The company was originally founded in Shanghai over a century ago. It moved to a small yard in Hong Kong in 1937, then to a much larger yard in 1940, and was occupied with building and repairing cargo ships. It diversified into building teak sailing yachts for export in 1956 and acquired a large site for a second yard on Lantau Island in 1960. The company commenced building motor yachts and building in GRP in 1961 and at present operates three divisions, one each for steel and composite commercial vessels, GRP workboats and GRP pleasure craft. The company has built over 4000 vessels since the current records commenced in 1950.

Tanjung Bakarang

Harbour Inspection and Service Launch delivered in June 1988.
Owner: Marine Department, Bandar Seri Begawan, Brunei Darussalam.

Principal Particulars

Length overall	25.84 m
Length waterline	22.2 m
Beam	6.43 m
Draught	1.82 m
Displacement	55 t
Crew	8
Passengers	65
Fuel capacity	13 620 l
Water capacity	2630 l
Propulsive power	2 × 662 kW
Maximum speed	23.5 knots
Operational speed	19 knots

Classification: Lloyds + 100A1 (Restricted Service) + LMC.
Structure: Moderate V bottom form with sponson chines. Construction in solid glass-reinforced plastic with foam core double skin for the decks. There is a two tier superstructure with wheelhouse and VIP lounge on the upper deck, galley and dinette-type seating on main deck. All accommodation is fully air-conditioned.
Propulsion: The main engines are 2 × MAN D2842 LXE, 662 kW each driving propellers through ZF BW 190 gearboxes.
Electrical system: 2 × Perkins/Stamford generator sets, 70 kVA 380 V, 50 Hz, 3-phase; 2 × 24 V 200 Ah starting battery sets; 2 × 24 V 120 Ah starting battery sets.

Discovery Bay 17

Fast passenger vessel delivered October 1988 and followed by a second, delivered to Penguin Boat Services Pte Ltd, Singapore, in 1991.
Owner: Hong Kong Resort Company Ltd.

Principal Particulars

Length overall	22.78 m
Length waterline	20.04 m
Beam	5.41 m
Draught	1.67 m
Displacement	36.1 t
Crew	4
Passengers	163
Fuel capacity	5100 l
Water capacity	450 l
Propulsive power	2 × 737 kW
Maximum speed	25 knots
Operational speed	23 knots

Penguin Progress, *sister vessel to* Discovery Bay 17   1990

Cheoy Lee 70 sports fisherman   1995

Classification: American Bureau of Shipping 100 A1 + AMS.
Structure: Deep V constant deadrise construction in solid GRP. It has a two tier superstructure with a wheelhouse and short passenger saloon on the upper deck forward half, after half and open under awning.
Propulsion: The main engines are 2 × Stewart and Stevenson Detroit Diesel Model 16V-92MCTAB, 737 kW each driving propellers through Nico MGN 273 gearboxes.
Electrical system: 1 × Mercedes-Benz/Stamford generator set, 32.5 kVA, 380 V, 50 Hz, 3-phase, 2 × 24 V 200 Ah starting battery sets, 1 × 24 V 120 Ah starting battery set.
Navigation and communications: 1 × Anritsu RA-72OUA daylight marine radar. Also 1 × Sailor VHF/RT 2048 compact VHF radiotelephone.

CHEOY LEE 70

Sport fishing yacht designed by American Naval Architect Tom Fexas.

Principal Particulars

Length overall	21.59 m
Length waterline	18.49 m
Beam	6.32 m
Draught	1.57 m
Displacement, minimum	37.6 t
Fuel capacity	7570 l
Water capacity	1514 l
Propulsive power	2 × 805 kW
Maximum speed	24 knots
Operational speed	21 knots

Structure: Moderate V bottom form with sponson chines. Hull decks and superstructure in GRP with extensive use of foam core materials.
Propulsion: The main engines are 2 × Detroit Diesel 12V 71TA diesels each developing 805 kW.
Electrical system: Two generating sets, one 32 kW and one 15 kW with 12 V starting.
Outfit: Open flybridge station with provision made for enclosing in unfavourable weather. The main deck houses the saloon and galley and also the master stateroom. Two guest staterooms are below deck aft and the crew area is forward. The crew area has separate access and includes a small galley, lounge and two crew cabins.

CHEOY LEE 83

Presently sold as a cockpit motor yacht, the hull of this craft is also used as the basis of a 'sports fisherman' vessel.

Principal Particulars

Length overall	25.27 m
Length waterline	22.29 m

Beam	6.42 m
Draught	1.62 m
Displacement, minimum	63.8 t
Fuel capacity	11 355 l
Water capacity	2650 l
Propulsive power	2 × 650 kW
Maximum speed	24 knots
Operational speed	17-19 knots

Structure: Moderate V bottom form with sponson chines; hull, decks and superstructure in GRP with extensive use of foam-cored sandwich construction.

Propulsion: 2 × Detroit Diesel 12V 71TA 650 kW each driving propellers through ZF BW 195 reverse/reduction gearboxes; underwater exhausts with idling bypasses.

Outfit: Flying bridge with L settees and table for guests. Open aft cockpit with access gate to swimming platform. Large main deck saloon with galley at forward end. Owner stateroom with double bed, and bathroom with whirlpool bath. Below deck, 2-berth crew cabin and three 2-berth guest cabins. Air-conditioned throughout.

Electrical system: 2 × Westerbeke or Onan 15 kW 230 V 50 Hz generator sets with hush covers, 2 × 24 V 180 Ah starting battery sets, 2 × 12 V 90 Ah starting battery sets.

CHEOY LEE 92

An enlarged version of the Cheoy Lee 83 cockpit motor yacht with similar layout and machinery except generator sets of 25 kW and a more elaborate bathroom for the aft cabin.

Caterpillar 3412 746 kW engines are fitted in the later models for a maximum speed of 25 knots.

Principal Particulars

Length overall	28.02 m
Length waterline	24.94 m
Beam	6.43 m
Draught	1.37 m
Displacement	67.85 t
Fuel capacity	15 000 l
Water capacity	2650 l
Propulsive power	2 × 746 kW

20 m SURVEILLANCE VESSEL

This vessel was constructed for the Environment Protection Council of Kuwait in 1993.

Principal Particulars

Length overall	19.8 m
Length waterline	17.65 m
Beam	5.54 m
Draught	1.57 m
Displacement	28 t
Crew	8
Fuel capacity	6000 l
Water capacity	400 l
Propulsive power	2 × 820 kW
Maximum speed	30 knots
Operational speed	25-28 knots

Structure: The hull and superstructure material is GRP.

Propulsion: The main engines are 2 × MAN D2842 LZE diesels, 820 kW each, driving 2 × propellers via 2 × ZF 195 2:1 reduction gearboxes.

Electrical system: 2 × Onan MDGBA 30 kW generators.

UPDATED

Cheoy Lee 83 cockpit motor yacht 1990

Recent version of Cheoy Lee 92 fast motor yacht 1995

CHUNG WAH SHIPBUILDERS LTD

41 Yau Tong Marine Lot, Cha Kwo Ling Road, Kwun Tong, Kowloon, Hong Kong

Telephone: +852 727 6333
Telex: 45803 WAHBU HX
Telefax: +852 347 3446

Brenda Lui Yee Man, *Director*
Edward Poh Choo Chye, *Director*
David Cho Lai Tong, *General Manager*

The company was established in 1940, and business covers shipbuilding, ship repairing, mechanical and electrical engineering, ship brokerage and consultancy.

PL71, one of 15 Chung Wah-built high-speed launches for the Royal Hong Kong Marine Police 1986

King class police launches built by Chung Wah   *1990*

The company has built and repaired marine craft in steel ranging from salvage tugs, deck container vessels, fire-fighting boats, supply vessels and cargo vessels to police patrol boats.

The company has completed a total of 34 steel police patrol launches for the Royal Hong Kong Marine Police and three command launches for the Customs and Excise Department of the Hong Kong Government. The success of these craft has been due to the joint efforts of Damen Shipyards (in the Netherlands) responsible for the basic design of the hull, and Chung Wah Shipbuilders Ltd (formerly called Chung Wah Shipbuilding and Engineering Company Ltd) responsible for the construction of the vessels.

KING CLASS
King Lai
   Police launch.
Principal Particulars
Length overall	26 m
Length waterline	24.6 m
Beam	5.6 m
Crew	18
Maximum speed	26 knots
Operational speed	24 knots
Electrical engine loitering speed	9 knots.

Structure: Constructed in steel.
Propulsion: The main engines are 2 × MTU 12V 396 TB 83 each delivering 1100 kW through ZF gearboxes; 1 × Benz 424A engine, with ZF gearbox.

2 × fixed-pitch propellers by SMM (MTU engines); 1 × KaMeWa steerable water-jet (Benz engine).
Electrical system: This is powered by 2 × Kosan 60 kVA alternators.
Navigation and communications: RM1226C 12 in, with 9 in slave radar and EMY1/C speed log repeater supplied by Racal Decca; 1 × Simrad echo-sounder; 1 × S G Brown 1000 gyro compass and repeater.
Control: Nautiservo BV electrohydraulic steering gear.
Operations equipment: An Avon sea rider launched or recovered by hydraulic crane operated from flying bridge.

UPDATED

ITALY

AZIMUT SpA

Corso M D'Azeglio 30, I-10125 Turin, Italy

Telephone: +39 (11) 650 2191
Telex: 220450 AZITO I
Telefax: +39 (11) 650 3478

Dr Paolo Vitelli, *President*
Dr Ing Vittorio Pippa, *Technical Manager*
Dr Massimo Perotti, *Director*
Dr Ugo Garassino, *Export Sales*

The company was founded in 1969 and concentrated on building motor yachts in GRP. In September 1985 Azimut took control of the Fratelli Benetti yard at Viareggio. With the acquisition of the Benetti facility, craft between 35 and 50 m are also able to be built in aluminium or steel.

The Viareggio yard encompasses approximately 3000 m², of which 2500 m² is fully enclosed; approximately 40 people are employed. In addition there are two other GRP fabrication yards employing 65 in total, and a fitting-out yard for the small boat division employing 20 people.

The company has expanded into the commercial boat markets offering a range of craft; there are fast passenger ferry, crew boat and fishing boat versions available.

Details of the following motor yachts built by Azimut are given in the 1992-93 edition of this book:
Rima
Atlantic Challenger
Athina R

VERIFIED

CANTIERI ING MOSCHINI SpA

Direzione e Cantieri di Bellocchi
Via De Nicola 5, I-1032 Fano, Pesaro, Italy

Telephone: +39 (721) 854236
Telefax: +39 (721) 854934

Cantieri del Porto
Lungomare Mediterraneo 2-4, I-1032 Fano, Pesaro, Italy

Telephone: +39 (721) 809988

Cantieri Ing Moschini SpA has been building GRP boats in the Pesaro area of Italy since 1970. The company now operates three yards and employs 175 people.

35 m ferry built by Cantieri Ing Moschini SpA and SIAR SpA   *1992*

The following are some of the high-speed vessels built in co-operation with SIAR SpA.

35 m FERRY

The hull and main deck of this vessel are built in GRP with the superstructure built in aluminium alloy. The passenger capacity is 350 and speed is 25 knots.

36 m FERRY
Ischiamar II

Launched in 1992 following experience gained with the 35 m ferry, this vessel is of all-GRP construction.

Principal Particulars

Length overall	36 m
Beam	7.1 m
Displacement, maximum	134 t
Passengers	350
Operational speed	28 knots

Propulsion: The main engines are 2 × MTU 12V 396 TE 94 diesels.

Sunliner IX

This Andrea Bacigalupo-designed vessel was built in Kevlar fibres by Cantieri Ing Moschini and fitted out by SIAR for Amital of Zurich.

Principal Particulars

Length overall	30 m
Beam	7.1 m
Displacement, maximum	120 t
Fuel capacity	40 000 l
Water capacity	4000 l
Propulsive power	2 × 1864 kW
Operational speed	32 knots

Propulsion: The main engines are 2 × MTU diesels, driving 2 × KaMeWa water-jets.

Sunliner X

Also designed by Andrea Bacigalupo, this vessel has a range which allows Atlantic crossing.

Principal Particulars

Length overall	35 m
Beam	7.1 m
Displacement, maximum	130 t
Fuel capacity	40 000 l
Water capacity	5000 l
Propulsive power	2 × 2610 kW
Operational speed	42 knots

Propulsion: The main engines are 2 × MTU diesels, driving propellers.

Sunliner IX   *1992*

Sunliner X   *1992*

21 m PATROL BOAT (DESIGN)
Principal Particulars

Length overall	21 m
Beam	6.1 m
Displacement, maximum	32 t

Structure: The hull and superstructure are constructed from Kevlar fibre.

Propulsion: The main engines are 2 × MTU 8V 396 TE 94 diesels, driving 2 × Levi surface drives.

UPDATED

CANTIERI NAVALI ITALCRAFT Srl

Via di Villa Emiliani 11, I-00197 Rome, Italy

Telephone: +39 (6) 807 5377/3650/0981
Telex: 613054 ITCRAF I
Telefax: +39 (6) 808 2701

Aristide Abbati, *Marketing Manager*

Italcraft, with a covered area of over 12 000 m², has built more than 2500 craft since 1953. Its latest design is the M78, at 56 knots one of the world's fastest production motor yachts, a development of its original 55 knot Drago class. The M78 is available in three yacht layout variations including an 'open' version with limited accommodation, named Ultra 70. There are also patrol craft and 100 passenger, 45 knot ferry versions. The patrol boat has a maximum speed of 52 knots and the ferry 45 knots.

M78 AEROMARINA

Fast motor yacht.
Principal Particulars

Length overall	22 m
Beam	5.45 m
Draught	1.2 m
Displacement, maximum	36 t
Maximum speed	56 knots
Operational speed	45 knots
Range	350 nm

Structure: Hull and deck constructed in GRP with aramidic fibre (Kevlar 49 Du Pont), impregnated with isophthalic resin. The superstructure consists of GRP and isophthalic resin. Four transverse bulkheads subdivide the hull.

56 knot Italcraft M78   *1989*

Propulsion: The main engines are 2 × MTU 12V 331 TC 92 diesels; 2 × reverse/reduction gearboxes are coupled by Aquamet 22 Armco shafts to 2 × surface-piercing Nibral propellers.
Electrical system: 1 × 12 kW diesel generator, 220 V AC 50 Hz, alternative by electric equipment 60 Hz standard USA.
Navigation and communications: Furuno or Vigil radar, 48 mile range; Loran C; echo-sounder; computerised electronic log; VHF, 55 channel 25 W. Internal communications: Intercom between wheelhouse, flying bridge, forecastle and quarter-deck; intercom in cabins, saloon and bridge.

Control: A dual station hydraulic steering system is coupled to rudders patented by Italcraft. Steering positions are in the wheelhouse and flying bridge.
Outfit: Deckhouse; wheelhouse, main saloon and galley Below decks; 3 double cabins, owner's toilet/shower, guest toilet/shower, crew toilet/shower, double-berth crew cabin. All accommodation is air-conditioned.

UPDATED

CANTIERI NAVALI LAVAGNA Srl

Via Dei Devoto 197, I-16033 Lavanga (GE), Italy

Telephone: +39 (185) 300341
Telex: 282693 CANACE I
Telefax: +39 (185) 306601

Dr Aldo Ceccarelli, *Chairman and Manager*

Cantieri Navali Lavagna builds the Admiral line of luxury high-speed motor yachts in aluminium or wood with sizes ranging from 22 to 45 m.

Over the past few years a number of the following craft have been launched:

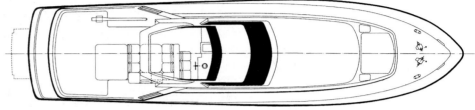

Admiral 27   1995

ADMIRAL 25
Principal Particulars
Length overall	25 m
Beam	6.5 m
Draught	2 m
Displacement, maximum	70 t
Fuel capacity	15 000 l
Water capacity	3500 l
Propulsive power	2 × 1137 kW
Maximum speed	26 knots
Range	900 nm

Propulsion: The main engines are 2 × MTU 8V 396 TE 94.

ADMIRAL 27
Principal Particulars
Length overall	27 m
Beam	6.8 m
Draught	2.05 m
Displacement, maximum	80 t
Fuel capacity	15 000 l
Water capacity	3500 l
Propulsive power	2 × 1432 kW
Maximum speed	30 knots
Operational speed	28 knots
Range	800 nm

Propulsion: The main engines are 2 × MTU 12V 396 TB 93.

ADMIRAL 28
Principal Particulars
Length overall	28 m
Beam	7 m
Draught	2.05 m
Displacement, maximum	86 t
Fuel capacity	20 500 l
Water capacity	3500 l
Propulsive power	2 × 1704 kW
Maximum speed	31 knots
Operational speed	29 knots
Range	780 nm

Propulsion: The main engines are 2 × MTU 12V 396 TE 94.

ADMIRAL 32
Principal Particulars
Length overall	32 m
Beam	7.25 m
Draught	1.2 m
Displacement, maximum	97 t
Fuel capacity	18 000 l
Water capacity	4000 l
Propulsive power	2 × 1946 kW
Maximum speed	32 knots
Operational speed	28 knots
Range	695 nm

Propulsion: The main engines are 2 × MTU 12V 396 TB 94.

UPDATED

CANTIERI POSILLIPO SpA

Località Porto del Bufalo, I-4016 Sabaudia (LT), Italy

Telephone: +39 (773) 57135
Telex: 680562 POS SA I
Telefax: +39 (773) 57139

Ing Giovanni Arrabatio, *Hull design, engines and propulsion*
Paola Galeazzi & Giovanni Zuccon, *Superstructures design, interior layout and furnishings*

Posillipo has been crafting and building pleasure boats since 1948 from a base on the west coast of Italy. While its beginnings were with the production of high performance mahogany runabouts, the company soon expanded its boundaries to meet the demands and tastes of an international market of boat enthusiasts.

In 1965, production began on larger day cruisers and cabin cruisers, fabricated in wood. This followed moving the shipyard from an area of natural caves of Cape Posillipo to Sabaudia between Rome and Naples. Soon after christening a new shipyard at Sabaudia where fibreglass construction was initiated, Posillipo directed its energies toward increasing its international markets, including the United States. Posillipo's principal contribution to the world of pleasure motor yachts is known as the 'Technema' line, ranging in size from 11 to 39 m.

In 1991 Cantieri Posillipo SpA was purchased by an American company, the first time an Italian shipyard has been sold to an American company.

TECHNEMA

A series of motor yachts ranging from 13 to 40 m in length with speeds from 29 to 50 knots and over. Propulsion options include direct drive, V-drive, Arneson drive and water-jets, with engine choices from Caterpillar, GM, MAN, MTU and Textron Lycoming.

A 27 m Posillipo Technema motor yacht   1993

VERIFIED

CANTIERI RIVA SpA

Via Predore 30, I-24067 Sarnico, Italy

Telephone: +39 (35) 910202
Telefax: +39 (35) 911059

Based on Lake Iseo in Northern Italy, Riva is the world's most prestigious manufacturer of luxury powerboats in the 27 to 70 foot range. Its customers include many Heads of State, senior industrialists and celebrities.

Riva has the capability to build between 30 and 40 powerboats each year. Its principal markets are in Europe and the Middle East, and the sales network is being expanded to take advantage of opportunities worldwide.

UK AGENTS: BK ElectroMarine Ltd, Hamble Point Marina, School Lane, Hamble, Hampshire SO31 4NB, UK

Telephone: +44 (1703) 455112
Telefax: +44 (1703) 455746

Brian Kaye, *Managing Director*

BLACK CORSAIR

Principal Particulars

Length overall	18.79 m
Beam	5.35 m
Draught	1.6 m
Fuel capacity	4500 l
Water capacity	800 l
Passengers	6 guests
Crew	1
Propulsive power	2 × 809 kW
Maximum speed	37 knots
Range	543 nm

Propulsion: 2 × MAN D2842 LZE diesels, 809 kW each.

CORSARO

A successor to the Black Corsair with increased space, more power and refined lines.

Principal Particulars

Length overall	19.72 m
Beam	5.35 m
Draught	1.65 m
Fuel capacity	4150 l
Water capacity	800 l
Crew	2
Passengers	8 guests
Maximum speed	32 knots
Range	507 nm

Propulsion: 2 × MTU 183 TE 92 diesel engines, 735 kW each.

RIVA 29 m GRANDYACHT (DESIGN)

Principal Particulars

Length overall	28.4 m
Beam	6.75 m
Draught	1.9 m
Fuel capacity	12 000 l
Water capacity	3000 l, desalinator: 3000 l/day
Propulsive power	2 × 1670 kW
Maximum speed	28 knots
Operational speed	25 knots cruising

Propulsion: 2 × MTU diesel engines, 1670 kW each.

UPDATED

Black Corsair   1995

Corsaro   1995

*Artist's impression of the Riva 29 m
Grandyacht
1992*

CRESTITALIA SpA

Via Armezzone, I-19031 Ameglia (SP), Italy

Telephone: +39 (187) 670800
Telex: 283042 CRESTI I
Telefax: +39 (187) 65282

A Melai, *Managing Director*
E Cossutta, *General Manager*

Crestitalia started building GRP craft in 1961 at Como and moved to a new shipyard at Ameglia (La Spezia) in 1971. The company build craft in GRP up to 40 m in length and since 1961 approximately 20 000 craft 4 to 11 m in length have been built. The Ameglia yard has recently been equipped with a new launching deck and sheds capable of building five 40 m craft simultaneously. Principal customers are the Italian Navy and Police, and overseas military and police forces.

MV100

Diving support and underwater exploration boat.
The MV100 is an enlarged version of the M85 (26 m), with a number of similarities in layout and equipment.

Principal Particulars

Length overall	30 m
Beam	6.9 m
Draught	1.05 m
Displacement, maximum	105 t
Maximum speed	27 knots
Range	560 nm (16.5 knots)

Structure: Semi-planing V-shaped hull in GRP with a GRP sandwich superstructure.
Propulsion: Two MTU 12V 396 TB 93 marine diesels, driving twin screws.
Electrical system: Two Mercedes OM 421 diesel generators providing 96 kW each.
Navigation and communications: One magnetic compass and one Anschutz gyro compass with two repeater compasses. One Sagem electromagnetic log, one RN 770 Decca radar, one Noak long-range searchlight, Elac LAZ51AT/LSE 133 echo-sounder, Zeiss Orion 80B night vision telescope and Decca Navigator Mark 21.
Control: Electric/hydraulic steering gear.
Outfit: Two twin-berth officers' cabins, two crew cabins, three berths in each, and one trainee cabin with six berths.
Operations equipment: Underwater exploration equipment is two Pluto RCVs equipped with search and identification sensors.

MV88

Multipurpose crew boat and quick deployment forces transport.

Principal Particulars

Length overall	27.28 m
Beam	6.98 m
Draught	1.1 m
Displacement, minimum	82 t
Crew	4
Passengers	250
Water capacity	2600 l
Propulsive power	2 × 1193 kW
Maximum speed	28 knots
Operational speed	23 knots

Structure: GRP.
Propulsion: The main engines are 2 × 1193 kW marine diesels, driving propellers or water-jets.

MV85 BIGLIANI CLASS

Fast patrol boat.

Principal Particulars

Length overall	27 m
Beam	6.95 m
Draught	1.15 m
Displacement, maximum	91 t
Propulsive power	2 × 2610 kW
Maximum speed	45 knots
Operational speed	40 knots
Range	850 nm

Classification: Registro Italiano Navale (RINa).
Structure: GRP.
Propulsion: Two MTU 16V 396 TB 94 diesels, driving two three-bladed Nibral alloy propellers.
Electrical system: Two diesel generators of 50 kW/50 Hz output, each capable of providing normal full load requirements, one emergency diesel generator of 10 kVA/380 V.
Navigation and communications: One GEM 732 radar, one Anschutz gyro compass, one Sagem electronic data log, one echo-sounder, and one ARPA radar; one complete radio station.
Control: remote engine room controls from wheelhouse and flying bridge
Outfit: Commanding Officer, four officers and eight ratings accommodated in single Commanding Officer's cabin, two double-berth officers' cabins and forward messdeck fitted with eight berths for ratings. Wardroom and galley situated in after part of wheelhouse structure.

MV70

Fast patrol boat.

Principal Particulars

Length overall	21.1 m
Beam	5.3 m
Draught	0.9 m
Displacement, maximum	40 t
Crew	4
Propulsive power	2 × 1044 kW
Maximum speed	35 knots
Operational speed	31 knots

Structure: GRP.
Propulsion: 2 × 1044 kW diesel engines, 2 × propellers.
Navigation and communications: Radar and echo-sounder, VHF-SSB-UHF.
Control: Mechanical remote controls to engines, hydraulic steering gear.

MV88 27 m multipurpose crew boat
1987

MV100 30 m diving support and underwater exploration boat

1988

31 m PASSENGER FERRY
Serena Lauro
Built in GRP 1988-89.
Principal Particulars

Length overall	31 m
Beam	6.9 m
Draught	0.9 m
Crew	3
Passengers	350
Propulsive power	2 × 820 kW
Maximum speed	24 knots
Operational speed	20 knots

Propulsion: The main engines are 2 × 820 kW high-speed diesels, driving propellers.

32 m PASSENGER FERRY (DESIGN)
Principal Particulars

Length overall	32.4 m
Beam	6.9 m
Draught	2 m
Crew	4
Passengers	200
Propulsive power	2 × 1339 kW
Maximum speed	30 knots
Operational speed	26 knots

Propulsion: The main engines are 2 × MTU 12V 396 TE 74L, driving propellers.

34 m PASSENGER FERRY (DESIGN)
Principal Particulars

Length overall	33.8 m
Beam	7 m
Draught	2 m
Passengers	250
Crew	4
Propulsion	2 × 1815 kW
Maximum speed	30 knots

Propulsion: The main engines are 2 × MTU 12V 396 TE 74, driving propellers.

37 m PASSENGER FERRY (DESIGN)
Principal Particulars

Length overall	37.2 m
Beam	7.9 m
Draught	2.1 m
Crew	4
Passengers	252
Propulsive power	2 × 1521 kW
Maximum speed	25.5 knots
Operational speed	22 knots

Propulsion: The main engines are 2 × MTU 12V 396 TE 74L, driving propellers.

UPDATED

MV85 27 m fast patrol boat   *1992*

Serena Lauro   *1990*

Freccia del Golfo   *1990*

FAZIOLI NAUTICA Srl

Via Della Scafa 135, I-00054 Fiumicino, Italy

Telephone: +39 (6) 658 3838/0355
Telefax: +39 (6) 652 3466

Previously known as Alfa Marine, this company builds a number of fast motor yachts, the largest of which is the Alfa 83.

ALFA 83 25 m FAST CRUISER
Principal Particulars

Length overall	25 m
Beam	6 m
Draught	1.5 m
Displacement, minimum	40 t
Displacement, maximum	43.75 t
Fuel capacity	8000 l
Propulsive power	1460 kW
Maximum speed	38 knots
Operational speed	34 knots

Structure: Built in GRP with V-keel with longitudinal side fins.

Propulsion: Two MTU 12V 396 TB 93, 1460 kW each driving propellers through BW 460 gearboxes.
    Manoeuvring: Bow thruster.

Electrical system: 2 × diesel generators 25 kW, central control and distribution panel 24 V, batteries 500 Ah, 24 V.

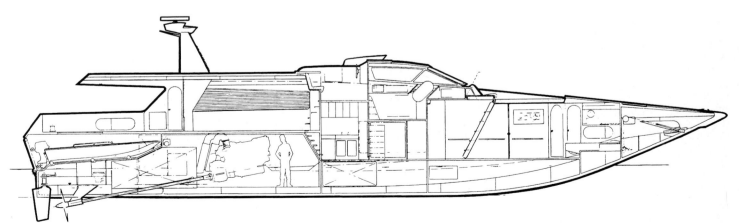

Interior arrangement of Alfa 83 25 m fast cruiser   *1995*

Navigation and communications: 40 mg radar, echo-sounder with optical plotting, GPS, automatic pilot. Communications are provided by a VHF 25 W 60-channel radio, SSB 1 828 MHz 220 W.
Outfit: Master cabin with bathroom and WC; 4 guest cabins, with bathroom and WC; kitchen, crew quarters, 2 bunk beds, piloting cabin, 2 seats, fly deck controls, 3 seats, fly sun deck, poop deck, lounge with bar, aft deck. Air-conditioning fitted.

UPDATED

Alfa Marine 25 m, 33 knot fast cruiser
1988

FINCANTIERI CANTIERI NAVALI ITALIANI SpA

Head Office: Via Genova 1, I-34121 Trieste, Italy
Naval Shipbuilding Division: Via Cipro, 11, I-16129 Genova, Italy

Telephone: + 39 (10) 59951
Telex: 270168 FINC GE I
Telefax: +39 (10) 599 5272

Mario De Negri, *Naval Shipbuilding Division General Manager*

Destriero

Destriero, which is owned by the Yacht Club Costa Smeralda, combines one of the largest light-alloy hull structures ever built, with a very high installed power level provided by three General Electric LM 1600 gas-turbines delivering a total of 44 742 kW.

Unconventional lightweight materials were used for the superstructure components. The hull is of a hard chine, semi-planing form.

Destriero was built at the Fincantieri Yards of Riva Trigoso (Genova) and Muggiano (La Spezia).

The design of *Destriero* started in March 1990. The contract was signed in May 1990, the vessel was launched in March 1991 and the sea trials were completed by the end of May 1991. On trials *Destriero* has reached 62.8 knots.

Measured noise levels in the accommodation and bridge areas are between 65 and 67 dBa.

Capacity is provided for 750 tonnes of fuel; each of the three engines burns up to 3.5 t/h.

Design and engineering of the vessel was undertaken by Fincantieri, hull forms by American naval architect Donald L Blount and styling by Pininfarina.

On 9 August 1992 *Destriero* broke the Blue Riband record for the fastest crossing of the Atlantic by more than 21 hours, completing the crossing from Ambrose lighthouse (New York) to Bishop Rock (Scilly Isles, UK), a distance of 3106 nm, in 58 hours 34 minutes and 50 seconds at an average speed of 53.09 knots.

It has been reported that on the initial westbound crossing of *Destriero* the starting displacement was 1070 tonnes with a corresponding speed of 43

The arrival of Destriero *at Bishop Rock, 9 August 1992*
1993

knots. As fuel was consumed speed increased, rising eventually to its maximum. The reported eastbound crossing time of 62 hours 7 minutes, together with the record westbound crossing time, also set a new double-crossing record of 159 hours 48 minutes and 15 seconds, a feat no other marine vessel has ever achieved.
Reference: *Interfacing the LM1600 Gas-Turbine with Advanced Marine Vessels*, Janna M Thames and Donald L Blount. *A Description of the Water Jets Selected for "Destriero"*, Rolf Svensson. Fast '91, Trondheim, Norway.

Principal Particulars

Length	67.7 m
Beam	12.9 m
Displacement, maximum	1070 t
Fuel capacity	750 t
Propulsive power	44 742 kW
Maximum speed	65 knots, light load
Operational speed	40 knots, full load
Range	>3000 nm

Classification: The vessel is classified according to

Det Norske Veritas Light Craft Rules, DnV having co-operated closely with the designers during design and construction; also Registro Italiano Navale.
Propulsion: The craft is powered by three GE LM 1600 gas-turbines, 14 914 kW each, packaged in resiliently mounted MTU modules, driving three KaMeWa 125 SII water-jets.
Reduction gears: Renk-Tacke Bus 255.
Structure: Aluminium alloy.
Control: Reverse thrust and steering affected by the 2 outer water-jets.

MDV 1200 *Pegasus*

The MDV 1200 *Pegasus* is a deep-V monohull fast ferry designed to maintain high speeds in exposed sea conditions. Three of these craft are currently on order from Ocean Bridge Investments for operation between Italy and Greece. The hull, tested at the Danish Maritime Institute, was specifically optimised to ensure excellent sea-keeping performance.

Wheelhouse of Destriero
1993

The three KaMeWa 125 SII water-jets of Destriero
1993

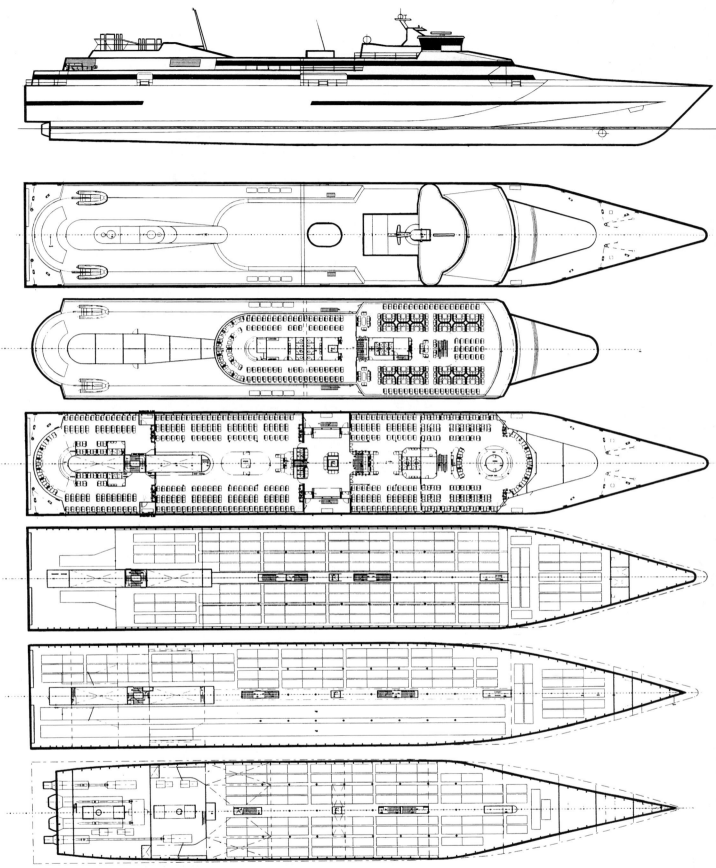

General arrangement of MDV 3000 Jupiter (design)

1995

The craft is capable of carrying 450 passengers and up to 150 cars at a speed of 40 knots.

Styling was defined jointly with Pininfarina.

Passenger and crew area subdivision into three main zones is protected by a sprinkler system. The hull is made of high tensile steel and the superstructures of light alloy.

The propulsion system and generating sets are split into two compartments in order to give the ship the 'go home capability' in case of failure of one engine room.

Principal Particulars

Length overall	95m
Length waterline	82 m
Beam	16.5 m
Draught	10.25 m
Passengers	600
Vehicles	170 cars
Propulsive power	24000 kW
Operational speed	36 knots
Range	300 nm

Classification: This design was developed in line with Category B of the new IMO Regulations for Fast Ferries and classed by Registro Italiano Navale.

Propulsion: Four MTU 20V 1163 TB 73L diesel engines each drive a Kamewa waterjet via a reduction gearbox.

Electrical system: Three main diesel generators and one emergency generator are specified.

MDV 3000 *Jupiter* (DESIGN)

The MDV 3000 *Jupiter* is a deep-V monohull fast ferry designed to transport passengers, cars and trucks at high speed.

The flexibility of the vessel allows it to be used in two different operating conditions: in a touristic service, where the cargo capability of the vessel is 420 cars - 1500 passengers (deadweight 800 t), with a speed of over 38 knots; and in a freight service, where the cargo capability of the vessel is 120 cars and 420 m of freight lanes (deadweight 1200 t), with a speed of over 34 knots.

Principal Particulars

Length overall	132.5 m
Beam	20.20 m
Passengers	1500 max
Vehicles	420 cars
Propulsive power	2 × 27 000 kW

Classification: This design has been developed in compliance with Category B of new IMO regulations.

Propulsion: The propulsion system and generating sets are split into two compartments and consist of two LM 2500 gas-turbines and two diesel engines with a total power installed of 54 000 kW.

UPDATED

INTERMARINE SpA

I-9038 Sarzana, La Spezia, Italy

Telephone: +39 (187) 671800
Telex: 271062 IMARIN I

23 m PATROL CRAFT
Principal Particulars

Length overall	23.8 m
Beam	8.4 m
Draught	1.2 m
Displacement	55 t
Crew	11
Propulsive power	2 × 1925 kW
Maximum speed	40 knots
Operational speed	35 knots
Range	450 nm

Structure: Constructed of GRP, the hull is of soft round form with fine entry forward, running into a hard chine constant deadrise aft.
Propulsion: The main engines are 2 × 1925 kW diesels, driving 2 × 3-blade, fixed-pitch propellers.

27 m PATROL CRAFT
Principal Particulars

Length overall	27.27 m
Beam	6.8 m
Draught	2.1 m
Displacement	85 t
Crew	15
Propulsive power	2 × 2575 kW
Maximum speed	40 knots
Operational speed	36 knots
Range	1000 nm

Structure: Same material and form as the 23 m patrol craft.
Propulsion: 2 × 2575 kW diesel engines, driving 2 × 3-blade, fixed-pitch propellers.
Electrical system: A generator of 76 kVA.

27 MTS PATROL CRAFT
Supplied to African navies.
Principal Particulars

Length overall	23.8 m
Beam	8.4 m
Draught	1.2 m
Displacement, maximum	55 t
Crew	11
Propulsive power	2 × 1925 kW

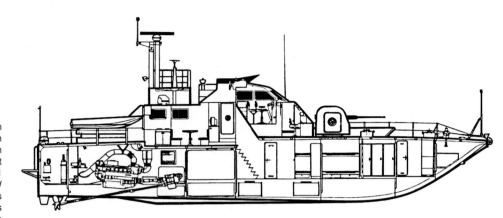
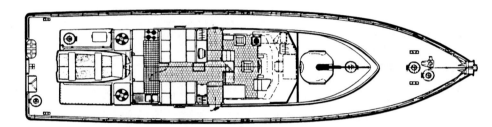
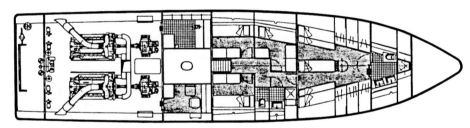

Intermarine 23 m patrol boat **1995**

Maximum speed	40 knots
Operational speed	35 knots
Range	450 nm

Structure: Same material and form as the 23 m patrol craft.

Propulsion: The main engines are 2 × 1925 kW diesel engines; driving 2 × 3-blade, fixed-pitch propellers.
Electrical system: 43 kVA generator.

UPDATED

RODRIQUEZ CANTIERI NAVALI SpA

22 Via S Raineri, I-98122 Messina, Italy

Telephone: +39 (90) 7765
Telex: 980030 RODRIK I
Telefax: +39 (90) 675294

Basbasso Gattuso, *President*
Giovanni Morace, *Managing Director*
Alcide Sculati, *Technical Manager*
Diego Mazzeo, *Sales and Marketing*

37 m FOIL-ASSISTED MONOHULL (MONOSTAB)

This is a patented concept for a stabilised monohull vessel matching the characteristics of a semi-planing hull with two automatically controlled surface-piercing foils, the object being to achieve a better overall performance than that obtained with a pure monohull, especially at Froude numbers near unity.

If water-jet propulsion is used for a semi-planing monohull, it is almost inevitable that with engines and auxiliary machinery also being at the stern, the

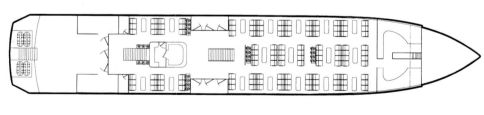
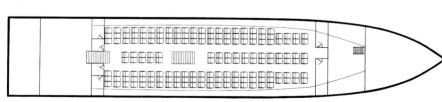

Deck layout of 37 m foil-assisted monohull **1995**

vessel will have a far aft centre of gravity with subsequently large changes in centre of gravity position from full load to light condition. Such machinery location also allows however for a hull shape with very fine entrance angles providing reduction in bow

wave generation and good sea-keeping performance especially in head seas.

The foil-assisted monohull concept reduces the difficulties of an excessively rear centre of gravity position by the provision of a pair of surface-piercing foils connected to moving arms, manually or automatically controlled and positioned at the rear of the craft. The effect is to allow for a true dynamic relief of weight load from abaft, thereby reducing the amount of craft weight supported by the combined buoyant/planing lift of the hull and effecting a planing trim reduction substantially equivalent to a forward shifting of the craft centre of gravity. This in turn leads to an improvement of cruising performance, because of the higher efficiency of foils in relation to hull efficiency in the range of speeds under consideration and, of the indirect advantage of being able to trim the craft correctly for any load condition. Further, with a considerable improvement in directional stability, with the dihedral effect of the foils generating correct banking in turns and the possibility of regulating the planing trim angle of the craft in head seas to reduce slamming, a large reduction of the hull bottom deadrise can be obtained, leading in turn to a better hydrodynamic efficiency of the hull.

Additional advantages of the concept, if trimmable foils are used, are that a strong roll and pitch damping effect is obtained, together with an increase in the transverse stability of the basic hull. These effects allow for a reduction in the waterline beam, improving hydrodynamic efficiency and rough water performance. With automatic control actuation of the moving arms a considerable increase in rough water performance can be obtained without involving unduly fast arm movements.

The first craft to be built according to the above principles was launched in 1989 and entered service with Aliscafi SNAV in April 1990 on the Naples to Capri and Ischia routes.

The 47 m foil-assisted monohull, in service with Adriatica SpA di Navigazione   **1995**

Principal Particulars

Length overall	37 m	Displacement, maximum	125 t
Length waterline	30 m	Passengers	350
Beam	7.5 m	Propulsive power	2 × 1920 kW
Draught	1.05 m	Operational speed	35 knots
Displacement, minimum	88 t	Range	200 nm

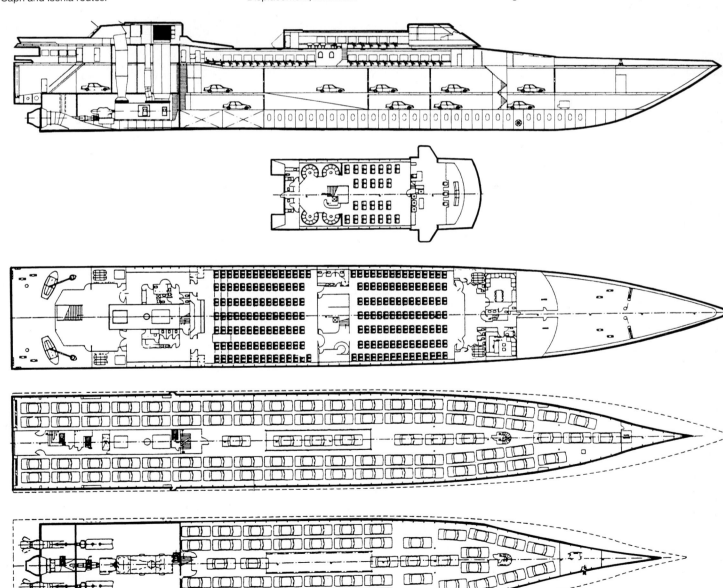

General arrangement of Aquastrada Guizzo

1995

Aquastrada Guizzo *in service with Tirrenia*

1995

Propulsion: Engines: 2 × MTU 16V 396 TB 84 diesels, 1920 kW each at 1940 rpm

47 m FOIL-ASSISTED MONOHULL

Two of these vessels have been bought by Adriatica di Navigazione SpA, one by Saremar and one by an unknown operator. The first vessel *Marconi* was delivered in December 1991 and the second *Pacinotti* in June 1992. The third vessel *Isola di San Pietro* was delivered to Saremar, a state owned company, in June 1993. Following the introduction of the 37 m foil-assisted monohull, these larger vessels accommodate 400 passengers. Interior design is by Ennio Cantu who has been responsible for many Adriatica di Navigazione SpA vessels. The two passenger saloons are air-conditioned. The third and fourth boats do not have aft stabilising foils but four Vosper Thornycroft stabilising fins, two forward and two aft.

Principal Particulars

Length overall	46.9 m
Length waterline	37.2 m
Beam	7.6 m
Draught	1.3 m
Displacement, maximum	154 t

Passengers	400
Propulsive power	2 × 2000 kW
Operational speed	34 knots
Range	200 nm

Propulsion: Engines: 2 × MTU 16V 396 TE 74L, 2000 kW each at 2000 rpm.
Thrust devices: 2 × KaMeWa water-jets (first two boats); 2 × Ulstein Propeller Speed-Z CPZ 60/42-125 CPP (third boat).

AQUASTRADA
Guizzo
Scatto

Two of these large fast monohull passenger/car ferries have been constructed for Tirrenia of Italy, with a third vessel of a very similar design under construction for Corsica Ferries, due for delivery in mid-1995.

The vessel's hulls are of a hard chine form and constructed of high tensile steel. The superstructures for the passenger accommodation are constructed of aluminium.

The capacities of the two Tirrenia vessels are similar although *Scatto* carries a slightly increased payload of 535 passengers and 156 cars as against 448 passengers and 126 cars. The performance penalty associated with this increased payload is small and equivalent to 1.5 knots of speed.

The Corsica Ferries vessel is slightly longer at 103.5 m as against 101.75 m and will be powered by three MTU 20V 1163 TB 74L diesel engines as opposed to the diesel/gas-turbine combination of the other vessels. The service speed of this vessel is understood to be 35 knots.

Principal Particulars

Length overall	101.75 m
Length waterline	85.3 m
Beam	14.5 m
Draught	2.05 m
Displacement, maximum	1057.5 t
Displacement, minimum	800.5 t
Passengers	450
Vehicles	126 cars
Propulsive power	24 065 kW
Operational speed	43 knots
Range	370 nm

Propulsion: Engines: 2 × MTU 16V 595 TE 70, 3565 kW each, 1 × GE LM 2500 gas-turbine, 20 500 kW; driving 2 × KaMeWa 100 SII, 1 × KaMeWa 180 SII.

UPDATED

TECNOMARINE SpA

Via Coppino 435, Viareggio, Italy

Telephone: +39 (584) 380381/3801
Telefax: +39 (584) 387630

Ms Anna Maria Marano, *President*

Tecnomarine was established in 1973 staffed with skilled labour and technicians from Picchiotti. The yard builds fast craft in wood, GRP, aluminium alloy and steel of from 14 to 120 m and is now one of the largest builders of luxury yachts in the world. Tecnomarine has a design staff of 45 and has long-

standing working relationships with Sparkman and Stephens on engineering design, Paola D Smith & Associates on interior design and Stefano Righini Design on styling. The total area of the company's various yards is 16 752 m².

TECNOMARINE 118
Motor yacht.
Principal Particulars

Length overall	36 m
Length waterline	31.16 m
Beam	7.33 m
Draught	2.25 m
Fuel capacity	14 000 l
Water capacity	4000 l

Propulsive power	2 × 1940 kW
Maximum speed	29-30 knots
Range	1000 nm

Structure: Construction in aluminium alloy or GRP.
Propulsion: 2 × MTU 16V 396 TB 93, 1940 kW at 2100 rpm each.

COBRA 76
Super Cobra

The first vessel of this new type named *Super Cobra* was launched in October 1990 for shipment to her owner in the USA.
Principal Particulars

Length overall	22.9 m
Beam	5.176 m

Draught	1.5 m
Displacement, maximum	42 t
Crew	2
Passengers	6
Fuel capacity	5000 l
Water capacity	2000 l
Maximum speed	34 knots
Range	360 nm

Classification: American Bureau of Shipping.
Structure: Hull and deck GRP, superstructure light alloy.
Propulsion: The main engines are 2 × GM 16V 92TA, DDC.

TECNOMARINE T90

The Tecnomarine T90 motor yacht is the latest vessel to come from this luxury yacht builder and was completed September 1991. With a GRP hull based on the proven 92 ft series and aluminium superstructure, speeds in excess of 30 knots are expected.

Principal Particulars

Length overall	27 m
Beam	6.42 m
Draught	2 m
Crew	4
Passengers	8
Fuel capacity	10 500 l
Water capacity	2300 l
Propulsive power	2 × 1462 kW
Maximum speed	31 knots
Operational speed	25 knots
Range	430 nm

Propulsion: The main engines are 2 × MTU 12V 396 TB 93.

TECNOMARINE T72

Motor yacht.

Principal Particulars

Length overall	21.8 m
Length waterline	17 m
Beam	6.1 m
Draught	1.9 m
Displacement, maximum	45 t
Fuel capacity	4800 l
Water capacity	2000 l
Propulsive power	2 × 895 kW
Maximum speed	28 knots
Operational speed	25 knots
Range	350 nm

Structure: GRP.
Propulsion: Main Engines: 2 × CAT 3412.

UPDATED

Tecnomarine T118 motor yacht Longitude Zero   *1989*

Tecnomarine T72   *1993*

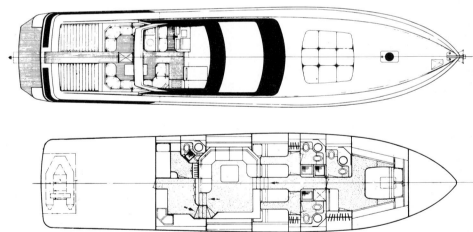

General arrangement of Super Cobra   *1991*

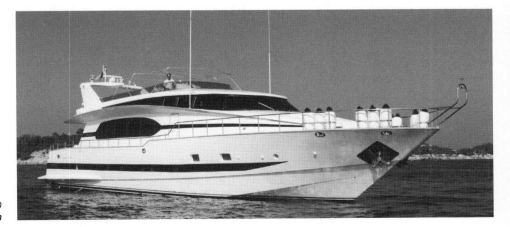

Tecnomarine T90
1993

CANTIERE NAUTICO VERSILCRAFT Srl

Via dei Pescatori 64, Viareggio (LU), Italy

Telephone: +39 (584) 384946
Telex: 624198 VERSIL I

Marketing
Versil Marine SA
Hinterbergstrasse 21, CH-6330 Cham-Zug,
Switzerland

Telephone: +41 (42) 418044
Telex: 865328 VEMA CH
Telefax: +41 (42) 416723

Versil Marine France
64 La Croisette, Palais Mirimar, F-06400
Cannes, France

Telephone: +33 93 43 56 66
Telex: 970836 VERSIL F

73 ft CHALLENGER
Principal Particulars

Length overall	22.26 m
Beam	6.1 m
Draught	1.83 m
Displacement, maximum	45 t
Crew	2
Passengers	6-8
Fuel capacity	9988 l
Water capacity	1614 l
Maximum speed	26 knots
Operational speed	23 knots

Structure: GRP.
Propulsion: 3 × GM 12V 92 TI.

83 ft SUPER CHALLENGER
Marcalec
Principal Particulars

Length overall	25.4 m
Beam	6.09 m
Draught	1.83 m
Displacement, minimum	40 t
Displacement, maximum	50 t
Crew	2-3
Passengers	6-8 berths

The Versilcraft 66 ft   *1990*

Fuel capacity	10 000 l
Water capacity	1600 l
Maximum speed	25 knots
Operational speed	22 knots
Range	572 nm

Structure: GRP.
Propulsion: 3 × GM 12V 92 TI diesel engines.

VERSILCRAFT 66 ft
Earl Grey
Principal Particulars

Length overall	19.8 m
Beam	5.6 m
Draught	1.5 m
Displacement, minimum	29 t
Crew	1-2
Passengers	6-8
Fuel capacity	5000 l
Water capacity	800 l
Propulsive power	2 × 597 kW

Propulsion: The main engines are 2 × MAN 597 kW diesels.

UPDATED

SCIOMACHEN

Via Massarenti 410, I-40138 Bologna, Italy

Telephone: +39 (51) 533043
Telefax: +39 (51) 531304

Franco Sciomachen, *Director*
Ernesto Sciomachen, *Director*
Aldo Sciomachen, *Director*

The Sciomachen name has been associated with yachts and boats since 1951. After the early years devoted mainly to sailing craft, the company's projects today encompass a full range of marine designs from high-speed power yachts to fast ferries, excursion vessels, fishing vessels, displacement yachts, as well as racing and cruising sailboats. Construction materials include fibreglass, steel, aluminium and wood, with sizes from about 7 m to over 45 m.

The company's yacht design experience is reflected in the attractiveness of its commercial vessels, where practicality is matched with aesthetically pleasing lines.

Sciomachen's European headquarters are in Bologna, Italy, while an office in San Diego, California, serves the Pacific area.

Neocastrum

Delivered in May 1993, this 35 m fast ferry was constructed at Cantiere Foschi's facilities in Cesenatico, Italy, for Foderaro Navigazione. The owners are also planning to order a sister ship to replace a 30 m vessel of similar design out of the same facilities. A third vessel is to be built for another owner.

Hull No 1 is equipped with a pair of Mitsubishi 1632 kW diesels for a top speed of 31 knots. Pass-

Neocastrum   *1993*

enger capacity is 350 with about two-thirds seated in the main deck saloon and one-third in the upper deck saloon. The Captain's cabin and a crew cabin are located just aft of the bridge. Forward of the main deck saloon, a crew mess and galley have direct access to the fore deck.

The vessel is operated between the south-west coast of Italy and the islands off the north coast of Sicily. The daily round trip is approximately 160 nm with about a three hour passage each way.

Principal Particulars

Length overall	35.4 m
Beam	7.6 m
Displacement, minimum	85 t
Passengers	350
Fuel capacity	12 000 l
Water capacity	2000 l
Propulsive power	2 × 1632 kW
Maximum speed	31 knots

Propulsion: 2 × Mitsubishi diesels.

Two smaller ferries have also been built, the 19.5 m *Neptunus* and the 18 m *Siro*, both delivered June 1992.

Recent fast ferry launchings include:
Hipponion
Delivered in May 1990.
Principal Particulars

Length overall	30.28 m
Beam	7.13 m
Displacement, minimum	52.15 t
Passengers	350
Propulsive power	2 × 1044 kW
Operational speed	26 knots

Propulsion: 2 × diesels.

Golfo Di Arzachena
Delivered in May 1992.
Principal Particulars

Length overall	23.68 m
Beam	6.11 m
Displacement, minimum	29.33 t
Passengers	200
Propulsive power	2 × 336 kW
Speed	22 knots

Propulsion: 2 × diesels.

37 m FAST FERRY
A new 37 m fast ferry is under construction at CN Fuschi in Cesenatico. The vessel is a development of *Neocastrum*.
Principal Particulars

Length overall	37.4 m
Length waterline	31.2 m
Beam	7.65 m
Displacement, minimum	90 t
Passengers	350
Propulsive power	2 × 2350 kW (diesels)
Fuel capacity	14 000 l
Operational speed	35-40 knots

40 m FAST FERRY (DESIGN)
Following the launching of two smaller vessels in 1994, Sciomachen developed an all-aluminium 40 m, 450 passenger fast ferry to IMO's International Code of Safety for High Speed Craft (Category B).

The service speed is 35 knots full load, with a top speed in excess of 40 knots in trial conditions. This speed is achieved with a triple diesel configuration driving three water-jets, although a gas-turbine propulsion system is also being considered.

In order to comply with Category B of the rules, the engine room is split into two units, capable of functioning independently from each other. Passenger accommodation is also split into three areas, protected by sprinkler systems, and each passenger has at least two routes to reach an alternative location in case of fire. A full alarm and monitoring system is installed throughout the ship. Passenger seats are designed to withstand the accelerations arising from a full speed collision.
Principal Particulars

Length overall	40 m
Beam	8.5 m
Draught	1.15 m
Passengers	450
Propulsive power	3 × 2000 kW or
	2 × 3000 kW
Maximum speed	40+ knots

Structure: Aluminium alloy throughout.
Propulsion: 3 × diesels, or 2 × gas-turbines.

UPDATED

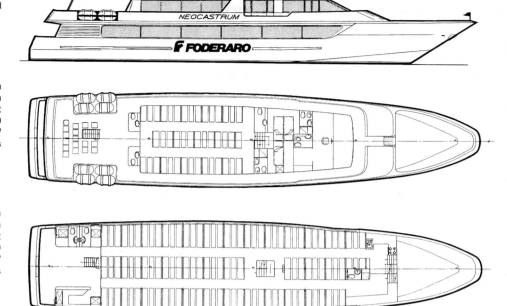

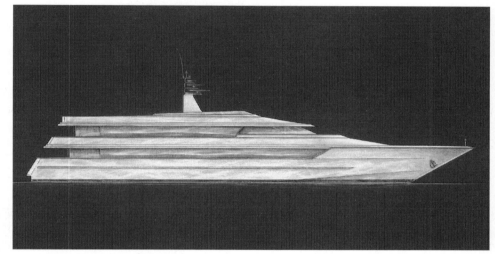

General arrangement of Neocastrum   **1995**

Sciomachen 40 m fast ferry (design)   **1995**

Hipponion
1993

JAPAN

ETOH MARINE CORPORATION

5-32 Shioya, Kurogawa-Cho, Imari City, Saga Prefecture, Japan 848-01

Telephone: +81 (955) 271288
Telefax: +81 (955) 271286

J Sireci, *Design Engineer*

Etoh Marine Corporation occupies a modern boat manufacturing facility in Imari City, completed in 1990 for the construction of aluminium craft. The company delivered the *Fuki 8*, a 232 passenger monohull ferry, in January 1994. The vessel will provide a service between Tomishima and Akashi in Japan.

Principal Particulars

Length overall	33.5 m
Length waterline	30.97 m
Beam	6.5 m
Draught	1 m
Fuel capacity	12 000 l
Water capacity	500 l
Operational speed	28 knots
Propulsive power	2 × 1200 kW
Range	600 nm

Propulsion: 2 × Yanmar V-16 Model 16LAK-STI diesel engines rated at 1200 kW each, driving 2 × 5-bladed propellers, through Niigata MGM 433 gearboxes.
Electrical system: A Yanmar 4CHL-N generator rated at 40 kW.

UPDATED

Fuki 8 *at speed*   *1994*

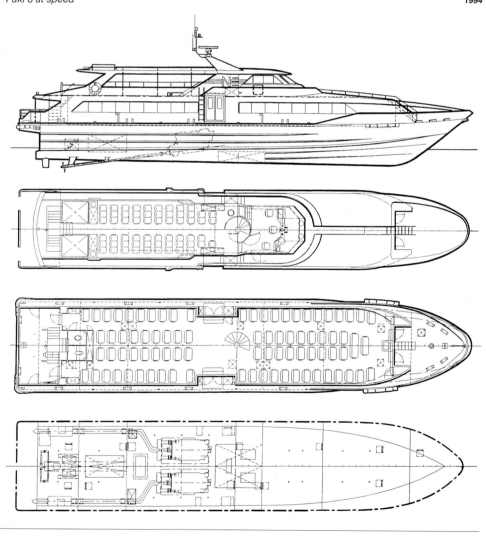

General arrangement of Fuki 8
1995

MITSUBISHI HEAVY INDUSTRIES LTD

5-1 Marunouchi 2-chome, Chiyoda-ku, Tokyo 100, Japan

Telephone: +81 (3) 3212 3111
Telex: 22443J
Telefax: +81 (3) 3212 9822

SHIMONOSEKI SHIPYARD AND MACHINERY WORKS

16-1 Enoura-cho, 6-chome Hikoshima, Shimono-seki, Japan

Telephone: +81 (832) 667989
Telex: 0682284J
Telefax: +81 (832) 661900

Seahawk

Please see the 1991 edition for an earlier built *Seahawk*.

Principal Particulars

Length overall	48.5 m
Beam	8.2 m
Passengers	301
Propulsive power	2 × 2051 kW
Maximum speed	29 knots

Propulsion: 2 × diesel engines, 2051 kW each, 1450 rpm.
Owner: Koshikishima Shosen Ltd.

Marine Star

Built in 1983 and originally in service with Oki Kisen Company Ltd, this craft has now been sold to a foreign owner.

Principal Particulars

Length overall	48.5 m
Beam	8.2 m
Passengers	351
Propulsive power	2 × 1805 kW
Maximum speed	30.7 knots

Propulsion: 2 × 1805 kW (2420 hp) high-speed diesels.

Seagrace

This vessel was delivered to its owner, Kyushu Shosen Ltd, in March 1993.

Principal Particulars

Length overall	48.5 m
Beam	8.2 m
Draught	3.95 m
Passengers	286
Maximum speed	30.11 knots
Propulsive power	2 × 2051 kW

Propulsion: 2 × diesels, 2051 kW each, 1450 rpm.
Control: Fin stabiliser, anti-pitching fin.

30 m FISHERY PATROL BOAT

Principal Particulars

Length overall	31.5 m
Beam	6.3 m
Crew	12
Propulsive power	2 × 1160 kW
Maximum speed	31 knots

Propulsion: 2 × 1160 kW engines (1520 hp) at 1840 rpm.
Owner: Yamaguchi Prefecture.

26 m FISHERY PATROL CRAFT

Principal Particulars

Length overall	26.03 m
Beam	5.73 m
Propulsive power	2 × 1160 kW
Maximum speed	36 knots

Propulsion: 2 × 1160 kW engines at 1840 rpm.
Owner: Nagasaki Prefecture.

UPDATED

Seahawk — 1992

Seagrace — 1993

Mitsubishi 30 m fishery patrol boat, Hiryu
1990

MOKUBEI SHIPBUILDING COMPANY

1-2-20 Imakatata, Otsu, Shiga Prefecture, Japan

Telephone: +81 (775) 722101
Telefax: +81 (775) 722111

Mamoru Nakano, *President*

Lansing

A water-jet-propelled sightseeing tourist boat built in 1982 for operation by the Biwa Lake Sightseeing Company on the very shallow Biwa Lake. Built in aluminium, the vessel has seating for 86 passengers and two crew. The fully laden power-to-weight ratio is 41.5 hp/t.

Principal Particulars

Length overall	22 m
Length waterline	19.8 m
Beam	4 m
Draught	0.55 m
Displacement, maximum	26 t
Crew	2
Passengers	86
Propulsive power	2 × 400 kW
Maximum speed	27 knots
Operational speed	30 knots

Propulsion: The main engines are 2 × MAN 254 MLE V12 diesels rated at 400 kW each, at 2230 rpm; driving two Hamilton Model 421 type directly driven from engine flywheel via torsionally flexible coupling and Cardan shaft.
Control: The vessel is fitted with an auxiliary diesel

Stern of Lansing *showing the Hamilton water-jet*
1987

AC generator which enables AC motor driven hydraulic power packs to be used for the water-jet unit controls. A tandem pump hydraulic power pack is used for the reverse ducts while a single pump hydraulic power pack operates the steering. At the helm, control for steering is via a wheel; the reverse is operated via a single electric joystick and two position indicators are fitted, one for the steering deflector angle and the other for the reverse duct position.

ESCORT BOAT
Kaiyo

A 25.5 m, 21.5 knot steel hull fire-fighting boat equipped to carry foam liquid, launched 19 February 1986 and owned by Sanyo-kaiji Company Ltd and Nihon-kaiji-kogyo Company Ltd.

Designer: Dr M Ikeda.

Principal Particulars

Length overall	25.5 m
Beam	5.6 m
Draught	1.1 m
Displacement, minimum	54.85 t
Crew	9
Propulsive power	2 × 746 kW

Propulsion: The main engines are 2 × Yanmar 12LAAK-UT1, 746 kW each at 1850 rpm, driving two fixed-pitch, 3-blade, aluminium bronze propellers, 1000 mm diameter, 1000 mm pitch, developed blade-area ratio: 0.90:1. Propeller shaft diameter: 99 mm, length 6500 mm; via NICO-MGN 332 gearboxes, shaft output MCR: 1000 hp at 907 rpm.

Mizusumashi II

Water quality research boat delivered 31 March 1989.

Principal Particulars

Length overall	23.5 m
Beam	4.8 m
Displacement, maximum	39.12 t
Crew	30
Propulsive power	2 × 1007 kW
Maximum speed	28 knots

Propulsion: 2 × DDC 16V 92TA, 1007 kW each, MCR, 2300 rpm; driving 2 × 5-blade propellers, 700 mm diameter, 884 mm pitch, developed area ratio: 1.0; via NICO MGN 332E reduction gearboxes, ratio: 1.42:1.

20 m COASTGUARD VESSEL
Takashima

Delivered on 31 October 1989 for operation on Lake Biwa, this vessel is owned by the Shiga police.

Principal Particulars

Length overall	19.8 m
Beam	4.7 m
Draught	0.8 m
Propulsive power	2 × 775 kW
Maximum speed	30.3 knots

Propulsion: The main engines are 2 × GM 12V 92TA, 775.5 kW each at 2300 rpm (100% MCR), 615 kW each at 2170 rpm (normal service).

UPDATED

Mokubei Lansing   1987

Kaiyo   1988

Takashima   1991

YAMAHA MOTOR COMPANY LTD

2500 Shingai, Iwata, Shizuoka 438, Japan

Telephone: +81 (538) 321145
Telex: YAMAHAMOTOR IWATA
Telefax: +81 (538) 374250

The Tsugaru

This boat was designed to engage in supervision and survey operations in Matsu Bay, Aomori Prefecture.

Principal Particulars

Length overall	19.55 m
Beam	4.4 m
Draught	0.8 m
Passengers	22
Fuel capacity	1900 l
Water capacity	200 l
Propulsive power	2 × 410 kW
Maximum speed	33.5 knots
Operational speed	29 knots
Range	240 nm

The Tsugaru *in Matsu Bay*   1993

Structure: The hull material is FRP, and is single skin.

Propulsion: The main engines are 2 × GM 8V 92TA diesels, 410 kW at 2240 rpm, 373 kW continuous at 2170 rpm; driving 2 × surface step drives.

Electrical system: 1 × 18.2 kW generator.

UPDATED

KOREA, SOUTH

SEMO COMPANY LTD

Shipyard: 1 Jangiri Donghaemyun, Kosung Kun, Kyung Nam, South Korea

Telephone: +82 (556) 723535
Telefax: +82 (556) 723570

Seoul Office: Sungwoo Building, 5th floor, 51-1 Dowhadong, Mapoku, Seoul, South Korea

Telephone: +82 (2) 702 3535
Telefax: +82 (2) 701 1780

SEMO 20 m PATROL BOAT
This boat type has been used by the Korean Office of Customs Administration for several years.

Principal Particulars

Length overall	19.9 m
Beam	4.76 m
Draught	0.87 m
Crew	10
Propulsive power	2 × 485 kW
Maximum speed	26 knots
Operational speed	20 knots

Propulsion: The main engines are 2 × DDC 8V 92TA diesels, 485 kW each at 2300 rpm, driving 2 × propellers.

VERIFIED

Semo 20 m patrol boat

1993

MALAYSIA

CHIONG BROTHERS SHIPYARD

and other yards, Sibu, Sarawak, East Malaysia

One of a number of builders of fast river ferries for Malaysian river services.

64 SEAT RIVER FERRY
Principal Particulars

Length overall	27.44 m
Beam	3.2 m
Displacement, minimum	15-16 t
Passengers	64
Fuel capacity	600 l
Maximum speed	32 knots

Structure: Cabin skin: 1.5 mm galvanised steel. Frames: 3 mm steel strip. Plating: 3 mm steel, 6 mm below engine room. Hull weight of steel: 10 t.
Propulsion: Engine: can be MAN, 260 kW (350 hp), cruise 2200 rpm, 87.5% of full power.

VERIFIED

WONG'S SHIPBUILDING CONTRACTOR & DESIGNER

3rd Floor, 27 Long Bridge, PO Box 497, 96007 Sibu, Sarawak, Malaysia

Telephone: +60 (84) 322098/331582
Telex: 72186 HWAHUN MA
Telefax: +60 (84) 331582/316310

Paul H L Wong, *Principal*

This yard reported that it had seven fast monohull ferries under construction at 9 September 1991.

Two vessels already built by Wong's Shipbuilding follow.

Ekspres Bahagia
Principal Particulars

Length overall	41.16 m
Beam	5.18 m
Passengers	250
Propulsive power	2 × 1490 kW
Maximum speed	40 knots
Operational speed	36 knots

Classification: NKK.
Structure: The hull material is mild steel.
Propulsion: The main engines are 2 × DDC 16V 149 TI, 1490 kW each at 2100 rpm, driving propellers.

Desa Intan
Operating area: Melacca and Dumai.
Principal Particulars

Length overall	40.78 m
Beam	5.5 m
Passengers	282
Propulsive power	3 × 902 kW
Maximum speed	35 knots
Operating speed	32 knots

Classification: NKK.
Structure: The hull material is mild steel.
Propulsion: The main engines are 3 × Yanmar 12LAK ST2, 902 kW each at 1910 rpm.

UPDATED

NETHERLANDS

KEES CORNELISSEN SHIPYARD

Waaldijk 11b, NL-6621 KG Dreumel, Netherlands

Telephone: +31 (8877) 2880
Telefax: +31 (8877) 2908

Kees Cornelissen, *Managing Director*

This shipyard was founded in 1978 and now employs a labour force of over 65. The yard builds fast aluminium yachts as well as larger low speed vessels.

Euroship 26 m motoryacht
1993

EUROSHIP 45.5 m MOTORYACHT

This all-aluminium motoryacht with transatlantic capability was delivered in 1994.

Principal Particulars
Length overall	45.5 m
Length waterline	39.5 m
Beam	8.6 m
Draught	2.15 m
Passengers	14 (including crew)
Fuel capacity	40 000 l
Water capacity	10 000 l
Maximum speed	26 knots
Operational speed	23 knots

Propulsion: The main engines are 2 × MTU 16V 396 TE 94 diesels, driving propellers via 2 × ZF BW 755 gearboxes.

Electrical system: Two Northern Lights 90 kW generators, one 45 kW generator.

EUROSHIP 26 m MOTORYACHT

Construction of this vessel began in February 1993 and it was delivered in 1994.

Principal Particulars
Length overall	26 m
Length waterline	21.5 m
Beam	6.25 m
Draught	1.6 m
Passengers	8
Fuel capacity	12 000 l
Water capacity	2500 l
Maximum speed	28 knots
Operational speed	24 knots
Range	1800 nm

Structure: The superstructure material is aluminium, and the hull material is steel.

Propulsion: The main engines are 2 × Deutz MWM diesels, driving propellers via 2 × ZF gearboxes.

Electrical system: Two 30 kW Northern Lights generators.

Euroship 45.5 m motoryacht   *1993*

UPDATED

ROYAL SCHELDE BV

PO Box 16, 165 Glacisstraat, 4380 AA, Vlissingen, Netherlands

Telephone: +31 1184 882973/82120/82118
Telex: 37815
Telefax: +31 1184 85010

Th P Winde, *Director of Shipbuilding*
A Van der Knapp, *Marketing and Sales of Fast Ferries*
H Keers, *Marketing and Sales of Fast Ferries*

Royal Schelde BV is well-known for the naval frigates and patrol craft designed and constructed by the shipyard. The first fast ferry produced by Royal Schelde was the SES Seaswift 23 in 1990. The company is now offering a range of SES, catamaran and monohull craft for passenger and vehicle transportation.

90 m PASSENGER/VEHICLE FERRY
(DESIGN)

This design, arranged for passenger, car and trailer transportation, was introduced in 1994. It is designed to the Code of Safety for High Speed Craft (Category A) and to be constructed of aluminium.

Principal Particulars
Length overall	103.4 m
Length waterline	90 m
Beam	15.4 m
Draught	2.9 m
Passengers	450
Vehicles	144 cars or 18 trailers
Maximum speed	38 knots
Operational speed	37 knots
Range	550 nm

Propulsion: The main engines are 4 × MTU 20V 1163 TB 73 diesel engines each driving through a reduction gearbox to a water-jet unit. The two inner water-jets are boosters only, and have no steering nozzles.

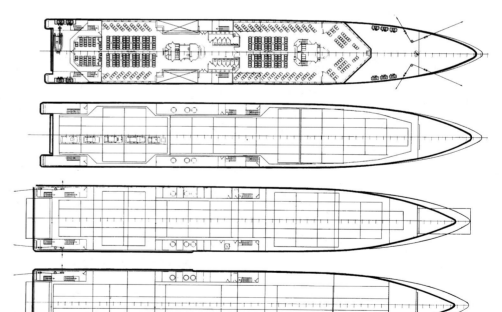

General arrangement of the 90 m passenger/vehicle ferry   *1995*

120 m PASSENGER/VEHICLE FERRY
(DESIGN)

This large fast monohull ro-ro ferry is designed to be constructed of high tensile steel and also to the Code of Safety for High Speed Craft (Category B).

Principal Particulars
Length overall	135 m
Length waterline	121.8 m
Beam	17.5 m
Draught	3.5 m
Passengers	750
Vehicles	150 cars + 6 coaches
Fuel capacity	80 000 l
Water capacity	7500 l
Propulsive power	4 × 7380 kW
Operational speed	34 knots
Range	400 nm

Propulsion: The main engines are 4 × diesel engines each rated at 7380 kW. Two diesels drive into one gearbox and then to one large booster water-jet, whilst the other two diesels each drive via individual gearboxes to steerable water-jet units. For higher speeds, gas-turbine propulsion is offered.

NEW ENTRY

NORWAY

BÅTUTRUSTNING A/S

Termetangen, N-5420 Rubbestadneset, Norway

Telephone: +47 (5) 427111
Telefax: +47 (5) 427602

Builder of many monohull vessels, Båtutrustning A/S was engaged in the construction of a 26 m 45 knot ferry in January 1989.

Askepott

Designed by Teknisk Modellcenter A/S, this three-engine 118 passenger 40 knot ferry was delivered to Per Vold in 1989. The vessel has an unusually high maximum speed capability of 47 knots.

Principal Particulars

Length overall	25.30 m
Length waterline	21.45 m
Beam	6 m
Passengers	118
Fuel capacity	6000 l
Propulsive power	872 kW
Maximum speed	47 knots
Operational speed	40 knots
Range	420 nm

Structure: The hull is GRP sandwich construction.
Propulsion: The main engines are 3 × MWM TBD 234 V16, each 872 kW max, 780 kW continuous; driving 3 × KaMeWa water-jet units, via Type 40S 3 × ZF BU250 gearboxes.

UPDATED

Askepott (Alan Bliault)   1990

MJELLEM & KARLSEN VERFT A/S

Thormøhlensgt 35/51, PO Box 2713 Møhlenpris, N-5026 Bergen, Norway

Telephone: +47 (55) 542200
Telefax: +47 (55) 542201

Paal Martens, *Vice President*
Steiner Draegebø, *Managing Director*

Mjellem & Karlsen signed a US$33 million contract in December 1993 with European Ferries Denmark AS to build a 95 m fast passenger and vehicle ferry in aluminium. This vessel is currently under construction and is scheduled for delivery in mid-1995. Mjellem & Karlsen's entry into the fast ferry market is based on extensive experience from ferries and fast naval vessels.

95 m PASSENGER/CAR FERRY

The ferry will be hired from European Ferries Denmark AS on a long-term bare boat charter by Driftsselskabet Grenaa Hundested A/S, to provide ferry service between the two ports of Grenaa and Hundested in Denmark. The ferry is scheduled to commence operations during the Summer of 1995.

The large aluminium hull will be manufactured in sections and assembled at Halsnøy Verth, a yard in the Mjellem & Karlsen group. The final outfitting will take place at Mjellem & Karlsen's main shipyard in Bergen.

One of the main features with the vessel is the very favourable payload capability that allows buses and trucks to be transported together with cars and 600 passengers.

The ferry is equipped with a bow and stern ramp system that is compatible with conventional ferry terminals and allows quick unloading of cars, buses and trucks. The six vehicle lanes run the full length of the vessel. A combination of fixed and hoistable 'tween-decks ensures maximum flexibility without too much of a weight penalty. With the hoistable 'tween-decks in the upper position, two lanes with six buses in each lane are available together with 52 cars.

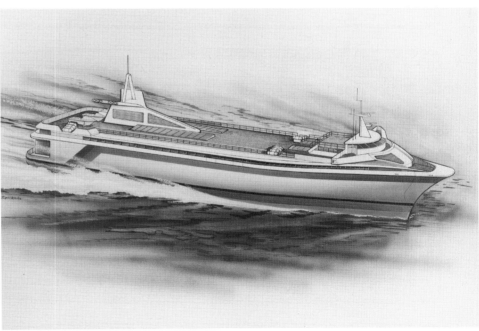

Artist's impression of Mjellem & Karlsen's 95 m passenger/car ferry   1994

Principal Particulars

Length overall	95 m
Beam	17.4 m
Draught	3.6 m
Passengers	600
Vehicles	160
Propulsive power	4 × 5800 kW
Maximum speed	35 knots
Operational speed	33 knots

Structure: The hull and superstructure are constructed from seawater resistant aluminium. The hull structure combines the use of plates and stiffeners with extruded profiles, depending on local and general strength requirements. Extensive computer modelling has been used to ensure crack resistance.

Propulsion: The main engines are 4 × MTU 20V 1163 TB 73 diesels, each producing 5800 kW at 1200 rpm; each driving KaMeWa 112 SII water-jets.
Control: All four water-jets are steerable, and two powerful bow thrusters have been fitted. Four computer-controlled fins will be fitted for stabilisation. The vessel will be controlled from an integrated bridge system.
Outfit: The passenger areas are located on one level, separated from the engine rooms by the car decks, so reducing noise from the machinery. The seating could be arranged in one or two classes either as aircraft style seating, table groups or combinations of these.

UPDATED

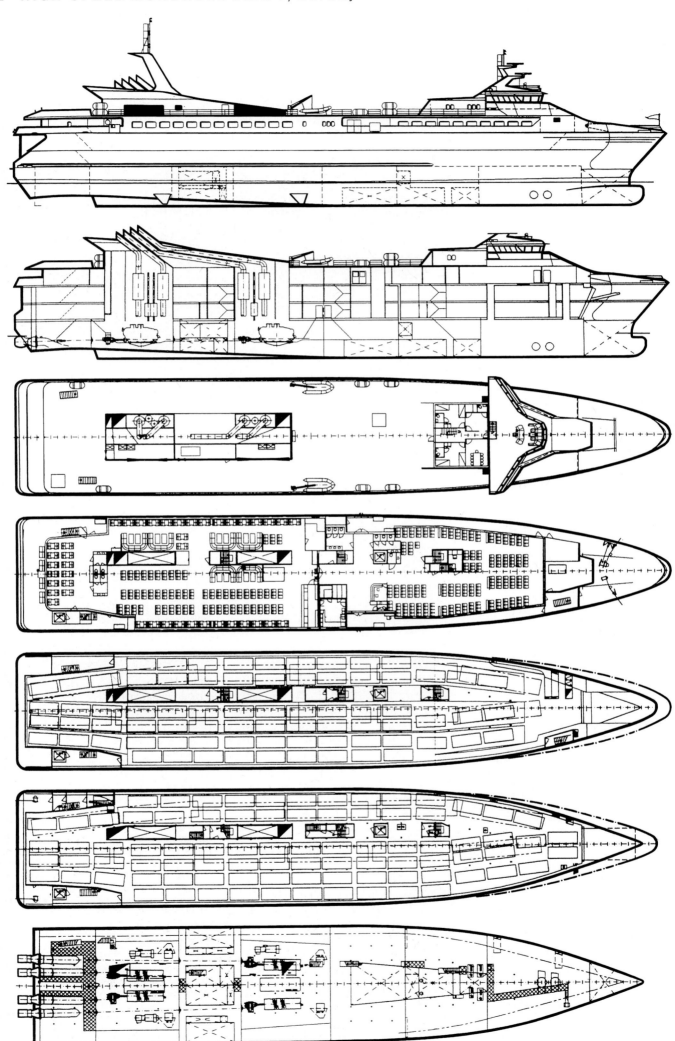

General arrangement of 95 m fast passenger/car ferry

1995

SINGAPORE

ALUMINIUM CRAFT (88) PTE LTD

55 Gul Road, Singapore 2262

Telephone: +65 862 4800
Telefax: +65 862 4803

Chang Seak Foo, *Director and General Manager*
Fong Weng Meng, *Technical Manager*
Gabriel Tan, *Marketing Manager*

A subsidiary of Singmarine Industries Ltd (a member of the Keppel Group), Aluminium Craft (88) Pte Ltd has accumulated more than 30 years of experience in the building and repairs of aluminium craft and industrial structures. It has the expertise to build sophisticated vessels such as the Surface Effect Ship, Navatek Ltd's SWATH (Small-Waterplane-Area Twin-Hull) and Lock Crowther's catamarans. Apart from its own proven monohull, the company also has a design team capable of building vessels to meet the specific requirements of its clients. It also provides a comprehensive range of repair services including jumboisation and conversion.

In 1991 two 27.5 m aluminium crew boats were delivered and two 15 m patrol boats.

27.5 m CREW BOAT
Borcos 112
Borcos 113
Principal Particulars

Length overall	27.5 m
Length waterline	25 m
Beam	6.2 m
Draught	1 m
Crew	6
Passengers	68
Payload	6 t (additional)

Borcos 112 *crew boat*   *1992*

Fuel capacity	6 t
Water capacity	2000 l
Operational speed	18 knots
Range	400 nm

Classification: Lloyd's + 100A1 + LMC for local trade limits, personnel carrier.

28 m FERRY
Delivered in the first quarter of 1993 for a Chinese owner, this 138 passenger vessel was classed and surveyed by the China Classification Society (ZC). A service speed of 28 knots is achieved with 1700 kW total output from two marine diesel engines.

35 m FERRY
Ordered by Penguin boat services in 1994, this 300 passenger vessel is scheduled for delivery in mid-1995.

UPDATED

MARINTEKNIK SHIPBUILDERS (S) PTE LTD

31 Tuas Road, Singapore 2263

Telephone: +65 861 1706
Telex: 53419 MARJET RS
Telefax: +65 861 4244

David C H Liang, *Group Chairman*
Patrick Cheung, *Managing Director*
Andrew Yeo, *Director and Technical Manager*
Susan Sim, *Business Manager*

Marinteknik Shipbuilders (S) Pte Ltd was established in 1984 for the building of high-speed vessels. To date, the yard has built more than 30 vessels of both monohull and catamaran type as passenger vessels and crew boats for customers worldwide. The length of these vessels varies from 27 to 41 m and they have a speed range of 18 to 40 knots.

Marinteknik Verkstads AB of Sweden, an associated company, ceased trading in 1994 and details of its craft are included in this entry in a separate table.

Rosaria Lauro *built at Öregrund*
1989

Craft built (high-speed monohull)

Designation	Yard No	Craft name	Owner/operator	Delivered	Engines	Classification	Payload	Speed
30 MCB (CV900)	102*	Hamidah	Ocean Tug Service	1985	2 × MTU 6V 396 TC 62	DnV R-30 Crew boat, light craft	50 passengers + 6.8 t	19 knots cruise
31 MCB	104	Zakat	Black Gold (M), Sdn Bhd, Malaysia	1986	2 × MTU, 440 kW each	GL+100A2, 30 miles	38 passengers + 13.38 t	37 knots
31 MCB	106	Amal	Black Gold (M), Sdn Bhd, Malaysia	1986	2 × MTU, 440 kW each	GL+100A2, 30 miles	38 passengers + 13.38 t	
35 MPV	107*	Discovery Bay 12	Discovery Bay Co	April 1987	2 × MWM TBD 604B V8, 840 kW each	HK Navy Dept, Cl2, Protected Waters	256 passengers	25 knots
35 MPV	108	Discovery Bay 15	Discovery Bay Co	May 1987	2 × MWM TBD 604B V8, 840 kW each	HK Navy Dept, Cl2, Protected Waters	256 passengers	25 knots
35 MPV	109	Discovery Bay 16	Discovery Bay Co	June 1987	2 × MWM TBD 604B V8, 840 kW each	HK Navy Dept, Cl2, Protected Waters	256 passengers	25 knots
35 MPV	110	Zhen Jiang Hu (ex Wu Yi Hu)	Jiangmen Jiang Gang Passenger Traffic Co, China	1987	2 × MTU 12V 396 TB 83, 1180 kW each		265 passengers + 3.12 t	27 knots contract
40 MPV-D	116	Celestina	Alilauro SpA	1988	2 × MTU, 1940 kW each	RINA/DnV	265 passengers	30 knots
35 MPV	122	Discovery Bay 19	Hong Kong Resort Co Ltd	1990	2 × MWM TBD 604B V8, 840 kW each	DnV R-25	256 passengers	25 knots
35 MPV	125	Discovery Bay 20	Hong Kong Resort Co Ltd	1990	2 × MWM TBD 604B V8, 840 kW	DnV R-25	256 passengers	25 knots
35 MPV	131	Discovery Bay 21	Hong Kong Resort Co Ltd	1992	2 × MTU 8V 396 TE 74 840 kW each	DnV R-3	300 passengers	25 knots
35 MPV	132	Discovery Bay 22	Hong Kong Resort Co Ltd	1993	2 × MTU 8V 396 TE 74 840 kW each	DnV R-3	300 passengers	25 knots

*hull built by Marinteknik Verkstads AB, Sweden and fitted-out by Marinteknik Shipbuilders (S) Pte Ltd, Singapore

Fast monohull craft built by Marinteknik Verkstads AB of Sweden which ceased trading in 1994

Designation	Yard No	Craft name	Owner/operator	Delivered	Engines	Payload	Speed
30 MCB (CV900)	58*	Hamidah	Ocean Tug Service	1985	2 × MTU 6V 396 TC82	50 passengers + 6.8 t cargo	19 knots cruise
MPV	64*	Discovery Bay 12	Discovery Bay	April 1987	2 × MTU, 840 kW each	22 t	25 knots
41 MPV	65	Cinderella West	City Jet Line Rederi AB	1987	4 × Scania DSI 14, 300 kW each	450 passengers	22 knots cruise
38 MPV	66	Cosmopolitan Lady	Private Cruise International I Ltd	1989	2 × MTU, 880 kW each	12 passengers	20 knots
41 MPV	68	Europa Jet	Alilauro SpA	1987	2 × MTU, 770 kW each	350 passengers	22 knots
41 MPV	71	Rosario Lauro, (ex Aurora Jet)	Alilauro SpA	1988			
41 MPV	72	Cinderella II	City Jet Line	1989	2 × MTU 12V 396 TB 83	450 passengers	28 knots
41 MPV	76	Iris	Kvaerner Express	1989	2 × MTU 12V 396 TB 83	350 passengers	28 knots
41 MPV	78	Cinderella	City Jet Line	1990	2 × MTU 12V 396 TB 83	450 passengers	28 knots
42 MPV	77**	Blue Crystal	Fyneside Shipping Caraibes	1991	2 × MTU 12V TBD 604B	12 passengers	27 knots
41 MPV	79	Diamant Express	Compagnie Maritime des	1991	2 × MTU 12V 396 TE 74	400 passengers	29 knots
43 MPV	80**	Northern Cross	Lillbacka Shipping	1991	2 × Caterpillar 3512 D	12 passengers	27 knots
41 MPV	83	Napoli Jet	Navigazione Libera del Golfo	1992	2 × MTU 12V 396 TE 74	400 passengers	29 knots
43 MPV	84**		BM Marine	1992	2 × MTU 12V 396 TE 94 1 × Lycoming TF40	12 passengers	45 knots
41 MPV	87	Adler Express	Hallia-und Inselreederei	1993	2 × MTU 12V 396 TE 74	400 passengers	29 knots

*Fitted-out by Fairey Marinteknik Shipbuilders (S) Pte Ltd, Singapore, now Marinteknik Shipbuilders (S) Pte Ltd
**Mini-cruise vessels

Discovery Bay 15 *built by FBM Marineteknik (S) Pte Ltd*

1988

The 265 seat, 27 knot Celestina

1989

35 m PASSENGER FERRY

A number of 35 m passenger ferries has been built to different operational requirements.
Owner: Yuet Hing Marine Supplies.
Principal Particulars

Length overall	35 m
Beam	7.7 m
Draught	1.25 m
Crew	14
Passengers	265

Fuel capacity	6000 l
Water capacity	1000 l
Propulsive power	2 × 1180 kW
Maximum speed	30 knots
Operational speed	27 knots

Classification: ZC + 100 A4K MCA and IMO code A373(x).
Structure: Deep-V forward and flat-V with flat chines aft. Constructed in marine grade aluminium T profile extrusions and plates welded by Robot MIG fully automatic welding machines. Provision is made for the main engines to be removed through two bolted access hatches.
Propulsion: The main engines are 2 × MTU 12V 396 TB 83 marine diesels, 1180 kW at 1940 rpm continuous each; driving 2 × KaMeWa Type 63/S62/60 water-jet propulsion units.

UPDATED

SINGAPORE SHIPBUILDING AND ENGINEERING LTD

7 Benoi Road, Singapore 2262
PO Box 138, Jurong Town Post Office, Singapore 9161

Boon Swan Foo, *Managing Director*
See Leong Teck, *Deputy General Manager*
Wong Kin Hoong, *Assistant General Manager, Commercial*
Tan Pheng Hock, *Assistant General Manager, Yard*

Telephone: +65 861 2244
Telex: 21206*SINGA RS
Telefax: +65 861 3028/1601

Singapore Shipbuilding and Engineering Ltd (SSE) was established in 1968 as a specialist shipyard. Current areas of expertise include the building of specialised commercial vessels, military engineering equipment fabrication and the reconstruction and modernisation of old vessels. SSE is located in a 30 acre site at the mouth of the Benoi Basin. In addition to the Swift class patrol boat described below SSE has built or have on order over 30 of its PT class patrol boats (14.54 m, 30 knots), 19 for the Singapore Marine Police, two for Singapore Customs and Excise Department and seven for the Royal Brunei Police Force; this last order was completed by the end of 1987. Please see the 1991 edition of this book for a general arrangement drawing of the Swift class patrol boat.

SSE has also completed a luxury motor yacht, 14.13 m, delivered to a Singapore owner.

In 1986 SSE completed its first air cushion vehicle, an Air Vehicles Tiger 40 and by 1991 they had delivered the 34 m catamaran ferry *Tai Ping*.

SWIFT CLASS PATROL BOAT

A fast patrol boat, 12 of which were built over the period 1979 to 1980 (Yard Nos 152 to 163) for the Singapore Navy.
Principal Particulars

Length overall	22.7 m
Length waterline	20 m
Beam	6.2 m
Draught	1.6 m
Displacement	47 t
Crew	12
Fuel capacity	7000 l
Water capacity	2000 l
Propulsive power	2 × 992 kW
Maximum speed	33 knots (Deutz)
	35 knots (MTU)
Operational speed	31 knots (Deutz)
	31 knots (MTU)
Range	550 nm

Structure: Hard chine planing form, welded aluminium.
Propulsion: Two Deutz SBA 16M 816 diesels, 992 kW each, at 2000 rpm or two MTU 12V 331 TC 92 diesels, 1100 kW each, at 2300 rpm.
Electrical system: Two diesel generating sets, each 440 V, 60 Hz, three-phase, can sustain 100 per cent ship's load.

UPDATED

SPAIN

BAZAN, EMPRESA NACIONAL

Paseo de la Castellana 55, E-28046 Madrid, Spain

Telephone: +34 (1) 441 5100
Telefax: +34 (1) 441 5090

Empresa Nacional Bazan is owned by the Spanish Government with its main activities being the design and construction of naval vessels for the Spanish Navy. The company has three shipyards, at Ferrol, Cartargena and San Fernando.

MESTRAL CAR FERRY

Late in 1992, two 96 m monohull car ferries were ordered by Companio Trasmediterranea from EN Bazan. Two further vessels were then ordered in 1994. The first vessel, *Albayzin*, was delivered from the San Fernando Shipyard in October 1994 and was immediately transferred to Buquebus. This Uruguayan company subsequently leased the vessel to the New Zealand operator Sea Shuttle in late 1994. The vessel is constructed entirely of aluminium with a deep-V hull form providing the seakeeping and powering performance specified for the Trasmediterranea ferry routes.

The second vessel is scheduled for delivery to Trasmediterranea in April 1995 with the third and fourth vessels to be delivered in April and May 1996.

The Mestral passenger/vehicle ferry Albayzin

1995

Principal Particulars

Length overall	96.2 m	Displacement, maximum	946 t
Length waterline	84 m	Crew	16
Beam	14.6 m	Passengers	450
Draught	2.1 m	Vehicles	84 cars
Displacement, minimum	774 t	Maximum speed	37 knots
		Operational speed	35 knots
		Range	300 nm

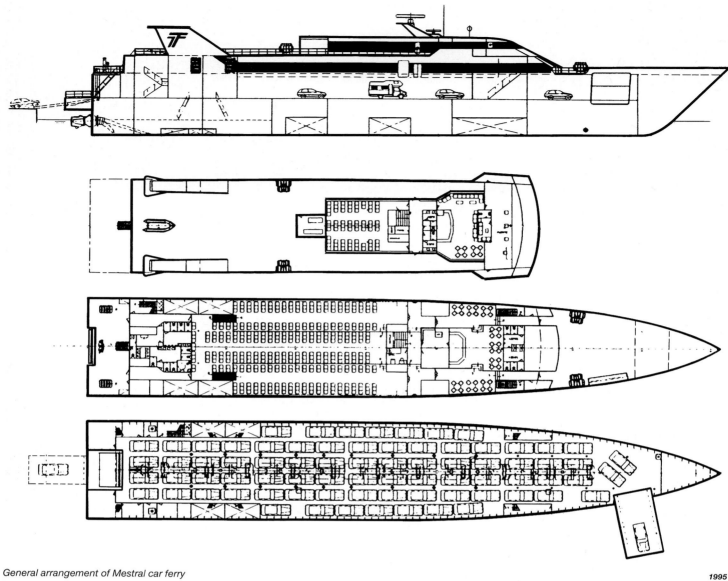

General arrangement of Mestral car ferry

1995

Classification: DnV +1A1 HSLC R1 Car Ferry A EO.
Propulsion: The vessel is powered by 4 × Caterpillar 3616 diesel engines, each driving a size 100 KaMeWa water-jet, the centre two jets being of a non-steering or reversing type.

Electrical system: Power is provided by 3 × Caterpillar 3408 diesels each rated at 270 kW.
Auxiliary systems: An active ride control system is provided on all vessels, the *Albayzin* having four Vosper Thornycroft stabiliser fins and the other

vessels having a system based on two active fins forward and two active transom flaps aft.

UPDATED

SWEDEN

BOGHAMMAR INTERNATIONAL AB

Nysaetravagen 6-8, S-181 61 Lidingoe, Sweden

Telephone: +46 (8) 766 0190
Telex: 14149 BOGBOAT S
Telefax: +46 (8) 766 1855

Boghammar International AB is situated at Lidingoe just outside Stockholm, approximately 15 minutes by car from Stockholm city and only 40 minutes from Stockholm International airport.

The company was formed in 1984 and is the international selling company for Boghammar Marine AB. The yard was formed in 1906, it is family owned and is today headed by the third generation.

Close to 1200 boats have been built over the years, some 90 per cent being of the yard's own design. Today the yard specialises in building all-aluminium constructed boats for commercial use such as high-speed monohull craft for patrol duty and day passenger transports.

August Lindholm

1993

The latest design of high-speed monohull craft for day passenger transports is the Kungsholm series. Three have now been built, *Gripsholm* in 1989, *Kungsholm* in 1990 and *August Lindholm* in 1992. The first two vessels are almost identical with some minor superstructure differences. The interior design of *Kungsholm* and its machinery and bridge are different to those of *Gripsholm*. *August Lindholm* also has two funnels instead of just one.

Gripsholm
Principal Particulars

Length overall	26.5 m
Beam	5.6 m
Draught	1.85 m
Crew	5
Passengers	125
Propulsive power	3 × 744 kW
Maximum speed	36 knots
Operational speed	33 knots

Propulsion: The main engines are 3 × MAN V12 D2842 LXE-LYE, 744 kW each at 2200 rpm; Servogear Petch VD propellers.

Kungsholm
Principal Particulars

Length overall	27.5 m
Beam	5.6 m
Draught	1.85 m
Propulsive power	3 × 723 kW
Maximum speed	35 knots
Operational speed	30 knots

Propulsion: The main engines are 3 × MWM TBD 234 V12, 723 kW each at 2300 rpm, driving 2 × Servogear CP propellers.

August Lindholm
This vessel (Yard No 1154) is the latest building from the Boghammar yard and is owned and oper-ated by Stockholm Sightseeing, a subsidiary of Bore Lines, Sweden.

Principal Particulars

Length overall	28.1 m
Beam	5.6 m
Draught	1.2 m
Displacement	41.5 t
Passengers	173
Fuel capacity	4800 l
Water capacity	600 l
Propulsive power	2 × 723 kW
Maximum speed	30 knots
Operational speed	25 knots

Propulsion: The main engines are 2 × MWM TBD 236 V12 diesels, 723 kW each at 2300 rpm, driving 2 × Michigan-Wheel propellers.

UPDATED

OSKARSHAMNS VARV AB

PO Box 704, S-572 28 Oskarshamn, Sweden

Telephone: +46 (491) 85550
Telefax: +46 (491) 15312

Curt Tappert, *Managing Director*
Olle Johansson, *Technical Manager*
Ronnie Petersson, *Repair and Production Manager*

Located on the east coast of Sweden, Oskarshamns Varv specialises in building aluminium and steel motor yachts, catamarans and military craft. The company is part of the Swede Ship Group. Craft are built in construction halls 90 × 31.5 m, 83 × 12 m and 40 × 31.5 m with overhead cranes, lifting 80 tonnes capacity. There are also machine shop and repair facilities with one floating dock with a lifting capacity of 2000 tonnes. Number of employees is about 170.

SWEDE SHIP 3700
Värmdö, Vånö, Väddö, Växo, Viberö
Five passenger vessels built for Waxholms Ångfartygs AB of Stockholm. The first vessel was delivered in 1990 and the last two were delivered in 1993.

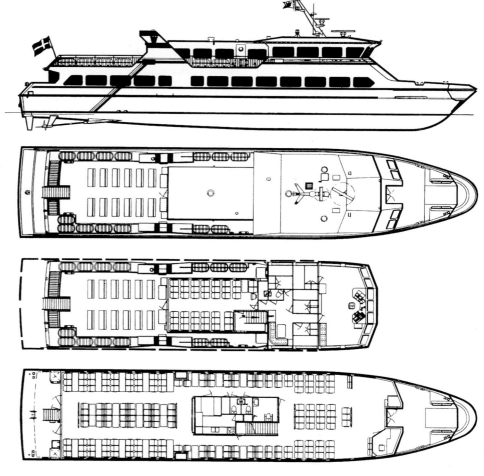

Swede Ship 3700
1995

Five Swede Ship 3700 class vessels

Principal Particulars

Length overall	37.7 m
Beam	7.5 m
Draught	1.28 m
Crew	4
Passengers	340
Fuel capacity	6000 l
Water capacity	2800 l

Propulsive power	3 × 600 kW
Operational speed	22 knots
Range	300 nm

Classification: National Swedish Administration of Shipping and Navigation.
Structure: The hull and superstructure material is aluminium, AlMg 4.5Mn.
Propulsion: The main engines are 3 × MAN D 2842 LYE, 600 kW each at 2150 rpm, driving 3 × Finn-screw fixed propellers via 3 × ZF BW 256 gearboxes.
Electrical system: One G&M 138 MDV generator, 126 kVA, one G&M 71 MDP 6T generator, 65 kVA.

UPDATED

THAILAND

TECHNAUTIC INTERTRADING COMPANY LTD

44/13 Convent Road, Silom, Bangkok 10500, Thailand

Telephone: +66 (2) 340730/9368
Telefax: +66 (2) 2376710

Capt Nirun Chitanon, *Director and General Manager*

The Technautic shipyard employs 150 people and has a total area of 7944 m², the main building occupying 2076 m². Over 52 craft in the 8 to 26 m range have been delivered, mainly patrol boats and workboats.

P86
Surveillance craft.
Principal Particulars

Length overall	26.2 m
Length waterline	22.6 m
Beam	6.3 m
Draught	1.1 m
Displacement, minimum	59 400 t
Displacement, maximum	70 000 t

Crew	14
Fuel capacity	18 050 l
Water capacity	2 545 l
Propulsive power	2350 kW
Maximum speed	27 knots
Operational speed	25 knots

P86 surveillance craft   *1990*

Structure: GRP sandwich with Airex PVC foam core.
Propulsion: Three Isotta Fraschini ID 36 8VSS engines, driving three Castoldi 07 water-jets.

UPDATED

UNITED KINGDOM

AILSA-PERTH SHIPBUILDERS LTD

Harbour Road, Troon, Ayrshire KA10 6DN, UK

Telephone: +44 (1292) 311311
Telex: 778027 AILSA G
Telefax: +44 (1292) 317613

Gregory Copley, *Chairman*
W Reid, *Managing Director*
Tom Jenkins, *Director and Naval Architect*
Alan Macdonald, *Marketing Manager*

Ailsa-Perth Shipbuilders' shipyard at Troon in Scotland has built vessels since 1886, including warships for the navies of Canada, New Zealand, other Commonwealth states, Mexico and the UK Ministry of Defence.

The covered building hall has two building ways and a 5860 m² (63 000 ft²) machine and fabrication shop for construction of vessels in steel, aluminium and GRP up to 114 m in length and 20.5 m beam.

Ailsa-Perth Shipbuilders (Typical Designs)

	Highlander corvette	Cresent/Cobra fast patrol	25 m fast patrol	13 m seek and arrest
Length overall	62 m	34 m	25 m	13 m
Beam	9.12 m	6.75 m	5.8 m	3 m
Draught	2.5 m	1.7 m	1.7 m	0.6 m
Displacement	480 t	146 t	85 t	13 t
Max continuous speed	25 knots	29 knots	25 knots	-
Sprint speed	35 knots	34 knots	39 knots	50 knots

There is a 130 m long fitting-out quay with a lifting capacity of 50 tonnes and two dry docks.

There are comprehensive facilities for naval architects and in-house technical services and an extensive collaboration programme with associated companies.

The yard specialises in designing for mission specific or general use respective of its size and speed.

Ailsa-Perth Shipbuilders offers worldwide after sales support with a flying squad available for repair, refit, training or other needs. The company can co-operate with clients to meet technology transfer, co-production or licence production needs. Technical teams can plan mid-life programmes for naval vessels to extend their service life, or can modify them to meet newly emerging threats or tasks.

UPDATED

BERTHON BOAT COMPANY LTD

The Shipyard, Lymington, Hampshire SO41 9YL, UK

Telephone: +44 (1590) 673312
Telex: 477831 BERTHN G
Telefax: +44 (1590) 676353

D O May, *Chairman*
B O May, *Managing Director*
J G Hemingway, *Director*
Dominic May, *Director, Sales*

Berthon 80' Dalvina
1990

BERTHON 80'
Dalvina

Completed 1 June 1989, this luxury motor yacht was designed by Laurent Giles Ltd of Lymington and the all-aluminium hull was built by Cougar Holdings of Hamble to Lloyd's approval and supervision.

A special feature of this vessel is the fitting of a hydraulically actuated MVS 2000 Koop Nautic roll stabilising system. With this system on *Dalvina* a mass of 1.14 tonnes can be moved athwartships across a 5 m horizontal track at up to 3.66 m/s. The movement is controlled by a computer that anticipates roll motion both underway and when stationary.

Another interesting feature of this vessel is that the superstructure is mounted on an aluminium frame fixed to the hull structure by rubber bushes.

Principal Particulars

Length overall	24.3 m
Length waterline	21.25 m
Beam	6.4 m
Draught	1.8 m
Displacement	75 t
Fuel capacity	13 620 l
Water capacity	2043 l
Propulsive power	2 × 969 kW
Maximum speed	22 knots
Operational speed	19.5 knots
Range	2000 nm

Propulsion: The main engines are 2 × MTU 8V 396 TB 93, 969 kW max each.

UPDATED

FBM MARINE GROUP

Cowes Shipyard, Cowes, Isle of Wight, UK

Telephone: +44 (1983) 297111
Telex: 86466 FAMBRO G
Telefax: +44 (1983) 299642

Michael Roberts, *Deputy Chairman*
Malcolm Keith, *Managing Director*
John Warbey, *International Sales Director*
Mike McSorley, *Sales Manager, Ferries*
Nigel Warren, *Chief Designer*
Heather Cox, *Marketing Manager*
Craig Moyes, *Sales Manager*

PROTECTOR 26
CUSTOMS AND EXCISE CUTTER

UK Customs and Excise Marine Branch placed an order for three 26 m Protector fast patrol cutters which entered service during 1988. The craft are a development of the 33 m Protector class, designed to meet the needs of HM Customs and Excise for operation anywhere round the coastline of the United Kingdom. A fourth 26 m Protector for HM Customs and Excise was built under licence by Babcock Thorn at the Rosyth Royal Dockyard in 1993.

Principal Particulars

Length overall	25.7 m
Beam	6.2 m
Draught	1.7 m
Crew	8
Propulsive power	2 × 1074 kW
Maximum speed	25 knots
Operational speed	8 knots (loiter)

Structure: Hull, deck and superstructure in welded marine grade aluminium, with integral alloy fuel tanks.

Protector 26   1992

Sorrento Jet   1991

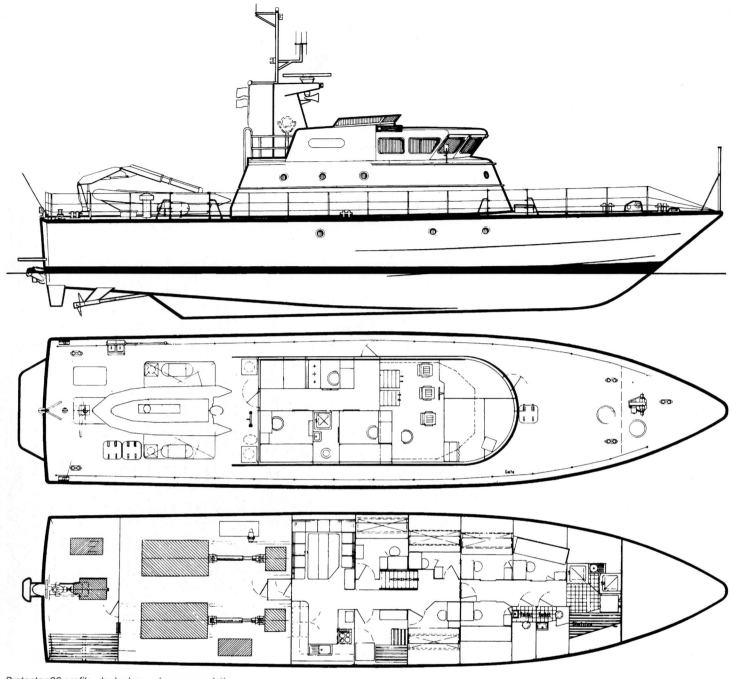

Protector 26 profile, deck plan and accommodation

1995

Propulsion: Two Paxman 12 SET CW marine diesel engines of 1074 kW each with ZF BW 460S gearboxes. These units drive two fixed-pitch propellers coupled to ZF BW 460S gearboxes via a V-drive. One single Perkins T6.3544 marine diesel engine of 159 kW driving a Hamilton 361 water-jet unit for cruise/loiter speeds.

Electrical system: Two 30 kW (continuous) diesel driven 240 V single-phase 50 Hz generator sets and engine driven alternators. Also a 24 V DC battery supplied system.

Navigation and communications: Equipment includes two navigational radars, one with ARPA plotter, gyro with repeaters, Decca Navigator Mk 53, direction-finder, log, echo-sounder, and autopilot.

One HF set and one marine 2182 kHz UHF set, telex, navtex and internal communications.

Control: Power-assisted hydraulic steering system operating twin-linked balanced aerofoil spade rudders. Primary controls are from the wheelhouse, with a secondary position on the open bridge.

Auxiliary systems: A hydraulic knuckle boom crane mounted on main deck for launch and recovery of rigid inflatable boarding boat.

Outfit: Single cabins for commanding officer and seven crew. Four cabins are fitted with pipe-cots for visitors.

41 m PASSENGER FERRY
Capri Jet
Sorrento Jet

Capri Jet, a 41 m passenger ferry, was completed in 1988 and operates on the Naples/Capri route.

A second similar vessel, *Sorrento Jet*, was ordered in May 1989 and was delivered in 1990.

Designer: Marinteknik Verkstads AB/FBM Marine Ltd.

Owner: Navigazione Libera Del Golfo SpA, Italy.

Principal Particulars

Length overall	41 m
Beam	7.8 m
Draught	1.1 m
Payload	27 t
Passengers	350
Fuel capacity	7000 l
Water capacity	1000 l
Propulsive power	2 × 1180 kW
Capri Jet	
Maximum speed	33.5 knots
Sorrento Jet	
Operational speed	29 knots

Classification: Built to rules of the Code of Safety for Dynamically Supported Craft comparable to the SOLAS and Load Line Conventions, class notation RINa is *100-A (UL) 1.1-Nav. S-TP.

Structure: The superstructure and hull are built in welded marine grade aluminium, subdivided into seven watertight compartments. A semi-planing hull with a deep-V forward progressing to a shallow-V aft with hard chines.

The extruded profiles are of quality Alcan B51 S WP. The sheets are of quality Alcan B54 S1/2.

Propulsion: Two MTU 12V 396 TB 83 marine diesels giving minimum 1180 kW each at MCR (1045 kW for *Sorrento Jet*), 1940 rpm at ambient air temperature of 27°C and seawater temperature at 27°C. Engines are coupled to ZF marine reduction gearboxes, and drive two MJP water-jet units, steering deflection angle is 30° port and starboard with an estimated reverse thrust of approximately half of the forward gross thrust.

Electrical system: Two Perkins 4.236M diesel generators each driving two 30 kVA alternators, Stamford MSC 234A.

Electrical supplies: 380 V AC, 50 Hz 3-phase, 220 V AC, 50 Hz single-phase, 24 V DC, shore supply connection.

Control: All controls and machinery instruments are within reach of the helmsman's seat. Steering and reversing buckets for the water-jets are controlled electrohydraulically from the wheelhouse. A retractable bow thruster unit is fitted.

22 m FAST CREW BOAT

The FBM Fast Crew Boat is a development of the Fairey Tracker patrol boat, suitably adapted for the rapid movement of personnel and cargo.

Principal Particulars

Length overall	21.8 m
Length waterline	19 m
Beam	5.3 m
Draught	1.25 m
Displacement, minimum	31 t
Fuel capacity	4.8 t
Water capacity	0.5 t
Propulsive power	2 × 605 kW
Maximum speed	24.9 knots
Range	550 nm

Propulsion: Engines: 2 × MWM 234 TBD V12, 605 kW each at 2200 rpm.

Structure: The hull is of mild steel with decks and superstructure of marine grade aluminium alloy.

UPDATED

McTAY MARINE

Port Causeway, Bromborough, Wirral, Merseyside
L62 4TP, UK

Telephone: +44 (151) 346 1319
Telex: 628052
Telefax: +44 (151) 334 0041

R McBurney, *Marketing Director*

McTay Marine is a subsidiary of the Mowlem Group. Although high-speed craft have not in the past been the main output of the shipyard, the company has completed two fast monohull craft. The most recent vessel was a 47 m Customs craft for the Greek Ministry of Finance, delivered in late 1994.

Chartwell

A high-speed survey vessel for hydrographic survey duties in the Thames and Thames estuary. The vessel has a longitudinally framed steel hull with an aluminium superstructure. The hull form is based on the NPL high-speed, round bilge series. The survey duties include echo-sounding, sonar sweeping, wire sweeping, marking obstructions, tidal stream observations and search and rescue.

Principal Particulars

Length overall	26.58 m
Beam	5.84 m
Propulsive power	2 × 1074 kW
Maximum speed	22.8 knots

Propulsion: The main engines are 2 × Paxman Diesels 12 SETCWM, 1074 kW each, 1500 rpm.

2 × fixed-pitch 3-blade Brunton propellers, driven via ZF BW 460 gearboxes, ratio 1.509:1.0. One PP Jets PP170 water-jet unit (for improved control at low speed) driven by Volvo Penta AMD121D diesel, 283 kW, 1800 rpm.

EUROPATROL 250

This 47 m Customs craft was delivered from the yard in November 1994. The design and build of this vessel was a result of a tripartite collaboration between McTay Marine, GEC-ALSTHOM (Paxman Diesels) and Vosper International. Vosper International provided the design of this vessel which is one of a family of offshore patrol and surveillance craft marketed by the company.

Principal Particulars

Length overall	47.3 m
Length waterline	43.5 m
Beam	7.5 m
Draught	2.5 m
Displacement	240 t
Crew	21
Propulsive power	9800 kW
Range	2000 nm

Chartwell   *1992*

Europatrol 250 on trials   *1995*

Structure: The hull and weatherdeck are of welded mild steel and the superstructure of welded aluminium alloy.

Propulsion: The vessel is propelled by three GEC Paxman VP185 diesels each driving a fixed-pitch propeller via a reverse reduction gearbox. The centre gearbox is fitted with a trolling valve to allow slow ship speeds of 2 to 4 knots.

UPDATED

VOSPER THORNYCROFT (UK) LTD

Victoria Road, Woolston, Southampton, Hampshire
SO9 5GR, UK

Telephone: +44 (1703) 445144
Telex: 47682 VTWOOL G
Telefax: +44 (1703) 421539

Vosper Thornycroft (UK) Ltd continues the shipbuilding business established over a century ago by two separate companies, Vosper Ltd and John I Thornycroft and Company Ltd. These companies merged in 1966, were nationalised in 1977, returned to the private sector in 1985, and floated on the London Stock Exchange in 1988. The company has designed, built and repaired warships of all sizes, and has always specialised in high-speed craft.

Since the early 1970s it has also developed the use of Glass-Reinforced Plastic (GRP) for warships, particularly Mine Countermeasures Vessels.

Within the past two years the company has invested in the extension and upgrading of its design and production facilities including the latest laser steel cutting and CAD/CAM equipment. Today, its shipyards at Southampton and Portsmouth on the southern coast of the UK are among the most modern in the world.

Diversified engineering work is also undertaken, including ship design consultancy for overseas builders, support services and the design and manufacture of roll damping fins, bow thrusters, water-jet propulsors and electronic control systems for marine and industrial use.

The company currently has under construction two 83 m corvettes for Oman and four 56 m fast attack craft for Qatar. Fast patrol craft designs range upwards from 30 m and the first of an updated 34 m patrol craft design has recentlly been completed for HM Customs and Excise.

30 m FAST PATROL BOAT
HAWK CLASS

The 30 m Hawk class patrol boat is designed for prolonged operation at speed in EEZ offshore roles. Three of these craft have been delivered to Jordan.

Principal Particulars

Length overall	30.45 m
Beam	6.87 m
Displacement	95 t
Crew	typical complement is three officers, two petty officers and eleven junior ratings
Maximum speed	28 knots

Structure: GRP and the superstructure is marine grade alloy both constructed to Lloyd's approved standards. Hull shape is hard chine with a moderately high deadrise, fine entry forward, and generous freeboard.

Propulsion: Two high-speed turbocharged marine diesels coupled to reverse reduction gearboxes, driving two fixed-pitch propellers; other configurations are optional.

Navigation and communications: Radar, electronic warfare and communications sets to suit operational requirements.

34 m FAST PATROL BOAT

Originally based on a 31 m Vosper Thornycroft design which was exported to many navies, the 34 m fast patrol boat has been developed using simplified construction techniques to reduce costs and enable relatively inexperienced shipyards to build an effective craft and develop their own technology.

There have been 49 of these craft built under licence by Bollinger Machine Shop and Shipyard, Louisiana, USA, for the US Coast Guard. For details of these craft see under the Bollinger entry.

34 m CUSTOMS BOAT

Developed from the earlier 103 ft, 106 ft and 110 ft designs, over 100 of which were built for many navies, the 34 m has been designed to operate all year round in the demanding environment of the UK offshore waters. It has a much improved machinery layout compared with the earlier 110 ft design and meets modern accommodation standards.

The first vessel of this improved design, HMCC *Sentinel*, entered service with the UK Customs and Excise on 3 December 1993.

Principal Particulars

Length overall	34.95 m
Length waterline	31.5 m
Beam	7.2 m
Draught	1.9 m
Displacement	155 t
Crew	17
Maximum speed	32 knots
Range	2300 nm

34 m Vosper Thornycroft designed US Coast Guard patrol boat   *1990*

Structure: The main structure, up to and including the weatherdeck and all transverse watertight bulkheads is constructed from welded mild steel. The superstructure is built from marine grade aluminium alloy and bonded to the hull by welding to an explosively bonded structural transition joint.

Propulsion: Two high-speed turbocharged marine diesels driving two fixed-pitch propellers via cardan shafts and reverse/reduction gearboxes. Trolling valves are fitted to the gearboxes to permit slow-speed main engine drive.

Auxiliary (Loiter) propulsion is provided and is a water-jet propulsor driven by an independent marine diesel.

Operations equipment: Light weapons, radar and passive sensors to suit operational requirements.

UPDATED

Vosper Thornycroft 30 m patrol boat on trials   *1994*

34 m Customs Boat Sentinel   *1995*

UNITED STATES OF AMERICA

ADMIRAL MARINE WORKS INC

919 Haines Street, Port Townsend, Washington, WA 98368, USA

Telephone: +1 (206) 385 4670
Telefax: +1 (206) 385 4256

D Wakefield, *President*
C McKinney, *Partner*
K Speer, *Partner*

Admiral Marine is a privately owned business specialising in the construction of high performance pleasure craft up to 60 m in length. The shipbuilding facility is based in Port Townsend at the entrance to Puget Sound.

MY Evvina

This vessel is the largest to have been built at Admiral Marine Works and was delivered in late 1993.

Principal Particulars

Length overall	48.8 m
Length waterline	40.2 m
Beam	9.2 m
Draught	2.4 m
Displacement, minimum	190 t
Displacement, maximum	245 t
Fuel capacity	74 000 l
Water capacity	4900 l
Maximum speed	30 knots
Range	6000 nm (12 knots)

Structure: The craft superstructure and interior is constructed of fibre reinforced plastic with extensive use of Nomex honeycomb and Kevlar fibre reinforcement. The main hull construction uses Airex foam core with polyester resin and glass fibre reinforced skins.

Propulsion: The vessel is powered by two MTU 16V 396 TB 94 diesel engines each driving through a ZF reverse reduction gearbox to a Lips fixed-pitch propeller.

UPDATED

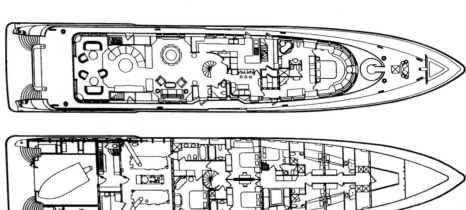

General arrangement of MY Evvina
1995

ALUMINUM BOATS INC
A company of the Trinity Marine Group
Crown Point, Louisiana, USA

25.9 m CREW BOAT
Osco Satria
Osco Perkasa

These fast crew boats delivered in August and September 1991 will seat 15 passengers inside and carry drilling supplies on their aft decks. Each vessel is equipped with a pollution control system consisting of oil spill dispersant tanks and two 3 m dispersant spray arms. In addition to the internal carbon dioxide and foam systems, external fire-fighting capabilities are added by two fire monitors provided aft. The two vessels are to operate in Indonesia.

Principal Particulars

Length overall	25.9 m
Length waterline	23.24 m
Draught	0.89 m
Beam	5.1 m
Displacement	43.4 t
Propulsive power	2 × 716 kW
Operational speed	30 knots

Propulsion: The main engines are 2 × DDC 16V 92TA diesels, 716 kW each, at 2100 rpm, driving through ZF Mod. BW 255, ratio 2.33:1 gearboxes.

26 m CREW BOAT
Maleo

This vessel was delivered in 1994 and outfitted for crew support, fire-fighting and oil dispersing duties.

Principal Particulars

Length overall	26 m
Beam	6.1 m
Draught	1.37 m
Payload	16 t
Crew	6
Passenger	45
Fuel capacity	15 000 l
Water capacity	2700 l
Maximum speed	26 knots
Operational speed	21 knots

Propulsion: Two Caterpillar 3412 DITA 500 kW diesels each driving a fixed-pitch propeller via a Twin Disc MG 518 reverse reduction gearbox.

Auxiliary systems: The vessel is equipped with a 20 000 l foam tank and a 1000 l oil dispersant tank with fire monitors and oil dispersant spray arms.

Majestic Princess
1992

Oil Sagbama
1995

26.2 m CREW BOAT
Abeer Three

Announced in October 1992 this vessel was the 25th designed and built by Aluminum Boats. *Abeer Three* is American Bureau of Shipping (ABS) certified and complies with US Coast Guard requirements. Delivered to Barberlines Arabian Navigation and Shipping Company Ltd of Saudi Arabia it replaces another Aluminum Boats vessel of the same name which was sold by its owners.

Principal Particulars

Length overall	26.2 m
Beam	6 m
Draught	1.7 m
Propulsive power	2 × 820 kW

Propulsion: The main engines are 2 × DDC 16V 92TA diesels, 820 kW each, at 2300 rpm; driving 2 × Rolla Nibral 5-blade propellers, through ZF gearboxes.
Electrical system: 2 × Kato 40 kW generators.

27 m PASSENGER FERRY
Greatland

This all-aluminium vessel was delivered to Kenai Tours, Seward, Alaska, in September 1992. The boat operates on the waterways and coastlines of national parks in Alaska as a sightseeing vessel.

Principal Particulars

Length overall	27.1 m
Beam	7.3 m
Fuel capacity	13 250 l
Water capacity	1900 l

Propulsion: The main engines are 2 × DDC 12V 92TA diesels, driving through ZF gearboxes.
Electrical system: The power is supplied by 2 × Northern Lights generators, 33 kW and 12 kW.

30.5 m FERRY
Majestic Princess

Operated by the Boston Harbor Commuter Service, the *Majestic Princess* is a high-speed ferry during the day and a dinner cruiser at night. The middle row of seats on the main deck is easily removed to provide floor space for dancing, bar and buffet tables.

The present operation is a 9.8 mile route between Boston's old Hingham Shipyard and Rowes Wharf; a water shuttle to Boston's Logan Airport is also operated.

26 m crew boat Maleo *1995*

Principal Particulars

Length overall	30.5 m
Beam	7.8 m
Passengers	325
Operational speed	30 knots

Propulsion: The main engines are 4 × DDC 12V 71TI diesels; Columbian Bronze propellers, via Twin Disc 514, 2:1 ratio gearboxes.
Electrical system: The generators are 2 × DDC 371, 75 kW.

32 m RESCUE BOAT
Oil Sagbama
Oil Siluko

These vessels were completed in late 1994, and delivered under their own power from the Aluminum Boats yard to Bonny in Nigeria where they operate. In addition to serving in an offshore role to accommodate 90 evacuees and seven crew members, the vessels are equipped to fight fires, disperse oil, tow up to 15 tonnes and rescue and retrieve people from the sea. Two 10 m spray arms can disperse 800 gallons/min of water and foam mixture from a 10 000 l foam tank.

The vessels are owned by O. I. L. Ltd of Woking, UK.

Principal Particulars

Length overall	31.85 m
Beam	7.16 m
Draught	1.6 m
Crew	7
Passengers	90
Fuel capacity	22 000 l
Water capacity	4800 l
Propulsive power	2 × 570 kW

Propulsion: The vessel is powered by two Caterpillar 3412 D1TA diesels developing 570 kW each at 2100 rpm. Each engine drives a five-bladed fixed-pitch propeller via a Twin Disc MG 518 reverse/reduction gearbox.

UPDATED

BLOUNT MARINE CORPORATION

461 Water Street, Warren, Rhode Island 02885, USA

Telephone: +1 (401) 245 8300
Telefax: +1 (401) 245 8303

Luther H Blount, *President*
Marcia L Blount, *Executive Vice President*
Ronald Baer, *Works Manager*

Blount Marine Corporation was formed in 1952 and, as of December 1994, had designed and built 300 vessels ranging in size from 5 to 80 m. Among the many types built has been the world's first small stern trawler and a significant number of all types of passenger/commuter vessels including mini-cruise ships, making Blount Marine one of the best known small passenger-boat builders in the USA. The Hitech composite hull was invented by Luther Blount.

Hitech Express

Hull No 251, Design No P452
A multipurpose craft design started in 1983 and built in 1984. The vessel has been granted USCG Certification for 149 passengers. Two smaller versions have been built.

Hitech Express has been engaged in demonstrating reliable, fast economical commuting service in the USA. It has made five runs to New York City from Warren, Rhode Island, a distance of 150 miles, in just over five hours (November 1984, May 1985, June 1985). It has made the run from the Battery, New York, to Staten Island fully loaded in 10 minutes, against 28 minutes via conventional ferry; also crossed the Hudson at mid-Manhattan in 2 minutes 46 seconds (in November 1984 and June 1985).

Principal Particulars

Length overall	23.48 m
Length waterline	22.66 m
Beam	6.1 m
Draught	1.12 m

Blount Marine Hitech Express *1993*

Displacement, maximum	56.39 t
Displacement, minimum	23.87 t
Payload	15 t
Crew	2
Passengers	149
Fuel capacity	1923 l
Propulsive power	2 × 380 kW
Maximum speed	27.8 knots

Operational speed	24.3 knots
Operational limitation	1.5 m waves
	4-5 Beaufort
Range	250 nm

Structure: Aluminium structural frames, bulkheads and decks with polyurethane foam sprayed over and a layed up glass fibre skin ¼ to ⅛ in thick forming the outer hull covering.

Propulsion: 2 × GM 12V-71 TI, 380 kW at 2300 rpm (each), driving 2 × 711 mm diameter, 622 mm pitch Columbian Bronze propellers.

Electrical system: Two 60 A alternators, one on each main engine providing 32 V DC power throughout vessel. Engine room area available for optional generator.

UPDATED

BOLLINGER MACHINE SHOP & SHIPYARD INC

PO Box 250, Lockport, Louisiana 70374, USA

Telephone: +1 (504) 532 2554
Telex: 584127

Richard Bollinger, *President*
George Bollinger, *General Manager*
Donald T Bollinger, *Chairman and CEO.*

Founded in 1946, Bollinger expanded from a machine shop/repair facility to building offshore workboats for the oil industry. In August 1985, the company was awarded a contract to build 16 of the Island class patrol boats for the US Coast Guard. The hull is the well proven 33.50 m patrol boat design by Vosper Thornycroft (UK) Ltd and the superstructure has been adapted to meet US Coast Guard operational requirements. All 16 vessels were successfully delivered by the end of June 1987.

In February 1987, Bollinger was awarded an additional 21 Island class (B class) patrol boats for the US Coast Guard. The 18th vessel of the 21 vessel order was delivered in September 1989 and the remaining vessels were delivered at 35 day intervals. A further 12 vessels were on order in January 1990.

ISLAND CLASS 33 m PATROL BOAT

Principal Particulars

Length overall	33.52 m
Beam overall	6.4 m
Draught	1.98 m
Displacement	167.76 t (A class)
	153 t (B class)
	137 t (C class)
Crew	18
Fuel capacity	39 295 l
Water capacity	6661 l
Propulsive power	2 × 4020 kW
Operational speed	26 knots
Maximum speed	26+ knots
Range	3928 nm

Structure: Designed by Vosper Thornycroft (UK) Ltd and built in steel with an aluminium superstructure.

Propulsion: Two Paxman Valenta 16RP 200M V type; 4020 kW at 1500 rpm (max), 2170 kW at 802 rpm (max). Engines are coupled to Zahnradfabrik (ZF) gearboxes, ratio 1.87:1. These drive two Vosper Thornycroft 5-blade (skewed) propellers,

1257 mm diameter, 1066 to 1549 mm pitch (0.7R).
Electrical system: Two Caterpillar 3304T, 99 kW generators.
Control: Vosper Thornycroft steering system. Paxman engine controls.

NAMED ISLAND CLASS 33 m PATROL BOATS

Forty-nine of these Vosper Thornycroft (UK) designed boats have now been named:

1301	*Farallon*
1302	*Manitou*
1303	*Matagorda*
1304	*Maui*
1305	*Monhegan*
1306	*Nunivak*
1307	*Ocracoke*
1308	*Vashon*
1309	*Aquidneck*
1310	*Mustang*
1311	*Naushon*
1312	*Sanibel*
1313	*Edisto*
1314	*Sapelo*
1315	*Matincus*
1316	*Nantucket*
1317	*Attu*
1318	*Baranof*
1319	*Chandeleur*
1320	*Chincoteague*
1321	*Cushing*
1322	*Cuttyhunk*
1323	*Drummond*
1324	*Key Largo*
1325	*Metomkin*
1326	*Monomoy*
1327	*Orcas*
1328	*Padre*
1329	*Sitkinak*
1330	*Tybee*
1331	*Washington*
1332	*Wrangell*
1333	*Adak*
1334	*Liberty*
1335	*Anacapa*
1336	*Kiska*
1337	*Assateague*
1338	*Grand Isle*
1339	*Key Biscayne*
1340	*Jefferson Island*
1341	*Kodiak Island*
1342	*Long Island*
1343	*Bainbridge Island*
1344	*Block Island*
1345	*Staten Island*
1346	*Roanoke Island*
1347	*Knight Island*
1348	*Mackinac Island*
1349	*Galvaeston Island*

Vessel Nos 1344 to 1349 inclusive were launched between May and November 1991.

52 m COASTAL PATROL BOAT

Designated primarily to fulfil coastal patrol, surveillance and interdiction roles and special warfare missions, the PC class was originally awarded by Naval Sea Systems Command to Bollinger in August 1990, as an eight vessel contract. A further five vessels were ordered in July 1991.

Based on an existing Vosper Thornycroft patrol craft hull platform, this multi-mission ship was modified to suit US Navy operational requirements.

Principal Particulars

Length overall	51.81 m
Beam	7.92 m
Draught	<2.4 m
Displacement	334 t
Fuel	48 500 l
Maximum speed	35 knots
Range	2500+ nm at 12 knots
Operational limitation	Sea State 5

Structure: Hull: steel.
Main deck: steel.
Superstructure: aluminium.

52 m Coastal Patrol Boats built

Ship name	Hull no	Delivery
USS *Cyclone*	PC-1	19 Feb 1993
USS *Tempest*	PC-2	21 May 1993
USS *Hurricane*	PC-3	21 Jul 1993
USS *Monsoon*	PC-4	20 Sep 1993
USS *Typhoon*	PC-5	29 Nov 1993
USS *Sirocco*	PC-6	28 Feb 1993
USS *Squall*	PC-7	9 May 1994
USS *Zephyr*	PC-8	16 Aug 1994
USS *Chinook*	PC-9	11 Nov 1994
USS *Firebolt*	PC-10	2 Feb 1995
USS *Whirlwind*	PC-11	11 Apr 1995
USS *Thunderbolt*	PC-12	20 Jun 1995
USS *Shamar*	PC-13	5 Sep 1995

UPDATED

Island class 33 m Patrol Boat Washington (Hull No 1331)   *1994*

United States Navy Coastal Patrol Boat (Cyclone class)   *1994*

BREAUX'S BAY CRAFT INC

PO Box 306, Loreauville, Louisiana 70552, USA

Telephone: +1 (318) 229 4246/7
Telefax: +1 (318) 229 8332

Roy Breaux, Jr, *President*
Royce Breaux, *Chairman and Executive Vice President*
Hugh Breaux, *Vice President*
Jerry Lagrange, *Secretary*
Velta Breaux, *Treasurer*

Agathe

Crew boat.
Owner: Compagnie des Moyens de Surfaces Adaptes à l'Exploitation des Océans (SURF), serving ELF offshore Cameroon fields five times weekly since 1982.

Principal Particulars

Length overall	34.9 m
Beam	7.32 m
Draught	1.93 m
Displacement, minimum	65 t
Displacement, maximum	100 t
Payload	33 t
Crew	3
Passengers	65
Fuel capacity	1300 l
Propulsive power	3 × 545 kW
Maximum speed	24 knots
Operational speed	22 knots
Range	1000 nm

Classification: Bureau Veritas.
Structure: Aluminium.
Propulsion: Three GM 16V-92 marine diesels, max rating 545 kW each at 2150 rpm; continuous 545 kW at 2000 rpm; driving three four-blade propellers.
Electrical system: The auxiliary engines are two generators Type Delco-GM 3L 71, 30 kW.
Navigation and communications: Two radars, one autopilot and one echo-sounder; one SSB radio and two VHF radios.
Safety equipment: In accordance with SOLAS regulations. One Zodiac inflatable and outboard.

Miss Peggy Ann

Owner: John E Graham & Sons, Bayou LaBatre, Alabama, serving the oil fields of the Gulf of Mexico.

Principal Particulars

Length overall	39.63 m
Beam	8 m
Draught	1.37 m
Crew	10
Passengers	64
Fuel capacity	36 336 l
Water capacity	70 969 l
Propulsive power	4 × 1521 kW
Operational speed	23.5 knots
Range	2160 nm

Classification: USCG Certified for 200 miles offshore ABS Load-Line Assignment.
Structure: All-welded aluminium construction with transverse non-floating frames.
Propulsion: The main engines are four DDC 12V-71TI 1521 kW (2040 hp) at 2100 rpm, driving 88.9 mm Aquamet No 17 stainless steel shafts and Michigan Nibral Dina Quad propellers 96.5 × 88.9 cm; via Twin Disc MG-514 gearboxes, with 2.5:1.0 reduction.
Electrical system: Auxiliary power is supplied by two 40 kW Detroit Diesel/Kato generator sets.
Navigation and communications: Radars, 2 × Furuno FR-810D; SSB, Stephens SEA 222; VHF, Cybernet CTX 2050; LORAN, Furuno LC-90; depth indicator, Datamarine 3000; loudhailer, Apelco HXL 1000.

Mexico III

This all-aluminium passenger ferry was delivered in April 1993 for use in rivers and protected waters.

Principal Particulars

Length overall	45.7 m
Beam	9.14 m
Draught	2.13 m
Passengers	800
Fuel capacity	23 000 l
Operational speed	24 knots

Propulsion: The main engines are 4 × DDC 16V 92TA diesels, driving via 4 × Twin Disc MGN273EV gearboxes.

Wildcat

This all-aluminium crew boat was delivered to the Pennzoil Exploration Company in 1993.

Principal Particulars

Length overall	46.33 m
Beam	8.99 m
Crew	8
Passengers	72
Payload	260 t
Fuel capacity	58 000 l

Propulsion: The main engines are 5 × Caterpillar 3412 diesels.

Miss Pearl Louise

This supply vessel was delivered in mid-1994 to John E Graham & Sons for operation in the Gulf of Mexico. Based on the earlier craft, *Miss Peggy Ann*, this vessel is slightly longer and faster.

Principal Particulars

Length overall	41.15 m
Beam	8.0 m
Draught	1.53 m
Crew	5
Passengers	10
Payload	180 t
Fuel capacity	42 000 l
Operational speed	25 knots

Propulsion: The vessel is powered by four 12V 92TA marine diesels each driving a fixed-pitch propeller via a reverse reduction gearbox.

UPDATED

Wildcat   *1994*

Mexico III
1994

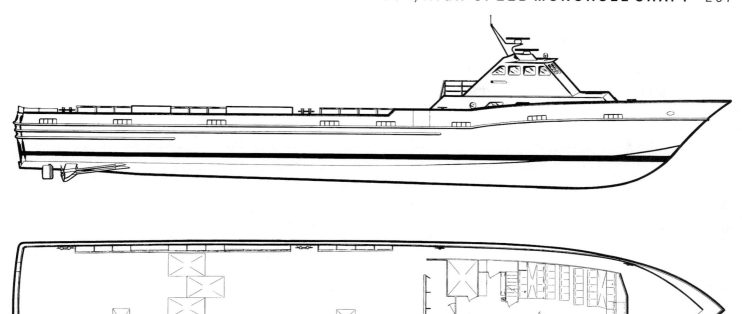

General arrangement of Wildcat

1995

CHRISTENSEN MOTOR YACHT CORPORATION

4400 Columbia Way, Vancouver, Washington 98661, USA

Telephone: +1 (206) 695 7671
Telex: 754607 CHRISTENSEN
Telefax: +1 (206) 695 6038

David H Christensen, *President*

The company builds production motor yachts of double Airex cored GRP construction; Kevlar and carbon fibre materials are also used in areas of high stress. A standard mould is used for building hulls from 29 to 39 m in length, which can be widened for different lengths and engine power requirements. Alternative superstructures are installed to meet individual owners' requirements. Unless otherwise specified, Christensen yachts are built under ABS standard inspections.

The company established a 6500 m² (70 000 ft²)

building facility in 1986 and by March 1992 had built 17 yachts and were employing 150 people working for customers in Belgium, Italy, Japan and the USA.

Royal Oak

Launched October 1988; a pilot-house motor yacht for a Japanese owner.

Principal Particulars

Length overall	39.6 m
Length waterline	35.7 m
Beam	8.2 m

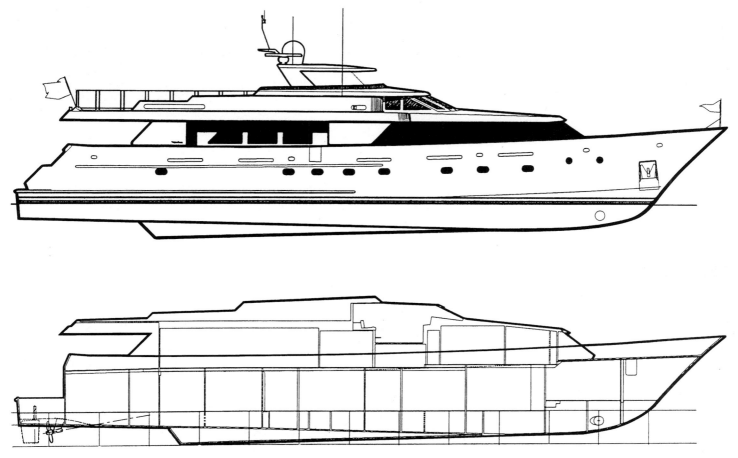

Christensen 120 ft raised pilot-house motor yacht

1995

Draught	1.8 m
Displacement, minimum	131.5 t
Displacement, maximum	172.3 t
Fuel capacity	30 280 l
Water capacity	5677 l
Propulsive power	2088 kW
Operational speed	20 knots

Propulsion: The engines are 2 × DDC 16V92TA, Model 8162-7400, dry weight 3538 kg, each

1044 kW at 2300 rpm (gross power), 932 kW at 1950 rpm cruising power.

120 ft MOTOR YACHT
Principal Particulars

Length overall	35.1 m
Length waterline	34 m
Beam	7.9 m
Draught	2 m

Fuel capacity	30 280 l
Propulsive power	1946 kW
Operational speed	22 knots

Propulsion: Engines: 2 × Deutz MWM TBD 604B V8 diesels, 973 kW each at 1800 rpm. Transmissions: 2 × ZF reduction gearboxes.
Electrical system: Generators: 2 × John Deere/ Lima 50 kW.

UPDATED

Royal Oak   *1990*

DENISON MARINE INC

PO Box 805, 750 North East 7th Avenue, Dania, Florida 33004, USA

Telephone: +1 (305) 920 0622
Telefax: +1 (305) 920 6553

Christopher Denison, *President*
Ann Denison, *Vice President, Secretary, Treasurer*
Carl Bischoff, *Vice President of Operations*
Robert Langlois, *Chief Operations Officer*

Denison Marine Inc specialises in the design and construction of aluminium motor yachts from 20 to 50 m in length. At its inception in 1983, the company integrated modern automation technologies in shipbuilding with traditional craftsmanship and attention to detail. Both conventional and modern yachts are manufactured in the USA.

Denison Marine has pioneered the use of water-jet and surface-drive propulsion in yachts over 30.5 m that exceed 34 knots. Denison has also produced the largest sport fishing boat built in the United States and also one of the largest custom yachts, the *Miss Turnberry*.

For Your Eyes Only
Raised bridge motor yacht, built December 1985, Hull No 103, fitted with trim tabs and bow thrusters.
Principal Particulars

Propulsive power	2 × 1439 kW
Operational speed	30 knots

Structure: Welded aluminium.

Quest   *1989*

Propulsion: The main engines are two MTU 12V 396 TB 93, 1439 kW (1930 bhp) each, at 2100 rpm, fitted with ZF BW 455, 2.27:1 reduction gears, driving two KaMeWa type 63 water-jet units.
Outfit: Sleeps eight in four staterooms, four berths for crew. The three guest staterooms have twin or queen-size berths, hanging lockers, drawers and

toilets with showers. Flybridge lounge area has over 8 m of seating, Mar Quipt hydraulic crane, 4.6 m Bayliner tender with 85 hp outboard and lighted helicopter landing pad. Push-button, automatic fold-forward mast to clear helicopter rotor blades. Fully equipped galley.

Recent motor yachts completed

	Dynamo V	Lady Anna	Big Bad John	Patricia	Astra Dee	Pharaoh
Launch date	1989	1990	1990	1990	1990	1991
Hull	Raised bridge cockpit motor yacht	Aluminium sports fisherman	Raised bridge cockpit motor yacht	Raised bridge cockpit motor yacht	Flush bridge motor yacht	Aluminium sports fisherman
Length overall	35.06 m	36.89 m	33.23 m	32.32 m	28.35 m	36.27 m
Beam	6.71 m	7.62 m	6.71 m	6.71 m	6.71 m	7.32 m
Draught	1.37 m	1.75 m	1.83 m	1.83 m	1.22 m	2.01 m
Engines	2	2	2	2	2	2
	MTU 12V 396 TB 83 1439 kW each	MWM TBD 604B 1919 kW each	DDC 16V 149 1790 kW each	MWM TBD 604B V12 1439 kW each	DDC 16V 149 1790 kW each	DDC 16V 149 1790 kW each
Propulsion	2 × KaMeWa S63 water-jet units	2 × turned propellers	2 × turned propellers	2 × turned propellers	2 × Arneson ASD-16 units	Props
Displacement	102 t	102 t	102 t	96.5 t	86.4 t	90 t
Berths	8 + 3 crew	6 + 4 crew	6 + 3 crew	8 + 3 crew	6 + 6 crew	6 + 4 crew
Speed	34 knots	32 knots	32 knots	30 knots	36 knots	35 knots

Quest

A bridge motor yacht completed in 1987, Hull No 116.

Principal Particulars

Length overall	31.39 m
Beam	6.71 m
Draught	1.22 m
Displacement	101.59 t
Fuel capacity	28 387.5 l
Water capacity	5677.5 l
Propulsive power	2 × 1440 kW
Maximum speed	36 knots

Propulsion: The main engines are two MTU 12V 396 TB 93, 1440 kW each, driving two KaMeWa 63 water-jets.
Electrical system: Two Northern Lights 55 kW and one Northern Lights 12 kW diesel generators.

Thunderball

Raised bridge motor yacht launched in August 1988, Hull No 114.

Principal Particulars

Length overall	33.53 m
Beam	6.71 m
Draught	1.22 m
Displacement	113.78 t
Crew	6
Passengers	8
Fuel capacity	38 985.5 l
Water capacity	3785 l
Maximum speed	46 knots

Structure: Marine grade aluminium.
Propulsion: The main engines are two MTU 16V 396 TB 94 marine diesels, driving via two KaMeWa 72 water-jets.

Miss Turnberry (ex Monkey Business II)

Motor yacht delivered in 1990, Hull No 115.

Principal Particulars

Length overall	42.67 m
Beam	8.23 m
Draught	1.83 m
Displacement, maximum	185 t
Fuel capacity	60 800 l
Propulsive power	2 × 2088 kW
Maximum speed	26 knots
Range	4800 nm

For Your Eyes Only   1987

Thunderball   1989

Structure: Marine grade aluminium.
Propulsion: Two Caterpillar 3516 marine diesel engines 2088 kW each, driving two Arneson ASD 18 drives with Rolla Nibral 5-blade surface-piercing propellers.

Electrical system: Two Northern Lights 100 kW diesel generating sets.

UPDATED

DERECKTOR SHIPYARDS

There are two shipyards in the group. They have built over 250 boats up to 36 m in length.

DERECKTOR-GUNNELL
(Florida)

775 Taylor Lane, Dania, Florida 33004, USA

Telephone: +1 (305) 920 5756
Telefax: +1 (305) 925 1146

DILLINGER 74

This vessel, completed in the Autumn of 1990, was designed by Frank Mulder, the Dutch naval architect designer of *Octopussy*. *Dillinger 74* is built in advanced carbon fibre pre-impregnated materials. A weight saving of between 2700 and 3200 kg over aluminium construction was expected.

Principal Particulars

Length overall	22.66 m
Length waterline	18.5 m
Beam	5.24 m
Draught	1.09 m
Fuel capacity	7570 l
Water capacity	1893 l
Maximum speed	55 knots

Propulsion: The main engines are 2 × MTU 12V 396 TB 93; 2 × KaMeWa S45 water-jet units.

ROBERT E DERECKTOR, INC
(New York)

311 E Boston Port Road, Mamaroneck, New York 10543, USA

Telephone: +1 (914) 698 5020
Telefax: +1 (914) 698 4641

Paul Derecktor, *President*

Dillinger   1992

Although primarily a builder of fast luxury yachts, this company is currently negotiating a contract for a number of 35 m fast ferries for New York Harbour.

MIT sea AH

This vessel was designed by Richard Liebowitz Design with Sparkman & Stephens and is the third and largest sea AH for the same owner.

Principal Particulars

Length overall	34.75 m
Length waterline	29.89 m
Beam	7.01 m
Draught	1.95 m
Propulsive power	2 × 1700 kW
Operational speed	29 knots

Propulsion: The main engines are 2 × MTU 12V 396 TE 94, 1700 kW each; driving 2 × propellers driven via ZF V-drive gearboxes, one Arneson surface drive.

S&S 105
Lady Francis

A high-speed water-jet-propelled motor yacht built in 1987, to American Bureau of Shipping Maltese Cross A1 for Yachting Service.

Designers: Sparkman & Stephens Inc, 79 Madison Avenue, New York 10016, USA.

Principal Particulars

Length overall	32 m
Length waterline	27.66 m
Beam	7.01 m
Draught	1.22 m
Fuel capacity	22 710 l
Water capacity	6056 l
Propulsive power	2 × 1462 kW
Maximum speed	31 knots
Operational speed	25 knots

Structure: Aluminium alloy, 5086 series welded aluminium, 6061 aluminium extrusions, teak main deck and boat deck.

Propulsion: The main engines are two MTU 12V 396 TB 93 diesel engines 1462 kW (1960 hp) each, driving two KaMeWa Series 63 water-jet units.

Electrical system: One 75 kW Northern Lights generator and one 30 kW slow-speed Northern Lights night generator.

Navigation and communications: One Raytheon NGR and one Raytheon 3710 radar, one Raytheon SNA9-8 colour charting IBM PC planning terminal, one Furuno F5N-70 satnav system, one North Star 800X Loran system, one Robertson-Shipmate Commander autopilot, one Raytheon weather fax system and Brookes and Gatehouse system instruments.

VHF Incom Sailor, SSB Furuno Skanti TRP 82585, 250 W, one Aiphone intercom system, Kenwood Bang & Olufsen stereo system, and ACR-EPIRB.

Auxiliary systems: Bow thrusters: Richfield 400 mm retractable hydraulic bow thrusters with two control stations.

Air-conditioning: three 60 000 Btu J D Nall water chiller units for air-conditioning throughout including engine room.

Outfit: Sun deck: pilot-house, saloon, boat deck with settees, seats and Jennaire electric barbecue Main deck: master stateroom and bathroom, entertainment centre with TV, VCR and radio, galley, main saloon entertainment centre.

Lower deck: two double-berth cabins and bathrooms, one cabin with two twin-size berths and bathroom. Captain's stateroom with double-berth and bathroom, double crew cabin with toilets and shower, crew lounge and kitchenette.

Fresh water: two Sea Recovery 2271 l/day reverse osmosis water makers.

Hot water: two 170 l hot water heaters with circulating pumps.

DERECKTOR 66
Wicked Witch III

High-speed motor yacht.
Owner: Donald Ford.
Principal Particulars

Length overall	20.11 m
Length waterline	16.38 m
Beam	5.41 m
Draught	1.67 m
Displacement, maximum	29.51 t
Propulsive power	2 × 649 kW
Maximum speed	33 knots

Structure: Aluminium alloy, stepped surface hull form, skeg on centreline.

MIT sea AH   1994

The Derecktor S&S 105 Lady Francis   1990

Propulsion: The main engines are two GM 12V-71 T marine diesels 649 kW each, coupled to 195 ZF, V-drive gearboxes; propeller shaft angle: 7°.

31 m MOTOR YACHT

Built in early 1989 this 31 m luxury yacht was designed by DIANA Yacht Design BV, Netherlands.

Principal Particulars

Length overall	31 m
Length waterline	26 m
Beam	7.5 m
Draught	1.4 m
Displacement, maximum	120 t
Fuel capacity	25 000 l
Water capacity	6000 l
Propulsive power	2 × 2040 kW

Structure: All-aluminium fully planing deep-V hull with transom stern, trim wedge, 3 spray rails and chine rail each side on bottom, flared bow, 3 watertight bulkheads. Fuel, water, oil and sanitary tanks built in double bottom.

Material of hull plating and superstructure: aluminium alloy grade 5083; remaining parts of construction to be aluminium alloy grade 6082.

Propulsion: The main engines are two diesel engines MTU 16V 396 TB 84, rating to ISO 3046/i, 2040 kW (2775 hp) each, driving two KaMeWa water-jet units Series 71.

Electrical system: 2 × Northern Lights 40 kW.

Auxiliary systems: Two 40 hp thrusters, by Cramm (Holland) mounted in engine room for low speed propulsion and manoeuvring, Schottel Bow

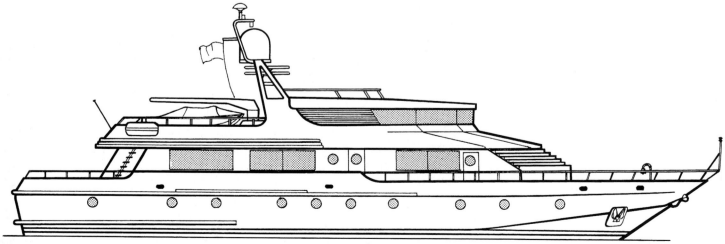

31 m (DIANA Yacht Design BV) water-jet luxury motor yacht built by R E Derecktor Shipyard   1995

Thruster, two deck cranes by Cramm, two Steen Anchor Windlass, windows supplied by WIGO, Holland.

Fire Island Clipper

Designed by Roper Associates, this vessel entered service 9 December 1979. It is built in 5086 aluminium alloy and powered by three GM 12V-71 diesel engines. The tunnel installed propellers are also protected by skegs. The craft has a length of 22.87 m, a beam of 6.71 m and a draught of 1.07 m. A full passenger load of 350 can be carried.

Fire Island Clipper is believed to be the first all-aluminium high capacity fast ferry to be built in the United States. There are nine sister vessels. *Fire Island Clipper* is owned by Wayfarer Leasing Corporation and is leased to Sayville Ferry Service, Inc, Long Island, New York.

See the *Operators* section for a photograph of this vessel.

22 m FEXAS EXPRESS MOTOR YACHT
Transition

Designed by Tom Fexas Yacht Design Inc, Florida, this vessel was delivered towards the end of 1990.

Principal Particulars

Length overall	22.6 m
Length waterline	19.5 m
Beam	5.8 m
Draught	0.92 m
Displacement, maximum	34.47 t
Fuel capacity	10 598 l
Water capacity	2498 l
Propulsive power	2 × 746 kW
Maximum speed	35 knots
Operational speed	30 knots
Range	1200 nm

Propulsion: The main engines are 2 × MAN D2842 LYE, 746 kW each.
Electrical system: Generators: 2 × 33 kW Northern Lights generators.

20 m SPORT FISHING BOAT

Designed by Tripp Design, this all-aluminium vessel is under construction in the New York yard.

Principal Particulars

Length overall	20 m
Length waterline	17.75 m
Beam	5.4 m
Draught	1.7 m
Propulsive power	2 × 950 kW
Operational speed	40 knots
Range	900 nm

Propulsion: 2 × MTU 8V 396 TE 94 rated at 950 kW each driving through a ZF BW 255S gearbox.

UPDATED

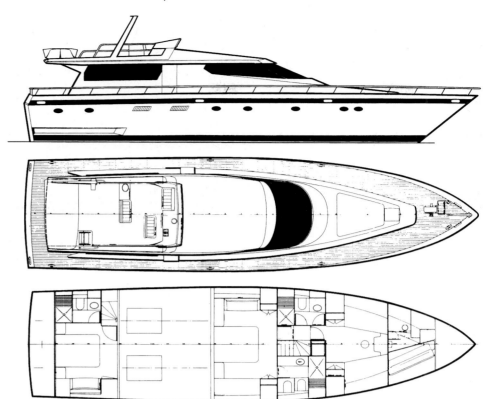

Derecktor 66, profile deck plan and accommodation 1995

Transition
1992

EQUITABLE SHIPYARDS INC

A company of the Trinity Marine Group

Industrial Canal, PO Box 8001, New Orleans, Louisiana 70182, USA
(Established 1921, acquired by Trinity Industries Inc, January 1973)

Telephone: +1 (504) 286 2500
Telefax: +1 (504) 286 2554

34 m FERRY
Kalama
Skagit

A contract valued at US$5 million was placed with Equitable Shipyards in 1988 for the supply of two air-conditioned 25 knot, 250-commuter passenger vessels for the Washington State Department of Transportation for service in 1989 between Vashon Island, Bremerton and downtown Seattle.

The 21.7 knot, 240 passenger Caribe Tide 1993

Skagit *at speed* 1990

The vessels were delivered in October 1989 but due to budget constraints they did not immediately enter service with Washington State Ferries but were chartered to the California Department of Transportation for use between San Francisco and the East Bay.

Principal Particulars

Length overall	34.07 m
Beam	7.49 m
Draught	2.13 m
Fuel capacity	15 140 l
Water capacity	2650 l
Propulsive power	4 × 716 kW
Operational speed	25 knots

Classification: USCG, sub-chapter T, ABS, under 100 GRT.
Structure: Aluminium.
Propulsion: 4 × DDA GM 16V 92TA, 716 kW each, at 2100 rpm; driving via 4 × ZF, ratio 2.5:1.0.
Electrical system: 2 × Detroit Diesel 4.71 diesel engines driving two 60 kW generators.

Caribe Tide

An air-conditioned 240 passenger ferry delivered in 1988 for serving cruise ship passengers in the US Virgin Islands.

Principal Particulars

Length overall	19.82 m
Beam	7.32 m
Draught	1.68 m

Classification: USCG.
Structure: Aluminium.
Propulsion: 4 × Cummins KT 19M, 380 kW each, at 2100 rpm; driving via Twin Disc MG 514, ratio 2:1.

24 m FAST PATROL BOAT

Equitable Shipyards Inc built and delivered eight of these fast patrol boats to the Phillipines Navy. These boats formed part of contracts with Halter Marine Inc and the US Navy, with funding coming from the US Foreign Military Sales Programme. There were also 17 craft built and delivered to Saudi Arabia.

This fast patrol boat is a new design from Halter Marine Inc which was selected after a US national competition.

Principal Particulars

Length overall	23.78 m
Beam	6.1 m
Draught	1.77 m
Displacement, maximum	57.3 t
Fuel capacity	18 925 l
Propulsive power	2 × 1044 kW
Operational speed	24 knots
Range	1200 nm

Propulsion: The main engines are 2 × DD 16V 92TAB, 1044 kW each.

24 m Fast Patrol Boat 1994

Extra Fast Patrol Boat Test (XFPB) 1994

EXTRA FAST PATROL BOAT TEST

Designed with Trinity Marine Group's expertise in patrol boat and offshore racing technology, the XFPB is an extremely stable, high-speed platform suitable for use as a pleasure craft or patrol craft. The XFPB hull cuts through water like a knife at a maximum speed of 62 knots and provides excellent handling and ride quality while minimising slamming.

The XFPB's modular design makes it extremely versatile in its potential applications. It is available in GRP, Kevlar, marine grade aluminium alloys and lightweight high strength steel.

Principal Particulars

Length overall	25 m
Beam	5.5 m
Draught	1.06 m
Displacement, maximum	49.9 t
Crew	9
Maximum speed	62 knots

Structure: The hull is deep-V, FRP/Kevlar or aluminium.

Propulsion: The main engines are Triple Marine diesels, driving Arneson Surface-Piercing Drives or water-jets.

ISLA CLASS PATROL BOAT

Two Isla class Patrol Boats were delivered to the Mexican Navy in the Autumn of 1993. Others are under contract and in construction. Built at Equitable Shipyards, these boats are derivatives of the Extra Fast Patrol Boat.

Principal Particulars

Length overall	25 m
Beam	5.5 m
Draught	1.06 m
Displacement, maximum	49.9 t
Crew	9
Maximum speed	50 knots
Range	700 nm

Classification: ABS.

Structure: The hull is deep-V, FRP/Kevlar or aluminium.

Propulsion: The main engines are Triple Marine diesels, driving Arneson Surface-Piercing Drives.

25 m SPECIAL OPERATIONS CRAFT

This vessel was designed to meet the US Navy's special operations requirements and was selected from two trials craft, the other being the Peterson/Cougar catamaran. The hull is based on the XFPB trials craft.

Principal Particulars

Length overall	24.75 m
Beam	4.72 m
Draught	1.07 m
Maximum speed	50 knots
Operational speed	35 knots
Range	675 nm

Propulsion: The craft is powered by two MTU 12V 396 TE 94 diesels rated at 1650 kW at 200 rpm, each driving a KaMeWa 50S water-jet.

25 m Special Operations Craft   *1995*

Isla class Patrol Boat   *1994*

Fjordland
Built for Kenai Tours in 1990 this vessel is almost identical to the *Greatland* briefly described in the entry for Aluminum Boats Inc, of Trinity Marine Group.

UPDATED

GLADDING-HEARN SHIPBUILDING

One Riverside Avenue, Box 300, Somerset, Massachusetts 02726-0300, USA

Telephone: +1 (508) 676 8596
Telefax: +1 (508) 672 1873

George R Duclos, *President*

This shipyard is a member of the Duclos Corporation and is known for its range of commercial workboats and fast ferry craft. The yard has built a large number of small pilot craft as well as its well-known Incat catamaran ferries.

19 m PILOT BOAT

Currently under construction, this all-aluminium Hunt-designed pilot boat is scheduled to be delivered to the Gulf of Mexico in late 1995.

20 m Gladding-Hearn pilot boat
1994

Principal Particulars

Length overall	19.3 m
Beam	5.56 m
Draught	1.73 m
Fuel capacity	3800 l
Propulsive power	1216 kW
Maximum speed	25 knots

20 m PILOT BOAT

Delivered in July 1993 to the San Francisco Bar Pilots, the boat was designed jointly with C Raymond Hunt Associates.

The deep-V, twin-screw vessel is designed and equipped to run 24 hours a day at speeds over 25 knots. The rugged, all-aluminium hull and superstructure was built with heavy-duty, low maintenance equipment, including keel-coolers and a 3800 litre remote-controlled ballast tank.

Principal Particulars

Length overall	20.42 m
Beam	5.33 m
Draught	1.83 m
Maximum speed	25.5 knots

24.5 m FERRY

Scheduled for delivery in May 1995, this craft is designed to run at 22 knots in 1.5 m of water.

Principal Particulars

Length overall	24.5 m
Beam	6.4 m
Draught	0.9 m
Passengers	400
Propulsive power	1823 kW
Operational speed	22 knots

30 m MONOHULLED FERRY

This is a new generation of monohulled fast ferries designed for fast offloading of passengers.

The first two all-aluminium vessels of this class, *Henry Hudson* and *Robert Fulton* were delivered to New Jersey-based Port Imperial Ferry Company for passenger service between New Jersey and New York City.

The third and fourth vessels *Empire State* and *Garden State* were delivered in 1994.

Monohulled passenger ferry Robert Fulton   **1994**

The vessel's unique bow-loading system safely offloads 100 passengers per minute.

Principal Particulars

Length overall	29.56 m
Beam	7.77 m
Draught	1.83 m
Passengers	400
Propulsive power	2 × 500 kW
Maximum speed	18 knots

Propulsion: The main engines are twin Caterpillar 3412 diesels, each rated at 500 kW at 1800 rpm. The engines drive two 1.07 m bronze propellers via ZF 2.57:1 reverse/reduction gears.

UPDATED

GULF CRAFT INC

3904 HWY182, Patterson, Louisiana 70392, USA

Telephone: +1 (504) 395 5254/6259

R Scott Tibbs, *President*

Gulf Craft Inc is a builder of high-speed aluminium conventional hull passenger ferries and crew boats. The *Caleb McCall* is a 44 m crew boat with a maximum speed of 27 knots. An interesting feature of this craft is that there are five engines which the owner claims gives better manoeuvrability and makes engine replacement or repair easier.

Caleb McCall

Crew boat.
Owner: McCall Boat Rental, Cameron, Louisiana, USA

Principal Particulars

Length overall	44.2 m
Beam	8.5 m
Draught	2.4 m
Crew	6
Passengers	75
Fuel capacity	45 420 l
Water capacity	75 700 l
Maximum speed	27 knots
Operational speed	23 knots

Classification: USCG approved Gulf of Mexico, 200 miles offshore.
Structure: Superstructure and hull are built in aluminium. Hull plating is in 5086 grade, 15.8 mm thick over the propellers, the remainder of the bottom is 12.7 mm thick with 8.4 mm side plating, superstructure is in 4.8 mm plate.
Propulsion: Five Cummins KTA19-M diesel engines coupled to Twin Disc MG 518, 2.5:1 reduction gearboxes, driving five three-blade Columbian Bronze FP propellers.
Electrical system: Two Cummins 6B5.8, 56 kW generators.
Navigation and communications: Raytheon/JRC colour and Furuno FR 8100 radars, Si-Tex Koden Loran, Datamarine sounder, Decca 150 autopilot.
Motorola Triton 20 SSB, Raytheon 53A VHF.
Control: Orbitrol/Charlynn steering and Kobelt engine controls. Duplicate engine controls also fitted on the upper bridge allowing operator to face aft with a clear view while working cargo at rigs and oil platforms.
Outfit: Three two-berth cabins, galley and mess room.

Annabeth McCall
Norman McCall

Two of four very large crew boats delivered in 1989 to McCall Boat Rental of Cameron, Louisiana. These boats combine increase in size (48.78 m long) for improved sea-keeping with a reasonably high speed of around 25 knots.

Principal Particulars

Length overall	48.78 m
Beam	9.15 m
Propulsive power	6 × 507 kW

Propulsion: The main engines are 6 × Cummins KTA19-M2 diesels, each 507 kW, giving a total power of 3042 kW.

Blair McCall

The previous world's largest crew boat of 47.25 m in length and powered by five Cummins diesels of 507 kW each.

Principal Particulars

Payload	200 t
Passengers	92
Propulsive power	5 × 507 kW
Maximum speed	23 knots

VERIFIED

HALTER MARINE INC

A company of the Trinity Marine Group

Formed in 1957, Halter Marine Inc has built over 1200 vessels since then and has designed and built more high-speed vessels than any other shipyard in the USA. The yard specialises in aluminium and high strength Corten steel hulls. The parent company is Trinity Industries of Dallas, Texas and the sister company is Equitable Shipyards.

The following craft descriptions represent some of the principal types of high-speed craft designed and built by Halter Marine Inc, having lengths of approximately 20 m or over with speeds over 20 knots.

HALMAR 65 (CREW BOAT TYPE)

This is a crew boat design but is also available in the following variants: customs launch, tanker service launch, pilot boat, ferry, communications launch, workboat and ambulance launch. The first of the type was designed and built in 1964 and by August 1985 112 had been built, with production continuing. The craft have been classified by various authorities including USCG, ABS and Lloyd's. Most are in service with the offshore oil industry.

Principal Particulars

Length overall	19.66 m
Beam	5.9 m
Draught	1.12 m
Crew	6
Fuel capacity	3596 l
Propulsive power	380 kW
Maximum speed	21 knots (aluminium hull)
	18 knots (steel hull)
Operational speed	19 knots (aluminium hull)
	16 knots (steel hull)
Operational limitation	Sea State 3 to 4

Structure: Corten steel, longitudinally framed; aluminium 5086, transverse framed.

Propulsion: Various options, the most popular being two GM 12V-71 TI, producing 380 kW each at 2100 rpm, driving 2 × Columbian Bronze propellers, 813 mm diameter, in Nibral.

Electrical system: 110/220 V AC, 60 Hz, generator 2-71 GM, 20 kW.

Control: Morse MD-24, manual, two stations. Steering hydraulic, 600 lb/in².

Outfit: 49 passengers and 2 crew (1 captain, 1 deckhand/engineer).

HALMAR 65 (PATROL BOAT TYPE)

Main particulars as for the Halmar 65 crew boat type but with the following differences:

Principal Particulars

Displacement, maximum	34.54 t
Fuel capacity	4546 l
Propulsive power	2 × 675 kW
Maximum speed	26 knots (aluminium hull)
	21 knots (steel hull)
Operational speed	22 knots (aluminium hull)
	18 knots (steel hull)

Propulsion: The most popular combination is two GM 12V-71 TI, 675 hp each at 2300 rpm; driving 2 × Columbian Bronze propellers, 838 mm diameter, in Nibral.

HALMAR 78 (PATROL BOAT TYPE)

The first Halmar 78 was completed in 1982 and 23 had been built by August 1985.

Principal Particulars

Length overall	23.78 m
Beam	5.64 m
Draught	1.43 m
Displacement	42.67 t
Payload	14 t
Fuel capacity	10 607 l
Propulsive power	503 kW
Maximum speed	22 knots
Operational speed	20 knots
Operational limitation	Sea State 4 to 5
Range	745 nm

Classification: Lloyd's class 100 A-1, November 1982.

Structure: Corten steel, longitudinally framed.

Propulsion: 2 × GM 12V-71 TI, producing 503 kW each at 2300 rpm; driving 2 × Columbian Bronze propellers, 864 mm diameter, in Nibral.

Electrical system: 220/440 V AC, 50 Hz, generator 2-71 GM, 20 kW.

Navigation and communications: Sailor RT-144 VHF and Decca 150 radar.

Control: Morse MD-24, manual, 2 stations.

Outfit: Captain, 2 officers, 8 crew. Below the main deck there are 4 staterooms, 3 toilets and a galley.

HALMAR 101 (CREW BOAT TYPE)

A crew boat design available in a full range of variants. Designed and first built in 1977-78, 37 had been delivered by August 1985, classified either by USCG or ABS.

Principal Particulars

Length overall	31 m
Beam	6.48 m
Draught	1.68 m
Displacement, minimum	55.88 t
Payload	30.48 t
Crew	6
Passengers	55
Fuel capacity	9092 l
Propulsive power	3 × 380 kW
Maximum speed	22 knots
Operational speed	20 knots
Operational limitation	Sea State 5
Range	500 nm

Structure: Aluminium 5086, transverse framed.

Propulsion: The main engines are 3 × GM 12V-71 TI, 380 kW each at 2100 rpm, driving via Twin Disc 2:1 reduction gears to 3 × Columbian Bronze propellers, 864 mm diameter, in Nibral (one vessel is fitted with three Rocketdyne water-jet units, two 406.4 mm diameter driven by two GM 16V-92 TI diesel engines and one 609.6 mm diameter driven by one Allison 501 gas-turbine).

Electrical system: 2 × generators, GM 3-71, 30 kW each 110/220 V AC, 60 Hz.

Navigation and communications: VHF, Sailor 144, SSB, Motorola, Radar, Decca D-150 36 mile range.

Control: Kobelt, pneumatic, 2 stations.

Halmar 65 20 knot crew boat, one of over 120 built 1986

Halmar 65 type patrol boats 1986

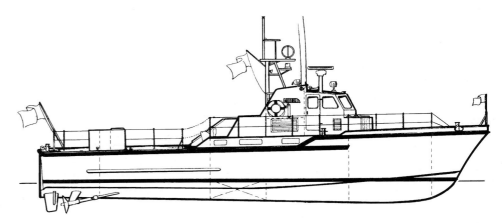

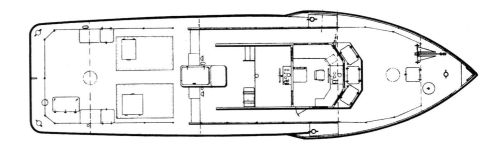

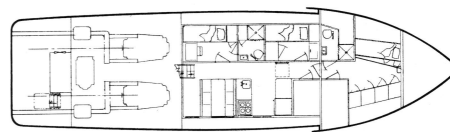

General arrangement of Halmar 65 type patrol boat 1995

Hebah
Marwa
Daina

The first of these three all-aluminium crew boats for Marine and Transportation Services, Saudi (Ltd) Damman, Saudi Arabia, was delivered in October 1988.

Principal Particulars

Length overall	33.74 m
Beam	6.61 m
Passengers	25
Fuel capacity	12 870 l
Water capacity	3785 l

Propulsion: The main engines are Detroit Diesel 12V-71 TI, 380 kW (510 hp) each, at 2100 rpm; driving through Twin Disc MG 514, ratio 2:1.

Halmar 78 crew boat Oil Conveyor II   *1987*

The ATCO Hebah, *25 passenger, 25 tonne cargo, crew boat built by Halter Marine Inc*   *1990*

Halter Marine 24 m patrol boat built for Republic of China Customs   *1994*

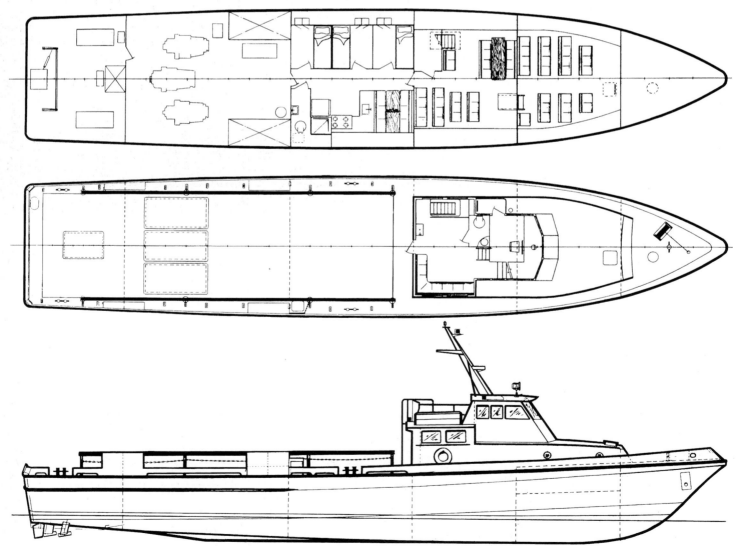

General arrangement of Halmar 101   *1995*

24 m PATROL BOAT

This craft was built by Halter Marine for the Republic of China (Taiwan) Customs.

Principal Particulars

Length overall	23.8 m
Beam	5.6 m
Draught	1.5 m
Crew	10
Operational speed	24 knots

Structure: The hull is aluminium.

Propulsion: The main engines are twin Marine diesels, driving 2 × Columbian Bronze propellers (4-bladed).

UPDATED

Halmar 122 deep-V hull crew boat
1986

MAGNUM MARINE CORPORATION

2900 Northeast 188th Street, North Miami Beach, Florida 33180, USA

Telephone: +1 (305) 931 4292
Telefax: +1 (305) 931 0088

Mrs Katrin Theodoli, *President and CEO*

Magnum Marine specialises in the construction of high performance, offshore pleasure and patrol craft from 8 to 21 m in length.

Magnum patrol craft are in service with the US Marine Patrol, US Customs, US Coast Guard and many other non-US agencies.

MAGNUM 63

This boat is built in accordance with the requirements of Lloyd's Register of Shipping and the American Bureau of Shipping. By August 1989 a total of 14 had been built; the first was completed in 1985. In August 1986 the Magnum 63 won the 370 mile Miami to Nassau to Miami offshore race. In 1987 a new and faster version of this Magnum 63 was developed and Magnum again won the race. The craft can be fitted out as a patrol boat. A flybridge version was shipped to Japan in November 1987.

Principal Particulars

Length overall	19.2 m
Length waterline	16.31 m
Beam	5.28 m
Draught	0.91 m
Crew	9
Fuel capacity	4320 l
Water capacity	720 l
Propulsive power	2 × 1074 kW
Maximum speed	52 knots
Range	400-500 nm

Magnum 70
1992

Structure: The boat is basically a four-piece construction consisting of a hull, deck, forward inner liner and cockpit liner, all laminated in GRP or for additional weight-saving the lamination can be of Du Pont Kevlar. Interiors may be built of Kevlar and Nomex honeycomb composite materials. Deadrise aft is 24°.

Propulsion: The main engines are 2 × DD 16V 92TA, 1074 kW each, driving 2 × Arneson surface drive SP2000 propeller units.

Electrical system: 8 × 12 V, 200 Ah batteries, four for each engine; 60 A engine driven alternators; 12 V and 24 V DC system; 100/220 V 60 Hz AC system; two automatic 60 A converters; Onan diesel generator, 7.5 kW.

MAGNUM 63 (1987 VERSION)
Maltese Magnum

Principal Particulars

Length overall	19.2 m
Beam	5.18 m
Draught	0.91 m
Fuel capacity	4542 l
Water capacity	946 l
Crew	6-10
Propulsive power	2 × 1380 kW
Maximum speed	65.8 knots

Structure: Constructed in Du Pont Kevlar, superstructure to suit individual requirements.

Propulsion: The main engines are 2 × CRM marine diesels, 1380 kW each at 2075 rpm coupled to two

1987 version of Magnum Marine 63, Maltese Magnum, *winner of the 1987 Miami to Nassau to Miami sea race at an average of 51 knots over 314.77 nm* **1988**

Arneson drives via 1.18:1 reduction gearboxes, driving 2 × five-blade Nibral propellers, 838 mm diameter, 143 mm pitch.

MAGNUM 70

The largest boat displayed at the 1991 Miami International Boat Show was the 21.34 m Magnum 70 Superyacht. This boat is built in Kevlar and in the standard version is powered by two Detroit Diesel 16V 92TA diesels.

Principal Particulars

Length overall	21.34 m
Beam	5.18 m
Draught	1.83 m
Crew	1-2
Passengers	6-8
Fuel capacity	4543 l
Water capacity	946 l
Propulsive power	2 × 1044 kW
Maximum speed	39 knots (standard shaft)
	48 knots (Arneson)
Operational speed	35 knots (standard shaft)
	44 knots (Arneson)

Propulsion: The standard engines are 2 × DDC 16V 92TA, 1044 kW each.

MAGNUM 90

A 27 m production motor yacht delivered in the Spring of 1992 with the same performance as the Magnum 70. The standard version is equipped with three Detroit Diesel 16V 92TA diesels coupled to Arneson surface drives. Lycoming gas-turbines can also be installed in the Magnum 90.

UPDATED

MUNSON MANUFACTURING INC

150 West Dayton Street, Edmonds, Washington 98020, USA

Telephone: +1 (202) 776 8222
Telefax: +1 (202) 672 0395

Christopher D Barry, *Chief Naval Architect*

Munson Manufacturing Inc produces high-speed aluminium craft up to 25 m in length and completed its first catamaran, a 15.24 m Hammercat, in 1991. The company is developing a high-speed vessel concept based on a proprietary hybrid hydrofoil system.

RIVER EXCURSION BOAT
Yukon Queen

Owned by Westours Inc the *Yukon Queen* operates on the Yukon River between Circle in Alaska and Dawson in Canada's Yukon Territory.

Principal Particulars

Length overall	19.5 m
Beam	5.18 m
Draught	0.84 m
Passengers	49
Fuel capacity	4353 l
Water capacity	1325 l
Propulsive power	3 × 410 kW
Maximum speed	26.8 knots
Operational speed	23 knots

Propulsion: The main engines are 3 × Lugger 6140A, 410 kW each, 2100 rpm, 6-cylinder turbocharged after-cooled in-line diesels, driving Hamilton 361 water-jets.

Yukon Queen *built by Munson Manufacturing Inc*   1992

20 m PASSENGER VESSEL

This vessel is owned by Lake Chelan Boat Company of Chelan, Washington.

Principal Particulars

Length overall	19.81 m
Beam	6.3 m
Draught	1 m
Displacement, maximum	40.64 t
Crew	100
Fuel capacity	1893 l
Propulsive power	2 × 805 kW
Maximum speed	30 knots
Operational speed	24 knots
Range	113 nm

Propulsion: The main engines are 2 × DDC 12V 92, 805 kW each, at 2300 rpm.

UPDATED

PETERSON BUILDERS INC

101 Pennsylvania Street, PO Box 650, Sturgeon Bay, Wisconsin 54235-0650, USA

Telephone: +1 (414) 743 5574
Telex: 263423
Telefax: +1 (414) 743 4784

Ellsworth L Peterson, *President and General Manager*
Allen A Powell, *Director Business Development*

Established builders of patrol boats and Mine CounterMeasure ships (MCMs), Peterson Builders has launched twelve 68 m MCM ships and one 20 m coastal patrol craft. It was announced in 1993 that Peterson had reached non-exclusive agreements with Royal Schelde Shipbuilding of the Netherlands and FBM Marine in the UK to market and produce under licence a wide range of high-speed passenger and passenger/car vessels. The designs to which Peterson now has access include a range of Surface Effect Ships (SES), high-speed catamarans, low-wash catamarans, fast displacement (SWATH type) catamarans, and high-speed monohulls.

PBI Mk 1

The PBI Mk 1 launched in 1983 is a twin-screw diesel-powered high performance coastal patrol craft, built of marine grade aluminium alloy.

It is presently based at St Petersburg, Florida.

A major rebuilding of main engines was accomplished in 1991 with the replacement of liners, injectors, intercoolers and other components,

Peterson Builders PBI Mk 1   1992

putting the engine in near new condition with factory warranty.

Principal Particulars

Length overall	20.17 m
Beam	5.48 m
Draught	1.64 m
Displacement	42.7 t
Crew	10
Fuel capacity	9085 l

Water capacity	1794 l
Propulsive power	1790 kW
Maximum speed	27.5 knots
Operational speed	20.5 knots
Range	683 nm
Operational limitation	Sea State 6

Propulsion: 2 × DDC 16V 92MTI, 1790 kW total.
Electrical system: Onan 30 kW driven by Ford 4-cylinder diesel.

12.8 m PCC

In September 1993 Peterson was awarded a contract by US Naval Sea Systems Command to build 10 12.8 m coastal patrol craft with an option for a further 15 vessels. Four of these craft have been delivered to date. These aluminium hull patrol craft are powered by twin MTU diesel engines, each driving a Hamilton water-jet.

UPDATED

SWIFTSHIPS INC

PO Box 1908, Morgan City, Louisiana 70381, USA

Telephone: +1 (504) 384 1700
Telefax: +1 (504) 384 0914

Dennis R Spurgeon, *Chairman*
Robert W Ness, *President*
Calvin J LeLeux, *Executive Vice President*
Mark H Dearing, *Treasurer/Controller*
Leslie Lallande, *Business Development Manager*
A J Blanchard, *Marketing Manager*
C C Clark, *Purchasing Manager*

Swiftships produces aluminium alloy craft up to 38 m and steel vessels from 45 to 76 m long. Swiftships employs approximately 900 personnel and apart from its fast crew boats has supplied fast aluminium patrol craft ranging from 8 to 45 m in length. These craft are in service with US armed forces, naval coastguard and police forces in some 20 countries throughout the world.

65′ PATROL BOAT

Patrol boats supplied to governments of Antigua, Dominica and St Lucia.

Principal Particulars

Length overall	19.81 m
Beam	5.56 m
Draught	1.52 m
Fuel capacity	4542 l

Structure: Superstructure and hull constructed in aluminium alloy.
Propulsion: 2 × GM 12V-71 TI marine diesel engines coupled to Twin Disc MG 514C reverse/reduction gearboxes, each to conventional propellers.

Swiftships 65′ patrol boats   1987

Control: Engine controls by Ponish with a Vickers/Charlynn steering system.

115′ CREW BOAT

Fast supply/crew boat.

Principal Particulars

Length overall	35.05 m
Beam	7.62 m
Draught	2.2 m
Payload	75.55 t
Crew	6
Passenger	49
Fuel capacity	14 000 l
Propulsive power	3 × 596 kW
Speed	23 knots
Range	750 nm

Propulsion: 3 × MTU 8V 396 TC 82 diesels providing 596 kW at 1845 rpm each, driving a 4-bladed bronze propeller via ZF BW 255 2:1 reduction gearboxes and a 101 mm diameter Aquamet 17 shaft.

135′ CREW BOAT

Principal Particulars

Length overall	41.15 m
Beam	7.92 m
Payload	100 t
Fuel capacity	38 600 l
Maximum speed	24 knots

Propulsion: 4 × MTU 12V 183 TE 72 diesel engines.

UPDATED

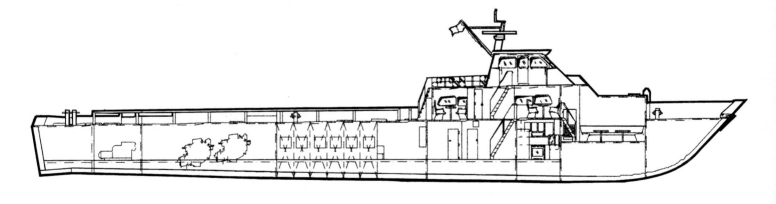

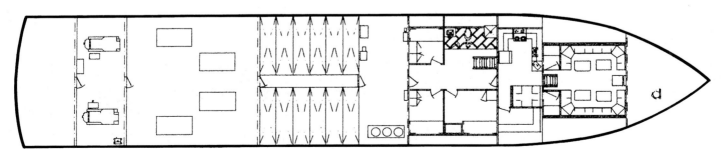

Swiftships 135′ crew boat, general arrangement   1995

TEMPEST YACHTS INC

3333 North East 188th Street, North Miami Beach, Florida 33180, USA

Telephone: +1 (305) 937 4400
Telefax: +1 (305) 937 3752

Adam Erdberg, *President*

Tempest Yachts Inc has established a reputation as an innovative manufacturer of high quality, diesel-powered vessels for a wide variety of applications. The company, with its new headquarters, is located on North Miami Beach, Florida where it currently produces 18 models ranging from 9.75 to 25.9 m in length. Tempest Yachts is a high technology oriented, growing company. The constantly developing state-of-the-art technology is complemented with extensive offshore experience and enables Tempest to produce vessels that are comfortable, practical and well designed for their particular application.

Due to its capabilities, Tempest Yachts was selected from among all American boat builders to design and construct an offshore Fast Coastal Interceptor (FCI) craft for the US Coast Guard. These patrol boats, 13.4 m in length, are currently operated in various areas in most weather conditions for a variety of applications ranging from rescue missions to anti-drug warfare.

Propulsion is provided by Tempest's T-Torque drive (US Patent 4919630) surface-piercing drive system.

TEMPEST 44 (FCI)

Fast Coastal Interceptor (FCI) craft first delivered to the US Coast Guard in April 1987.

Principal Particulars

Length overall	13.4 m
Beam	2.9 m
Draught	0.1 m
Displacement, maximum	8 t
Fuel capacity	11 750 l
Propulsive power	2 × 317 kW
Operational speed	45 knots

Propulsion: 2 × Caterpillar 3208 TA 317 kW diesels each driving a T-Torque surface-piercing propeller.

TEMPEST 60

High-speed offshore performance craft available for both pleasure and commercial applications.

Principal Particulars

Length overall	18.29 m
Beam	4.8 m
Draught	1.07 m
Displacement, maximum	22.68 t
Fuel capacity	3785 l
Water capacity	1060 l
Propulsive power	2 × 783 kW
Maximum speed	50 knots

Structure: FRP, ABS class.
Propulsion: The main engines are 2 × Caterpillar 3412 TA diesels, 783 kW (1050 hp) each; driving Tempest's own T-Torque surface-piercing drive system.
Electrical system: 220 V AC, 110 V AC, 24 V DC, 12 V DC.
Navigation and communications: VHF, Loran, radar, autopilot, depthsounder.
Control: Kobelt mechanical engine controls, single station hydraulic power steering system.

TEMPEST 74

Added to the Tempest range in 1991, the Tempest 74 is an ocean-going cockpit motor yacht, also available for various commercial applications.

Principal Particulars

Length overall	22.55 m
Beam	6.1 m
Draught	1.07 m
Displacement, maximum	43.13 t
Fuel capacity	8327 l
Water capacity	1135 l
Propulsive power	2 × 783 kW
Maximum speed	26 knots

Structure: The hull material is FRP, ABS class; the deck material is Aluminium 5086.
Propulsion: 2 × Caterpillar 3412 TA diesels, 783 kW each; driving Tempest T-Torque surface-piercing drive system.

Tempest 60 sport yacht   1990

Tempest 74 cockpit motor yacht   1992

Tempest 80 enclosed motor yacht   1994

Electrical system: 220 V AC, 110 V AC, 24 V DC, 12 V DC.

Control: Dual station, hydraulic power steering system, Vosper stabilisers.

TEMPEST 80

Ocean-going enclosed sport yacht, also available in various commercial applications.

Principal Particulars

Length overall	24.39 m
Beam	6.1 m
Draught	1.22 m
Displacement, maximum	36.28 t
Fuel capacity	7570 l
Water capacity	1135 l
Propulsive power	2912 kW
Maximum speed	36 knots

Structure: The hull and deck are FRP.

Propulsion: The main engines are 2 × Detroit Diesel 16V 92TA, 1081 kW each plus 1 × Lycoming Y-53 gas-turbine of 750 kW; driving T-Torque surface-piercing drive system (US Patent 4919630).

Electrical system: 220 V AC, 110 V AC, 24 V DC, 12 V DC.

TEMPEST 84

Ocean-going sky lounge motor yacht, also available in various commercial applications.

Principal Particulars

Length overall	25.61 m
Beam	6.1 m
Draught	1.3 m
Displacement, maximum	56.69 t
Fuel capacity	8705 l
Water capacity	1135 l
Propulsive power	2912 kW
Maximum speed	26 knots

Structure: The hull is FRP and the deck is aluminium 5086.

Propulsion: The main engines are 2 × Detroit Diesel 16V 92TA, 1081 kW each plus 1 × Lycoming T-53 gas-turbine of 750 kW; driving T-Torque surface-piercing drive system (US Patent 4919630).

Electrical system: 220 V AC, 110 V AC, 24 V DC, 12 V DC.

TEMPEST 85

Ocean-going raised pilot-house motor yacht also available in various commercial applications.

Principal Particulars

Length overall	25.91 m
Beam	6.4 m
Draught	1.52 m
Displacement, maximum	61.22 t
Fuel capacity	13 248 l
Water capacity	2650 l
Propulsive power	2 × 783 kW
Maximum speed	30 knots

Structure: The hull is FRP, ABS class, and the deck is aluminium 5086.

Propulsion: The main engines are 2 × Caterpillar 3412 TA diesels, 783 kW (1050 hp) each; driving 4-blade Nibral propellers.

Electrical system: 220 V AC, 110 V AC, 24 V DC, 12 V DC.

Navigation and communications: VHF, Loran, radar, autopilot, depthsounder, SATNAV, SATCOM, facsimile, SSB.

Control: Kobelt pneumatic, 2 stations, hydraulic power steering system, hydraulic bow thruster.

Fire extinguishing system: Halon 1301.

UPDATED

Tempest 84 sky lounge motor yacht   *1994*

Tempest 85 raised pilot-house motor yacht   *1991*

TRINITY MARINE GROUP

A Trinity Industries Company

PO Box 3029, 13085 Industrial Seaway Road, Gulfport, Mississippi 39503, USA

Telephone: +1 (601) 896 0029
Telex: 6821246 HALMAR
Telefax: +1 (601) 897 4866

John Dane III, *President*
Vince Almerico, *Snr. Vice President, Operations*
Harvey Walpert, *Snr. Vice President, Administration*
James G Rivers, *Vice President, International Sales*
Anil Raj, *Vice President, Government Projects*
Sidney Mizell, *Vice President, Sales*

Details of high-speed vessels built in the Trinity Marine Group are given in the entries for the relevant shipyards.

Shipbuilding companies within the group:
Halter Marine Inc
Moss Point Marine Inc
Trinity Yachts Inc
Aluminum Boats Inc
Equitable Shipyards Inc
HBC Barge Inc
Gretna Machine and Iron Works Inc

Shipbuilding Facilities:
Trinity Marine Panama City, Florida, USA
Trinity Beaumont, Beaumont, Texas, USA
Equitable Halter, New Orleans, Louisiana, USA

Trinity Madisonville, Madisonville, Louisiana, USA
Halter Moss Point, Moss Point, Mississippi, USA
Halter Lockport, Lockport, Louisiana, USA
Moss Point Marine, Escatawpa, Mississippi, USA
Moss Point Marine South, Escatawpa, Mississippi, USA
Aluminum Boats Inc, Crown Point, Louisiana, USA
Gretna Machine and Iron Works, Gretna, Louisiana, USA
Trinity Brownsville, Brownsville, Pennsylvania, USA
Trinity Marine Gulfport, Gulfport, Mississippi, USA
Trinity Marine Carothersville, Carothersville, Missouri, USA
Platzer Shipyards Inc, Houston, Texas, USA
Port Allen Marine, Baton Rouge, Louisiana, USA

UPDATED

TRINITY YACHTS INC

A company of the Trinity Marine Group

Leda

Trinity Yachts Inc delivered the 29.5 m motor yacht *Leda* in March 1991. It was designed by naval architect Gerhard Gilgenast.

Although *Leda* is under 30 m and has a sleek hull and low profile, she offers expansive, luxurious accommodation including four double staterooms with private baths and a unique formal dining salon with a panoramic view over the bow. *Leda's* most impressive feature is her exceptional low noise and vibration levels, previously not considered possible on a yacht with her performance and equipment.

Principal Particulars

Length overall	29.57 m
Length waterline	25.3 m
Draught	1.4 m
Fuel capacity	26 495 l
Water capacity	3028 l
Maximum speed	20 knots
Operational speed	18 knots

Propulsion: The main engines are 2 × MTU 8V 396 TB 93, driving 2 × 4-bladed skew propellers.

22 m SPORT YACHT

This sport fishing yacht was delivered in 1994.

Principal Particulars

Length overall	22.13 m
Beam	6.04 m
Draught	1.4 m
Fuel capacity	10 500 l
Water capacity	1000 l
Maximum speed	32 knots
Operational speed	27 knots
Range	750 nm

Propulsion: Two DDEC 16V 92TA diesels rated at 1100 kW at 2300 rpm.

UPDATED

Leda   *1994*

22 m Sport Yacht
1995

WESTPORT SHIPYARD INC

PO Box 308, Westport, Washington 98595, USA

Telephone: +1 (206) 268 0117
Telefax: +1 (206) 268 0119

Randy Rust, *General Manager*

Westport Shipyard was established in 1964 and sold to the present owners in 1977. The yard has a workforce of 110 and consists of 5110 m² (70 000 ft²) of covered building sheds and workshops plus four acres of fenced storage space. The range, in length, of craft built is from 10.4 to 36.6 m. Hulls of the larger craft are built with a sandwich-type construction of Airex PVC and GRP, which the builder claims yields a tougher and lighter hull than an all-GRP type. Hull moulds are adjustable for length and beam enabling craft to be built in the following length ranges: 16.15 to 19.8 m, 19.8 to 29 m and 27.4 to 36.6 m. The company has built over 50 vessels to USCG 'S' classification since 1977.

The yard currently has under construction six yachts in the 32 m range.

Westship Lady

Designed by Jack Sarin, this vessel was delivered in the Spring of 1993.

Principal Particulars

Length overall	32.33 m
Beam	6.91 m
Draught	1.68 m
Displacement, maximum	95 t
Crew	14
Fuel capacity	18 950 l
Water capacity	2840 l
Maximum speed	28 knots
Operational speed	25 knots
Range	2000 nm

Structure: The hull is FRP/Airex core and the superstructure is FRP/composite.
Propulsion: The main engines are 2 × MTU 8V 396 TE 94.

Kenai Explorer

Delivered in the Spring of 1993, *Kenai Explorer* operates as a tour vessel in the Kenai Fjords area of Alaska and is certified to operate within 20 miles of a harbour of safe refuge. The hull is built with Airex core and fire retardant resin with plywood bulkheads and stringers of fibreglass and foam. The superstructure is of fibreglass and core type construction.

Principal Particulars

Length overall	27.44 m
Beam	6.71 m
Passengers	149
Fuel capacity	11 355 l
Water capacity	1135 l
Propulsive power	2 × 969 kW
Operational speed	26 knots

Propulsion: The main engines are 2 × DDC 16V 92TA diesels, 969 kW each at 2300 rpm.

Lady Kathryn   *1993*

Northstream   *1992*

Kenai Explorer   *1995*

Westship Lady   *1994*

Chugach

Delivered in May 1992 this vessel, designed by Jack Sarin, is owned and operated by Stan Stephens Charters, Valdez, Alaska.

Principal Particulars

Length overall	24.4 m
Beam	6.4 m
Draught	1.5 m
Passengers	149
Fuel capacity	7570 l
Water capacity	416 l
Propulsive power	626 kW
Maximum speed	22.6 knots
Operational speed	18 knots

Propulsion: The main engines are 2 × Lugger L6170A diesels, 626 kW each at 2100 rpm.

WESTSHIP 98
Lady Kathryn

Designed by Jack Sarin, this vessel was delivered at the end of 1992.

Principal Particulars

Length overall	29.88 m
Beam	6.91 m
Draught	1.73 m
Displacement, minimum	74.83 t
Passengers	10
Fuel capacity	17 000 l
Water capacity	2840 l
Maximum speed	23 knots
Operational speed	19 knots
Range	1720 nm

Structure: Hull: FRP/Airex core.
Superstructure: FRP/composite.
Propulsion: The main engines are DDC 12V 92.

Northstream

Delivered in the Spring of 1990, this Sports fisherman type was designed by Jack Sarin, with acoustic engineering by Joe Smullin.

Principal Particulars

Length overall	32.7 m
Beam	7.32 m
Displacement, minimum	80 t
Displacement, maximum	93 t
Fuel capacity	22 330 l
Maximum speed	27 knots
Operational speed	22 knots

Structure: Hull: double-cored Airex bottom, single-cored Airex sides; superstructure: composite with Airex core.
Propulsion: The main engines are 2 × DDC 16V 92TA with DDEC system.
Control: Stabilisers: Naiad 301s with 0.56 m² fins. Bow thruster: Wesmar 12.2 kW.

Heritage

An ocean-going motor yacht, built in advanced plastics. The hull construction is in fibreglass with vacuum-bonded 1 in Airex core on the sides and a double layer of ¾ in Airex on the bottom. Where appropriate unidirectional and biaxial materials are used extensively. All structural bulkheads, lower soles, exterior decks and superstructure are fibreglass composite. All stringers are foam and fibreglass. The exterior skin is laid up with isophthalic resin for added blister resistance. The bottom is triple-coated with International Paint 2000 epoxy and then double-coated with Hysol antifouling paint.

Principal Particulars

Length overall	29.88 m
Beam	6.71 m
Displacement, minimum	65.3 t
Displacement, maximum	83 t
Propulsive power	2 × 805 kW
Maximum speed	26 knots
Operational speed	22.5 knots

Propulsion: The main engines are 2 × DDC 12V 92TAB, 805 kW each at 2300 rpm, driving 2 × Michigan Wheel Dynaquad, 4-blade, 1067 × 91.4 mm Nibral Alloy propellers.

Tahiti

Delivered in the Spring of 1991, this is the second in the Westship Series and was designed by Jack Sarin.

Principal Particulars

Length overall	29.12 m
Beam	6.91 m
Draught	1.68 m
Displacement	74.83 t

Catalina Express   *1995*

Alaskan Explorer   *1995*

Passengers	10
Fuel capacity	13 250 l
Water capacity	2840 l
Maximum speed	24 knots
Operational speed	18 knots

Structure: The hull is FRP/Airex core, and the superstructure is FRP/composite.
Propulsion: The main engines are Caterpillar 3412.

Bluefin

This boat was delivered to California Fish and Game in Spring 1991.

Principal Particulars

Length overall	19.77 m
Beam	5.84 m
Passengers	9
Fuel capacity	9463 l
Water capacity	1135 l
Maximum speed	30 knots

Structure: The hull is FRP/Airex core, and the superstructure is wood/fibreglass.
Propulsion: The main engines are 2 × DDC 12V 92TAB.

30 m FERRY
Catalina Express
Islander Express

Delivered in 1994 these two vessels operate off the coast of Southern California for Catalina Express Lines. Licensed for coastwise service (20 miles from harbour of safe refuge), the boats will carry 149 passengers at speeds of up to 32 knots.

The hull form features modified propeller tunnels for increased propeller efficiency.

Principal Particulars

Length overall	30 m
Beam	6.71 m
Passengers	149

Fuel capacity	9500 l
Water capacity	418 l
Propulsive power	2 × 1491 kW
Operational speed	32 knots

Structure: The vessels are constructed from Fibre Reinforced Plastic (FRP) sandwich with an Airex core and fire retardant resin. The vessels were the first to be built in a new Westport adjustable hull mould.
Propulsion: The main engines are 2 × 16V 149TIB DDEC Detroit diesels, driving propellers.
Electrical system: The electrical power is supplied by two Northern Lights generators.

Alaskan Explorer

This vessel was scheduled to be delivered to Kenai Fjords Tours in the Spring of 1995. The vessel is based in Seward, Alaska, for day tours to the scenic Kenai Fjords national park area.

The hull form incorporates propeller tunnels, and was designed by Jack Sarin based on Westport's 8500 series high-speed hull mould.

Principal Particulars

Length overall	30 m
Beam	6.71 m
Passengers	149
Fuel capacity	11360 l
Water capacity	1135 l
Propulsive power	2 × 1305 kW
Operational speed	28 knots

Propulsion: The main engines are 2 × Caterpillar 3512 DITA diesels, each producing 1305 kW at 1800 rpm; driving propellers via a ZF460 gearbox.
Electrical system: The power is supplied by 2 × Northern Lights generators, 40 kW and 20 kW.

UPDATED

WING-IN-GROUND-EFFECT CRAFT

Company Listing by Country

China, People's Republic
CSSRC
Maric

Commonwealth of Independent States
Central Design Bureau of Hydrofoils
Krylov Shipbuilding Research Institute

Germany
Botec Ingenieursozietät GmbH
Rhein-flugzeugbau GmbH (Rfb)

Japan
Chiba Marine Development Corporation
Dr Shigenori Ando
Tottori University

CHINA, PEOPLE'S REPUBLIC

CSSRC

**CHINA SHIP SCIENTIFIC
RESEARCH CENTER**
Wuxi, Jiangsu, People's Republic of China

Telephone: +86 (051) 668012
Telex: 362016 CSSRC CN
Telefax: +86 (051) 201164

RAM-WING VEHICLE 902

A single-seat test vehicle.

The research plan behind the development of the 902 was begun in 1979 and a programme of theoretical and wind tunnel experimental research was carried out which provided solutions for the particular problem of longitudinal stability encountered by such craft when operating in and out of ground-effect. The 902 was built in 1983 and first flew on 12 November 1984.

Take off can be achieved in waves up to 0.4 or 0.5 m with winds of Beaufort 6 to 7. The craft can be flown in and out of ground-effect and in the surface-effect region of 0.6 to 8 m altitude it can fly safely without any automatic stabilising device.

Principal Particulars
Length overall	9.55 m
Span	5.8 m
Weight, maximum	0.4 t
Weight, minimum	0.3 t
Payload	0.1 t
Take off distance	150 m
Take off speed	40.5 knots
Operational speed	65 knots
Operational limitation	wave height 0.5 m
	Beaufort force 6-7

Propulsion: The main engines are 2 × HS-350A, 15 kW each, aircraft piston engines, driving 2 × fixed-pitch, aircraft type propellers.

XTW-1

Following the success of the 902 a larger ram-wing craft was built, the XTW-1, for lake and river communications duties. This craft has a weight of 950 kg and is powered by two 30 kW piston engines giving it a cruise speed of 70 knots, with four people on board. A retractable undercarriage is incorporated for slipway handling.

XTW-2

With the experience gained with the 902 and XTW-1, a much larger project was embarked upon in 1988. The XTW-2 was built in 1990 and performance testing was due to be completed 1992 but no further information is available. The main centre hull is fitted with a passenger cabin with 14 seats. Provision is made for two pilots as long distance operations are envisaged. The aisle width in the passenger cabin is 40 cm and ceiling height allows for standing of passengers when entering and disembarking. Food cupboards, luggage storage cabinets and a lavatory are installed and a high standard of comfort is

XTW-1 in cruising flight **1991**

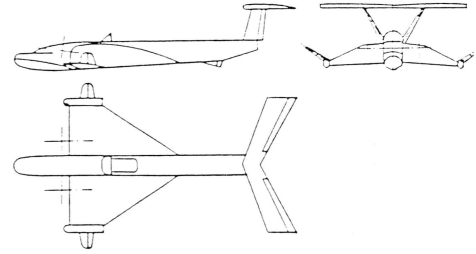

Wing-in-ground-effect craft built by China Ship Scientific Research Center **1989**

provided throughout.

Principal Particulars
Length overall	18.5 m
Span	12.72 m
Weight, maximum	3.6 t
Payload	1.2 t
Propulsive power	448 kW (take off)
Operational speed	80-100 knots
Flight altitude	1 m
Range	485 nm
Operational limitation	Sea State 3

Propulsion: The main engines are 2 × IO-540 K1B5 aircraft piston engines.

Reference: *Analysis of Hydrodynamic Performance & Characteristics of Ram-Wing Craft* by Li Kaixie and Li Shuming. Second International Conference for High Performance Vehicles. CSNAME, Shenzhen, China 12-15 November 1992.

UPDATED

MARIC

**MARINE DESIGN AND RESEARCH
INSTITUTE OF CHINA**
314 Sichuan Road, Central, PO Box 002-053, Shanghai, People's Republic of China

Telephone: +86 (21) 321 5044
Telex: 33029 MARIC CN
Telefax: +86 (21) 329 0929

Sun Songhe, *Director*
Yun Liang, *Deputy Chief Naval Architect*

PAR WIG TYPE 750

This two-seat experimental Power-Assisted Ram-Wing-In-Ground-effect (PAR WIG) craft was completed in 1985, and over the period March 1985 to June 1987 over 40 trial flights were performed, exploring various operating conditions.

Over-water behaviour: can take off and fly steadily in wave heights of 0.5 to 0.7 m with Beaufort 4 to 5

MARIC PAR WIG Type 750 coming ashore **1991**

and gust 6 wind conditions. In horizontal flight, average pitch is 0.3° and roll, 0.53°.

Principal Particulars

Length overall	8.47 m
Span	4.8 m
Weight, maximum	0.8 t
Payload	0.2 t
Propulsive power	4 × 22 kW
Take off distance	160 m
Take off speed	24 knots
Maximum speed	71 knots
Flight altitude	0.5 m
Range	70 nm

Structure: Built in GRP with aircraft construction techniques.

Propulsion: Four 22 kW piston engines driving four ducted propellers Type DT-30.

PAR WIG TYPE 751 (AF-1)

This 20 passenger PAR WIG is currently under construction and expected to be completed during 1994.

MARIC PAR WIG Type 750

1991

Reference: *20-Passenger Power-Augmented-Ram-Wing-In-Ground-Effect Craft (PAR WIG) Type AF-1* by Hu An-ding and Wang Gou-zhong, MARIC, Second International Conference for High Performance Vehicles. CSNAME, Shenzhen, China 12-15 November 1992.

UPDATED

COMMONWEALTH OF INDEPENDENT STATES

CENTRAL DESIGN BUREAU OF HYDROFOILS

51 Svobody Street, Nizhni Novgorod, Russia, CIS

Telephone: +7 (831) 225 1037
Telex: 151348
Telefax: +7 (831) 225 0248

B V Chubikov, *General Director, Chief Designer*
V V Sokolov, *Chief Designer, Ekranoplan Programme*
and

KRYLOV SHIPBUILDING RESEARCH INSTITUTE

44 Moskovskoye Street, 196158 St Peterburg, Russia, CIS

Telephone: +7 (812) 293 5482

Prof V M Pashin, D Sc (Tech), CMAS, *Director*

The above two organisations are working in co-operation on wing-in-ground-effect designs.

SDVPs

SDVP is a Russian abbreviation for Dynamic Air Cushion Vehicles.

In 1990 first details were published in the USSR, on a series of designs of wing-in-ground-effect craft developed under the direction of Dr R Ye Alekseev of the Central Design Bureau of Hydrofoils. The need for these craft arises from the speed limitations of hydrofoils and the appreciable draught and limited speed of catamarans in long distance river operations. The type of wing-in-ground-effect craft under development employ the power-assisted-lift

Craft Type Name						
Characteristics	**Volga-2**	**Raketa-2**	**Raketa-2.2**	**Meteor-2**	**Kometa-2**	**Vykhr-2 (Whirlwind)**
Passenger capacity	8	50	90	120	150	250
RF River Register class	R	O	O	O	M	M
Weight	2.5 t	16 t	31 t	32 t	42 t	105 t
Length	11.3 m	26.2 m	34.8 m	36 m	25 m	54 m
Width	7.63 m	14.9 m	19.8 m	20 m	N/K	28 m
Draught	0.2 m	0.35 m	0.5 m	0.45 m	0.5 m	0.7 m
Engine	2	2	3	2	2	2
	VAZ-413 RPD	TVD-10 Type M601 turboprop	TB7-117C turboprop	AP-24 turboprop	D-36 turbofan	D-36 turbofan
	2 × 95 kW	2 × 662 kW	3 × 1795 kW	2 × 1840 kW	2 × 6500 kg thrust	2 × 6500 kg thrust
Speed	120 km/h 65 knots	150 km/h 80 knots	150-180 km/h 80-97 knots	170 km/h 92 knots	185 km/h 100 knots	280 km/h 150 knots
Range	500 km (270 nm)	500 km (270 nm)	800 km (432 nm)	800 km (432 nm)	930 km (500 nm)	1500 km (800 nm)
Seaworthiness (wave height)	0.5 m	1.25 m	1.25 m	1.5 m	wind force 4	wind force 5
Crew						
watch	1	3	3	4	4	6
total aboard	2	6	6	8	8	12

Volga-2 8 passenger, 65 knot wing-in-ground-effect craft (A Belyaev)

1995

principle, or PAR WIG (Power-Assisted Ram-Wing-In-Ground-effect) as it is sometimes known. The designs have over-hard-surface as well as over-water capability.

The first design to be built is the Volga-2.

VOLGA-2

This craft can overcome uneven surfaces and obstacles up to 0.4 m in height. The engines for Volga-2 are two VAZ-413 'rotor-piston' engines, believed to be rotary engines. Experimental data gained during trials of Volga-2 show propulsion economics to be on a level with existing hydrofoils. Further details of this craft are given in the table that follows.

An interesting aspect of the SDVP designs is the use of soft balloon-type structures to give the craft amphibious capabilities; the main structures are built in light alloys.

The Gorky Institute of Water Transportation Engineers (GIIVTOM), together with the Scientific Industrial Society (NPO) of the Central Design Bureau of Hydrofoils and the United Volga River Shipping Line (VORP), have carried out research appraising the technical possibilities and economic expediency of using these wing-in-ground-effect craft. As an example it was found that the route Nizhni Novgorod to Kazan, 432 km, could show positive economic results if wing-in-ground-effect craft were to be used for passenger-carrying services.

In the accompanying table the Raketa, Meteor, Kometa and Vykhr craft are design studies; Volga-2 has been built.

A.90.150 EKRANOPLAN

There were five of these craft built, with three remaining. Working prototypes of cargo versions have been built enabling the economics of future passenger-carrying versions to be predicted. The fuselage is of a relatively simple girder and stringer design and, like the wings, is divided into watertight compartments so that the craft will float while at rest. The fuselage is divided into three parts; the nose section with the flight deck and crew service area, a middle section containing the cargo or passenger area, and the tail section which houses auxiliary machinery.

A.90.150 Ekranoplan in flight (A Belyaev)   **1995**

The nose-mounted jet engines have pivoted exhaust nozzles; during take off the jet exhaust streams are directed beneath the wing to boost the ram-air pressure beneath the wing. On changing to cruising flight the nozzles are redirected to provide horizontal thrust, accelerating the craft until cruising speed is reached; the take off jet units are then shut down. The same procedure is used when landing the craft to reduce hydrodynamic loading. The fuselage nose location of the jet units allows their intakes to be positioned in the contours of the nose in such a way as to minimise aerodynamic resistance.

In cruising flight the craft is propelled by the NK-12 turboprop installation mounted high at the fin and tailplane intersection in order to keep the intake away from sea spray as far as it is feasible.

Pitching stability is more difficult to achieve for a craft operating in ground-effect mode than in normal free flight, because it is influenced by the flight altitude as well as the angle of attack. The Ekranoplan has a very large tailplane to counter this problem, which is greater increased in efficiency by the propeller slipstream.

Principal Particulars

Length overall	58 m
Span	31.5 m
Height	15 m
Weight, normal take off	110 t
Weight, maximum	125 t
Passengers	100-150 (single-deck version)
	350 (twin deck version)
Fuel capacity	33 000 l (max)
	17 650 l (normal)
Propulsive power	11 000 kW
Operational speed	216 knots
Range	1080 nm
Operational limitation	Beaufort force 4 to 5

A.90.150 Ekranoplan loading cargo   **1992**

A.90.150 Ekranoplan taking off **1995**

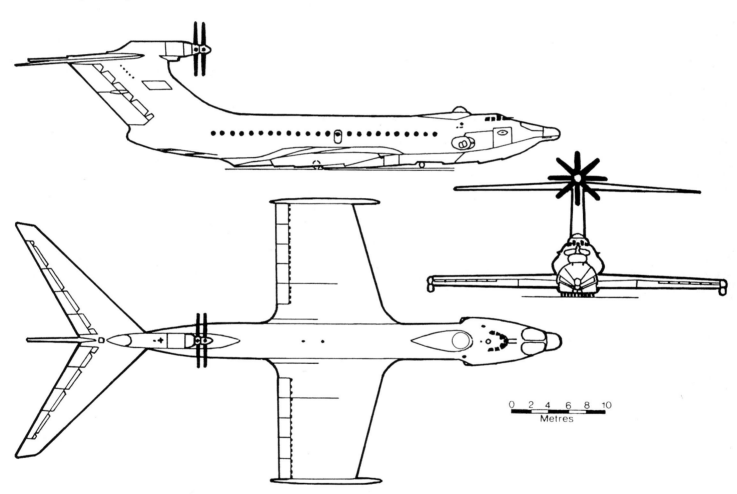

General arrangement of A.90.150 Ekranoplan **1995**

Propulsion: The main engines are 2 × Kuznetsov NK-8 turbofan engines, up to 10.5 t thrust, for take off, and 1 × Kuznetsov NK-12, 11000 kW, turboprop for sustained cruising.

Outfit: Passenger cabin length: 25 m
width: 3.3 m
height: 3 m
volume: 240 m³.

A.90.150 EKRANOPLAN, CARGO VERSION

During the development of the cargo model, a version was designed to have the fuselage split in two vertically, in order to facilitate loading. It is a unique project, with no equivalent known of anywhere else.

Principal Particulars

Payload	30 t
Range	540 nm

Outfit: Cargo section length: 25 m
width: 3.3 m
height: 3 m.

70 m HAWK

Three of these craft are reported to have been constructed, with production of passenger-carrying versions scheduled to start in 1995.

Principal Particulars

Length overall	70 m
Beam	35 m
Weight, maximum	160 t
Maximum speed	300 knots

LUN (CASPIAN MONSTER)

The Russians built the first large scale WIG craft in the 1960s; the 500 t, so called Caspian Monster, which remained secret to the West until very recently. There have been several (at least five), of these military craft built to various designs since, with at least two protoypes completed in 1982, and one craft of the Lun design currently building at the Central Design Bureau of Hydrofoils. The original Caspian Monster prototype is reported to have crashed and sunk in the Caspian Sea in 1980.

The craft are ideally suited for rapid transportation of forces, with a greater payload capacity, greater range, and less fuel consumption than conventional aircraft, whilst operating at a comparable speed.

The Caspian Monster Lun design apparently went

Caspian Monster at speed (A Belyaev)

1995

into military service in 1989, but all of these craft are now reported to have been withdrawn from military activities. The craft and associated technology are reportedly now up for sale.

The craft is propelled by eight turbofan engines, and the craft is armed with six anti-ship missiles.

Principal Particulars

Length overall	75 m
Span	41 m
Weight	400 t
Flight altitude	4 m
Maximum speed	300 knots
Range	1620 nm

UPDATED

Caspian Monster SM-8 development craft (A Belyaev)

1995

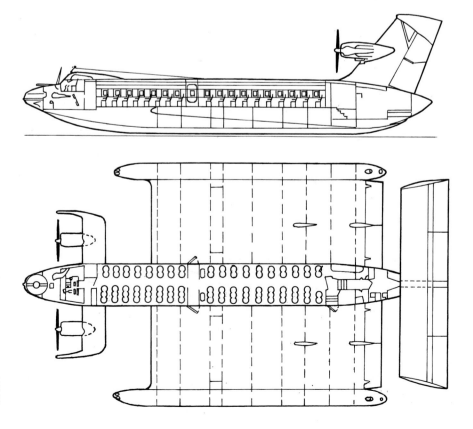

Raketa-2 design, a 90 passenger, 90 knot craft
1992

GERMANY

BOTEC INGENIEURSOZIETÄT GmbH

Entwicklung und Konstruktion von bodeneffektstartenden Fahrzeugen

Odenwaldring 24, D-64401 Gross-Bieberau, Germany

(DESIGN COMPANY)

Telephone: +49 (6162) 3624/1013
Telefax: +49 (6162) 1014

Günther W Jörg, *Principal*

Günther W Jörg was for a number of years a constructor, works manager and development engineer for various West German Vertical Take Off and Landing (VTOL) projects. He sees his Aerodynamic Ground-Effect Craft (AGEC) concept as a means of providing fast, economical and comfortable long distance travel. His experiments began in the 1960s with a series of radio-controlled models. Wind tunnel tests were also undertaken and the results were checked by a computer. The first Günther Jörg ramwing, a two-seater powered by a modified Volkswagen engine, was designed in 1973 and first flew in 1974. After an extensive test programme, Jörg II was designed, performing its first flight in 1976. This incorporated more than 25 design improvements and has travelled more than 10 000 km. During 1978 and 1979, Jörg designed a glass fibre-hulled four- to six-seater Jörg III, which would have been put into series production in Poland had there not been political tension. The first prototype was completed in 1980. Designs are being prepared for larger and faster craft capable of carrying heavier loads over greater distances.

Stabilisation about the pitch and roll axes and maintaining the flying height of the AGEC can be regulated independently by the ground/water surface reaction and therefore requires only a simple steering control for movement around the vertical axis. This basic requirement led to the development of a tandem wing configuration, the handling characteristics of which were first tested on models and then on two-seat research craft. Tests showed that the tandem wings had good aerodynamic

TAF VIII-2 in service in Asia   *1995*

The Jörg two-seat TAF VIII-1 on road trailer. Total time for loading and unloading: ½ hour   *1989*

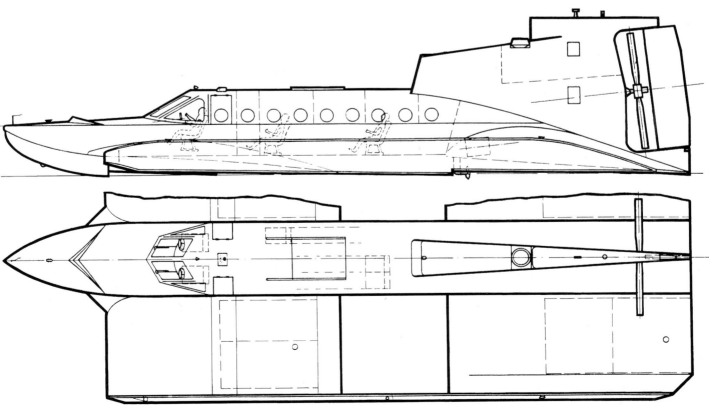

General arrangement of Jörg TAF VIII-5 Flairboat   *1995*

TAF VIII-4S during ground test   1992

A Jörg Airfoil Flairboat at high speed showing condensation trails, not spray   1992

qualities, even above turbulent water, with or without water contact.

AGECs have ample buoyancy and are seaworthy, even while operating at low speed (cruising in displacement condition). After increasing speed the craft lifts off the surface of the water and the resulting air cushion reduces the effects of the waves. After losing water contact the boat starts its ramwing flight at a height of 4 to 8 per cent of the profile depth. A two-seater with a wing span of 3.2 m and a profile length of 3.05 m will have a flying height above the water surface of up to 1 m at a speed of 96.6 km/h. The low power requirement of this type of craft is achieved through the improved lift-to-drag ratio of a wing-in-ground-effect as compared to free flight.

A craft of more than 300 tonnes would have a wing chord of 36 m and fly under ground-effect conditions between 3.5 and 7 m. It would have a wing span of 40 m and a length of 100 m, requiring engine thrust of 40 000 kW. Cruising speed would be 250 km/h from 7350 kW and craft of this size could travel all year round over 90 per cent of the world's sea areas.

The following operational possibilities are foreseen:

Inland Waterways and Offshore Areas: Suitable for rescue boats, customs, police, coastguard units, patrol boats, high-speed ferries, leisure craft.

Coastal Traffic: Large craft would be operated as fast passenger and passenger/car ferries and mixed traffic freighters.

Overland: Suitable for crossing swamps, flat sandy areas, snow and ice regions. Another possible application is as a high-speed tracked skimmer operating in conjunction with a guide carriage above a monorail.

Small craft, displacing 1 tonne or more, can travel over the supporting surface at a height of 304 mm or more at a speed of 96.6 to 144.8 km/h.

Larger craft, weighing 10 to 50 tonnes will be able to fly at a height of 914 mm to 1.98 m at a speed of 129 to 177 km/h.

Coastal craft displacing more than 100 tonnes will fly at a height of 3 m or more.

The basic advantage of the AGEC is its ability to transport passengers and freight far quicker than conventional ship, rail or road transport. The ratio between empty weight and service load is approximately 2:1 but can certainly be improved. Fuel consumption is 80 to 85 per cent lower than that of a boat of similar construction. A high degree of ride comfort is achieved with these craft.

The Airfoil-Flairboats of Jörg design are designed in accordance with International marine standards.

Details of early Jörg craft can be found in the 1992-93 edition of this book.

JÖRG V
TAF VIII-4S

This new Jörg craft underwent its first ground tests in September 1986. Open sea tests in the North Sea started in September 1987.

Principal Particulars

Length overall	17.95 m
Weight, maximum	3.5 t
Passengers	5-8
Propulsive power	485 kW
Operational speed	45-90 knots
Flight altitude	0.6 m
Range	269 nm

Propulsion: The main engine is 1 × 485 kW Textron Lycoming LTX 101 turboshaft with water-methanol injection available for 10% power increase for take off. One diesel engine driving a retractable marine propeller, MT-P 4-blade, 2.9 m diameter, cable/hydraulically controlled; via 9 × V-belts transmissions (Optibelt, Höxter, Germany).

PROJECT DESIGNS

Details of three project designs with passenger capacities of 15, 135 and 400 are given in *Jane's Surface Skimmers 1985*.

A new project design for 1990s development is the 19.8 m Flairboat TAF VIII-5.

FLAIRBOAT TAF VIII-5

Intended for river and inter-island traffic. The first TAF VIII-5 was under construction on the Oder River in the Autumn of 1991.

Principal Particulars

Length overall	19.8 m
Span	8.5 m
Draught, hullborne	0.4 m
Weight, maximum	9.2 t
Payload	1.5 t
Crew	2
Passengers	12-15
Propulsive power	2 × 550 kW
Maximum speed	108 knots
Operational speed	95 knots
Range	200 nm

Structure: Aluminium and composite plastics.

Propulsion: The main engines are 2 × 550 kW petrol engines or 1 × 1015 kW 12-cylinder diesel. Water propulsion: retractable propeller for harbour manoeuvring.

Reference: For further information on Jörg Aerodynamic Ground-Effect Craft please see paper: *History and Development of the Aerodynamic Ground-Effect Craft (AGEC) with tandem wings* by Dipl Ing G W Jörg. Proceedings of Ram-Wing and Ground-Effect Craft Symposium, Royal Aeronautical Society, London, 19 May 1987.

14 m FLAIRBOAT TAF VIII-3

Construction of this new project began in Germany at the beginning of 1991. It is being built as an eight-seat patrol boat and is due to go into series production. The first craft was launched at the end of August 1991 and high-speed tests on the Oder River followed in September 1991.

Principal Particulars

Length overall	14 m
Span	5.85 m
Hull beam	1.6 m
Weight, minimum	2.2 t
Take off speed	39 knots
Operational speed	76 knots
Maximum speed	84 knots
Flight altitude	0.35 m

Propulsion: The engine is a 7.8 l, V8.

FLAIRSHIP TAF VIII-5/25

This design is for a luxury craft (equivalent to a motor yacht specification) carrying up to 10 people. The craft is scheduled for delivery in 1995.

Principal Particulars

Length overall	25.2 m
Length waterline	24.2 m
Span	13.4 m
Weight, maximum	15 t
Crew	3
Propulsive power	1540 kW
Operational speed	90 knots
Flight altitude	0.75-0.93 m
Range	432 nm

Propulsion: The engine is 1 × 18-cylinder diesel, 1540 kW, driving 1 × 4.5 m diameter air propeller, 2 × steerable, retractable water propellers.

UPDATED

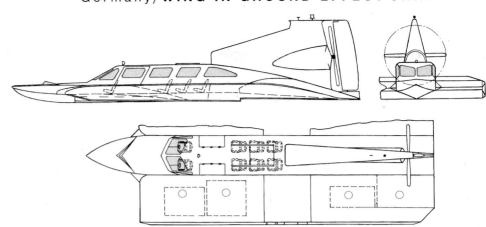

General arrangement of Flairboat TAF VIII-3   1992

Jörg TAF VIII-3 with engine cover raised   1992

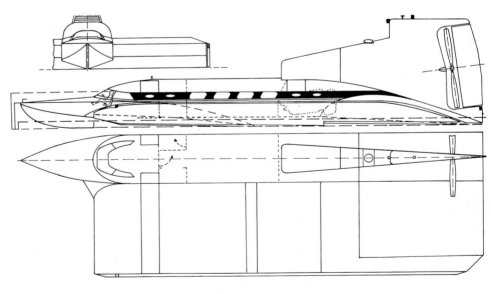

Flairship TAF VIII-5/25
1993

RHEIN-FLUGZEUGBAU GmbH (RFB)

Head office and main works: Flugplatz, PO Box 408, D-4050 Mönchengladbach 1, Germany

Telephone: +49 (2161) 682243
Telefax: +49 (2161) 682273

Other works:
Flugplatz, D-2401 Lübeck-Blankensee, Germany

Dipl-Ing Hartmut Stiegler, *President*

RFB is engaged in the development and construction of airframe structural components, with particular emphasis on wings and fuselages made entirely of glass fibre-reinforced resins. Research and design activities include studies for the Federal German Ministry of Defence.

Current manufacturing programmes include the series production of Fantrainer 400/600 and components and assemblies made of light alloy, steel, glass and carbon fibre-reinforced resins for aircraft and quantity production; manufacturing and maintenance of ejection seats and energy-absorbing armoured seats for helicopters; emergency overhead oxygen boxes for airliners.

As a result of Dr Lippisch's work on the wing-in-ground-effect machine X-112 in the USA, RFB bought several of his patents and further developed the wing-in-ground-effect technology in close co-operation with Dr Lippisch.

After elaborate towing and wind tunnel tests supplemented by radio control model tests, the X-113 was derived, a 1:1.7 scaled down version of a four-seat craft. This single seat trimaran-type craft, built of composite materials in a special sandwich construction developed by RFB, successfully underwent tests on Lake Constance in October 1970.

During additional trials, which were performed in Autumn 1972 in the Weser estuary and the North Sea coastal region over rough water, the X-113's design and the chosen composite construction method proved fully effective.

The flight performance measurements confirmed the analytically expected improvements with respect to lift and drag resulting in gliding angles of 1:23 close to the surface. Even flights out of ground-effect were successfully performed with gliding angles of 1:7 because of the low aspect ratio during this flight phase.

The X-113 showed inherent stabilities even with respect to altitude keeping. Speeds of 97 knots (180 km/h) were achieved with a power of 28 kW (38 hp) in ground-effect. The ability to achieve bank attitudes permits very small curve radii and excellent manoeuvrability. Remarkably good sea behaviour was shown from the outset. Take offs and landings in wave heights of about 0.75 m presented no problem.

RFB X-114 AND -114H AEROFOIL BOATS

Evolved from the X-113, this six- to seven-seater has a maximum take off weight of 1500 kg and is fitted with a retractable wheel undercarriage, enabling it to operate from land or water.

Power is provided by a 200 hp Lycoming IO-360 four-cylinder, horizontally opposed air-cooled engine driving a specially designed Rhein-Flugzeugbau ducted fan. Range, with 100 kg of fuel, is more than 1000 km. Operational speed is 75 to 200 km/h.

An initial trials programme was successfully completed in 1977. A new series of trials is now being undertaken after hydrodynamic modifications which included the fitting of hydrofoils beneath the sponsons, raising maximum take off weight to 1750 kg. In this configuration it is known as the X-114H.

The vehicle is designed to operate over waves up to 1.5 m in ground-effect and can therefore be used without restriction during 80 per cent of the year in the Baltic Sea area and 60 per cent of the year in the North Sea. In high seas of more than 1.5 m, take off and landing takes place in waters near the coast. Flying is virtually unrestricted, providing due allowance is made for the loss in economy.

Fuel consumption costs, while flying in ground-effect, are lower than those for cars. RFB states that its economics cannot be matched by any other form of transport aircraft.

Although built primarily as a research craft to extend the experience gained with the X-113 Am single seater, Aerofoil boats of the size of the X-114 are suitable for air taxi work along coastlines, the supervision of restricted areas, patrol, customs and coastguard purposes, and search and rescue missions.

Without any significant new research the construction of a vehicle with a take off weight of approximately 18 000 kg is possible. On a vehicle of this size, the ratio of empty weight to take off weight is less than 50 per cent.

RFB X-113 Am during flight demonstration over Wattenmeer   **1987**

RFB X-114 Aerofoil boat with hydrofoils extended   **1987**

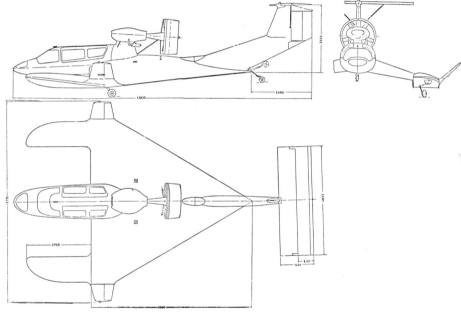

General arrangement of RFB X-114   **1987**

The RFB Airfish FF-2 showing its inflated wing structure   **1989**

Principal Particulars

Length overall	12.8 m
Span	7 m
Weight, maximum	1500 kg (X-114)
	1750 kg (X-114H)
Payload	500 kg
Maximum speed	108 knots
Operational speed	81 knots
Range	1160 nm

AIRFISH FF1/FF2

Further application of the ground-effect technology resulted in a prototype for a new two-seat sports vehicle, the Airfish FF1/FF2. Unlike the X-113 and X-114, which were operational out of ground-effect in free flight, the FF1 and FF2 are solely operational in ground-effect. These craft were developed and successfully tested in 1988 with the objective of optimising the handling of the craft as a 'boat' in ground-effect.

AIRFISH 3 (FLARECRAFT)

The first pre-production craft Airfish 3 successfully passed all function tests in September/October 1990 and proved all performance data.

Built from composite plastics, metal and fabric, an interesting feature of this craft is the incorporation of a retractable water rudder integrated with an electrically driven propeller with two forward and one reverse gears for maximum manoeuvrability in harbour areas. The two-cylinder BMW Boxer engine with an output of 60 kW (75 hp) drives the ducted reduction gear-controlled six-bladed propeller.

By virtue of its specific aerodynamic layout the vehicle always stays close to the surface over which it is operating, but permitting single 'dynamic jumps' over obstacles. This capability is made possible by

Airfish 3 (Flarecraft) engaged in performance tests in September 1990   **1991**

using the stored kinetic energy but which does not however permit continued free flight out of ground-effect. Thus the vehicle, like a hovercraft, can be considered as a boat thereby avoiding the necessity of applying aircraft regulations and having a licensed pilot for its operation.

To make the boat more manoeuvrable in ports its width may be reduced by 1.5 m by pivoted winglets folded electrically by a push-button in the cockpit.

For road transport the Airfish loaded on a boat trailer can be towed by a motor car.

Principal Particulars

Weight, minimum	425 kg
Weight, maximum	650 kg
Fuel capacity	35 kg
Take off speed	39 knots
Operational speed	65 knots
Maximum speed	78 knots
Flight altitude	0.1-1 m
Range	175 nm

VERIFIED

JAPAN

CHIBA MARINE DEVELOPMENT CORPORATION

Yusuke Uzawa, *Head*

with

DR SHIGENORI ANDO

Motoige 17-75, Iwasaki, Nissin-Cho, Aichi Prefecture, 470-01 Japan

Telephone: +81 (5617) 33246

Dr Ando has developed a number of designs for Power-Assisted Ram-Wing-In-Ground-effect (PAR WIG) craft. Radio-controlled models have been built of several configurations, these developments following his earlier work with Nagoya University.

Reference: *PAR-WIG Performance Prediction during Acceleration from Water-Borne to Air-Borne*, by Dr Shigenori Ando and Michiyo Kato. Transactions of the Japan Society for Aeronautical and Space Sciences Vol 34, No 105, 1991.

VERIFIED

PAR WIG model development by Dr Shigenori Ando   **1992**

TOTTORI UNIVERSITY

Department of Applied Mathematics and Physics, Faculty of Engineering, Koyama, Tottori 680, Japan

Telephone: +81 (857) 280321
Telefax: +81 (857) 310882

Syozo Kubo, *Professor*

μSKY I AND μSKY II (MARINE SLIDER PROGRAMME)

This ram wing project was first announced by Mitsubishi on 1 February 1990. Both prototypes were aimed at the eventual production of a commercial craft for leisure use but it is understood that this work has now been suspended.

μSky I

μSky I first flew in December 1988. The structure is rigid; an earlier craft, Rameses I (USA built), employed a flexible structure.

Principal Particulars

Length overall	4.4 m
Span	3.5 m
Weight, minimum	0.2 t
Weight, maximum	0.3 t
Crew	1
Propulsive power	48 kW
Take off speed	35 knots
Maximum speed	44 knots

Propulsion: The engine is a water-cooled gasoline engine 48 kW (Rotax 532), driving a 4-blade, fixed-pitch propeller.
Structure: Hull: GFRP.
Wing: GFRP.
Tail: aluminium plus cloth.

μSky II

μSky II first flew on 8 February 1990 at Kobe, Hyogo Prefecture.

The prototype craft obtained the Ship Inspection Certificate on 17 July 1990, and five pre-production craft on 11 September 1991 from the Japanese Government.

Principal Particulars

Length overall	5.95 m
Span	4.32 m
Weight, minimum	0.3 t
Weight, maximum	0.4 t
Crew	2
Propulsive power	48 kW
Take off speed	33.5 knots
Maximum speed	46 knots
Flight altitude	0.5 m

Propulsion: The engine is a water-cooled gasoline 48 kW (Rotax 532); propeller diameter: 1.54 m.

Propeller number of blades: 3.
Propeller pitch: fixed.
Propeller material: GFRP.
Structure: Hull: GFRP.
Wing: aluminium plus cloth.
Tail: aluminium plus cloth.
Control: Air and water rudders are fitted.
The vehicle may be dismantled for transportation.

VERIFIED

μSky I   1992

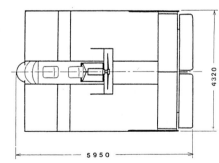

μSky II   1992

μSky II   1992

CIVIL OPERATORS OF HIGH-SPEED CRAFT

Company Listing by Country

Antilles / St Maarten
D & R Ferries

Argentina
Alimar SA
Ferry Lineas

Australia
Boat Torque Cruises Pty Ltd
Fantasea Cruises
Gordon River Cruises Pty Ltd
Great Adventures
Great Keppel Island Tourist Services Ltd
Hayman Resort
Mackenzies Marine
Peel's Tourist and Ferry Services Pty Ltd
P & O Heron Island Resort
Pure Pleasure Cruises
Queensland Government
Quicksilver Connections Ltd
Rottnest Express Pty Ltd
Roylen Cruises
State Transit Authority of New South Wales
Tangalooma Island Resort Ltd

Bahrain
Coastguard Directorate

Belgium
Eurosense Hoversounding NV
Oostende Lines

Bolivia
Crillon Tours SA

Brazil
Norsul Offshore SA
Transtur

Bulgaria
Navibulgar

Canada
Badlands Hovertours
Canadian Coast Guard Hovercraft Units
West Coast Canada
Eastern Canada
Chominco Snip Operation

Chile
Patagonia Travelling Service

China, People's Republic
Cactec
Changjiang Shipping Corporation
China Merchant Development Company
Chongqing Shipping Companies
Dalian Steamship Co
Dalian Yuan Feng Ferry Company
Geophysical Surveys Inc (USA)
Guangdong Province Navigation Company
Nantong High-Speed Passenger Ship Company
Ningbo Huagang Ltd
Sanfu Shipping China
Shanghai Free Flying Transport
Shen Zhen Shipping
Wuzhou Navigation Company
Yantai Marine

Commonwealth of Independent States
Azov Shipping Company
Black Sea Shipping Company
Caspian Shipping Company
Far Eastern Shipping Company
Murmansk Shipping Company
Northern Shipping Company
Novorossiysk Shipping Company
Soviet Danube Shipping Company

Croatia
Atlas Turistička Plovidba
Kvarner Express International DD

Denmark
Dampskibsselskabet (Dsøresund Ø) A/S
Gråhunbus
Pilen (Köpenhamns Pilen AB)
Supply-Trans A/S

Estonia
City Jet
Sukkula
Tallink Express

France
Bateaux Gallus
Channiland
Emeraude Lines
Naviland
Snat
Surf SA
Vedettes de L'Odet Ferry Company

French Polynesia
Aremiti Pacific Cruises (Bora Bora Navette)
Leprado
SPI Maritime

Germany
AG EMS
Hallig-und Inselreederei
Köln-Düsseldorfer Deutsche Rheinschiffahrt AG (KD)

Greece
Advanced Technology Cruises
Ceres Hydrofoil Services
Dodecanese Hydrofoils
Hermes
Ilio Lines
Nomikos
Paraskevas Shipping Company (Takistours)
Piraiki Naftiliaki SA
Renatour SA
Santa Lines
Sonia Shipping, Melina Trading

Guadeloupe
Antilles Trans-express
Société de Transports Maritimes Brudey Frères

Hong Kong
Castle Peak Power Company Ltd
Chu Kong Shipping Company Ltd
Yuet Hing Marine Supplies Company Ltd
Customs and Excise Department
Discovery Bay Transportation Services Ltd Hong Kong Resort Company
Far East Hydrofoil Company Ltd
Hong Kong Hi-Speed Ferries Ltd
Hong Kong Macao Hydrofoil Company Ltd
The Hong Kong & Yaumati Ferry Company Ltd
Royal Hong Kong Police Force, Marine Region
Hong Kong Parkview Ferry Services
Panyu Nan Sha Shipping

Hungary
Mahart Tours

India
Ministry of Surface Transport (Shipping Corporation)
New India Business House Ltd

Indonesia
Bahtera Segara Persanda
Bali Hai Cruises
Citra Bahari Nustraindo
P T Bintan Baruna Sakti
PT Hover Maritim Semandera
PT Mabua Intan Express (PT Mahasara Buana)
PT Satmarindo
Pulau Seribu Marine Resort
Quicksilver

Iran
Valfajre 8 Shipping

Italy
Adriatica di Navigazione Spa
Albadria
Alilauro SpA
Aliscafi Snav SpA
Caremar
Covemar Italia
Foderaro Navigazione
Linee Lauro Srl
Ministero Dei Trasporti
Ministero Della Marina Mercantile
Misano Alta Velocita' Srl
Navigazione Lago di Como
Navigazione Libera Del Golfo SpA
Navigazione Lago Maggiore
Navigazione Sul Lago di Garda
Siremar
Tirrenia Navigazione
Toremar
Vetor Srl

Japan
Awaji Ferry Boat Company
Awashima Kisen Company Ltd
Biwako Kisen Company Ltd
Enoh Kisen
Fuke Kaiun Company Ltd
Geibi Shosen Company Ltd
Goto Ryokaykusen Company Ltd
Hankyu Kisen Company Ltd
Hayatekaiun Company Ltd
Higashi-Nihon Ferry Company
Hiroshima Imabari Kosokusen Company Ltd
Imabari Kosokusen Company Ltd
Iromote Kanko Kaiun Company Ltd
Ishizaki Kisen Company Ltd
Iwakuni Hashirajima Kosokusen Company Ltd
Japan Ocean Cruise Line
Kagoshima Shosen Company Ltd
Kaijo Access Company
Kasumigaura Jet Line KK
Kato Kisen Company Ltd/Kansai Kisen Company Ltd
Kumejima Ferry Company Ltd
Kyodo Kisen Kaisha Ltd
Kyushi Ferry Boat Company
Kyushu Railway Company
Kyushu Shosen Company Ltd
Kyushu Yusen Company Ltd
Maritime Safety Agency of Japan
Marunaka Kisen Company Ltd
Maruto Kisen Company Ltd
Meitetsu Kaijo Kankosen Company Ltd
Mihara Kanko Kisen Company Ltd

Mikatagoko Yuransen
Nankai Ferry Company Ltd
Ohmi Marine
Oita Hover Ferry Company Ltd
OKI Kisen KK
Ryobi Unyu
Sado Kisen Kaisha
Sea-Com Cruise Corporation
Setonaikai Kisen Company Ltd (Seto Inland Sea Lines)
Shikoku Ferry Company (Bridge Line)
Tenmaya Marine Company Ltd
Third District Port Construction Bureau
Tokai Kisen
Tokushima Shuttle Line Company Ltd
Ueda Kaiun KK
Wakasawan Kanko Company Ltd
Yaeyama Kanko Ferry Company
Yasuda Sangyo Kisen Company Ltd

Jordan
Jordan Ports Corporation

Korea, South
Dae-A Ferry Company Ltd
Daeheung Sang-Sa
Dong Bu Express
Geo Je Haewoon
Government
Jeo-Kyung Ferry Company
Jung Ahang Express Company
Kumsan Hungup
Nam Hae Express Company
Semo Company Ltd Marine Craft
Seo Kyung Haewoon
Won Kwang Shipping

Malaysia
Asie Crewboat Sdn Bhd
Kuala Perlis Langkawi Ferry Service Sdn Bhd
Lada Langkawi Holdings
Misc
Pomas Sdn Bhd
Rawa Safaris

Malta
Gozo Channel Company Ltd
Virtu Ferries Ltd

Mexico
Cruceros Maritimos del Caribe SA De CV
Pemex

Netherlands
Rederji G Doeksen en Zonen BV

New Zealand
Fiordland Travel Ltd NZ
Fullers Cruises Northland Ltd
Gulf Ferries Ltd
Hovercraft Adventures
Stewart Island Marine
Wanaka Lake Services Ltd

Norway
Bergen Nordhordland Rutelag A/S
North Cape Minerals A/S
Finnmark Fylkesrsrederi og Ruteselskap
Fosen Trafikklag A/S
Fylkesbaatane i Sogn og Fjordane
Helgeland Trafikkselskap A/S
HSD
L Rødne and Sønner A/S
Møre og Romsdal Fylkesbåtar A/S
Namsos Trafikkselskap A/S
Nesodden-Bundefjord Dampskipsselskap A/S
Rogaland Trafikkselskap A/S
Saltens Dampskibsselskap A/S
Simon Møkster Shipping A/S
Torghatten Trafikkselskap A/S
TFDS
Vest-Trafikk A/S

Pakistan
Pakistan Water and Power Development Authority

Paraguay
Aliscafos Itaipu SA

Philippines
Aboitez Supercat

Poland
Przedsiebiorstwo Usiug Turystycznych Pomerania
Zegluga Gdanska
Zegluga Szczecinska

Portugal
Regiao Autonoma da Madeira Direcçao Regional de Portos

Puerto Rico
Puerto Rico Ports Authority

Saudi Arabia
Dery Shipping Lines
Saudi Aramco

Sierra Leone
Sierra Link

Singapore
Auto Batam Ferries
Bintan Resort Ferries
Igsa Transport
J & N Cruise Pte Ltd
Pelayaran Bintan Baruna Sakti
Resort Cruises (S) Pte Ltd
Shell Eastern Petroleum (Pte) Ltd
Sinba Shipping
Tan Pia Law
Tian San Shipping Pte Ltd
Yang Passenger Ferry Service

Slovakia
Slovenská Plavba Dunajská Závod Osobnej Lodnej
Dopravy (Passenger Transport Division)

Slovenia
Kompas International DD

Spain
Compania Trasmediterranea SA
Flebasa Lines
Lineas Fred Olsen
Trasmapi
Yasmine Line SA
Islena de Navegacion SA

St Pierre Et Miquelon
Armement Borotra Frères

Sweden
City Jet Line
Sea Containers Sweden AB

Taiwan
Tien Peng Yang Hovertravel Corporation
Tung Hsin Steamship Company Ltd

Thailand
Fast Ferry Siam Ltd
Jet Cat Tour Company Ltd
Thai General Transport Ltd

Trinidad
Sun Island Cruises

Tunisia
Sea Bus SA

Turkey
Istanbul Deniz Otobüsleri

United Arab Emirates
Zadco Productions

United Kingdom
Condor Ltd
Hoverspeed Ltd
Hovertravel Ltd
Hoverwork Ltd
Isle of Man Steam Packet Company
Red Funnel Ferries
Sea Containers Ltd
Sea Containers Scotland Ltd
Stena Sealink Line
White Horse Ferries Ltd
Wightlink Ltd

United States of America
Alaska Travel
Arnold Transit Company
Bar Harbor Whale Watch
Blue and Gold Fleet
Bottom Time Adventures
Catalina Channel Express Lines
Catalina Passenger Services
Clipper Navigation Inc
Department of Transportation, United States Coast Guard
Express Navigation Inc
Glacier Bay Yacht Tours Inc (Catamaran Cruise Lines)
Golden Gate Ferry
Harbor Bay Maritime
Hawaiian Cruises Ltd
Kenai Fjords Tours
NY Waterway
Party Line Cruise Company
Phillips Cruises & Tours (Yukon River Cruises)
Put-In-Bay Boat Line
Red and White Fleet
Sayville Ferry Service Inc
Sea Jet Cruise Line
Sea Princess (Guam) Corporation
Shepler's Mackinac Island Ferry
Star Line
Washington State Ferries

Uruguay
Belt SA
Buquebus
Transportes Anfibios SA

Venezuela
Intumaca Inversiones Turisticas Margarita Ca
Maraven SA

Virgin Islands (Us)
Nautical Trading Ltd

CIVIL OPERATORS OF HIGH-SPEED CRAFT

The following abbreviations are used in this section:

ALH	Air-Lubricated-Hull craft
CAT	CATamaran vessel
FAMH	Foil-Assisted MonoHull vessel
F-CAT	Foil-CATamaran vessel
HOV	HOVercraft, amphibious capability
HYD	HYDrofoil, surface-piercing foils, fully immersed foils
MH	MonoHull vessel
SES	Surface-Effect Ship or sidewall hovercraft (non-amphibious)
SWATH	Small-Waterplane-Area Twin-Hull vessel
TRI	TRImaran
WPC	Wave-Piercing Catamaran

ANTILLES / St MAARTEN

D & R FERRIES

St Maarten

High-speed craft operated

Type	Name	Seats	Additional payload	Delivered
CAT Westamarin W86	*Flycat*	135	8.2 t cargo	December 1991

Operations
St Maarten to Saba to St Eustatius and to St Barth.

UPDATED

ARGENTINA

ALIMAR SA

Avenida Cordoba 1801 (Esq Callao), Codigo Postal 1120, Buenos Aires, Argentina

Telephone: +54 (41) 6919/5914
Telex: 0121510 ALMAR AR

High-speed craft operated

Type	Name	Seats	Delivered
HYD Rodriquez PT 50	*Flecha de Buenos Aires*	125	1962
HYD Rodriquez PT 50	*Flecha de Colonia*	125	1963

Operations
Buenos Aires to Colonia, Uruguay (32 nm) and on by coach to Montevideo, operated jointly with Belt of Uruguay.

VERIFIED

FERRY LINEAS

Darsena Sud, Puerto Buenos Aires, Argentina

Telephone: +54 (361) 4161/0346/3140
Telex: +54 (361) 5921

High-speed craft operated

Type	Name	Seats	Additional payload	Delivered
CAT InCat Australia 74 m	*Atlantic II (ex Sea Cat Calais, ex Sea Cat Tasmania)*	432	80 cars	1993

(*Atlantic II* is chartered from Sea Containers Ltd, UK.)

Operations
Buenos Aires to Colonia, Uruguay (32 nm).

AUSTRALIA

BOAT TORQUE CRUISES PTY LTD

PO Box 189, South Perth, Western Australia 6151, Australia

Telephone: +61 (9) 474 1497
Telefax: +61 (9) 368 1656

Trevor A Kitcher, *Managing Director*

High-speed craft operated

Type	Name	Seats
MH WaveMaster 32.3 m	*Sea Raider I*	250
MH WaveMaster 41 m	*Star Flyte*	506
MH WaveMaster 45 m	*Super Flyte*	585

Operations
Perth and Fremantle to Rottnest Island.

UPDATED

FANTASEA CRUISES

PO Box 616, Airlie Beach, Queensland 4802, Australia

Telephone: +61 (79) 466999
Telefax: +61 (79) 469297

D G Hutchen, *Managing Director*

High-speed craft operated

Type	Name	Seats	Delivered
CAT NQEA InCat 24 m	*Quickcat II*	195	1985
CAT InCat 31 m WPC	*2000*	226	March 1988
CAT NQEA InCat 29 m	*Monarch* (ex *South Molle* and *Telford Capricorn*)	332	1994
CAT NQEA InCat 22 m	*Princess* (ex *South Molle* and *Telford Reef*)	195	1994

Operations
Specialising in cruises to the Great Barrier Reef daily from Hamilton, Hayman, Daydream, South Molle, Club Med Lindeman and Long Islands as well as mainland resorts.

UPDATED

GORDON RIVER CRUISES PTY LTD

PO Box 40, Strahan, Tasmania 7468, Australia

Telephone: +61 (004) 717187/7281
Telex: 59284 AA
Telefax: +61 (004) 717317

R F Kearney, *Proprietor*
J A Kearney, *Proprietor*

High-speed craft operated

Type	Name	Seats	Delivered
MH SBF Eng 27.7 m	*James Kelly II*	200	1983
MH WMI Eng 32.3 m	*Gordon Explorer*	250	1985
MH SBF Eng 22.5 m	*Wilderness Seeker*	100	1986

NEW ENTRY

Operations

High-speed cruising in Macquarie Harbour and Gordon River World Heritage area, 4½ hour trips.

The three vessels have been carrying 90 000 passengers annually to the Gordon River.

UPDATED

James Kelly II   *1989*

Wilderness Seeker   *1989*

GREAT ADVENTURES

PO Box 898, Cairns, Queensland 4870, Australia

Telephone: +61 (70) 515644
Telex: 48284 GRTADV AA
Telefax: +61 (70) 517556

John Finnin, *General Manager*
Jeff Sharp, *Sales and Marketing Manager*

High-speed craft operated

Type	Name	Seats	Delivered
CAT InCat (Hobart) 20 m	*Fitzroy Flyer*	169	June 1981
CAT NQEA InCat 22 m	*Green Island Express*	200	June 1982
CAT NQEA InCat 22 m	*Reef Adventure III*	214	March 1984
CAT NQEA InCat 30 m	*Reef Cat*	309	June 1986
CAT NQEA InCat 30 m	*Reef King*	390	December 1987
CAT Lloyd's 35 m	*Reef Queen*	390	February 1993
CAT Lloyd's 38 m	*Reef Prince*	393	(May 1995)

Operations (daily from Cairns City)

Two outer Barrier Reef destinations
-Norman Reef via Green Island
-Moore Reef via Fitzroy Island
Three Island destinations
-Green Island
-Fitzroy Island
-Two Island

UPDATED

GREAT KEPPEL ISLAND TOURIST SERVICES LTD

(previously operating as Hydrofoil Seaflight Services Pty Ltd)
168 Denison Street, Rockhampton, Queensland, Australia

Telephone: +61 (079) 336744/272948

Claude Diehm, *Director*
Claude Diehm Jr, *Director*
David Diehm, *Director*
Andrew Diehm, *Director*
Helen Jackson, *Director/Secretary*

High-speed craft operated

Type	Name	Seats	Delivered
CAT SBF Engineering	*Victory III*	448	1985
MH SBF Engineering	*Aqua Jet*	48	1985

Operations

Rosslyn Bay (Yeppoon) to Great Keppel Island
Rosslyn Bay (Yeppoon) to Carricornia Section, Great Barrier Reef, 90 minutes.

VERIFIED

HAYMAN RESORT

Hayman Island, Queensland 4801, Australia

Telephone: +61 (79) 469100
Telex: 48163 AA
Telefax: +61 (79) 469410

Akos Niklai, *Managing Director*
T A Klein, *General Manager*

High-speed craft operated

Type	Name	Seats	Delivered
MH Wavemaster International Ltd 35 m	*Sun Goddess*	146	1984
MH Oceanfast 34.75 m	*Sun Paradise*	96	1987
MH Precision 22 m	*Reef Goddess*	60	1987
MH Steber 15 m	*Sun Aura*	18	1989

Operations

Hayman Island to Great Barrier Reef
Hayman Island to Hamilton Island.

UPDATED

Reef Cat *at the Norman Reef Pontoon*   *1993*

Reef Queen   *1993*

Sun Paradise *and* Sun Goddess   *1992*

MACKENZIES MARINE

Esperance, Western Australia

High-speed craft operated

Type	Name	Seats	Delivered
CAT SBF 20 m	*Seabreeze*	116	1994

Operations
Esperance to Woody Island.

NEW ENTRY

PEEL'S TOURIST AND FERRY SERVICES PTY LTD

PO Box 197, Lakes Entrance 3909, Victoria, Australia

Telephone: +61 (051) 551246

Barrie Peel, *Managing Director*

High-speed craft operated

Type	Name	Seats	Delivered
CAT InCat (Hobart) 20.4 m Bulls Marine Pty Ltd	*Thunderbird*	190	December 1984

Operations
Three routes are operated on Gippsland Lakes. These range from 35 to 70 km with journey times between 2 and 2½ hours.

UPDATED

Peel's InCat Thunderbird   *1987*

P & O HERON ISLAND RESORT

Queensland, Australia

High-speed craft operated

Type	Name	Seats	Additional payload	Delivered
CAT Precision Marine 30 m	*Reef Adventurer II*	130	10 t cargo	1987

Operations
Heron Island to Gladstone, Australia.

VERIFIED

PURE PLEASURE CRUISES

PO Box 1831, Townsville, Queensland 4810, Australia

High-speed craft operated

Type	Name	Seats	Delivered
CAT International Cats, 31 m WPC	*2001*	196	1989

Operations
Townsville to Kelso Reef, Magnetic Island and Orpheus Island.

UPDATED

QUEENSLAND GOVERNMENT

Department of Harbours, Marine Boating and Fisheries Patrol, Thursday Island, Queensland, Australia

High-speed craft operated

Type	Name	Delivered
CAT NQEA InCat, 22 m Cheetah Class	*Wauri*	1988

VERIFIED

QUICKSILVER CONNECTIONS LTD

PO Box 171, Port Douglas, North Queensland 4871, Australia

Telephone: +61 (070) 995455
Telex: 48969 LOWISL AA
Telefax: +61 (070) 995525

Mike Burgess, *Managing Director*
John F Lergessner, *Operations Manager*

High-speed craft operated

Type	Name	Seats	Delivered
WPC InCat 37.2 m	*Quicksilver V*	340	November 1988
WPC InCat 37.2 m	*Quicksilver VII*	340	September 1989
WPC NQEA/InCat 44 m	*Quicksilver VIII*	400	(May 1995)

Operations
Port Douglas to Agincourt Reef North, 39 nm, 1 hour 30 minutes
Port Douglas to Cairns, 36 nm, 1 hour 10 minutes
Port Douglas to Low Isles.

UPDATED

37.2 m wave-piercing catamaran operated by Quicksilver Connections   *1991*

ROTTNEST EXPRESS PTY LTD

Lot 33, Cockburn Road, South Coogee, Western Australia 6166, Australia

High-speed craft operated

Type	Name	Seats	Delivered
MH SBF 30 m	*Osprey V*	257	1994

Operations
Fremantle to Rottnest Island.

NEW ENTRY

ROYLEN CRUISES

(A Division of McLean's Roylen Cruises Pty Ltd)
PO Box 169, Mackay, Queensland 4740, Australia

Telephone: +61 (79) 553066
Telefax: +61 (79) 553186

Barry J Dean, *Manager*

High-speed craft operated

Type	Name	Seats	Delivered
CAT InCat (Hobart) 29 m	*Spirit of Roylen*	290	1982
CAT InCat (NQEA) 24 m	*Roylen Sunbird*	240	1987

Operations
Mackay to Great Barrier Reef (140 km return)
Mackay to Hamilton Island (120 km return)
Mackay to Brampton Island (40 km return)
Mackay to Lindeman Island (100 km return)

Fares (one day excursion)

Destination	Fare
Great Barrier Reef	A$85, includes lunch and coral viewing
Brampton Island	A$40, includes lunch
Hamilton Island	A$40
Lindeman Island	A$75, includes lunch

Fares (one way transfers)

Destination	Fare
Brampton Island	A$20
Hamilton Island	A$36
Lindeman Island	A$30

VERIFIED

STATE TRANSIT AUTHORITY OF NEW SOUTH WALES

Level 29, 100 Miller Street, North Sydney, NSW 2059, Australia

Telephone: +61 (2) 956 4770
Telefax: +61 (2) 956 4771

L Harper, *Chief Executive*
G Slee, *Chairman*

High-speed craft operated

Type	Name	Seats	Delivered
CAT NQEA 36 m InCat	*Blue Fin*†	250	March 1990
CAT NQEA 36 m InCat	*Sir David Martin*†	280*	December 1990
CAT NQEA 36 m InCat	*Sea Eagle*†	280*	April 1991
CAT NQEA 35 m RiverCat	*Dawn Fraser*††	172**	May 1992
CAT NQEA 35 m RiverCat	*Betty Cuthbert*††	172**	May 1992
CAT NQEA 35 m RiverCat	*Shane Gould*	172**	January 1993
CAT NQEA 35 m RiverCat	*Marlene Matthews*	172**	January 1993
CAT NQEA 35 m RiverCat	*Evonne Goolagong*	172**	September 1993
CAT NQEA 35 m RiverCat	*Marjorie Jackson*	172**	September 1993

* 250 inside, 30 outside
** 150 inside, 22 outside

Operations
†Sydney (Circular Quay) to Manly, 7 nm, 15 minutes
Fare, single: A$4.60
††Sydney (Circular Quay) to Parramatta, 14 nm, 60 minutes
Fare, single: A$4.00

UPDATED

36 m Jetcat Blue Fin   **1995**

35 m Low-Wash RiverCat Evonne Goolagong   **1995**

TANGALOOMA ISLAND RESORT LTD

PO Box 1102, Eagle Farm, Queensland 4007, Australia

Telephone: +61 (7) 268 6722
Telefax: +61 (7) 268 6106

Brian Osborne, *Director*

High-speed craft operated

Type	Name	Delivered
CAT InCat 20 m	*Tangalooma*	December 1981

Operations
Brisbane to Moreton Island, 26 nm, 1 hour 10 minutes
During the period 1 July 1993 to 30 June 1994, 43 000 passengers and 1000 tonnes of cargo were carried each way between Brisbane and Moreton Island.

UPDATED

BAHRAIN

COASTGUARD DIRECTORATE

Ministry of the Interior, Public Secretary, PO Box 13, Bahrain

Telephone: +973 700000
Telex: 9572 CGD BN
Telefax: +973 700728

Col Abdul Aziz A Al-Khalifa, *Director*

High-speed craft operated
HOV Air Vehicles Tiger

Operations
General-purpose search and rescue.

VERIFIED

BELGIUM

EUROSENSE HOVERSOUNDING NV

Main office: Nervierslaan 54, B-1780 Wemmel, Belgium

Telephone: +32 (2) 460 7000
Telex: 26687 B
Telefax: +32 (2) 460 4958

E Maes, *Managing Director*
J Van Sieleghem, *Project Leader*

Zeebrugge office: New-Yorklaan, B-8380 Zeebrugge, Belgium

Telephone: +32 (50) 546438
Telex: 26687 B
Telefax: +32 (50) 547486

High-speed craft operated

Type	Name	Delivered
BHC SR. N6 Mk 6	*Beasac III*	November 1989

Operations
Eurosense Hoversounding NV employs a converted BHC SR. N6 Mk 6 for Belgian coast hydrographic survey and remote sensing work. The craft is based at Zeebrugge on behalf of the Ministry of Works.

The Eurosense SR. N6 Mk 6, BEASAC III   **1991**

OOSTENDE LINES

Madouplein 1, B-1030 Brussels, Belgium

Telephone: +32 (2) 219 5555
Telefax: +32 (2) 223 0309

E Depraetere, *Managing Director*
R Beyen, *Technical Director*
F Engelen, *Commercial Director*
J Carlier, *Nautical Director*

High-speed craft operated

Type	Name	Seats	Delivered
HYD Boeing Jetfoil 929-115	*Princesse Clémentine*	280	May 1981
HYD Boeing Jetfoil 929-115	*Prinses Stephanie*	280	July 1981

Operations
Ostend to Ramsgate, 67 nm, 1 hour 45 minutes
Passengers carried in 1989: 326 641
Passengers carried in 1990: 351 400
Passengers carried in 1991: 360 605
Passengers carried in 1992: 334 170
Passengers carried in 1993: 286 315

UPDATED

Prinses Stephanie   1995

BOLIVIA

CRILLON TOURS SA

PO Box 4785, Avenida Camacho 1223, La Paz, Bolivia

Telephone: +591 (2) 350363/374566/374567/372970
Telex: 2557 CRITUR BV
Telefax: +591 (2) 391039

Darius Morgan, *President*
Elsa Morgan, *General Manager*
Helmut Kock, *Hydrofoil Designer and Consultant*

USA office: 1450 South Bayshore Drive 815, Miami, Florida, USA

Telephone: +1 (305) 358 5353
Telefax: +1 (305) 372 0054

Crillon Tours SA was founded in 1958 by Darius Morgan and started its hydro-foil services on Lake Titikaka in 1966. The company's first craft was the *Inca Arrow,* an Albatross type built by the Ludwig Honold Manufacturing Company. Three more hydrofoils were added in the next ten years, followed in 1976 by the first Bolivian hydrofoil, the *Bolivia Arrow.* In 1979 the Italian built *Sun Arrow* was added to the fleet.

A sister operation is undertaken on Lake Itaipu in Paraguay by Darius Morgan's other company, Aliscafos Itaipu SA. Since 1991 the fleet has been serving the "Andean Roots" cultural complex.

High-speed craft operated

Type	Name	Delivered
HYD Ludwig Honold Manufacturing Co	*Inca Arrow*	1966
HYD Ludwig Honold Manufacturing Co	*Copacabana Arrow*	1964
HYD Ludwig Honold Manufacturing Co	*Andes Arrow*	1965
HYD Ludwig Honold Manufacturing Co	*Titikaka Arrow*	1963
HYD Ludwig Honold Manufacturing Co	*Bolivia Arrow*	1976
HYD Seaflight SpA H.57	*Sun Arrow*	1979
HYD Batumi Ship Building Plant, CIS	*Glasnost Arrow*	1990

Operations
Lake Titikaka, serving La Paz, Huatajata, Sun Island, Copacabana, Juli, Puno, Tiahuanacu, Guaqui, Pako Island. Daily national and international itineraries (Bolivia/Peru).

UPDATED

BRAZIL

NORSUL OFFSHORE SA

Av. Augusto Severo, 8-5th floor, Rio de Janeiro, RJ CEP 20021-040, Brazil

Telephone: +55 (21) 292 0122
Telex: (021) 22115
Telefax: +55 (21) 252 8881

Carlos Temke, *Managing Director*
Aristido Reichert, *Administrative and Financial Director*
Oswaldo Thielmann Jnr, *Commercial Director*
Rufo Belligotti, *Technical and Operational Director*

High-speed craft operated

Type	Name	Seats	Delivered
MH Swiftships	*Parintins*	70	1972
MH Swiftships	*Penedo*	70	1972
MH Breaux's Bay	*Piracicaba*	56	1975
MH Halter Marine	*Atalaia*	70	1980
MH Halter Marine	*Capela*	70	1980
MH Inace	*Norsul Paracuru*	60	1986
MH Inace	*Norsul Pindare*	60	1986
MH Inace	*Norsul Parnaiba*	60	1986
MH Inace	*Norsul Propria*	60	1986

Operations
Offshore support along Brazilian coast with bases in Rio, Macaé, Natal, Fortaleza and Aracaju.

VERIFIED

Atalaia *operated by Norsul Offshore SA*   1993

TRANSTUR

Aerobarcos do Brasil, Transportes Maritimos e Turismo SA

Praça Iaiá Garcia, 3 Ribeira, Rio de Janeiro, Brazil

Telephone: +55 (21) 396 3567/2282/5940
Telefax: +55 (21) 396 3965

Hamilton Amarante Carvalho, *Director President*
Luiz Paulo Amarante Carvalho, *Superintendent*
Vicente Oliveros Perez, *Director of Administration and Finance*

High-speed craft operated

Type	Name	Seats	Delivered
HYD Rodriquez PT 20	*Flecha do Rio*	85	1970
HYD Rodriquez PT 20	*Flecha de Niterói*	85	1970
HYD Rodriquez PT 20	*Flecha das Ilhas*	85	1971
HYD Rodriquez PT 20	*Flecha de Itaipú*	85	1971
HYD Rodriquez PT 20	*Flecha de Ipanema*	83	1977
HYD Rodriquez PT 20	*Flecha de Icarai**	83	1977
HYD Rodriquez PT 20	*Flecha da Ribeira*	83	1978
HYD Rodriquez PT 20	*Flecha Fluminense*	85	1971

*Laid up
Operations
Rio de Janeiro to Niterói, 5 minutes, 2.8 miles
Rio de Janeiro to Paquetá Island, 20 minutes, 9.2 miles.

UPDATED

Rodriquez PT 20 *operated by TRANSTUR*   1993

BULGARIA

NAVIBULGAR

Navigation Maritime Bulgare

1 Chervenoarmeiski Blvd, 9000 Varna, Bulgaria

Telephone: +359 (52) 222474
Telex: 77525/77352 NAVIBULGAR
Telefax: +359 (52) 222491

Dimitar Mavrov, *Director General*
Ivan Borisov, *Managing Director*
Stefan Gramatikov, *Passenger Department Manager*

High-speed craft operated

Type	Name	Seats	Additional payload	Delivered
HYD S Sormovo	*Kometa 1*	108	0.7 t	1978
HYD S Sormovo	*Kometa 2*	108	0.7 t	1979
HYD S Sormovo	*Kometa 3*	108	0.7 t	1980
HYD S Sormovo	*Kometa 7*	108	0.7 t	1974
HYD S Sormovo	*Kometa 8*	108	0.7 t	1974
HYD S Sormovo	*Kometa 12*	108	0.7 t	1977

Operations
Varna to Bourgas to Sozodol, 66 nm, 3 hours
120 000 passengers were carried in 1990

VERIFIED

CANADA

BADLANDS HOVERTOURS

PO Box 940, 100 Willow Avenue, Drumheller, Alberta T0J 0Y0, Canada

Telephone: +1 (403) 8235100
Telefax: +1 (403) 8235005

Keith J J Barry, *President*

This operation uses the original Griffon 2500 TD built for Expo '86 in Vancouver which has been recertified for Canadian passenger service and registered as CH-BAD.

High-speed craft operated

Type	Name	Seats	Delivered
HOV Griffon 2500 TD	*Raindance*	26	February 1993

Operations
Red Deer River tourist operation, 25 km in either direction from Drumheller.

VERIFIED

Griffon 2500 TD Raindance *in operation with Badlands Hovertours* **1993**

CANADIAN COAST GUARD HOVERCRAFT UNITS

Headquarters Administration: Fleet Aviation Office, Fleet Systems Directorate, Canadian Coast Guard (CCG), 8th Floor, Tower 2, Canada Building, 344 Slater Street, Ottawa, Ontario K1A 0N7, Canada

Telephone: +1 (613) 998 1617
Telefax: +1 (613) 995 4700

C D O'Halloran, *Manager*

Operations
The CCG operates two Hovercraft Units, administered from CCG Headquarters in Ottawa, with operational tasking controlled by the region in which they are based.

VERIFIED

WEST COAST CANADA

Canadian Coast Guard Hovercraft Unit: PO Box 23968, AMF, Vancouver International Airport, British Columbia V7N 1T9, Canada

Telephone: +1 (604) 273 2556

J McGrath, *Officer in Charge*

High-speed craft operated

Type	Delivered
HOV BHC SR. N6, Serial No 039, CH-CGB, purchased from BHC	1977
HOV BHC SR. N6, Serial No 030, CH-CCG, rebuilt by Unit	April 1986

(HOV BHC SR. N5, Serial No 021, was retired and scrapped in April 1986 and No 031 was withdrawn from service in November 1992)

Operations
The Canadian Coast Guard Hovercraft Unit in Vancouver was formed in 1968 for hovercraft evaluation in search and rescue and other coastguard duties.

The patrol area is the Straits of Georgia and Gulf Islands (500 square miles), although search and rescue duties are undertaken outside this area. The average patrol distance is 80 miles.

The Unit commenced operations with SR. N5 021 in 1968 in the search and rescue role and quickly established itself. Within five years it was responding to over 900 calls per year. The craft's speed and versatility made it ideal for other CCG roles, amongst which are light station servicing, buoy maintenance, ship inspections, shore patrols, pollution control and emergency work with other agencies. In 1977, the additional work justified a second craft and SR. N6 039 was purchased. Soon afterwards new fishing fleet activities resulted in a northward extension of the SAR cover provided. In 1980-81, the first of two old SR. N6 craft previously purchased was completely rebuilt and commissioned by Unit personnel, enabling a sub-base at Parkesville 90 km north of Vancouver to be built and equipped with one SR. N6, becoming operational in early 1982. This sub-base was closed in November 1992 and SR. N6, Serial No 031 was removed from service.

VERIFIED

EASTERN CANADA

Laurentian Region ACV Unit
850 Nun's Island Boulevard, Nun's Island, Quebec H3E 1H2, Canada

Telephone: +1 (514) 283 0681

D L'Heureux, H Goulet, *Craft Captains*

High-speed craft operated

Type	Name	Delivered
HOV BHC AP1-88/200 Serial No 201, registration CH-CGC	*Waban-Aki*	September 1987

Operations
This Unit started operations by evaluating the potential of hovercraft in the Montreal District of the Laurentian Region, and in 1980 was integrated into the CCG Fleet operating in that region. In 1974-75, the *Voyageur* demonstrated remarkable capabilities for ice-breaking in the St Lawrence and its tributaries, and has been used extensively every winter to break and manage ice in shallow water and for flood relief.

Voyageur was replaced in September 1987 with a BHC AP1-88/200, designed with a forward well-deck and equipped with an easily removable crane, together with a hydraulic capstan and winch. As well as ice-breaking in the winter, *Waban-Aki* maintains marine aids to navigation along 350 miles of the St Lawrence river and also responds to SAR incident calls.

VERIFIED

Waban-Aki breaking ice in a tributary of the St Lawrence, to prevent flooding **1991**

CHOMINCO SNIP OPERATION

Bag 9000, Smithers, British Columbia V0J 2N0, Canada

Telephone: +1 (604) 662 0800
Telefax: +1 (604) 662 0847

Merlyn Royer, *Project Manager*
Paul Morrison, *Chief Pilot*

Chominco Metals acquired an AP1-88 in 1990 (built by NQEA Australia) for the transport of diesel fuel in its Wrangell gold mining operations at Bronson Creek in north-west British Columbia. The craft was first on site 11 July 1990. Conversion of the AP1-88 *Hover Mirage II* was undertaken by NQEA Australia to a freighter version AP1-88/300. The craft operates over a 70 mile route mostly on the unnavigable Iskut and Stikine rivers.

VERIFIED

Chominco AP1-88/300 operating in north-west British Columbia (R Wade) **1994**

CHILE

PATAGONIA TRAVELLING SERVICE

Chile

High-speed craft operated

Type	Name	Seats	Delivered
CAT AYSN Båtservice Sea Lord 28	*Patagonia Express*	60	1991

Operations
Puerto Montt to Termas de Puyuhvapi to San Rafael Lagoon.

VERIFIED

CHINA, PEOPLE'S REPUBLIC

CACTEC
China Air Cushion Technology Development Corporation
9 Qi Xiang Nan Li, Binhu Road, Tianjin, People's Republic of China

Telephone: +86 (22) 331859/333339
Cable: 3333

171 Gaoxion Road, Shanghai, People's Republic of China

Telex: 770539

Formed in 1984, CACTEC, subordinated to China State Shipbuilding Corporation (CSSC), is a specialised business corporation. The corporation deals, jointly with MARIC, with a wide variety of applications of the air cushion principle, and lays emphasis on the research, development, design and production of both amphibious hovercraft and sidewall hovercraft.

High-speed craft operated

Type	Seats	Delivered
SES MARIC 7203	81	September 1982
SES MARIC 719	186	1984
HOV MARIC 716 II	32	1985

VERIFIED

CHANGJIANG SHIPPING CORPORATION

Shanghai, People's Republic of China

High-speed craft operated

Type	Delivered
SES Vosper Hovermarine HM 218, Serial No 129*	1983
SES Vosper Hovermarine HM 218, Serial No 130*	1983

*purchased from The Hong Kong & Yaumati Ferry Company Ltd

Operations
Shekou (China) to Pearl River and Aberdeen (Hong Kong).

VERIFIED

CHINA MERCHANT DEVELOPMENT COMPANY

People's Republic of China

High-speed craft operated

Type	Name	Seats	In service
SES Hovermarine HM 218	*Yin Bin 1*	84	1986
SES Hovermarine HM 218	*Yin Bin 2*	84	1986
CAT Mitsui CP 20	*Yin Bin 3*	250	1987
SES Huangpu MARIC 7211	*Yin Bin 4*	162	1993
CAT Cougar 32 m	*Yin Bin 5*	—	1993

Operations
Shekou to Hong Kong Central.

UPDATED

CHONGQING SHIPPING COMPANIES

Head Office: Chongqing Shipping Company, 21 DaoMenKou, Chongqing, People's Republic of China

High-speed craft operated

Type	Name	Seats	Delivered
SES Dong Feng MARIC 717 III	*Ming Jiang*	54-60	September 1984
SES Dong Feng MARIC 717 III	*Jin Sha Jiang*	54-60	1987
SES Dong Feng MARIC 717 III	*Jin Ling Jiang*	54-60	1989
SES Dong Feng MARIC 717 II	*Chong Qing*	70	October 1984
SES Dong Feng MARIC 717 II	*Yu Xiang*	70	1989

Operations
Chong Qing to Yi Bin, 200 nm
Chong Qing to Lu Zhou, 135 nm
Yangtze River between Chong Qing and Fu Ling, 65 nm
Yu Xiang, delivered in September 1989, operates from Hang Zhou to Chong Qing, 1512 nm along the Great Canal and Yangtze River through the spectacular 'Three Gorge' area.

UPDATED

DALIAN STEAMSHIP CO

People's Republic of China

High-speed craft operated

Type	Name	Seats	Delivered
CAT Fjellstrand (S) Flying Cat 40 m	*Hai Ou*	400	January 1993
CAT Fjellstrand (S) Flying Cat 40 m	*Hai Yan*	400	January 1993

Operations
Dalian to Nantai.

UPDATED

DALIAN YUAN FENG FERRY COMPANY

People's Republic of China

High-speed craft operated

Type	Name	Delivered
CAT Fjellstrand 38.8 m	*Fei Yu*	1993
CAT Wavemaster 49 m	*Fei Long*	1994

Operations
Dalian to Yantai.

NEW ENTRY

GEOPHYSICAL SURVEYS INC (USA)

People's Republic of China

High-speed craft operated

Type	Delivered
HOV Griffon Hovercraft 1000 TD	1985
HOV Griffon Hovercraft 1000 TD	1985
HOV Griffon Hovercraft 1000 TD	1985

Operations
Survey contract in China.

VERIFIED

GUANGDONG PROVINCE NAVIGATION COMPANY

People's Republic of China

High-speed craft operated

Type	Name	Seats	Delivered
CAT A Fai InCat 21.9 m	*Mingzhu Hu*	150	1982
CAT A Fai InCat 21.9 m	*Yin Zhou Hu*	150	1982
CAT A Fai InCat 21.9 m	*Liuhua Hu*	150	1982

Operations
Taiping and Jiangmen to Hong Kong.

VERIFIED

NANTONG HIGH-SPEED PASSENGER SHIP COMPANY

Nantong, People's Republic of China

High-speed craft operated

Type	Name	Seats	Delivered
CAT Austal Ships 36 m	*Tong Zhou*	430	1990

Operations
Shanghai to Nantong.

VERIFIED

NINGBO HUAGANG LTD

No 2-2 86 Lane, Bai Sha Road, Ningbo, People's Republic of China

High-speed craft operated

Type	Name	Seats	Delivered
CAT Fjellstrand 38.8 m	*Yong Xing*	312	November 1985

Operations
Ningbo to Shanghai.

VERIFIED

Fjellstrand 38.8 m Yong Xing   *1987*

SANFU SHIPPING CHINA

People's Republic of China

High-speed craft operated

Type	Name	Seats	Delivered
CAT A Fai InCat 21 m	*Jin San Hu*	150	1985
CAT WaveMaster 32 m	*Yin San Hu*	252	July 1989

VERIFIED

SHANGHAI FREE FLYING TRANSPORT

People's Republic of China

High-speed craft operated

Type	Name	Seats	Delivered
SES Wu-Hu Shipyard MARIC 719 II	—	257	August 1988
CAT Austal 40 m	*Free Flying*	—	1994

Operations
Shanghai to Ningbo.

UPDATED

MARIC 719 II 257 seat, 28 knot SES built by Wu-Hu Shipyard   *1989*

SHEN ZHEN SHIPPING

People's Republic of China

High-speed craft operated

Type	Name	Seats	Delivered
CAT A Fai InCat 21 m	*Yue Hai Chun*	169	1984
CAT A Fai InCat 21 m	*Shen Zhen Chun*	169	1985
CAT A Fai InCat 21 m	*Ling Nan Chun*	169	1987
CAT A Fai InCat 21 m	*Nan Hai Chun*	169	1989
CAT A Fai InCat 21 m	*Dong Fang Chun*	169	1991
CAT A Fai InCat 21 m	*Zhu Hai Chun*	169	1986
CAT A Fai AMD 28 m	*Jin Xiang*	242	1993

Operations
Shen Zen to Zhu Hai.

UPDATED

WUZHOU NAVIGATION COMPANY

People's Republic of China

High-speed craft operated

Type	Name	Seats	Delivered
CAT A Fai InCat 21 m	*Lijiang*	150	1983
CAT A Fai AMD 170	*Wuzhou*	150	1994

Operations
Wuzhou to Hong Kong.

UPDATED

YANTAI MARINE

People's Republic of China

High-speed craft operated

Type	Name	Seats	Delivered
CAT Fjellstrand 40 m	*Xin Shi Ji*	—	1993

NEW ENTRY

COMMONWEALTH OF INDEPENDENT STATES

AZOV SHIPPING COMPANY

89 Admirala Lunina Pr, Zhdanov 341010, CIS

Telex: 412601/2, 115156

High-speed craft operated

Type	Name	Delivered
HYD Kometa	*Kometa 19*	1973
HYD Kometa	*Kometa 22*	1974

VERIFIED

BLACK SEA SHIPPING COMPANY

1 Lastochkina Str, Odessa 270026, CIS

Telex: 232711, 412677

High-speed craft operated

Type	Name	Seats	Delivered
HYD S Ordzhonikidze Kometa	Kometa 13	116	1968 (Odessa)
HYD S Ordzhonikidze Kometa	Kometa 16	116	1969 (Odessa)
HYD S Ordzhonikidze Kometa	Kometa 27	116	1975 (Yalta)
HYD S Ordzhonikidze Kometa	Kometa 32	116	1977 (Yalta)
HYD S Ordzhonikidze Kometa	Kometa 37	116	1978 (Odessa)
HYD S Ordzhonikidze Kometa	Kometa 40	116	1979 (Yalta)
HYD S Ordzhonikidze Kometa	Kometa 41	116	1979 (Yalta)
SES Sosnovka Rassvet		80	
HYD-Feodosia Tsiklon	—		November 1987
CAT Westamarin W 4100S	Krymskaya Strela	298	April 1990
CAT Westamarin W 4100S	Golubaya Strela	300	April 1990

Operations
Daily services, Odessa to Ochakov, Kherson and Nikolaev. Services also from Yalta to Istanbul and Piraeus.
Black Sea Kometas carry over 1.5 million passengers a year and are mostly based in the ports of Sochi, Tuapse, Novorossiysk, Yalta, Odessa and Izmail.

UPDATED

Kolkhida craft at Odessa   *1988*

CASPIAN SHIPPING COPMANY

Astrakhan, CIS

D Gashumov, *President*

High-speed craft operated

Type	Name	Delivered
HYD Kometa	Kometa 21	1974
HYD Kometa	Kometa 28	1975

VERIFIED

FAR EASTERN SHIPPING COMPANY

ul 25-go Oktyabrya 15, Vladivostok 690019, CIS

High-speed craft operated

Type	Name	Seats	Delivered
CAT Fjellstrand 38.8 m	Mercury	286	March 1990
HYD Kometa	Kometa 20	116	1973
HYD Kometa	Kometa 29	116	1976
HYD Kometa	Kometa 31	116	1977

Operations
Vladivostok to Nakhodka to Preobrazhemie to Olga to Rudnaya Pristan (264 nm)
Vladivostok to Slavyanka (60 nm).

VERIFIED

MURMANSK SHIPPING COMPANY

Murmansk, CIS

High-speed craft operated

Type	Name	Delivered
HYD Kometa	Kometa 30	1976

VERIFIED

NORTHERN SHIPPING COMPANY

Archangelsk, CIS

High-speed craft operated

Type	Name	Seats	Delivered
CAT Fjellstrand 38.8 m	Solovki*	230	March 1990
HOV BHC AP1-88/100	North Wind (ex Siverko)	68	September 1991

*Currently leased to another operator

Operations
Archangelsk to Petrominsk to Solovetskiy.

UPDATED

NOVOROSSIYSK SHIPPING COMPANY

1 ul Svobody, Novorossiysk 353900, CIS

Telephone: +7 (86134) 51276
Telex: 279113
Telefax: +7 (86134) 64255

High-speed craft operated

Type	Name	Seats	Delivered
HYD Kometa	Kometa 10	116	1967
HYD Kometa	Kometa 19	116	1973
HYD Kometa	Kometa 22	116	1974
HYD Kometa	Kometa 24	116	1975
HYD Kometa	Kometa 33	116	1976
HYD Kometa	Kometa 53	116	1982
CAT Westamarin W 4100S	Irbis	292	August 1990
CAT Westamarin W 4100S	Sirius	292	September 1990

Operations
Novorossiysk to Pertominsk to Solovetskiy, 188 nm
Novorossiysk to Solovetskiy, 166 nm
Novorossiysk to Istanbul and Pireaus.

UPDATED

Westamarin W 4100S prior to delivery to Novorossiysk Shipping Company (Alan Bliault)   *1991*

SOVIET DANUBE SHIPPING COMPANY

2 Pr Suvorova, Izmail 272630, CIS

Telex: 412699, 232817

High-speed craft operated

Type	Name	Delivered
HYD Kometa	Kometa 34	1977
HYD Kometa	Kometa 35	1978
HYD Kometa	Kometa 36	1978

VERIFIED

CROATIA

ATLAS TURISTIČKA PLOVIDBA

50000 Dubrovnik, Pile 1, Croatia

Telephone: +38 (50) 44222
Telex: 27517, 27583 CRO
Telefax: +38 (50) 411100/442720

Owned by leading Croatian Travel Agency Atlas, Turistička Plovidba operates three Kometa and two Kolkhida hydrofoils for passenger and tourist services on the Adriatic sea, namely: *Krila Dubrovnika, Krila Brăca, Krila Hvara, Krila Dalmacije* and *Krila Istre.*

UPDATED

KVARNER EXPRESS INTERNATIONAL DD

Marsala Tita 186, 51410 Opatija, PO Box 92, Croatia

Telephone: +385 (51) 271111
Telefax: +385 (51) 271549/741

Radomir Premuš, *Managing Director*

In 1985 Kvarner Express introduced high-speed daily ferry services from Opatija to the Island of Rab and to Venice.

High-speed craft operated

Type	Name	Seats	Delivered
HYD S Ordzhonikidze Kolkhida	*Mirta*	145	1986
MH Marinteknik 41 MPV	*Iris*	350	1989

Operations
Opatija to Rab, 50 nm, Mali Losin, 53 nm
Opatija to Venice and in Spring 1987 to Ancona and Rimini
Istrian Penisula to Venice, Kornati Islands, Rimini, Ravenna, Pesaro
Rab and Mali Losin to Venice, Rimini, Zadar
Rueica to Venice, Silba and Rimini
Zadar to Sirenic and Ancona.

UPDATED

Marinteknik Iris   *1995*

DENMARK

DAMPSKIBSSELSKABET (DSØRESUND Ø) A/S

Havnegade 49, PO Box 1509, DK 1020 Copenhagen K, Denmark

Telephone: +45 3314 7770
Telefax: +45 3393 1330

Finn Zoega Olesen, *Managing Director*
Jens Nygaard, *Director*

High-speed craft operated

Type	Name	Seats	Delivered
CAT Marinteknik Marinjet	*Lommen* (Yard No 56)	235	December 1985
CAT Marinteknik 33 m	*Ørnen*	235	May 1986
CAT Fjellstrand 38.8 m	*Løberen*	256	September 1990
CAT Fjellstrand 38.8 m	*Springaren*	256	July 1991
CAT Fjellstrand 40 m Flying Cat	*Saelen*	288	May 1993
CAT Fjellstrand 40 m Flying Cat	*Søbjørnen*	—	May 1993
CAT Fjellstrand 40 m	*Kraka Viking*	—	1994
CAT Fjellstrand 40 m	*Sifka Viking*	—	1994

UPDATED

GRÅHUNBUS

Denmark

High-speed craft operated

Type	Name	Seats	Delivered
MH Boghammar 29.5 m	*Grasoelen*	—	1993

NEW ENTRY

PILEN (KÖPENHAMNS PILEN AB)

Havenegade 28, DK-1058 København, Denmark

Telephone: +45 3323 1260
Telefax: +45 3332 2794

High-speed craft operated

Type	Name	Seats	Delivered
CAT Westamarin W 3700	*Pilen 3* (ex *Vindile*)	315	1989
CAT Westamarin W88	*Delfinen*	170	1994

Operations
Copenhagen to Malmö in 45 minutes.

UPDATED

SUPPLY-TRANS A/S
(Wholly owned by Temdex A/S)

Kongevejen 64, DK-3450 Allerød, Denmark

Telephone: +45 4814 3515
Telefax: +45 4814 0515

Peter Krumbak, *Director*

Operator of specialised high-speed craft for the construction industry.

High-speed craft operated

Type	Name	Seats	Delivered
MH	*Kato I*	30	—
MH	*Nanok*	30	—
MH	*Imera*	30	—
MH	*Fremad II*	30	December 1994

UPDATED

ESTONIA

CITY JET

Regati PST 1-6K324A Tallin, EE 0019, Estonia

High-speed craft operated

Type	Name	Seats	Delivered
SES Cirrus 120P	*San Peitro*	—	1993
SES Cirrus 105P	*Ulstein Surfer*	—	1994

Operations
Tallin to Helsinki.

NEW ENTRY

SUKKULA

Estonia

High-speed craft operated

Type	Name	Seats	Delivered
CAT Teknicraft 22 m	*Sea Shuttle I*	—	1994

Operations
Tallin to Helsinki.

NEW ENTRY

TALLINK EXPRESS

Ädala 4A, Tallin, EE 0006, Estonia

High-speed craft operated

Type	Name	Seats	Delivered
HYD Morye Cyclone	*Liisa*	—	1992
HYD Morye Olympia	*Laura*	—	1993

Operations
Tallin to Helsinki.

NEW ENTRY

FRANCE

BATEAUX GALLUS

24 quai Lunel, F-06300 Nice, France

Telephone: +33 93 55 33 33
Telefax: +33 93 26 54 60

Salvatore Lauro, *Managing Director*

High-speed craft operated

Type	Name	Seats	Delivered
HYD Ordzhonikidze Kolkhida	*Gallus 6*	155	1991
HYD Ordzhonikidze Kolkhida	*Gallus 7*	155	1991
HYD Ordzhonikidze Kolkhida	*Gallus 8*	155	1991

Operations
Cote d'Azur (Monaco, Nice, Cannes, St Tropez, San Remo) and between Nice and Calvi, Corsica.

VERIFIED

CHANNILAND

3 rue Georges Clémenceau et Gare Maritime, BP 319, F-50400 Granville, France

High-speed craft operated

Type	Name	Delivered
CAT Westamaran 86	*Brittania*	1992
CAT Marinteknik 42 m	*Saint Malo* *	1993

*Damaged during grounding off Jersey (April 1995)

Operations
Granville to Jersey (April to October)
Jersey to Sark and Guernsey (April to September)
Jersey to Guernsey (April to November)
St Malo to Jersey (April to November).

VERIFIED

EMERAUDE LINES

BP 16, Gare Maritime, F-35401 Saint Malo Cedex, France

Telephone: +33 99 40 48 40
Telex: 950271 F
Telefax: +33 99 81 28 73

Pierre Legras, *Chairman*
Jean-Luc Griffon, *Commercial Director*
Jean-Francois Negre, *General Manager*

High-speed craft operated

Type	Name	Seats	Additional payload	Delivered
CAT Westamarin W95	*Trident 3*	205		
CAT Westamarin W95	*Trident 4*	218		May 1988
CAT Westamarin W95	*Trident 5*	200		
CAT Westamarin W95 D	*Trident 7*	201		1990
CAT Westamarin W95 D	*Trident 8*	201		
MH SBCN Hydro Jet	*Mont Orgueil*	140		January 1991
Leroux & Lotz 66 m Corsair	*Emeraude* *	400	42 cars	late 1994

*Withdrawn from service early 1995

Note: *Trident 6* was sold in 1994

Operations
Saint Malo to Jersey to Guernsey to Sark
Granville to Jersey to Guernsey
Carteret to Jersey to Guernsey
St Quay Portrieux to Jersey to Guernsey
Portbail to Jersey.

UPDATED

Emeraude *(no longer in service with Emeraude Lines)*   1995

NAVILAND

Parc du Golfe, F-56000 Vannes, France

Naviland was formed in 1993 by Sealink SNAT and took over the Navix SA fleet.

High-speed craft operated

Type	Name	Delivered
MH SFCN 28 m	*Nicholas Bouchard*	1988

Operations
Belle Ile en Mer to La Trinité, La Turballe, Noirmoutier, Port Valalo and Vannes.

VERIFIED

SNAT

France

High-speed craft operated

Type	Name	Seats	Delivered
CAT Westamaran 86	*Jaguar*	145	1992

VERIFIED

SURF SA

(Cie des Moyens de Surfaces Adaptes a l'Exploitation des Oceans)
148 rue Sainte, F-13007 Marseilles, France
BP 48, F-13262 Marseilles Cedex 7, France

Telephone: +33 91 54 92 29
Telex: 401042 SURF F
Telefax: +33 91 33 85 70

High-speed craft operated

Type	Name	Seats	Delivered
MH SFCN 34.9 m	*Aida*	90	April 1986
MH SFCN 34.9 m	*Angelica*	90	April 1986
CAT Marinteknik Verkstads 40 m	—		January 1992

Operations
Offshore support, off Congo coast and Cameroon, Pointe Noir to Emeraude North and South oil-fields and to the Likouala oil-field.

VERIFIED

Trident 3 *in service with Emeraude Lines*   1992

SURF's Angelica *and* Aida   1989

VEDETTES DE L'ODET FERRY COMPANY

F-29118 Benodet, France

High-speed craft operated

Type	Name	Seats	Delivered
MH SBCN 28 m	*Atlante*	165	1990

Operations
Concarneau to Iles de Glénan. **VERIFIED**

FRENCH POLYNESIA

AREMITI PACIFIC CRUISES (*BORA BORA NAVETTE*)

French Polynesia

High-speed craft operated

Type	Name	Seats	Delivered
CAT Sabre Catamarans, 17 m	*Aremiti*	—	1990
CAT Sabre Catamarans, 29 m	*Aremiti II*	288	1992
CAT Fjellstrand 40 m	—	300	1994

Operations
Papeete to Moorea. **UPDATED**

LEPRADO

French Polynesia

High-speed craft operated

Type	Name	Delivered
CAT InCat 23 m	*Tamahine Moorea*	1992
WPC InCat 37 m	*Tamahine Papeete* (Ex *Seaflight*)	1993

Operations
Tahiti to Moorea. **NEW ENTRY**

SPI MARITIME

French Polynesia

High-speed craft operated

Type	Name	Seats	Delivered
CAT Austal 48 m	*Ono-Ono*	—	1994

Operations
Papeete to Bora Bora. **NEW ENTRY**

GERMANY

AG EMS

PO Box 1154, Am Borkumkai, D-26691 Emden 1, Germany

Telephone: +49 (21) 890722
Telefax: +49 (21) 890742

High-speed craft operated

Type	Name	Seats	Delivered
CAT Fjellstrand 38.8 m	*Nordlicht*	272	March 1989

Operations
Emden to Borkum.

VERIFIED

Nordlicht *operated by AG Ems* **1992**

HALLIG-UND INSELREEDERI

D-25980 Westerland, Sylt, Germany

High-speed craft operated

Type	Name	Delivered
MH Marinteknik 42 m	*Adler Express*	1993

NEW ENTRY

KÖLN-DÜSSELDORFER DEUTSCHE RHEINSCHIFFAHRT AG (KD)

Frankenwerft 15, D-50667 Köln, Germany

Telephone: +49 (221) 20880
Telefax: +49 (221) 208 8229

High-speed craft operated

Type	Name	Seats
HYD Sormovo Raketa	*Rheinpfeil (Rhine Arrow)*	64

Operations
Cologne to Koblenz to Bingen to Mainz and many intermediate stops, 9 April to 24 October.

VERIFIED

Raketa, Rheinpfeil, *operated by Köln-Düsseldorfer (KD) German Rhine Line* **1992**

GREECE

ADVANCED TECHNOLOGY CRUISES

67 Iroon Polytechniou Avenue, GR-18536 Pireas, Greece

Telephone: +30 (1) 451 1017/418 0341/4181263
Telefax: +30 (1) 452 3876/4181266

Michail Theocharis, *Managing Director*

High-speed craft operated

Type	Name	Seats	Delivered
SES Polyship 30 m	*Manto*	200	1993
SES Polyship 33 m	*Alexandros**	250	1994

*Transferred to West Coast 1994

Operations
Services from Pasei to Corfu to Brindisi.

UPDATED

CERES HYDROFOIL SERVICES

8 Akti Themistokleus, Freattys, Piraeus, Greece

Telephone: +30 (1) 428 0001
Telex: 240107 HYDR GR
Telefax: +30 (1) 428 3526

Services started in 1975 with the Piraeus to Hydra route.

High-speed craft operated

Type	Name	Seats*	Delivered
HYD S Ordzhonikidze Kometa-M	*Flying Dolphin I*	132	1975
HYD S Ordzhonikidze Kometa-M	*Flying Dolphin II*	132	1975
HYD S Ordzhonikidze Kometa-M	*Flying Dolphin III*	132	1976
HYD S Ordzhonikidze Kometa-M	*Flying Dolphin V*	132	1976
HYD S Ordzhonikidze Kometa-M	*Flying Dolphin VI*	132	1976
HYD S Ordzhonikidze Kometa-M	*Flying Dolphin VII*	132	1976
HYD S Ordzhonikidze Kometa-M	*Flying Dolphin IV*	132	1977
HYD S Ordzhonikidze Kometa-M	*Flying Dolphin VIII*	132	1977
HYD S Ordzhonikidze Kometa-M	*Flying Dolphin IX*	132	1978

High-speed craft operated

Type	Name	Seats*	Delivered
HYD S Ordzhonikidze Kometa-M	Flying Dolphin X	132	1978
HYD S Ordzhonikidze Kometa-M	Flying Dolphin XI	132	1979
HYD S Ordzhonikidze Kometa-M	Flying Dolphin XII	132	1979
HYD S Ordzhonikidze Kometa-M	Flying Dolphin XIV	132	1981
HYD S Ordzhonikidze Kometa-M	Flying Dolphin XV	132	1981
HYD S Ordzhonikidze Kometa-M	Flying Dolphin XVI	132	1981
HYD S Ordzhonikidze Kolkhida	Flying Dolphin XVII	155	1986
HYD S Ordzhonikidze Kolkhida	Flying Dolphin XVIII	155	1986
HYD S Ordzhonikidze Kometa	Flying Dolphin XX	132	1988
HYD S Ordzhonikidze Kometa	Flying Dolphin XXI	132	1988
HYD S Ordzhonikidze Kometa	Flying Dolphin XXII	132	1989
HYD S Ordzhonikidze Kometa	Flying Dolphin XXIII	132	1989
HYD S Ordzhonikidze Kometa	Flying Dolphin XXIV	132	1989
HYD S Ordzhonikidze Kometa	Flying Dolphin XXV	132	1989
HYD S Ordzhonikidze Kolkhida	Flying Dolphin XIX	155	1990
CAT K Fjellstrand Flying Cat	Flyingcat I	352	1990
HYD S Ordzhonikidze Kometa	Flying Dolphin XXVI	132	1991
HYD S Ordzhonikidze Kometa	Flying Dolphin XXVII	132	1991
HYD S Ordzhonikidze Kometa	Flying Dolphin XXVIII	132	1991
HYD S Ordzhonikidze Kolkhida	Flying Dolphin XXIX	155	1993

(*Flying Dolphins IV, V* and *XII* are owned by Ceres Hydrofoils Shipping and Tourism SA. *Flying Dolphins VIII, IX* and *X* are owned by Ceres Hydrocomets Shipping and Tourism SA. *Flying Dolphins VI, VII, XI* and *XXIX* are owned by Ceres Express Ways Shipping and Tourism SA. *Flying Dolphins XIV, XV, XVI* and *XVII* are owned by Ceres Hydrolines Shipping Company.)
*MTU engines are being fitted to all Ceres Kometas enabling seat numbers to be increased to 132

Operations
Aghios Konstantinos to Volos to Skiathos to Glossa to Skopelos to Aionissos
Piraeus (Zea) Aigina to Poros to Hydra to Ermioni to Spetsai to Porto Heli to Leonidi to Kiparissi to Monemvassia to Kythira and Neapoli
Macedonia to Thessaloniki
Halkidiki to Moudania and Marmaras.

VERIFIED

Fjellstrand Flying Cat I *in service 1990 with Ceres Hydrofoil Services*   *1991*

DODECANESE HYDROFOILS

56 Panepistimiou Street, GR-10678 Athens, Greece

High-speed craft operated

Type	Name	Seats	Delivered
HYD Kometa	Marilena	—	1981
HYD Kometa	Tzina	—	1981
HYD Kometa	Marilena II	—	1993
HYD Kometa	Georgios M	—	1993
HYD Kometa	Aristea M	—	1993
HYD Kometa	Tzina II	—	1993

Operations
Inter-Dodecanese islands.

NEW ENTRY

HERMES

153 Koloktroni Street, GR-18536 Piraeus, Greece

High-speed craft operated

Type	Name	Seats	Delivered
HYD Rodriquez RHS 70	Nikos	—	1993
HYD Rodriquez RHS 70	Iptamenos Hermes II	—	1993
HYD Rodriquez RHS 140	Iptamenos Hermes I	—	1993
HYD Rodriquez RHS 160	Iptamenos Hermes III	—	1994

NEW ENTRY

ILIO LINES

1 Makras Stoas Street, GR-18531 Piraeus, Greece

High-speed craft operated

Type	Name	Seats	Delivered
HYD Kometa	Delfini I	102	1992
HYD Kometa	Delfini II	102	1992
HYD Kometa	Delfini III	102	1992
HYD Kometa	Delfini IV	102	1992
HYD Kometa	Thraki I	102	1992
HYD Kolkhida	Delfini V	—	1992
HYD Kometa	Delfini VII (ex Kometa 42)	102	1992
HYD Kometa	Delfini VIII	102	1992
HYD Kometa	Thassan Dolfin	102	1992
HYD Kometa	Delfini XVIII	102	1992
HYD Kometa	Delfini XX	102	1992
HYD Kolkhida	Delfini XXI	—	1992
HYD Kolkhida	Delfini XXII	—	1992

Delfini XVI ran aground and sank in gale conditions on 18 August 1993
    Delfini V was damaged in a collision in 1994

UPDATED

NOMIKOS

Greece

High-speed craft operated

Type	Name	Delivered
HYD Kometa	Flying Ikaros I (ex Wanda)	1990
HYD Kometa	Flying Ikaros II (ex Maria)	1990
HYD Kometa	Flying Ikaros III	1990

VERIFIED

PARASKEVAS SHIPPING COMPANY (TAKISTOURS)

Bouboulinas 6, Dapia, GR-18050 Spetsai, Greece

Telephone: +30 (298) 73025/72888
Telex: 214528
Telefax: +30 (298) 74315

Takis Paraskevas, *Owner, Managing Director*

High-speed craft operated

Type	Name	Seats	Delivered
CAT Westamarin W86	Supercats (ex Sauda)	168	1990

Operations
Pireaus to Agistri, Aegina and Epidaurus.

UPDATED

PIRAIKI NAFTILIAKI SA

Akti Kondyli 26-28, GR-18545 Piraeus, Greece

Telephone: +30 (1) 422 1042/1045
Telefax: +30 (1) 412 8112/8473

A M Karageorgis, *Managing Director*

High-speed craft operated

Type	Name	Seats	Delivered
SES Ulstein CIRR 120P	Catamaran II	316	1992

Operations
Piraeus to Rafina.

UPDATED

Catamaran II in service with Piraiki Naftiliaki SA   *1994*

RENATOUR SA
Rethimniaki Naftiliaki Touristiki

250 Arkadiou Rethymno, Crete, Greece

Telex: 291226 GR

High-speed craft operated

Type	Name	Seats	Delivered
CAT Westamarin W100D	Nearchos (ex Venture 83, launched as Rosario)	245	May 1982

Operations
Réthimnon to Santorini (Thira).   *VERIFIED*

SANTA LINES

Greece

High-speed craft operated

Type	Name	Delivered
HYD Kometa	Santa	1992
HYD Kometa	Santa II	1993
HYD Kometa	Santa III	1993

Operations
Kavala to Thassos and Limenaria.

NEW ENTRY

SONIA SHIPPING, MELINA TRADING

Greece

High-speed craft operated

Type	Name	Delivered
CAT Westamarin W95T	Karmen (ex Alisur Azul)	1989

Operations
African Coast.   *VERIFIED*

GUADELOUPE

ANTILLES TRANS-EXPRESS

Gare Maritime, Quai Gatine, 97110 Pointe à Pître, Guadeloupe

Telephone: +590 911343
Telefax: +590 911105

C H Munier, *General Manager*
L Labatut, *Operating Manager*

High-speed craft operated

Type	Name	Seats	Delivered
CAT Marinteknik 41 m CPV	Jetkat Express II	380	1992
CAT Marinteknik 34 m CPV	Emeraude Express	242	1986
CAT Marinteknik 34 m CPV	Antilles Express	297	1992
CAT Marinteknik 41 m CPV	Saphir Express	—	1994

Operations
Pointe à Pître to Marie Galante, 45 minutes
Pointe à Pître to Les Saintes, 45 minutes
Pointe à Pître to Dominique to Martinique, 3 hours 45 minutes
Pointe à Pître to Dominica (Roseau), 1 hour 30 minutes
    Transit in Roseau 30 minutes
Dominica to Martinique (Fort de France), 2 hours
Pointe à Pître to Martinique, 2 hours 50 minutes

High-speed sea transport of passengers between Guadeloupe and its dependencies Marie Galante and Les Saintes, as well as the neighbouring islands of Dominica and Martinique. In addition to its regular lines ATE organises charter trips and other activities.

UPDATED

SOCIÉTÉ DE TRANSPORTS MARITIMES BRUDEY FRÈRES

Quai de la Darse BP 783, 97174 Pointe à Pître, Guadeloupe

Telephone: +590 900448
Telex: 919810 GL
Telefax: +590 821562

Brudey Doenis, *Shipowner*
Vala Claude, *Commercial Director*

High-speed craft operated

Type	Name	Seats	Additional payload	Delivered
MH Esterel 35 m	Tropic	250		1988
CAT Westamarin 3700S 37 m	Maria	320		1990
CAT Westamarin 27 m	Flycat (ex Kogelwieck)	140		1992
CAT Westamarin 5000CF 50 m	Madikera*	352	35 cars	1993

*conversion of Anne Lise

Operations
Pointe à Pître to Dominique to Port de France, 3 hours
Pointe à Pître to Les Saintes, 21 miles, 45 minutes
Pointe à Pître to Marie Galante, 25 miles, 55 minutes.

UPDATED

HONG KONG

CASTLE PEAK POWER COMPANY LTD

Hong Kong

High-speed craft operated

Type	Name	Seats	Delivered
CAT A Fai InCat 16 m	Kwong Fai	40	June 1984

UPDATED

CHU KONG SHIPPING COMPANY LTD

7/F 28 Connaught Road West, Hong Kong

Chu Kong Shipping Company Ltd is registered in Hong Kong but owned by a People's Republic of China organisation. It acts as the general manager in Hong Kong for the Guangdong Province Hong Kong Macao Navigation Company, the organisation responsible for all the transportation companies in the ports around Guangdong Province. These transportation companies include:
Hui Yang County
Jiang Men Passenger Shipping
Jiuzhou Port Administration
Ping Gang Transportation Corporation
San Fu Shipping Company
Shun Gang Passenger Transport
Taishan Guanghai Port Corporation
Xin Gang Passenger Transport
Zhon Gang Steamer Navigation Company
Zhong Shan Shipping
Zhu Hai Jiuzhou Port Administration

High-speed craft operated

Type	Name	Seats	Delivered
CAT Fjellstrand 31.5 m	Hai Shan (ex Bei Xiu Hu)	289	1984
CAT Fjellstrand 31.5 m	Li Wan Hu	289	1984
CAT Fjellstrand 31.5 m	Xiu Li Hu	291	1984
CAT A Fai InCat 21 m	Jin Shan Hu	150	1985
CAT Fjellstrand 31.5 m	Hai Tian (ex Peng Lai Hu)	291	1985
CAT Fjellstrand 38.8 m	He Shan (ex Long Jin)	312	1985
CAT Fjellstrand 31.5 m	Yi Xin (ex Yi Xian Hu)	291	1985
CAT Marinteknik JC-3000	Hai Shan	—	1986
CAT Fjellstrand 31.5 m	Lian Hua Hu	291	1986
CAT Marinteknik 34 m	Jiu Zhou	—	1987
CAT Precision Marine 40 m	Shun Feng	—	1988
CAT Precision Marine 40 m	Xin Ning	—	1988
CAT WaveMaster 32 m	Yin Shan Hu	252	1989
CAT Italthai Marine 32.5 m	Dou Men	—	1990
CAT Italthai Marine 32.5 m	Zhong Shan Hu	—	1990
CAT WaveMaster 34.5 m	Zheng Xing Hu	310	1990
CAT Austal 40 m	Shun Shui	354	1991
CAT Singapore Shipbuilding 35 m	Tai Ping	—	1991
CAT WaveMaster 39 m	Wu Yi Hu	—	1992
CAT Austal 40 m	Xin Duan Zhou	338	1992
CAT Austal 40 m	Shun De	354	1992
CAT Austal 40 m	Zhu Hai	338	1992
CAT Austal 40 m	Nan Gui	338	1992
CAT Austal 40 m	Kai Ping	368	1992

High-speed craft operated

Type	Name	Seats	Delivered
CAT Austal 40 m	*Lian Shan Hu*	338	1992
CAT WaveMaster 39 m	*Peng Lai Hu*	—	1992
CAT Austal 40 m	*Xan Xing*	354	1993
CAT Austal 40 m	*Hai Chang*	—	1993
CAT Aluminium Craft (88) 35 m	*Dong Tai An*	—	1993
CAT Austal 40 m	*Hui Yang*	—	1993
CAT Austal 40 m	*Tai Shan*	—	1993
CAT Austal 40 m	*Gang Zhou*	—	1993
CAT Austal 40 m	*Gao Ming*	—	1993
CAT Austal 40 m	*Gui Feng*	—	1993
CAT Austal 40 m	*San Bu*	—	1993
CAT WaveMaster 39 m	*Peng Jiang*	—	1993
CAT Austal 40 m	*Shunjing*	355	1994
CAT Austal 40 m	*Lian Gang Hu*	355	1994
CAT Austal 40 m	*Yi Xian Hu*	355	1994
CAT Austal 40 m	*Xin He Shan*	300	1994
CAT Austal 40 m	*Zhong Shan*	355	1994

Vessels are ordered through the subsidiary company Yuet Hing Marine Supplies Company Ltd.

UPDATED

YUET HING MARINE SUPPLIES COMPANY LTD

25/F Yardley Commercial Building, 1-3 Connaught Road West, Hong Kong

Telephone: +852 815 0333
Telex: 65317 YHMSC HX
Telefax: +852 815 2188

Liang Jian Tao, *Managing Director*
Lin Zao Yu, *Director and Deputy General Manager*

Yuet Hing Marine Supplies Company Ltd is an associate company of Chu Kong Shipping and has ordered the building of over 40 various high-speed passenger vessels in aluminium alloy since 1980 for companies in the ports of Guangdong Province.

UPDATED

CUSTOMS AND EXCISE DEPARTMENT

8th Floor, Harbour Building, 38 Pier Road, Central, Hong Kong

Telephone: +852 852 3386
Telex: 65092 CUSEX HX
Telefax: +852 854 1959

Raymond Li, *Assistant Commissioner (Operations)*
Vincent Poon, *Head of Command, Marine and Land Enforcement*

High-speed craft operated

Type	Name
MH Chung Wah Shipbuilding and Engineering Co Ltd King Class Yard No 204	*Customs 6 Sea Glory*
MH Chung Wah Shipbuilding and Engineering Co Ltd King Class Yard No 205	*Customs 5 Sea Guardian*
MH Chung Wah Shipbuilding and Engineering Co Ltd King Class Yard No 206	*Customs 2 Sea Leader*

UPDATED

Hong Kong Customs and Excise fleet 1991

DISCOVERY BAY TRANSPORTATION SERVICES LTD HONG KONG RESORT COMPANY

2nd floor, Jardine House, Central, Hong Kong

Telephone: +852 987 7351
Telex: 65179 HKRCL HX
Telefax: +852 987 5246

Eric Chu, *Executive Director*
Andrew Kwong, *Executive Director*

High-speed craft operated

Type	Name	Seats	Delivered
SES Hovermarine HM 218	*RTS 201*	100	October 1986
SES Hovermarine HM 218	*RTS 202*	100	March 1987
SES Hovermarine HM 218	*RTS 203*	100	December 1986
MH Marinteknik Sweden/ Singapore 35 MPV	*Discovery Bay 12*	300	May 1987
MH Marinteknik (S) 35 MPV	*Discovery Bay 15*	300	May 1987
MH Marinteknik (S) 35 MPV	*Discovery Bay 16*	300	June 1987
MH Marinteknik (S) 35 MPV	*Discovery Bay 19*	300	January 1990
MH Marinteknik (S) 35 MPV	*Discovery Bay 20*	300	May 1990
MH Marinteknik (S) 35 MPV	*Discovery Bay 21*	300	June 1992
MH Marinteknik (S) 35 MPV	*Discovery Bay 22*	300	March 1993
MH Cheoy Lee 22.8 m	*Discovery Bay 17*	170	October 1988
MH Cheoy Lee 22.8 m	*Discovery Bay 10*	170	May 1986
MH Cheoy Lee 22.8 m	*Discovery Bay 11*	170	July 1986
MH Cheoy Lee 22.8 m	*Discovery Bay 18*	170	January 1989
MH Cheoy Lee 19.7 m	*Discovery Bay 23* (ex *Discovery Bay 3*)	100	August 1982
MH Cheoy Lee 19.7 m	*Discovery Bay 8*	100	July 1983
MH Cheoy Lee 19.7 m	*Discovery Bay 9*	100	September 1983
CAT Marinteknik (S) 42 m	*Discovery Bay 1*	500	1995
CAT Marinteknik (S) 42 m	*Discovery Bay 2*	500	(1995)
CAT Marinteknik (S) 42 m	*Discovery Bay 3*	500	(1995)

Operations
Discovery Bay, Lantau to Central, Hong Kong, 9 nm, 25 minutes
Approximately 600 000 passenger trips per month.

UPDATED

Discovery Bay 16 1995

FAR EAST HYDROFOIL COMPANY LTD

Penthouse, 39th Floor, Shun Tak Centre, 200 Connaught Road, Central, Hong Kong

Telephone: +852 859 3111
Telex: 74200 SEDAM HX
Telefax: +852 559 6471

Stanley Ho, *Group Executive Chairman*
David Hill, *Executive Director*
Andrew Tse, *Group Operations Director*
Jenning Wang, *Engineering Manager*
Edmund Cheng, *Fleet Operations Manager*

The company started hydrofoil service in 1963 with a PT 20 and gradually built up to a total of 14 surface-piercing hydrofoils. The Far East Hydrofoil Company began the world's first commercial Jetfoil service in April 1975. Subsequently the Jetfoils took over the bulk of the traffic due to passenger demand and the surface-piercing hydrofoils were gradually phased out and additional Jetfoils purchased. All surface-piercing hydrofoils were removed from service by the end of 1983 and subsequently sold. In 1993 FEH Jetfoils carried 77.1 per cent of all Hong Kong to Macau passenger traffic with 49 283 crossings and 10.6 million passengers. By June 1994 FEH Jetfoils had carried a total of 109 369 784 passengers. The fitting of new seats and interior decoration to the entire FEH fleet began in April 1993.

High-speed craft operated

Type	Name	Seats	Delivered
STEC			
HYD Boeing Jetfoil 929-100	*Madeira*	268	1975
HYD Boeing Jetfoil 929-100	*Santa Maria*	268	1975
HYD Boeing Jetfoil 929-100	*Flores* (ex *Kalakaua '78*)	268	1978
HYD Boeing Jetfoil 929-100	*Corvo* (ex *Kamehameha*)	268	1978
HYD Boeing Jetfoil 929-100	*Pico* (ex *Kuhio*)	268	1978
HYD Boeing Jetfoil 929-100	*Saõ Jorge* (ex *Jet Caribe I '80*, ex *Jet de Oriente '78*)	268	1980
HYD Boeing Jetfoil 929-100	*Acores* (ex *Jet Caribe II*)	268	1980
HYD Boeing Jetfoil 929-100	*Ponta Delgada* (ex *Flying Princess II*)	268	1981
HYD Boeing Jetfoil 929-115	*Terceira* (ex *Normandy Princess*)	268	1981
HYD Boeing Jetfoil 929-100	*Urzela* (ex *Flying Princess*)	268	1981
HYD Boeing Jetfoil 929-115	*Funchal* (ex *Jetferry One '83*)	268	*1983*
HYD Boeing Jetfoil 929-115	*Horta* (ex *Jetferry Two*)	268	1983
HYD Boeing Jetfoil 929-115	*Lilau* (ex *HMS Speedy*)	268	1987
HYD Boeing Jetfoil 929-100	*Guia* (ex *Okesa*)	268	1990
HYD Boeing Jetfoil 929-115	*Taipa* (ex *Princesa Guaeimara*)	268	*1991*
HYD Boeing Jetfoil 929-115	*Cacilhas* (ex *Princesa Guayarmina*)	268	1991
HYD China Shipbuilding PS-30	*Balsa*	274	1994
HYD China Shipbuilding PS-30	—	274	1995

*converted 929-320

Operations
Hong Kong to Macau, 38 to 40 nm, 24 hour service since March 1989
Services operate four times per hour each way between 07.00 and 20.00 and twice an hour from 20.00 to 02.30 and then two more sailings at 04.00 and 06.00.

UPDATED

Funchal, *Jetfoil Model 929-115*   *1990*

Saõ Jorge (Paul Beaver)   *1995*

HONG KONG HI-SPEED FERRIES LTD

13/F, V Huen Building, 138 Queen's Road, Central, Hong Kong

Telephone: +852 815 2789
Telex: 89846 HKHPF HX
Telefax: +852 543 0324/544 4392

Dr Stanley Ho, *Chairman*
Captain P N Parashar, *General Manager*

High-speed craft operated

Type	Name	Speed	Seats	Delivered
MH Vosper Thornycroft 62.5 m	*Cheung Kong*	26 knots	659	May 1985
MH Vosper Thornycroft 62.5 m	*Ju Kong*	26 knots	659	May 1985

Operations
Hong Kong to Macau, journey time approximately 105 minutes.
Seven departures on weekends and holidays, six departures on weekdays.

Fares
Weekends and public holidays: HK$58 to HK$95
Weekdays: HK$35 to HK$71
Exclusive of embarkation fee of HK$26 from Hong Kong and HK$22 from Macau

Traffic carried
820 874 passengers in 1993

UPDATED

Cheung Kong   *1989*

HONG KONG MACAO HYDROFOIL COMPANY LTD

Suite 2903, 29th Floor, 9 Queen's Road, Central, Hong Kong

Telephone: +852 521 8302
Telefax: +852 810 0952

Tony Lee, *General Manager*

This company started hydrofoil service in 1964 with two Rodriquez Supramar PT 20, 68-seat craft operating between Hong Kong and Macau. It now operates a fleet of seven catamaran ferries.

High-speed craft operated

Type	Name	Seats	Delivered
CAT Marinteknik 41 CPV	*Oregrund*	306	January 1989
CAT Marinteknik 41 CPV	*Camoes/Cowes*	306	July 1989
CAT Marinteknik 41 CPV	*Estrela do Mar*	306	August 1989
CAT Marinteknik 41 CPV	*Lusitano*	306	January 1991
CAT Marinteknik 41 CPV	*Vasco Da Gama*	306	May 1991
CAT Marinteknik 41 CPV	*Santa Cruz*	306	July 1991
CAT Marinteknik 41 CPV	*Magellan*	306	December 1991

Operations

Hong Kong to Macau, 37 nm, 1 hour
Tsimshatsui to Macau, 37 nm, 1 hour.

UPDATED

Vasco Da Gama *operated by Hong Kong Macao Hydrofoil Company* **1992**

THE HONG KONG & YAUMATI FERRY COMPANY LTD

Central Harbour Services Pier, 1st Floor, Pier Road, Central, Hong Kong

Telephone: +852 542 3081
Telex: 83140 HYFCO HX
Telefax: +852 542 3958

Colin K Y Lam, *Chairman*
Peter M K Wong, *President and Chief Executive Officer*
David C S Ho, *General Manager*

The world's largest operator of sidewall hovercraft (SES).

High-speed craft operated

Type	Name	Seats	Delivered
SES Hovermarine HM 216 (HM 2 Mk III)	HYF 103	74	1975
SES Hovermarine HM 216 (HM 2 Mk III)	HYF 104	74	1975
SES Hovermarine HM 218 (HM 2 Mk IV)	HYF 105	100	1976
SES Hovermarine HM 218 (HM 2 Mk IV)	HYF 106	100	1976
SES Hovermarine HM 218 (HM 2 Mk IV)	HYF 107	100	1976
SES Hovermarine HM 218 (HM 2 Mk IV)	HYF 111	105	1979
SES Hovermarine HM 218 (HM 2 Mk IV)	HYF 112	105	1979
SES Hovermarine HM 218 (HM 2 Mk IV)	HYF 113	105	1980
SES Hovermarine HM 218 (HM 2 Mk IV)	HYF 114	105	1980
SES Hovermarine HM 218 (HM 2 Mk IV)	HYF 115	105	1980
SES Hovermarine HM 218 (HM 2 Mk IV)	HYF 116	74	1980
SES Hovermarine HM 218 (HM 2 Mk IV)	HYF 117	105	1980
SES Hovermarine HM 218 (HM 2 Mk IV)	HYF 118	105	1980
SES Hovermarine HM 218 (HM 2 Mk IV)	HYF 119	105	1980
SES Hovermarine HM 218 (HM 2 Mk IV)	HYF 120	105	1980
SES Hovermarine HM 218 (HM 2 Mk IV)	HYF 121	105	1980
SES Hovermarine HM 218 (HM 2 Mk IV)	HYF 122	105	1980
SES Hovermarine HM 218 (HM 2 Mk IV)	HYF 123	105	1980
SES Hovermarine HM 218 (HM 2 Mk IV)	HYF 124	105	1980
SES Hovermarine HM 218 (HM 2 Mk IV)	HYF 125	105	1980
SES Hovermarine HM 218 (HM 2 Mk IV)	HYF 126	105	1980
SES Hovermarine HM 218 (HM 2 Mk IV)	HYF 127	105	1980
SES Hovermarine HM 218	HYF 128	105	1985
SES Hovermarine HM 218	HYF 130	74	1982
SES Vosper Hovermarine HM 527	Tejo	200	1983
SES Vosper Hovermarine HM 527	Douro	200	1983
SES Vosper Hovermarine HM 527	Sado	200	1983
SES Vosper Hovermarine HM 527	Mondego	200	1983
CAT Kværner Fjellstrand 40 m	HKF I	422	1993
CAT Kværner Fjellstrand 40 m	HKF II	422	1993

Operations	Crossing time	1993 Passengers
Hong Kong Central to:		
Tuen Mun	42 min (SES)	3 756 000
	30 min (CAT)	57 000
Tsuen Wan	22 min	1 576 000
Goad Coast	45 min	269 000
Tsim Sha Tsui East	5-8 min	659 000
Mui Wo/Peng Chau	35 min	106 000
Cheung Chau	35 min	154 000
Macau	80 min	527 000
Shekou	70 min	197 000
Whampoa	175 min	51 000
Wanchai to Tuen Mun	45 min	10 000

UPDATED

ROYAL HONG KONG POLICE FORCE, MARINE REGION

25 Salisbury Road, Tsim Sha Tsui, Kowloon, Hong Kong

Telephone: +852 366 5827
Telex: 65367 HX
Telefax: +852 311 5564

Lim Sak-yeung, *Regional Commander, Assistant Commissioner*
Foo Tsun-kong, *Deputy Regional Commander, Chief Superintendent*
J L Pettengell, *Chief Staff Officer, Chief Superintendent*

High-speed craft operated

Type	Name
MH Chung Wah Shipbuilding and Engineering Co Ltd 26.3 m, Yard No 178, Mk II Patrol	PL 57 Mercury
MH Chung Wah Shipbuilding and Engineering Co Ltd 26.3 m, Yard No 179, Mk II Patrol	PL 58 Vulcan
MH Chung Wah Shipbuilding and Engineering Co Ltd 26.3 m, Yard No 180, Mk II Patrol	PL 59 Ceres
MH Chung Wah Shipbuilding and Engineering Co Ltd 26.5 m, Yard No 166, Mk I Patrol	PL 60 Aquarius
MH Chung Wah Shipbuilding and Engineering Co Ltd 26.5 m, Yard No 167, Mk I Patrol	PL 61 Pisces
MH Chung Wah Shipbuilding and Engineering Co Ltd 26.5 m, Yard No 168, Mk I Patrol	PL 62 Argo
MH Chung Wah Shipbuilding and Engineering Co Ltd 26.5 m, Yard No 169, Mk I Patrol	PL 63 Carina
MH Chung Wah Shipbuilding and Engineering Co Ltd 26.5 m, Yard No 170, Mk I Patrol	PL 64 Cetus
MH Chung Wah Shipbuilding and Engineering Co Ltd 26.5 m, Yard No 171, Mk I Patrol	PL 65 Dorado
MH Chung Wah Shipbuilding and Engineering Co Ltd 26.5 m, Yard No 172, Mk I Patrol	PL 66 Octans
MH Chung Wah Shipbuilding and Engineering Co Ltd 26.5 m, Yard No 173, Mk I Patrol	PL 67 Vela
MH Chung Wah Shipbuilding and Engineering Co Ltd 26.5 m, Yard No 174, Mk I Patrol	PL 68 Volans
MH Chung Wah Shipbuilding and Engineering Co Ltd 26.5 m, Yard No 189, Mk III Patrol	PL 70 King Lai
MH Chung Wah Shipbuilding and Engineering Co Ltd 26.5 m, Yard No 190, Mk III Patrol	PL 71 King Yee
MH Chung Wah Shipbuilding and Engineering Co Ltd 26.5 m, Yard No 191, Mk III Patrol	PL 72 King Lim
MH Chung Wah Shipbuilding and Engineering Co Ltd 26.5 m, Yard No 192, Mk III Patrol	PL 73 King Hau
MH Chung Wah Shipbuilding and Engineering Co Ltd 26.5 m, Yard No 193, Mk III Patrol	PL 74 King Dai
MH Chung Wah Shipbuilding and Engineering Co Ltd 26.5 m, Yard No 194, Mk III Patrol	PL 75 King Chung
MH Chung Wah Shipbuilding and Engineering Co Ltd 26.5 m, Yard No 195, Mk III Patrol	PL 76 King Shun
MH Chung Wah Shipbuilding and Engineering Co Ltd 26.5 m, Yard No 196, Mk III Patrol	PL 77 King Tak
MH Chung Wah Shipbuilding and Engineering Co Ltd 26.5 m, Yard No 197, Mk III Patrol	PL 78 King Chi
MH Chung Wah Shipbuilding and Engineering Co Ltd 26.5 m, Yard No 198, Mk III Patrol	PL 79 King Tai
MH Chung Wah Shipbuilding and Engineering Co Ltd 26.5 m, Yard No 199, Mk III Patrol	PL 80 King Kwan
MH Chung Wah Shipbuilding and Engineering Co Ltd 26.5 m, Yard No 200, Mk III Patrol	PL 81 King Mei
MH Chung Wah Shipbuilding and Engineering Co Ltd 26.5 m, Yard No 201, Mk III Patrol	PL 82 King Yan
MH Chung Wah Shipbuilding and Engineering Co Ltd 26.5 m, Yard No 202, Mk III Patrol	PL 83 King Yung
MH Chung Wah Shipbuilding and Engineering Co Ltd 26.5 m, Yard No 203, Mk III Patrol	PL 84 King Kan
MH Australian Shipbuilding Industries 32.6 m	PL 51 Protector
MH Australian Shipbuilding Industries 32.6 m	PL 52 Guardian
MH Australian Shipbuilding Industries 32.6 m	PL 53 Defender
MH Australian Shipbuilding Industries 32.6 m	PL 54 Preserver
MH Australian Shipbuilding Industries 32.6 m	PL 55 Rescuer
MH Australian Shipbuilding Industries 32.6 m	PL 56 Detector

This organisation also operates a range of high-speed craft including eleven 10 m inshore patrol launches, four 11 m logistic launches and thirteen 8 m 40 knot interceptors.

UPDATED

26.5 m Chung Wah Patrol Boat Mk I **1994**

HONG KONG PARKVIEW FERRY SERVICES

11 F Worldwide House, 19 Des Voeux Road, Central, Hong Kong

High-speed craft operated

Type	Name	Seats	Delivered
CAT K Fjellstrand (S) FlyingCat 40 m	*Universal Mk I*	262	December 1992
CAT K Fjellstrand (S) FlyingCat 40 m	*Universal Mk II*	262	December 1993
CAT K Fjellstrand (S) FlyingCat 40 m	*Universal Mk III*	263	October 1993
CAT FBM Tricat 35 m	*Universal Mk VI*	160	December 1993
CAT FBM Tricat 45 m	*Universal Mk 2001*	340	January 1995

Operations
Hong Kong to Shenzhen airport, China.

UPDATED

Universal Mk 2001   *1995*

PANYU NAN SHA SHIPPING

Hong Kong

High-speed craft operated

Type	Name	Delivered
HYD PTS 75 Mk II	*Nan Sha No 1*	1992
HYD Rodriquez RHS 140	*Nan Sha No 3*	1992
HYD Rodriquez RHS 140	*Nan Sha No 5*	1993
CAT WaveMaster 39 m	*Nan Sha No 2*	December 1992
CAT WaveMaster 42 m	*Nan Sha No 18*	1994
CAT WaveMaster 42 m	*Nan Sha No 28*	1994

Operations
Hong Kong to People's Republic of China.

UPDATED

HUNGARY

MAHART TOURS

1056 Budapest, Belgrád rakpart, Nemzetközi Hajóállomás, Hungary

Telephone: +36 (1) 118 1743/1704/1586
Telex: 225412
Telefax: +36 (1) 118 7740

MAHART (Magyar Hajózási Részvénytársaság) introduced three Raketa hydrofoils on the River Danube between Hungary and Austria in 1962. Since the mid-1970s the Raketas have been replaced by Meteor and Voskhod hydrofoils. In 1993 four Polesye type vessels were introduced on the same routes, these craft have a very low draft of 0.40 m on foils. The cruise speed of all vessels is between 38 and 42 knots. MAHART carries between 30 000 and 40 000 passengers a year. Hydrofoils and traditional boats are also available for private hire.

High-speed craft operated

Type	Name	Seats	Delivered
HYD Sormovo Meteor	*Sólyom I*	108	1975
HYD Sormovo Voskhod	*Vöcsök I*	62	1977
HYD Sormovo Voskhod	*Vöcsök II*	62	1986
HYD Sormovo Voskhod	*Vöcsök III*	62	1987
HYD Sormovo Voskhod	*Vöcsök IV*	62	1987
HYD Sormovo Meteor	*Solyom II*	104	1988
HYD Polesye	*Bíbic I*	44	1992
HYD Polesye	*Bíbic II*	44	1992
HYD Polesye	*Bíbic III*	44	1993
HYD Polesye	*Bíbic IV*	44	1993

Operations
Between Budapest and Vienna, 282 km, 4 to 5 hours (depending on the current), April to October, daily. Budapest to Esztergom, June to August weekends, 73 km, 1 hour.

VERIFIED

Sormovo Meteor Sólyom I operated by MAHART   *1986*

INDIA

MINISTRY OF SURFACE TRANSPORT (SHIPPING CORPORATION)

Nehru Centre, Discovery of India Building, Dr Annie Besant Road, Worli, Bombay 400018, India

High-speed craft operated

Type	Name	Seats	Delivered
CAT Tille Shipyards 31.9 m	*Khadeeja Beevi*	100	1990
CAT Tille Shipyards 31.9 m	*Hameedath Bee*	100	1990

Operations
Lakshadweep area of South West India.

UPDATED

NEW INDIA BUSINESS HOUSE LTD

Arvind Complex Plot No 156, Opp. Maharashtra Nagar, Lokmanya Tilak Road, Boivali (West), Bombay 400092, India

High-speed craft operated

Type	Name	Seats	Delivered
HOV Griffon 4000 TD	*Shri Bajarangtasbapa*	51	1992
HOV Griffon 4000 TD	*Shri Saibaba*	51	1992

VERIFIED

INDONESIA

BAHTERA SEGARA PERSANDA

Indonesia

High-speed craft operated

Type	Name	Delivered
CAT Precision 31 m	*Bahtera Princess*	1990
CAT 26 m	*Bahtera Express*	1991
MH Aluminium Craft 88	*Penguin Success*	1992

NEW ENTRY

BALI HAI CRUISES

PO Box 548, Den Pasar 80001, Bali, Indonesia

High-speed craft operated

Type	Name	Seats	Delivered
CAT Austal 36 m	*Bali Hai II*	332	1994

Operations
Benoa to Lembongan Island.

NEW ENTRY

CITRA BAHARI NUSTRAINDO

JLRE Martatinata, Sukupang Pulau Datam, Jakarta, Indonesia

High-speed craft operated

Type	Name	Seats	Delivered
CAT NQEA 24 m InCat	*Supercat II*	180+	1990

VERIFIED

P T BINTAN BARUNA SAKTI

Pelabuhan Sekupang - Ferry Terminal, Batam Island, Indonesia

Telephone: +62 (778) 22639
Telefax: +62 (778) 322901

Pipin Kusnadi, *President*
Daniel Chendra, *Managing Director*

High-speed craft operated

Type	Name	Seats	Delivered
MH Setouchi Craft Co Ltd	*Sea Prince*	140	1976
MH SBF Shipbuilders	*Seaflyte*	220	1981
MH WaveMaster International	*Sea Raider II*	250	1984
MH Wavemaster International	*Golden Raider*	240	1985
MH Wavemaster International	*Jet Raider*	350	1991
MH Wavemaster International	*Ocean Raider*	350	1992

Operations
Singapore to Sekupang
Singapore to Tonjong Pinang.

VERIFIED

PT HOVER MARITIM SEMANDERA

Jalan Gondangdia Lama 26, Jakarta 10350, Indonesia

Telephone: +62 (21) 325608/310 3358
Telex: 45746 SHARCO IA
Telefax: +62 (21) 310 3357

Air Marshal, Suharnoko Harbani Rtd, *Chairman*
H M Suharnoko, *Vice Chairman*
H Wijaya, *Commissioner*
Ir A W Suharnoko, *President, Director*
Isamaya P Asrah, *Director*

High-speed craft operated

Type	Name	Seats	Delivered
SES Vosper Hovermarine HM 218 Mk IV	*Semandera Satu*	78	1986
SES Vosper Hovermarine HM 218 Mk IV	*Semandera Dua*	78	1986

Operations
   Tanjung Priok (Port of Jakarta) to P Kotok Besar and P Antuk Timur (Holiday resort islands north-west of Jakarta), distance 40 to 45 nm, trip time 1 hour 20 minutes, commercial service started February 1987, one and occasionally two trips per day, four days per week. Departures: Jakarta 07.00, Islands 16.00, contract with resort operator (subsidiary of Japan Airlines).
   Hover Maritim Semandera is also offering a two day cruise package to the Ujung Kulon National Park from Jakarta, distance 135 nm, trip time 4 hours 25 minutes, service started September 1987, major holidays only. Departures: 07.00 from Jakarta.
   Since November 1989, the company has provided offshore crew transfer services.

VERIFIED

Vosper Hovermarine HM 218 Mk IV Semandera Satu   *1989*

PT MABUA INTAN EXPRESS (PT MAHASARA BUANA)

Jakarta, Indonesia

High-speed craft operated

Type	Name	Seats	Delivered
CAT K Fjellstrand (S) Flying Cat 40 m	*Mabua Express*	248	1992

Operations
Bali to Lombok.

VERIFIED

PT SATMARINDO

Indonesia

High-speed craft operated

Type	Name	Seats	Delivered
MH SBF Engineering (Phil Curran design)	*Satrya Express*	62	1985

Crew boat with capacity for two 8 tonne deck containers

Operations
Servicing of the Hudbay Oil Lalang oil and gas fields in the Strait of Malacca.

VERIFIED

PULAU SERIBU MARINE RESORT

Indonesia

High-speed craft operated

Type	Name	Delivered
MH Yamaha 19.5 m	*Lumba-Lumba*	1989
MH Yamaha 20 m	*Pantara VII*	1993

Operations
Jakarta to Pulau Seribu.

VERIFIED

QUICKSILVER

Bali

High-speed craft operated

Type	Name	Delivered
WPC NQEA InCat 37 m	*Quicksilver Beluga*	1992

Operations
Benoa to Nusa Penida.

NEW ENTRY

IRAN

VALFAJRE 8 SHIPPING

Karimkhan-Zand Avenue, Abyar Alley, 15875 Tehran, Iran

High-speed craft operated

Type	Name	Seats	Delivered
CAT WaveMaster 44 m	*Negeen*	242	1994

Operations
Khoramshahr to Kuwait city.

UPDATED

ITALY

ADRIATICA DI NAVIGAZIONE SpA

PO Box 705, I-30123 Venice, Italy

Telephone: +39 (41) 781611
Telex: 410045 ADRNAV I

High-speed craft operated

Type	Name	Seats	Delivered
HYD Rodriquez RHS 160	*Diomedea* (launched as *Flying Phoenix*)	168	1975
HYD Rodriquez RHS 160F	*Monte Gargano*	212	1989
Rodriquez Monostab 47	*Marconi*	400	1991
Rodriquez Monostab 47	*Pacinotti*	400	1992

Operations
1991 schedule June to September
Pacinotti: Vieste to Tremiti, 1 hour
Peschici to Tremiti, 1 hour 10 minutes
Rodi to Tremiti, 35 minutes
Marconi: Operations on longer routes along Adriatic coast
Diomedea: Vasto to Tremiti, 1 hour 15 minutes
Monte Gargano: Termoli to Tremiti, 45 minutes.

VERIFIED

Marconi *operated by Adriatica di Navagazione*   1992

ALBADRIA

Italy

High-speed craft operated

Type	Name	Seats	Delivered
SES Cirrus 120P	*La Vikinga*	—	1993

Operations
Bari to Kerkira and Durres.

NEW ENTRY

ALILAURO SpA

Via F Caracciolo 11, I-80122 Naples, Italy

Telephone: +39 (81) 761 1004/4249
Telex: 720354 ALILAR I
Telefax: +39 (81) 761 4250

Captain Salvatore Lauro, *President*
Dott Nicola D'Abundo, *Managing Director*

High-speed craft operated

Type	Name	Seats	Delivered
HYD Rodriquez PT 50	*Alimarte* (ex *Alivit*)	140	1969
HYD Sormovo Kometa-M	*Aliapollo* (ex *Alitunisi*, 1984 ex *Alispan Secondo*, 1980 ex *Atalanta*, 1971)	116	1971
HYD Sormovo Kometa-M	*Freccia Vulcano*	116	1971
HYD Sormovo Kometa-M	*Alivulcano* (ex *Alispan Primo*, 1977 ex *Lepa Vida*, 1970)	116	1972
HYD Sormovo Kometa-M	*Alivenere* (ex *Aligiglio*)*	116	1972
HYD Sormovo Kometa-M	*Alisorrento**	116	1972
HYD Sormovo Kometa-M	*Alivesuvio**	116	1973
HYD Kolkhida	*Aligea*	155	1987
CAT Marinteknik Marinjet 33 CPV	*Giove Jet*	280	1989
HYD S Ordzhonikidze Kolkhida	*Aliatlante*	155	1986
HYD S Ordzhonikidze Kolkhida	*Alieolo*	155	July 1986
MH Marinteknik Verkstads AB 34 MPV	*Europa Jet* (ex *Europa 1* '87)	350	September 1987

High-speed craft operated

Type	Name	Seats	Delivered
CAT FBM Marinteknik Shipbuilder (S) Pte Ltd Marinjet 34 CPV	*Acapulco Jet*	300	1989
MH FBMM (S)	*Celestina*	350	1988
CAT Marinteknik Verkstads AB	*Nettuno Jet*	300	1988
CAT Marinteknik Verkstads AB 34 CPV	*Giunone Jet*	300	1988
MH Marinteknik Verkstads AB 41 MPV	*Rosaria Lauro*	350	1988
CAT Marinteknik Verkstads 36 CPV	*Airone Jet*	316	1988
HYD Kolkhida	*Alikenia*	115	1989
HYD Kolkhida	*Aliflorida*	115	1988
HYD Kometa	*Alieros*	116	1973
HYD Kometa	*Alisaturno*	116	1972
HYD Kometa	*Alischia*	116	1977
HYD Kometa	*Alicapri*	116	1983
HYD Kolkhida	*Aliantares*	115	1991
HYD Kolkhida	*Aliaturo*	115	1991

*These Kometas were fitted with MTU 8V 396 TB 83 engines in the order shown in 1984, 1985 and 1986
The first *Nettuno Jet* was bought back by Marinteknik Verkstads AB and sold to SURF, France, 1987
The first Marinteknik JC-F1 JetCat, *Alitirreno I*, was sold to a Spanish operator in 1989

Operations
Naples to Ischia Porto
Naples to Forio
Naples to Sorrento
Sorrento to Capri
Sorrento to Fiumicino
Capri to Ischia
Salerno to Amalfi to Positano to Capri to Napoli
Naples to Capri and the ports of the Cilento coast
Naples to Positano
Formia to Ischia to Capri to Sorrento to Napoli
Sorrento to Ischia
Fiumicino to Ponza to Ventotene to Ischia to Capri to Sorrento
Trapani to Egadi
Lampedusa to Linosa.

VERIFIED

Nettuno Jet   1992

ALISCAFI SNAV SpA

Società di Navigazione Alta Velocita
Subsidiary Company of Rodriquez SpA

Via S Raineri 22, I-98100 Messina, Italy

Telephone: +39 (90) 7775
Telefax: +39 (90) 717358

Main Terminal: Via F Caracciolo 10, I-80122 Naples, Italy

Telephone: +39 (81) 761 2348
Telefax: +39 (81) 761 2141

High-speed craft operated

Type	Name	Seats	Built
HYD Rodriquez PT 20	*Freccia delle Eolie*	70	1957
HYD Rodriquez PT 20	*Freccia del Tirreno*	70	1957
HYD Rodriquez PT 50	*Freccia di Sorrento*	140	1959
HYD Rodriquez PT 50	*Freccia del Sud* (ex *Princefoil* '78 ex *Vingtor* '74)	110	1960

High-speed craft operated

Type	Name	Seats	Built
HYD Rodriquez PT 20	*Freccia dello Stretto*	140	1960
HYD Rodriquez PT 50	*Freccia Atlantica* (ex *Sirena '67*)	—	—
HYD Westermoen Hydrofoil A/S PT 50	*Freccia del Mediteraneo*	125	1963
HYD Rodriquez PT 50	*Freccia di Sicilia* (ex *Condor 1*)	130	1964
HYD Rodriquez PT 20	*Freccia del Vesuvio*	70	1966
HYD Rodriquez PT 50	*Sun Arrow*	140	1968
HYD Rodriquez PT 50	*Freccia Adriatica*	140	1969
HYD Rodriquez PT 50	*Freccia di Casamicciola*	140	1970
HYD Rodriquez RHS 200	*Superjumbo*	250	1981
HYD Rodriquez RHS 150	*Dynasty*	161	1984
HYD Rodriquez RHS 160F	*Alijumbo Stromboli*	210	1986
HYD Rodriquez RHS 160	*Fast Blu*	180	1986
HYD Rodriquez RHS 160	*Sinai*	180	1986
HYD Rodriquez RHS 150	*Salina*	161	1990
HYD Rodriquez RHS 150	*Panarea*	210	1990
FAMH Rodriquez	*Procida*	180	1990
HYD Rodriquez RHS 160F	*Cittiships*	210	1990
HYD Rodriquez RHS 160F	*Moretto I*	210	1991
HYD Rodriquez RHS 160F	*Zibibbo*	210	1991
HYD Rodriquez RHS 160F	*Alijumbo Messina*	210	1992
HYD Rodriquez MEC	*MEC Ustia*	—	1992
HYD Rodriquez RHS 160F	*Alijumbo Eolie*	210	1991
CAT Fjellstrand 40.0 m	*Alcione Primo*	357	1990

Operations

Eolie to Napoli to Eolie
Lipari to Vulcano to S M Salina to Panarea to Stromboli to Napoli and back

Milazzo to Isole Eolie
Milazzo to Lipari to Vulcano to S M Salina to Rinella to Filicudi to Alicudi to Filicudi to Rinella to S M Salina to Lipari to Panarea to Stromboli to Panarea to S M Salina to Lipari to Vulcano to Milazzo to Vulcano to Lipari to Vulcano to Milazzo

Isole Eolie to Messina to Reggio C
S M Salina to Vulcano to Lipari to Messina to Reggio C to Messina to Vulcano to Lipari to S M Salina to Rinella to Lipari to Vulcano to Messina to Reggio C to Messina to Reggio C to Messina to Vulcano to Lipari to Rinella to S M Salina

Messina to Reggio C to Isole Eolie
Messina to Reggio C to Messina to Vulcano to Lipari to Milazzo to Lipari to Vulcano to Panarea to Stromboli to Messina to Reggio C to Messina to Stromboli to Panarea to S M Salina to Lipari to Vulcano to Messina to Reggio C to Messina

Messina to Isole Eolie Bis
Messina to Reggio C to Messina to Stromboli to Panarea to S M Salina to Lipari to Vulcano to Messina to Reggio C to Messina to Vulcano to Lipari to S M Salina to Rinella to Lipari to Vulcano to Panarea to Stromboli to Messina to Reggio C to Messina

Isole Eolie to Palermo
Vulcano to Lipari to S M Salina to Rinella to Filicudi to Alicudi to Palermo and back

Palermo to Cefalu' to Eolie
Palermo to Cefalu' to Alicudi to Filicudi to Rinella to S M Salina to Vulcano to Lipari to Milazzo to Vulcano to Lipari to S M Salina to Rinella to Lipari to Vulcano to S M Salina to Rinella to Filicudi to Alicudi to Cefalu' to Palermo

Messina to Reggio C
Napoli to Capri
Napoli to Procida to Casamicciola
Napoli to Sorrento to Capri
Portoferraio to Livorno to Capraia to Bastia

UPDATED

SNAV Rodriquez RHS 160F　　　　　　　　　　*1992*

CAREMAR
Campania Regionale Marittima SpA
Molo Beverello 2, I-80133 Naples, Italy

Telephone: +39 (81) 551 5384
Telex: 720054

High-speed craft operated

Type	Name	Seats	Delivered
HYD Rodriquez RHS 140	*Albireo*	140	1977
HYD Rodriquez RHS 160	*Algol*	180	1978
HYD Rodriquez RHS 160	*Alioth*	180	1979
HYD Rodriquez RHS 160F	*Anilam*	210	1986
HYD Rodriquez RHS 160F	*Aldebaran*	210	1986
CAT Rodriquez Seagull 400	*Achernar*	354	1993

Operations
Naples to Capri
Naples to Ischia Porto
Naples to Procida
Formia to Ponza/Ventotene.

VERIFIED

Campania Regionale Marittima's Algol　　　　　*1990*

COVEMAR EOLIE

Via Capp M Scala 21, Milazzo ME, Sicily, Italy

High-speed craft operated

Type	Name	Seats
HYD Rodriquez PT 50S	*Star Capricorn* (ex *Springeren*, 1967)	117

Operations
Lipari to Filicudi to Alicudi
Lipari to Panarea to Stromboli
Lipari to Vulcano to Milazzo
S M Salina to Lipari.

VERIFIED

FODERARO NAVIGAZIONE

Italy

High-speed craft operated

Type	Name	Seats	Delivered
MH C N Foschi, Sciomachen 290	*Neocastrum*	350	1993
MH C N Foschi, Sciomachen 290	—	350	1994

Operations
Vibo Marina to Tropea to Vakano to Lipari to Stromboli to Tropea to Vibo Marina.

VERIFIED

LINEE LAURO Srl

Via Roma 1, I-80078 Pozzuoli, Naples, Italy

Telephone: +39 (81) 551 3352/552 2828
Telefax: +39 (81) 991889

Salvatore Lauro, *Chairman*
A M Lauro, *Managing Director*

High-speed craft operated

Type	Name	Seats	Delivered
MH Crestitalia	*Serena Lauro*	350	1988
MH Crestitalia	*Freccia Del Golfo*	290	1989

VERIFIED

MINISTERO DEI TRASPORTI
(Gestione Governativa Navigazione Laghi)

Via L Ariosto 21, I-20145 Milan, Italy

Telephone: +39 (2) 481 2086/6230
Telex: 311294 NAVIGE I

Dott Ing Pietro Santini, *Government Manager*

The Italian Ministry of Transport has three subsidiary hydrofoil-operating companies which run services on Lake Como, Lake Garda and Lake Maggiore as detailed in the following entry. Passengers carried in 1988 totalled 6 674 108.

VERIFIED

MINISTERO DELLA MARINA MERCANTILE

In 1987 a Rodriquez PT 50 hydrofoil was adopted for anti-pollution work. The vessel was previously operated by Aliscafi SNAV SpA.

High-speed craft operated

Type	Name	Delivered
HYD Rodriquez PT 50	*Freccia di Sorrento* (ex *Freccia di Reggio '70*, ex *Freccia del Caribe '64*)	1959

VERIFIED

Rodriquez PT 20 Freccia di Sorrento in service with the Italian Ministero della Marina Mercantile for anti-pollution work **1988**

MISANO ALTA VELOCITA' Srl

Corso Garibaldi 96/98, I-72100 Brindisi, Italy

Telephone: +39 (831) 529771
Telex: 813384
Telefax: +39 (831) 527968

Anacleto Ippati - Brindisi
Fabio Fazzina - Brindisi
Nicola Bonetti - Ravenna

Misano Alta Velocita' Srl operates the SES *Santa Eleonora* as detailed below and is a joint venture company between Misano di Navigazione and The Virtu Steamship Company Ltd, Malta.

High-speed craft operated

Type	Name	Seats	Delivered
SES Ulstein UT 904	*Santa Eleonora*	354	February 1992

Operations
Brindisi to Corfu
Brindisi to Pasci.

UPDATED

Santa Eleonora   *1993*

NAVIGAZIONE LAGO DI COMO
(Gestione Governativa Navigazione Laghi)

Via Rubini 22, 22100 Como, Italy

Telephone: +39 (31) 273324/260234
Telefax: +39 (31) 270305

Dott Ing F Parigi, *Director*

High-speed craft operated

Type	Name	Seats	Delivered
Rodriquez PT 20	*Freccia delle Azalee*	80	1967
Rodriquez RHS 70	*Freccia delle Betulle*	80	1974
Rodriquez RHS 70	*Freccia delle Gardenie*	80	1976
Rodriquez RHS 150SL	*Freccia delle Valli*	180	1981
Rodriquez RHS 150SL	*Guglielmo Marconi*	180	1983
Rodriquez RHS 150SL	*Voloire*	180	1989

Operations
Como to Argegno to Lezzenno to Lenno to Tremezzo to Bellagio to Menaggio to Varenna to Bellano to Dongo to Gravedona to Domaso to Gera to Colico.

VERIFIED

Freccia delle Valli (Aerea I Buga)   *1993*

NAVIGAZIONE LIBERA DEL GOLFO SpA

Molo Beverello, I-80133 Naples, Italy

Telephone: +39 (81) 552 0763/7209
Telex: 722661 NAVLIB I
Telefax: +39 (81) 552 5582

High-speed craft operated

Type	Name	Seats	Delivered
MH FBM Marine 41 m	*Capri Jet*	394	26 July 1988
MH FBM Marine 41 m	*Sorrento Jet*	394	June 1990
MH Marinteknik 41 m	*Napoli Jet*	394	May 1992
MH Marinteknik 41 m	*Amalfi Jet*	350	1993
MH Marinteknik 41 m	*Ischia Jet*	350	1994

Operations

Naples to Capri, 40 minutes
Sorrento to Capri, 20 minutes.

UPDATED

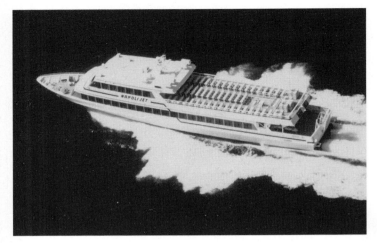

Napoli Jet   *1993*

NAVIGAZIONE LAGO MAGGIORE
(Gestione Governativa Navigazione Laghi)

Via le F Baracca 1, I-28041 Arona, Italy

Telephone: +39 (322) 46651
Telefax: +39 (322) 249530

Dott Ing Piero Ferrozzi, *Director*

High-speed craft operated

Type	Name	Seats	Delivered
Rodriquez RHS 70	Freccia delle Ortensie	80	1974
Rodriquez RHS 70	Freccia delle Camelie	80	1974
Rodriquez RHS 70	Freccia delle Magnolie	80	1975
Rodriquez RHS 150SL	Freccia dei Giardini	176 + 20	1981
Rodriquez RHS 150SL	Enrico Fermi	200	1984
Rodriquez RHS 150FLS	Lord Byron	200	1989

Operations

RHS 70: Luino to Cannero to Cannabui. RHS 150: Arona to Angera to Ispra to Belgirate to Stresa to Baveno to Isola
Madre to Intra to Pallanza to Luino to Cannobio to Brissago to Ascona to Locarno.

UPDATED

Rodriquez RHS 150SL Freccia dei Giardini   *1994*

NAVIGAZIONE SUL LAGO DI GARDA
(Gestione Governativa Navigazione Laghi)

Piazza Matteotti 2, I-25015 Desenzano del Garda, Italy

Telephone: +39 (30) 914 1321/2/3
Telefax: +39 (30) 914 4640

High-speed craft operated

Type	Name	Seats	Delivered
HYD Rodriquez RHS 70	Freccia dei Benaco	80	1974
HYD Rodriquez RHS 70	Freccia dei Gerani	80	1976
HYD Rodriquez RHS 150SL	Freccia delle Riviere	200	1981
HYD Rodriquez RHS 150SL	Galileo Galilei	200	1982
HYD Rodriquez RHS 150FL	Goethe	200	1988
CAT Conavi 22 m	Catullo	105	1992
CAT Conavi 22 m	Parini	105	1993

Operations

Peschiera del Garda to Desenzano to Sirmione to Bardolino to Garda to Salò to Gardone to Torri to Maderno to Gargnano to Malcesine to Limone to Torbole to Riva del Garda.

Traffic carried

180 000 passengers in 1991

UPDATED

Rodriquez RHS 150FL Goethe   *1991*

SIREMAR
Sicilia Regionale Marittima SpA
Via Principe di Belmonte, 1/C, I-90139 Palermo, Sicily, Italy

Telephone: +39 (91) 582688
Telex: 910135 SIRMAR I
Telefax: +39 (91) 582267

High-speed craft operated

Type	Name	Seats	Delivered
Rodriquez PT 50	Pisanello	130	1961
Rodriquez RHS 140	Duccio	140	1977
Rodriquez RHS 160	Donatello	184	1980
Rodriquez RHS 160	Botticelli	184	1980
Rodriquez RHS 160F	Masaccio	210	1987
Rodriquez RHS 160F	Mantegna	210	1989
Rodriquez RHS 160F	Giorgione	210	1989
Rodriquez RHS PT50	Giotto*	130	1992
Rodriquez Foilmaster	Tiziano	220	1994

Giotto was damaged in a storm in 1994

Operations

Milazzo to Eolie (Vulcano to Lipari to Salina to Panarea to Stromboli to Filicudi to Alicudi)
Palermo to Ustica
Trapani to Egadi (Favignana to Levanzo to Marettimo)

UPDATED

Sicilia Regionale Marittima's Giorgione   *1991*

TIRRENIA NAVIGAZIONE

Rione Sirignano 2, I-80121 Naples, Italy

High-speed craft operated

Type	Name	Seats	Additional payload	Delivered
MH Rodriquez Aquastrada	*Guizzo*	450	126 cars	1993
MH Rodriquez Aquastrada	*Scatto*	450	126 cars	1994

Operations
Civitavecchia and La Spezia to Olbia.   **NEW ENTRY**

Tirrenia Aquastrada Guizzo   **1995**

TOREMAR
Toscana Regionale Marittima SpA
Via Calatati 6, I-57123 Livorno, Italy

Telephone: +39 (586) 22772
Telex: 590214 I

High-speed craft operated

Type	Name	Seats	Delivered
HYD Rodriquez RHS 160F	*Fabricia*	160	1987

Operations
Portoferraio to Cavo to Piombino (Elba to mainland).
                                                         UPDATED

VETOR Srl

Italy

High-speed craft operated

Type	Name	Seats	Delivered
HYD Kometa	*Vetor 944*	102	1984
HYD Kometa	*Freccia Pontina*	102	1985
HYD Kolkhida	*Gabri*	120	1989
HYD Kolkhida	*Vemar*	120	1991

Operations
Anzio to Naples
Anzio to Ponza to Ventotene
Formia to Ponza to Ventotene.   **UPDATED**

JAPAN

AWAJI FERRY BOAT COMPANY

4-1-1 Sotohama, Suma-Ku, Kobe 654, Japan

High-speed craft operated

Type	Name	Seats	Delivered
CAT Mitsui CP25 Supermaran	*Queen Rokko*	250	June 1988

                                                         VERIFIED

Mitsui catamaran ferry Queen Rokko *operated by Awaji Ferry Boat Company*   **1989**

AWASHIMA KISEN COMPANY LTD

1-67 Iwafuneminato-machi, Murakami-shi Niiga-ken 958, Japan

High-speed craft operated

Type	Name	Speed	Seats	Delivered
MH Sumidagawa Zosen Co Ltd	*Iwayuri*	24 knots	144	May 1979
MH Sumidagawa Zosen Co Ltd	*Asuka*	24 knots	173	May 1989

Operations
Awashima to Iwafune.   **VERIFIED**

Asuka operated by Awashima Kisen   **1992**

BIWAKO KISEN COMPANY LTD
(Biwa Lake Sightseeing Company)

5-1 Hamaotsu, Otsu-City 520, Shiga Prefecture, Japan

Telephone: +81 775 24 500

High-speed craft operated

Type	Name	Speed	Seats	Delivered
MH Mokubei Shipbuilding Co Ikeda 22 m	*Lansing*	27 knots	78	April 1982

Operations
Biwa Lake, sightseeing.   **UPDATED**

The Mokubei Shipbuilding Company water-jet-propelled Lansing **1995**

ENOH KISEN

Japan

High-speed craft operated

Type	Name	Seats	Delivered
MH New Japan Marine Co Ltd	*Edajima No 2*	60	February 1975
MH New Japan Marine Co Ltd	*Edajima No 3*	60	January 1976
MH New Japan Marine Co Ltd	*Edajima No 5*	74	November 1982

Operations
Ujina to Fujinowaki.   **VERIFIED**

FUKE KAIUN COMPANY LTD

3-3-25 Hon-machi, Sumoto-City 656, Japan

High-speed craft operated

Type	Name	Seats	Delivered
MH Miho 24 m	*Hikari*	—	1978
MH Miho 24 m	*Itchigo*	—	1978
MH Miho 24 m	*Nigo*	—	1978
MH Miho 24 m	*Hirari Sango*	—	1978
CAT Sanuki 36 m	*Iris*	250	1990
CAT IHI SSTH 30	*Trident*	68	1992
F-CAT Hitachi Superjet 30	*Trident Ace*	200	1993
F-CAT Hitachi Superjet 30	*Artemis*	200	1993
F-CAT Hitachi Superjet 30	*Apollon*	200	1994

Operations
Fuke to Sumoto
Fuke excursions
Fuke to Kansai Airport.   **UPDATED**

GEIBI SHOSEN COMPANY LTD

1-11-23 Ujinakaigan, Minami-Ku, Hiroshima-City 734, Japan

High-speed craft operated

Type	Name	Seats	Delivered
MH Miho Zosenjyo Co Ltd	Chidori No 5	70	March 1979

Operations
Nakamachi to Ujina.

GOTO RYOKAYKUSEN COMPANY LTD

5-35 Matsugae-machi, Nagasaki-City 850, Japan

Telephone: +81 (958) 251631
Telefax: +81 (958) 252537

Sakichi Yasuda, *President and main stock holder*

High-speed craft operated

Type	Name	Seats	Delivered
MH Nankai	New Gotoh	193	June 1984

Operations
Gonokubi to Wakamatsu, 4.5 km, 10 minutes; Wakamatsu to Kirifurusato, 6.5 km, 15 minutes; Kirifurusato to Doinoura, 8.0 km, 15 minutes; Doinoura to Naru, 14 km, 15 minutes; Naru to Fukue, 19.8 km, 30 minutes.

VERIFIED

HANKYU KISEN COMPANY LTD

45 Harima-Cho, Chuo-Ku, Kobe-City 650, Japan

Telephone: +81 (78) 331 5191

Asaziro Katsumata, *Maritime Director*

High-speed craft operated

Type	Name	Seats	Delivered
HYD Hitachi Zosen PT 50	Zuiho	123	January 1972
HYD Hitachi Zosen PT 50	Hoo	123	March 1972
HYD Hitachi Zosen PT 50	Kaio	123	February 1974
HYD Hitachi Zosen PTS 50 Mk II	Housho	123	January 1983

Operations
Kobe to Kameura (Naruto)
Kobe to Tokushima.

VERIFIED

HAYATEKAIUN COMPANY LTD

148-15 Maesatosoe, Irabu-cho, Miyako-Gun, Okinawa-ken 906-05, Japan

High-speed craft operated

Type	Name	Seats	Delivered
MH Setouchi Craft Co Ltd	Hayate No II	70	March 1984

Operations
Sarahama to Hirara.

VERIFIED

HIGASHI-NIHON FERRY COMPANY

Minami 4-jo, Nishill-chome Chuo-Ku, Sapporo 064, Japan

High-speed craft operated

Type	Name	Seats	Delivered
HYD KHI Jetfoil 929-117	Unicorn	—	1990

Operations
Aomori to Hakodate.

HIROSHIMA IMABARI KOSOKUSEN COMPANY LTD

853 Miyajima-Cho, Saeki-Gun, Hiroshima-Ken 739-05, Japan

High-speed craft operated

Type	Name	Seats	Delivered
MH Miho Zosenjyo Co Ltd	Waka	84	July 1984
MH Miho Zosenjyo Co Ltd	Seto	84	August 1984

Operations
Ujina to Imabari.

VERIFIED

IMABARI KOSOKUSEN COMPANY LTD

1-2 Katahara-Cho, Imabari-City 794, Japan

High-speed craft operated

Type	Name	Seats	Delivered
MH Miho Zosenjyo Co Ltd	Kamome No 2	52	November 1973
MH Miho Zosenjyo Co Ltd	Kamome No 5	80	May 1976
MH Miho Zosenjyo Co Ltd	Chidori No 7	70	January 1980
MH Miho Zosenjyo Co Ltd	Kamome No 7	93	April 1982

Operations
Imabari to Iguchi
Imabari to Onomichi.

VERIFIED

IRIOMOTE KANKO KAIUN COMPANY LTD

2 Misaki-Cho, Ishigaki-City 907, Japan

High-speed craft operated

Type	Name	Seats	Delivered
MH Sumidagawa Zosen Co Ltd	Marine Star	141	March 1979

Operations
Ishigaki to Funaura.

VERIFIED

ISHIZAKI KISEN COMPANY LTD

1-4-9 Mitsu, Matsuyama-City 791, Ehime Prefecture, Japan

Telephone: +81 (899) 510128

High-speed craft operated

Type	Name	Seats	Delivered
HYD Hitachi Zosen PT 20	Kansei*	66	1962
HYD Hitachi Zosen PT 50	Kosei	125	1969
HYD Hitachi Zosen PT 50	Saisei	126	1974
HYD Hitachi Zosen PT 50	Shunsei	123	1975
HYD Hitachi Zosen PT 20	Ryusei	69	1981
F-Cat Hitachi Superjet 30	Suiko	200	1994
F-Cat Hitachi Superjet 30	Shoko	200	1994

*Spare craft
Operations
Matsuyama to Hiroshima (PT 50s)
Matsuyama to Onomichi (PT 20s).

UPDATED

IWAKUNI HASHIRAJIMA KOSOKUSEN COMPANY LTD

Iwakuniko 4, Shinminato-machi, Iwakuni-City 740, Japan

High-speed craft operated

Type	Name	Seats	Delivered
MH Kiso Zosen Tekko Co Ltd	Suisei	96	November 1982

Operations
Iwakuni to Hashirashima.

VERIFIED

JAPAN OCEAN CRUISE LINE

Japan

High-speed craft operated

Type	Name	Seats	Delivered
HYD Kawasaki Jetfoil 929-117	Nagasaki	180	September 1989

VERIFIED

KAGOSHIMA SHOSEN COMPANY LTD

12-2 Kamoikeshinmachi, Kagoshima 890, Japan

High-speed craft operated

Type	Name	Seats	Delivered
HYD Kawasaki Jetfoil 929-117	Toppy	265	June 1989
HYD Kawasaki Jetfoil 929-117	Toppy 2	265	1992

Operations
Kagoshima to Nishinoomote to Miyanoura.

UPDATED

KAIJO ACCESS COMPANY

9-1 Minatojima, Chuo-Ku, Kobe 650, Japan

High-speed craft operated

Type	Name	Delivered
HYD Kawasaki Jetfoil 929-117	—	March 1994
HYD Kawasaki Jetfoil 929-117	—	March 1994

Operations
Kobe to airport Kensai.　　*UPDATED*

KASUMIGAURA JET LINE KK

Japan

High-speed craft operated

Type	Name	Delivered
MH Yamaha Motor Co Ltd	*Superjet Kasumi*	1985

Operations
Tsuchiura to Itako.　　*VERIFIED*

KATO KISEN COMPANY LTD/KANSAI KISEN COMPANY LTD (Jet Line)

7-15 Benten 6-Chome, Minato-Ku, Osaka 552, Japan

High-speed craft operated

Type	Name	Delivered
HYD Boeing Jetfoil 929-115	*Jet 7* (ex *Spirit of Friendship*)	August 1980
HYD Boeing Jetfoil 929-115	*Jet 8* (ex *Spirit of Discovery*)	April 1985

Operations
Started 1987, Seto Inland Sea.　　*UPDATED*

KUMEJIMA FERRY COMPANY LTD

3-25-25 Maejima, Naha 900, Japan

High-speed craft operated

Type	Name	Seats	Delivered
CAT Mitsui CP20 Supermaran	*Blue Sky* (ex *Blue Hawk*)	162	1987

　　UPDATED

KYODO KISEN KAISHA LTD

5 Kaigan-dori, Chuo-Ku, Kobe 650, Japan

Telephone: +81 (78) 391 2726
Telex: 5622665 KBKYD J
Telefax: +81 (78) 391 8010

High-speed craft operated

Type	Name	Seats	Delivered
MH Miho Shipyard Co Ltd	*Ryokufu*	150	February 1985
MH Miho Shipyard Co Ltd	*Seifu*	150	July 1986
CAT MES CP15	*Aquajet I*	196	March 1989
CAT MES CP15	*Aquajet II*	196	June 1989
CAT MES CP15	*Aquajet III*	190	July 1990
CAT MES CP15	*Aquajet IV*	190	October 1990
CAT Miho Shipyard Co Ltd	*Aquajet Super I*	—	March 1993
CAT Miho Shipyard Co Ltd	*Aquajet Super II*	—	May 1993
CAT Miho Shipyard Co Ltd	*Aquajet Super III*	—	July 1994

Operations
Osaka (Honshu) to Sumoto via Tsuna (Awaji Island)
Kobe (Honshu) to Sumoto via Tsuna (Awaji Island).　　*UPDATED*

Aquajet Super I, II and III　　*1995*

Aquajet III *(top)* and Aquajet IV *designed by Michelotti*　　*1992*

KYUSHI FERRY BOAT COMPANY

Japan

High-speed craft operated

Type	Name	Seats	Additional payload	Delivered
WPC Kawasaki/ AMD 1500	*Hayabusa*	460	94 cars	1995

Operations
Yawatahama to Usuki.　　*NEW ENTRY*

Hayabusa　　*1995*

KYUSHU RAILWAY COMPANY

14-1 Okihamacho, Hakata-Ku, Fukuoka 812, Japan

High-speed craft operated

Type	Name	Seats	Delivered
HYD Kawasaki Jetfoil 929-117	*Beetle 2*	263	1991

　　NEW ENTRY

KYUSHU SHOSEN COMPANY LTD

16-12 Motofune-Cho, Nagasaki-City 850, Japan

High-speed craft operated

Type	Name	Seats	Delivered
HYD Kawasaki Jetfoil 929-117	*Pegasus*	282	March 1990
MH Mitsubishi 48.5 m	*Sea Grace*	—	March 1993

Operations
Nagasaki to Narao to Fukue
Sasebo to Narao.　　*VERIFIED*

KYUSHU YUSEN COMPANY LTD

1-27 Kamiya, Hakata, Fukuoka 812, Japan

High-speed craft operated

Type	Name	Seats	Delivered
HYD Kawasaki Jetfoil 929-117	*Venus*	263	March 1991

Operations
Hakata to Ashibe
Gonoura to Izuhara.

VERIFIED

MARITIME SAFETY AGENCY OF JAPAN

2-1-3 Kasumigaseki, Chiyoda-ku, Tokyo, Japan

Telephone: +81 (3) 3591 6361
Telefax: +81 (3) 3597 9420

Hiroharu Hagihara, *Director of Ship Division, Equipment and Technology Department*

High-speed craft operated

Type	Name	Delivered
23 m patrol craft type		
MH Mitsubishi Heavy Industries Ltd	*Hayagiri*	February 1985
MH Hitachi Zosen	*Shimagiri*	February 1985
MH Hitachi Zosen	*Setogiri*	March 1985
MH Sumidagwa Zosen Co Ltd	*Natsugiri*	January 1990
MH Sumidagwa Zosen Co Ltd	*Suganami*	January 1990
180 ton patrol vessel type		
Mitsubishi Heavy Industries Ltd	*Mihashi*	September 1988
MH Hitachi Zosen	*Saroma*	November 1989
MH Mitsubishi Heavy Industries Ltd	*Inasa*	January 1990
MH Hitachi Zosen	*Kirishima*	March 1991
MH Mitsubishi Heavy Industries Ltd	*Takatsuki*	March 1992
MH Hitachi Zosen	*Nobaru*	March 1993
MH Hitachi Zosen	—	1994
MH Mitsubishi Heavy Industries Ltd	—	1994
MH Mitsubishi Heavy Industries Ltd	*Kamui*	January 1994
MH Hitachi Zosen	*Bizan*	January 1994

Only those craft with a maximum speed of over 30 knots have been listed here.

Operations
The Maritime Safety Agency of Japan (JMSA) was established in May 1948 for the protection of life and property at sea.

UPDATED

Suganami *23 m patrol craft*   *1992*

Kirishima *180 tonne patrol vessel*   *1992*

MARUNAKA KISEN COMPANY LTD

Japan

High-speed craft operated

Type	Name	Seats	Delivered
CAT Miho Zosensho	—	280	1991

Operations
Onagawa to Ayukawa to Kin Kazan.

VERIFIED

MARUTO KISEN COMPANY LTD

2235-17 Minato-machi, Mihara-City 723, Japan

High-speed craft operated

Type	Name	Seats	Delivered
MH Tohkai Boat Co Ltd	*Queen Romance*	115	June 1976
MH Hayami Zosen Co Ltd	*Queen Romance No 2*	126	April 1982

Operations
Setoda to Mihara.

VERIFIED

MEITETSU KAIJO KANKOSEN COMPANY LTD

18-1 Sanbonmatsu-Cho, Atsuta-Ku, Nagoya-city 456, Japan

High-speed craft operated

Type	Name	Seats	Delivered
MH Suzuki Zosen Co Ltd	*Ohtoki*	97	February 1981
MH Suzuki Zosen Co Ltd	*Ohtoki 2*	97	July 1981
MH Suzuki Zosen Co Ltd	*Ohtoki 3*	97	March 1982
MH Suzuki Zosen Co Ltd	*Kaien 5*	61	March 1982
MH Suzuki Zosen Co Ltd	*Kaien 6*	79	July 1982
MH Mitsubishi 25 m	*Hiryu 1*	70	July 1988
MH Mitsubishi 25 m	*Hiryu 3*	70	July 1988
MH Mitsubishi 25 m	*Hiryu 2*	70	July 1988

Operations
Shinojima to Morozaki to Himakajima
Gamagohri to Toba
Nishiura to Higashihaza
Morozaki to Irako
Kowa to Irako.

VERIFIED

MIHARA KANKO KISEN COMPANY LTD

2235-17 Minato-machi Mihari-City 723, Japan

High-speed craft operated

Type	Name	Seats	Delivered
MH Setouchi Craft Co Ltd	*Nishi Nikko No 3*	150	October 1976
MH Setouchi Craft Co Ltd	*Nishi Nikko No 5*	81	February 1981
MH Setouchi Craft Co Ltd	*Nishi Nikko No 8*	81	October 1981

Operations
Mihara to Setoda.

VERIFIED

MIKATAGOKO YURANSEN

1-5 Hayase, Mihama-Cho, Mikata-Gun, Fukui-Ken 919-11, Japan

High-speed craft operated

Type	Name	Seats	Delivered
MH Ohtani	*Suisei No 3*	50	July 1975
MH Ohtani	*Suisei No 5*	50	July 1975
MH Ohtani	*Suisei No 6*	50	August 1976
MH Ohtani	*Suisei No 7*	50	August 1976
MH Ohtani	*Suisei No 8*	50	May 1981

Operations
Hayase to Mikatasanbashi.

VERIFIED

NANKAI FERRY COMPANY LTD

6-5 Chikkoh, Wakayama 640, Wakayama Prefecture, Japan

High-speed craft operated

Type	Name	Seats	Delivered
CAT Mitsui CP30	*Marine Hawk*	280	July 1983
CAT Mitsui CP30 Mk 4	*Argo*	—	December 1992

Operations
Wakayama to Tokushima.

VERIFIED

OHMI MARINE

11-12 Yasukiyo-Cho, Hikone City 522, Japan

High-speed craft operated

Type	Name	Seats	Delivered
MH Mokubei	*Wakaayu No 5*	160	March 1983
MH Mokubei	*Wakaayu No 8*	62	March 1984
MH Mokubei	*Wakaayu No 6*	100	July 1984

Operations
Hikone to Chikubushima
Imazu to Chikubushima
Iiura to Chikubushima. **UPDATED**

OITA HOVER FERRY COMPANY LTD

1-14-1 Nishi-shinchi, Oita 870, Japan

Telephone: +81 (975) 58 7180
Telefax: +81 (975) 56 6247

Keiichiro Isayama, *President*
Kiyoshi Iwai, *General Director*

Oita Hover Ferry Company Ltd was established in November 1970 and began operating in October 1971. Annual traffic is approximately 450 000.

High-speed craft operated

Type	Name	Seats	Delivered
HOV Mitsui MV-PP5 Mk 2	*Hakuchyo No 3*	75	June 1970
HOV Mitsui MV-PP5	*Hobby No 6* (ex *Akatombo 51* and stretched)	75	
HOV Mitsui MV-PP5	*Angel No 5*	75	April 1975
HOV Mitsui PP-10	*Dream No 1*	105	April 1980
HOV Mitsui PP-10	*Dream No 2*	105	April 1981

Operations
Oita city to Oita Airport, 15.6 nm, 24 minutes
Oita city to Beppu city, 6.5 nm, 10 minutes. **UPDATED**

Oita Hover Ferry Mitsui PP-10 Dream No 2 **1992**

OKI KISEN KK

Nakamachim, Saigo-cho, Okigun, Shimane Prefecture, Japan

Telephone: +81 (85) 122 1122
Telex: 628966 J

High-speed craft operated

Type	Name	Seats	Delivered
F CAT Mitsubishi Super Shuttle 400	*Rainbow*	341	April 1993

Operations
Sakai to Okinoshima. **VERIFIED**

RYOBI UNYU

1-1-8 Bancho, Okayama City, Japan

High-speed craft operated

Type	Name	Seats	Delivered
MH Miho Zosen	*Princess Olive*	94	July 1981
MH Miho Zosen	*Queen Olive*	94	October 1981

Operations
Okayama to Tonosho. **VERIFIED**

SADO KISEN KAISHA

9-1 Bandaijima, Niigata City 950, Japan

Telephone: +81 (252) 452311
Telefax: +81 (252) 478830

S Nakamura, *Jetfoil Director*

High-speed craft operated

Type	Name	Seats	Delivered
HYD Boeing Jetfoil 929-115	*Mikado*	266	May 1979
HYD Boeing Jetfoil 929-115	*Ginga* (ex *Cu na Mara*)	260	July 1986
HYD Kawasaki Jetfoil 929-117	*Tsubasa*	266	April 1989
HYD Kawasaki Jetfoil 929-117	*Suisei*	262	April 1991

The Boeing Jetfoil *Okesa* formerly owned by this company was sold to the Far East Hydrofoil Company Ltd of Hong Kong in November 1990.

Operations
Niigata, Honshu Island, to Ryotsu, Sado Island, 36.3 nm, 1 hour
Naoetsu, Honshu Island to Ogi, Sado Island, 42.1 nm, 1 hour

The number of passengers carried in 1993 was 743 648

UPDATED

Kawasaki Jetfoil Tubasa *in service with Sado Kisen Kaisha* **1994**

SEA-COM CRUISE CORPORATION

7 Taiso Marine Building, 4-23 Kaigandouri, Naka-ku, Yokohama 231, Japan

High-speed craft operated

Type	Name	Seats	Delivered
CAT Yamaha 291	*Bay Bridge*	230	1989
CAT Yamaha 291	*Bay Dream*	178	1989
CAT Yamaha 291	*Bay Frontier*	230	1989
CAT InCat 40 m WPC	*SeaCom 1*	265	1990

Operations
Yokohama Minatomirai Pier and Hakkeijima Sea Paradise. **UPDATED**

SETONAIKAI KISEN COMPANY LTD (SETO INLAND SEA LINES)

1-12-23 Ujinakaigan, Minami-ku, Hiroshima 734, Japan

Telephone: +81 (82) 255 3344
Telex: 653625 STSHRM J
Telefax: +81 (82) 251 6743

Nobue Kawai, *Tour Co-ordinator of Akinada Line*

Setonaikai Kisen Company has been operating transport services linking the islands in the Inland Sea for many years. It now has a fleet of 38 vessels, operating regular services along nine routes between Hiroshima and Shikoku, including a main route between Hiroshima and Matsuyama as well as Hiroshima to Kobe and Osaka.

High-speed craft operated

Type	Name	Seats	Delivered
HYD Hitachi Supramar PT 50	Ohtori No 2*	113	February 1970
HYD Hitachi Supramar PT 50	Ohtori No 3*	113	October 1972
HYD Hitachi Supramar PT 50	Hikari No 2*	123	March 1975
HYD Hitachi Supramar PT 50	Ohtori No 5	113	May 1973
MH Miho Zosenjo	Marine Star 2	103	November 1979
MH Miho Zosenjo	Marine Star 3	120	January 1983
Setouchi Craft MH	Akinada	125	May 1989
HYD Hitachi Supramar PT 50	Ohtori*	118	June 1968
HYD Hitachi Supramar PT 50	Condor	32 knots	118
HYD Hitachi Supramar PT 50	Condor 2	118	June 1968
HYD Hitachi Supramar PT 50	Condor 3	32 knots	118
MH Miho 22 m	Waka	84	June 1984
MH Miho 22 m	Seto	84	July 1984
F-CAT Hitachi Superjet 30	Dogo	200	1993
F-CAT Hitachi Superjet 30	Miyajima	200	1994

*spare craft

Operations
Miyajima to Hiroshima to Omishima Island (Port of Inokuchi) to Setoda *(Akinada)*
Hiroshima to Matsuyama 1 hour *(Ohtori No 2, 3 and Ohtori No 5)*, some services stopping at Kure, then 1 hour 10 minutes *(Hikari No 2)*
Mihara to Imabari 1 hour *(Marine Star 2, Marine Star 3)*, some services stopping at Setoda, then 1 hour 7 minutes.

UPDATED

Akinada, *introduced into service by Setonaik Kisen in May 1989*   **1990**

SHIKOKU FERRY COMPANY (BRIDGE LINE)

10-32 Tamamo-cho, Takamatsu City 760, Japan

High-speed craft operated

Type	Name	Delivered
CAT Sanuki Shipbuilding and Iron Works 30 m	Sea Chateau	1988

VERIFIED

TENMAYA MARINE COMPANY LTD

Japan

High-speed craft operated

Type	Name	Seats	Delivered
CAT Mitsui CP5 Supermaran	Mon Cheri	58	May 1988

VERIFIED

THIRD DISTRICT PORT CONSTRUCTION BUREAU

Japan

High-speed craft operated

Type	Name	Delivered
SWATH Mitsubishi 27.01 m	Ohtori	March 1981

VERIFIED

TOKAI KISEN

1-11-1 Kaigan, Minato-ku, Tokyo 105, Japan

Telephone: +81 (3) 432 4551

High-speed craft operated

Type	Name	Seats	Delivered
MH Mitsubishi Heavy Industries Ltd	Seahawk 2	401	February 1980
SWATH Mitsui	Seagull 2	420	December 1989

Operations
Seagull
Atami to Ohshima
Tokyo to Ohshima*
Tokyo to Niijima*
Ohshima to Tokyo
Seahawk 2
Inatori to Ohshima
Ito to Ohshima
Atami to Ohshima*
*Summer services only

VERIFIED

TOKUSHIMA SHUTTLE LINE COMPANY LTD

3-1-3 Sannomiya-Cho, Chao-Ku, Kobe 650, Japan

Hiromu Harada, *President*

High-speed craft operated

Type	Name	Delivered
CAT MES CP30 Mk II	Marine Shuttle	February 1986
CAT MES CP30 Mk III	Blue Star	1987
CAT MES CP30 Mk III	Sun Rise	1987
CAT MES CP30 Mk IV	Sun Shine	1991
CAT MES CP30 Mk IV	Soleil	1991
CAT MES CP30 Mk IV	Polar Star	1993
CAT MES CP30 Mk IV	Venus	1993

Operations
Wakayama to Tokushima, Shikoku Island.

VERIFIED

UEDA KAIUN KK

Japan

Charterer of Mitsui Supermaran CP10 from KK Seto Naikai Cruising formed in 1987 as a joint venture of MES, the Chutetso Group and the Ueda Group.

High-speed craft operated

Type	Name	Seats	Delivered
CAT Mitsui CP10	Marine Queen	88	April 1987

VERIFIED

WAKASAWAN KANKO COMPANY LTD

1-3-2 Kawasaki, Obama City 917, Japan

High-speed craft operated

Type	Name	Seats	Delivered
MH Obama Zosen	Wakasa	180	April 1973

Operations
Obama to Sodohmon.

VERIFIED

YAEYAMA KANKO FERRY COMPANY

1-3 Misaki-cho, Isigaki-City 907, Okinawa, Japan

Telephone: +81 (98) 082 5010
Telex: 792681 K

High-speed craft operated

Type	Name	Seats	Delivered
MH Miho Zosenjyo Co Ltd	Hayabusa	88	December 1974
MH Sumidagawa 26 m	Marine Star	—	1979
MH Shinju Shipyard Co Ltd 27.3 m	Tropical Queen	150	July 1982
MH Suzuki 19 m	Hirugi No 2	—	1986
MH Toukai 15 m	Hirugi No 3	—	1987
MH Gouriki 17 m	Hirugi No 5	—	1989
MH Gouriki 16 m	Hirugi No 7	—	1990

Operations
Ishigaki to surrounding islands.

UPDATED

YASUDA SANGYO KISEN COMPANY LTD (YASUDA OCEAN GROUP) AIRPORT LINE

5-35 Matsugae-machi, Nagasaki-City 850, Japan

Telephone: +81 (958) 260188
Telex: 755556
Telefax: +81 (958) 242182

Sakichi Yasuda, *President and main stockholder*

High-speed craft operated

Type	Name	Seats	Delivered
MH Nankai	Erasumus	123	October 1984
MH Nankai	Airport Liner 5	44	July 1985
MH Nankai	Airport Liner 7	66	March 1986
MH Nankai	Airport Liner 8	66	March 1986
MH Nankai	Airport Liner 10	66	December 1986
MH Nankai	Airport Liner 11	66	February 1987
MH Nankai	Airport Liner 13	66	April 1987
MH Nankai	Airport Liner 15	66	June 1987
MH Nankai	Airport Liner 17	66	June 1987
MH Nankai	Nagasaki 8	39	June 1987
MH Nankai	Nagasaki 10	39	August 1987
MH Nankai	Taiyo	231	March 1988
MH Shinju	Toliton	150	June 1986
MH Uehara	Ocean Liner 1	88	April 1988
MH Euhara	Ocean Liner 3	88	September 1988
MH Uehara	Ocean Liner 5	97	February 1989
MH Nankai	Ocean Liner 7	97	February 1989
MH Nankai	Ocean Liner 8	97	February 1989
SES Brødrene Aa CIRR 120P	Nissho	320	September 1990

Operations
Nagasaki Airport to Nagasaki (Togitsu), 17 km, 20 minutes
Nagasaki Airport to Ohkusa, 8.8 km, 10 minutes
Nagasaki Airport to Nagasaki Holland Village, 27 km, 40 minutes
Nagasaki Airport to Sasebo, 38 km, 50 minutes
Nagasaki Holland Village to Sasebo, 23 km, 35 minutes
Nagasaki Holland Village to Hirado, 63 km, 65 minutes
Nagasaki Holland Village to Higashisonogi, 22 km, 30 minutes
Mogi to Obama, 30 km, 40 minutes
Mogi to Tomioka, 33.7 km, high-speed passenger ship, 40 minutes, car ferry, 170 minutes
The total number of passengers per year is 600 000
Nagasaki to Kagoshima (Kushikino) began March 1991 with 320 seat Brødrene Aa 35.24 m SES. Route length 135 km, 100 minutes.

UPDATED

JORDAN

JORDAN PORTS CORPORATION

PO Box 115, Aquaba, Jordan

Telephone: +962 (3) 314031
Telefax: +962 (3) 316204

Dr Duried Mahasneh, *Director general*
Aakef Abu Tayeh, *Deputy Director General*
Samir Mustafa, *Manager, Boats and Crafts*

High-speed craft operated

Type	Name	Delivered
SES Hovermarine HM 218	Amira Sumaiah	1980
SES Hovermarine HM 218	Amira Badeaah	1980

Operations
Aquaba to Farohirland, 10 nm, 20 minutes
(These craft were both out of service through 1994).

VERIFIED

KOREA, SOUTH

DAE-A FERRY COMPANY LTD

140-6 Dongbin 2 Ga, Pohang City, Kyung buk, South Korea

Telephone: +82 (562) 425111
Telephone: +82 (562) 425114

C K Kim, *Technical Manager*

High-speed craft operated

Type	Name	Seats	Delivered
CAT Fjellstrand	Dae Won Catamaran	392	November 1988
SES Ulstein CIRR 120P	Sea Flower	345	August 1991
SES Ulstein UT 904	Ocean Flyer	341	January 1992

Operations
Mukho to Ullung Do, 86 nm, 3 hours, US$25
Pohang to Ullung Do, 117 nm, 3½ hours, US$33
Hupo to Ullung Do, 86 nm, 3 hours, US$25.

VERIFIED

DAEHEUNG SANG-SA

South Korea

High-speed craft operated

Type	Name	Seats	Delivered
HYD Hitachi Zosen PT50	Dae Heung (ex Tobiuo No 1 '81)	133	1973

VERIFIED

DONG BU EXPRESS

South Korea

High-speed craft operated

Type	Name	Seats	Delivered
SES KTMI 17 m	Que-Ryong II	—	1988

NEW ENTRY

GEO JE HAEWOON

5 Ga 16, Jung-Ang Dong, Jung Gu, Pusan City 600, South Korea (terminal)

Telephone: +82 (51) 463 0354

K S Kim, *President*

High-speed craft operated

Type	Name	Seats	Delivered
SES Korea Tacoma Marine Industries Ltd 18 m	Cosmos	60	1980

Operations
Masan to Geo Je Island.

UPDATED

GOVERNMENT

South Korea

High-speed craft operated

Type	Name	Delivered
HOV Korea Tacoma Industries Ltd Turt IV type, 12 m	Eagle II	1984

VERIFIED

JEO-KYUNG FERRY COMPANY

5 Ga 16, Jung-Ang Dong, Jung Gu, Pusan City 600, South Korea

Telephone: +82 (51) 445994

J S Park, *President*

High-speed craft operated

Type	Name
SES Korea Tacoma Marine Industries Ltd 18 m	Air Ferry

Operations
Pusan to Gejae Island.

VERIFIED

JUNG AHANG EXPRESS COMPANY

South Korea

High-speed craft operated

Type	Seats	Delivered
MH Miwon Trading and Shipping Co 28 m	20	August 1986
MH Miwon Trading and Shipping Co 28 m	128	September 1986

Operations

A four-craft fleet operates on the man-made Choong Joo Dam where it is engaged in sightseeing tours.

VERIFIED

KUMSAN HUNGUP

South Korea

High-speed craft operated

Type	Name	Seats	Delivered
SES Korea Tacoma Marine Industries Ltd 18 m	Sun Star	60	1990

Operations

Yeosu to various islands.

NEW ENTRY

NAM HAE EXPRESS COMPANY

Hang-Dong 1 ka 6, Passenger Boat Terminal 201, Mokpo City, South Korea

High-speed craft operated

Type	Name	Seats	Delivered
HYD Hitachi PT50	Nam Hae No 1	—	1974
CAT MES CP20	Nam Hae No 7	—	1978
CAT Fjellstrand 38.8 m	Nam Hae Star	350	1989
CAT Marinteknik (S) 41 CPV	Nam Hae Prince	354	January 1993
CAT Fjellstrand 40 m	Nam Hae Queen	—	1994

Operations

Mokpo City to Hong-do Island.

UPDATED

SEMO COMPANY LTD MARINE CRAFT

5 Ga 16-5 Jung-Ang Dong, Jung-Gu, Busan 600-015, South Korea

Yeong Rok Son, *President*
Sang Gyun Mok, *General Manager*
Yong Seong Lee, *Ferry Operating Manager*

Semo Company Ltd Marine Craft is the ferry operating division of the Semo Company. In January 1989 Semo took over operation of three of the Han Ryeo Development Company vessels, *Angel I*, *Angel III* and *Angel IX,* and on 1 March 1990 they took control of vessels previously operated by the Shin Young Shipbuilding and Engineering Company.

High-speed craft operated

Type	Name	Seats	Delivered
HYD Rodriquez PT 20	Angel I	71	1970
HYD Hitachi PT 20	Angel III	71	1978
HYD Hyundai PT 20	Angel IX	71	1985
SES Korea Tacoma	Duridoongsil	158	1983
SES Korea Tacoma	Dudoongsil	200	1983
SES Korea Tacoma	Soonpoong	158	1983
SES Ulstein CIRR 120P	Perestroika	346	1990
SES Semo 36	Democracy	336	1992
SES Semo 40	Democracy II	350	1994
SES Semo 40	Democracy III	400	1994

Democracy *operating from Inchon to Bagryung Island*   *1994*

Operations
Southern coast of South Korea
Busan to Yeosu·
Yeosu to Gemun Island
Inchon to Bagryung Island
Busan to Geoje Island
Cheju to Mokpu
Chungmu to Cheju.

UPDATED

Perestroika *operated by Semo Company Ltd Marine Craft*   *1994*

SEO KYUNG HAEWOON

South Korea

High-speed craft operated

Type	Name	Delivered
SES KTMI 18 m	Air Ferry	1990
F-CAT Daewoo 40 m	Royal Ferry	1994

Operations
Pusan to Geo Je.

UPDATED

WON KWANG SHIPPING

South Korea

High-speed craft operated

Type	Name	Delivered
CAT Fjellstrand 40 m	Paradise	1994

NEW ENTRY

MALAYSIA

ASIE CREWBOAT SDN BHD

10th Floor Menara Apera ULG, 84 Jalan Raja Chulan, 50200 Kuala Lumpur, West Malaysia

Telephone: +60 (3) 261 0831/0935
Telex: 30531 AHSB MA
Telefax: +60 (3) 261 8051

Khalil Akasah, *Chairman*
Kamaruzaman Akasah, *Executive Director*
Captain Joe Hiew, *Operations Manager*

High-speed craft operated

Type	Name	Seats	Additional payload	Delivered
MH Halter Marine Sea Shuttle 34.1 m	Asie I	60	80 tonnes	1982
MH Halter Marine Sea Shuttle 34.1 m	Asie II	60	80 tonnes	1982-3
CAT Fjellstrand 31.5 m	Asie III	150	10 tonnes	March 1984
MH Halter Marine Sea Shuttle 31 m	Asie IV	52	30 tonnes	February 1985
MH Halter Marine Sea Shuttle 31 m	Asie V	52	30 tonnes	March 1985
MH Halter Marine Sea Shuttle 31 m	Asie VI	52	30 tonnes	July 1985
MH Halter Marine Sea Shuttle 31 m	Asie VII	52	30 tonnes	February 1985

Operations
For Esso Production Malaysia Inc (EPMI), Sarawak Shell Bhd, Union Oil of Thailand and others
Offshore support, Malaysia, Thailand, Indonesia, South China Sea and Singapore, transport of cargo and passengers, inter-fields offshore of Trengganu. Area of operation to include offshore southern Thailand, Sabah and Sarawak waters.

VERIFIED

KUALA PERLIS LANGKAWI FERRY SERVICE SDN BHD

37-39, Jalan Pandak Mayah 5, Pusat Bandar Kuah, 07000 Langawi, Kedah, Malaysia

Telephone: +60 (4) 9667868/9667878
Telefax: +60 (4) 9667190

Ooi Cheng Choon, *Managing Director*

High-speed craft operated

Type	Name	Seats	Delivered
MH Miho 19.5 m	Pantas Ekspres	70	1978
MH Binan 23.5 m	Saga Ekspres	87	1986
MH WaveMaster 31 m	Kita Ekspres	152	1987
MH WaveMaster 27 m	Suka Ekspres	140	1988
MH WaveMaster 27 m	Sinar Ekspres	130	1989
CAT Marinteknik 36 m	Selesa Ekspres	350	1990
MH WaveMaster 36 m	Langkawi Ekspres (ex Barbaros)	248	1991
CAT K Fjellstrand (S) Flying Cat 40 m	Perdana Ekspres	356	March 1992
CAT Marinteknik 30 m	Mustika Ekspres	209	1993
MH Wavemaster 33 m	Langawi II	—	1994
MH Wavemaster 33 m	Langawi III	—	1994

Operations
Langkawi Island to Kuala Kedah, Kuala Perlis, Penang and Thailand. Penang to Medan, Indonesia. Lumut to Medan.

UPDATED

Selesa Ekspres 1995

LADA LANGKAWI HOLDINGS

Malaysia

High-speed craft operated

Type	Name	Seats	Delivered
CAT SBF 32 m	Lada Satu	250	1993
CAT SBF 32 m	Lada Dua	250	1993
CAT SBF 32 m	Lada Tiga	250	1994
CAT SBF 32 m	Lada Empat	250	1994
CAT SBF 20 m	Lada Lima	—	1994

NEW ENTRY

MISC
Malaysian International Shipping Corporation Berhad

2nd Floor Wisma Misc, No 2 Jalan Conlay, PO Box 10371, 50712 Kuala Lumpur, Malaysia

Telephone: +60 (3) 242 8088/240 5360
Telex: 30428/31057/31058/30325 NALINE MA
Telefax: +60 (3) 241 6651

Ariffin Alias, *Managing Director*
Captain Ghani Ishak, *Director Petroleum Services*

High-speed craft operated

Type	Name	Seats	Delivered
34 m FBM Marinteknik (S)	Layar Sentosa	70	June 1987
34 m FBM Marinteknik (S)	Layar Sinar	70	June 1987

*hull built in Sweden

Operations
Both of these crew boats are on time charter to a multinational oil company in coastal waters off Malaysia.

UPDATED

MISC crew boat Layar Sentosa 1988

POMAS SDN BHD

Hovermarine Wharf, Bintawa, Kuching, Sarawak, Malaysia

High-speed craft operated

Type	Name	Seats	Delivered
SES Hovermarine HM 218	Pomas No 1	95	April 1986

Operations
Kuching to Sarikei to Sibu (daily), 90 nm.

VERIFIED

RAWA SAFARIS

Mersing Tourist Centre, Jalang Ismail, Mersing Jahore, Malaysia

High-speed craft operated

Type	Name	Delivered
HYD Vosper Singapore PT 20B Mk II	Rawa Bird	1987

Operations
Mersing, Pulau Rawa and Pulau Tioman (not in monsoon season).

VERIFIED

MALTA

GOZO CHANNEL COMPANY LTD

Sa Maison Wharf, Pieta, Malta

Telephone: +356 243964/5/6
Telex: 1580
Telefax: +356 284007

J Engerer, *Operations Manager*

High-speed craft operated

Type	Name	Seats	Delivered
SES Hovermarine International HM 218	Calypso	84	May 1988

Operations
Ferries to Mgarr, 25 minutes
Mgarr to Sa Maison, 26 minutes
Also services to Sliema and Mgarr (Gozo Island) and to Marsalforn and Comino Island.

VERIFIED

VIRTU FERRIES LTD

(A joint venture between The Virtu Steamship Company Ltd, PO Box 315, Valletta CMR 01, Malta and Misano di Navigazione SpA, Ravenna, Italy)
PO Box 285, Valletta, Malta

Telephone: +356 317088/071/316766
Telex: 1214/1667 SHIPAZ MW
Telefax: +356 314533/4633

F A Portelli, *Director*
C A Portelli, *Director*
M A Portelli, *Director*
J M Portelli, *Director*

High-speed craft operated

Type	Name	Seats	Delivered
SES Ulstein CIRR 120P	San Frangisk	330	1990

Operations
Valetta, Malta to Pozzallo, Sicily, 52 nm, 1 hour 30 minutes
Valetta, Malta to Catania, Sicily, 113 nm, 3 hours
Valetta, Malta to Licata, Sicily, 80 nm, 2 hour 30 minutes.

VERIFIED

San Frangisk *at Grand Harbour Valletta, Malta*   *1991*

MEXICO

CRUCEROS MARITIMOS DEL CARIBE SA DE CV

Calle 6 Nte No 14, Cozumel, Quintana Roo, Mexico

Telephone: +52 (987) 21508/88
Telefax: +52 (987) 21942

Venado 30, m18, SM 20, Cancún, Mexico

Telephone: +52 (988) 46846/46656

Jose Trinidad Molina Caceres, *Chairman of the Board*
Mario Arturo Molina Caceres, *Chief Executive Officer*
Rogelio Molina Caceres, *Managing Director*
Captain Manuel Pirez, *Operations Manager*
Javier Guillermo Clausell, *Operative Executive Officer*
Captain Luis Claudio Fernández, *Marine Superintendent*

High-speed craft operated

Type	Name	Seats	Delivered
CAT Fjellstrand 38.8 m	*Mexico*	390	February 1986
MH Breaux's Baycraft 30 m	*Mexico II*	250	November 1988
MH Breaux's Baycraft 43 m	*Mexico III*	800	April 1993

Operations
Mexican Caribbean area tourist service
Cancún to Cozumel, 43 nm
Cozumel to Playa del Carmen, 10 nm.

VERIFIED

Mexico II   *1993*

PEMEX
Petroleos Mexicanos

Tampico, Mexico

High-speed craft operated

Type	Name	Seats	Delivered
CAT Harding Verft A/S 26 m	*Havstril*	200	January 1990

This vessel was purchased from Simon Møkster by the US company Daysland

Operations
Transport of oil workers in Gulf of Mexico.

VERIFIED

NETHERLANDS

REDERJI G DOEKSEN EN ZONEN BV

PO Box 40, 8880 AA Terschelling-West, Netherlands

Telephone: +31 (5620) 2141
Telefax: +31 (5620) 3241

H Oosterbeek, *Managing Director*

High-speed craft operated

Type	Name	Seats	Delivered
CAT Harding Verft 35 m	*Koegelwieck*	300	June 1992

Operations
Harlingen to Terschelling, 45 minutes
Harlingen to Vlieland, 45 minutes
Terschelling to Vlieland, 15 minutes.

UPDATED

Koegelwieck *operated by BV Rederij G Doeksen en Zonen*   *1993*

NEW ZEALAND

FIORDLAND TRAVEL LTD NZ

PO Box 1, Te Anau, New Zealand

High-speed craft operated

Type	Name	Seats	Delivered
CAT NQEA InCat 22 m Peak	*Commander*	140	September 1985

Operations
Milford and Doubtful Sounds.

UPDATED

FULLERS CRUISES NORTHLAND LTD

PO Box 145, Maritime Building, Paihia, Bay of Islands, New Zealand

Telephone: +64 (09) 402 7421
Telefax: +64 (09) 402 7831

Chris Jacobs, *Director*
Roger Dold, *Director*
Mike Simm, *Director*

The Fullers Company is privately owned. Fullers has plied the Bay of Islands since 1886 and the company presently operates a fleet of eight vessels including an 18 m 40 passenger underwater viewing craft.

High-speed craft operated

Type	Name	Seats	Delivered
CAT Wanganui Boats InCat 22 m	*Tiger III* (ex *Tiger Lily III*)	240	1986
CAT NQEA InCat 26 m	*Tiger IV* (ex *Taupo Cat*)	250	1993
CAT Terry Bailey 11 m	*Tutunui*	35	1993

Operations
Cape Brett 'Hole in the Rock' cruise, 4 hours, fare NZ$49.
Whale watching, swimming with dolphins, 4 hours NZ$65.

UPDATED

Tiger III *coming through the 'Hole in the Rock'*   *1991*

GULF FERRIES LTD

9th Floor, Downtown House, 21 Queen Steet, Auckland, New Zealand

Telephone: +64 (9) 367 9100/9102
Telefax: +64 (9) 379 9105

George R Hudson, *Chairman*
Douglas G Hudson, *Managing Director*

High-speed craft operated

Type	Name	Seats	Delivered
CAT SBF Engineering 33.37 m	*Quickcat*	600+	March 1987
MH WaveMaster Int 37 m	*Jet Raider*	400	December 1990
CAT Fast Craft	*Seaflyte*	170	December 1993
CAT Sabre	*Quickcat II*	200	December 1993

Gulf Ferries' InCat 26 m *Taupo Cat* was sold to Fullers Northland in 1993.

Operations
Auckland to Waiheke Island, 30 minutes
Auckland to Great Barrier Island
plus Gulf cruises.

UPDATED

Jet Raider *operated by Gulf Ferries Ltd*   *1991*

HOVERCRAFT ADVENTURES

PO Box 656, Queenstown, New Zealand

Telephone: +64 (04) 28034

Ewen J McCammon, *Owner*

High-speed craft operated

Type	Name	Delivered
HOV Hovercraft Manufacturers (NZ)	*Riverland Surveyor 8*	1984

Operations
30 minute tourist trips over mud flats, sand banks and river rapids in Queenstown area.

VERIFIED

STEWART ISLAND MARINE

New Zealand

High-speed craft operated

Type	Name	Seats	Delivered
CAT Sabre Catamarans	*Foveaux Express*	67	1992

Operations
Stewart Island to Bluff (Foveaux Strait).

VERIFIED

WANAKA LAKE SERVICES LTD

PO Box 20, Wanaka, New Zealand

Telephone: +64 (03) 443 7495
Telefax: +64 (03) 443 1323

Paul Miller, *Director*

High-speed craft operated
HOV *Riverland Surveyor 8*. Originally operated by Airborne Hovercraft Services

Operations
30 minute tourist trips over farm land and in river and lake areas of Lake Wanaka, Ram Island, Matukituki River and Glendhu Bay.

VERIFIED

NORWAY

BERGEN NORDHORDLAND RUTELAG A/S

Lars Hilles gt. 26, PO Box 4204, Nygårdstangen, N-5028 Bergen, Norway

Telephone: +47 (55) 548700
Telefax: +47 (55) 317403

Oddvar Vigestad, *Managing Director*

High-speed craft operated

Type	Name	Seats	Delivered
CAT Fjellstrand Aluminium Yacht Alumaran 165	*Manger*	189	1979
CAT Fjellstrand 31.5 m	*Lygra*	292	1981

Operations
Bergen to Frekhaug to Knarvik to Frekhaug to Bergen. Round trip 1 hour 40 minutes to 1 hour 45 minutes.

VERIFIED

An early Fjellstrand catamaran Manger *operated by Bergen Nordhordland Rutelag*   *1988*

NORTH CAPE MINERALS A/S

N-9543 Stjernsund, Norway

Telephone: +47 78 434555
Telefax: +47 78 436267

Mr Martinsen, *Works Manager*

High-speed craft operated

Type	Name	Seats	Additional payload	Delivered
MH Fjellstrand 26 m	*Nefelin IV*	84	32 m³	1980

Operations
This craft operates a 47 km route from Alta to Sjernoey three times a day with a crossing time of 70 minutes.

UPDATED

Fjellstrand Nefelin IV *operated by North Cape Nefelin*   **1986**

FINNMARK FYLKESRSREDERI OG RUTESELSKAP

PO Box 308, N-9601 Hammerfest, Norway

Telephone: +47 (78) 411000
Telex: 64257N
Telefax: +47 (78) 412773

Stig Solheim, *Managing Director*

High-speed craft operated

Type	Name	Seats	Additional payload	Delivered
CAT Westamarin W86	*Brynilen*	94	cargo	June 1975
CAT Westamarin W86	*Hørnøy*	136	—	October 1979
MH Brødrene Aa Båtbyggeri	*Tanahorn*	49	cargo	1986
CAT Brødrene Aa Båtbyggeri 25.5 m	*Ingøy*	48	4 cars	July 1987
CAT Fjellstrand 38.8 m	*Varangerfjord*	164	3 cars	June 1990
CAT Fjellstrand 40 m	*Vargøy*	—	—	1994

Operations
Masry to Hammerfest to Sørøysundbass
*Masry to Havrøysund to Hammerfest
Kirkenes to Murmansk (CIS) Summer service.

UPDATED

FOSEN TRAFIKKLAG A/S

Pirterminalen, N-7005 Trondheim, Norway

Telephone: +47 (73) 525540
Telex: 65720
Telefax: +47 (73) 524133

High-speed craft operated

Type	Name	Seats	Delivered
CAT Westamarin W86	*Kongsbussen* (Yard No 27)	161	April 1973
CAT Westamarin W86	*Hertugbussen* (Yard No 28)	161	May 1973
CAT Lindstøl	*Fosningen* (Yard No 298)	118	June 1991
CAT Mjosundet	*Frøyfart*	72 + cargo	June 1991
CAT Harding	*Agdenes*	210	July 1991
CAT Fjellstrand 38.8 m	*Ternen* (Yard No 1595)	290	July 1994

Operations
Trondheim to Brekstad to Storfosna to Hestvika to Fjellvoer to Fillan to Sistranda to Mausundvøer to Vadsøysund to Bogoyvøer to Sula
Sistranda to Sula to Froan
Trondheim to Kristansund, 3.5 hours
Trondheim to Vanvikan, 25 minutes.

UPDATED

Ternen operated by Fosen Trafikklag   **1995**

FYLKESBAATANE I SOGN OG FJORDANE

PO Box 354, N-6901 Florø, Norway

Telephone: +47 (57) 746200
Telex: 40646
Telefax: +47 (57) 743760

Per Drageset, *Director*

High-speed craft operated

Type	Name	Seats	Delivered
CAT Westamarin W86 (Yard No 21)	*Fjordglytt*	140	May 1971
MH Brødrene Aa A/S	*Hyen*	156	1980
CAT Fjellstrand 38.8 m	*Fjordprins*	201	October 1987
CAT Fjellstrand 38.8 m	*Sognekongen*	201	December 1987
CAT Fjellstrand 40 m Flying Cat	*Kommandøren*	252	June 1990
CAT Brødrene Aa 20 m	*Alden*	—	1990
CAT Brødrene Aa 17 m	*Tornerose*	—	1990
MH Eikefjord 22 m	*Høydalsfjord*	—	1991
MH Båtutrustning 20 m	*Hennøy*	—	1993
CAT Fjellstrand 38.8 m	*Solundir*	—	1993

Operations
Askvoll to Bulandet, Årdalstragen to Bergen, Bergen to Flåm
Eivindvik to Nåra and Anneland, Florø to Svanøy, Flåm to Balestrand, Fjaerland and Kaupanger
Måloy to Forø
Selje to Bergen.

VERIFIED

Hyen (Alan Bliault)   **1991**

Kommandøren *at Bergen* (Alan Bliault)   **1991**

HELGELAND TRAFIKKSELSKAP A/S

PO Box 603, N-8800 Sandnessjøen, Norway

Telephone: +47 (86) 43066
Telefax: +47 (86) 40256

Jarl Høberg, *Chairman of the Board*
Robert Kolvik, *Managing Director*
Roger Hansen, *General Manager*

High-speed craft operated

Type	Name	Seats	Additional payload	Delivered
CAT Fjellstrand Alumaran 165 25.6 m	*Traena*	128	6 t	1976
MH Fjellstrand 25.9 m	*Råsa*	93	4 t	1979
CAT Fjellstrand 31.5 m	*Helgeland*	160	8 t	1983

Operations
Sandnessjøen to Herøy and Veger
Sandnessjøen to Lovund and Træna.

VERIFIED

HSD
Hardanger Sunnhordlandske Dampskipsselskap

PO Box 2005, N-5024 Nordnes, Bergen, Norway

Telephone: +47 (55) 238700
Telex: 42607 HSD N
Telefax: +47 (55) 238701

Arne Dvergsdal, *Managing Director*

High-speed craft operated

Type	Name	Seats	Delivered
CAT Westamarin W86	*Tedno I*	140	June 1973
CAT Westamarin W95	*Sunnhordland*	180	April 1975
CAT Westamarin W88	*Midthordland*	—	1981
CAT Westamarin W86	*Teisten* (ex *Øygar*)	140	September 1975
MH Båtutrustning	*Tranen* (ex *Concorde II*)	58	1990
CAT Fjellstrand 38.8 m	*Draupner*	—	1991
CAT Fjellstrand 38.8 m	*Sleipner*	—	1991
CAT Harding 29 m	*Tedno*	173	December 1992
CAT Holen 24 m	*Baronen*	—	1994
CAT Holen 24 m	*Baronessa*	—	1994

Operations
Bergen to Austevoll to Sunnhordland approximately 80 nm
Os to Sunnhordland approximately 50 nm
Odda to Norheimsund approximately 45 nm.

UPDATED

Sleipner   *1994*

L RØDNE AND SØNNER A/S

Skagenkaien 18, N-4006 Stavanger, Norway

Telephone: +47 (4) 5189 5270
Telefax: +47 (4) 5189 5202

High-speed craft operated

Type	Name	Seats	Delivered
MH Brødrene Aa 24.4 m	*Clipper*	120	1981
MH Batutrustning TMS 19.3 m	*Clipper Skyss*	88	1990

Operations
Stavanger to Pulpit Rock and Lysebotn.

VERIFIED

MØRE OG ROMSDAL FYLKESBÅTAR A/S

Gotfred Lies Plas 2, PO Box 216, N-6401 Molde, Norway

Telephone: +47 71219500
Telefax: +47 71219501

Olav Smørdal, *Managing Director*
Harald Ekker, *Assistant Director*
Anker Grøvdal, *Head of Department*
Olav Saunes, *Technical Maritime Manager*
Ottar Lillevik, *Head, Quality Department*
Kåre Sandøy, *Nautical Personnel Manager*
Øivind Ohr, *Traffic Manager*
Rolf D Holten, *Economics Manager*

High-speed craft operated

Type	Name	Seats	Delivered
CAT Fjellstrand 31.5 m	*Hjørungavåg*	250	1983
CAT Brødrene Aa Båtbyggeri CIRR 265P	*Fjørtoft*	120	June 1988
MH Brødrene Aa Båtbyggeri	*Romsdalsfjord*	89	—
CAT Harding	*Lauparen* (ex *Steufdik*)	200	April 1992
CAT Fjellstrand 38.8 m *	*Ternen*	290	July 1994

*Operated in cooperation with Fosen Trafikklag under the name *Kystekspressen*

Operations
Ålesund to Valderøy to Hareid, 300 000 passengers in 1994
Molde to Helland to Vikebukt, 130 000 passengers in 1994
Ålesund to Nordøyane, 100 000 passengers in 1994
Kristiansund to Edøy to Trondheim, 85 000 passengers in 1992.

UPDATED

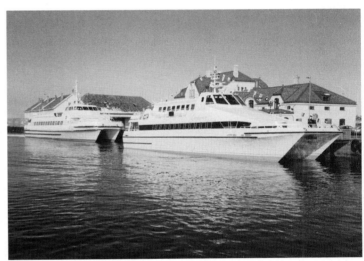

Hjørungavåg *(background) and* Lauparen   *1993*

Fjørtoft   *1994*

NAMSOS TRAFIKKSELSKAP A/S

PO Box 128, D-S Kaia, N-7801 Namsos, Norway

Telephone: +47 (77) 72433
Telex: 55492 NTS N
Telefax: +47 (77) 72467

High-speed craft operated

Type	Name	Seats	Delivered
CAT Lindstøl Skip 22.5 m	*Namdalingen*	107	August 1990

Operations
Leka to Rørvik to Namsos.

VERIFIED

Namdalingen   *1993*

NESODDEN-BUNDEFJORD DAMPSKIPSSELSKAP A/S

Stranden 1, N-0250 Oslo, Norway

Telephone: +47 (2) 833072
Telefax: +47 (2) 2483 0948

Ulf Nygaard, *Managing Director*

High-speed craft operated

Type	Name	Seats	Delivered
CAT Westamarin 28 m	*Princess*	175	November 1990

Operations
Nesoddtangen to Fornebo to Lysaker and Iltjernet
Oslo to Drøbak (May to August).

UPDATED

ROGALAND TRAFIKKSELSKAP A/S

PO Box 7033, Jorenholmen, N-4004 Stavanger, Norway

Telephone: +47 (51) 890499
Telex: 33032 N
Telefax: +47 (51) 531361

High-speed craft operated

Type	Name	Seats	Delivered
CAT Båtservice Sea Lord 28	*Fjordbris*	150	1991
CAT Båtservice Sea Lord 28	*Fjorddrott*	150	1990
CAT Båtservice Sea Lord 28	*Fjordsol*	150	1991
MH Boghammar 26.5 m	*Fjordtind*	130	1989
CAT Westamarin W86	*Ryfylke*	186	1992

VERIFIED

Båtservice Fjordbris (Alan Bliault)   *1991*

SALTENS DAMPSKIBSSELSKAP A/S
(A Subsidiary of Ofotens og Vesteraalens DSS A/S

PO Box 1064, N-8000 Bodø, Norway

Telephone: +47 (75) 521020
Telefax: +47 (75) 520835

High-speed craft operated

Type	Name	Seats	Additional payload	Delivered
MH Fjellstrand 26 m	*Rødøyløven*	—		1977
MH Fjellstrand 23 m	*Tysfjord*	—		1981
MH Fjellstrand 25.5 m	*Øykongen*	—		1982
MH Fjellstrand 25.5 m	*Øydronningen*	—		1982
CAT Brødrene Aa Båtbyggeri CIRR 27 m	*Helgelandsekspressen*	184		June 1985
CAT Westamarin 3600SC	*Salten*	186	65 m³	1988
CAT Westamarin 3000	*Børtind*	130	30 m³	1989
CAT Westamarin 3600SC	*Ofoten*	184	65 m³	1991
CAT Harding Verft 29 m	*Skogoy*	130	30 m³	1991

VERIFIED

SIMON MØKSTER SHIPPING A/S

PO Box 108, Skogstøstraen 37, N-4001 Stavanger, Norway

Telephone: +47 (51) 546001
Telex: 33101 MOKS N
Telefax: +47 (51) 546587

Per Haram, *Managing Director*
Atle W Holgersen, *Operations Manager*

High-speed craft operated

Type	Name	Seats	Delivered
MH Fjellstrand 26 m	*Veslestril*	94	1981
CAT Westamarin W86	*Strilbris* (ex *Carib Link*)	113	1975

UPDATED

The 25 knot Fjellstrand Veslestril *owned by Simon Møkster Shipping A/S*   *1986*

TORGHATTEN TRAFIKKSELSKAP A/S

PO Box 103, N-8901 Brønnøysund, Norway

Telephone: +47 (75) 022311
Telex: 55089 N
Telefax: +47 (75) 021719

High-speed craft operated

Type	Name	Seats	Additional payload	Delivered
MH Brødrene Aa Båtbyggeri 27 m	*Torgtind*	86	—	1981
CAT Brødrene Aa Båtbyggeri 25 m	*Heilhorn*	48	4 cars	1987
CAT Rosendal Verft 29 m	*B. No.264*	100	—	1994

Operations
Brønnøysund to Vega to Sandnessjøen and Bindalsflorden.

UPDATED

TFDS
Troms Fylkes Dampskibsselskap A/S

PO Box 548, N-9001 Tromsø, Norway

Telephone: +47 (77) 686088
Telex: 64457 TTDS N
Telefax: +47 (77) 688710

Bjørn Kald , *Managing Director*
Jan M Leinebø, *Financial Manager*
Kjell Ravnbø, *Technical Manager*
Reider Klingenberg, *Marine Superintendent*

High-speed craft operated

Type	Name	Seats	Delivered
CAT Westamarin W86	*Fjorddronningen*	174	January 1976
CAT Westamarin W86	*Fjordprinsessen*	163	March 1977
CAT Westamarin W95	*Tromsprinsen*	210	June 1981
MH Brødrene Aa Båtbyggeri	*Gapøy*	43	June 1980
MH Djupviks Varv	*Reinfjord*	49	June 1984
CAT Fjellstrand 40 m	*Fjordkongen II* (ex *Fjordkongen*)	320	1994

Operations

Fjordkongen, Tromsø to Harstad
Fjorddronningen, *Fjordprinsessen* and *Gapøy* operate Harstad area, *Tromsprinsen*, Tromso area, and *Reinfjord*, Skjervøy area

UPDATED

Fjordprinsessen (Alan Bliault)   *1992*

VEST-TRAFIKK A/S

N-5353 Straume, Norway

Telephone: +47 (56) 323500
Telefax: +47 (56) 323560

B O Børnes, *Managing Director*

High-speed craft operated

Type	Name	Seats	Delivered
CAT Båtservice Sea Lord 32	*Beinveien*	177	December 1992

Operations

Bergen to Kleppestø, 2.8 nm, 7 minutes.

VERIFIED

PAKISTAN

PAKISTAN WATER AND POWER DEVELOPMENT AUTHORITY

WAPDA Offices Complex, Hussainabad, Fatima Jinnah Road, Hyderabad, Pakistan

High-speed craft operated

Type	Name	Seats	Delivered
HOV Griffon Hovercraft Ltd 1000 TD (008) (GH 9456)	—	—	1987
HOV Griffon Hovercraft Ltd 1000 TD	—	—	1993

VERIFIED

Griffon Hovercraft 1000 TD (008) operated by the WAPDA of Pakistan   *1992*

PARAGUAY

ALISCAFOS ITAIPU SA

Yegros 690, Asunción, Paraguay
Main harbour: Hernandarias, Alto Panama, Paraguay

Telephone: +595 063479
Telex: 264 IE PY

Darius Morgan, *President*
Erminio Gatti, *Vice President*

High-speed craft operated

Type	Name	Seats	Delivered
HYD Ludwig Honald Manfacturing Co Albatross	*Flecha Guarani**	22	June 1985
HYD Ludwig Honald Manfacturing Co	*Flecha de Itaipu*	22	June 1985

*built 1964, overhauled and re-engined in Miami

Operations

Tourist use on Itaipu Lake on the border between Brazil and Paraguay
Puerto Hernandarias to Puerto Guarani.

VERIFIED

One of the boarding points for Aliscafos Albatross hydrofoils operating on Lake Itaipu in Paraguay (Darius Morgan)   *1987*

PHILIPPINES

ABOITEZ SUPERCAT

Philippines

High-speed craft operated

Type	Name	Delivered
CAT Cat Craft 27 m WPC	*Supercat I*	1993

VERIFIED

POLAND

PRZEDSIEBIORSTWO USIUG TURYSTYCZNYCH POMERANIA

Szczecin, Poland

High-speed craft operated

Type	Name	Delivered
HYD S Ordzhonikidze Meteor	*Adriana*	1973

VERIFIED

ZEGLUGA GDANSKA

Ul Wartka 4, Gdansk, Poland

Telephone: +48 (58) 311975

High-speed craft operated

Type	Name	Delivered
HYD Sormovo Kometa	*Poszum*	1973
HYD Sormovo Kometa	*Poweiw*	1973
HYD Sormovo Kometa	*Poswist*	1975
HYD Sormovo Kometa	*Poryw*	1976
HYD Sormovo Kometa	*Pogwizd*	1977
HYD Sormovo Kometa	*Polot*	1977

Operations
Gdynia to Hel, 25 minutes
Gdansk to Hel, 55 minutes
Gdynia to Jastarnia, 25 minutes
Sopot to Hel, 25 minutes
Gdynia to Sopot, 10 minutes
Gdynia to Hel to Wladyslawowo.

ZEGLUGA SZCZECINSKA

Ul Energetyka 55, PL-70-656 Szczecin, Poland

Telephone: +48 (91) 45561/47051
Telex: 0422158 PL

Michal Bardasz, *Director*

High-speed craft operated

Type	Name	Delivered
HYD Sormovo Kometa	*Lida*	1971
HYD S Ordzhonikidze	*Daria* (ex *Kometa 4 '76*)*	1975
HYD Sormovo Kometa	*Liwia**	1978

Operations
Szczecin to Świnoujście, 1 hour 15 minutes
*operating *en route* Kolobrzeg to Roenne/Bornholm, Denmark, 2 hours 30 minutes.

PORTUGAL

SERVICO DE TRANSPORTES MARITIMOS

Avenida Sá Carneiro, 3, 4 e 5, P-9000 Funchal, Portugal

Telephone: +351 (91) 225281/7
Telefax: +351 (91) 228881

Miguel Homem de Freitas, *Director for Madeira Island harbours*
Captain José Carlos Caldeira, *Co-ordinator of Maritime Transport Services*

High-speed craft operated

Type	Name	Seats	Delivered
CAT Westamarin W100 (Yard No 76)	*Independencia* (ex *Gimle Bird*)	244	November 1983
Swath FBM Marine FDC400	*Patria*	400	March 1990

Operations
Funchal to Porto Santo Island, 42 nm, 1 hour 35 minutes

Independencia traffic 1992: 33 437 passengers
Patria traffic 1992: 63 119 passengers

VERIFIED

Patria   *1990*

PUERTO RICO

PUERTO RICO PORTS AUTHORITY

Apartado 2829, San Juan, Puerto Rico 00936

Edwin Rodríquez Colón, *Manager, Acuaexpreso Project*

High-speed craft operated

Type	Name	Seats	Delivered
CAT Nichols Bros InCat 22 m	*Martin Peña*	167	August 1989
CAT Nichols Bros InCat 22 m	*Amelia*	167	November 1989
CAT Nichols Bros InCat 22 m	*Covadonga*	167	December 1989
CAT Nichols Bros InCat 22 m	*San Jerónimo*	167	April 1990
CAT Nichols Bros InCat 22 m	*Viejo San Juan*	167	April 1990
CAT Nichols Bros InCat 22 m	*Cristobal Colón*	167	June 1990

VERIFIED

SAUDI ARABIA

DERY SHIPPING LINES

Saudi Arabia

High-speed craft operated

Type	Name	Delivered
CAT Westamarin W95	*Salem* (ex *Tryving*)	1990

VERIFIED

SAUDI ARAMCO

Saudi Arabia

High-speed craft operated

Type	Name	Delivered
CAT Båtservice Sea Lord 36	*Ain Dar 7*	1992
CAT Båtservice Sea Lord 36	*Ain Dar 8*	1992

Operations
Pollution control vessels.

VERIFIED

SIERRA LEONE

SIERRA LINK

(an Aliscafi SNAV Company)

PO Box 73, Freetown, Sierra Leone

High-speed craft operated

Type	Name	Seats	Delivered
CAT Westamarin W95	*Nastro Azzuwo* (ex *Martini Bianco*)	220	1991

Operations
Freetown to Conakry.

VERIFIED

SINGAPORE

AUTO BATAM FERRIES

1 Maritime Square, 02-04 World Trade Centre, Singapore 0409

High-speed craft operated

Type	Name	Seats	Delivered
SES Hovermarine 218	*Auto Batam 1*	—	1982
MH Bintan Senpokau 26 m	*Auto Batam 2*	—	1982
MH SBF Engineering 30 m	*Auto Batam 6*	200	1990
MH SBF Engineering 30 m	*Auto Batam 7*	200	March 1991
CAT NQEA InCat 30 m	*Diamond 2*	—	1994

UPDATED

Equator Triangle   *1992*

Auto Batam 1 *in Singapore harbour* (M Daley)   *1990*

PELAYARAN BINTAN BARUNA SAKTI

1 Maritime Square, 09-01 World Trade Centre, Singapore 0409

High-speed craft operated

Type	Name	Seats	Delivered
MH SBF 31 m	*Sea Flyte*	240	1985
MH WaveMaster 32 m	*Sea Raider II*	250	1986
MH WaveMaster 32 m	*Golden Raider III* (ex *Sea Spirit*)	250	1989
MH WaveMaster 37 m	*Jet Raider III*	330	1991
MH WaveMaster 39 m	*Ocean Raider*	339	1992

Operations
Singapore to Sekupang
Singapore to Tanjong to Pinang.

VERIFIED

BINTAN RESORT FERRIES

Singapore

High-speed craft operated

Type	Name	Seats	Delivered
CAT Fjellstrand 40 m	*Indera Bupala*	—	1994
CAT Fjellstrand 40 m	—	—	1994

NEW ENTRY

IGSA TRANSPORT

International Plaza 35-09, Anson Road, Singapore 0105

Telephone: +65 222 1500

High-speed craft operated

Type	Name	Seats	Delivered
SES Hovermarine HM 216	*Batam Express Dua*	60	
CAT NQEA InCat 30 m	*Supercat III*	358	1989

UPDATED

J & N CRUISE PTE LTD

1 Maritime Square, 12-04 World Trade Centre, Singapore 0409

Telephone: +65 270 7100
Telefax: +65 278 4367

Tokuhisa Asayama, *Chief Executive Officer*

High-speed craft operated

Type	Name	Seats	Delivered
CAT Austal Ships 38 m	*Equator Triangle*	216	May 1991

Operations (Cruises)
Singapore to Batam to Singapore
Singapore to Desaru (West Malaysia) to Singapore
Local harbour cruises.

VERIFIED

RESORT CRUISES (S) PTE LTD

337 Telok Blangah Road, 02-03 Shing Loong Building, Singapore 0409

Telephone: +65 278 4677
Telefax: +65 278 3301

High-speed craft operated

Type	Name	Seats	Delivered
CAT Aluminium Craft (88) 34 m	*Island Pearl*	200	1990
CAT Aluminium Craft (88) 34 m	*Sea Pearl*	211	1991
CAT NQEA InCat 30 m	*Island Jade*	—	1992

Operations
Singapore to Tioman Island and excursions.

VERIFIED

SHELL EASTERN PETROLEUM (PTE) LTD

PO Box 1908, Pulau Bukom, Singapore 9038

Telephone: +65 229 4150
Telex: 21251 RS

Captain V K Nanda Kumar, *Marine Manager*

Operator: Kapal Management Pte Ltd
15 Hoe Chiang Road 10-05, Sanford Building, Singapore 0208

Telephone: +65 225 9338

High-speed craft operated

Type	Name	Seats	Delivered
SES Vosper Hovermarine 218	*Bukom Deras*	90	1983
SES Vosper Hovermarine 218	*Bukom Pantas*	90	1983
SES Vosper Hovermarine 218	*Bukom Lekas*	90	1983
SES Vosper Hovermarine 218	*Bukom Maju*	90	1983
SES Vosper Hovermarine 218	*Bukom Jaya*	90	1983

Operations
Pasir Panjang to Pulau Bukom refinery.

VERIFIED

SINBA SHIPPING

Singapore

High-speed craft operated

Type	Name	Seats	Delivered
ALH Stolkraft	Batam Express III	45	1988

VERIFIED

TAN PIA LAW

Singapore

High-speed craft operated

Type	Seats	Delivered
CAT Aluminium Craft SS23	130	July 1989
CAT Aluminium Craft SS23	130	July 1989

VERIFIED

TIAN SAN SHIPPING PTE LTD

Singapore

High-speed craft operated

Type	Seats	Built
MH 28 m Troika Class	150	1990
MH 28 m Troika Class	150	1990
MH 28 m Troika Class	150	1990
MH 28 m Troika Class	150	1990

VERIFIED

YANG PASSENGER FERRY SERVICE

407 Jalan Besar, Singapore 0820

Telex: 56408 YANGFE RS

Yong Kian Chin, *Director*

High-speed craft operated

Type	Name	Seats	Delivered
CAT Lloyd's Ships 36.5 m	Auto Batam 8	—	1989

(previously owned by Auto-Shipping, Singapore and Union Hydraulic Jack (Pte) Ltd)

Operations
Singapore to Batam Island (Indonesia).

VERIFIED

SLOVAKIA

SLOVENSKÁ PLAVBA DUNAJSKÁ ZÁVOD OSOBNEJ LODNEJ DOPRAVY (PASSENGER TRANSPORT DIVISION)

Fajnorovo nábr. 2, 811 02 Bratislava, Slovakia

Telephone: +42 (7) 363518/331115
Telefax: +42 (7) 363516

Miroslav Gerhát, *Director*

High-speed craft operated

Type	Name	Seats	Built
HYD Meteor	Koske	112	1977
HYD Meteor	Trnava	112	1982
HYD Meteor	Myjava	112	1987
HYD Meteor	Modra	112	1990
HYD Meteor	Bratislava	112	1989
HYD Voskhod	Piestany	71	1980

Operations
Vienna to Bratislava, 1 hour
Bratislava to Vienna, 1 hour 15 minutes
Bratislava to Budapest, 3 hours 30 minutes
Budapest to Bratislava, 4 hours.

UPDATED

Piestany   1995

Bratislava   1995

SLOVENIA

KOMPAS INTERNATIONAL DD

PO Box 307/IV, Prazakova 4, 61001 Ljubljana, Slovenia

Telex: 31209 KOMPAS SI
Telefax: +386 (61) 318262

Janez Urbas, *Director*

High-speed craft operated

Type	Name	Seats	Delivered
CAT Westamarin W100	Poreč 1	250	1982
CAT NQEA Wave-piercer InCat	Prince of Venice	303	1989

Operations
Prince of Venice operates Portorož to Venice, *Poreč* to Venice, Venice to Mali Lošinj and along the Istrian Coast. *Poreč 1* operates to Cyprus.
Between April and October 1993, *Prince of Venice* carried 30 000 passengers
Services are operated from April until October each year.

UPDATED

Prince of Venice   1994

SPAIN

COMPAÑIA TRASMEDITERRANEA SA

Plaza Manuel Gómez Moreno s/n, Edificio Bronce-Centro Azca, E-28020 Madrid, Spain

Telephone: +34 (1) 455 0049/456 0009
Telex: 27666 TRASM E

High-speed craft operated

Type	Name	Seats	Additional payload	Delivered
HYD Rodriquez RHS 160F	*Pez Volador*	220	—	1988
HYD Rodriquez RHS 160F	*Barracuda*	204	—	1989
HYD Rodriquez RHS 160F	*Marrajo*	204	—	1989
HYD Rodriquez RHS 160F	*Tintorera*	204	—	1990
HYD Kawasaki Jetfoil 929-117	*Princesa Dacil*	286	—	1990
HYD Kawasaki Jetfoil 929-117	*Princesa Teguise*	286	—	1991
HYD Rodriquez RHS 160F	*Alijumbo Stromboli*	204	—	1994
MH EN Bazán Mestrel 96 m	*Albayzin*	450	76 cars	1995
MH EN Bazán Mestrel 96 m	—	450	76 cars	(1995)

Operations

Las Palmas, Grand Canaria to Santa Cruz de Tenerife, 52 nm, 1 hour 20 minutes
Las Palmas to Morro Jable, 1 hour 30 minutes
Algeciras to Ceuta, 15 nm, 30 minutes
Cristianos to Gomera, Canary Islands, 21 nm, 45 minutes
Valencia to Ibiza (July to September).

UPDATED

FLEBASA LINES

Spain

High-speed craft operated

Type	Name	Delivered
HYD Rodriquez RHS 140	*Rapido de Ibiza* (ex *Viggen*)	1988
CAT Westamarin W95	*Rapido de Formentera* (ex *Sunnhordland*)	1991
HYD Rodriquez RHS 200	*Rapido de Mallorca*	1994

Operations

Ibiza to La Savina.

UPDATED

Rapido de Formentera (Duncan P Trillo)   *1992*

LINEAS FRED OLSEN

Santa Cruz de Tenerife, Canary Islands, Spain

High-speed craft operated

Type	Name	Delivered
SES Cirrus 120 P	*Bahia*	1994

Operations

Lanzarote to Fuerteventura.

NEW ENTRY

TRASMAPI

Avenida Santa Eulalia, 17-5 Bajos Edificio Cabiro, Spain

High-speed craft operated

Type	Name	Delivered
CAT Marinteknik JC-F1	*Formentera Jet*	1990
CAT Westamarin W95	*Ibiza Jet* (ex *Tunen*)	1993
CAT Westamarin W95	*Tagomago Jet* (ex *Tranen*)	1993

Operations

Ibiza to La Savina.

UPDATED

YASMINE LINE SA

Avenida de Alay 27, Galerías Diana, E-29630 Benalmádena-Costa, Málaga, Spain

Telephone: +34 (52) 445576
Telefax: +34 (52) 561627

Kjell K Trofast, *Director and Manager*

High-speed craft operated

Type	Name	Seats	Delivered
CAT Marinteknik Verkstads 34 m	*Saud*	255	1989

Operations

Benalmádena to Ceuta, 60 nm
Benalmádena to M'Diq (Morocco), 75 nm
Malaga to Ceuta
Marina Smir to Gibraltar.

VERIFIED

Saud   *1993*

ISLENA DE NAVEGACION SA

Avenida Virgen del Carmen, Nos 3 & 5, Algeciras, Spain

Telephone: +34 (56) 652000/950/561
Telex: 78132

V S Lopez, *President*

High-speed craft operated

Type	Name	Seats	Delivered
CAT Fjellstrand 38.8 m	*Sevilla 92* (ex *Caribbean Princess*)	310	1990
CAT Fjellstrand 38.8 m	*Rapido de Algeciras* (ex *Bahamian Prince*)	310	1990

Operations

Algeciras to Centa.

UPDATED

ST PIERRE ET MIQUELON (France)

ARMEMENT BOROTRA FRÈRES

PO Box 4218, F-97500 St Pierre et Miquelon

Telephone: +508 412078
Telex: 914407
Telefax: +508 414608

High-speed craft operated

Type	Name	Seats	Delivered
MH SFCN 35 m	*St Eugene 5*	200	March 1988

Operations

St Pierre to Miquelon, 55 minutes.

UPDATED

SWEDEN

CITY JET LINE

PO Box 183, S-185 23 Vaxholm, Sweden

Telephone: +46 (8) 5413 3460
Telefax: +46 (8) 5413 2284

Captain Bjørn Justine, *Director*

High-speed craft operated

Type	Name	Seats	Delivered
MH Marinteknik 41 m	*Cinderella II*	450	1989
MH Marinteknik 41 m	*Cinderella III*	450	1990

Operations
Stockholm to Archipelago
Malmö to Copenhagen.   **VERIFIED**

SEA CONTAINERS SWEDEN AB

Base 4040, S-400 40 Goteborg, Sweden

Telephone: +46 (31) 775 4200
Telefax: +46 (31) 420015

Magnus Brannberg, *Managing Director*
Lars Nilsson, *Sales and Marketing Manager*
Hakan Siewers, *Operations Manager*

Sea Containers Sweden AB, a subsidiary of Sea Containers Limited, was formed in May 1993 to operate an InCat 74 m wave-piercing catamaran on the cross Kattegat route between Sweden and Denmark. It has carried more than 603 000 passengers and 109 000 vehicles since the service started.

High-speed craft operated

Type	Name	Seats	Delivered
CAT InCat Australia 74 m WPC	*SeaCatamaran Danmark*	450	1993

Operations
Gothenburg to Frederikshavn, 1 hour 45 minutes.   **UPDATED**

TAIWAN

TIEN PENG YANG HOVERTRAVEL CORPORATION

Koahsiung, Taiwan

High-speed craft operated

Type	Name	Seats	Delivered
HOV NQEA BHC AP1-88	*Tien peng yang*	94	May 1990

VERIFIED

TUNG HSIN STEAMSHIP COMPANY LTD

Ping Tung, Taiwan

High-speed craft operated

Type	Name	Seats	Delivered
MH SBF 26.55 m	*Tung Hsin*	193	February 1993

VERIFIED

THAILAND

FAST FERRY SIAM LTD

Bangkok, Thailand

High-speed craft operated

Type	Name	Seats	Delivered
SES Karlskronavarvet Jet Westamarin Rider 3400 37 m	*Jet Cruise 2* (ex *Jet Prince*)	292	1991
SES Karlskronavarvet Jet Westamarin Rider 3400 37 m	*Jet Cruise 3* (ex *Jet Princess*)	292	1991
CAT Westamarin W100	*Jet Cruise 1* (ex *Gibline I*)	250	1991

Operations
Phuket to Phi Phi Island.   **VERIFIED**

JET CAT TOUR COMPANY LTD
(a subsidiary of Seatran Travel Company)

599/1 Chua Phloeng Road, Klontoey, Bangkok 10110, Thailand

Telephone: +66 (2) 240 2582
Telefax: +66 (2) 249 5656

Tanan Tanphaibul, *Managing Director*
Pornrat Tanphaibul, *General Manager*

High-speed craft operated

Type	Name	Seats	Delivered
MH Mitsubishi 45 m	*Seatran Express*	N/K	1990
CAT Fjellstrand Flying Cat 40 m	*Jet Cat* (ex *Pattaya Express*)	272	1991

Operations
Phuket to Similan, 2 hours.   **UPDATED**

40 m Fjellstrand Flying Cat Jet Cat   *1994*

THAI GENERAL TRANSPORT LTD

3/63-63 The Teppukdee Building, 4th Floor, Rachadabhisek Road, Hueykhwang, Bangkok, Thailand

Telephone: +66 (2) 7653 1344

High-speed craft operated

Type	Seats	Delivered
HOV Griffon 3000 TD	30	1991
HOV Griffon 3000 TD	30	1991

VERIFIED

TRINIDAD

SUN ISLAND CRUISES

Trinidad

High-speed craft operated

Type	Name	Seats	Delivered
WPC ASL/InCat 49 m	*Condor 9*	450	1994

Operations
Trinidad to Tobago.   **NEW ENTRY**

TUNISIA

SEA BUS SA

PO Box 108, 4089 el Kantaoui, Tunisia

Telephone: +216 (3) 41791
Telefax: +216 (3) 42663

High-speed craft operated

Type	Seats	Delivered
HOV Griffon 2000 TDX	20	March 1991
HOV Griffon 2000 TDX	20	March 1991

VERIFIED

TURKEY

ISTANBUL DENIZ OTOBÜSLERI

81110 Bostanci, Istanbul, Turkey

There were 10 Fjellstrand 38.8 m, 449 passenger catamarans purchased to provide a ferry service for commuters across the Strait of Bosphorus. Five have a 24 knot cruise speed capability and five, 32 knots. Two monohull craft were purchased from Austal in 1994.

High-speed craft operated

Type	Name	Seats	Delivered
CAT Fjellstrand 38.8 m	Umer Bey	449	April 1987
CAT Fjellstrand 38.8 m	Sarica Bey	449	August 1987
CAT Fjellstrand 38.8 m	Uluç Ali Reis	449	January 1988
CAT Fjellstrand 38.8 m	Nusret Bey	449	March 1988
CAT Fjellstrand 38.8 m	Hezarfen Çelebi	449	September 1988
CAT Fjellstrand 38.8 m	Çaka Bey	449	February 1987
CAT Fjellstrand 38.8 m	Yeditepe I	449	May 1987
CAT Fjellstrand 38.8 m	Ulubatli Hasan	449	September 1987
CAT Fjellstrand 38.8 m	Karamürsel Bey	449	March 1988
CAT Fjellstrand 38.8 m	Cavli Bey	449	September 1988
MH Austal 30 m	Aksemseddin		November 1994
MH Austal 30 m	Ertugrul Gazi		November 1994

Operations
Bostanci to Kabatas, 10 nm, 18 minutes
Bostanci to Karakoy to Atakoy, 39 minute round trip
Kabatas to Buyukada. ***UPDATED***

UNITED ARAB EMIRATES

ZADCO PRODUCTIONS

Abu Dhabi, United Arab Emirates

High-speed craft operated

Type	Name	Seats	Additional payload	Delivered
CAT Sing Koon Seng Pte InCat 30 m	Ipo Ipo 3001	15	60 t	1984

VERIFIED

UNITED KINGDOM

CONDOR LTD

Commodore House, Bulwer Avenue, St Sampson's, PO Box 10, Guernsey, Channel Islands, UK

Telephone: +44 (1481) 48771
Telefax: +44 (1481) 45049

D C Butcher, *Chairman*
R N Adams, *Managing Director*
A R White, *Technical Manager*
S R Maycock, *Financial Director*
S G Spindlow, *Marketing Manager*
R W Sumner, *Operations Manager*

Condor Ltd operates a fast passenger network between St Malo in France and Jersey, Sark, Guernsey and Weymouth in the UK. The company carries approximately 430 000 passengers yearly. In 1991 over 250 000 passengers were carried by *Condor 9* which ran from 7 April to the end of October with only one weather cancellation. In 1992, TNT, an Australian based company, became a joint partner in Condor Ltd. In 1993 Condor Ltd started a passenger/car ferry service employing its first Incat Australia 74 m WPC operating on routes between Weymouth and the Channel Islands.

High-speed craft operated

Type	Name	Seats	Additional payload	Delivered
CAT Marinteknik (S)	Condor 8	300	—	June 1988
CAT Incat Australia 74 m WPC	Condor 10	580	80 cars	April 1993

Operations
St Malo to Jersey, 38 nm, 1 hour 10 minutes
Jersey to Sark, 27 nm, 45 minutes
Jersey to Guernsey, 28 nm, 1 hour
St Malo to Guernsey, 57 nm, 1 hour 20 minutes
Guernsey to Weymouth, 70 nm, 2 hours 15 minutes
Jersey to Weymouth, 3 hours. ***UPDATED***

HOVERSPEED LTD

International Hoverport, Western Docks, Dover, Kent, UK

Telephone: +44 (1304) 240101
Telefax: +44 (1304) 240099

Geoffrey Ede, *Managing Director*
Dave Stafford, *General Europe Manager*
John Smith, *Marketing Manager*

Sea Containers' Hoverspeed subsidiary has been an important part of its ferry operations since it was purchased in 1986. It is the prominent high speed cross-channel car ferry operator. Two Mark III Hovercraft underwent major refits in 1992 and parts have been purchased to enable them to continue in service until the end of the decade. Seacat Great Britain broke the record for the fastest trans-Atlantic crossing by a passenger craft during her delivery voyage from Tasmania, winning the prestigious Hales trophy and Blue Riband in the process. Hoverspeed carries more than 2 000 000 passengers and 400 000 vehicles across the channel each year.

Operations
Dover to Calais, 23 nm, 35 minutes by SR. N4
Folkestone to Boulogne, 28 nm, 55 minutes by SeaCat.

Traffic carried by SR. N4 hovercraft and SeaCats

	Passengers	Vehicles
1985	1 645 000	238 000
1986	1 575 000	257 000
1987	1 587 600	287 200
1988	1 738 578	334 096
1989	1 722 110	316 633
1990	1 640 514	277 329
1992	1 980 000	393 000
1993	2 100 000	411 000
1994	2 110 000	373 000

Up to 12 return trips daily on the Dover to Calais route.

High-speed craft operated

Type	Name	Seats	Additional payload	Delivered
HOV BHC SR. N4 Modified to Mk 3 in 1979	The Princess Margaret (GH 2006)	390	55 cars	1968
HOV BHC SR. N4 Mk 1 modified to Mk 3 in 1978	The Princess Anne (GH 2007)	390	55 cars	1969
CAT InCat Australia 74 m WPC	Hoverspeed Great Britain	600	90 cars	August 1990

Note: Capacity of Hoverspeed Great Britain increased from 450 passengers and 80 cars in 1993-94 refit.

UPDATED

Hoverspeed SR. N4 Mk 3 The Princess Margaret *and* Hoverspeed Great Britain
1995

HOVERTRAVEL LTD

12 Lind Street, Ryde, Isle of Wight PO33 2NR, UK

Telephone: +44 (1983) 565181
Telex: 86513 HOVERWORK G
Telefax: +44 (1983) 812859

Terminal offices: Quay Road, Ryde, Isle of Wight (Tel: +44 (1983) 811000);
Clarence Pier, Southsea (Tel: +44 (1705) 811000)

C D J Bland, *Chairman and Managing Director*
E W H Gifford, *Director*
J Gaggero, *Director*
R K Box, *General Manager (Solent Services)*
G M Palin, *Company Secretary*
B A Jehan, *Operations Manager*

Hovertravel Ltd, the world's longest established commercial hovercraft company, was formed in 1965 using two SR. N6 Winchester hovercraft to operate the service. Today the 98 seat AP1-88 hovercraft make the crossing between Ryde and Southsea in under 10 minutes and carry over 650 000 passengers per year. The company is also a registered carrier of Royal Mail and a high-speed freight service is provided on each crossing. In the last year *Courier* has returned from Gibraltar for refurbishment and eventual sale. By December 1994 the company had carried over 13.8 million passengers.

High-speed craft operated

Type	Name	Seats	Delivered
HOV BHC/HW AP1-88 GH 2107	*Double O Seven*	98	1989
HOV BHC/HW AP1-88 GH 2114	*Freedom 90*	98	1990
HOV BHC/NQEA AP1-88 GH 2108	*Courier*	84	1986

AP1-88 *Perseverance* and *Resolution* were sold to Textron Marine for delivery to the US Navy for training purposes.

Operations
Ryde, Isle of Wight to Southsea, Portsmouth

VERIFIED

Courier *arriving on the beach*   **1995**

HOVERWORK LTD

12 Lind Street, Ryde, Isle of Wight PO33 2NR, UK

Telephone: +44 (1983) 565181
Telex: 86513 HOVERWORK G
Telefax: +44 (1983) 812859

C D J Bland, *Managing Director*
R H Barton, *Director*
R K Box, *Director*
E W H Gifford, *Director*
G M Palin, *Director*
B A Jehan, *Operations Manager*

Hoverwork is a wholly owned subsidiary of Hovertravel Ltd which provides a hovercraft service linking Portsmouth on the mainland to the Isle of Wight; the service operates 13 hours a day, 363 days a year.

Hoverwork has access to all the craft operated by Hovertravel, which includes 80 and 98 seat AP1-88 diesel-powered hovercraft built under licence at the company's engineering facility on the Isle of Wight.

High-speed craft operated

Type	Name	Seats	Delivered
HOV BHC/HW AP1-88 GH 2087	*Tenacity*	80	1983

Operations
The company has trained over 60 hovercraft captains and received some 40 charter contracts, including film sequences and the operation of hovercraft for mineral surveys throughout the world. The company operated the passenger

hovercraft service during Expo '67 at Montreal, the Algiers Trade Fair Expositions in 1970 and 1976, and supplied operating crews for Expo '86 linking Victoria and Vancouver, a route of 70 nm.

Hoverwork is the largest international operator of hovercraft, having access to Hovertravel's SR. N6 and its AP1-88 fleet. The company has undertaken operations in over 25 countries from the Arctic to the equator, which include logistics, passenger services, mineral surveys and medical evacuation duties.

In 1991 *Tenacity* completed a passenger service contract in Sierra Leone connecting the international airport with the capital Freetown. The 25 minute journey by hovercraft saves a 117 mile road trip or crossing by conventional ferry.

VERIFIED

ISLE OF MAN STEAM PACKET COMPANY

Imperial Buildings, Douglas, Isle of Man

High-speed craft operated

Type	Name	Seats	Additional payload	Delivered
CAT WPC InCat Australia 74 m	*SeaCat Isle of Man*	450	90 cars	1994

Operations
Douglas to Belfast, Dublin, Fleetwood and Liverpool.

NEW ENTRY

RED FUNNEL FERRIES

12 Bugle Street, Southampton, Hampshire SO14 2JY, UK

Telephone: +44 (1703) 333042
Telefax: +44 (1703) 639438

A Whyte, *Managing Director*
O H Glass, *Marketing Director*
N Palmer, *General Manager*
J Sheard, *Group Chief Accountant*
R A Marshall, *Technical Manager*

High-speed craft operated

Type	Name	Seats	Delivered
HYD Rodriquez RHS 70	*Shearwater 5*	67	1980
HYD Rodriquez RHS 70	*Shearwater 6*	67	1982
CAT FBM Marine 31.5 m	*Red Jet 1*	130	1991
CAT FBM Marine 31.5 m	*Red Jet 2*	130	1991

Operations
Southampton to West Cowes, Isle of Wight, 10.8 nm, 20 minutes
Fares: single £5.90, return £10.60, day return £8.80 (from 1 February 1994)

Passengers carried
In 1993 780 000 passengers were carried

UPDATED

Red Jet 1   **1992**

SEA CONTAINERS LTD

Sea Containers House, 20 Upper Ground, London SE1, UK

Telephone: +44 (171) 928 6969
Telefax: +44 (171) 928 1469

Also: 41 Cedar Avenue, PO Box HM1179, Hamilton, Bermuda, HMFX

James B Sherwood, *President*
Michael Stracey, *Executive Vice President*
Daniel O'Sullivan, *Senior Vice President, Finance*
Robert Ward, *Senior Vice President, Containers*
David Benson, *Vice President, Ferries and Ports*

Sea Containers Ltd is the parent company of Hoverspeed, Sea Containers Scotland, Wightlink and Sea Containers Sweden. Between them these subsidiary companies operate three Tasmanian built InCat 74 m SeaCats, two Mk 3 Hovercraft and two passenger-only InCat 30 m catamarans. Wightlink also operates a number of conventional car ferries. Sea Containers Ltd holds a 42 per cent share of the Isle of Man Steam Packet Company and, in addition to its status as a world leader in the design, manufacture and lease of containers, has extensive leisure industry interests. Sea Containers is the world's leading fast ferry operator and the UK's third major ferry company. It handles nearly eight million passengers and 1.6 million vehicles worldwide each year.

UPDATED

SEA CONTAINERS SCOTLAND LTD

34 Charlotte Street, Stranraer DG9 7EF, UK

Telephone: +44 (1776) 702755
Telefax: +44 (1776) 705894

Hamish Ross, *Managing Director*
John Burrows, *Route General Manager*

Sea Containers Scotland Ltd is a subsidiary of Sea Containers Ltd and was formed in 1992 to operate the Irish Sea route from Stranraer to Belfast. *SeaCat Scotland*, an InCat 74 m wave-piercing catamaran operates on this route.

High-speed craft operated

Type	Name	Seats	Additional payload	Delivered
WPC InCat Australia 74 m	*SeaCat Scotland*	450	90 cars	1992
WPC InCat Australia 74 m (Currently on charter to Isle of Man Steamship Company)	*SeaCat Isle of Man*	450	90 cars	

Operations
Belfast to Stranraer.

Passengers carried
1.1 million passengers and 250 000 vehicles since June 1992

UPDATED

STENA SEALINK LINE

Charter House, Park Street, Ashford, Kent TN24 8EX, UK

Telephone: +44 (1233) 647022
Telex: 965181
Telefax: +44 (1233) 620364

W G Cooper, *Managing Director*
M Storey, *Ship and Port Management Director*
J Hannah, *Communications Director*

Stena Sealink Line operates one 78 m Wave-Piercing Catamaran (WPC) alongside its conventional ferry fleet on the Holyhead to Dun Laoghaire route. This craft is scheduled to be replaced by the 120 m Stena HSS catamaran in 1995.

Stena Sea Lynx   1995

High-speed craft operated

Type	Name	Seats	Additional payload	Delivered
WPC InCat Australia 74 m	*Stena Sea Lynx*	450	90 cars	June 1993
WPC InCat Australia 78 m	*Stena Sea Lynx II*	600	120 cars	June 1994

Operations
Holyhead (UK) to Dun Laoghaire (Ireland). Crossing time 110 minutes, service speed 35 knots. Maximum vehicle height 3 m, maximum vehicle length 6 m Fishguard to Rosslare. Crossing time 99 minutes, service speed 35 knots. Maximum vehicle height 3 m, maximum vehicle length 6 m.

UPDATED

Stena Sea Lynx II   1995

WHITE HORSE FERRIES LTD

Head Office: Stanley House, 65 Victoria Road, Swindon, Wiltshire SN1 3BB, UK
Boatyard: Clifton Slipway, West Street, Gravesend, Kent DA11 0BS, UK

Telephone: +44 (1474) 533610
Telefax: +44 (1474) 533123

Harold Peter Lay, *Director*
Sidney Richard Lay, *Director*
Spencer Lloyd Lay, *Director*
Lawrence Lester Lay, *Director*

White Horse Ferries Ltd operates passenger ferry services on the River Thames and Southampton Water.
The company currently operates one medium-speed catamaran and one high-speed trimaran river taxi. A further two river taxis are currently under construction.

High-speed craft operated

Type	Name	Seats	Delivered
TRI Griffon Trimaran	*Ebenezer Scrooge*	12	1993

UPDATED

12 seat Fast River Taxi Ebenezer Scrooge   1994

WIGHTLINK LTD

70 Broad Street, Portsmouth, Hampshire PO1 2LB, UK

Telephone: +44 (1705) 812011
Telex: 86440 WIGHTL G
Telefax: +44 (1705) 855475

Mel Williams, *Managing Director*
William Kennerly, *Commercial Manager*
Jill Adams, *Marketing Services Controller*

Wightlink Ltd, a subsidiary of Sea Containers Ltd, operates ferry services on three routes across the Solent to the Isle of Wight. The two vessels on the Portsmouth to Ryde route are high-speed passenger catamarans. The seven other conventional ferries on the other two routes, Portsmouth to Fishbourne and Lymington to Yarmouth, carry all sizes of vehicles as well as passengers. In 1993 Wightlink carried 4.9 million passengers and 898 000 vehicles on all its services.

High-speed craft operated

Type	Name	Seats	Delivered
CAT International Catamarans Pty Ltd 30 m	*Our Lady Patricia*	452	March 1986
CAT International Catamarans Pty Ltd 30 m	*Our Lady Pamela*	452	July 1986

Operations
Portsmouth Harbour to Ryde Pier, Isle of Wight, 15 minutes.

UPDATED

Our Lady Pamela   *1994*

UNITED STATES OF AMERICA

ALASKA TRAVEL

Alaska, USA

High-speed craft operated

Type	Name	Seats	Delivered
CAT Allen 24 m	*Golden Spirit*	—	1987

NEW ENTRY

ARNOLD TRANSIT COMPANY

PO Box 220, Mackinac Island, Michigan 49757, USA

Telephone: +1 (906) 847 3351

Robert Brown, *General Manager*

High-speed craft operated

Type	Name	Seats	Delivered
CAT Gladding-Hearn InCat 25 m	*Mackinac Express*	350	1987
CAT Gladding-Hearn InCat 25 m	*Island Express*	300	1988

Operations
Mackinaw City to Mackinac Island
St Ignace to Mackinac Island, 14 minutes, May to November.

Arnold Transit's Island Express   *1991*

BAR HARBOR WHALE WATCH

29 Cottage Street, Bar Harbor, Maine 04609, USA

High-speed craft operated

Type	Name	Delivered
CAT Gladding-Hearn InCat 28 m	*Friendship IV*	1994

NEW ENTRY

BLUE AND GOLD FLEET

Pier 29, Box Z-2, San Francisco, California, USA

High-speed craft operated

Type	Name	Delivered
CAT Nichols Bros InCat 22 m	*Olone Spirit*	1989
CAT Nichols Bros InCat 31 m	*Bay Breeze*	1994
CAT Gladding-Hearn InCat 31 m	*Jet Cat Express*	1994

NEW ENTRY

BOTTOM TIME ADVENTURES

PO Box 11919, Fort Lauderdale, Florida, 33339-1919, USA

Telephone: +1 (305) 921 7798

A J Bland, *Director*

High-speed craft operated

Type	Name	Seats	Delivered
CAT Atlantic and Gulf Boat Building 23.8 m InCat	*Bottom Time II*	49 (14 cabins)	August 1986

Operations
Diving expeditions, dolphin research, movie support vessel and naturalist group charters (Bahamas, Florida, Gulf of Mexico and Caribbean).

VERIFIED

CATALINA CHANNEL EXPRESS LINES

Berth 95, San Pedro, California 90731, USA

Telephone: +1 (310) 519 1212/7971
Telefax: +1 (310) 548 7389

Doug Bombard, *President*
Greg Bombard, *Vice President and General Manager*
Audrey Bombard, *Secretary/Treasurer*
Tom Rutter, *Vice President Operations*
Elaine Vaughan, *Vice President Marketing*

High-speed craft operated

Type	Name	Seats	Delivered
MH Westport 56	*Channel Express*	60	1981
MH Westport Shipyard Inc 27.44 m 90	*Catalina Express*	149	1984
MH Westport Shipyard Inc 27.44 m 90	*Two Harbors Express*	149	1986
MH Westport 95	*Catalina Super Express*	149	1989
MH Westport 95	*Avalon Super Express*	149	June 1990
MH Westport 30.5 m	*Catalina Express*	—	1994
MH Westport 30.5 m	*Islander Express*	—	1994

Operations
San Pedro to Avalon and Two Harbors, Santa Catalina Island, fare US$17.50
Long Beach to Avalon, Catalina Island, fare US$17.50.

UPDATED

CATALINA PASSENGER SERVICES

USA

High-speed craft operated

Type	Name	Seats	Delivered
CAT Nichols Bros InCat 36 m	*Catalina Flyer*	500	May 1988

Operations
Newport Beach to Catalina Island, 26 nm, 75 minutes.

VERIFIED

CLIPPER NAVIGATION INC

2701 Alaskan Way, Pier 69, Seattle, Washington 98121, USA

Telephone: +1 (206) 443 2560
Telefax: +1 (206) 443 2583

254 Belville Street, Victoria, British Columbia V8V 1W9, Canada

Telephone: +1 (604) 382 8100
Telefax: +1 (604) 382 2152

Merideth Tall, *President*
Leonard Tall, *Executive Vice President*
Darrell E Bryan, *Vice President and General Manager*

High-speed craft operated

Type	Name	Seats	Delivered
CAT Fjellstrand 38.8 m	*Victoria Clipper*	300	April 1986
CAT Gladding-Hearn InCat 31 m	*Victoria Clipper III* (ex *Audubon Express*)	239	1991
CAT Fjellstrand Flying Cat 40 m	*Victoria Clipper IV*	324	May 1993

Operations
Seattle to Victoria, British Columbia, Canada, 71 nm, 2 hours 30 minutes
Fares vary by season: single US$49-55, return US$79-89.

UPDATED

Victoria Clipper IV *departing from Seattle*   1994

DEPARTMENT OF TRANSPORTATION, UNITED STATES COAST GUARD

2100 Second Street SW, Washington DC 20593-0001, USA

Telephone: +1 (202) 267 2997
Telefax: +1 (202) 267 0025

High-speed craft operated
(Sea Bird class)

Type	Name	Delivered
SES Bell Halter Model 522A (110 Mk 1)	*Sea Hawk* (WSES-2)	October 1982
SES Bell Halter Model 522A (110 Mk 1)	*Shearwater* (WSES-3)	October 1982
SES Bell Halter Model 522A (110 Mk 1)	*Petrel* (WSES-4)	June 1983

Operations
Based at Key West, Florida and engaged in anti-drug smuggling patrols in the Caribbean Sea.

UPDATED

EXPRESS NAVIGATION INC

Two First Avenue, Atlantic Highlands, New Jersey 07716, USA

Telephone: +1 (908) 872 2628
Telefax: +1 (908) 872 9691

Mark J Stanisci, *President*
Gary R Dunzleman, *Operations Manager*

High-speed craft operated

Type	Name	Seats	Delivered
MH Gladding-Hearn InCat 24 m	*Express I*	265	February 1989
MH Gladding-Hearn InCat 24 m	*Express II* (ex *Vineyard Spray*)	296	June 1990

Operations
Monmouth County, New Jersey and Brooklyn, New York to Wall Street, 45 minutes.

UPDATED

Express I *and* Express II   1992

GLACIER BAY YACHT TOURS INC (CATAMARAN CRUISE LINES)

Seattle, Washington, USA

Robert Giersdorf, *President*
Bert Nordby, *Vice President*

High-speed craft operated

Type	Name	Seats	Delivered
CAT Nichols Brothers InCat 30 m	*Executive Explorer*	25 staterooms*	October 1986
CAT Nichols Brothers InCat 30 m	*Hawaii Express*	400	6 December 1986
CAT Nichols Brothers InCat	*Gold Rush* (ex *Glacier Express 1985*)	220	1988 (built 1985)

*49 passengers

Operations
Summer months (June to mid-September): Alaska, based in Juneau, *Executive Explorer* calls at Skagway, Haines/Pt Chilkoot, Glacier Bay Lodge, Sitka and Ketchikan
Hawaii Express operates one day excursions out of Maui's Maalaea harbour to Molokai and Lanai and to Molokini Island; started early 1987.

VERIFIED

GOLDEN GATE FERRY

Golden Gate Bridge, Highway and Transportation District, 101 East Sir Francis Drake Boulevard, Larkspur, California 94939, USA

Telephone: +1 (415) 457 8800
Telefax: +1 (415) 925 5510

James L Harberson, *President*
Robert McDonnell, *1st Vice President*
John E Fraser, *2nd Vice President*
Carney J Campion, *General Manager*
Eric A Robinson, *Division Manager*
Carl D Harrington, *Operations/Maintenance Manager*

The Ferry Division was formed in 1970 to operate water-borne mass transit on San Francisco Bay, operating between Marin County and San Francisco. In

1976, service was expanded with three semi-planing, triple gas-turbine, 25 knot, water-jet-propelled vessels. For economic reasons these three vessels have now been repowered with twin diesel engines using conventional propellers and rudders and with a resulting speed of 20.5 knots. The last of the three vessels modified was delivered in its new form in October 1985. See the *High-Speed Monohull Craft* section.

High-speed craft operated

Type	Name	Seats	Delivered
MH Campbell Industries Spaulding S-165 51.2 m	*Marin*	partially open deck 118 open deck 42 enclosed decks 372	December 1976
MH Campbell Industries Spaulding S-165 51.2 m	*Sonoma*	partially open deck 118 open deck 42 enclosed decks 372	March 1977
MH Campbell Industries Spaulding S-165 51.2 m	*San Francisco*	partially open deck 118 open deck 42 enclosed decks 372	September 1977

Operations
San Francisco to Larkspur, Marin County, 45 minutes.

VERIFIED

The Golden Gate Ferry vessel Sonoma   ***1986***

HARBOR BAY MARITIME

1141 Harbor Bay Parkway, Alameda, California 94501, USA

High-speed craft operated

Type	Name	Seats	Delivered
CAT Gulfcraft 24.5 m	*Harbor Bay Express*	—	1991
CAT USA Catamarans	*Harbor Bay Express II*	—	1994

NEW ENTRY

HAWAIIAN CRUISES LTD

Hawaii, USA

Telephone: +1 (808) 848 6360

High-speed craft operated

Type	Name	Seats	Delivered
SWATH Navatek	*Navatek 1*	430	1991
SWATH Navatek	*Navatek 2*	149	1994

Operations
Daytime and evening cruises off Oahu's Gold Coast and whale watching when in season.

VERIFIED

KENAI FJORDS TOURS

524 West 4th Avenue, Suite 101, Anchorage, Alaska, USA.

High-speed craft operated

Type	Name	Delivered
MH Westport 90	*Kenai Explorer*	1993
MH Westport 95	*Alaskan Explorer*	(1995)

NEW ENTRY

NY WATERWAY

Pershing Road, Weehawken, New Jersey 07087, USA

Telephone: +1 (201) 902 8700

Arthur E Imperatore, *President*

High-speed craft operated

Type	Name	Seats	Delivered
MH Blount Marine Corporation	*Port Imperial*	149	1984
MH Blount Marine Corporation	*Port Imperial Manhattan*	149	1986
MH Gulf Craft	*New Jersey*	350	1988
MH Gulf Craft	*George Washington*	399	1989
MH Gulf Craft	*Thomas Jefferson*	399	1989
MH Gulf Craft	*Alexander Hamilton*	399	1989
MH Gulf Craft	*Abraham Lincoln*	399	1989
MH Gulf Craft	*West New York*	149	1990
MH Gladding-Hearn	*Henry Hudson*	397	1992
MH Gladding-Hearn	*Robert Fulton*	397	1993
MH Gladding-Hearn	*Empire State*	397	1994
MH Gladding-Hearn	*Garden State*	397	1994

Operations
Weehawken (New Jersey), to 38th Street and 12th Avenue Manhattan, every 15 minutes from 06.45 to midnight.
Weehawken (New Jersey), to slip 5 in Lower Manhattan during the rush hours.
Hoboken (New Jersey), to the World Financial Centre, Manhattan, every 5 minutes during peak and every 20 minutes off-peak from 0630 to 2200.
Colgate pier in Jersey City (New Jersey), to the World Financial Centre, Manhattan every 15 minutes from 0645 to 2200.
Hunters Point in Queens, New York, to East 34th Street, Manhattan, every 15 minutes during rush hours.

UPDATED

The 350 passenger 24 knot Port Imperial Manhattan   ***1990***

PARTY LINE CRUISE COMPANY

903 South American Way, Miami, Florida 33132, USA

Telephone: +1 (305) 381 6360
Telefax: +1 (305) 381 6831

John Martin, *President*
Antoine Gurrey, *General Manager*

High-speed craft operated

Type	Name	Seats	Delivered
SWATH Swath Ocean Super 4000	*Cloud Ten*	365	(July 1995)

Operations
Miami to Key West.

UPDATED

PHILLIPS CRUISES & TOURS (YUKON RIVER CRUISES)

509 West Fourth Avenue, Anchorage, Alaska 99501, USA

Telephone: +1 (907) 276 8023
Telefax: +1 (907) 276 5315

Brad Phillips, *President/Owner*
Helen Phillips, *Executive Vice President*

High-speed craft operated

Type	Name	Seats	Delivered
CAT Nichols Brothers InCat 22 m	*Klondike*	210	1985
CAT Nichols Brothers InCat 30 m	*Klondike Express*	330	1992

Operations
Whittier to Alaska to College Fjord to Barry Arm to Harriman Glacier. 110 miles, 6 hours. Fare (1994) US$119 + tax.

UPDATED

Klondike Express *operated by Phillips Cruises & Tours*   **1995**

PUT-IN-BAY BOAT LINE

South Bass Island, Lake Erie, Ohio, USA

High-speed craft operated

Type	Name	Seats	Delivered
CAT Gladding-Hearn InCat 28 m	*Jet Express I*	380	May 1989
CAT Gladding-Hearn InCat 29 m	*Jet Express II*	400	May 1992

Operations
Put-In-Bay to Port Clinton, 13 nm, 22 minutes.

VERIFIED

RED AND WHITE FLEET
(a subsidiary of Crowley Maritime Corporation)

Pier 41, Fisherman's Wharf, San Francisco, California 94133, USA

Telephone: +1 (415) 546 2800

Alan Zurawski, *Vice President and General Manager*
Carolyn Horgan, *Operations Manager*

High-speed craft operated

Type	Name	Seats	Delivered
CAT Nichols Brothers InCat 26 m	*Catamarin*	274	1985
CAT Nichols Brothers InCat 26 m	*Dolphin*	274	1986

Operations
Marin County area commuter and cruise services
Catamarin and *Dolphin* operating ferry services between San Francisco and Sausalito, Tiburon on San Francisco Bay.

UPDATED

Catamarin *operated by the Red and White Fleet*   **1992**

SAYVILLE FERRY SERVICE INC

41 River Road, PO Box 626, Sayville, Long Island, New York 11782, USA

Telephone: +1 (516) 589 0810
Telefax: +1 (516) 589 0843

Captain Kenneth Stein, *President*

Sayville Ferry Service has a total fleet of eight vessels with passenger capacities of from 88 to 350. Most of them are operated at between 15 and 20 knots but the *Fire Island Clipper* can cruise at 26 knots at full load.

High-speed craft operated

Type	Name	Seats	Delivered
MH Derecktor Shipyard	*Fire Island Clipper*	350	1979

Operations
Sayville, Long Island (South Shore) to Fire Island, 5 nm, serving three Summer communities, stops at Cherry Grove and Fire Island Pines. The ferries also serve Sunken Forest and Sailor Haven Federal Parks.

VERIFIED

Sayville Ferry Service Fire Island Clipper   **1988**

SEA JET CRUISE LINE

San Diego, California

Telephone: +1 (619) 585 2100
Telefax: +1 (619) 585 2116

High-speed craft operated

Type	Name	Seats	Delivered
CAT Nichols Bros InCat 37 m WPC	*SeaJet I* (ex *Metro Atlantic*)	400	1992
SES Avondale Air Ride 109	— (ex *Metro Manhattan*)	327	1993

VERIFIED

SEA PRINCESS (GUAM) CORPORATION

790 North Marine Drive, Box 432, Tamuning, Guam 96911, USA

Telephone: +671 477 5680
Telefax: +671 477 5666

Graham Poon, *General Manager*

The 30 m, 222 passenger catamaran *Sea Princess* operates as a dinner cruise boat out of Guam.

VERIFIED

SHEPLER'S MACKINAC ISLAND FERRY

PO Box 250, Mackinaw City, Michigan 49701, USA

High-speed craft operated

Type	Name	Seats	Delivered
MH Camcraft Boats Inc (Hargrave) 18.3 m	*The Welcome*	120	1969
MH Camcraft Boats Inc (Hargrave) 17.1 m	*Felicity*	150	1972
MH Bergeron 19.9 m (Hargrave)	*Hope*	150	1975
MH Bergeron 23.5 m (Hargrave)	*Wyandot*	265	1979
MH Aluminium Boats Inc (Hargrave) 23.78 m	*Captain Shepler*	265	1986

Operations
St Ignace (Upper Peninsula) and Mackinaw City (Lower Peninsula) to Mackinac Island, Michigan on Lake Huron.

UPDATED

STAR LINE

590 North State Street, St Ignace, Michigan 49781, USA

High-speed craft operated

Type	Name	Seats	Delivered
MH Gulf Craft 19.8 m	Maquette	150	1979
MH Gulf Craft 19.8 m	La Salle	150	1983
MH Gulf Craft 19.8 m	Nicolet	150	1985
MH Gulf Craft 25.9 m	Radisson	350	1988
MH Gulf Craft 19.8 m	Cadillac	150	1990
MH Gulf Craft 20 m	Juliet	150	1993

UPDATED

MH Gulf Craft Radisson *in service with Star Line*   1994

WASHINGTON STATE FERRIES

Seattle Ferry Terminal, 801 Alaska Way, Seattle, Washington 98104-1487, USA

Telephone: +1 (206) 464 7866

High-speed craft operated

Type	Name	Seats	Delivered
CAT Nichols Bros InCat 26 m	Tyee (ex Express)	245	October 1986
MH Equitable 34 m	Kalama	253	1990
MH Equitable 34 m	Skagit	253	1990

Operations
Seattle to Bremerton, 14 nm
Seattle to Vashon.

VERIFIED

Skagit *operated by Washington State Ferries*   1992

URUGUAY

BELT SA

Plaza Cagancha 1124, Montevideo, Uruguay

Telephone: +598 (2) 924004
Telefax: +598 (2) 922626

Juan Carlos Deicas, *Managing Director*

High-speed craft operated

Type	Name	Seats	Delivered
HYD Rodriquez RHS 140	Tyrving	145	1979
HYD Rodriquez RHS 140	Colonia del Sacramento (ex Condor 3)	134	1979
HYD Rodriquez RHS 140	Farallón (ex Løberon '85)	134	1985

Operations
Colonia to Buenos Aires and Colonia to La Plata
Montevideo to Colonia to Buenos Aires
Montevideo to Colonia to La Plata

Annual traffic
180 000 to 200 000 passengers

VERIFIED

BUQUEBUS

Rio Negro 1400, Montevideo, Uruguay

High-speed craft operated

Type	Name	Seats	Additional payload	Delivered
CAT InCat Australia WPC 74 m	Patricia Olivia	515	90 cars	September 1992
CAT InCat Australia WPC 74 m	Juan L	600	110 cars	1993
CAT InCat Australia K55	—	450	63 cars	1995

Operations
Montevideo (Punta del Este) to Buenos Aires, 100 nm.

UPDATED

TRANSPORTES ANFIBIOS SA

Rivera 236, Colonia, Postal 70 000, Uruguay

Telephone: +598 5224978/4982
Telefax: +598 5223144

Esteban Moreira Vina, *President*

High-speed craft operated

Type	Name	Seats	Delivered
HOV NQEA AP1-88/100	Hover	96	May 1992

Operations
Colonia to Buenos Aires.

VERIFIED

VENEZUELA

INTUMACA
INVERSIONES TURISTICAS MARGARITA CA

Coracrevi, Apartado Postal 101, Caracas, Venezuela

High-speed craft operated

Type	Name	Seats	Delivered
MH Swiftships 38 m	Gran Cacique I	300	1978
MH Swiftships 38 m	Gran Cacique II	300	1980
MH Swiftships 38 m	Gran Cacique III	300	1980

Operations
Puerto La Cruz to Margarita Island.

Gran Cacique I *operating off the Venezuelan coast*   1988

MARAVEN SA

Apartado 829, Caracas 1010-A, Venezuela

Telephone: +58 (2) 908 2111
Telex: 23535/23536 CCAR
Telefax: +58 (2) 908 2383

Francisco Guedez, *Director*
Alberto S Finol, *Exploration and Production Manager*
David Escojido, *Product Division General Manager*

High-speed craft operated

Type	Name	Seats	Delivered
SES Vosper Hovermarine HM 218	*Zumbador*	70	1979
SES Vosper Hovermarine HM 218	*Zumaya*	70	1980
SES Vosper Hovermarine HM 218	*Barroso*	70	1980

Operations

Support duties for oil production platforms on Lake Maracaibo.

VERIFIED

VIRGIN ISLANDS (US)

NAUTICAL TRADING LTD
Transportation Services of St John

St John, US Virgin Islands

High-speed craft operated

Type	Name	Seats	Delivered
ALH Atlantic and Gulf Boatbuilding Air Ride 65	*Caribe Air Ride* (ex *Air Ride Express*)	149	1987*
MH Equitable Shipyards 25.9 m	*Caribe Tide*	232	1988

*Launched March 1983, originally delivered to South Florida Offshore Services Ltd, Plantation, Florida

Operations

St John to St Thomas Airport.

VERIFIED

PRINCIPAL ENGINEERING COMPONENTS FOR HIGH-SPEED CRAFT

Engines
Transmissions
Air propellers
Marine propellers
Water-jet units
Air cushion skirt systems
Ride control systems

ENGINES

Company Listing by Country

Canada
Pratt & Whitney Canada, Inc

Commonwealth of Independent States
A Ivchenko (AI)
Kuznetsov Design Bureau NK-12/14
Transmash Plant
Zvezda Production Association

France
Moteurs Baudouin
SACM
Semt Pielstick
Turbomeca

Germany
Deutz (Klöckner-Humboldt-Deutz AG)
Deutz MWM
MAN
MTU

Italy
CRM Motori Marini SpA
Fiat Aviazione SpA
Fincantieri
Iveco Aifo SpA
Seatek SpA
Seatek Marine Power

Japan
Mitsubishi Heavy Industries Ltd
Niigata Engineering Company Ltd

Norway
Kværner Energy A/S
Ulstein Turbine A/S

Sweden
Scania
Volvo Penta AB

United Kingdom
GEC Alsthom Paxman
GEC Alsthom Ruston Diesels Ltd
Perkins Group of Companies
Rolls-Royce Industrial and Marine Gas Turbines
Ltd

United States of America
Allied Signal Engine Division
Allison Engine Company
Caterpillar Inc
Caterpillar, Solar Turbines Inc
Cummins Engine Company Inc
Detroit Diesel Corporation
General Electric Company
United Technologies International Inc

CANADA

PRATT & WHITNEY CANADA, INC

A United Technologies Company

1000 Marie-Victorin Boulevard, Longueuil, Quebec
J4G 1A1, Canada

Telephone: +1 (514) 677 9411/651 3633 (Industrial
and Marine Division)

L D Caplan, *President and Chief Executive Officer*
G P Ouimet, *Executive Vice President*
R F Steers, *Vice President, Finance*
C J Pascoe, *Vice President, Counsel and Corporate Secretary*
J B Haworth, *Vice President, Industrial and Marine Division*
W M Coffin, *Manager of Marketing, Industrial and Marine Division*

ST6 gas-turbine   1986

In addition to its wide range of small gas-turbine aero-engines, Pratt & Whitney Canada (P&WC) also manufactures industrial and marine derivatives supplied by its Industrial and Marine (I&M) Division. Engines are rated from 410 kW (550 shp) upwards (see table) and are of the simple-cycle, free turbine type. They run on Nos 1 and 2 diesel or aviation turbine fuels.

Typical marine applications are the ST6K-77 driving the auxiliary power unit on the Flagstaff 2 class hydrofoils built for the Israeli Navy, and the ST6T-76 Twin Pac powering LACV-30 hovercraft built by Bell Aerospace Textron (now Textron Marine Systems) for the US Army. Including aero-engine installations, more than 38 000 of P&WC's turbines have been delivered. They have accumulated in excess of 217 million hours of operation.

Engine features: All ST6 engines have a single spool gas generator and a multi-stage compressor (three axial plus one centrifugal stage) driven by a single stage axial turbine. The larger models have cooled vanes. The radial diffuser incorporates P&WC patented diffuser pipes. The burner section has a reverse flow annular combustor. A single- or two-stage free turbine provides a direct high-speed output or drives through a reduction gearbox.

Air intake is located at the rear of the engine and is through a screened annular inlet.

The ST6T-76 Twin Pac is a dual version of the ST6 with two power sections mounted side by side coupled to a twinning reduction gearbox. The gearbox incorporates automatic clutches which permit emergency operation of one side independent of the other.

SPW124-2

The SPW124-2 is an industrial and marine version of the PW124 aero turboprop. This engine benefits from the experience gained by its aero counterparts with 9 million hours of operation.

Engine features: The SPW124 is a three-shaft engine. The low pressure and high pressure centri-

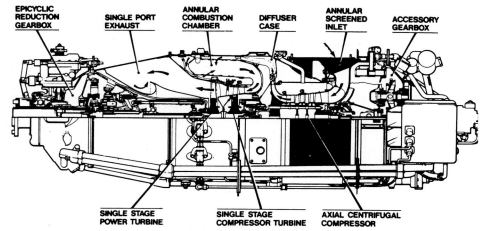

Main components of ST6   1986

fugal compressors (combined pressure ratio 15:1) are each driven independently by single stage compressor turbines. This allows both compressors to operate at their optimum efficiencies without the need for complex variable geometry. Other features comprise P&WC patented pipe diffusers, reverse annular combustor, low pressure and high pressure stator cooling and turbine blade cooling. The two-stage power turbine retains the free turbine concept of the ST6 engine.

SPW901/1

This is a direct drive gas-turbine of rugged design intended for industrial and marine use.

Engine features: A free turbine engine incorporating a cast aluminium air intake casing, centrifugal

compressor, patented P&WC pipe diffusers, reverse flow annular combustor, single stage high turbine with cooled vanes and disk. The ball and roller bearings which support the gas generator rotor assembly and power turbine shaft have under-race lubrication. Thermal insulation blankets are selectively installed on the external surfaces of the engine to maintain surface temperature below 450°F.

PW901A

The PW901A is an auxiliary power unit which is fully marinised, lightweight and compact, delivering 551 lb/min of air at 54 lb/in² absolute. In addition it has provision to drive two 90 kVA electrical generators.

ST6 and SPW SERIES ENGINE DATA SUMMARY (GUARANTEED PERFORMANCE)										
Sea Level Standard Pressure at 15°C Inlet Temperature										
Model	Max kW	Max SFC	Normal kW	Normal SFC	RPM direct drive	RPM integral gearbox	Length	Width	Height	Engine dry weight
ST6L-794	639	0.358	569	0.365	33 000	2200 6188 1300	1346 mm	559 mm	533 mm	139 kg
ST6L-812	777	0.344	674	0.357	30 000	1700 2000 5700	1447 mm	483 mm	559 mm	164 kg
ST6T-76 Twin Pac	1380	0.374	1076	0.395	33 000	6600	1676 mm	1118 mm	838 mm	336 kg
SPW901-A	1303	0.362	1225	0.363	24 625	available	1194 mm	660 mm	1041 mm	209 kg
SPW124-2	1843	0.294	1585	0.307	20 000	available	1524 mm	660 mm	838 mm	300 kg
SPW200	395	0.344	255	0.345	-	6000	914 mm	483 mm	559 mm	111 kg

Engine data with integral gearbox available on request
Engine data shown are for direct drive

UPDATED

COMMONWEALTH OF INDEPENDENT STATES

The following information has been received on the gas-turbine engine for the Tsiklon Hydrofoil.

M37 GAS-TURBINE SYSTEM

This system consists of the DO37 gas-turbine and the RO37 two-stage reduction gear with built-in supporting bearings. The M37 is used to power the Tsiklon (Cyclone) 250-passenger, 42 knot hydrofoil.

Principal Particulars (M37):
Length: 6350 mm
Width: 1900 mm
Height: 2200 mm
Shaft power, max: 5880 kW
　　normal: 5150 kW
Specific fuel consumption: 295 g/kWh
Time between overhauls: 8000 h
Weight: 7000 kg
Another proposed power-plant installation for hydrofoils consists of two DO37 gas-turbine units driving a common reduction gear and offering a total output of 11 760 kW.

VERIFIED

M37 gas-turbine system　　　　　　　　　　　*1986*

The largest Russian passenger hydrofoil which is fitted with the M37 gas-turbine system, Yalta 1990
(Antonio Scrimali)
1992

A IVCHENKO (AI)

This design team, which was headed by the late A Ivchenko, is based in a factory at Zaporojie in Ukraine, where all prototypes and pre-production engines bearing the 'AI' prefix are developed and built.

The first engine with which Ivchenko was associated officially was the 40 kW AI-4G piston engine used in the Kamov Ka-10 ultralight helicopter. He later progressed via the widely used AI-14 and AI-26 piston engines, to become one of the Soviet Union's leading designers of gas-turbine engines.

Two AI-20s in derated, marinised form and driving two three-stage water-jets power the Burevestnik, the first Soviet gas-turbine hydrofoil. The integrated lift and propulsion system of the Sormovich ACV was derived from the 1894 kW gas-turbine AI-20 DK. The two AI-20s, each rated at about 2700 kW continuous, are also thought to power the Lebed amphibious assault landing craft.

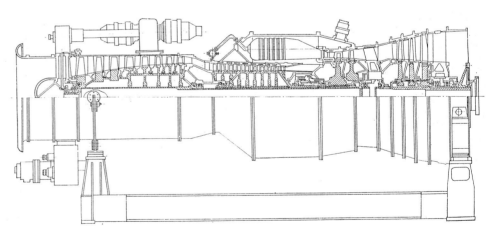

1750 hp Ivchenko AI-23-CI marine gas-turbine　　　*1992*

IVCHENKO AI-20

The Ivchenko design bureau is responsible for the AI-20 turboprop engine which powers the Antonov An-10, An-12 and Ilyushin Il-18 airliners and the Beriev M-12 Tchaika amphibian.

AI-20K Rated at 3000 kW. Used in Il-18V, An-10A and An-12.

AI-20M Uprated version with T-O rating of 3100 kW. Used in Il-18D/E, An-10A and An-12.

Conversion of the turboprop as a marine power unit for hydrofoil water-jet propulsion (as on the Burevestnik) involved a number of changes to the engine. In particular it was necessary to hold engine rpm at a constant level during conditions of varying load from the water-jet pump. It was also necessary to be able to vary the thrust from the water-jet unit from zero to forward or rearwards thrust to facilitate engine starting and vessel manoeuvring.

The AI-20 is a single-spool turboprop, with a 10-stage axial flow compressor, cannular combustion chamber with 10 flame tubes and a three-stage turbine, of which the first two stages are cooled. Planetary reduction gearing, with a ratio of 0.08732:1, is mounted forward of the annular air intake. The fixed nozzle contains a central bullet fairing. All engine driven accessories are mounted on the forward part of the compressor casing, which is of magnesium alloy.

The AI-20 was designed to operate reliably in all temperatures from −60 to +55°C at heights up to 10 000 m. It is a constant speed engine, the rotor speed being maintained at 21 300 rpm by automatic variation of propeller pitch. Gas temperature after turbine is 560°C in both current versions. TBO of the AI-20K was 4000 hours in the Spring of 1966.

Weights
Dry
　AI-20K: 1080 kg
　AI-20M: 1039 kg
Performance Ratings
Max T-O
　AI-20K: 3000 kW
　AI-20M: 3100 kW
Cruise rating at 630 km/h at 8000 m
　AI-20K: 1700 kW
　AI-20M: 2000 kW
Specific Fuel Consumption
At cruise rating
　AI-20K: 288 g/kWh
　AI-20M: 264 g/kWh
Oil Consumption
Normal: 1 l/h

IVCHENKO AI-24

In general configuration this single-spool turbo-prop engine, which powers the An-24 transport aircraft, is very similar to the earlier and larger AI-20.

Dimensions
Length, overall: 2435 mm
Weight
Dry: 499 kg

Performance Rating
Max power with water injection: 2102 kW

UPDATED

KUZNETSOV DESIGN BUREAU NK-12/14

In its original form the NK-12M developed 8948 kW. The later NK-12MV is rated at 11 033 kW and powers the Tupolev Tu-114 transport, driving four-blade, contrarotating propellers of 5.6 m diameter. As the NK-12MA, rated at 11 185 kW, it powers the Antonov An-22 military transport, with propellers of 6.2 m diameter.

The NK-12M has a single 14-stage axial flow compressor. Compression ratio varies from 9:1 to 13:1 and variable inlet guide vanes and blow off valves are necessary. A cannular-type combustion system is used. Each flame tube is mounted centrally on a downstream injector, but all tubes merge at their maximum diameter to form an annular secondary region. The single turbine is a five-stage axial. Mass flow is 56 kg/s.

The casing is made in four portions from precision welded sheet steel. An electric control for variation of propeller pitch is incorporated to maintain constant engine speed.

The NK-14 is the modern derivative of the same engine, providing similar power outputs. The Kuznetsov design bureau is currently working on low NOx combustor designs for this engine, scheduled to be available in 1995/96.

Dimensions
Length: 6000 mm

Kuznetsov NK-14E (Ken Fulton) 1995

Diameter: 1150 mm
Weight
Dry: 2350 kg
Performance Ratings
Maximum power: 11 033 kW

Nominal power: 8826 kW at 8300 rpm
Idling speed: 6600 rpm

UPDATED

TRANSMASH PLANT

Industrial Union, Transport Machine Building, Barnaul Plant (IU Barnaultransmash), 656037 Barnaul, Russia, CIS

Telephone: +7 (095) 772013

Yuri S Cherviakov, *Chief Designer*

The Transmash Plant produces a range of high-speed diesel engines for applications in sea and river craft types including hydrofoil vessels.

3K Δ12H-520 DIESEL ENGINE

The 3K Δ12H-520 diesel engine is designed to be installed on sea and river ships of various applications as their main propulsion engine. The engine is a four-stroke, high-speed engine, with 12 cylinders, V-type cylinder arrangement, liquid cooling, direct fuel injection, and supercharging.

Principal Particulars
Cylinder diameter: 150 mm
Piston stroke: 180 mm
Full power: 382 kW (520 hp)
Crankshaft rotation speed at full power: 1500 rpm
Specific fuel consumption, g/kWh (g/hph): 220 + 11 (162+8)
Dimensions
Length: 2030 mm
Width: 1108 mm
Height: 1178 mm
Dry weight: 1750 kg

3 Δ12A DIESEL ENGINE

The 3 Δ12A diesel engine is designed to be employed by sea and river ships of various applications as their main propulsion engine. The engine is a four-stroke, high-speed type, with 12 cylinders, V-type cylinder arrangement, liquid cooling and direct fuel injection.

The engine is equipped with a reversing reduction gear comprising a reduction gear and a friction clutch to couple the screw propeller with and disengage it from the crankshaft and to reverse the screw propeller sense of rotation.

Transmash 3K Δ12H-520 diesel engine 1992

Transmash 3 Δ12A diesel engine
1992

The driving force in fast ferries

For proven performance choose lightweight robust PAXMAN high speed or RUSTON medium speed marine diesel engines.
From 500 to 6875 kWb our engines offer low fuel consumption, dependable performance and extended service intervals, backed by worldwide Customer Support.

GEC ALSTHOM Diesels - a leader in diesel technology.

▼
GEC ALSTHOM
DIESELS

GEC ALSTHOM Paxman Diesels, Paxman Works, Hythe Hill, Colchester, Essex CO1 2HW, England.
Telephone UK + 44 1206 795151   Fax UK + 44 1206 797869
GEC ALSTHOM Ruston Diesels, Vulcan Works, Newton-le-Willows, Merseyside WA12 8RU, England.
Telephone UK + 44 1925 225151   Fax UK + 44 1925 222055

Principal Particulars
Cylinder diameter: 150 mm
Piston stroke: 180 mm
Full power at reversing reduction gear driven shaft flange, emf
at ahead running: 300 hp
at astern running, not more than: 180 hp
Crankshaft rotation speed at full power: 1500 rpm
Gear ratio
at ahead running: 1.22 or 2.04 or 2.95
at astern running, not more than: 2.18
Specific fuel consumption, g/emf h: 172 + 8
Dimensions
Length, with power take off shaft: 2464 mm
Length, without power take off shaft: 2390 mm
Width: 1052 mm
Height: 1210 mm
Dry weight: 1814 kg

3 Δ20C2 DIESEL ENGINE

The 3 Δ20C2 diesel engine is designed to be employed by sea and river ships as their main propulsion engine and is a four-stroke, high-speed engine, with six cylinders, V-type cylinder arrangement (at an angle of 120°), liquid cooling and direct fuel injection.

The crankcase unit of the engine is of tunnel type, made integral with the cylinder jackets. The crankshaft is mounted on roller bearings. The connecting rods are of central type. The engine is provided with a first order inertial force balancing mechanism.

The engine can be equipped (on request) with an auxiliary power take off shaft (up to 22.4 kW (30 hp) at 2200 rpm). The power take off shaft is installed coaxially with the crankshaft on the side opposite to the flywheel.

Principal Particulars
Cylinder diameter: 150 mm
Piston stroke: 150 mm
Power: rated, 175 kW (235 hp), max 194 kW (260 hp)
Rotational speed: corresponding to rated power 2200 rpm, corresponding to max power 2270 rpm
Specific fuel consumption at rated power, g/emf h: 170 + 8
Dimensions
Length: 1122 mm
Width: 1140 mm
Height: 767 mm
Dry weight: 770 kg

UPDATED

Transmash 3 Δ20C2 diesel engine

1992

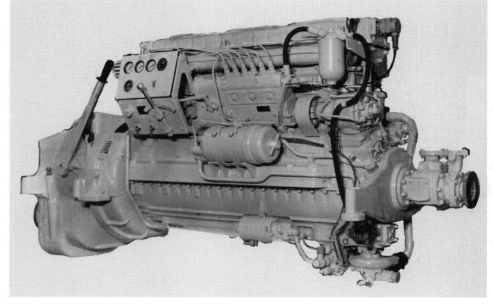

Transmash 3 Δ6C2 diesel engine
1992

ZVEZDA PRODUCTION ASSOCIATION

123 Babuschkina Str, 193012 St Petersburg, Russia, CIS

Telephone: +7 (267) 3156/(262) 1327

Zvezda produces diesels of two sizes; ΔH 18/20 and ΔH 16/17. Diesels of both families have many features in common; main housing parts are cast in aluminium alloy and highly loaded parts are made in nitrided alloy steels. These features provide for the diesels' low specific weights and high specific volumetric powers. The engines are used as main marine diesels in high-speed boats and ships where powerful, compact propulsion plants are required and similarly for hydrofoil vessels.

Diesels of both families have a dry crankcase lubrication system. The cooling system has a double circuit, the inner cooling circuit (of fresh water) is closed with excessive pressure at inlet of centrifugal pumps of the cooling system, which is mounted on diesel.

Zvezda M400
1986

The seawater pump is mounted on the diesel. The water and oil coolers are installed outside the diesel and are not delivered with the engine.

At low ratings of engine and vessel reversing, the water pump provides the priming of water through water and oil coolers, as well as water supply for gas exhaust watering; at high ratings the cooling flow for the coolers is provided by the dynamic pressure of the vessel motion, but watering of gas exhaust and water priming through air-water radiators (if there are any) are carried out by the pump.

Diesel starting is by compressed air under the pressure of 15.0 to 8.0 MPa. Availability of full load of the fully warmed up diesel is possible within a short time (not over 15 seconds).

Diesels of both types are equipped and delivered with a system of emergency warning signalling and protection and a complete set of control-measuring devices, adapted for automatic remote-control.

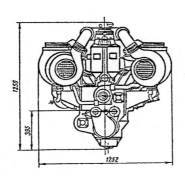

Zvezda M401A

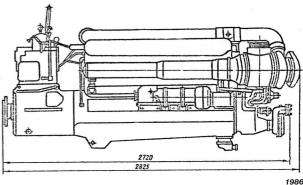

1986

Main technical characteristics of diesel type ΔH 16/17 and for type 12 ΔH 18/20 are given in the accompanying tables.

Both types of these diesel engines may be purchased from PO 'Zvezda', St Petersburg.

PARAMETERS OF MAIN VARIATIONS OF MARINE DIESELS ΔH 16/17 TYPE BEING MANUFACTURED AT THE PRODUCTION ASSOCIATION "ZVEZDA"

Table 1

	Unit of measurement	Plant designation of diesels						
		M503A	M503B	M504A	M504B	M517	M520	M521
Type of diesel		4-stroke, star-shaped with gas-turbo-compressor, connected kinematically to the crankshaft, equipped by the emergency warning signalisation and protection						
Purpose		Main marine diesel for light high-speed ships						
Number of cylinders	-	42	42	56	56	56	56	56 × 2
Nominal power	kW	2425	1840	3493	3676	3493*	3600	6654*
Maximal power	kW	2942	-	-	-	-	3965	-
Revolutions at full (nominal) power	min⁻¹	2000	1780	1950	2000	2000	1900	2000
Mean effective pressure	MPa	1.01	0.86	1.12	1.15	1.09	1.16	1.04
Standard specific fuel consumption	g/kWh	211⁺¹¹	204⁺¹¹	211⁺¹¹	210⁺¹¹	211⁺¹¹	213⁺¹¹	217⁺¹¹*
Cooling of supercharging air	-	no	no	yes	yes	yes	yes	yes
Length	mm	3700	3900	4650	4400	4400	4400	7000
Width	mm	1555	1555	1676	1676	1676	1676	1820
Height	mm	1560	1560	1654	1654	1654	1654	2495
Mass in full completing	kg	5400	5600	7500	7250	7250	7250	17100
Engine life until 1st full overhaul	h	1000	3500	2500	2500	1600	1500	2500
Total engine life	h	2500	9000	6500	6500	4500	4500	6500
Transmission ratio of reducer	-	0.514	0.179	0.268	0.514	0.514	0.514	0.311

* during operation in tropics

PARAMETERS OF MAIN VARIATIONS OF MARINE DIESELS 12 ΔH 18/20 TYPE BEING MANUFACTURED AT THE PRODUCTION ASSOCIATION "ZVEZDA"

Table 2

	Unit of measurement	Plant designation of diesels				
		M400	M401A	M419A	M417A	PA-210B
Type of diesel		4-stroke, V-shaped, 12 cylinders, 18/20 dimensions with supercharging				
Purpose		Main marine engine for hydrofoils, hovercraft and so on				Main marine engine for ships with propeller of regulated- or fixed-pitch
Nominal power	kW	736	736	809	736	809
Maximal power	kW	809	809	890	809	890
Nominal revolutions	min⁻¹	1700	1550	1550	1550	1550
Mean effective pressure	MPa	0.93	0.93	1.03	0.93	1.03
Standard specific fuel consumption	g/kWh	217⁺¹⁰	203⁺¹⁰	200⁺¹⁰	205⁺¹⁰	200⁺¹⁰
Standard specific oil consumption	g/kWh	2.3	2.2	2.2	2.2	2.2
Cooling of supercharging air	-	no	no	yes	no	yes
Supercharging unit	-	MS	TK-18(2ps)	TK-18(2ps)	TK23	TK-18(2ps)
Length	mm	2600	2825	2825	2678	2715
Width	mm	1200	1260	1260	1220	1260
Height	mm	1250	41250	1250	1600	1272
Mass in full completing	kg	1800	2100	2200	2200	2350
Engine life until 1st full overhaul	h	1500	3500	4500	3500	4000
Total engine life	h	6000	9000	10 000	9000	10 000
Reversing transmission	-	friction cam	friction cam	friction cam	disc clutch	non-reversible planetary
Transmission ratio of reducer						
forward run		1.0	1.0	1.0	1.0	0.241
rear run		0.8	0.8	0.8	0.705	-
Power of suspended electric generator (28 V)	kW	1.0	3.0	3.0	1.0	-

UPDATED

FRANCE

MOTEURS BAUDOUIN

165 boulevard de Pont-de-Vivaux, BP 62, F-13362
Marseilles Cedex 10, France

Telephone: +33 91 83 85 00
Telex: 410944 MOBOD F
Telefax: +33 91 79 09 38

12 P 15.2 SR7

Fitted to the SBCN 38 m patrol boat.
Type: four-stroke direct injection diesel engine
Cylinders: 12 cylinders, V-form, rigid wet type
cylinder liners
Aspiration: turbocharged with air cooler
Cooling: by water from closed-circuit with fresh
water/raw water heat exchanger integrated with
engine
Lubrication: gear pump with full flow cartridge type
oil filters
Injection: monoblock injection pump with mechanical governor
Technical Data
Swept volume: 31.8 l
Compression ratio: 14:1
Max rating: 1030 kW at 2000 rpm
Mean effective pressure: 19.44 bar at 2000 rpm
Fuel consumption: 265 l/h
Dry weight, without gearbox: 3000 kg

BAUDOUIN VTi SERIES

A new series of diesel engines was announced in
1989, four-stroke, direct injection, water-cooled, 6 or
12 in 90° V cylinders and turbocharged with charge
air intercooling.

V6Ti330

243 kW at 3200 rpm, dry weight: 815 kg

V12BTi840

618 kW at 3000 rpm, dry weight: 1360 kg

V12BTi1200

883 kW at 2000 rpm, dry weight: 3002 kg

V12BTi1400

Characteristics
1030 kW at 2000 rpm for high-speed craft
Diesel engine, 4-stroke, direct injection turbocharged with charge air intercooling
Bore and stroke: 150 × 150 mm
Number of cylinders: 12 in 90° V
Total sweep volume: 3181 dm³
Compression ratio: 14/1
Number of valves per cylinder: 4
Engine rotation to ISO 1204 standard:
counterclockwise
Idling speed: 700 min⁻¹
Weight without water and oil: 3020 kg
Weight to power ratio (rating RP): 2.1 kg/HP

Baudouin 12 P 15.2 SR7 marine diesel engine   *1988*

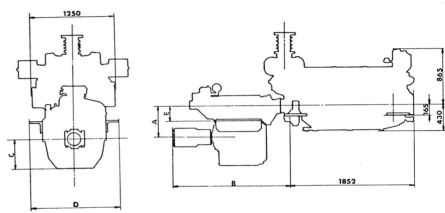

Dimensions of Baudouin Series 12 P 15.2 SR7 engines/gearboxes   *1987*

	A	B	C	D	E	Approx weight without water or oil
12 P 15.2 SR7						3000 kg
12 P 15.2 SRC IRS	355 mm	1229 mm	340 mm	1084 mm	165 mm	3970 kg
12 P 15.2 SRC IRX	488 mm	1839 mm	460 mm	1356 mm	226 mm	5105 kg
12 P 15.2 SRC RHS	355 mm	1611 mm	340 mm	1084 mm	165 mm	3965 kg
12 P 15.2 SRC RHX	488 mm	2071 mm	460 mm	1356 mm	226 mm	5105 kg

VERIFIED

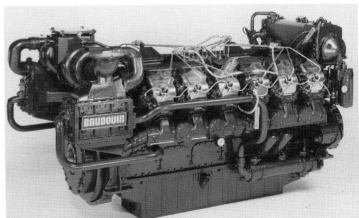

Baudouin V6 Ti330 243 kW   *1990*

Baudouin V12BTi1400 1030 kW
1990

SACM

SOCIÉTÉ ALSACIENNE DE CONSTRUCTIONS MÉCANIQUES DE MULHOUSE

Division Uni diesel

1 rue de la Fonderie, BP 1210, F-68054 Mulhouse Cedex, France

Telephone: +33 89 46 01 08
Telex: 881699 F
Telefax: +33 89 56 52 76

Division Poyaud
16 avenue de la Gare, BP 13, F-17700 Surgeres, France

Telephone: +33 46 07 62 10
Telex: 790 831 F
Telefax: +33 46 07 64 02

The SACM-M company designs, manufactures and markets a range of modern high-speed diesel engines from 150 to 8000 kW. Over 25 000 engines have been supplied over 30 years under the trade names Poyand, MGO and AGO and have now regrouped under the trade name Uni diesel. These engines are designed to meet sophisticated requirements for propulsion and power supply applications.

The SACM-M company has joined with Wärtsilä in producing diesel engines and now ranks among the world leaders for high performance vessel propulsion, heavy and armoured vehicle powering and nuclear plant safeguard generator sets.

Over five per cent of the turnover of SACM-M is devoted to research and development.

Technical Characteristics

Compact through high integration of equipment.
Low operating costs:
    easy to maintain,
    low fuel consumption.
Performance range of engine adapted to particular resistance curves of various hulls.
Optimisation of propulsion line (engine reversing reducing gear-shaft line-propeller) in association with shipyards.
Calling on high technology superchargers, a wide range of speeds and a large degree of control over mechanical stresses, give these engines an extremely wide performance range.

SACM-M UD33 V12 M7D 2020 kW engine

1989

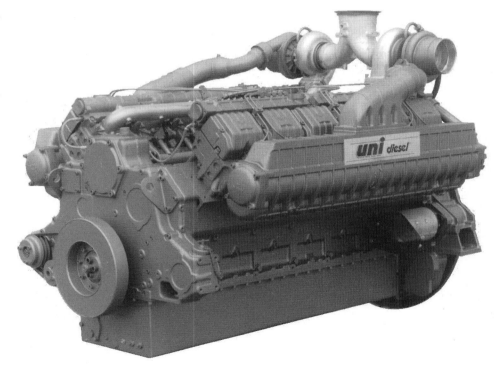

SACM-M UD23 V12 M5D 735 kW engine
(Phot'indus)
1989

Type of engine	Swept volume	Bore	Stroke	rpm	kW	hp	Length	Width	Height	Dry weight
UD23										
UD23 V12 M5D	2.6 l³	142 mm	166 mm	1800	735	1000	1975 mm	1380 mm	1450 mm	2650 kg
UD33										
UD33 V12 M6D					1765	2400	2950 mm	1700 mm	2280 mm	7500 kg
UD33 V12 M7D					2020	2745	2950 mm	1700 mm	2280 mm	7500 kg
UD33 V16 M6D	5.5 l³	195 mm	180 mm	1600	2355	3200	4030 mm	1700 mm	2280 mm	9000 kg
UD33 V16 M7D					2690	3660	4030 mm	1700 mm	2280 mm	9000 kg
UD45										
UD45 V12 M7D					2850	3875	3800 mm	2000 mm	2700 mm	12 100 kg
UD45 V16 M7D	10.2 l³	240 mm	220 mm	1350	3800	5170	4400 mm	2000 mm	2700 mm	19 000 kg
Wärtsilä 12V 200	—	200 mm	240 mm	1500	2400	3260	3640 mm	1636 mm	2345 mm	12 600 kg
Wärtsilä 16V 200	—	200 mm	240 mm	1500	3200	4290	—	—	—	—
Wärtsilä 18V 200	—	200 mm	240 mm	1500	3600	4890	—	—	—	—

Rating at engine PTO fuel stop power according to ISO 3046.1

SEMT PIELSTICK

2 quai de Seine, F-93202 Saint-Denis Cedex 1, France

Telephone: +33 (1) 48 09 76 00
Telex: 233 147F
Telefax: +33 (1) 48 09 78 78

SEMT Pielstick was founded in 1947. It designs and develops four-stroke high- and medium-speed diesel engines which are built under licence all over the world. The high-speed catamaran *Sun* built by Mitsui shipyard in Japan is powered by two Pielstick 16 PA4-200 VGA engines built under licence by Niigata.

The PA range of high-speed diesel engines offers four types of engines:
PA4-185 rated from 590 kW to 2215 kW and from 1200 to 1500 rpm
PA4-200 rated from 1060 kW to 2650 kW and from 1200 to 1500 rpm
PA5-255 rated from 1050 kW to 3960 kW and from 900 to 1000 rpm
PA6-280 rated from 1745 to 7920 kW and from 720 to 1050 rpm

The PA4 types are fitted with a variable geometry combustion chamber.

The PA engines are available in a gas version with low pollutant emission versions also being available.

These engines are used in marine propulsion, railway traction, dumpers, land-based power generation and generating sets including emergency sets for nuclear power-plants.

UPDATED

TURBOMECA

F-64511 Bordes, Cedex, France

Telephone: +33 59 12 50 00
Telex: 560928 F
Telefax: +33 59 53 15 12

S Meton, *President*
J L Chenard, *Director*

EURODYN

Turbomeca is involved in the development programme, Eurodyn, the aim of which is to produce a high efficiency industrial gas-turbine in the 2500 to 3000 kW power range.

The engine is intended for applications in the fast surface transport market such as train or boat propulsion, as well as in the more traditional market for gas-turbines of electric generation and drive of pumps or compressors.

In this Franco-Scandinavian co-operation, programme leader Turbomeca (France) holds 50 per cent, Ulstein (Norway) 30 per cent and Volvo Flygmotor (Sweden) 20 per cent.

The Eurodyn turbine is a two-shaft engine, making extensive use of radial technology, based on an advanced and patented design.

The efficiency targets set for the Eurodyn are impressive for turbines in this power class with an efficiency of 35 per cent.

In 1992 the Eurodyn programme partners achieved a significant milestone with tests of the Eurodyn prototypes in the Turbomeca and Ulstein facilities.

The two engines underwent extensive testing during 1994, and will be further tested in a high-speed vessel in Norway and a high-speed train in France in 1995.

MAKILA T I

Turbomeca has developed a new industrial marine gas-turbine, which the company designates Makila T I, rated 1200 kW under ISO conditions and base load. Its modern design and the use of state-of-the-art technology have contributed to its 28 per cent efficiency; exceptionally high for this class of prime mover.

This new industrial turbine is a derivative of the Makila turboshaft model and some 1200 units have been built for the Super Puma helicopter manufactured by Aerospatiale. Consequently the reliability of all major components has been proven in several years of service.

In 1988 the Makila T I was introduced as propulsion units on French turbotrains. At the same time Makila T I was adapted to run on natural gas and dual fuel at 1200 kW.

Makila T I production rate is at about three per month. Development work continues to increase engine performance.

The Makila T I gas-turbine comprises six main modules:
(1)Auxiliary drive and air intake module
(2)Three axial compressor stages with thick airfoils and fixed stators
(3)The gas generator module housing the centrifugal compressor stage, an annular combustion chamber for homogeneous temperature distribution and the two uncooled high pressure turbine stages with inset blades and nozzle guide vanes manufactured from refractory alloys
(4)Rear bearing casing and nozzle guide vanes of power turbine
(5)The power turbine module including the two low pressure axial turbine stages and an integrated gearbox which reduces the power output speed from 22 000 to 800 rpm as required by the operation

Turbomeca Makila T I industrial gas-turbine rated at 1200 kW   **1990**

(6)The dedicated electronic computer module, based on a multiprocessor and multilayered flexible card technology, performs start up, control and regulation of the engine parameters. This module includes facilities for in-line auto-test and off-line failure detection and identification.

The Makila T I is intended for generator and mechanical drive applications in land and marine based industries.

Main Characteristics
Length overall: 1.8 m
Width overall: 0.7 m
Weight, basic engine: 480 kg (for 6300 rpm ouput version)
Power rating, ISO base load: 1200 kW
Thermal efficiency: 28%
Specific fuel consumption: 300 g/kWh
Compressor pressure ratio: 9.6:1
Exhaust gases flow: 5.5 kg/s
Exhaust gases temperature: 505°C

UPDATED

GERMANY

DEUTZ (KLÖCKNER-HUMBOLDT-DEUTZ AG)

Deutz-Mülheimer-Strasse 111, D-51005 Cologne, Germany

Telephone: +49 (221) 8220
Telex: 88120
Telefax: +49 (221) 822 3525

Group companies:
Motoren-Werke Mannheim AG and MWM Diesel und Gastechnik GmbH, Carl-Benz-Strasse 5, D-68140 Mannheim, Germany

UK subsidiary:
KHD Great Britain Ltd, 2 St Martin's Way, London SW17 0UT, UK

Telephone: +44 (181) 946 9161
Telex: 8954136 KHDLON G
Telefax: +44 (181) 947 6380

KHD Deutz air-cooled engines of the Type 913C and 513 family have been in large scale production for a number of years. The BF6L 913C engine is a 141 kW engine with high power to weight ratio suitable for smaller hovercraft. For larger craft the 513 series is available as 6-, 8-, 10- and 12-cylinder V types in naturally aspirated, turbocharged and

Deutz BF12L 513C air-cooled diesel as fitted to BHC and NQEA AP1-88 hovercraft   **1986**

turbocharged/charge-cooled versions. The 513 engines encompass the power range 64 to 386 kW and can be extended to 441 kW. The latest variation, the BF8L 513LC, a long-stroke cylinder version of the 513 family, meets EURO 1 exhaust emission requirements and has recently also been introduced into hovercraft applications.

BF6/8/10/12L 513C

8-, 10- and 12-cylinder versions of this engine are installed in a variety of hovercraft.

Type: Air-cooled four-stroke diesel with direct fuel injection naturally aspirated or turbocharged; BF12L 513C with air-charge cooling system.

Cylinders: Individually removable cylinders made in grey cast-iron alloy, each with one inlet and one exhaust valve and overhead type. The valves are controlled via tappets and pushrods by a camshaft running in three metal bearings in the upper part of the crankcase. The camshaft is crankshaft driven via helical spur gears arranged at the flywheel end of the engine.

Pistons: Each is equipped with two compression rings and one oil control ring and is force oil-cooled.

Cooling system: Air-cooled, mechanically driven axial type cooling air blower with optional load-dependent, electronic control.

Lubrication: Force-fed by gear type pump. Oil is cleaned by full-flow paper filters. A centrifugal filter is installed in the fan hub as a high efficiency secondary flow filter.

BF12L 513C

Power, max (intermittent duty): 386 kW at 2300 rpm
Number of cylinders: 12
Bore/stroke: 125/130 mm
Capacity: 19.144 l
Compression ratio: 15.8:1
Rotational speed: 2300 rpm
Mean piston speed: 9.96 m/s
Specific fuel consumption (automotive rating flywheel net at max torque): 205 g/kWh
Shipping volume: 3.16 m³

Dimensions
Length: 1582 mm
Height: 1243 mm
Width: 1196 mm
User: British Hovercraft Corporation and NQEA Australia AP1-88

BF12L 513CP

This engine is a variant of the turbocharged and intercooled V12 which, by utilising a remotely mounted air-to-air intercooler, raises the intermittent power to 441 kW at 2300 rpm.

This is used by BHC on its latest well-deck version of the WAP1-88 for lift and propulsion and

Deutz-powered Griffon hovercraft, left to right: two 3000 TD (twin Deutz BF8L 513 diesels), two 2000 TDX (single Deutz BF8L 513 diesel) and one 2000 TD (single Deutz BF6L 913C diesel)   **1992**

RECENT APPLICATIONS

KHD Deutz engines are installed by the following hovercraft manufacturers:

Griffon Hovercraft Ltd	1000 TD/1500 TD/2000 TD	BF6L 913C
	2500 TD	BF6L 913C × 2
	2000 TDX/M	BF8L 513/LC
	3000 TD	BF8L 513 × 2
	4000 TD	BF10L 513 × 2
Slingsby Aviation Ltd	SAH 2200	BF6L 913C or
ABS Hovercraft Ltd	M10	BF8L 513
		BF12L 513C × 2
Westland Aerospace	WAP1-88	BF12L 513C × 4 or
		BF12L 513CP × 4

MARIC types 7210 and 716II use the BF6L 913C
Korea Tacoma Marine Industries Ltd and Mitsui-Deutz also use 913 and 513 engines for hovercraft.

also by Mitsui-Deutz in Japan for various other hovercraft applications.

BF8/10L 513

Turbocharged 8/10-cylinder engines with similar basic engine data to the BF12L 513C except that the outputs vary as follows:
BF8L 513: 235 kW (intermittent) at 2300 rpm
    211 kW (cruise) at 2300 rpm
BF10L 513: 294 kW (intermittent) at 2300 rpm
    263 kW (cruise) at 2300 rpm

BF8L 513LC

Turbocharged, charge-cooled eight-cylinder long stroke engine derived from the 513 engine series but giving increased power with emissions below EURO 1 levels.
Max power: 265 kW at 2100 rpm
Bore/stroke: 125/140 mm
Capacity: 13.744 l

BF6L 913C

Built to the same specification as the 513, this six-cylinder in-line engine is also available for hovercraft applications. It is fitted with an exhaust turbocharger and charge air-cooler.
Max (intermittent duty) power: 141 kW at 2500 rpm
Number of cylinders: 6
Bore/stroke: 102/125 mm
Capacity: 6.128 l
Compression ratio: 15.5:1
Rotational speed: 2500 rpm
Mean piston speed: 10.4 m/s
Specific fuel consumption (automotive rating at max torque): 214 g/kWh
Shipping volume: 0.8 m³
Dimensions
Length: 1245 mm
Height: 991 mm
Width: 711 mm
Dry weight: 510 kg

UPDATED

DEUTZ MWM

Motoren-Werke Mannheim AG

Carl-Benz-Strasse 5, D-68140 Mannheim, Germany

Telephone: +49 (621) 3840
Telex: 462341 D
Telefax: +49 (621) 384328

Group companies:
Klöckner-Humboldt-Deutz AG, Deutz-Mülheimer-Strasse 147, D-51005 Cologne, Germany

UK subsidiary:
KHD Great Britain Ltd, 2 St Martin's Way, London SW17 0UT, UK

Telephone: +44 (181) 946 9161
Telex: 8954136 KHDLON G
Telefax: +44 (181) 947 6380

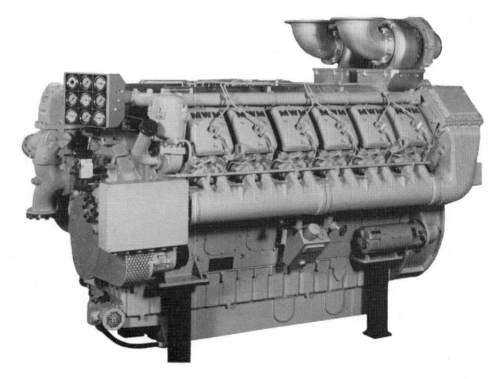

Deutz MWM TBD 604B V12 diesel engine
1987

Since 1985 when Motoren-Werke Mannheim AG was taken over by Klöckner-Humboldt-Deutz AG, the company has offered a combined range of medium sized and large water-cooled engines from 100 to 7250 kW. The principal engine ranges suitable for high-speed surface craft and hovercraft are in the table overleaf.

DEUTZ MWM TBD 616

In Spring 1993, the Deutz MWM division of the KHD Group announced the high-speed 616 engine series. It was established from the predecessor 234 series that the displacement for the engines could be enlarged by 22 per cent if the bore was enlarged from 128 to 132 mm and the stroke extended from 140 to 160 mm. It was necessary to introduce four-valve technology with a central injector arrangement in order to realise the potential for minimising exhaust emissions while maintaining a high degree of efficiency. The 616 series covers turbocharged, charge air-cooled diesel engines with 8, 12 and 16 cylinders.

DEUTZ MWM TBD 604B

The series 604B engine type is a compact high-speed diesel engine giving excellent power to weight ratios and a very favourable fuel consumption of only 190 g/kWh. The engine is four-stroke, turbocharged and intercooled, this gives a power spread of 420 kW (563 bhp) at 1000 rpm up to 2240 kW (3046 bhp) at 1860 rpm. The engine is available with an in-line six-cylinder, together with 90° V 8-, 12- and 16-cylinder variants. It is fitted with the HALLO swirl system, allowing optimum combustion even under idling and other low load conditions. This engine has been widely used for the main propulsion of high-speed ferries and patrol craft.

DEUTZ MWM TBD 620

For the main propulsion of high-speed craft, Deutz MWM has provided cylinder powers up to 140 kW for the 620 series. There are powers from 880 to 2240 kW (IOFN) available at speeds up to 1860 rpm for application in yachts, catamarans, SESs and similar fast craft.

The maximum power corresponds to a net brake fuel stop power as per DIN 6271 and ISO 3046/1. It is limited to 0.5 hours within a period of six hours. The maximum continuous power (ICFN) is now 127 kW per cylinder which means a power coverage by the series from 1016 to 2032 kW.

Specific fuel consumption of the 620 engines is as low as 195 g/kWh, related to the ICFN output and only 192 g/kWh at the optimal point of about 85 per cent output.

Considerable modifications were made to the exhaust system. Instead of the pulse charging system using several exhaust manifold pipes, Deutz MWM applied the pearl (pulse energy recovery line) exhaust system to the 620 series. In station-

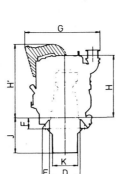
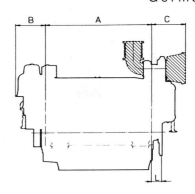
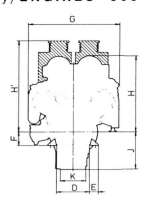

Engine type	Dimensions in mm											
	A	B	C	D	E	F	G	H	H'	J	K	L
TBD 604B L 6	1353	300	541	490	105	180	1143	1015	1168	567	390	203

Deutz MWM TBD 604B and 620 series weights and dimensions 1993

Deutz MWM 616 V16 diesel engine 1994

MODEL SUMMARY

Type	Number of cylinders and configuration	Power according to DIN 6271 and ISO 3046/1		Length mm	Weight kg
		Continuous net brake fuel stop power kW	Marine propulsion rpm		
TBD 616 V8	V8	480	2100	1720	1720
TBD 616 V12	V12	720	2100	2100	2100
TBD 616 V16	V16	960	2100	2550	2600
TBD 604B L6	L6	640	1800	2194	2115
TBD 620 V8	V8	1016	1800	1913	3000
TBD 620 V12	V12	1524	1800	2629	4075
TBD 620 V16	V16	2032	1800	3129	5495
TBD 440-6 K	L6	900	1000	3065	7500
TBD 440-8 K	L8	1200	1000	3675	9000
BV 6 M 628	L6	1350	1000	3537	9500
BV 8 M 628	L8	1800	1000	4233	11 500
BV 9 M 628	L9	2025	1000	4544	13 400
BV 12 M 626	V12	2700	1000	4343	16 300
BV 16 M 628	V16	3600	1000	5126	21 200
TBD 645 L6	L6	2550	600	5195	25 500
TBD 645 L8	L8	3400	600	6235	32 500
TBD 645 L9	L9	3825	600	7111	37 000
BV 6 M 640	L6	2650	650	6348	29 000
BV 8 M 640	L8	3530	650	7664	37 000
BV 12 M 640	V12	5290	650	6641	48 000
BV 16 M 640	V16	7060	650	7983	60 000

ary duty it provides for fuel savings up to 3 g/kWh over the complete load range in comparison with conventional exhaust systems. For main propulsion and auxiliary drive, the range of the 620 series engines includes the 90° V configuration, available as 8-, 12- and 16-cylinder models. The compression ratio of the direct injection engines is 13.5.

DEUTZ MWM 645

Deutz MWM presented, at Europort '91 in Amsterdam, the medium-speed diesel engines of the 645 series as an addition to its engine range in the upper power class. They are long-stroke in-line models, initially with six and eight cylinders covering a power spectrum of 2500 to 3740 kW and operating at a rated speed of 600 rpm. A nine-cylinder version is

DEUTZ MWM series 616, 604B and 620

TYPE	kW	kg	Air intake temperature
TBD 616 V8	480	1720	25°C
TBD 616 V12	720	2100	25°C
TBD 616 V16	960	2600	25°C
TBD 604B L6	640	2115	45°C
TBD 620 V8	1016	3000	25°C
TBD 620 V12	1524	4075	25°C
TBD 620 V16	2032	5495	25°C

also planned for the near future. With an increased speed and a higher brake mean effective pressure an output of 500 kW/cylinder will be obtained at a speed of 650 rpm, thus extending the power spectrum of the series up to 4500 kW. The engines are mainly used as marine main and auxiliary drives and prime movers for power generating and pump sets. A pre-production series became available in 1992.

UPDATED

MAN
MAN Nutzfahrzeuge AG

Nuremberg Works, PO Box 440 100, Frankenstrasse 15, D-8500 Nüremberg 44, Germany

Telephone: +49 (911) 186013
Telex: 622914-0 MN D
Telefax: +49 (911) 437455

MAN Marine diesels are in widespread use and have been supplied to the following shipyards: Anne Wever; BAIA; Camuffo; Canados; Eder/Knoche; Ladenstein; San Lorenzo; Lowland; Marchi; Mochi Craft; Neptunus; Posillipo; Riva; Sunseeker; Tecnomarine; Marine Projects; Gestione; Best Yachts; Rizzardi; Storeboo; Oskarshamns; Lux-Shipyard; Seggendorf Shipyard; Viking; Vosper Thornycroft; Hatteras; Bertram; Dalla Pieta; Golfo; Piantoni; Cantieri della Pasquaz; Engitalia; Fairline; Henriques and Guy Couach.

MAN marine diesel engines are blocked for different marine applications, rating 1, rating 2 and rating 3. Please see the table for rating definitions.

D 0826L

Type: Four-stroke diesel engine, six-cylinder vertical in-line water-cooled with turbocharger and intercooler. Direct injection system. High unit output, low noise level and quiet running with low fuel consumption. Long service life and low upkeep and all parts to be serviced are readily accessible.

Crankcase: One-piece crankcase and cylinder block. Replaceable dry cylinder liners. Seven bearing crankshaft with forged on balance weights. Induction-hardened main bearing and connecting rod bearing journals, additional hardening of journal radii. Main and connecting rod bearing journals in ready-to-install three-component bearing. Torsional vibration damper fitted at front of six-cylinder engines. Die-forged, straight split connecting rods, which are removable through top of cylinder. Three-ring pistons of special aluminium alloy with ring carrier for the top piston ring. Piston crown cooled by lubricating oil jet.

Cylinder heads and valve train: Cross-flow cylinder head for each pair of cylinders with cast swirl inlet and exhaust channels on opposite sides. Shrunk-fit inlet and outlet valve seat inserts and replaceable pressed-in valve guides. One inlet and outlet valve per cylinder arranged in overhead position. Forged camshaft with induction-hardened cams and bearing supports.

Lubrication: Force-fed lubrication with gear oil pump for crankshaft, connecting rod and camshaft bearings as well as valve train and turbocharger. Oil filter/oil cooler combination with coolant-covered, flat-tube oil cooler. Lubricant cleaned in full flow by easy maintenance screw-on filters with fine disposable filter cartridge of paper.

Fuel system: Bosch injectors. Bosch-MW in-line injection pump. Mechanical engine speed governor and timing device. Switch-off via separate stop lever and solenoid. Fuel pre-supply pump, fuel filter with easy maintenance screw-on disposable cartridges.

Intake and exhaust system: Wet air filter, water-cooled manifold cooled by engine water.

Supercharging: Exhaust gas turbocharger, water-cooled by engine water, seawater-cooled intercooler.

MAN Model D 2840 LE401 marine diesel

1988

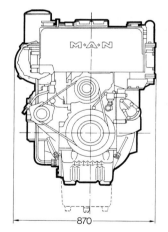
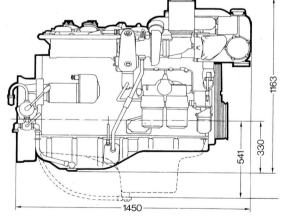

MAN Model D 2866 LE, dimensions (mm)

1988

Electrical system: Two-pole starter, 4 kW, 24 V and two-pole alternator 28 V, 35 A.

Applications: Workboats, customs and police patrol boats, yachts.

Technical Data for 108 mm bore
Bore/stroke: 108/120 mm
Swept volume: 6.6 l
Compression ratio: 17:1
Rotation looking on flywheel: anti-clockwise
Flywheel housing: SAE 2
Weight of engine dry, with cooling system: 640 kg
Max rating 3: 199 kW at 2600 rpm
Mean effective pressure: 13.9 bar at 2600 rpm
Torque: 860 Nm at 1700 rpm
Starter motor: Bosch solenoid-operated starter Type KB, 24 V, 5.4 kW.

Technical Data for 128 mm bore
Bore/stroke: 128/155 mm

Swept volume: 11.97 l
Compression ratio: 15.5:1
Max rating 3: 324 kW at 2200 rpm.
Mean effective pressure: 14.8 bar at 2200 rpm
Torque: 1406 Nm at 2200 rpm
Fuel consumption (+5% tolerance) at max rating 3: 215 g/kWh at 2200 rpm.

D 2848 LX
Type: Four-stroke, direct injection.
Cylinders: Eight-cylinder, V-form, wet replaceable cylinder liners.
Aspiration: Turbocharged, intercooled.
Cooling: Water circulation by centrifugal pump fitted on engine.
Lubrication: Force-fed lubrication by gear pump, lubrication oil cooler in cooling water circuit of engine.

Injection: Bosch in-line pump with mechanical Bosch speed governor fitted.
Generator: Bosch three-phase generator with rectifier and transistorised governor Type K1, 28 V, 35 A.
Starter motor: Bosch solenoid-operated starter, Type KB, 24 V, 6.5 kW.

Technical Data
Bore/stroke: 128/142 mm
Volume: 14.62 l
Compression ratio: 13.5:1
Max rating 3: 500 kW at 2300 rpm
Mean effective pressure: 17.8 bar at 2300 rpm
Torque: 2290 Nm at 1700 rpm
Fuel consumption (+5% tolerance): 214 g/kWh at 2300 rpm.

D 2840 HLE401
(Supersedes D 2840 LXE)

Type: Four-stroke marine diesel engine, 10-cylinder, V-form, water-cooled with turbocharger and intercooler. Direct injection system.
Crankcase: Grey cast-iron cylinder block, six-bearing crankshaft with screwed-on balance weights, three-layer type bearings, die-forged connecting rods. Replaceable wet-type cylinder liners.
Cylinder heads and valve train: Individual cylinder heads of grey cast-iron, overhead valves, one intake and one exhaust valve per cylinder, valve actuation via tappets, pushrods and rocker arms. Six-bearing camshaft, shrunk-fit valve seat inserts.
Lubrication: Force-fed lubrication by gear pump, oil-to-water oil cooler, full-flow oil filter, changeover type optional.
Fuel system: Bosch in-line injection pump with mechanical speed governor, fuel supply pump, fuel filter, changeover type optional.
Intake and exhaust system: Viscous air filter, water-cooled exhaust manifold connected in engine cooling circuit.
Supercharging: Turbochargers, water-cooled in fresh water circuit, seawater-cooled intercooler Waste Gate System.
Electrical system: Two-pole starter, 6.5 kW, 24 V, two-pole alternator 28 V, 120 A, additional alternator 28 V available with 35 A, 55 A or 120 A on request.
Applications: Yachts, customs and police patrol boats.

Technical Data
Bore/stroke: 128/142 mm
Swept volume: 18.271 l
Compression ratio: 13.5:1
Rotation looking on flywheel: anti-clockwise
Weight of engine, dry with cooling system: 1380 kg
Speed: 2300 rpm
Max rating 3: 603 kW/820 hp
Mean effective pressure: 17.2 bar
Fuel consumption: 215 g/kWh

D 2866 LX
Type: Four-stroke, direct injection.
Cylinders: Six-cylinder in-line, wet replaceable cylinder liners.
Aspiration: Turbocharged intercooled.
Cooling: Water circulation by centrifugal pump fitted on engine.
Lubrication: Force-fed lubrication by gear pump, lubrication oil cooler in cooling water circuit of engine.
Generator: Bosch three-phase generator with rectifier and transistorised governor type K1, 28 V, 35 A.
Mean specific fuel consumption (+5%): 215 g/kWh.

D 2842 HLE402
(Supersedes D 2842 HLZE)

Type: Four-stroke marine diesel engine, 12-cylinder, V-form, water-cooled with turbocharger and intercooler. Direct injection system.
Crankcase: Cylinder block of grey cast-iron. Replaceable wet-type cylinder liners. Seven-bearing crankshaft with screwed-on balance weights, three-layer type bearings, die-forged connecting rods.
Cylinder heads and valve train: Individual cylinder heads of grey cast-iron, overhead valves, one intake and one exhaust valve per cylinder, valve actuation via tappets, pushrods and rocker arms. Seven-bearing camshaft, shrunk-fit valve seat inserts.
Lubrication: Force-fed lubrication by gear pump, oil-to-water oil cooler, full flow oil filter, changeover type optional.
Fuel system: Bosch in-line injection pump with

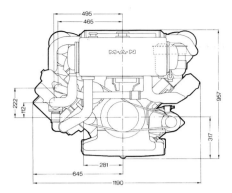 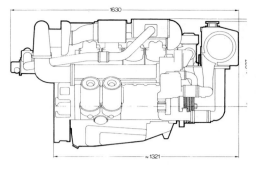

MAN Model D 2848 LE, dimensions (mm)   *1987*

Model Summary

Model	No of cylinders/ configuration	Bore/ stroke in mm	Displacement in litres	Dry weight in kg	Speed rpm	Rating @ kW	ps/hp	Rating @ kW	ps/hp	Rating @ kW	ps/hp
D 0226 ME	6	102/116	5.69	520	2400	79	107	83	113	-	-
					2800	87	118	95	130	-	-
					3000	-	-	-	-	100	136
D 0226 MTE(T)	6	102/116	5.69	530	2600	110	150	121	170	-	-
					2800	-	-	125	-	135	184
D 0226 MLE(L)	6	102/116	5.69	545	2600	125	170	125	170	-	-
					2800	-	-	147	200	154	210
D 0826 LE(L)	6	108/120	6.60	640	2600	-	-	-	-	199	270
					1500	125	170	132	180	-	-
					1800	151	205	162	220	-	-
D 2866 E	6	128/155	11.97	985	2100	165	224	178	242	-	-
					2200	-	-	-	-	185	252
					1800	190	258	206	280	-	-
D 2866 TE(T)	6	128/155	11.97	1000	2100	-	-	227	300	-	-
					2200	-	-	-	-	235	320
					1800	246	326	-	-	-	-
D 2866 LE(L)	6	128/155	11.97	1035	2100	-	-	260	354	-	-
					2200	-	-	280	380	300	408
D 2866 LXE(LX)	6	128/155	11.97	1045	2200	-	-	-	-	324	440
					1800	280	380	294	400	-	-
D 2848 LE(L)	V8	128/142	14.62	1210	2100	-	-	331	450	-	-
					2300	-	-	347	472	375	510
D 2840 LE(L)	V10	128/142	18.27	1350	1800	346	470	365	496	-	-
					2100	-	-	412	560	-	-
					2300	-	-	433	590	467	635
D 2848 LXE(LX)	V8	128/142	14.62	1200	2100	-	-	370	500	-	-
					2300	-	-	-	-	500	680
D 2842 LE(L)	V12	128/142	21.93	1550	1800	420	571	441	600	-	-
					2100	-	-	496	675	-	-
					2300	-	-	520	707	559	760
D 2840 LE401	V10	128/142	18.27	1370	2100	-	-	478	650	-	-
					2300	-	-	-	-	603	820
D 2842 LE401	V12	128/142	21.93	1580	2100	-	-	-	-	735	1000
D 2842 LE402	V12	128/142	21.93	1600	2100	-	-	-	-	800	-
					2300	-	-	-	-	809	1100

T = Turbocharged model
L = Turbocharged and intercooled model

DEFINITION OF RATING CLASSIFICATION OF MAN MARINE PROPULSION ENGINES

	Rating 1	Rating 2	Rating 3
Kind of operation	Heavy duty (MCR)	Medium duty	Light duty (commercial and private)
Operating hours per year	3000 up to 8000	1000 up to 3000	up to 1000
Percentage of time at full load	30 up to 50%	10 up to 30%	5 up to 20%
Average load application	50 up to 85%	50 up to 70%	25 up to 50%
Particular operating conditions		no wide open throttle with reduced rpm	no wide open throttle with reduced rpm
Typical application	Fishtrawler	Escort boats	Yachts
	Tug boats	Pilot boats	Lightweight fishing boats
	Pushing vessels	Fishing boats	Patrol boats for customs, coastguard, police, port authorities, navy
	Freighters	Ferries	Fast boats in emergency service
	Ferries	Cruising vessels	Bow thruster
			Fire pumps

mechanical speed governor, fuel supply pump, fuel filter, changeover type optional.

Intake and exhaust system: Viscous air filter, water-cooled exhaust manifold connected in engine cooling circuit.

Supercharging: Turbochargers, water-cooled in fresh water circuit, seawater-cooled intercooler Waste Gate System.

Electrical system: Two-pole starter, 6.5 kW, 24 V, two-pole alternator 28 V, 120 A, additional alternator 28 V with 35 A, 55 A or 120 A on request.

Applications: Yachts, customs and police boats.

Technical Data

Bore/stroke: 128/142 mm
Volume: 21.931 l
Compression ratio: 13.5:1
Rotation looking on flywheel: anti-clockwise
Weight of engine, dry with cooling system: approx 1600 kg
Speed: 2300 rpm
Max rating 3: 809 kW at 2300 rpm
Mean effective pressure: 19.2 bar
Torque: 3820 Nm at 1700 rpm
Mean specific fuel consumption (+5%): 217 g/kWh

UPDATED

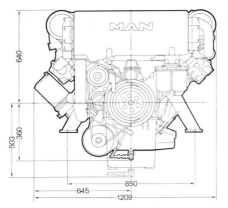
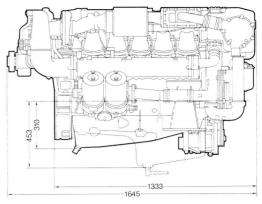

MAN Model D 2842 LZE, dimensions (mm)

1989

MAN Model D 2842 HLE402 marine diesel
1991

MTU

Motoren- und Turbinen-Union Friedrichshafen GmbH

D-88040 Friedrichshafen, Germany

Telephone: +49 (7541) 900
Telex: 734280-0 mtd
Telefax: +49 (7541) 902247

MTU Friedrichshafen, which is part of AEG Daimler-Benz Industrie, offers diesel engines for marine, heavy vehicle, electric-power generation and rail applications in the 35 to 7400 kW power range.

MTU 12V 183 TE 72
1989

Main dimensions (mm) for series 183 engine family
1988

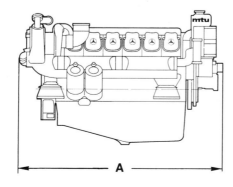
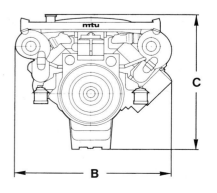

Engine model		A	B	C
6R 183 TE 72	(OM 447LA)*	1575	885	1120
8V 183 TE 72	(OM 442LA)*	1405	1255	1165
12V 183 TE 72	(OM 444LA)*	1845	1280	1195

*original Mercedes-Benz designation on which types the corresponding MTU engines are based.

MTU 16V 396 TE 74L

1990

Main dimensions (mm) for series 396 engine family
1986

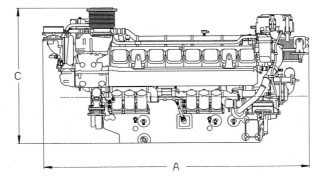

Engine model	A	B	C
8V 396 TE 74	2300	1540	1520
8V 396 TE 74L	2330	1540	1520
12V 396 TE 74	2830	1540	1600
12V 396 TE 74L	2870	1540	1600
16V 396 TE 74	3350	1540	1650
16V 396 TE 74L	3430	1540	1750

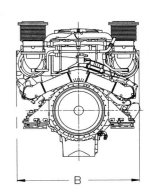

MTU Friedrichshafen is the development and production centre for high performance diesel engines of Maybach and Mercedes-Benz origin, and embodies the experience of these companies in diesel engine technology. In addition to diesel engines, MTU Friedrichshafen is responsible for industrial and marine gas-turbine sales and application engineering.

In the field of hydrofoils, surface-effect ships, catamarans and other high-speed craft, MTU can draw from decades of experience with over 1000 engines having been supplied for the propulsion of hydrofoils and catamarans starting as early as 1955 when an MB 820 engine was delivered for the first PT 20 hydrofoil built by Cantiere Navale Rodriquez (now Rodriquez Cantieri Navali SpA) in Messina.

Currently the 099, 183, 396, 595 and 1163 engine families are offered for propulsion of these special types of craft. These engines cover a wide range of power. In the accompanying table the standard power outputs are listed; these, however, may have to be adjusted depending on the application, the power demand and the operating profile. The outputs are based on DIN/ISO 3046.

MTU diesel engines for catamaran, hydrofoil and Surface Effect Ships (SES) propulsion and similar

Engine model		Engine speed rpm	Fuel stop power kW	hp (metric)	Engine dry weight kg
		A	B	C	
6R 183 TE 72	(OM 447LA)*	1900	305	415	1185
8V 183 TE 72	(OM 442LA)*	2100	405	551	1420
12V 183 TE 72	(OM 444LA)*	2100	610	830	1690
8V 396 TE 74		1900	840	1142	2890
12V 396 TE 74		1900	1260	1714	3900
16V 396 TE 74		1900	1680	2285	5000
8V 396 TE 74L		1900	1000	1360	2890
12V 396 TE 74L		1900	1500	2040	3900
16V 396 TE 74L		1900	2000	2720	5000
12V 595 TE 70		1700	2700	3672	9070
16V 595 TE 70		1700	3600	4896	11 360
12V 595 TE 70L		1750	2945	4005	9070
16V 595 TE 70L		1750	3925	5338	11 360
16V 1163 TB 73		1200	4320	5875	17 550
20V 1163 TB 73		1200	5400	7344	20 650
16V 1163 TB 73L		1200	4800	6528	17 550
20V 1163 TB 73L		1200	6000	8160	20 650

* original Mercedes-Benz designation on which types the corresponding MTU engines are based

In addition to the delivery of the propulsion engine, MTU can lay out, design and deliver complete propulsion packages including the interface engineering and the technical assistance during installation and the start up phase.

UPDATED

MTU 12V 595 TE 70
1991

Engine model	A	B	C
12V 595 TE 70	3390	1500	2570
16V 595 TE 70	3980	1500	2600
12V 595 TE 70L	3390	1500	2570
16V 595 TE 70L	3980	1500	2600

Main dimensions (mm) for series 595 engine family
1991

Engine model	A	B	C
16V 1163 TB 73	4515	1660	2850
20V 1163 TB 73	5310	1660	2940
16V 1163 TB 73L	4515	1660	2850
20V 1163 TB 73L	5310	1660	2940

Main dimensions (mm) for series 1163 engine family
1992

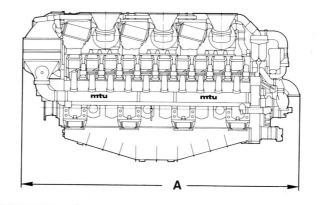
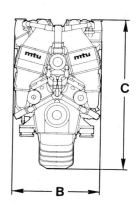

ITALY

CRM MOTORI MARINI SpA

Head Office and Works: I-21053 Castellanza, Via Marnate 41, Italy

Telephone: +39 (331) 501548
Telex: 334382 CREMME I
Telefax: +39 (331) 505501

G Mariani, *Director*
Ing B Piccoletti, *Director*
Ing S Rastelli, *Director*
Ing G Venturini, *Director*

CRM has specialised in building lightweight diesel engines for more than 40 years. The company's engines are used in large numbers of motor torpedo boats, coastal patrol craft and privately owned motor yachts. The engines have also been installed in hydrofoils (*Tehi*).

The range of engines comprises the 12-cylinder 12 D/S and 12 D/SS and the 18-cylinder 18 D/SS, BR-1 and BR-2. All are turbocharged with different supercharging ratios. The 12 cylinders are arranged in two banks of six and the 18 cylinders are set out in an unusual 'W' arrangement of three banks of six.

All engines are available in non-magnetic versions; the perturbation field is reduced to insignificant amounts when compensated with the anti-dipole method.

CRM 18-CYLINDER

First in CRM's series of low weight, high-speed diesel engines, the CRM 18-cylinder is arranged in a 'W' form. Maximum power is 1213 kW at 2075 rpm for the 18 D/SS, 1335 kW at 2075 rpm for the BR-1 and 1544 kW at 2120 rpm for the BR-2.

The following description relates to the 18D/SS, BR-1 and BR-2:

Type: 18-cylinder in-line W-type, four-stroke, water-cooled, turbocharged with different supercharging ratios: 2.4 (18 D/SS); 2.6 (BR-1) and 3 (BR-2).

Cylinders: Bore 150 mm (5.91 in). Stroke 180 mm (7.09 in). Swept volume 3.18 l/cylinder. Total swept volume 57.3 litres. Compression ratio 14:1. Separate pressed-steel cylinder frame side members are surrounded by gas-welded sheet metal water-cooling, jacket-treated and pressure-coated internally to prevent corrosion. Lower half of cylinder is ringed by a drilled flange for bolting to crankcase. Cylinder top also houses a spherical-shaped pre-combustion chamber as well as inlet and exhaust valve seats. The pre-combustion chamber is in high strength, heat- and corrosion-resistant steel. A single cast light alloy head, carrying valve guides, pre-combustion chambers and camshaft bearings bridges each bank of cylinders. The cylinder head is attached to cylinder bank by multiple studs.

Pistons: Light alloy forgings with three rings, the top ring being chrome-plated and bottom ring acting as oil scraper. Piston crowns (hard anodised top) shaped to withstand high temperatures especially in vicinity of pre-combustion chamber outlet ports.

Connecting rods: Comprise main and secondary articulated rods, all being completely machined I-section steel forgings. Big end of each main rod is bolted to ribbed cap by six studs. Big end bearings are white metal lined steel shells. Each secondary rod anchored at its lower end to a pivot pin inserted in two lugs protruding from big end of main connecting rod. Both ends of all secondary rods and small ends of main rods have bronze bushes.

Crankshafts: One-piece hollow shaft in nitrided alloy steel, with six throws equally spaced at 120°. Seven main bearings with white metal lined steel shells. There are 12 balancing counterweights.

Crankcase: Cast light alloy crankcase bolted to bed plate by studs and tie bolts. Multiple integral reinforced ribs provide robust structure. Both sides of each casting braced by seven cross ribs incorporating crankshaft bearing supports. Protruding sides of crankcase ribbed throughout length.

Valve gear: Hollow sodium-cooled valves of each bank of cylinders actuated by twin camshafts and six cams on each shaft. Two inlet and two outlet valves

CRM 18 D/SS, BR-1   *1988*

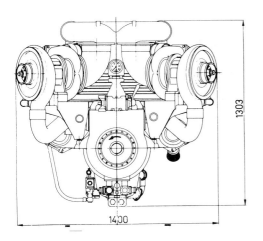

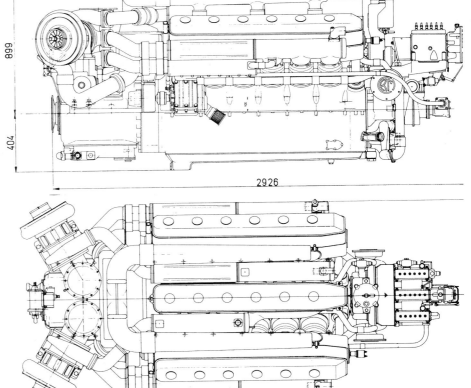

CRM 18 D/SS, BR-1   *1987*

	18 D/SS	BR-1	BR-2	12 D/S	12 D/SS
Dimensions					
Length	2305 mm	2305 mm	2305 mm	1909 mm	2147 mm
Width	1400 mm	1400 mm	1400 mm	1210 mm	1210 mm
Height	1303 mm	1303 mm	1303 mm	1204 mm	1310 mm
Reverse gear	621 mm	621 mm	621 mm	621 mm	621 mm
Weights, dry					
Engine	1950 kg	1950 kg	1950 kg	1380 kg	1560 kg
Reverse gear	340 kg	340 kg	750 kg	340 kg	340 kg
Reduction gear	150-300 kg	150-300 kg	—	150-300 kg	150-300 kg
Ratings					
Max power	1213 kW (1650 hp) at 2075 rpm	1335 kW (1815 hp) at 2075 rpm	1544 kW (2100 hp) at 2120 rpm	687 kW at 2075 rpm	1010 kW at 2075 rpm
Continuous rating	1103 kW (1500 hp) at 2020 rpm	1213 kW (1650 hp) at 2020 rpm	1403 kW (1910 hp) at 2050 rpm	625 kW at 2010 rpm	918 kW at 2020 rpm
Specific fuel consumption	0.224 ±5% kg/kWh	0.230 ±5% kg/kWh	0.240 ±5% kg/kWh	0.227 ±5% kg/kWh	0.238 ±5% kg/kWh
Specific oil consumption	0.002 ±5% kg/kWh	0.002 ±5% kg/kWh	0.002 ±5% kg/kWh	0.002 kg/kWh	0.002 kg/kWh

CRM 18 D/SS, BR-2, section **1992**

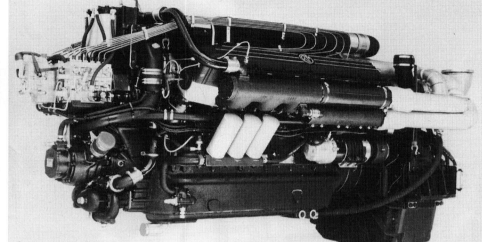

CRM 18 D/SS, BR-2 **1994**

per cylinder and one rocker for each valve. End of stem and facing of exhaust valves fitted with Stellite inserts. Valve cooling water forced through passage formed by specially shaped plate welded to top of cylinder.

Fuel injection: Pumps fitted with variable speed control and pilot injection nozzle.

Pressure charger: Two turbochargers, Brown Boveri type, on the 18 D/SS and BR-1; three turbochargers, KKK type, on the BR-2.

Accessories: Standard accessories include oil and fresh water heat exchangers with thermostats mounted on the engine; oil filters, air filters and fresh water tank with preheating system; engine room instruments panel with warning system and exhaust gas temperatures indicator; wheel room instruments panel; pre-lubrication electric pump; salt water and

fuel hand pumps and expansion joints for exhaust piping separate from the engine.

Cooling system: Fresh water.

Fuel: Fuel oil having specific gravity of 0.83 to 0.84.

Lubrication: Dry sump type with circulating and scavenge oil pumps.

Oil: Mineral oil to SAE 40 HD, MIL-L-2104D.

Oil cooling: Salt water circulating through heat exchanger.

Starting: 24 V 15 kW electric motor and 85 A, 24 V alternator for battery charge, or compressed air.

Mounting: At any transverse or longitudinal angle tilt to 20°.

CRM 12-CYLINDER

Second in the CRM series of low weight diesels, the CRM 12-cylinder is a unit with two blocks of six

cylinders set at 60° to form a V assembly. The bore and stroke are the same as in the CRM 18 series and many of the components are interchangeable including the crankshaft, bedplate, cylinders and pistons. The crankcase and connecting rod assemblies are of a modified design; the secondary rod is anchored at its lower end to a pivot pin inserted on two lugs protruding from the big end of the main connecting rod. The fuel injection pump is modified to single block housing all 12 pumping elements located between the cylinder banks.

Type: 12-cylinder V-type, four-stroke, water-cooled, turbo-supercharged with medium supercharging ratio (2.15 for 12 D/S) and light supercharging ratio (2.85 for 12 D/SS).

Pressure charger: Two KKK type.

UPDATED

FIAT AVIAZIONE SpA

Marine and Industrial Products Department, Via Nizza 312, PO Box 1389, I-10127 Turin, Italy

Telephone: +39 (11) 330 2543
Telex: 221320 FIATAV I

The LM 500 gas-turbine is a compact high performance marine and industrial power unit in the 3000 to 6000 shaft horsepower class. General Electric's Marine and Industrial Engine Division and Fiat Aviazione SpA, in a co-operative undertaking, initiated the design programme in July 1978. In January 1980 the first engine began full load testing and the LM 500 went into production.

The LM 500 is a simple-cycle, two-shaft gas-turbine engine with a free power turbine. It incorporates a variable stator compressor, with excellent stall margin capability, driven by an air-cooled, two-stage turbine. It is derived from the TF34 high bypass turbofan aircraft engine which was

designed for marine operation in the US Navy's S-3A aircraft and later incorporated in the US Air Force's A-10 aircraft, with the same materials and marine corrosion protection as employed in the very successful LM 500 marine gas-turbine. The LM 500 incorporates the latest in proven design technology and corrosion-resistant materials to provide a mature design with maximum reliability, component life and time between inspections and overhaul. The LM 500 demonstrates higher efficiency than currently available gas-turbines in its class and is suited for marine applications requiring low weight and fuel economy.

General Electric Company and Fiat Aviazione SpA have designed the LM 500 gas-turbine to produce power for marine applications requiring significant fuel economy, compactness, light weight, minimum maintenance, high tolerance to fouling/deposits and reliable operation. Such applications include military land craft, hydrofoils, air cushion vehicles, fast patrol boats, cruise power propulsion and onboard electric power generators.

LM 500

The LM 500 is a simple-cycle, two-shaft gas-turbine engine. The single shaft gas generator consists of a 14-stage high pressure compressor with variable inlet guide vanes and variable stator vanes in the first five stages, an annular machined ring combustor with 18 externally mounted fuel injectors and an air-cooled, two-stage HP gas generator turbine. The free power turbine has four stages and the output shaft connecting flange is at the air inlet end of the engine.

Air intake: The LM 500 offers, as optional equipment, an air inlet collector to guide the inlet air from the customer's intake ducting into the engine. The inlet duct is made from aluminium and provides the structural connection for the forward engine mounts or for the reduction gearbox containing the forward mounts.

An off-engine inlet screen is also offered to prevent objects from entering the compressor.

Compressor: The compressor is identical to the TF34 and consists of the front frame, accessory

LM 500 1986

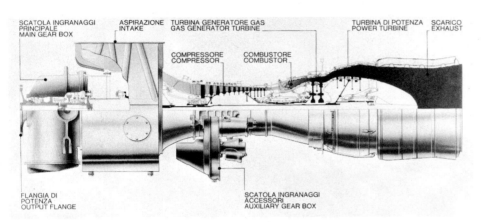

Cutaway of LM 500 1986

Power turbine: The LM 500 power turbine is a four-stage, uncooled, high performance design incorporating aerodynamic and mechanical features and materials identical to the TF34 low pressure turbine. The power turbine rotor structural components are made of inconel 718 material. The four turbine discs carry tip shrouded turbine blades that are attached to the discs with single tang dovetails. The blades are made of René 77 material with the first stage Codep-coated. The durability of René 77 alleviates the need for coatings on the other stages. At operating gas temperatures 111°C less than the TF34, the LM 500 blades have virtually infinite stress rupture life. The structural integrity of the power turbine rotor has been demonstrated to a speed of 9030 rpm, 29 per cent over the normal rated speed of the LM 500 engine.

Lubrication: The LM 500 lubricating oil system provides the following functions: lubricates and cools the gas-turbine main bearings; supplies hydraulic fluid for the variable geometry actuation system and fuel metering valve actuator.

The main engine bearings are lubricated from an accessory gearbox-driven lube pump. The scavenge circuit is based on a dry sump system and each bearing sump is scavenged by a separate pump or pump elements driven off the accessory gearbox. All scavenge oil is filtered (coarse screens) prior to entry into the pump elements.

Fuel: The LM 500 is designed to operate with marine diesel, diesel and JP fuels. The fuel system consists of on- and off-engine components. Filtered fuel is supplied by the customer to the fuel pump, which is mounted on the accessory gearbox, where the fuel pressure is increased by a centrifugal boost element and then ported externally to an on-engine last chance fuel filter. From the filter the fuel is routed to an off-engine Fuel Regulating Assembly (FRA) which meters the engine fuel flow according to signals received from the off-engine Main Electronic Control Assembly (MECA). Also included in the FRA are two fuel shut-off valves, mounted in series for redundancy, which are used to shut off the fuel to the engine during normal shut downs and automatic shut downs. Fuel is then routed to the on-engine fuel distributor which divides the fuel through separate hose assemblies to 18 fuel injectors.

Specifications
Basic engine
Length overall: 2184 mm
Width: 864 mm
Weight: 580 kg
With optional inlet and axial exhaust duct, starter kit and output gearbox
Length overall: 3307 mm
Width: 1179 mm
Weight: 1031 kg

drive assembly, compressor rotor and case/vane assembly. The front frame is an uncomplicated four-strut aluminium casting and is designed to provide the compressor inlet flowpath, the forward structural support for the engine, support the forward bearings and seals for the gas generator and power turbine rotors, and support the accessory gearbox.

Combustor: The LM 500 combustor is of the TF34 flight engine design. It is an annular through flow combustor using a machined ring liner construction for long life. Metered fuel is distributed and introduced through 18 central, individually replaceable injectors.

High pressure turbine: The LM 500 high pressure turbine is a two-stage, fully air-cooled design, identical to the TF34 turbine except for minor changes to improve performance and meet the requirements for marine and industrial applications.

FINCANTIERI DIESEL ENGINES DIVISION

Isotta Fraschini

Bagnoli Della Rosandra 334, I-34018 Trieste, Italy

Telephone: +39 (40) 3195648
Telefax: +39 (40) 810246

Fincantieri, the largest and most diversified shipbuilding organisation in the Mediterranean and one of the biggest in Europe, is the company in the IRI group which unifies the capacities and facilities of the oldest and most important Italian enterprises in the sector.

The company, with continuous experience and technology acquired since the beginning of the century, is now giving new impulse to the long established Isotta Fraschini name.

The Diesel Engines Division, with its headquarters at Trieste, carries out the functions of a typical industrial enterprise for the production and sale of diesel, gas and dual-fuel engines in the marine, industrial and rail traction sectors.

IF L 1306 T2 marine engine
1993

Following the merging of Isotta Fraschini Motori SpA, the Diesel Engines Division of Fincantieri - with the two trademarks GMT and IF - a range of engines covering power outputs from 400 to 22 000 kW per unit is now available.

The Division has two production plants, one situated at Trieste and one at Bari. The Trieste factory extends, in the industrial zone of Trieste, over a site of 530 000 m², 150 000 m² of which are presently occupied by the offices and workshops.

The Bari factory extends on the total area of 200 000 m² of which 24 000 m² are covered.

ISOTTA FRASCHINI 1300

The 1300 family comprises a six-cylinder in-line unit and 8- and 12-cylinder 90° Vee models. A 130 mm bore and a stroke of 142 mm on the in-line unit are principal features of the 1300 family. The stroke is reduced to 126 mm for the Vee models. The in-line engine has a cylinder displacement of 1885 cm³, while the Vee units have a cylinder of 1672 cm³. The 1300 engines have an impressive power-to-weight ratio, being highly standardised and extremely reliable engines of modular type. Introduced as marine engines, these diesels will also serve the power generation and industrial market segments.

The 1300 family specification may be summarised as follows:
Four-stroke diesel engines, direct injection, exhaust gas turbo-charging, supercharging air-cooling through water/air exchangers, engine double-circuit water-cooling, complete with heat exchanger, cooling system complete with centrifugal pumps, thermostats for internal circuit water and oil control, engine water-cooled exhaust manifolds, force-feed lubrication through gear pump, injection pump complete with mechanical governor, fuel feed pump, oil exchanger with replaceable/cartridge oil filters, fuel oil filter, dry air filter, crankshaft vibration damper, flywheel and flywheel housing SAE standard, battery charger generator, 24 V electric starter.

ISOTTA FRASCHINI 1700

The 1700 family comprises 8 to 16 cylinder models arranged with a 90° V on a high tensile alloy iron crankcase.

These engines feature a direct injection system with four valves per cylinder. They are built using a modular concept, with most components common to all units. A special amagnetic version is available for mine warfare vessels.

UPDATED

Engine model	Cylinder arrangement	Engine ratings (brake power)									
		High performance special craft		Fast special craft		Commercial craft light duty		Commercial craft medium duty		Commercial craft heavy duty	
		kw	rpm	kw	rpm	kw	rpm	kw	rpm	kw	rpm
L 1306 T2	6 in line	370	2400	350	2400	320	2300	280	2200	220	1800
L 1308 T2	8 vee	500	2700	500	2700	450	2600	390	2400	330	2100
L 1312 T2	12 vee	780	2700	750	2700	675	2600	585	2400	495	2100
V 1708 T2	8 vee	955	2000	900	2000	815	1935	750	1935	700	1800
V 1712 T2	12 vee	1680	2000	1540	2000	1400	1940	1260	1935	1050	1800
V 1716 T2	16 vee	2350	2100	2140	2030	1925	1980	1730	1960	—	—

IF V 1308 T2 marine engine   *1993*

IF ID 36 SS 16V marine engine
1993

IVECO AIFO SpA

Viale dell'Industria, 15/17, I-20010 Pregnana Milanese, Milan, Italy

Telephone: +39 (2) 935101
Telex: 352328 AIFO I
Telefax: +39 (2) 9359 0029

Pietro Bruno, *Commercial Operations Manager*
E Bettina, *Marketing Manager*

Iveco Aifo manufactures a range of marine diesel engines from 44 to 626 kW. The accompanying table details the more powerful engines.

UPDATED

Type	No of cylinders and arrangement	Displacement	Output Light duty commercial	Output Continuous duty	Length basic engine	Weight
8361 SM 20	6-cylinder/L	8.1 l	140 kW	129 kW	1271 mm	700 kg
8361 SRM 32	6-cylinder/L	8.1 l	184 kW		1271 mm	893 kg
8210 M 22	6-cylinder/L	13.8 l		162 kW	1495 mm	1130 kg
8210 SRM 36	6-cylinder/L	13.8 l	265 kW	243 kW	1627 mm	1290 kg
8460 SRM 19	6-cylinder/L	9.5 l		140 kW	1478 mm	1130 kg
8460 SRM 28	6-cylinder/L	9.5 l		206 kW	1487 mm	1140 kg
8460 SRM 50	6-cylinder/L	9.5 l	270 kW		1487 mm	1140 kg
8281 M 32	8-cylinder/V	17.2 l	236 kW	206 kW	1291 mm	1455 kg
8281 SRM 44	8-cylinder/V	17.2 l		324 kW	1460 mm	1690 kg
8291 SRM 75	12-cylinder/V	25.8 l	626 kW	552 kW	2362 mm	2450 kg

M=Naturally aspirated
SRM=Turbocharged intercooled

The 331 kW Iveco Aifo 8460 SRM 50
1993

SEATEK SpA

Via Provinciale 71, 22040 Annone Brianza (Co), Italy

Telephone: +39 (341) 579335
Telefax: +39 (341) 579317

Ing P Molla, *Chairman*
Ing F Buzzi, *Managing Director*
P Fumagalli, *General Manager*
Dr A Bonomi, *Director*

SEATEK MARINE POWER USA

Harbour Town Marina, 850 North East 3rd Street, Suite 101, Dania, Florida 33004, USA

Telephone: +1 (305) 927 4266
Telefax: +1 (305) 927 4288

G Campau, *Director*

Builders of high-speed marine diesel engines which are noted for their power-to-weight and power-to-size ratios as well as fuel economy and low emissions.

In 1988 a Seatek powered boat won the Italian, European and World offshore Class One Championships and since this time Seatek powered craft have continually won Class One and Two offshore races worldwide.

Seatek Model 6.4V.9D diesel with dry weight per kW of 1.66 kg
1992

MODEL 6.4V.9D

Recently available as a production engine this four-cycle diesel has the following characteristics.

Principal Particulars
Length: 1540 mm
Width: 721 mm

Cylinder number: 6 in line
Dry weight: 800 kg
Compression ratio: 15:1
Power output: 463 kW
rpm: 3150
Fuel consumption: 210 g/kWh

MODEL 6.4V.10D

Dry weight: 780 kg
Power output: 530 kW
rpm: 3000

UPDATED

JAPAN

MITSUBISHI HEAVY INDUSTRIES LTD

5-1 Maranouchi 2-chome, Chiyoda-ku, Tokyo, Japan

Telephone: +81 (3) 3212 3111
Telex: 22443 J

S16R-S

In 1992 Mitsubishi announced the development of a new high-speed diesel engine aimed at the growing market of high performance marine vessels.

The S16R-S has been developed from the S16R series and has the following basic characteristics:

Principal Particulars
Type: direct injection, 4-cycle, water-cooled
Turbocharger: Mitsubishi TD15
Cylinders: 16 in 60° V
Base: 170 mm
Stroke: 180 mm
Displacement: 65.4 l output, MCR: 2100 kW at 2000 rpm and bmep 19.3 bar
Specific fuel consumption: 218 g/kWh
Weight: 5500 kg
Weight per kW: 2.54 kg/kW

Four of these engines power the Mitsubishi Super Shuttle 400 *Rainbow*, a 350 passenger, 40 knot catamaran.

NIIGATA ENGINEERING COMPANY LTD

4-1 Kasumigaseki 1-chome, Chiuoda-ku, Tokyo 100, Japan

Telephone: +81 (3) 3504 2473
Telefax: +81 (3) 3591 4764

Niigata has introduced a range of high speed marine diesel engines specifically for use in fast marine craft. The FX series, as they are known, were introduced in 1993 with the first engines being installed in the Superjet 30 craft constructed by Hitachi Zosen.

The company also builds the SEMT Pielstick PA 4 series diesels under licence.

NEW ENTRY

Type	Continuous output kW	Speed rpm	Length mm	Width max mm	Height max mm	Weight kg
8L16FX 1000	1950	2589	1130	1046	3300	—
12V16FX	1545	1950	2084	1360	1006	4500
16V16FX	2023	1950	2614	1360	1156	5500
12V26FX	3420	1150	3744	2215	1725	17300
16V26FX	4560	1150	4634	2325	1780	22 200
18V26FX	5149	1150	5080	2325	1780	24 600
12V32FX	5291	920	5000	2750	2420	29 500
16V32FX	7061	920	6010	2750	2420	38 600
12V41FX	900	700	6250	4000	2900	66 000
16V41FX	12 000	700	7750	4000	2900	85 000

Niigata 16V26FX
1995

NORWAY

KVÆRNER ENERGY A/S

PO Box 9277, Grønland, N-0134 Oslo, Norway

Telephone: +47 (22) 666666
Telex: 71650 KV N
Telefax: +47 (22) 193765

Odd Sandøy, *General Manager*

Kværner Energy supplies the high-speed craft market with complete propulsion modules, including gas-turbines and water-jets.

Kværner/General Electric's marine and industrial gas-turbine modules are compact, high performance power units. Each, from the LM 500 to the LM 6000, is a simple-cycle gas-turbine derived from highly reliable aircraft engines. In a wide range of applications they have provided years of troublefree, unattended operation. Built incorporating the latest design technologies and corrosion resistant materials, each GE LM engine provides maximum reliability and parts life along with outstanding performance.

Kværner Energy's workshop which specialises in the overhaul, repair and testing of gas-turbines is located at Ågotnes, on the outskirts of Bergen. This workshop is one of the few of its kind worldwide with authorisation from GE to carry out maintenance and servicing on the gas-turbines at all levels. Please see General Electric entry for technical details.

LM 500

The LM 500 is a simple-cycle, two-shaft gas-turbine, derived from GE's TF34 aircraft engine. This engine powers a Danish Navy patrol boat, a Japanese PG Class hydrofoil patrol craft and the Kværner Fjellstrand Flying Foilcat class passenger ferry.

LM 1600

The LM 1600 is a simple-cycle three-shaft gas-turbine engine, derived from GE's F404 engine. It is designed with 50 to 60 per cent fewer parts than other gas-turbines in its class. This engine has been selected as the power unit for two large high-speed vessels: the *Destriero* powered by three LM 1600 engines and Eco powered by one LM 1600 engine.

The LM 1600 is a fuel efficient simple-cycle

engine. Lightweight, compact and modular it combines the latest in blade-loading design, cooling technology and corrosion-resistant materials and coatings.

LM 2500

The LM 2500 is a simple-cycle two-shaft gas-turbine engine, derived from GE's military TF39 and the commercial bypass turbofan engines. Two LM 2500s in father and son configuration with two LM 1600s, will power the two 125 m Stena high-speed catamarans for delivery in 1995 and 1996. Its current experience base comprises over 250 ships and 19 navies.

Compact, lightweight and powerful the LM 2500 is adaptable to a broad range of ships. The LM 2500 has good reliability and fuel efficiency, it boasts an outstanding record for over 6 million hours of consistent, cost-effective, troublefree service for marine and industrial applications.

LM 6000

The LM 6000 is a simple-cycle, two-shaft high performance gas-turbine engine, derived from GE's most powerful and reliable aircraft engine, the CF6-80C2. Delivering more than 40 MW at over 40 per cent thermal efficiency, the powerful LM 6000 is very fuel efficient.

All components of the LM 6000 incorporate corrosion-resistant materials and coatings to provide maximum parts life and time between overhaul, regardless of the unit's operational environment.

UPDATED

Kværner/GE LM 2500 gas-turbine module nearing completion   *1994*

ULSTEIN TURBINE A/S

Kongsberg Næringspark, PO Box 1023, N-3601 Kongsberg, Norway

Telephone: +47 (32) 737300
Telefax: +47 (32) 737320

Jan Halle, *Managing Director*
Ivar Austrem, *Technical Manager*

The Ulstein Group of Norway has purchased the technology and patents related to the unique engine design of the Radial Turbine operations, which belonged to the former Kongsberg Vaapenfabrikk. Ulstein, a leading manufacturer of maritime machinery and equipment, has seen a large potential for the new, high power density turbine engine design for high-speed surface transportation in general and marine propulsion in particular.

Ulstein is implementing the Eurodyn turbine development plans through a new company, Ulstein Turbine A/S, situated in Oslo. Ulstein Turbine A/S is structured as a design and development company with some 15 turbine engine experts employed.

When the new turbine engine is in production, it will have a positive effect on more than 30 companies in the Ulstein Group, especially for Ulstein Bergen A/S, the only remaining Norwegian owned diesel engine manufacturer.

EURODYN

The purpose of the Eurodyn programme, designated EU159 in the European Eureka projects frame, is to develop and produce a high efficiency industrial gas-turbine in the 2 to 3 MW power range. The engine is intended for applications in the fast surface transport market such as train or boat propulsion, as well as in the more traditional market for gas-turbines of electric generation and drive of pumps or compressors.

In this Franco-Scandinavian co-operation Turbomeca (France) holds 50 per cent, Ulstein (Norway) 30 per cent and Volvo Aero Corporation AB (Sweden) 20 per cent.

The efficiency targets set for the Eurodyn are impressive for turbines in this power class. An efficiency of 35 per cent is the ultimate goal with an interim target of 33 per cent, making the compact and lightweight Eurodyn turbine a formidable competitor for existing turbines and high-speed diesel engines.

The Eurodyn engine is particularly well suited to high-speed craft propulsion, such as catamarans and surface effect ships.

The engine provides a performance characteristic that is superior to any known, simple-cycle, gas-turbine of comparable size. It is a fully marinised industrial engine of rugged design.

A significant milestone was reached late in 1992 with the first engine test of the Eurodyn demonstrators. The first tests successfully demonstrated

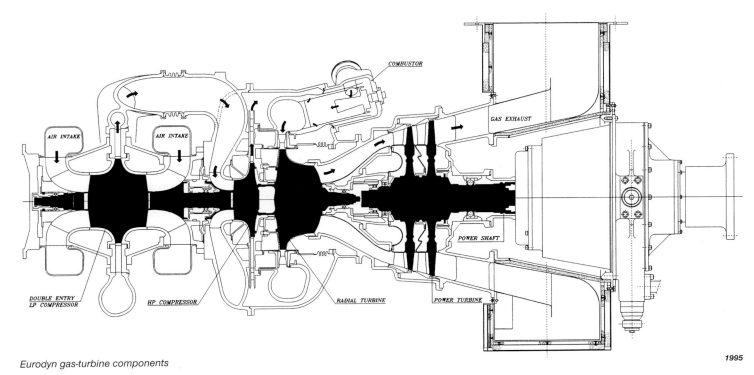

Eurodyn gas-turbine components   *1995*

the high performance characteristics of the engine. The demonstrator engines were subjected to an extensive testing programme during 1993 in France and Norway.

The first pilot applications are underway, with pre-serial engines being tested in industrial, marine and railway applications. The market launch will be in 1995.

The high pressure ratio compressor, comprising a dual entry first stage and a single entry second stage, was developed by Turbomeca, which also supplies the auxiliary gearbox and engine accessories.

The engine hot section, featuring a multiple can low-emissions combustor with multi-fuel capability and a radial gas generator turbine was developed by Ulstein Turbine A/S, a company within the Ulstein Group. It also supplied the compact reduction gearbox, adaptable to both industrial and marine applications.

The inter turbine duct and free power turbine section comprising two axial stages were developed by Volvo Aero Corporation AB and its subsidiary Volvo Aero Turbines AB. They are also responsible for the engine management and fuel control system.

Each partner will manufacture its respective parts and the final engine assembly and testing will be performed in Norway and France.

The new turbine engine will have lower fuel consumption than any other turbine engine in its power range of 2 to 3 MW. The engine will be compact and will weigh significantly less than the lightweight diesels now used for high-speed surface applications. Furthermore, the engine will be largely vibration free, have a very low noise level and most importantly, will satisfy the strictest exhaust emissions regulations.

Principal Particulars

Length overall: 3260 mm
Height overall: 1300 mm
Weight: 1900-2300 kg (inc' gearbox), depending on equipment specification
Power range: 2200-2900 kW (ISO conditions)
Thermal efficiency: 33-35%
Airflow: 11.5 kg/s
Specific fuel consumption: 240-250 g/kWh

Ulstein has built a UT 905 catamaran containing two Eurodyn engines for propulsion. The vessel will enter an extensive sea trial period in early 1995. The Norwegian Navy is joining the trials to verify the engine for future navy programmes.

UPDATED

The Eurodyn gas-turbine

1995

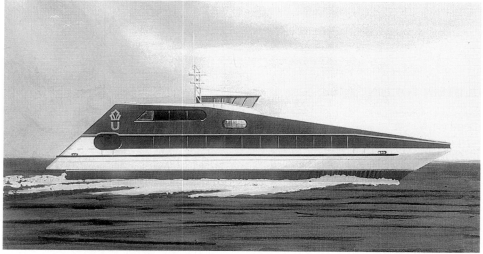

Ulstein test vessel, UT 905 catamaran

1995

SWEDEN

SCANIA

Industrial and Marine Engines
S-151 87 Södertälje, Sweden

Telephone: +46 (8553) 81000
Telex: 10200 SCANIA S
Telefax: +46 (8553) 82993

Scania marine diesels cover a power output range of 153 to 497 kW with weights of 875 to 1400 kg. Power test code ISO 3046.

Scania marine engines have recently been radically redeveloped and constitute an almost new range, still however, built for economical operation and long service life.

Scania claims that the excellent performance and low fuel consumption of its engines result from new injection equipment, carefully optimised turbochargers and a cylinder design with a top liner ring (Scania Saver Ring) which is complementary to the Keystone-type piston ring. Together they eliminate coking, keep piston ring grooves clean, prevent bore polishing and reduce lube oil consumption by more than 50 per cent.

A recent and interesting application of Scania

Marine diesel engines
RATINGS

Engine type with heat exchanger	Turbo	Inter-cooled	Displace-ment dm³	Config-uration	Propulsion	
					High-speed workboats, patrol, and so on kW (hp) rpm	Specific fuel consumption at 1500 rpm g/kWh
DS 9	T	-	8.5	6 L	195(265)2200	201
DSI 9	T	I	8.5	6 L	220(300)2200	-
DS 11	T	-	11	6 L	242(329)2100	210
DSI 11	T	I	11	6 L	288(392)2100	206
DSI 11	T	I	11	6 L	315(428)2100	204
DSI 11	T	I	11	6 L	368(500)2100	207
DSI 14	T	I	14.2	V 8	356(484)2100	207
DSI 14	T	I	14.2	V 8	414(563)2100	206
DSI 14	T	I	14.2	V 8	460(625)2100	213
DSI 14	T	I	14.2	V 8	497(675)2100	213
with keel cooling						
DS 9	T	-	8.5	6 L	165(224)2200	207
DS 9	T	-	8.5	6 L	195(265)2200	208
DS 11	T	-	11	6 L	242(329)2100	210
DSI 11	T	I	11	6 L	286(389)2100	212
DSI 14	T	-	14.2	V 8	356(484)2100	207
DSI 14	T	I	14.2	V 8	414(563)2100	206

diesels is the use of two DSI 11 engines in the FBM Marine Thames Class RTL Hydrocat catamarans for the London City Airport service. These 62 passenger, 26 knot catamarans have extremely slender hulls to minimise wash, and high power-to-weight ratio engines are essential for the same reason.

Turbocharged and intercooled models feature a new high efficiency charge air-cooler, matched on marine engines to a two-compartment heat exchanger and effective gallery cooling of the piston crown. The crown is anodised for extended resistance to fatigue.

WEIGHTS

Engine type	Max dimensions (mm)			Weight dry (kg)
	Length	Width	Height	
with heat exchanger				
DS 9	1352	786	977	895
DSI 9	1413	786	977	900
DS 11	1556	750	1041	1100
DSI 11	1556	750	1104	1115
DSI 14	1302	1172	1176	1400
with keel cooling				
DS 9	1330	754	1084	875
DS 11	1493	715	1003	1010
DSI 11	1493	715	1104	1035
DSI 14	1302	1172	1176	1325

Weights and dimensions. Quoted values are only a guide; there are variations for each engine type. Weights exclude oil and water.

UPDATED

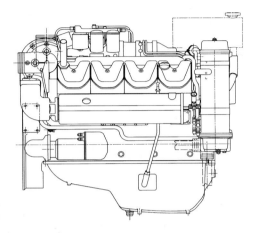
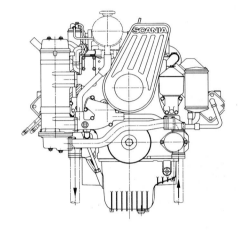

DSI 14 Marine
1988

VOLVO PENTA AB

S-405 08 Gothenburg, Sweden

Telephone: +46 (31) 235460
Telex: 20755 PENTA S
Telefax: +46 (31) 510595

The Board of Volvo Penta:
Christer Zetterberg, *Chairman*
Jan Walldorf, *President*
Olle Johansson, *Director*
Anders Lindstrom, *Director*
Bo Egerdal, *Director*
Hans Eric Ovin, *Director*
Union Group: Bengt Segeheden
Gösta Gendenberg

Executive Marine Management:
Jan Walldorf, *President*
Orvar Lundberg, *Director Marine Commercial*

AB Volvo Penta designs, manufactures and markets engines, transmissions, accessories and equipment for marine and industrial use.

Part of the Volvo Group, the sales of Volvo Penta engines account for around four per cent of sales within the transport equipment sector. The engines are used in ferries, pilot vessels, fishing boats and all types of leisure craft, as well as for industrial propulsion or power generation applications.

Production facilities are in the USA and Brazil plus four locations in Sweden. Volvo Penta products are sold in 100 countries worldwide. Approximately 2600 people are employed either directly or indirectly by Volvo Penta.

Volvo Penta diesels for commercial craft can provide up to 550 hp. The company has updated the entire engine range covering two-, three- and four-cylinder commercially rated diesels as well as the in-line six series.

New to the range are the heavy diesels TAMD 162, TAMD 122 and TAMD 102.

All eight units in the 31 and 41 series feature direct injection which reduces thermal stress, heat and pressure loss resulting in lower fuel consumption and longer life expectancy. Fuel consumption is

Volvo Penta TAMD 41
1988

around 15 per cent less than with the equivalent prechamber ignition diesels. The new turbocharger is fresh water-cooled and the pistons are oil-cooled to increase engine life.

Further up the power range are the six and seven litre models TAMD 61 and TAMD 71. Both are turbocharged, after-cooled in-line, six diesels for which the latest three-dimensional computer techniques have been used as a means towards reducing engine weight and providing optimum rigidity. Interesting design features of the new 16 litre in-line six-cylinder diesel engine TAMD 162 include efficient cooling of the cylinder head with four valves per cylinder, for high efficiency. The cylinder head is bolted to the block without gaskets for increased service life and low maintenance costs. A new fast injection

pump on the cold side of the engine gives good economy and environmental properties in combination with a smoke limiter.

A responsive turbo and after-cooler with low internal resistance gives efficient combustion and cleaner exhausts, as well as increasing engine service life.

The new TAMD 122 has between four and seven per cent higher power output than the previous 121 generation.

The new technical features of the engine include new cylinder head and gaskets, new cylinder linings with flame barriers and improved sealing. The engine has a new injection pump with smoke limiter and new, five-hole nozzles for better combustion and less smoke.

Volvo Penta TAMD 122   **1988**

Volvo Penta TAMD 102A   **1993**

The new 10 litre engine for workboats has the designation TAMD 102 and will be of particular significance for sales to Japan, a market where Volvo has been active for 30 years. With its light duty configuration of 297 kW and its bore of 120 mm, the engine meets the requirements made by the authorities for power units fitted in light, fast fishing boats in Japan.

VOLVO PENTA THREE TO TWELVE LITRE MARINE PROPULSION ENGINES

TAMD 31

	hp	kW	rpm
Propeller shaft output ISO 3046,			
light duty	124	91	3800
medium duty	105	77	3250

Weight: 385 kg including MS4 gearbox
Displacement: 2.39 l

TAMD 41

	hp	kW	rpm
Propeller shaft output ISO 3046,			
light duty	192	141	3800
medium duty	163	120	3250
heavy duty	145	107	2500

Weight: 465 kg including MS4 gearbox
Displacement: 3.59 l

TAMD 61

	hp	kW	rpm
Flywheel output,			
light duty	306	225	2800
medium duty	228	168	2500

Weight: 760 kg excluding gearbox
Displacement: 5.48 l

TAMD 71

	hp	kW	rpm
Flywheel output,			
light duty	357	263	2500
medium duty	292	213	2500
heavy duty	222	163	2000

Weight: 880 kg excluding gearbox
Displacement: 6.73 l

TMD 102

	hp	kW	rpm
Flywheel output,			
medium duty	272	200	2000
heavy duty	238	175	1800

Weight: 1140 kg excluding gearbox
Displacement: 9.6 l

TAMD 102

	hp	kW	rpm
Flywheel output,			
light duty	400	297	2200
medium duty	360	268	2000

Weight: 1190 kg excluding gearbox
Displacement: 9.6 l

TAMD 122

	hp	kW	rpm
Flywheel output,			
light duty	450	331	2000
medium duty	400	294	1900
heavy duty	380	279	1800

Volvo Penta TAMD 71 in-line, six turbocharged and after-cooled seven litre engine   **1988**

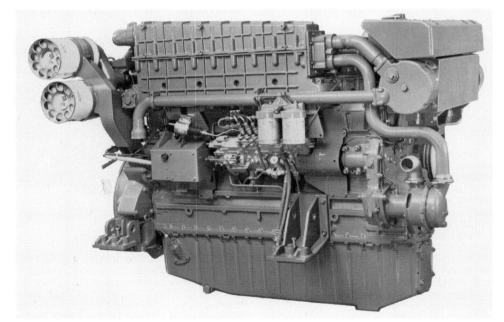

Volvo Penta TAMD 162   **1989**

Weight: 1300 kg excluding gearbox
Displacement: 11.98 l

TAMD 162

	hp	kW	rpm
Flywheel output,			
light duty	550	405	1900
medium duty	550	405	1900
heavy duty	510	375	1800

Weight: 1705 kg excluding reverse gear
Displacement: 16.12 l

The following definitions define the duty ratings given in the accompanying table.

LD: Light Duty

Engines with this power setting are for applications where rated power for rated speed is utilised for short periods only, followed by cruising at reduced speed; also when operating time is short and does not exceed 500 hours per year.

Examples: Certain patrol boats, fire boats, rescue boats and charter craft.

MD: Medium Duty

Engines with this power setting are intended for applications where rated power at rated speed is utilised during part of the operating time only (up to ⅓), followed by cruising at reduced speed. Operating time should not exceed 2000 hours per year, or on average, one shift per working day.

Examples: Patrol boats, pilot boats, police boats and certain fishing vessels.

HD: Heavy Duty

Engines with this power setting are intended for applications where neither LD nor MD applies and rated power at rated speed could be needed continuously. No interruption or load cycling is expected other than for service and maintenance.

Examples: Tugboats, ferries, fishing boats and most commercial applications in displacement vessels.

UPDATED

UNITED KINGDOM

GEC ALSTHOM PAXMAN DIESELS LTD

A Management Company of GEC ALSTHOM Diesels Ltd

Paxman Works, Hythe Hill, Colchester, Essex CO1 2HW, UK

Telephone: +44 (1206) 795151
Telex: 98151 GENERAL G
Telefax: +44 (1206) 797869

GEC ALSTHOM Paxman Diesels manufactures compact high-speed diesel engines suitable for high-speed marine craft propulsion duties, backed up by comprehensive worldwide product support.

The Paxman range of well proven Valenta and Vega engines was joined in 1993 by the VP 185, of which the 12-cylinder version was launched first. This new range of engines is a breakthrough in low-cost, low maintenance high-speed diesel engines in the 1760 to 3960 kW power range, and will eventually be available in 8-, 16- and 18-cylinder versions as well as the 12-cylinder engine shown. To support all engine and component manufacture Paxman has invested heavily in new design and manufacturing technology.

Paxman Valenta 18 CM
1994

Paxman Vega 16 CM
1994

VALENTA	Maximum Brake power	rpm	Length	Width	Height Weight	Dry
6 CM	1020 kW	1600 rpm	2673 mm	1070 mm	1943 mm	4363 kg
8 CM	1515 kW	1600 rpm	2133 mm	1460 mm	2273 mm	6108 kg
12 CM	2480 kW	1640 rpm	2497 mm	1568 mm	2338 mm	8590 kg
16 CM	3300 kW	1640 rpm	2953 mm	1568 mm	2466 mm	10 706 kg
18 CM	3710 kW	1640 rpm	3245 mm	1575 mm	2397 mm	11 670 kg
VEGA						
12 CM	1310 kW	1745 rpm	2129 mm	1595 mm	1738 mm	4996 kg
16 CM	1745 kW	1800 rpm	2816 mm	1686 mm	2092 mm	6087 kg

Measurements and weights are for complete engines ready for installation. These may vary slightly depending on application.

12 VP 185						
12 VP 185	2611 kW	1950 rpm	2646 mm	1440 mm	2030 mm	7119 kg

12 VP 185 measurements and weights are for complete engine ready for installation.

Paxman 12VP 185

1995

	Valenta (60° V)	Vega (60° V)	VP 185 (90° V)
Housing	High grade cast-iron or fabricated steel	High grade cast-iron	High grade cast-iron
Crankshaft and main bearings	Forged steel nitride hardened carried in tin aluminium steel-backed bearing shells	Forged steel induction hardened carried in lead bronze steel-backed bearing shells	Nitride hardened forged steel carried in tin aluminium steel-backed bearings
Connecting rods	Fork and blade rods with steel-backed aluminium tin, lined forked rod big end bearings and lead bronze lined blade rod bearings	Side by side with lead bronze steel-backed big end bearings	Side by side with tin aluminium steel-backed big end bearings
Pistons	Aluminium alloy with top compression ring fitted in an 'Alfin' bonded cast-iron insert	Aluminium alloy with top compression ring fitted in an 'Alfin' bonded bonded cast-iron insert	Cast-iron
Cylinder head	Cast-iron with four valve direct injection system	Cast-iron with four valves and unit pump injector	Cast-iron with four valves and unit pump injector
Cylinder liner	Wet type seamless steel tube, chrome-plated and honeycombed for oil retention	Wet type seamless steel tube, chrome-plated and honeycombed for oil retention	Centrifugally cast-iron
Fuel injection	Single unit pumps driven from engine via pump camshaft, multi-hole injectors retained by clamp to heads	Combined fuel pump and injector unit operated by pushrods from engine camshaft	Combined fuel pump and injector unit operated by pushrods from engine camshaft
Governor	Electronic, hydraulic or pneumatic	Electronic, hydraulic or pneumatic	Electronic or hydraulic
Pressure charging and intercooling	Single water-cooled exhaust gas turbocharger, air to water intercooler	Single air-cooled exhaust gas turbocharger mounted on each bank Intercooled using seawater or jacket water	Two stage exhaust gas turbochargers Four interchangeable low pressure and two high pressure turbochargers, mounted in a common water jacketed housing inter-cooled and after-cooled
Fresh water cooling	Single water pump driven from free end, thermostatic control	Two pumps driven from free end, thermostatically controlled	Primary and secondary fresh water cooling system each with their own water pump driven from the free end. Thermostatically controlled
Lubrication	Wet sump, single pump pressurised system with external-mounted oil coolers, full flow single or duplex oil filters	Wet sump, externally mounted oil pump pressurised system with jacket water oil cooler on each bank. Three canister oil filters to each bank	Wet sump, externally mounted oil pump, pressurised system, thermostatically controlled, with oil cooler. Canister oil filters
Exhaust	Single outlet from turbocharger, water-cooled manifolds	Dry manifold system with individual outlet from each turbocharger	Dry manifold with air/water jacket cooling
Starting	Air, electric or hydraulic starting	Air or electric starting	Electric or air starting

Recent customers for high-speed craft include:
Hyundai Heavy Industries
US Navy (Cyclone class PC)
Vosper Thornycroft (fast strike craft)
Batservice 49 m catamaran ferry
McTay Marine Customs Patrol Boat
HM Customs and Excise (UK)
Oceanfast 146′ Superyatch

GEC ALSTHOM RUSTON DIESELS LTD

A Management Company of GEC ALSTHOM Diesels Ltd

Vulcan Works, Newton-le-Willows, Merseyside WA12 8RU, UK

Telephone: +44 (1925) 225151
Telex: 627131-2
Telefax: +44 (1925) 222055

In late 1988 GEC ALSTHOM Ruston diesels received an order for four 16RK270 engines to power *Hoverspeed Great Britain*, a 74 m wave-piercing catamaran built by InCat Tasmania. This was the first large passenger/car carrying high-speed ferry to enter commercial service and successfully obtain the Blue Riband award for a record transatlantic crossing on its delivery voyage to the UK. The success of *Hoverspeed Great Britain* led owners Sea Containers to continue using Ruston engines for their subsequent vessels and Condor and Stena Sealink to specify the engines from their catamarans. The first catamarans were powered by four 16-cylinder engines each producing 3650 kW at 750 rpm and the later vessels producing 4050 kW at 762 rpm all directly coupled to the water-jet propulsion units.

These vessels have accumulated over 250 000 engine hours during service in a wide variety of sea conditions in the English Channel, Irish Sea, Baltic, Mediterranean, Europe and in South America and Australia providing Ruston with a unique experience of fast ferry propulsion applications.

Ruston power continues to be specified by owners/operators with orders in hand for two new 78 m catamarans which are a logical development of the earlier 74 m vessels. These are to be powered by four 16RK270 engines producing 4320 kW brake power at 782 rpm, in a direct drive installation.

Following the success of the Ruston engines in their first generation SeaCats, Sea Containers has demonstrated its confidence by specifying them for

Ruston 16 RK270 engine

1995

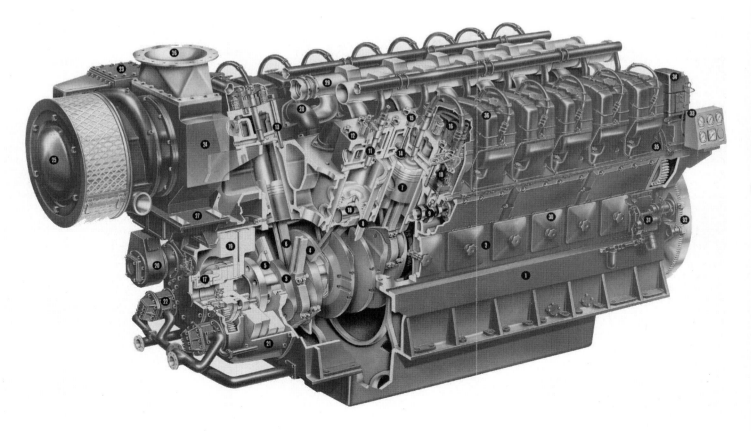

Cutaway drawing of Ruston 16 RK270
Key: **1** *Bedplate;* **2** *Crankcase;* **3** *Crankshaft web;* **4** *Crankshaft balance weight;* **5** *Main bearing cap;* **6** *Connecting rod;* **7** *Piston;* **8** *Cylinder liner;* **9** *Camshaft;* **10** *Fuel injection pump;* **11** *Injector;* **12** *Cylinder head;* **13** *Cylinder head stud;* **14** *Inlet valve;* **15** *Valve spring;* **16** *Rocker lever;* **17** *Auxiliary drive gear;* **18** *Gudgeon pin;* **19** *Viscous vibration dampers;* **20** *Seawater pump;* **21** *Pump drive casing;* **22** *Lubricating oil pump;* **23** *Charge cooler;* **24** *Turbocharger;* **25** *Air intake filter/silencer;* **26** *Exhaust uptake adaptor;* **27** *Turbocharger/charge cooler bracket;* **28** *Air inlet bend;* **29** *Exhaust manifold branch;* **30** *Crankcase door;* **31** *Starter motor;* **32** *Flywheel;* **33** *Instrument panel;* **34** *Governor;* **35** *Hand throttle lever;* **36** *Valve gear cover.*

1992

the first, with an option for four more, 79 m Super SeaCats to be built by Austal Ships Pty Ltd of Australia. The four Ruston 16-cylinder engines, each producing 5500 kW at 1000 rpm, will drive water-jets through gearboxes to provide a service speed of 39 knots.

Ruston engines provide an output of 750 to 5500 kW at speeds of 720 to 1000 rpm, from a range of 6-, 8-, 12- and 16-cylinder engines. The RK270 is suitable for a wide variety of applications including industrial power generation, marine propulsion, marine auxiliary power generation and rail traction duties.

GEC ALSTHOM Ruston Diesels offers comprehensive support packages tailored to the demands of both the shipbuilder and shipowner to ensure that projects are completed on time and to specification. Full after sales service programmes are available to meet the individual operator's specific requirements worldwide.

RK270

The RK270 follows the proven design features of the renowned RK range of engines, with the bedplate manufactured from a high grade mechanite iron casting. Robust construction with transverse diaphragms for each main bearing provides rigid support for the crankshaft.

Crankshaft: The crankshaft is machined from a single piece alloy steel forging, produced by the continuous grain flow method with bolted on balance weights and an integrally forged coupling flange to which the flywheel is registered and bolted. The camshaft drive gear is split to facilitate replacement.

Bearings: The main bearings are pre-finished, steel-backed shells lined with high grade bearing material having a lead-tin surface flashing to facilitate running-in. The bearings are retained in the housings by caps drilled to direct oil to the bearings. These caps are located transversely in large registers in the bedplate and held in position by studs and nuts. The bearings are easily removable through the crankcase doors.

Crankcase: The cylinder housing with integral air chest is machined from a rigid grey iron casting, with transverse diaphragms between each cylinder to provide water compartments around the cylinder liners. Detachable doors facilitate access to the connecting rod and main bearings and to the camshaft and governor drive gear train.

Explosion relief valves are appropriately positioned on the crankcase doors and on the integrally cast charge air chest.

Cylinder liners: Separate wet type liners cast in alloy iron are flanged at their upper ends and secured by the cylinder heads. The lower ends of the liners are located in the crankcase and sealed by synthetic rubber rings. The liners are machined all over and the bore is hone finished to provide good piston liner compatibility for long service life.

Connecting rods: A feature of the connecting rods is an oblique split large end with the cap located by serrations on the joint face, optimised to reduce bending and shear loads across the joint. As a result, distortion of the large end housing is minimised.

The small end features a stepped configuration large diameter pin to distribute the load evenly between piston and connecting rod, allowing operation at very high firing pressures.

Cylinder head: Individual cylinder heads are manufactured from iron castings. Each cylinder head carries two inlet and two exhaust valves and a side entry air inlet port which is connected to the crankcase air manifold.

Piston: The standard piston is of single piece aluminium alloy construction with a combustion bowl of the Hesselman design. Cooling oil is fed from the connecting rod, through the small end bush and drillings in the gudgeon pin and piston body to the cast-in cooling gallery. For some duties, including heavy fuel operation, a steel crown, aluminium skirt and two-piece piston is used.

Valve gear: Each pair of valves is operated via short stiff pushrods and conventional rockers. The pushrods are driven from the side entry camshafts, one per bank of cylinders via roller cam followers. Hardened steel cams are used throughout.

A single shaft for each cylinder has few component parts and removal and replacement of cam clusters is simple and straightforward. The cam-

shafts are side-mounted in the crankcase and can be easily inserted or removed from the side of the engine.

The camshafts and auxiliary drive are driven through a train of hardened and ground steel spur gears from the crankshaft split gear.

Flywheel: The mild steel flywheel, suitable for mounting flexible couplings when required, is fitted with a ring gear for starting and hand barring and is statically balanced before bolting to the integrally forged crankshaft flange.

Governor: A sensitive hydraulic governor is bevel gear driven from the camshaft.

Overspeeding is prevented by a separate safety trip mechanism which returns the control shaft to the 'no fuel' position.

For generator drive applications an electric load-sensing governor is employed.

Auxiliary drives: Auxiliaries are driven from the free end of the engine through a spring drive and spur gears. The standard arrangement includes one water pump for the jacket water, one water pump for the charge-air cooler and lubricating oil cooler circuits and a gear type lubricating oil pump.

An extension shaft may be fitted to allow power to be taken from the free end of the engine.

Instrumentation: An engine-mounted instrument panel is provided to indicate engine speed, lubricating oil pressure and temperature, jacket water pressure and air chest pressure.

Engines are fitted with thermocouples for indicating cylinder exhaust outlet, turbine inlet and outlet temperatures. A multi-point indicator with compen-

sating multi-core cabling is supplied for off engine mountings.

Turbochargers: Turbochargers and charge-air coolers are fitted as standard equipment. The standard location of the single turbocharger is at the free end of the engine. However, a flywheel end-mounted turbocharger may be offered at customer's request. For rail traction applications the turbocharger is mounted above the alternator.

A high efficiency compressor is driven by an axial flow exhaust gas-turbine and delivers air to the air chest through a charge-air cooler. Lubricating oil to the plain bearings and cooling water is provided from the engine systems.

By careful turbocharger matching, engine output is achieved with a favourable air to fuel ratio resulting in low thermal loading.

Exhaust manifold: Exhaust manifolds, of cast-iron construction, feature bolted flanges with heavy-duty joints. Where required, these are lagged with non-asbestos material, protected by a metallic skin.

Lubrication: The system includes single or twin engine driven oil pumps, full flow filtration, thermostat and oil cooler. The oil pressure is controlled by one or two spring-loaded relief valves.

Cooling system: The jacket cooling system is thermostatically controlled and includes an engine driven water pump.

Starting system: Air or electric motor starting is standard, using one or two motors, operating via spur gears onto the flywheel ring gear which is also employed for hand barring.

Fuel injection: The fuel injection system features

Number of cylinders		6	8	12	16
Cylinder configuration		In-line	In-line	45° V	45° V
Dry weight (with flywheel)	kg	13 000	17 500	22 000	26 000
Oil sump capacity	l	340	410	654	691
Length	mm	4020	5300	5100	5600
Width	mm	1990	1700	2100	2050
Height	mm	2800	3050	2900	3050
Turbocharger no Position		one free end	one free end	two free end	two free end and drive end
Charge cooler no Position		one free end	one free end	two free end	two free end and drive end

Marine unrestricted service power

Engine	Speed rpm	Distillate Brake power kW	bhp	Electrical kW
6 RK270	750	1555	2085	1445
	900	1875	2515	1655
	1000	2063	2765	1790
8 RK270	750	2075	2783	1925
	900	2500	3350	2210
	1000	2750	3688	2390
12 RK270	750	3110	4170	2890
	900	3750	5030	3310
	1000	4125	5530	3580
16 RK270	750	4150	5565	3850
	900	5000	6700	4420
	1000	5500	7375	4780
20 RK270	750	519	6955	4956
	900	6250	8375	5969
	1000	6875	9212	6566

Electrical power output will depend on actual generator efficiency

Name	Type	Nos of engines
Hoverspeed Great Britain	InCat 74 m	4 × 3650 kW at 750 rpm
Atlantic II	InCat 74 m	4 × 3650 kW at 750 rpm
Isle of Man	InCat 74 m	4 × 3650 kW at 750 rpm
SeaCat Denmark	InCat 74 m	4 × 4050 kW at 760 rpm
SeaCat Scotland	InCat 74 m	4 × 3650 kW at 750 rpm
Condor 10	InCat 74 m	4 × 4050 kW at 760 rpm
Stena Sea Lynx II	InCat 78 m	4 × 4050 kW at 760 rpm
Condor 11	InCat 78 m	4 × 4320 kW at 782 rpm
—	InCat 78 m	4 × 4320 kW at 782 rpm
Super SeaCat	Austal 79 m	4 × 5500 kW at 1000 rpm

(Option for four more Super SeaCat craft)

individual pumps and injectors for each cylinder. Governing is by a Regulateurs Europa or equivalent unit, the governor drive being taken from the camshaft via bevel gears.

Technical Data (RK270)
Type: Turbocharged and charge-cooled diesel
Cycle: 4-stroke
Bore: 270 mm
Stroke: 305 mm
Compression ratio: 12.8
Mean piston speed: 10.16 m/s at 1000 rpm
Standard rotation: Counter-clockwise looking on the drive end of the crankshaft
Standard Equipment
Flywheel
Air filter/silencer mounted on turbocharger
Air motor starting
Crankcase explosion relief valves
Water to air charge-air coolers
Jacket water cooler

Lubricating oil cooler
Speed governor - type 1100
Lubricating oil pressure relief valve
Lubricating oil filter:
  simplex type for generator sets
  duplex type for propulsion
Lubricating oil pressure pump, engine driven
Fuel oil filter - duplex type
Pre-start lubricating oil priming pump
Engine cooling water pump, engine driven
Electric tachometer
Engine-mounted instrument panel
Remote exhaust temperature indicator
Charge-air temperature alarm
Jacket water temperature alarm and shut down
Lubricating oil pressure alarm and shut down
Hand barring gear
Lagged exhaust manifold
Cylinder pressure relief valve/compression release valve and indicator

Exhaust silencer non-spark arrester type
Exhaust uptake adaptor and bellows
Tools for routine maintenance
Optional Equipment
Auto starting
Reverse direction of rotation
Alternative type of speed governor
Power take off from free end of crankshaft
Seawater/secondary water pump, engine driven
Overload switch
Fuel limiter
Residual fuel build
Centrifugal bypass lubricating oil filter
Alternative exhaust silencer, for example spark arrester/improved attenuation
Turbocharger mounted at drive end (6-, 8- and 12-cylinder)
Handed engine control
Tools for engine overhaul

UPDATED

PERKINS GROUP OF COMPANIES

Frank Perkins Way, Eastfield, Peterborough, Lincolnshire PE1 5NA, UK

Telephone: +44 (1733) 67474
Telex: 32501 PERKEN G
Telefax: +44 (1733) 582240

J A Gilroy, *Managing Director*

The Condor family, built at the Perkins Shrewsbury plant, is the latest addition to the Perkins range of marine engines. Three ratings are available: 700 bhp (522 kW) and 800 bhp (597 kW) for pleasure applications and 600 bhp (448 kW) for light duty commercial usage.

CONDOR M800Ti

Type: 8 cylinders in 90 'V' form, water-cooled
Power, max: 597 kW at 2300 rpm
Bore: 135 mm
Stroke: 152 mm
Capacity: 17.41 l
Cycle: 4-stroke
Aspiration: turbocharged, charge-cooled
Combustion system: direct injection
Rotation: anti-clockwise viewed from rear
Fuel pump: 8 element in-line with mechanical governor
Operating angle: maximum continuous operating angle, 20 nose up, 8 nose down, 30 thwartships
Weight, dry: 1818 kg with ZF MPM 1RM350A and PL gearbox.

Standard Equipment
Fresh water heat exchanger cooled engine with gear driven, self-priming raw and fresh water pumps
Fresh water-cooled exhaust manifolds
Twin fresh water-cooled turbochargers
Raw water-cooled charge-air coolers
Dry type air cleaners. Closed circuit engine breather system

Perkins Condor engine   *1991*

High inclination lube oil sump with lube oil drain facility
Fresh water-cooled lube oil system with spin-on lube oil filters
SAE 1 flywheel housing with flywheel suitable for range of marine reverse/reduction transmissions
Adjustable engine support brackets
Engine stop solenoid
Single water-injected exhaust outlet

CONDOR M700Ti
Details as for M800Ti but max power is 522 kW at 2100 rpm and dry weight is 1818 kg with ZF 1RM 350 A gearbox.

UPDATED

ROLLS-ROYCE INDUSTRIAL AND MARINE GAS TURBINES LTD

Ansty, Coventry, West Midlands CV7 9JR, UK

Telephone: +44 (1203) 624000
Telex: 37645
Telefax: +44 (1203) 623250

Jim Roberts, *Head of Marketing*

Rolls-Royce offers a range of aero-derived industrial and marine gas-turbines suitable for a wide variety of applications. Over 2700 marine and industrial gas turbines have been sold or are on the order book world-wide with over 42 million operating hours' experience. Twenty-five navies and civil operators have selected Rolls-Royce engines.

Spey SM1C module
1991

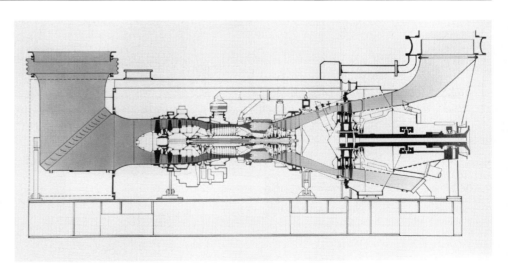

MARINE SPEY

The Marine Spey module is a complete marine propulsion package for all types of large fast ferry and large high-speed surface transport.

It is a highly efficient fully marinised machine based on the Aero Spey and incorporating much of the state-of-the-art technology incorporated in the Aero Tay which is a development of the Spey.

There are two types available for light craft, both offering high thermal efficiency (in excess of 35 per cent). They are designed to provide the main propulsion power for all current and future large fast ferries, in addition to their existing role of providing high-speed and cruise propulsion power for all types of fast attack craft, patrol vessels, frigates and destroyers.

The Marine Spey module is a complete marine propulsion package for all types of large fast ferry and large high-speed surface transport.

The unit comprises a marinised version of the Spey aero-engine which powers the BAC 1-11 and Fokker F28. Both aircraft are used predominantly in short haul and shuttle operations which are very similar in their operating profile to any ferry operation.

The marinisation of the Aero Spey and the design and development of the complete Marine Spey module has been carried out by Rolls-Royce under contract from the British Ministry of Defence initially to provide a robust reliable naval main propulsion engine. Rolls-Royce pioneered the concept of aero-derivative marine gas-turbines over 35 years ago, current sales total over 1000 marine engines to 25

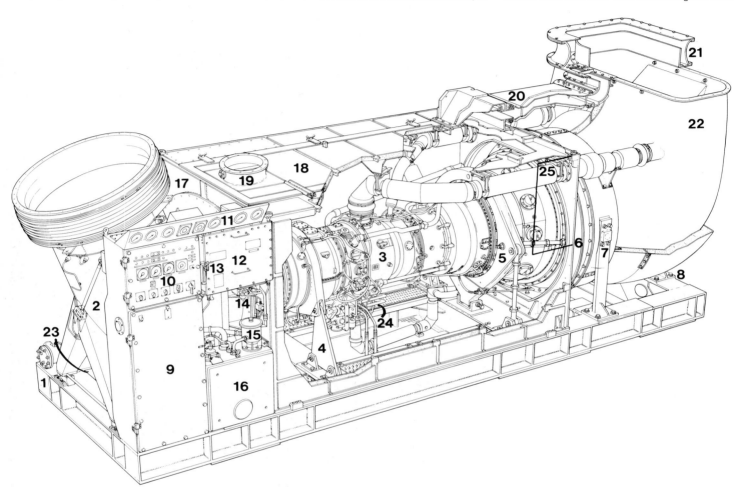

Rolls-Royce Marine Spey SM1C **1** *Baseplate;* **2** *Air intake cascade;* **3** *Gas generator;* **4** *Gas generator front mounting;* **5** *Gas generator rear mounting;* **6** *Power turbine;* **7** *Power turbine front mounting;* **8** *Power turbine rear mounting;* **9** *Plant control unit;* **10** *Local control panel;* **11** *Auxiliary gauge panel;* **12** *Fuel system enclosure;* **13** *Emergency shutdown lever;* **14** *Manual throttle control;* **15** *Air/oil separator;* **16** *Lubricating oil tank;* **17** *Enclosure;* **18** *Hinged roof panel for gas generator removal;* **19** *Enclosure ventilation inlet duct;* **20** *Enclosure ventilation exhaust duct;* **21** *Exhaust bellows assembly;* **22** *Exhaust volute;* **23** *Module's self-contained gas generator lubricating oil system, cooler and filters;* **24** *Spey engine's starter motor;* **25** *Fire extinguisher system*

1993

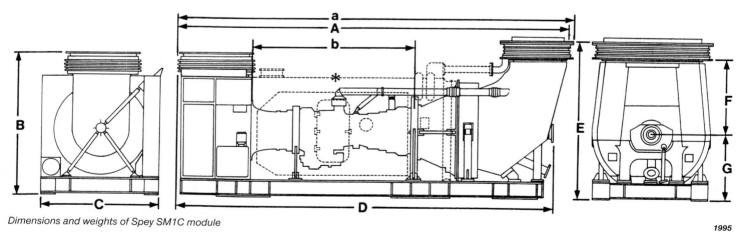

Dimensions and weights of Spey SM1C module

1995

Notes

A = 7500 mm
B = 2800 mm
C = 2285 mm
D = 7320 mm
E = 3090 mm
F = 1475 mm
G = 1300 mm

a. SM1C module complete
(dry, inclusive of gas generator): 23.4 tonnes
b. SM2C module complete
(dry, inclusive of gas generator): 19 tonnes
c. Gas generator 1.9 tonnes

nations, and over 4 million total operating hours. By 1993 the Marine Spey alone achieved over 1 million operating hours in service.

The Marine Spey first went to sea with the Royal Navy in 1985 and by 1993 142 units were on order or in service with three navies in six classes of warship. The latest 'C' rated version entered service in 1990 and has been formally adopted by the MoD (UK) as a standard marine propulsion engine for all future warships. It has also been selected by the Japanese Defence Agency to power a new class of DD destroyer.

Module

The module has been designed for ease of installation by the shipbuilders. It is a complete self-contained unit which incorporates as standard the gas generator, power turbine and all of the ancillary systems mounted on a common baseplate. The unit's interfaces are clearly defined and have been kept to a minimum.

Two variants of the module are available:

SM1, a fully enclosed version, which provides full acoustic and heat insulation

SM2, a lightweight version, without an acoustic enclosure.

Performance

Max shaft power: 19 500 kW at 5650 rpm
Specific fuel consumption: 0.229 kg/kWh
Max civil marine rated shaft power: 18 000 kW at 5000 rpm
Specific fuel consumption: 0.234 kg/kWh
at atmospheric pressure 101.3 kPa
air intake temperature 15.ldC
fuel calorific value: 42 800 kJ/kg
no inlet or exhaust losses

Weights

SM 1C module complete: 23.4 t
SM 2C module complete: 19 t
Gas generator: 1.9 t

Power Turbine

The power turbine is a long-life high efficiency two stage design with short, rugged shrouded blades capable of withstanding significant foreign object damage. The rotor system is supported on hydrodynamic bearings housed in a rigid centrebody, and is available with either clockwise or anti-clockwise output shaft rotation.

Gas Generator

The Marine Spey gas generator is a high efficiency second-generation unit of twin spool design, providing excellent operational flexibility, rapid acceleration and good aerodynamic stability. This unit incorporates the latest technology from the Tay aero-engine. The unit operates on class 'A' diesel fuel and produces no visible exhaust smoke at any power level.

Control System

The module is designed for UMS operation and is supplied with a fully integrated electronic control system which interfaces with a ship control system and controls the engine starting, stopping, accelerating and decelerating functions.

The module mounted plant control unit cabinet, contains a full authority local control panel which enables the engine to be started, stopped and operated from the machinery space. It also contains all the instrumentation and control requirements, to permit the engine to remain fully operational includ-

Spey SM1C for HMS Brave *conversion*   1991

ing throttle control, under electrical blackout conditions.

Ancillary Systems

The module as standard is complete with the following ancillaries:

Comprehensive electronic control system and local control panel
Compressor wash system
Fire-fighting system with IR fire detection system
Self-powered enclosure ventilation system
Engine starter system
Air intake cascade bend and exhaust volute, complete with flexible connecting bellows

Acoustic enclosure with access door, viewing portholes, and power points and all associated pipes and fittings
Engine mounting system.

Module Options

To enable the Marine Spey module to be tailored to an individual craft design a number of equipment options is available:
With or without acoustic enclosure
Hydraulic or air engine starting
Cross-connection of engine starting systems
Solid or VLV (Very Low Vibration) module mounting in the craft

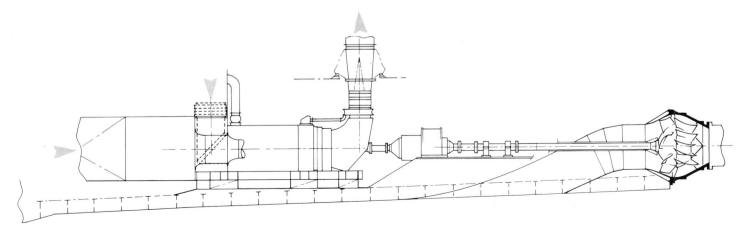

Optional air intake arrangements for Spey SM1C   1993

Various air intake configurations
With or without fire detection/extinguishing system
(SM2C only).

Propulsion Machinery Packaging

Rolls-Royce, if required, offers a complete propulsion package tailored to suit individual craft designs comprising:
Marine Spey module
Speed reducing gearbox, designed to match the individual craft water-jet or propeller and the machinery space design
Spey module/gearbox interconnecting flexible drive coupling.

Maintenance

The Marine Spey uses the highly developed aero-practice of exchanging sections of the gas generator rather than overhauling the complete unit. The engine comprises five Maintenance Assembly Change Units (MACUs) which can be changed independently, considerably reducing the repair cost and downtime of the unit.

The Marine Spey has inherited long life and low maintenance from its Aero Spey and Tay background, coupled with the approach that scheduled maintenance should be carried out without impinging on the craft operating schedule.

WR-21 INTERCOOLED RECUPERATED MARINE GAS-TURBINE

In December 1991, the US Navy awarded an intercooled recuperated gas-turbine design and development contract to a Westinghouse-led team. The team members are: Westinghouse Marine Division as the prime contractor and system integrator; Rolls-Royce, gas-turbine design/development; Allied Signal, recuperator and intercooler developer; and CAE Electronics, controller developer. The WR-21, as it is now known, will become the next prime mover on US Navy new construction surface combatant ships and has been specifically designed, since its outset, to meet the USN future need for a more economical operating system than the existing simple-cycle engine. The WR-21 is derived from the Rolls-Royce family of RB211 engines. Changes to the aero com-

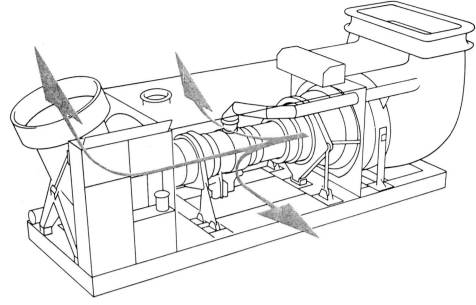

Optional engine removal routes for Spey SM1C   *1993*

ponents have been kept to a minimum to take advantage of the large commercial engine production base and also to profit from the aero engine technological base and accrued reliability. During 1992 and 1993 the initial design of the WR-21 was developed using a combination of analytical and rig/model tests. The results of these tests have been used to validate the design or, where neccessary, provide direction for design changes. The WR-21 has been designed from concept through to detail design with maintainability being of prime importance.

The design phase is now complete, the compo-

nents have been manufactured and the first engine has been built. The current phase of WR-21 development is to test the full engine system. Initial testing commenced in July 1994 and is taking place at the Royal Navy test facility at Pyestock, UK. A second facility, the US Navy test site in Philadelphia, USA, will be available in 1995.

The prime benefit of this 25.2 MW gas-turbine development will be the low specific fuel consumption of below 0.19 kg/kWh with an overall module weight of 46 tonnes.

UPDATED

UNITED STATES OF AMERICA

ALLIED SIGNAL ENGINE DIVISION

550 Main Street, Stratford, Connecticut 06497, USA

Telephone: +1 (203) 385 3863
Telex: 964242
Telefax: +1 (203) 385 3255

Carroll R Oates, *Group Manager for Turboshaft Sales and Marketing*

Previously Textron Lycoming, Allied Signal manufactures a wide range of gas-turbine engines for helicopters, regional jetliners and armoured vehicles, as well as marine and industrial applications. The marine version of the turboshaft and turbofan T55 family is designated the TF40. Over 400 TF40B engines have been supplied for the US Navy LCAC programme, currently involving a fleet of 90 craft.

With over 750 000 hours of operational experience in the LCAC and other craft, the TF40 has passed the Navy's rigorous 1000 hour qualification test and is the world's only 3000 kW class marine turbine Navy certified for shipboard propulsion applications.

By September 1994, there were three new TF40 gas-turbine applications in fast ferries, megayachts and patrol boats:
Two TF40s for one 40 m Swath ferry built by Nichols Brothers of Seattle, Washington
Eight TF40s for four 40 m catamaran ferries built by Austal Ships of Fremantle, Australia
Two TF40s for lift engines on the Super-Technoliner SES ferry prototype in Japan.
Allied Signal has a joint CODAG agreement with Detroit Diesel to sell and service the TF40 worldwide. As a result, several TF40s are being placed in megayachts through the Detroit Diesel network.

Cutaway of TF40 marine/industrial gas-turbine rated at 2983 kW (4000 shp) continuous, 3430 kW (4600 shp) 'boost' power   *1988*

TF40 AND TF40B
(The 'B' designation is for military use)

The TF40, at 3430 kW and weighing 1325 lbs, has the highest power-to-weight ratio of any engine in its class. It is relatively small (about the size of an aver-

age office desk), and can go from 'cold' to maximum power in less than 45 seconds. It produces virtually no vibration, smoke or loud noise which means that it conforms to today's more rigid environmental regulations. The engine is modular in design with only two of its five modules containing moving parts that require maintenance; these are the combustor-power turbine and gas producer modules. The others are the inlet housing, the accessory gearbox and the oil sump (which only lubricates the bearings, meaning minimal oil consumption). Modules can be detached separately and serviced in place or easily removed through standard-size shipboard hatches.

Scheduled inspections are required after 2000 hours. These can generally be accomplished in less than eight hours and involve disassembling the hot section of the engine to check for wear. Major maintenance intervals are at 24 000 hours. Since the TF40 is cantilevered off the gearbox, repairs do not disturb the engine's alignment, a feature which simplifies most maintenance operations.

There are plans for an upgraded version of the TF40 with a growth potential to approximately 5300 shp to be produced by 1997.

Air intake: Side inlet casting of aluminium alloy housing internal gearing and supporting power producer section and output drive shaft. Integral or separately mounted gears are optional. Provision for intake filters and/or silencers. Integral water-wash nozzles are provided.

Compressor: Seven axial stages followed by a single centrifugal stage. Two piece aluminium alloy stator casing, with seven rows of steel stator blades bolted to steel alloy casing diffuser, to which combustion chamber casing is attached. The rotor comprises seven stainless steel discs and one titanium impeller, and is mounted on a shaft supported in a forward thrust ball bearing and a rear roller bearing. TF40 pressure ratio is 8.4:1.

Combustion chamber: Annular reverse flow type. Steel outer shell and inner liner. Twenty-eight fuel nozzles with downstream injection.

Control system: Electronic fuel control with power and/or speed control available. All cabling and instrumentation supplied as standard. Fully automatic starting and safety systems.

Fuel grade: MIL-T-5624, JP-4, JP-5, MIL-F-16884 diesel, standard and wide-cut kerosene.

Turbine: Two mechanically independent axial flow turbines. First turbine, with two stages, drives compressor. It has cored-out cast blades and is flange-bolted to outer coaxial drive shaft. Second two stage turbine drives output shaft. It has solid blades and is mounted on inner coaxial drive shaft. (Other features include: integral cast-cooled first turbine nozzle, cooled turbine blades in both first and second stages, second turbine vane cooling and second turbine disc and blade cooling.)

Exhaust unit: Fixed area nozzle, with inner cone, supported by six radial struts.

Accessories: Electric, air or hydraulic starter, fuel/oil heat exchanger, fuel and oil pumps and all plumbing and valves are engine-mounted.

Lubrication: Recirculating type. Integral oil tank and cooler.

Oil grade: Synthetic base oils.

Weight: 600 kg

Dimensions
Length: 1.32 m
Width: 0.88 m
Height: 1.11 m

Performance Ratings
Max intermittent (at 15°C sea level): 3430 kW
Max continuous (at 15°C sea level): 2983 kW

Fuel Consumption
At max continuous rating: 300 g/kW h (0.494 lb/hph)
Oil consumption: 0.24 l/h (max allowed).

UPDATED

ALLISON ENGINE COMPANY

General offices: PO Box 420 SCU5, Indianapolis, Indiana 46206, USA

Telephone: +1 (317) 230 5617
Telefax: +1 (317) 230 2900

H L Holzworth, *Marine Sales Manager, Industrial Gas Turbines*

Allison has been active in the development of gas-turbines for aircraft, industrial and marine use for many years. Production of the first Allison gas-turbine began in the 1940s, when the company built the power-plant for the P-39, the first jet-powered aircraft to fly in the USA.

Later, the Allison T56 turboprop aircraft engine was developed. It demonstrated outstanding reliability and the same basic design has been adapted for industrial and marine applications. In the early 1960s, the first Allison 501-K gas-turbine-powered electric power-plant went into service. Today, in excess of 1600 501-K industrial series engines are used not only in electric power-plants but also in industrial and marine applications. The two-shaft marine engine powers the Boeing/Kawasaki Jetfoil and is installed in the Israeli Shipyard Ltd M161 hydrofoil craft for primary propulsion.

By the end of September 1994, Allison had 152 Model 501-KF gas-turbines in operational use, with approximately 690 000 hours of successful operation in Boeing and Kawasaki Jetfoil and military applications.

Principal features of the Allison 501-K type engine (dimensions in inches)   1986

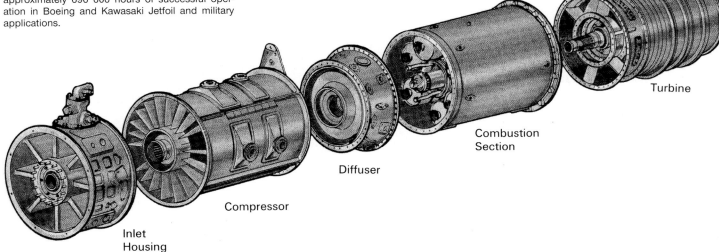

Inlet Housing

Compressor

Diffuser

Combustion Section

Turbine

Accessory Housing

Allison 571-KF   1986

Since the introduction of the 570/571 KF unit, there have been 23 units placed in operation with 21 000 hours of operation.

Allison markets its marine gas-turbine engines by selling commercial packages through Stewart & Stevenson Services, Houston, Texas. For Foreign Military Sales (FMS) Allison sells direct or in conjunction with Allison's authorised distributor and for US military Allison sells direct.

ALLISON DISTRIBUTORS

Centrax Limited Gas Turbine Division, Shaldon Road, Newton Abbott, Devon TQ12 4SQ, UK

Telephone: +44 (1626) 52251
Telex: 42935
Telefax: +44 (1626) 52250

Guy West, *Sales Marketing Manager*

Detroit Engine and Turbine Company, PO Box 188, Adelaide, South Australia 5084, Australia

Telephone: +61 (8) 2602299
Telex: 82427 DETCO AA
Telefax: +61 (8) 3494142

Trevor Sando, *Engineering Manager*

Stewart & Stevenson Services Inc, 16415 Jacintoport, Houston, Texas 77015, USA

Telephone: +1 (713) 452 3610
Telefax: +1 (713) 452 7550

David Whisenhunt, *Director of Sales*

Tominaga & Company Ltd, Shuwa Asakusabashi Nishiguchi Building, 4-2-2. Asakusabashi, Taito-Ku, Tokyo 111, Japan

Telephone: +81 (3) 568 70040
Telefax: +81 (3) 568 70147

Jihei Kuniyoshi, *Director and General Manager*

US Turbine Corporation, 7685 South State Route 48, Maineville, Ohio 45039, USA

Telephone: +1 (513) 683 6100
Telex: 247358
Telefax: +1 (513) 683 6939

Charles Brown, *Manager Allison Products*

ALLISON 501-K SERIES

The Allison 501-K series industrial gas turbine incorporates a 14 stage axial flow compressor, with bleed valves to compensate for compressor surge.

Of modular design, it comprises three main sections: the compressor, combustor and turbine. Each section can be readily separated from the other. Modular design provides ease in handling and servicing of the engine.

The first stage of the four stage turbine section is air-cooled, permitting the engine to be operated at higher than normal turbine inlet temperatures.

The combustor section of the 501-K consists of six combustion chambers of the through-flow type, assembled within a single annular chamber. This multiple provides even temperature distribution at the turbine inlet, thus eliminating the danger of hot spots.

The 501-K series engines are available in single-shaft or free turbine design.

The lightweight, compact size of the 501-K lends itself to multiple engines driving a single shaft through a common gearbox, or as a gas generator driving a customer-furnished power turbine.

The engine can be operated on a wide range of liquid fuels. Designation of the marine model is 501-KF5, a brief specification for which follows.

ALLISON 501-KF5

The marine version of the industrial 501-K engine at ISO, SL conditions
Principal Particulars
Continuous power: 3881 kW
Weight: 1134 kg
Length: 2667 mm

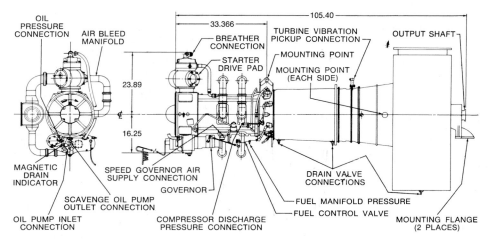

General arrangement of Allison 501-KF   *1989*

Allison 501-KF   *1986*

Height: 1378 mm
Calculated temperature: 1058°C
Exhaust gas temperature: 534°C
Power turbine rpm: 14 200
Specific fuel consumption: 305 g/kWh
Dimensions in inches are shown on the accompanying general arrangement drawing.
Inlet airflow: 26 000 ft³/min
Exhaust airflow: 81 000 ft³/min
Engine jacket heat rejection: 6000 Btu/min
Lubricating heat rejection (Gasifier): 1270 Btu/min

Max liquid fuel flow: 1476 l (390 ghp)
Liquid fuel: DF-1, DF-2 per Allison EMS66
Lubricant: Synthetic oil per Allison EMS35 and 53
Required auxiliaries:
25 hp starter
20-29 V DC electrical power
Power take off shaft and couplings
Temperature and speed controls from engine furnished signals
Oil cooler
Auxiliary lubricating pump

571-KF three-stage gas-turbine

	Maximum	Continuous
Power shp (kW)		
15°C (59°F)	8288 (6180)	7694 (5738)
26.7°C (80°F)	7602 (5669)	6908 (5151)
Fuel consumption 15°C (59°F)		
g/kW	246	249
lb/hph	0.405	0.408
Power turbine temperature		
°C	835	803
°F	1535	1477
Compression ratio	12.8	12.3
Corrected airflow		
kg/s	20.1	19.7
lb/s	44.2	43.4
Power turbine speed (rpm)	11 500	11 500
Weight		
kg	789	789
lb	1740	1740
Length		
m	1.87	1.87
in	74	74

For tough cases

Powerful, thrifty, durable and environment-friendly

High-speed in-line and V marine diesels from MAN have proven
themselves in long term operation in the most arduous conditions
in workboats, passenger ferries, fishing boats and rescue boats
alike. They are economical in operation and maintenance costs for
both marine propulsion and auxiliary power units and cover the
power range 60 – 809 kW (60 – 1100 HP).
Excellent after sales service is available from MAN's extensive
marine dealer network.

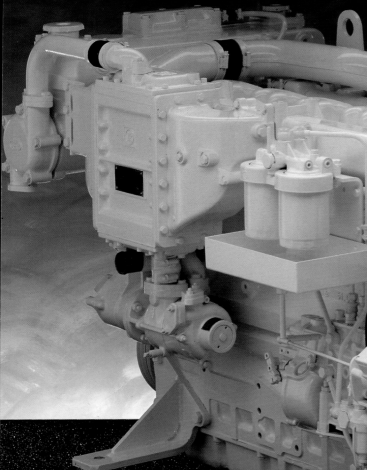

MAN Nutzfahrzeuge
Aktiengesellschaft
Nuremberg Works
Dept. VEM-N
P.O. Box 44 01 00
D-90206 Nuernberg

Tel.: (0049) 0911/420-6218
Fax: (0049) 0911/437455

MAN Truck & Bus UK Ltd.
Engine and Components Division
Frankland Road

Blagrove, SWINDON SN5 8YU

Tel.: 01793/488116
Fax: 01793/615058

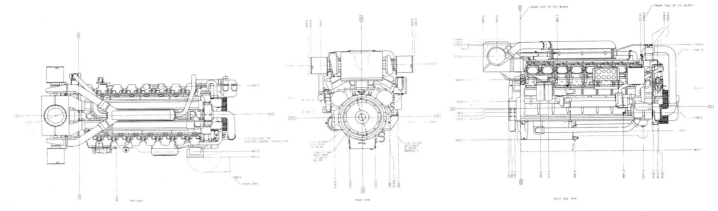

Engineering drawings of Caterpillar 3516 engine

1993

hph (206 g/kWh) at 1925 rpm and .330 lb/hph (201 g/kWh) at 1600 rpm, with a tolerance of +3 per cent, with all engine driven pumps and conforms to ISO 3046/1 and SAE J1349 for fuel having an LHV of 18 390 Btu/lb (42 780 kJ/kg) and weighing 7.001 lb/US gal (838.9 g/l).

The higher power density and lower fuel consumption of the 3516 High Performance engine compared to other versions of the 3516 can be attributed to several redesigned components including an improved air intake and exhaust system, increased efficiency turbocharger, high pressure unit injector fuel system and a two piece piston design. While several components have been changed to increase the horsepower and reduce the weight the High Performance 3516 shares many parts with the proven standard versions of the 3500 Series.

Like all Caterpillar Marine Engines the 3500 Series engines are expertly supported by the Caterpillar worldwide network of dealers and parts warehouses. Caterpillar Marine product support is never far away.

In addition to the developments in the 3600 and 3500 families, Caterpillar announced improvements to several of its smaller engines. Many of these product development programmes resulted in substantial increases in the performance and horsepower to weight ratio of several models. Most notably the 3408 and 3412 were fitted with new electronically controlled fuel systems to boost their outputs from 585 bhp (436 kW) to 800 bhp (597 kW), and from 1000 bhp (746 kW) to 1200 bhp (895 kW) respectively. The increased power output of these engines has lowered their weight to horsepower ratio down to 5.0 lbs/bhp (3.0 kg/kW) for the 3408 and to 4.25 lbs/bhp (2.6 kg/kW) for the 3412. Modifications to the popular 3116TA and 3208TA engines also increased their ratings. The 3116TA increased from 300 bhp (224 kW) to 350 bhp (261 kW) with no increase in weight. At only 4.3 lb/bhp (2.6 kg/kW) the 3116TA is a leader in the 350 bhp (224 kW) range. The improvements made to the 3208TA over the years have allowed it to stay at the top of its class. While the last round of improvements were aimed at improving the performance and sociability of the engine, a small gain in power output was made. The 3208TA increased from 425 bhp (317 kW) to 435 bhp (325 kW) without a change in the weight of 2080 lbs (943 kg).

3600 Diesel Product Group

Production of the Caterpillar 3600 Series in-line engine commenced in 1985, with vee engine production following in 1986. By early 1993, over 550 had been produced, approximately 250 of which were marine engines. The longest running marine engine had 50 000 hours. Caterpillar 3600 marine engines evolved from the heavy fuel (up to 700 cSt), 750 rpm robust version. To meet the needs of fast, weight-sensitive vessels Caterpillar offers a distinct high performance distillate version. This high performance design is significantly lighter, offers more

power and has a longer Time Between Overhauls (TBO) than the basic HFO engine. To do this, the high performance design incorporates numerous changes, including reduced mass and special alloy components, lube and air systems optimised for use with distillate fuels, while not affecting the fundamental reliability of the basic engine.

September 1992 saw the first installation of 3600s in fast ferry operation, with four 3616s being installed in the *Patricia Olivia* operated by Buquebus Lines between Buenos Aires and Montevideo, a 74 m wave-piercer built by International Catamarans Tasmania Pty Ltd. Rated at 4020 kW at 765 rpm, they propel the 780 dwt vessel up to a light ship top speed of 42 knots and a loaded cruising speed of 38 knots.

The 3600 engine family includes in-line 6- and 8-cylinders and vee 12- and 16-cylinders, all versions turbocharged and aftercooled. Displacement is 18.5 l/cylinder, with 280 × 300 mm bore and stroke. At rated speeds of 720 to 1000 rpm, piston speeds average 7.2 to 10.0 m/s. Peak cylinder pressure is 162 bar and BMEP ranges from 22.0 to 23.7 bar at maximum continuous ratings. Specific fuel consumption with all pumps is 188 to 197 g/kWh, based

on ISO 3046/1 with +5 per cent tolerance for fuel having an LHV of 42, 780 kJ/kg and weighing 838.9 g/l.

The advantage of the Caterpillar 3600 family is high power to weight ratio combined with long Time Between Overhauls (TBO) and low maintenance costs. At Continuous Service Ratings (CSR) 40 000 hours of operation before the first major overhaul can be expected, with most major components such as pistons and liners being reusable.

The maximum continuous rating, or 'MCR @ 1000' is the maximum rating at which the engine can be continuously applied. Engine ratings between CSR and MCR for specific applications can be matched to owners' specific requirements of TBO, based on their load profile. MCR ratings are also available at the lower engine speeds.

Weights shown include dry engine with all pumps, filters, flywheel, torsional damper, air starter, manifold shields, flexible plate coupling and resilient mounts.

In contrast to many other makes, Caterpillar 3600 engines include integral lube oil and cooling pumps, providing ease of installation and a clean engine room.

Model	Bore	Stroke	Weight	D rating	D rating	E rating	E rating
3116TA	105 mm	127 mm	681 kg	205 kW	2600 rpm	224 kW	2800 rpm
3116TA	105 mm	127 mm	681 kg	231 kW	2600 rpm	261 kW	2800 rpm
3208NA	114 mm	127 mm	789 kg	157 kW	2800 rpm	157 kW	2800 rpm
3208T	114 mm	127 mm	816 kg	224 kW	2800 rpm	239 kW	2800 rpm
3208TA	114 mm	127 mm	853 kg	254 kW	2800 rpm	280 kW	2800 rpm
3208TA	114 mm	127 mm	943 kg	—	—	325 kW	2800 rpm
3304BTA	121 mm	152 mm	832 kg	134 kW	2200 rpm	142 kW	2200 rpm
3306BTA	121 mm	152 mm	1120 kg	250 kW	2200 rpm	265 kW	2200 rpm
3406BTA	137 mm	165 mm	1470 kg	365 kW	2100 rpm	403 kW	2100 rpm
3408BTA	137 mm	152 mm	1681 kg	399 kW	2100 rpm	436 kW	2100 rpm
3408BTA	137 mm	152 mm	1814 kg	—	—	597 kW	2300 rpm
3412TA	137 mm	152 mm	2459 kg	641 kW	2100 rpm	641 kW	2100 rpm
3412TA	137 mm	152 mm	2313 kg	—	—	895 kW	2300 rpm
3508TA	170 mm	190 mm	5216 kg	858 kW	1800 rpm	—	—
3512TA	170 mm	190 mm	6532 kg	1305 kW	1800 rpm	—	—
3516TA	170 mm	190 mm	8029 kg	1641 kW	1800 rpm	—	—
3516TA	170 mm	190 mm	7840 kg	2088 kW	1880 rpm	2237 kW	1925 rpm

Rating Guidelines:
D - for use in patrol, customs, police and some fire boats **E** - for use in pleasure craft with planing hulls, as well as for patrol, pilot and harbour master boats (Some fish boats may operate on duty cycles where **D** or **E** engine ratings apply.)

Model	CSR (kW) 750	800	900	1000	MCR 1000	Weight (kg)
3616	3960	4160	4600	4920	5420	28 500
3612	2980	3120	3460	3700	4060	23 250
3608	1980	2080	2300	2460	2710	17 950
3608	1490	1560	1730	1850	2030	14 600

UPDATED

CATERPILLAR, SOLAR TURBINES INC

2200 Pacific Highway, PO Box 85376, San Diego, California 92186-5376, USA

Telephone: +1 (619) 544 5000
Telex: 695045
Telefax: +1 (619) 544 5864

Solar Turbines has designed and manufactured marine gas-turbines since the mid-1940s. In 1950, it became the first company to provide an acceptable gas-turbine of original design for the US Navy's Bureau of Ships. The Solar gas-turbine was a 335 kW (450 hp) axial flow unit which the Navy later procured for main propulsion, generating power for launching shipboard missiles and for driving pulse generators on mine-sweepers. In a subsequent programme for the US Navy, Solar designed the 1 MW class Saturn gas-turbine engine which has subsequently become the world's most widely used industrial gas-turbine with nearly 5000 units sold. Today, the company produces industrial and marine gas-turbines in the 1000 to 11 000 kW range, and more than 9200 of Solar's Saturn, Centaur and Mars gas-turbines installed offshore and onshore in some 80 nations, have logged more than 450 million operating hours, including over 1500 units with some 95 million hours in this marine environment.

TAURUS MARINE GAS-TURBINE

The first propulsion application for Solar's Taurus gas-turbine will be aboard five new 334 passenger, high-speed Tricat ferry boats being manufactured by FBM Marine (UK) Ltd in the Isle of Wight. Two Taurus marine gas-turbines will provide power on each of the 45 m long vessels. The Taurus gas-turbines will drive water-jets capable of propelling the Tricat vessels at speeds over 47 knots.

The Taurus marine gas-turbine is a robust, modularly constructed, proven industrial power-plant that includes selected design features adapted from aero-derivative engines such as cooled first stage turbine nozzles and turbine blades for high performance and long life. The Taurus gas-turbine is a simple-cycle, two-shaft machine with a free power turbine assembly for high efficiency and power extraction. It is made with materials selected for outstanding durability in a marine environment.

Air compressor: The Taurus gas-turbine's air compressor has 12 axial flow stages providing an 11.2:1 compression ratio. The first four stages have variable geometry stators and inlet guide vanes to facilitate smooth and reliable starting. All compressor stages have factory applied corrosion-resistant coatings.

Combustor assembly: The engine has a single annular-type combustor equipped with 12 high precision vortex-stabilised fuel injectors for highly efficient operation, low nitrous oxide emissions, a uniform temperature profile and extremely stable

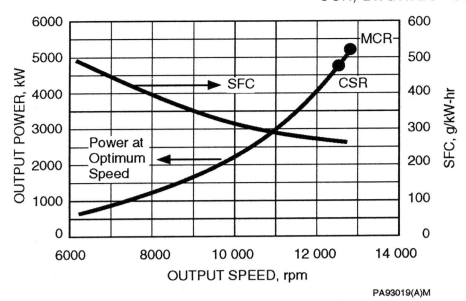

Taurus gas-turbine performance, power and SFC (specific fuel consumption) vs speed *1993*

PA93019(A)M

combustion over a broad range of operating loads and conditions. The combustor liner's advanced alloys and film-air cooling technology contribute to a long and troublefree life.

Gas generator turbine assembly: The first two stages in the Taurus gas-turbine drive its air compressor. The advanced alloy materials, corrosion-resistant coatings and state-of-the-art cooling technology maximise turbine reliability and efficiencies.

Power turbine assembly: The Taurus marine gas-turbine's two stage free power turbine assembly provides a broad range of output speeds for propulsion applications. Power output is delivered from its hot (rear) end through speed-reduction gearing to the driven equipment such as a water-jet propulsion system or propeller.

Fuel system: The fuel system for the Taurus gas-turbine is designed for use with No 1 and No 2 fuel oil and No 1 and No 2 diesel fuel, with an option for kerosenes (JP-4, JP-5, or Commercial Grade). Its

major components include a high pressure fuel pump, boost pump and strainer, main fuel control valve, filters and pressure valve.

Lubrication: The Taurus engine is lubricated by an integral, closed-loop scavenging system that uses synthesised hydrocarbon oils.

Control system: Solar's microprocessor-based Turbotronic™ control system monitors and regulates the static and dynamic parameters of the gas-turbine system and auxiliary devices. The Turbotronic™ control system is available with serial link interfaces for connection to other control systems.

Starting system: The Taurus marine gas-turbine is equipped with a hydraulic start system or AC electric start system.

Dimensions
Length: 3786 mm
Width: 1786 mm
Height: 1786 mm
Weight: 3045 kg

PERFORMANCE, Taurus Marine Gas-turbine*

	Max continuous	Continuous service
Output Power, kW	5250	4890
Specific Fuel Consumption, g/kWh	263	265
Inlet Air Flow, kg/s	21.6	21
Exhaust Gas Temperature. °C	500	480
Output Speed, rpm	12 760	12 500

*ISO Conditions: SL/15°/no inlet, or gear losses/60% RH
Liquid fuel, LHV = 42 780 kJ/kg

UPDATED

CUMMINS ENGINE COMPANY INC

PO Box 3005, Columbus, Indiana 47202-3005, USA

Telephone: +1 (812) 377 5000
Telefax: +1 (812) 377 3554

David Crompton, *Marine Marketing Manager*

Formed in 1919 in Columbus, Indiana, the Cummins Engine Company produces a wide range of marine diesel engines which are now manufactured and distributed internationally. In addition to manufacturing plants in the United States, the company also produces diesel engines in Brazil, China, India, Japan, Mexico and the United Kingdom. All these plants build engines to the same specifications thus ensuring interchangeability of parts and the same quality standards. These standards meet design approvals for worldwide agency certification.

VTA-903-M

Type: Four-stroke cycle, turbocharged, after-cooled V-8 diesel engine.

After-cooler: Large capacity after-cooler plumbed for raw water cooling.

Bearings: Replaceable, precision-type, steel-backed inserts. Five main bearings, 95 mm diameter. Connecting rod bearings, 79 mm diameter.

Camshaft: Single camshaft precisely controls valve and injector timing. Lobes are induction hardened for long life. Five replaceable precision-type bushings, 63 mm diameter.

Camshaft followers: Induction hardened, roller type for long cam and follower life.

Connecting rods: Drop forged, I-beam section 208 mm centre-to-centre length. Rifle drilled for pressure lubrication of piston pin. Rod tapered on piston pin end to reduce unit pressures.

Cooling systems: Gear-driven centrifugal engine coolant pump. Large volume water passages provide even flow of coolant around cylinder liners, valves and injectors. Modulating bypass thermostat regulates coolant temperature. Spin-on corrosion resistor checks rust and corrosion, controls acidity and removes impurities.

Crankshaft: Fully counter-weighted and spin-balanced high tensile strength steel forging with induction hardened fillets.

Cylinder block: Alloy cast-iron with removable wet liners. Cross bolt support to main bearing cap provides extra strength and stability.

Cylinder heads: Alloy cast-iron. Each head serves four cylinders. Drilled fuel supply and return lines. Valve seats are replaceable corrosion-resistant inserts. Valve guides and cross head guides are replaceable inserts.

Cylinder liners: Replaceable wet liners dissipate heat faster than dry liners and are easily replaced without reboring the block.

Fuel system: Low pressure system with wear compensating pump and integral dual flyweight governor. Camshaft actuated fuel injectors give accurate metering and precise timing. Fuel lines are internal drilled passages in cylinder heads. Spin-on fuel filter.

Gear train: Timing gears and accessory drive gears are induction hardened. Spur gears driven from the crankshaft and located at rear of block.

Lubrication: Large capacity gear pump provides pressure lubrication to all bearings. Oil cooler and full-flow filters maintain oil condition and maximise oil and engine life.

Pistons: Aluminium alloy, cam ground and barrel-shaped to compensate for thermal expansion, ensures precise fit at operating temperatures. One oil and two compression rings.

Piston pins: Full floating, tubular steel retained by snap rings, 44 mm diameter.

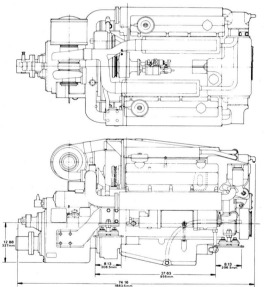

Cummins KTA19-M turbocharged after-cooled diesel engine

1986

Turbocharger: Exhaust gas-driven turbocharger mounted at rear of engine. Turbocharging provides more power, improved fuel economy and lower smoke and noise levels.

Valves: Dual 48 mm diameter poppet-type intake and exhaust valves. Wear-resistant face on exhaust valves.

Power Ratings
High output: 336 kW
Rated rpm: 2600
Medium continuous: 283 kW
Rated rpm: 2600
Continuous duty: 239 kW
Rated rpm: 2300
Bore and stroke: 140 × 121 mm
Displacement: 14.8 l
Oil pan capacity: 19 l
Net weight, dry*: 1660 kg
*With selected accessories and Capitol HY-22000 marine gear.

6BT5.9-M

This engine is now replacing the VT-555-M type. Its compact size provides for ease of installation and easy access for routine maintenance. Fewer parts enables less inventory, faster maintenance and repair to be achieved, and allows engines to be serviced and repaired with ordinary hand tools.

Type: Four-stroke cycle, turbocharged, direct injection, in-line, six-cylinder diesel engine.

Skirted block: Cast-iron with main bearing supports between each cylinder, for maximum strength and rigidity, low weight and optimum crankshaft support.

Fuel injection system: Direct, with high swirl intake ports for thorough mixing of air and fuel to provide low fuel consumption.

Crankshaft: Forged steel with integral counterweights, allowing high power output from a compact size.

Connecting rods: Forged steel, I-beam cross-section, with angle split cap-to-rod interface and capscrew attachment for maximum structural strength and ease of service.

Camshaft: Side-mounted gear drive for low engine height and minimum maintenance.

Alternator and water pump drive: Single-belt with self-tensioning idler for minimum belt maintenance.

Cylinder head: Single piece cross flow for short length and maximum structural stiffness of the block/head assembly and for fewer head gasket problems.

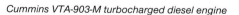

Cummins VTA-903-M turbocharged diesel engine

1986

Valves per cylinder: Two with single valve springs for fewer parts.

Turbocharger: Water-cooled exhaust manifold and water-cooled turbocharger can be configured for top-out or rear-out exhaust for added flexibility.

Power Ratings
High output: 157 kW
Rated rpm: 2600
Medium continuous: 134 kW
Rated rpm: 2500
Bore and stroke: 102 × 120 mm
Displacement: 5.9 l
Oil pan capacity: 14.2 l
Net weight, dry: 579 kg*
*Heat-exchanger-cooled and MG-502 marine gear.

6BTA5.9-M

As for 6BT5.9-M except:

Type: Four-stroke cycle, turbocharged, after-cooled, direct injection, in-line, six-cylinder diesel engine.

Jacket water after-cooler: Mounted on top of intake manifold.

Turbocharger: Water-cooled exhaust manifold and water-cooled turbocharger, configured for rear-out exhaust for lower profile.

Power Ratings
High output: 186 kW (250 bhp)
Rated rpm: 2600
Medium continuous: 164 kW (220 bhp)
Rated rpm: 2500
Bore and stroke: 102 × 120 mm
Displacement: 5.9 l
Oil pan capacity: 14.2 l
Net weight, dry: 613 kg*
*Heat-exchanger-cooled and MG-506A marine gear.

KTA19-M

Type: Four-stroke cycle, turbocharged, after-cooled diesel.

After-cooler: Large capacity after-cooler results in cooler, denser intake air for more efficient combustion and reduced internal stresses for longer life. After-cooler is located in engine coolant system, eliminating need for special plumbing.

Bearings: Replaceable, precision-type, steel-backed inserts. Seven main bearings, 140 mm in diameter. Connecting rod bearings 102 mm in diameter.

Camshaft: Single camshaft precisely controls the valve and injector timing. Lobes are induction hardened for long life. Seven replaceable precision-type bushings 76 mm in diameter.

Camshaft followers: Induction hardened, roller type for long cam and follower life.

Connecting rods: Drop forged, I-beam section 290 mm centre-to-centre length. Rifle drilled for pressure lubrication of piston pin. Rod is tapered on piston pin end to reduce unit pressures.

Cooling system: Gear driven centrifugal pump. Large volume water passages provide even flow of coolant around cylinder liners, valves and injectors. Modulating bypass thermostats regulate coolant temperature. Spin-on corrosion resistor checks rust and corrosion, controls acidity and removes impurities.

Crankshaft: High tensile strength steel forging with induction hardened fillets and journals. Fully counter-weighted and dynamically balanced.

Cylinder block: Alloy cast-iron with removable wet liners. Cross bolt support to main bearing cap provides extra strength and stability.

Cylinder heads: Alloy cast-iron. Each head serves one cylinder. Drilled fuel supply and return lines. Valve seats are replaceable corrosion-resistant inserts. Valve guides and cross head guides are replaceable inserts.

Cylinder liners: Replaceable wet liners dissipate heat faster than dry liners and are easily fitted without reboring the block.

Fuel system: Cummins PT self-adjusting system. Integral dual flyweight governor provides overspeed protection independent of main engine governor. Camshaft actuated fuel injectors give accurate metering and timing. The fuel lines are internal drilled passages in the cylinder heads. Spin-on fuel filters.

Gear train: Timing gears and accessory drive gears are induction hardened helical gears driven from the crankshaft and located at front of block.

Lubrication: Large capacity gear pump provides pressure lubrication to all bearings and oil supply for piston cooling. All pressure lines are internal drilled passages in the block and heads. Oil cooler, full flow filters and bypass filters maintain oil condition and maximise oil and engine life.

Pistons: Aluminium alloy, cam ground and barrel shaped to compensate for thermal expansion assures precise fit at operating temperatures. CeCorr grooved skirt finish provides superior lubrication. Oil-cooled for rapid heat dissipation. Two compression and one oil ring.

Piston pins: Full floating, tubular steel retained by snap rings, 61 mm in diameter.

Turbocharger: AiResearch exhaust gas-driven turbocharger mounted on right side of engine. Turbocharging provides more power, improved fuel economy, altitude compensation and lower smoke and noise levels.

Valves: Dual 56 mm diameter poppet-type intake and exhaust valves. Wear-resistant face on exhaust valves.

Power Ratings
Continuous duty: 373 and 432 kW
Rated rpm: 1800
Intermittent duty: 507.3 kW** and 410 kW
Rated rpm: 2100
Bore and stroke: 159 × 159 mm
Displacement: 19 l
Oil pan capacity: 38 l
Net weight, dry: 3084 kg*
*Heat-exchanger-cooled and MG-502 marine gear.
**Limited production.

KTA38

This engine was introduced in 1994 with a 38 litre, 12-cylinder V configuration, producing 1000 kW maximum and 900 kW continuous brake power both at 1800 rpm.

6CTA8.3-M

Type: Four-stroke cycle, turbocharged, aftercooled in-line, six-cylinder diesel.

After-cooler: Large capacity after-cooler results in cooler, denser air for more efficient combustion and reduced internal stress for longer life.

Bearings: Replaceable precision-type aluminium steel-backed. Seven main bearings 98 mm diameter. Connecting rod bearings 2.99 in (76 mm) diameter.

Camshaft: Forged steel for increased wear resistance and long life. Seven replaceable precision-type bushings 2.36 in (60 mm) diameter.

Connecting rods: Drop forged I-beam section, 8.50 in (216 mm) centre-to-centre length. Rod is tapered on piston pin end to reduce unit pressures.

Crankshaft: Eight counter-weight fully balanced high tensile strength steel forging with induction hardened fillets and journals.

Cylinder block: Alloy cast-iron with removable wet liners.

Cylinder head: One piece cross flow cylinder head for short length and maximum structural stiffness of block/head assembly. Contains replaceable valve guides and seat inserts.

Cylinder liners: Mid-stop replaceable wet liners feature a new liner clamping method which seals at the middle of the liner with a press fit at the top. This design eliminates the need for packing rings and crevice seals.

Valves per cylinder: Two, with single valve springs for fewer parts.

Water-cooled exhaust manifold and water-cooled turbocharger: Configured for rear-out exhaust for lower profile.

Power Ratings
High output: 302 kW**
Rated rpm: 2600
Medium continuous: 223 kW
Rated rpm: 2500
Continuous: 209 kW
Rated rpm: 2200
Bore and stroke: 114 × 135 mm
Displacement: 8.3 l
Net weight, dry: 824 kg*
*With heat exchanger cooling and MG-507A marine gear.
**Limited production.

NTA-855-M

Type: Four-stroke cycle, turbocharged, after-cooled, in-line, six-cylinder diesel.

After-cooler: Large capacity after-cooler results in cooler, denser intake air for more efficient combustion and reduced internal stresses for longer life and lower exhaust emissions.

Bearings: Replaceble, precision-type, steel-backed. Seven main bearings, 4.5 in (114 mm) diameter. Connecting rod bearings 3.125 in (79 mm).

Camshaft: Single large diameter camshaft precisely controls valve and injector timing. Lobes are induction hardened for increased wear resistance and long life. Seven replaceable precision-type bushings 2.5 in (64 mm) diameter.

Camshaft followers: Induction hardened, roller type for long cam and follower life.

Connecting rods: Drop forged, I-beam section 12 in (305 mm) centre-to-centre length. Rifle drilled for pressure lubrication of piston pin. Rod is tapered on piston pin end to reduce unit pressures.

Crankshaft: Fully counter-weighted high tensile strength steel forging with induction hardened fillets and journals.

Cylinder block: Alloy cast-iron with removable wet liners.

Cylinder head: Alloy cast-iron. Each head serves two cylinders. Drilled fuel supply and return lines. Valve seats are replaceable corrosion-resistant inserts. Valve guides and cross head guides are replaceable inserts.

Cylinder liners: Replaceable wet liners dissipate heat faster than dry liners and are easily replaced without reboring the block.

Filters: Fleetguard. Lubricating oil, spin-on full flow and bypass type, mounted on engine oil cooler. Fuel, spin-on type, mounted. Corrosion resistor, spin-on type, mounted.

Fuel system: Cummins exclusive low pressure PT system with wear compensating pump.

Power Ratings
Medium continuous: 298 kW
Rated rpm: 2100
Continuous: 261 kW
Rated rpm: 1800
Bore and stroke: 140 × 152 mm
Displacement: 14 l
Net weight, dry: 205.5 kg*
*With selected accessories and MG-514 marine gear.

UPDATED

DETROIT DIESEL CORPORATION

13400 Outer Drive West, Detroit, Michigan 48239-4001, USA

Telephone: +1 (313) 592 5000
Telex: 4320091
Telefax: +1 (313) 592 7288

A A Kozel, *Vice President, Marine Sales*

Detroit Diesel Corporation has its headquarters in Detroit, Michigan and has the design, manufacturing and sales responsibilities for a complete line of heavy-duty diesel engines, supported by a worldwide distributor/dealer network.

DDC 16V-149TI
1993

A range of marine diesel engines is available with maximum power levels between 187 and 1790 kW. The following table gives the maximum marine ratings for these engines:

Model	Max hp	rpm	Cyl	Displacement	Weight
DD500 T	187 kW	3200	8	8.2 l	639 kg
DD500 TI	224 kW	3200	8	8.2 l	655 kg
4-71	242 kW	2600	4	4.7 l	817 kg
6V-53TI	298 kW	2800	6	5.22 l	898 kg
6-71TI	362 kW	2500	6	6.9 l	1170 kg
6V-92TA	410 kW	2300	6	9.0 l	1223 kg
6V-92TA (DDEC)	421 kW	2300	6	9.0 l	1239 kg
8V-92TA	548 kW	2300	8	12.1 l	1570 kg
8V-92TA (DDEC)	567 kW	2300	8	12.1 l	1577 kg
12V-71TA	671 kW	2300	12	13.9 l	1793 kg
12V-71TA (DDEC)	671 kW	2300	12	13.9 l	1807 kg
12V-92TA	805 kW	2300	12	18.1 l	2225 kg
12V-92TA (DDEC)	828 kW	2300	12	18.1 l	2239 kg
16V-92TA	1044 kW	2300	16	24.1 l	2714 kg
16V-92TA (DDEC)	1082 kW	2300	16	24.1 l	2727 kg
12V-149TI (DDEC)	1343 kW	2100	12	29.3 l	5063 kg
16V-149TI (DDEC)	1790 kW	2100	16	39.1 l	6114 kg

DDC 6V-92TA   *1993*

DDC 12V-92TA   *1994*

GENERAL ELECTRIC COMPANY

GE Aircraft Engines

1 Neumann Way, Mail Drop N109, Cincinnati (Evendale), Ohio 45215-6301, USA

Telephone: +1 (513) 243 6136

Eugene F Murphy, *President and Chief Executive Officer*
Dennis R Little, *Vice President and General Manager, GE Marine and Industrial Engines Division*
Robert R Bass, *Manager, Marketing Communications*

General Electric Company's Dr Sanford A Moss operated the first gas-turbine in the USA in 1903 and produced the aircraft turbo-supercharger, first flown in 1919 and mass produced in the Second World War for US fighters and bombers.

The company built its first aircraft gas-turbine in 1941, when it began development of a Whittle-type turbo-jet, under an arrangement between the British and American governments.

Since then General Electric has produced over 82 000 aircraft gas-turbines for military and commercial aircraft, as well as aircraft derivative gas-turbines for marine and industrial uses.

General Electric offers three gas-turbines for marine service: the LM 2500, the LM 500 and the LM 1600.

LM 2500

The LM 2500 marine gas-turbine is a two-shaft, simple-cycle, high efficiency engine derived from the General Electric military TF39 and the commercial CF6 high bypass turbofan engines for the US Air Force C-5 Galaxy transport and DC-10, 747 and A300 commercial jets. The compressor, combustor and turbine are designed to give maximum progression in reliability, parts life and time between

LM 2500   *1990*

overhauls. The engine has a simple-cycle efficiency of more than 37 per cent, which is due to advanced cycle pressures, temperatures and component efficiencies.

Two GE LM 2500s power the Rodriquez 101 m high-speed monohull passenger/car ferries designated Aquastrada. Two LM 2500s have been chosen to power the Stena High-Speed Service (HSS) ferry, the world's largest car/passenger ferry.

The LM 2500 marine gas-turbine provides foil-borne power for the US Navy PHM hydrofoils. The six PHM Pegasus class vessels were built by the Boeing Company, Seattle, Washington. In addition to the Pegasus hydrofoils, GE LM 2500 marine gas-turbines propel over 310 ships. These ships include the 'Perry' class FFG-7 frigates, 'Spruance' class DD-963 destroyers, 'Kidd' class DDG-993 destroyers, 'Ticonderoga' class Aegis CG-47 cruisers, 'Burke' class DDG-51 Aegis destroyers and the supply class AOE-6 auxiliary ships of the US Navy.

In combination with diesels the LM 2500 powers several classes of high-speed patrol boats with top speeds of more than 40 knots. LM 2500 gas-turbines and diesel combinations also provide propulsive power for a broad cross-section of 37 ship programmes for 24 navies throughout the world, including aircraft carriers, cruisers, destroyers, frigates and corvettes.

Total operating time of LM 2500 engines in all marine service is more than four million hours.

Type: Two-shaft, axial flow, simple-cycle.

Air intake: Axial, inlet bellmouth or duct can be customised to installation.

Combustion chamber: Annular.

Fuel grade: Kerosene, JP4, JP5, diesel, distillate fuels and natural gas.

Turbine: Two stage gas generator, six stage power turbine.

Jet pipe: Vertical or customised to fit installation.

Oil specification: Synthetic turbine oil (MIL-L-23699) or equal.

Mounting: At power turbine and compressor front frame.

Starting: Pneumatic, hydraulic.

Dimensions
Length: 6630 mm
Width: 2100 mm

Performance rating: 24 310 kW (32 600 shp) at 15°C at sea level.

Specific fuel consumption: 0.226 g/kWh.

LM 500

The LM 500, derived from GE's TF34 high bypass aircraft engine, is a simple-cycle, two-shaft gas-turbine engine that powers the Danish Navy's Flyve-fisken (Stanflex 300) patrol boat, a Japanese PG class hydrofoil patrol craft, and the Kværner Fjellstrand Flying FoilCat class passenger ferry. Throughout its operating range, the LM 500 is characterised by outstanding efficiency, which is attributable to the high pressure ratio of the compressor, high turbine inlet temperature, improved component efficiency and conservation of cooling airflow.

Type: Two-shaft, axial flow, simple-cycle.

Air intake: Axial; vertical inlet duct can be customised to installation.

Combustion chamber: Annular.

Fuel grade: Kerosene, JP4, JP5, diesel, distillate fuels, and natural gas.

Turbine: Two stage gas generator, four stage power turbine.

Jet pipe: Vertical or axial or customised to fit installation.

Oil specification: Synthetic turbine oil (MIL-L-23699) or equivalent.

Mounting: At turbine frame and front frame.

Dimensions
Length: 2187 mm
Width: 864 mm

Performance rating: 4474 kW (6000 shp) at 15°C at sea level.

Specific fuel consumption: 270 g/kWh.

LM 1600

The LM 1600 is derived from GE's F404 engine, which powers the F/A-18 Hornet and F-117 Stealth Fighter. A simple-cycle, three-shaft gas-turbine engine, the LM 1600 has been selected as the power-plant for two large high-speed vessels. The *Destriero*, which set the speed record for a trans-atlantic crossing without refuelling, is powered by three LM 1600 engines developing up to a total 44 740 kW (60 000 bhp). The other vessel, designed by Martin Francis and built by the Blohm+Voss shipyard, named *Eco*, is powered by one LM 1600 engine in a CODOG configuration.

MTU (Motoren- und Turbinen-Union) of Germany and GE Aircraft Engines have entered into an arrangement whereby MTU will package the LM 1600 gas-turbine in marine modules for all types of naval applications.

Type: Three-shaft, axial flow, simple-cycle.

Air intake: Axial, inlet bellmouth or duct can be customised to installation.

Combustion chamber: Annular.

Fuel grade: Kerosene, JP4, JP5, diesel, distillate fuels and natural gas.

Turbine: Two stage gas generator, two stage power turbine.

Jet pipe: Vertical or customised to fit installation.

Oil specification: Synthetic turbine oil (MIL-L-23699) or equivalent.

LM 500   1991

LM 1600   1991

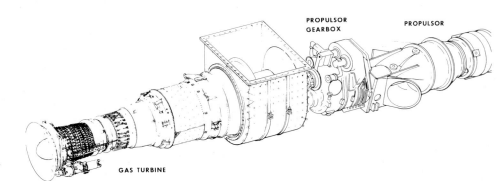

LM 2500 installation for PHM Pegasus class hydrofoil   1986

Mounting: At turbine frame and front frame.

Starting: Pneumatic, hydraulic.

Dimensions
Length: 4890 mm
Width: 2032 mm

Performance rating: 14 913 kW (20 000 shp) at 15°C at sea level.

Specific fuel consumption: 226 g/kWh.

VERIFIED

UNITED TECHNOLOGIES INTERNATIONAL INC

Turbo Power and Marine Systems Inc

Aircraft Road, PO Box 611, Middletown,
Connecticut 06457, USA

Telephone: +1 (203) 343 2000
Telex: 221432 TPM UTC
Telefax: +1 (203) 343 2266

R J Hogan, *Vice President and General Manager*
Dr W H Day, *Director Advanced Engineering*
M A Cvercko, *Director, Marketing and Sales*

Turbo Power and Marine Systems Inc designs, builds and markets industrial and marine gas-turbine power plants and related systems throughout the world. It also provides a systems support for its installations. The current gas-turbine product line includes the 25 MW class FT8, and a 50 MW class FT8 Twin Pac (electric power generation only). Support of the existing fleet of FT4 gas-turbines is also continued.

Canadian sales of Turbo Power and Marine (TPM) are handled by Pratt & Whitney Canada (qv) which also manufactures and sells the 1.0 MW ST6 marine gas-turbine.

The FT8 is marketed by Turbo Power's licensee/engine packaging partner MAN Gutehoffnungshutte GmbH (MAN GHH). The unit is marketed in the People's Republic of China by Turbo Power's licensee China National Aero-Technology Import and Export Corporation (CATIC).

A modified version of the FT8 called the MFT8, which consists of the GG8 gas generator and a light-weight power turbine designed and manufactured by Mitsubishi Heavy Industries, is marketed for marine and other applications by MHI and TPM.

MARINE GAS-TURBINES

TPM's FT4 marine gas-turbines were first used for boost power in military vessels, including two Royal Danish Navy frigates, 12 US Coast Guard Hamilton class high endurance cutters and four Canadian Forces DDH-280 'Iroquois' class destroyers. Another boost power application of the FT4 is in the Fast Escort and ASW vessel *Bras d'Or* also built for the Canadian Forces. Another application is in two 12 000 tonne Arctic icebreakers for the US Coast Guard. With three FT4 marine gas-turbines, these vessels are capable of maintaining a continuous speed of 3 knots through ice 1.8 m thick, and are able to ram through ice 6.4 m thick. One of these vessels actually cut through the polar ice cap to reach the North Pole.

TPM's marine gas-turbines were used for both the main and boost propulsion in the four Canadian DDH-280 destroyers. These are the first military combatant vessels to be designed for complete reliance on gas-turbine power.

FT4 gas-turbines are also used in the *Finnjet,* a high-speed Finnlines passenger liner which cut the Baltic crossing time in half, routinely maintaining 30 knots, with an engine availability of over 99 per cent. The record time for an engine replacement is 1 hour 20 minutes.

FT8 MARINE GAS-TURBINE

TPM has recently introduced a new model, the FT8 marine gas-turbine based on the Pratt & Whitney JT8D aircraft engine, which incorporates advanced technology from Pratt & Whitney PW4000 and PW2000 series commercial aircraft gas-turbine engines. Eighteen FT8 units are already in commercial operation in five countries. The nominal 24 609 kW, (33 000 hp) size is expected to fit marine applications.

Three MFT8 gas-turbine engines have been supplied to Mitsubishi Heavy Industries for the Techno-Superliner demonstration programme in Japan. This vessel achieved 55 knots on sea trials in 1994. The full-scale vessel is to be propelled by four such engines.

The FT8 aero-derivative marine gas-turbine is of a modular design with major components designed to be easily removed for servicing. With a spare gas generator to replace the one removed, the ship's power-plant can be changed in a matter of hours.

Production model of FT4 with 38 600 shp base load 1986

MFT8 gas-turbine 1995

FT8 marine gas-turbine 1993

Borescope inspection features allow internal inspection without disassembly.

GAS GENERATOR

Type: Simple-cycle two-spool gas generator. A low pressure compressor is driven by a two stage turbine and a high pressure compressor is driven by a single stage turbine. The burner section has nine burner cans each equipped with one fuel nozzle.

Air intake: Steel casing with radial struts supporting the front compressor bearing.

Low pressure compressor: Eight stage axial flow on inner of two concentric shafts driven by two stage turbine and supported on ball and roller bearings. Variable geometry inlet guide vanes and the first two stages of vanes improve part power efficiencies and reduce the start up power requirements.

High pressure compressor: Seven stage axial flow on outer hollow shaft driven by single stage turbine and running on ball and roller bearings.

Combustion chamber: Nine burner cans located in an annular arrangement and enclosed in a one piece steel casing. Each burner has one fuel nozzle.

Turbines: Steel casing with hollow guide vanes. Turbine wheels are bolted to the compressor shafts and are supported on ball and roller bearings. A single stage turbine drives the high pressure compressor and a two stage turbine drives the low pressure compressor.

POWER TURBINE

Power turbine (MFT8): The MFT8 power turbine was developed by Mitsubishi Takasago Works as a lightweight substitute for those FT8 power turbines directed to land-based applications. The weight of the three stage 5000 rpm MFT8 power turbine is 2600 kg. The MFT8 employs a cantilevered rotor design as opposed to the straddle arrangement used on the FT8.

Control system: The control system is a digital system based on the Woodward Governor Company's Netcon 5000 controller. All software is developed by TPM, and can be integrated with ship systems.

Accessory drive: Starter, fluid power pump, tachometer drives for the low pressure compressor shaft and the high pressure compressor shaft.

Lubrication: Scavenge pump return system and supply system pumps.

Oil specifications: Synthetic lubricating oil, PWA-521.

Starting: Pneumatic, hydraulic or electric.

Dimensions
Length: 6373 mm
Width: 1962 mm
Height: 2440 mm

Fuel Specifications
Marine diesel, Aviation grade kerosene, light distillate (naptha) TPM-FR-1.

Treated crude and residual oil, refer to manufacturer.

MFT8 DESIGN PARAMETERS
59°F, Sea Level, No Losses, 43 MJ/Kg
Shaft Output (kW): 25800
Heat rate (kg/kWh): 0.219

Airflow: 85.3 kg/s
Pressure ratio: 20.3:1
Combustor exit temperature: 1174°C
Power turbine exhaust temperature: 443°C

UPDATED

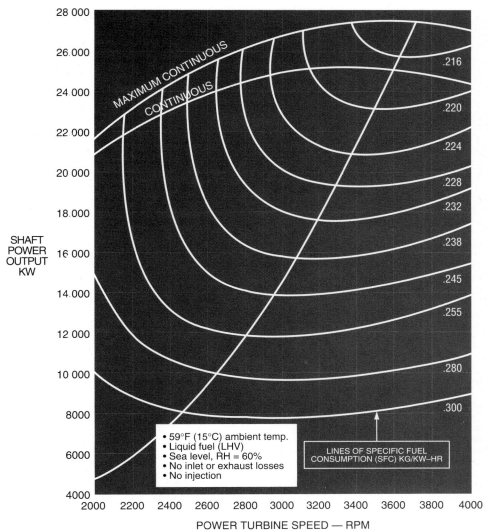

- 59°F (15°C) ambient temp.
- Liquid fuel (LHV)
- Sea level, RH = 60%
- No inlet or exhaust losses
- No injection

LINES OF SPECIFIC FUEL CONSUMPTION (SFC) KG/KW–HR

SHAFT POWER OUTPUT KW

POWER TURBINE SPEED — RPM

FT8 marine gas-turbine, expected performance 1993

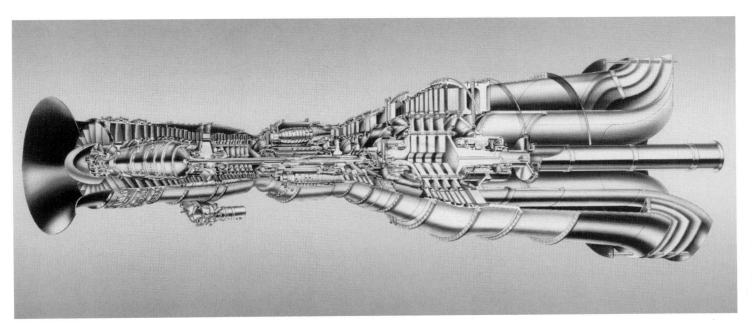

FT8 marine gas-turbine, internal configuration 1993

TRANSMISSIONS

Company Listing by Country

Germany
Lohmann + Stolterfoht GmbH
Reintjes GmbH
Renk Tacke GmbH
ZF Marine

Italy
FB Design SRL
Rexroth SpA

Japan
Niigata Converter Co Ltd

Norway
Servogear A/S
Ulstein Propeller A/S

Singapore
Nico Transmission (S) Pte Ltd

Switzerland
Maag Gear Company Ltd

United Kingdom
Allen Power Engineering Ltd

United States of America
The Cincinnati Gear Company
Detroit Diesel Corporation
Twin Disc Inc

GERMANY

LOHMANN + STOLTERFOHT GmbH

PO Box 1860, D-58408 Witten, Germany

Telephone: +49 (2302) 8770
Telex: 8229005
Telefax: +49 (2302) 877400

Lohmann and Stolterfoht manufactures a range of gearboxes, reduction gearboxes, reverse reduction gearboxes, twin output/single output gearboxes,

Type	Torque	Reduction ratios available
Navilus GUU	5.0 to 16 kNm	1.5 to 6.5:1.0
Navilus GWC	15.5 to 190 kNm	2.0 to 6.0:1.0
Navilus GCS/GUC	39.0 to 2200 kNm	1.5 to 6.0:1.0
Navilus GUT	570.0 to 3580 kNm	1.5 to 12.0:1.0
Navilus GVA/GVE	50.0 to 1620 kNm	2.0 to 6.0:1.0
Navilus GVG	690 to 3580 kNm	2.0 to 6.0:1.0

clutches and couplings for torques ranging from 5 kNm to 3580 kNm for marine propeller transmissions.

UPDATED

REINTJES GmbH

PO Box 101344, D-31784 Hameln, Germany

Telephone: +49 (5151) 1040
Telefax: +49 (5151) 104300

UK representative: European Marine and Machine Agencies, 22-26 Gore Road, New Milton, Hampshire BH25 6RX, UK

Telephone: +44 (1425) 618704
Telefax: +44 (1425) 617424

Reintjes has specialised in the manufacture of marine gearboxes for harbour craft and sea-going vessels for more than 65 years. The company has produced over 70 000 gearboxes.

Reintjes manufactures gearboxes ranging from 800 to 5000 kW for fast vessels with marine propeller transmissions, and up to approximately 6000 kW for water-jet drives.

GEARBOXES FOR FAST VESSELS

The gearboxes of the Types WVS/WLS and VLJ have been designed specially for fast vessels and for vessels with water-jet drive, such as marine craft, patrol boats or yachts, as well as all types of vessels with similar exacting requirements.

Owing to their specific design for these fields of application, the hydraulically operated reverse reduction gearbox of Type WVS and the hydraulically operated reduction gearboxes of Types WLS and VLJ have special advantages to offer, which are: high efficiency, low weight per horsepower due to light metal housing and light construction, small size, excellently synchronised engagement and optimum smooth running.

For application in fast vessels with water-jet propulsion Reintjes has developed reduction gearboxes with and without clutches. By using various distances and arrangements of output and input the most favourable arrangement of engine and water-jet can be selected for hulls, each with either one or two engines. Requested reduction ratios are tailor-made enabling the water-jet to operate with the best possible efficiency.

Built-in disc clutches enable a diesel engine start-up with water-jet being disengaged. The gearboxes are provided with connection facilities for

Type	Reduction ratios	N/n1 kW/rpm	Max input speed (rpm)
WVS/WLS 234	1.179-2.542	0.385	2400
	2.958	0.248	2400
	3.571	0.213	2400
	4.053	0.180	2400
WVS/WLS 334	1.122-2.538	0.470	2400
	2.956	0.400	2400
	3.521	0.320	2400
WVS/WLS 430 L	1.184-3.550	0.365	2300
WVS/WLS 430	1.184-2.458	0.600	2300
	2.904	0.520	2300
	3.315	0.450	2300
	3.550	0.420	2300
WVS/WLS 730 L	1.414-3.047	0.700	2100
	3.541	0.670	2100
	3.954	0.600	2100
WVS/WLS 730	1.414-3.047	0.950	2100
	3.541	0.670	2100
	3.954	0.600	2100
WVS/WLS 930 L	1.348-3.043	1.000	2100
	3.541	0.930	2100
	3.958	0.830	2100
	4.409	0.720	2100
WVS/WLS 930	1.348-3.043	1.340	2100
	3.541	0.930	2100
	3.958	0.830	2100
	4.409	0.720	2100
WVS/WLS 2232	1.725-3.037	2.280	1700/2100
	3.451	2.080	1700/2100
	3.954	1.900	1700/2100
	4.590	1.600	1700/2100

Reintjes WVS 2232 (2.025:1) gearbox   *1992*

Power range of Reintjes gearboxes for fast vessels

1995

hydraulic pumps required for water-jet control. The projected gearboxes are available for engine ratings to approximately 6000 kW and in numerous configurations. Standard type is VLJ 930.

US NAVY PATROL BOAT GEARBOXES

WVS 2232/2.025:1 Installed in US Navy Patrol Boats. Each vessel incorporates four Paxman engines rated individually at 2500 kW at 1500 rpm. Thus, 10 000 kW is available in total, enough to give a top speed exceeding 30 knots. Each engine is mated to a series WVS 2232 hydraulically operated reverse reduction gearbox with vertically offset shafts and a 2.025:1 reduction ratio. The gearboxes are fitted with built-in thrust bearing, seawater-resistant oil cooler, oil pump, duplex filter and electrically actuated control and trolling valve facility. This allows operation at low propeller speeds with slipping clutch and can be used in ahead and astern running and for manoeuvring. The gear's spur wheels are helically toothed, case-hardened and tooth flank ground.

WAVE-PIERCER CATAMARAN
Condor 9

The power input is from four MWM diesel engines, Type 16 V 604 B, having an output of 1.690 kW each. The diesel engines run in connection with a Reintjes reduction gear equipped with a hydraulically operated clutch, especially developed for operation in fast vessels with water-jet propulsion Type VLJ 930 HL/HR, having a reduction ratio of 1.8056:1.0. The installed water-jet is MJP Type J 650 R-DD.

Due to the built-in disc clutch the diesel engine can be started with the water-jet disengaged.

The gears of the Reintjes gearbox are horizontally offset, that is, they are equipped with horizontally left and horizontally right output shafts. The gear mounting is rigid on the foundation. Gear brackets are seated on Chock-Fast. The horizontal gear design for *Condor 9* allows an optimum arrangement of diesel engines and water-jets in the individual hulls. As *Condor 9* would operate as a ferry, there was a demand for fitting a complete spare propulsion plant at short notice. Due to the variable gear design it is possible for the first time to have a suitable replacement with only one gearbox for all four propulsion plants. Slight modification work only is required. The gears are supplied with connections for hydraulic pumps for the water-jet control system.

The gears can also be delivered vertically offset. Either a rigid or resilient gear mounting can be provided.

UPDATED

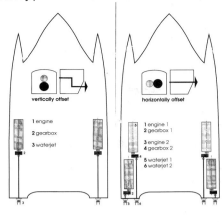
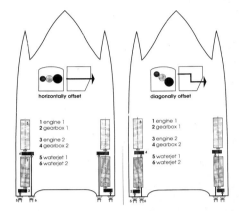
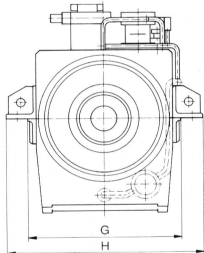
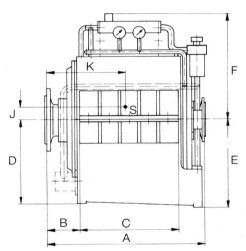

Examples of gearbox drive arrangements
1993

RENK TACKE GmbH

Augsburg Works, Gögginger Strasse 73, D-86159 Augsburg 1, Germany

Telephone: +49 (821) 57000
Telex: 53781
Telefax: +49 (821) 570 0460

Rheine Works, Rodder Damm 170, D-48432 Rheine, Germany

Telephone: +49 (5971) 7900
Telex: 981637
Telefax: +49 (5971) 790208

PLS AND PWS GEARBOXES

Renk Tacke's marine planetary gear units (PLS and PWS series) have been specifically developed for use in fast ships such as corvettes, speedboats, mine-sweepers, mine-layers, OPVs and IPVs. Designed for a performance range between 800 and 10 000 kW, they cover a very wide range of applications. The specific characteristics and advantages of disconnectable planetary gear units (PLS) and planetary reversing gear units (PWS) are: ratios 1.5 to 4.8

Renk Tacke PLS and PWS series gearboxes (see table for dimensions)
1995

Gear unit Type	A		B	C	Dimensions D	E	F	G	H	J	K	Weight, dry		Thrust	Oil content
	i<2.8 i>5	i>2.8 i<5										i<2.8 i>5	i>2.8 i<5		
Size	mm	mm	mm	mm	mm	mm	mm	mm	mm	mm	mm	kg	kg	kN	litres
PLS															
18	900	800	200	480	530	560	710	850	1120	80	400	1350	1200	130	90
25	1000	900	225	530	600	630	800	950	1250	90	450	1750	1550	160	110
35.5	1120	1000	250	600	670	710	900	1060	1400	100	500	2350	2050	200	130
50	1250	1120	280	670	750	800	1000	1180	1600	115	560	3000	2650	250	150
71	1400	1250	315	750	850	900	1120	1320	1800	125	630	3800	3450	320	185
100	1600	1400	355	850	950	1000	1250	1500	2000	140	710	4800	4300	400	230
PWS															
18	1060	950	200	600	530	560	710	850	1120	80	480	1600	1450	130	120
25	1180	1060	225	670	600	630	800	950	1250	90	530	2150	1950	160	145
35.5	1320	1180	250	750	670	710	900	1060	1400	100	600	3000	2800	200	170
50	1500	1320	280	850	750	800	1000	1180	1600	112	670	4200	3900	250	200
71	1700	1500	315	950	850	900	1120	1320	1800	125	750	5750	5300	320	235
100	1900	1700	355	1060	950	1000	1250	1500	2000	140	850	8100	7300	400	280

UPDATED

PWS series efficiencies 97.5 to 98 per cent

PLS series efficiencies 98.5 to 99 per cent

compact design, permitting favourable engine room concepts

low power-to-weight ratio of less than 0.5 kg/kW

coaxial input and output shafts for optimum power plant layouts

high shock resistance due to planetary design

insensitivity of transmission elements to hull distortion, providing high operational reliability even under extreme service conditions

high efficiency due to epicyclic concept

starboard and port gear units offer identical connection interfaces and with PWS units this means completely identical starboard and port gear units, even for multi-propeller ships

forward and reverse gears of PWS units are both designed for 100 per cent loads, engines can therefore operate with the same direction of rotation without affecting the gear unit

on request, these gear units can be built under the supervision of any classification society. Anti-magnetic versions are available

high reliability

suitable for use with gas-turbines

if required, low-speed gear can be provided

special design with vertically offset shafts for V drives.

PWS gearbox
1995

ZF MARINE

A Division of ZF Friedrichshafen AG

D-88038 Friedrichshafen, Germany

Telephone: +49 (7541) 770
Telex: 734207-17 ZF D
Telefax: +49 (7541) 775942

F Petilli, *Managing Director and General Manager*
R Mosbacher, *Marine Department Manager*

ZF produces marine transmission systems in its three plants in Friedrichshafen, Germany, Padua, Italy and São Paulo, Brazil. ZF marine reduction and reversing gearboxes range from 75 to 7300 kW for high-speed craft application and from 75 to 3000 kW for workboats. All gears can be supplied with classification approval.

ZF marine transmission systems have been fitted in a large number of high performance, naval, commercial and pleasure craft throughout the world.

The Italian office of ZF Marine is known as ZF-MPM and has the following contact details:

Via Penghe 48, I-35030 Caselle di Selvazzano, Padua, Italy

Telephone: +39 (49) 829 9311
Telex: 430320 MPM PD I
Telefax: +39 (49) 829 9550

F Petilli, *Managing Director and General Manager*

Type	Possible ratios	Max input torqued Nm*		Max input speed rpm	Length between flange faces mm	Centre distance mm	Weight kg
		Continuous	Intermittent				
IRM 50PL ⅔	1.57-3.12	464	658	5000	492	110	30
IRM 220PL	1.19-3.00	570	880	5500	info on request	–	–
IRM 320PL1	1.03-2.48	1269	2010	3000	526	170	165
IRM 320-1	2.96-4.95	1269	1532	2400	526	245	270
IRM 350PL	1.03-2.86	1465	2499	3000	503	175	220
IRM 350	3.97-6.54	1624	1863	2400	489	335	500
BW 61	2.62-4.64	637	756	3200	378	210	105
BW 160	1.11-3.04	1980	3100	3000	484	200	263
BW 161	3.61-6.42	1980	2275	2600	489	365	560
BW 165	1.11-2.59	3100	3880	3000	484	200	264
BW 190	1.09-3.00	2930	4120	3000	577	220	333
BW 191-1	3.50-6.46	2470	2690	2600	567	390	680
BW 195	1.09-2.57	4120	5000	3000	577	220	333
BW 196	2.92-4.04	3000	5000	3000	670	310	415
BW 250	1.04-3.45	3300	4820	2500	716	235	437
BW 251	3.31-5.90	3300	4820	2500	776	360	830
BW 255	1.04-3.45	3300	5450	2500	716	235	440
BW 256	3.31-5.90	4410	6000	2500	776	360	630
BW 450-1	1.18-3.48	4750	6095	2300	727	310	695
BW 451-1	2.37-5.63	4750	5230	2300	822	460	1330
BW 452-1	2.37-7.62	4750	5230	2300	1041	150	1542
BW 456-1	2.37-5.63	5230	6095	2300	822	460	977
BW 457-1	2.37-7.62	6370	7420	2300	1041	150	1160
BW 460	1.18-3.48	5750	7465	2300	727	310	699
BW 461	2.37-5.63	6635	6635	2300	822	460	1338
BW 465	1.18-3.23	8085	8820	2300	727	310	703
BW 466	2.27-5.63	8085	8745	2300	822	460	985
BW 487	1.50-4.45	8085	9380	1820	1041	150	1165
BW 750	1.16-3.23	7900	10 300	2300	746	340	895
BW 751	4.0-6.8	8900	10 780	2300	920	600	2300
BW 755	1.16-3.23	10 465	12 190	2300	746	340	900
BW 1200	1.10-2.22	16 100	17 200	2000	1085	320	1340
BW 1201	1.70-3.59	16 100	17 200	2000	1055	450	1550
BW 1202	1.48-2.53	16 100	17 200	2000	1350	130	1870
BW 1500	1.10-1.84	-	21 730	2000	1085	320	1350
BW 1501	1.70-3.03	-	21 730	2000	1055	450	1560
BW 1502	1.70-3.03	-	21 730	2000	1350	130	1880
BW 1555	1.10-2.22	-	22 920	2000	1105	320	1370
BW 1556	1.70-3.59	-	23 000	2000	1055	450	1570
BW 1557	1.70-3.59	-	23 000	2000	1350	130	1895
BW 2002	1.48-2.53	-	28 590	1520	1350	130	1880
BW 2057	1.42-2.99	-	27 610	1665	1350	130	1895
BW 2356	1.42-3.58	17 000	25 440	2000	1154	440	2100

*The stated maximum torque ratings and speeds do not apply to all ratios

ZF MARINE GEARS WITH PARALLEL OFFSET INPUT AND OUTPUT SHAFTS

ZF MARINE GEARS WITH COAXIAL INPUT AND OUTPUT SHAFTS							
Type	Possible ratios	Max input torqued Nm* Continuous	Intermittent	Max input speed rpm	Length between flange faces mm	Centre distance mm	Weight kg
IRM 41I	1.00	314	440	5000	info on request	0	30
IRM 50I	1.00	464	785	5000	info on request	0	50
IRM 301 PL2	1.11-2.69	712	1399	3000	433	0	87
IRM 310 PL	1.08-2.56	1037	1726	3000	451	0	135
BWK 450-1	1.18-4.71	4750	6095	2300	946	0	902
BWK 455-1	1.18-4.71	6370	7460	2300	946	0	907
BWK 485	1.19-2.75	8050	9380	1820	946	0	907
BWK 750	1.16-4.62	7900	10 300	2300	915	0	1135
BWK 755	1.16-4.62	10 780	12 190	2300	915	0	1140
BWK 785	0.95-2.64	13 180	14 905	1880	915	0	1140
BWK 1200	1.10-2.22	16 100	17 200	2000	1380	0	1640
BWK 1500	1.10-1.84	-	21 730	2000	1400	0	1650
BWK 1555	1.10-2.22	-	21 610	2000	1400	0	1675
BWK 2000	1.15-1.53	-	28 590	1665	1400	0	1650
BWK 2356	1.42-5.12	17 000	25 440	2000	1154	-	2450
BWK 2386	1.12-1.76	34 550	51 700	1000	1154	-	2450

*The stated maximum torque ratings and speeds do not apply to all gear ratios

ZF MARINE GEARS WITH DOWN ANGLED OUTPUT SHAFTS							
Type	Possible ratios	Max input torqued Nm* Continuous	Intermittent	Max input speed rpm	Length between flange faces mm	Centre distance mm	Weight kg
IRM 41A ⅔	1.03-2.47	-	440	5000	440	122	30
IRM 50A ⅔	1.03-2.47	464	658	5000	492	122	32
IRM 180A	1.18-2.44	480	680	4500	359	138	50
IRM 220A-1	1.24-2.45	576	890	4500	336	145	57
IRM 220V-2	1.24-2.45	576	890	4500	-	145	59
IRM 220VLD	1.21-2.49	576	890	4500	-	247	90
IRM 280A	1.15-2.52	640	1090	3200	351	147	68
IRM 301A-2	1.19-2.90	650	1227	3000	415	56.2	89
IRM 302VLD	1.30-3.16	701	1381	3000	-	270	127
IRM 310A	1.08-2.56	1036	1726	3000	435	37	140
IRM 311A	1.09-2.03	1150	1950	3000	431	37	139
IRM 320A-1	1.55-2.52	1268	2009	3000	499	212.1	165
IRM 350A	1.29-2.95	1455	2500	3000	501	196	219
IRM 350 VLD	1.32-2.03	1455	2500	3000	—	416	249
BW 160A	1.53-2.96	1980	3100	3000	548.8	276	286
BW 160V	1.53-2.96	1980	3100	3000	—	276	286
BW 165A	1.53-2.96	-	3880	3000	549	276	288
BW 165V	1.53-2.96	-	3880	3000	-	276	288
BW 190A	1.27-2.92	2930	4120	3000	554	296	330
BW 190V	1.27-2.92	2930	4120	3000	-	296	340
BW 195A	1.27-2.45	-	5000	3000	554	296	332
BW 195V	1.27-2.45	-	5000	-	296	342	—

*The stated maximum torque ratings and speeds do not apply to all gear ratios

UPDATED

ITALY

FB DESIGN Srl

Via Provinciale 73, I-22040 Annone Brianza (Co), Italy

Telephone: +39 (341) 260105
Telefax: +39 (341) 260108

Ing Fabio Buzzi, *Director and Administrator*

TRIMAX SURFACE DRIVE

FB Design produces the TRIMAX range of surface drive systems using Rolla surface-piercing propellers. The most popular model is the TR2100 which has been responsible for many offshore race wins over the last ten years. This is a self-aligning system built entirely in stainless steel. The largest unit available is the TR4000 which is used in the offshore power boat *Super Hawaii*. This craft is fitted with two

Super Hawaii fitted with two FB Design TR4000 transmission systems
1992

The TF40, Seatek diesel and FB Design installation in Super Hawaii   *1992*

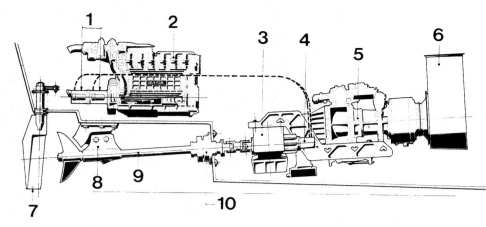

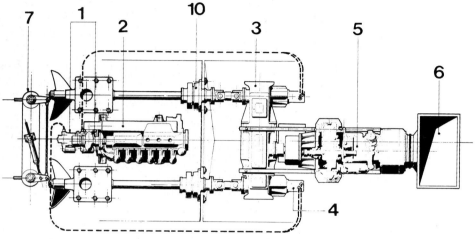

TRIMAX drive for a single gas-turbine installation with opposite-rotation surface-piercing propellers.
Key: **1** Hydraulic pumps; **2** Seatek engine; **3** FB/ZF gearbox; **4** Hydraulic engines; **5** Lycoming TF40 gas-turbine; **6** Turbine exhaust; **7** Rudders; **8** Self-aligning supports; **9** 4 in propeller shafts; **10** Spherical thrust sets   *1992*

FB/ZF gearbox and TF40 gas-turbine for Super Hawaii
1992

TR4000s and a FB/ZF splitting gearbox and is powered by one Lycoming TF40 gas-turbine with one Seatek diesel (for low-speed operation). Propulsion is by means of opposite-rotation surface-piercing propellers. In 1991, the 19.2 m *Super Hawaii* won the P3 class in the Venice to Monte Carlo 1500 mile endurance race at an average speed of 52 knots (96 km/h).

FB Design is also involved in various high-speed patrol boats, its "46 Racing" being adopted by the Italian Guardia di Finanza for patrolling against smugglers. This type also came first overall in the Venice to Monaco, Monaco to Porto Cervo to Monaco and Round Sicillian Island races winning the Martini endurance trophy in 1992.

UPDATED

REXROTH SpA

Subsidiary of Mannesmann Rexroth GmbH

Via Di Vittorio 1, I-20063 Cernusco S Naviglio, Milan, Italy

Telephone: +39 (2) 923 651/924 9706
Telex: 331695 REXRTH I
Telefax: +39 (2) 923 65237/924 8840

Dr Ing Hanno Speich, *Managing Director*

POWER SHAFT HS-5000 HYDROSTATIC PROPULSION SYSTEM

Some of the first details of this power transmission system were given in the 1989 edition of this book and are repeated below. Using Rexroth hydraulic components the Hydromarine system is being marketed by the Hydromarine company in Italy. The development of propellers for the system has been undertaken by Marintek in Trondheim, Norway, achieving an efficiency of 85 per cent for the propeller component of the system.

The concept now developed is called Power Shaft HS-5000 and designs for units of four power levels are presently available from 350 to 2000 kW.

Design Particulars

Incorporation of the power shaft into the design of a high-speed craft leads to the following advantages over conventional propulsion systems, it is claimed:
reduction in installed power
increased carrying capacity
lower fuel consumption
higher average speeds in transit
greater passenger comfort gained through drastic reduction in noise levels and improved sea-keeping
longer life of drive unit and longer servicing intervals
flexibility of application and ease of installation given by mutual independence in positioning power shaft and diesel engine
general improvements in structural design of craft, from the functional standpoint
availability of spare parts worldwide.

Horizontal Fixed-Pitch Tractor Propeller

Propulsion is obtained using a tractor propeller, with correct alignment to the water flow. The propeller is driven by a high efficiency hydraulic motor installed within the power shaft, on which the rudder is also mounted.

Propeller cavitation problems are very greatly reduced by virtue of the fact that the propulsion stream is absolutely uniform and symmetrical about the rotation axis. In this way, the propeller enjoys ideal operating conditions, giving high efficiency and generating no vibration or noise through the vessel. The power shaft and its propellers have been optimised to give speeds up to 50 knots.

The power shaft is flange-mounted to the bottom of the hull, selecting the most advantageous position in terms of hydrodynamics and propulsion.

Inside and outside the power shaft, hydraulic connections to the motor driving the propeller consist exclusively of hoses running from a hydraulic pump mounted direct to the diesel engine.

Both pump and motor are axial piston units manufactured by Mannesmann Rexroth; these components have been tried and proven, and further refinements have been made to ensure their complete suitability for marine propulsion.

Overall Efficiency and Power Range

Overall efficiency ratings of the power shaft system

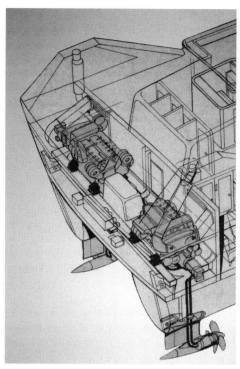

Simplified illustration of hydrostatic propulsion for a high-speed craft   *1991*

Tractor propeller power shaft installations on Baglietto motor yacht   *1991*

are higher than of the water-jet and conventional mechanical drives with inclined axis and pusher propeller. Adopting tractor-type propulsion in the power shaft signifies that the propeller operates in ideal hydrodynamic conditions; in addition, the pod-and-strut structure (which also carries the rudder and its actuator system) has been designed to recover a high percentage of the rotary kinetic energy generated by the propeller, in the form of thrust.

According to the applications, overall efficiency ratings including ratings of hydraulic transmission, propeller, power shaft (due to the water friction on its external surfaces) amounts to about 60 per cent.

The power shaft also includes the rudder and its

drive, and can be supplied for nominal powers from 350 to 2000 kW (under development).

Noise and Vibration Reduction

The design and positioning of the power shaft create particularly good hydrodynamic conditions for the propeller, with the result that overall propulsion noise is reduced to a level never achieved hitherto with propeller drives. The elastic suspension arrangement (patented) designed for the hydraulic motor and propeller drive assembly damp out vibrations generated by the motor and propeller. The flexible components incorporated into the mountings prevent vibrations from being

transmitted to the hull through the power shaft. The fact that the engine and power shaft are connected by nothing other than a set of hoses enhances sound isolation, as does the fact that the initial location of the engine unit can be selected to ensure minimal noise.

An additional factor contributing to the reduction in noise and vibration is the distance which separates the propeller blades from the hull, with the propeller set well away from the structure of the vessel. Axial water inflow to the propeller eliminates the fluctuating forces that cause much of the vibration experienced with inclined shafts.

The final noise reduction expedient is that of suspending the diesel engine and pump equipment on anti-vibration mountings; the pumps can be either flange-mounted direct to the engine or bolted to the same baseplate. This type of installation can reduce vibration through the structure of the craft by as much as 20 dBA.

Power Shaft as Torque Converter

The combination of variable displacement pump and fixed displacement motor provides a speed/torque converter.

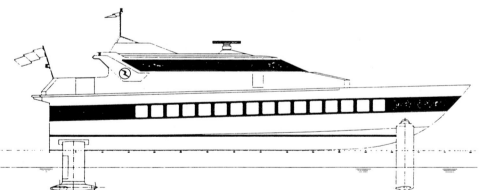

The hydrofoil craft MEC 1 of the Rodriquez shipyard in Messina with semi-submerged foils and hydrostatic tractor propeller propulsion. The power shafts are integrated in the foil structure   *1991*

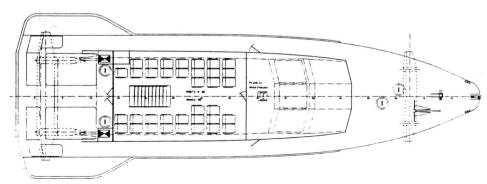

The hydrofoil craft MEC 1-SF of the Rodriquez shipyard in Messina with fully submerged foils, tractor propeller and hydrostatic transmission. The hull of the ship is the same as that with semi-submerged foils   *1991*

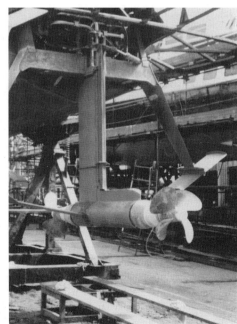

Test installation on a PT 20 hydrofoil   *1991*

Hydromarine hydrostatic propulsion installation on MEC 1　　　　1993

Accordingly, the possibility exists of installing diesel engines with reduced power, size and weight specifications. With torque and speed thus variable the craft is able to accelerate and reach its cruising speed earlier, requiring significantly less time to plane, or to lift onto its foils than in the case of a hydrofoil. The power shaft's fixed-pitch propeller therefore functions substantially as a variable-pitch one. The transmission's flexibility in operation means that full power can also be extracted from the engine in taking craft to higher cruising speeds.

Propeller and Engine Speed Balance

With mechanical transmission eliminated, the speed reduction from engine to propeller is no longer tied to fixed ratios specified by reduction gear manufacturers, but simply a matter of choice. There is also the facility to adjust the transmission ratio during operation to suit conditions of loading, or of the sea state.

Absence of Mechanical Transmission Components

The fluid connection between hydraulic pump and motor eliminates a complete mechanical driveline incorporating speed reducing gears, shafting, bevel gears, reversing gears and clutches. Nor are there any problems arising from the close fit tolerances prescribed for mechanical components and their mounting to marine structures of limited rigidity. By contrast, the hydrostatic transmission effectively compensates for lack of rigidity.

Propeller Control

The operation of docking becomes especially swift and accurate because of the speed and precision with which the propeller can be controlled, reversing included; engine speed remains constant throughout all such manoeuvres.

The running speed and direction of the propeller are controlled from the bridge. By shifting a handle connected to a potentiometer, a signal is produced that commands the pump servo control to produce a variation in flow, hence in the speed of rotation of the hydraulic motor.

Alternatively, the same remote-control effect can be obtained by adopting a pneumatic remote-control, likewise operated from the bridge.

Lightweight, Compact Drive

The power shaft brings advantages of weight and dimensions, especially when compared to water-jet propulsion, as there is no heavy mass of water drawn into the craft through jet ducts.

Approval of Maritime Insurance Agencies

The following agencies have expressed their approval of Hydromarine's power shaft propulsion

MEC 1　　　　1993

system: Germanischer Lloyd, Det Norske Veritas, Bureau Veritas, Lloyd's Register of Shipping, American Bureau of Shipping and Registro Italiano Navale.

Preliminary Results

At the High Performance Vehicle Conference, Shanghai, China, 2-5 November 1988, papers were presented giving details of a Rexroth hydrostatic transmission system fitted to a Rodriquez Supramar PT 20 hydrofoil. Trials started in June 1988 and finished in October 1988. Bench tests carried out on the prototype by Rexroth SpA have enabled the following efficiencies to be established:

hydraulic pump: 0.896
hydraulic piping: 0.966
hydraulic motor: 0.910
propeller: 0.72
pump coupler: 0.98
overall efficiency: 0.556

The efficiency levels for the original PT 20 single propeller inclined shaft drive system are:

gearbox: 0.98
shafting line: 0.979
inclined shafting line: 0.987
propeller: 0.65
overall efficiency: 0.606

Trials were run at various conditions, for example:

main engine revs: 1500 rpm

power (calculated): 937 kW
overall propeller thrust: 3082 kg
vessel speed: 34.75 knots
hydraulic pump delivery pressure: 257 bar
hydraulic motor inlet pressure: 235 bar
calculated overall efficiency: 0.577

Some of the advantages of the total propulsion system made possible by the Rexroth hydrostatic transmission may be listed as follows:

freedom to optimise the power-plant in the logical optimum position (engine noise distanced from passengers), avoidance of 'designing around the engine'

avoidance of inclined shaft hydrodynamic resistance

freedom to optimise passenger cabin layouts

compactness and flexibility of power transmission from engine to propeller

the ability to vary propeller speeds, quickly and accurately

variable speed ratio between engine and propeller enabling the full power of the engine to be used at low craft speeds

simple provision of neutral and reverse drive capability.

UPDATED

JAPAN

NIIGATA CONVERTER CO LTD

27-9, Sendagaya 5-chome, Shibuya-ku, Tokyo 151, Japan

Telephone: +81 (3) 3354 6931
Telex: 2323105 NICOTO J
Telefax: +81 (3) 3341 5365

Works: Kamo, Niigata Prefecture and Omiya, Saitama Prefecture
Kyugo Kobayashi, *Managing Director*

Niigata Converter Company Ltd is licensed by Twin Disc Inc of Racine, Wisconsin, USA for the production and marketing of marine reverse and reduction gears for high-speed engines.

Niigata Converter Company Ltd (NICO), well-known for the manufacture and marketing of diversified lines of marine products, has a new series of marine reverse and reduction gears in lightweight and compact design utilising aluminium alloy housings. There are 16 models in both of the standard and U-drive versions available in the 224 to 2145 kW range. These marine gears are ideal for such vessels as pleasure craft, passenger ferries, patrol boats and crew boats for which the essential requirement is high speed.

Built-in hydraulic clutches, cooled by the same type of oil used in the engines, give the marine gears smooth and instantaneous shifting from ahead to astern and vice versa.

Standard equipment on all models includes filters, pump(s), temperature gauges, heat exchangers for salt or fresh water cooling, output companion flanges and manually actuated range selectors and control valves.

Optional equipment such as X-control or trailing pump is available on request.

UPDATED

MARINE GEAR CAPACITIES FOR HIGH-SPEED MARINE CRAFT

(Parallel shaft models)

Model	SAE Hsg.	Standard ratios	kW/rpm PC	Max speed (rpm)	Dry weight (kg)
MGN 123	2, 1	1.52, 1.97, 2.57	0.134		190
		3.08	0.126	3300	
		3.46	0.118		
MGN 133	2, 1, 0	1.65, 2.00, 2.48	0.178		235
		2.92	0.173	2800	
		3.25	0.168		
		3.43	0.164		
MGN 153	2, 1, 0	1.65, 2.00, 2.48	0.221		250
		2.92	0.215	2800	
		3.25, 3.43	0.203		
MGN 173	1, 0	1.53, 1.97	0.248		345
		2.44	0.243	2600	
		2.93	0.233		
MGN 232E	1, 0	1.29, 1.50, 1.76, 1.96	0.389	2600	370
		2.48	0.303		
MGN 233E	1, 0	2.52	0.389		410
		2.96	0.336	2600	
		3.52	0.283		
MGN 272	1, 0	1.18, 1.50, 1.74, 2.04	0.479	2500	470
MGN 273E	1, 0	2.55	0.479	2500	525
		3.12	0.414		
MGN 332G	1, 0	1.00, 1.45, 1.71, 2.04	0.622	2500	600
		2.36	0.567		
MGN 433E	0	1.18, 1.53, 1.71, 2.06	0.774	2500	870
MGN 433G	0	2.52	0.780	2500	980
MGN 472	0	1.53, 2.11	0.998	2150	1200
		2.52	0.987		
MGN 473	0	2.48, 3.03, 3.31, 3.48	0.998	2150	1270

(Down angle and U-drive models)

Model	SAE Hsg.	Standard ratios	kW/rpm PC	Max speed (rpm)	Dry weight (kg)
MGNV 172 MGNV 172-C	1, 0	1.55, 2.03	0.232	2600	350
		2.34	0.220		
MGNV 232E MGNV 232E-C	1, 0	1.54, 1.73, 1.96	0.389	2600	460
		2.43	0.281		
MGNV 271E MGNV 271E-C	1, 0	1.18	0.479		470
		1.44	0.415	2500	
		1.86	0.349		
MGNV 272E MGNV 272E-C	1, 0	1.66, 2.06	0.479	2500	530
		2.46	0.437		
MGNV 332G MGNV 332G-C	1, 0	1.53, 1.72, 1.93	0.622	2500	630
		2.43	0.567		
MGNV 432 MGNV 432-C	0	1.52, 2.03	0.781	2500	1000
		2.53	0.628		
MGNV 472 MGNV 472-C	0	1.52, 1.95	0.997	2100	1300
		2.46	0.864		

Niigata gearbox configuration   **1990**

NORWAY

SERVOGEAR A/S

N-5420 Rubbestadneset, Norway

Telephone: +47 53 427380
Telefax: +47 53 427783

Servogear, established in 1973, produces lightweight gears to its own design with in-built servo systems for controllable-pitch propellers and hydraulic shaft clutches. Servogear gearboxes are specifically designed for high-speed craft where low weight and small size are particularly important.

Since Servogear started production in 1975 over 700 gearboxes and propeller systems have been delivered, of which more than 300 have been delivered for high-speed craft with engines from 225 to 2240 kW and speeds from 20 to 40 knots.

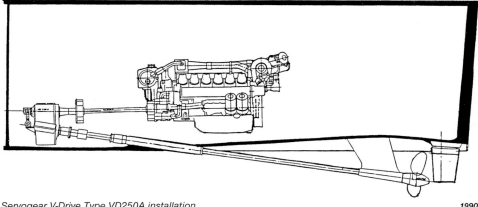

Servogear V-Drive Type VD250A installation   1990

Delivered	Gearbox/ Servo system	Propeller system	Engine kW	Type of ship	Length (m)	Speed (knots)	Owner
1991	ZF465	VD820B	2 × 840	Catamaran	28	33	Salten DS
1991	ZF250	VD820C	2 × 470	Catamaran	23	20	Fosen Trafikklag
1991	ZF250	VD820C	2 × 470	Catamaran	32	24	Fosen Trafikklag
1991	ZF465	VD820B	2 × 1275	Catamaran	28	36	Fosen Trafikklag
1991	ZF250	VD800A	2 × 671	Patrol vessel	22	27	NSSR Norway
1991	ZF465	VD820C	2 × 1275	Passenger vessel	27	38	Per Vold
1991	ZF255	VD9644	2 × 953	Patrol vessel	20	30	Limbongan Timor BHD
1991	VD250C	VD800	2 × 783	Lifeboat	21	24	NSSR
1991	ADF250C	VD800B	2 × 634	Ambulance	19	34	Bjarköy Kommune
1992	ZF755	VD820A	2 × 1551	Oil pollution catamaran	36	20	Saudi Aramco
1992	VD250A	VD800B	2 × 559	Catamaran	21	28	Public board N Italian lake
1992	ADF250A	VD800B	2 × 466	Research vessel	24	20	University of Berge
1992	VD250A	VD770	2 × 352	Passenger vessel	19	20	NPA Nigeria
1992	ZF250	VD810B	2 × 850	Personnel transport	33	26	Norwegian Navy
1992	ZF190	VD810B	2 × 1081	Sports fishing boat	28	28/52	Petosa Brothers
1992	VD250C	VD800A	2 × 686	Passenger vessel	24	28	L Rödne & Sonner

UPDATED

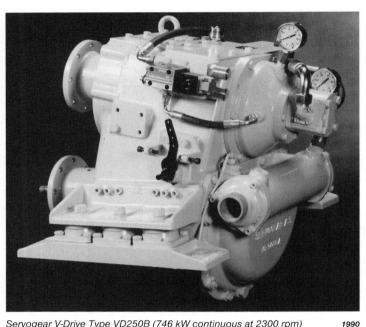

Servogear V-Drive Type VD250B (746 kW continuous at 2300 rpm)   *1990*

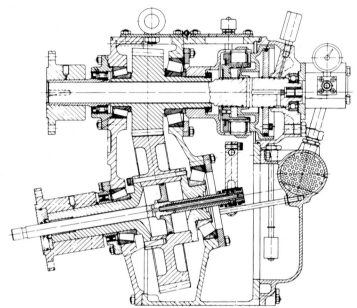

Section through a Servogear gearbox   *1989*

ULSTEIN PROPELLER A/S

N-6065 Ulsteinvik, Norway

Telephone: +47 (700) 14000
Telex: 42848 UP N
Telefax: +47 (700) 14017

Stig Ulstein, *Managing Director*
Jarle Hessen, *Sales Manager*

Ulstein Propeller A/S manufactures marine propeller and water-jet transmissions in addition to the Speed-Z system. Please see the *Marine propellers* section for details of the Ulstein propeller systems and the *Water-jet units* section for details of Ulstein developments in this area.

UPDATED

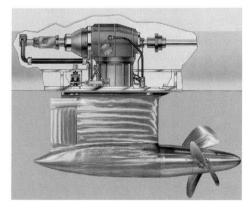

Ulstein Speed-Z drive system
1991

SINGAPORE

NICO TRANSMISSION (S) PTE LTD

46 Gul Crescent, Jurong Town, Singapore 2262

Telephone: +65 862 1332
Telex: 25983 NICOSN RS
Telefax: +65 862 1762

Nico Transmission (S) Pte Ltd is a wholly owned subsidiary company in Singapore of Niigata Converter Company Ltd (NICO), Tokyo, Japan.

The company acts as Regional Marketing Centre in Asia and supervises the activity of its distributors in each country and assists them in providing the function of a depot of units and spares of NICO products for ex-stock sales upon request of the customers.

The business lines of the company naturally follow the product lines of its parent company NICO which covers the wide ranges of power transmission equipment, such as marine reverse and reduction gearboxes of all sizes, three-stage torque converters for railway applications, power shift transmissions for

various industrial vehicles, Omega-drive clutches (slipping clutches), hydraulic couplings and planetary gearboxes for gas-turbines.

VERIFIED

SWITZERLAND

MAAG GEAR COMPANY LTD

Hardstrasse 219, Postfach, CH-8023 Zurich, Switzerland

Telephone: +41 (1) 278 7878
Telex: 822 704 MZZ CH
Telefax: +41 (1) 278 7880

The Maag Gear Company Ltd designs and manufactures a wide range of marine gears and synchronous clutch couplings.

Recent applications include:

Stena HSS catamarans, the largest high-speed vessels ordered to date, fitted with two HPG-185/C gearboxes, each taking an input from a GT LM 2500/LM 1600 combination. Each gearbox outputs to two water-jets. Total power transmission is 80 000 kW.

Kværner Fjellstrand Flying Cat now in series production, fitted with two MPU-24/G-50 gearboxes, each taking an input of 4500 kW at 7000 rpm from a GE LM 500 gas-turbine. Output is at 900 rpm to a water-jet propulsor.

Austal Ships series of gas-turbine powered craft. Each craft is fitted with two MPG-80 gearboxes, each taking an input of 3088 kW from a Textron Lycoming TF-40 gas-turbine with a reduction from 16 400 rpm to 920 rpm.

UPDATED   *MAAG HPG-185/C gearbox for the Stena HSS*   **1995**

UNITED KINGDOM

ALLEN POWER ENGINEERING LTD

Atlas Works, Pershore, Worcestershire WR10 2BZ, UK

Telephone: +44 (1386) 552211
Telefax: +44 (1386) 554491

D J Taft, *General Manager*
D E Yates, *Technical Manager*
P M Johnson, *Sales Manager*
C F W Brimmel, *Marketing Manager*

Allen Gears first became associated with high-speed surface craft in the early 1950s when the Royal Navy commissioned two Vosper prototype aluminium hull vessels. Each triple-screw craft was powered by three Rolls-Royce Proteus gas-turbines driving fixed-pitch propellers. The turbines had a rating of 3500 hp at a speed of 11 600 rpm, and an Allen epicyclic gear was incorporated to reduce engine speed to 5000 rpm. The secondary reduction Allen gearbox consisted of bevel gears for a shaft angle of 15°, driving into a double-train epicyclic reversing section. Since their introduction and subsequent uprating to 4250 hp, over 260 primary gear sets have been supplied by Allen Gears to many of the world's navies.

C FORM GEARBOX

In 1978 Allen Gears fitted its C form gearboxes in a Don Shead-designed 29 m, 45 knot luxury yacht. The yacht cruises on two wing, diesel engine driven jets, and a gas-turbine provides power for maximum speed. The turbine is a Textron Lycoming Super TF40 which produces 4600 hp at 15 400 rpm and drives a Rocketdyne jet pump running at 1664 rpm. The gearbox has a C drive configuration, both input and output shafts are at the aft end, and consists of a primary epicyclic train with a single helical parallel-shaft secondary train. An idler is required to cover the necessary centre distance from the gas-turbine to the Rocketdyne jet pump and also matches their standard rotations. The jet pump houses the main thrust bearing, therefore secondary gearbox bearings need only accommodate the thrust imposed by single helical gearing. A caliper disc brake is fitted to the free end of the secondary pinion enabling the main jet pump to be held stationary when using wing engine propulsion.

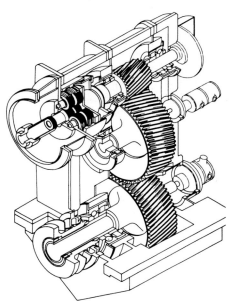

A section view of the Allen C form drive gearbox showing first and second stage reduction gears   **1988**

The Allen five-shaft C form 12 000 to 681 rpm reduction gearbox as fitted to an Fr Lürssen Werft luxury yacht, two 5406 kW (7250 hp) gas-turbines   **1988**

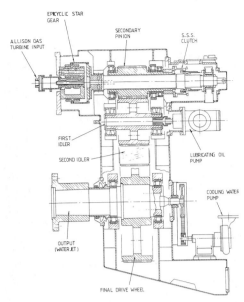

Sectioned view of one drive line of the five-shaft C form reduction gearbox   **1990**

FIVE-SHAFT C FORM DRIVE GEARBOX

As a follow-on from uprated gears for the Royal Navy, Allen Gears constructed a combined epicyclic and parallel-shaft C drive gearbox for a 46 m, 45 knot luxury yacht built by Fr Lürssen Werft of Germany. The yacht was powered by two Allison 570 gas-turbines driving KaMeWa water-jets. In addition there were two wing engines driving small water-jets of 1500 hp. Total available power was 17 500 hp. The gas-turbines were positioned aft, driving forward into the gearbox. Each of the turbines has a maximum input of 7250 hp at 12 000 rpm giving an output speed, to the water-jet unit from gearbox, of 681 rpm. A five-shaft configuration gearbox was adopted to accommodate the centre distance between the gas-turbines and the output shaft. The input is taken from the primary epicyclic train through quill-shafts, within the secondary pinion, to SSS self-synchronising clutches at the forward end of the gear case. This arrangement permits the second gas-turbine to be introduced to the drive line or to be disconnected without interruption of power.

HOVERCRAFT TRANSMISSIONS

Allen Gears' association with the Spanish Company CHACONSA and its VCA-36 craft has moved on to future developments with an overseas navy for a similar sized craft. This prototype vessel which more than surpassed expectation on trials utilises Pratt & Whitney gas-turbines for the lift system and Allied Signal gas-turbines for the propulsion system. In both cases the reduction gears are of Allen Gears' lightweight construction using the very latest gear technology. In order to achieve the best machinery layout and to meet the necessary weight targets Allen provided multi-stage parallel shaft gears in aluminium gear cases using gear components constructed according to proven aircraft methods. All techniques were fully tested with careful stress analysis in all areas prior to manufacture.

CODAG PROPULSION SYSTEM

The first seven ships of the Royal Danish Navy 'Standard Flex 300' multi-role vessel programme use a 'CODAG' propulsion plant powered by MTU 16V 396 TB 94 diesels for cruise and a GE LM 500 gas-turbine for boost. The engines drive through Allen vertically offset custom-engineered lightweight parallel shaft gearboxes with integral lubricating system. Each gearbox is equipped with a hydraulic motor which forms part of a hydraulic system (powered by a General Motors diesel) to meet the requirements of auxiliary propulsion during silent mine-hunting and economic loitering at nearly stationary patrols.

Port and starboard multi-stage hovercraft propulsion gearboxes   **1990**

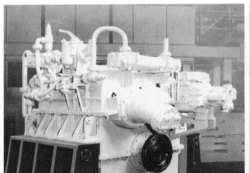

UPDATED   *Gas-turbine boost and diesel engine cruise gearboxes for 'Standard Flex 300'*   **1990**

UNITED STATES OF AMERICA

THE CINCINNATI GEAR COMPANY

5657 Wooster Pike, Cincinnati, Ohio 45227, USA

Telephone: +1 (513) 271 7700
Telefax: +1 (513) 271 0049

Steven J Crowell, *Marketing Manager*
Rob W Rye, *Marine Sales Manager*
Ken M Kiehl, *Advanced Programs Sales Manager*

The Cincinnati Gear Company, founded in 1907, specialises in high performance parallel shaft and epicyclic marine drives. Successful installations include the Jetfoil passenger ferry, the LCAC air cushion landing craft, the T-AO 187 class oiler, and the AOE 6 class support ship.

A leader in the design and manufacture of high power density gearing for gas-turbine and diesel applications, Cincinnati Gear offers a wide variety of gearbox and propulsion system designs. These include parallel shaft units ideal for offset installations and epicyclic units, featuring coaxial input and output shafts, for in-line arrangements.

Cincinnati Gear has utilised its extensive experience with military and commercial high-speed craft to develop the MA and MD series of standard marine reduction gearboxes. The MA and MD series offer the advantages of quicker delivery and lower cost than custom designs.

A CINTI MA-107 reduction gear with close coupled TF40 gas-turbine. This 3400 kW reduction gear is one of the MA series gearboxes being produced for vessels such as high-speed ferries and megayachts **1994**

Two CINTI dual input, locked train reversing reduction gears provide power transmission from LM 2500 gas-turbines to fixed-pitch propellers on the AOE 6 Class fleet support ships. These are the first surface hardened reverse reduction gears of their size in a US ship **1994**

Two CINTI parallel shaft gearboxes are used on each Kawasaki hydrofoil passenger ferry. Each gearbox transmits power from a 501-KF gas-turbine to a water-jet **1994**

Two CINTI parallel shaft gearboxes are used on a T-AO 187 class fleet oiler to transmit power from Colt Pielstick 10PC4.2V diesel engines. These gearboxes contain the largest carburised hardened and precision ground bull gears in Navy history **1994**

The MA series features highly versatile modular gearbox designs for gas-turbine-powered vessels such as megayachts, high-speed ferries and fast patrol boats. Standard MA gearboxes are available for a variety of gas-turbines, ranging from 800 to 25 000 kW. Available designs include epicyclic and single and dual input parallel shaft units in C- or Z-drive configurations as well as CODOG or CODAG arrangements.

The MD series was developed for marine applications using medium-speed diesels in the 3000 to 15 000 kW range, such as tankers and container ships. Standard MD designs are available for single and dual input applications, each with a number of clutch, thrust bearing and lube system options to suit most craft requirements.

UPDATED

Three different gearboxes, eight total, transmit lift and propulsion power for the LCAC hovercraft using TF40 gas-turbines
1995

DETROIT DIESEL CORPORATION

13400 Outer Drive West, Detroit, Michigan 48239-4001, USA

Telephone: +1 (313) 592 5000
Telex: 4320091
Telefax: +1 (313) 592 7288

Detroit Diesel Corporation provides a full range of transmissions to give an optimum match for each DDC engine. These transmissions are manufactured by Twin Disc Inc.

DETROIT DIESEL MARINE TRANSMISSIONS

Engine model	Configuration	Gear ratios
8.2L	10° Down Angle	1.54, 2.00
6V-53	Inline & 7° Down Angle	1.10, 1.51, 1.77, 1.98
6-71	Inline & 7° Down Angle	1.10, 1.51, 1.77, 1.98
	Vertical Offset	1.45, 1.71, 2.04
6V-92	Vertical Offset	1.45, 1.71, 2.00, 2.04
	7° Down Angle	1.45, 1.73, 1.96
8V-92	Vertical Offset	1.50, 1.74, 2.04
	7° Down Angle	1.48, 1.92
12V-71	Vertical Offset	1.29, 1.50, 1.76, 1.96, 2.48
	10° Down Angle	1.52, 1.77, 1.97
12V-92	Vertical Offset	1.29, 1.50, 1.64, 1.76, 1.83, 1.96, 2.03, 2.48, 2.55
	10° Down Angle	1.52, 1.66, 1.77, 1.97, 2.06, 2.48
16V-92	Vertical Offset	1.00, 1.45, 1.74, 2.04, 2.55
	10° Down Angle	1.53, 1.71, 1.92, 2.38
16V-149	Vertical Offset	2.52

UPDATED

DDC gearbox installation　　　*1990*

TWIN DISC INC

1328 Racine Street, Racine, Wisconsin 53403, USA

Telephone: +1 (414) 638 4000
Telex: 170336
Telefax: +1 (414) 638 4480

M E Batten, *Chairman, Chief Executive Officer*
M H Joyce, *President, Chief Operating Officer*
L J Melik, *Vice President, Marketing*
J McIndoe, *Vice President, International Marketing*

Twin Disc Incorporated manufactures marine propulsion systems including marine transmissions, electronic propulsion controls and Arneson Surface Drives.

Twin Disc marine transmissions feature helical gearing in most models for quieter operation; hydraulic-controlled and oil-cooled clutches for smooth, fast shifting; identical ratios in forward and reverse with full power in forward and reverse in most cases and minimal external plumbing. Down angle output configurations provide for near level engine installation and space saving remote and direct mounted V-drive models are also available.

Operational trolling valves are available for most Twin Disc models. This feature provides the ability to obtain lower propeller speeds than would be possible at engine idle with the clutch fully engaged. Omega Power Control, available on the MG-514M and MG-530M, is similar to the trolling valve except that it allows clutch modulation at higher engine speeds and provides an internal governor.

Optional torsional input couplings are available for most models and a number of power take-off options exists for many Twin Disc marine transmissions.

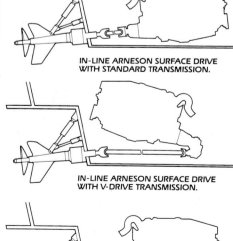

IN-LINE ARNESON SURFACE DRIVE WITH STANDARD TRANSMISSION.

IN-LINE ARNESON SURFACE DRIVE WITH V-DRIVE TRANSMISSION.

DROP-CENTER ARNESON SURFACE DRIVE WITH STANDARD TRANSMISSION.

Three possible layouts for Arneson Surface Drives
1993

Model	ASD 6	ASD 7	ASD 8	ASD 10	ASD 12	ASD 14	ASD 16	ASD 18
Horsepower acceptance								
petrol:	to 450-55-	to 730	to 1200	to be determined				
diesel:	to 235-300			to 3500 (subject to application)				
Unit weight, dry, with								
hydraulic cylinders (in-line):	61 kg		129 kg	189 kg			900 kg A	1769 kg A
(drop centre):	72 kg	147 kg	220 kg	272 kg	352 kg	515 kg	1150 kg B	2268 kg B
Overall external length:	914-991 mm	1114 mm	1067 mm	1270 mm	1638 mm	1805 mm	2184 mm	2896 mm
Steering angle:	40°	40°	40°	40°	40°	40°	36°	36°
Trim angle (max travel inclusive):	15°	15°	15°	15°	15°	15°	15°	13°
Materials								
socket:	A or B	A or B	B	B	B	B	A or B	A or B
thrust tube:	A or B	A or B	B	B	B	B	A or B	A or B
ball:	B	B	B	B	B	B	A or B	A or B
propeller shaft:		Aquamet 17 stainless steel						

A - aluminium alloy
B - manganese bronze

Twin Disc 'Power Commander' marine electronic propulsion controls feature precise, single lever control of clutch and throttle functions.

Twin Disc Arneson Surface Drives combine surface-piercing propeller technology with hydraulically actuated steering and trim control through angular displacement of the propeller shaft, providing greater propulsion and manoeuvring effectiveness. In most applications, elimination of underwater shafts, struts and rudders results in marked improvement in vessel performance and efficiency.

This concept allows complete flexibility of engine location, weight placement and effective reduction of noise and vibration. Hydraulic steering and propeller depth control provide outstanding manoeuvrability and shallow draft capability limited only by the draft of the vessel itself.

Twin Disc Arneson Surface Drives serve the commercial, military and pleasure craft markets. Differentiated by torque capacity, these drives are available for use with gasoline, diesel and gas-turbine engines up to approximately 5000 horsepower.

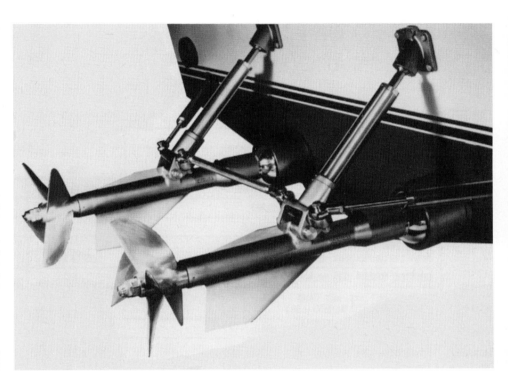

Arneson ASD 10 in-line unit
1993

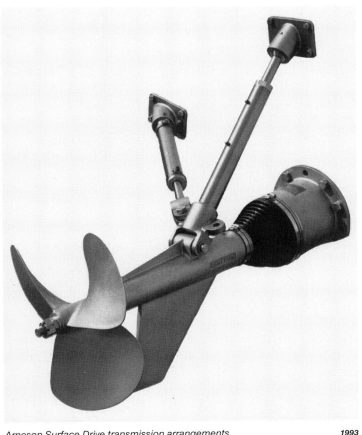

Arneson Surface Drive transmission arrangements   1993

Twin Disc Inc MG-5062V, V-drive marine transmission   *1994*

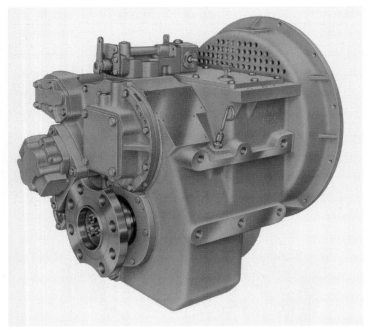

Twin Disc Inc MG-5141 marine transmission **1993**

Twin Disc MGNV-232E marine transmission **1994**

TWIN DISC MARINE TRANSMISSION

Model	Reduction Ratio (:1)	kW Intermediate @2100 rpm	hp Pleasurecraft @2300 rpm
MG-5010	1.11, 1.50, 2.00	90(121)	122(164)
	2.39	76(102)	122(154)
MG-5010A	1.44, 1.90	90(121)	122(164)
	2.39	76(102)	122(164)
MG-5010V	1.14, 1.55, 2.04	90(121)	122(164)
	2.46	76(102)	122(164)
MG-502-1	1.54, 2.00	100(140)	165(221)
MG-502	2.47	88(118)	138(185)
MG-5050	1.23, 1.53, 1.71, 2.04	139(186)	214(287)
	2.45, 3.00	139(186)	196(263)
MG-5050A & MG-5050V	1.12, 1.26, 1.50, 1.80	139(186)	214(287)
	2.04, 2.50	139(186)	196(263)
MG-506-1 & MG-506A	1.09, 1.50, 1.97	121(162)	192(260)
	2.50, 2.96	121(162)	172(230)
MG-506	3.79, 4.48	119(159)	—
MG-5061	1.15, 1.48, 1.77, 2.00, 2.43	187(250)	263(353)
	3.00	187(250)	245(329)
MG-5061A & MG-5061V	1.13, 1.54, 1.75, 2.00, 2.47	187(250)	263(353)
MG-5062V	1.19, 1.53, 1.83, 2.07, 2.51	187(250)	263(353)
MG-507-1 & MG-507A-1	0.75, 0.81, 0.92	254(340)	313(420)
	1.10, 1.51, 1.77, 1.98	235(315)	298(400)
	2.54	201(207)	239(320)
	2.99	179(240)	213(285)
MG-507-2 & MG-507A-2	1.10, 1.51, 1.77	—	373(500)
	1.98	—	336(450)
MG-5081	1.12, 1.51, 1.97	298(400)	433(580)
	2.48	242(325)	343(460)
MG-509	1.45, 2.00	235(315)	291(390)
	2.48	235(315)	275(370)
	2.95	216(290)	242(325)
	3.39	165(220)	195(260)
	3.83, 4.50	235(315)	—
	4.95	180(242)	—
MG-5091	1.17, 1.45, 1.71, 2.04	343(460)	503(675)
	2.45	321(430)	474(635)
	2.95	321(430)	418(560)
	3.38	(205(275)@1800)	

TWIN DISC MARINE TRANSMISSION

Model	Reduction Ratio (:1)	kW Intermediate @2100 rpm	hp Pleasurecraft @2300 rpm
MG-5091	3.82	321(430)	—
	4.50	298(400)	—
	5.10	(205(275)@1800)	
MG-5090A	1.45, 1.73, 1.96	343(460)	503(675)
	2.43	321(430)	418(560)
MG-5111	1.12, 1.50, 1.74, 2.04	429(575)	597(800)
	2.54	358(480)	548(735)
	3.10	321(430)	418(560)
	3.28	380(510)	574(770)
	3.92, 4.43	373(500)	—
	4.95	(283(380)@1800)	
MG-5111A & MG-5111V	1.20, 1.48, 1.75, 1.92	395(530)	597(800)
	2.44	358(480)	522(700)
MG-5112V	1.06, 1.23, 1.52, 1.80, 1.98	429(575)	597(800)
	2.51	358(480)	548(735)
MG-5113	5.50, 6.05, 6.48	(291(390)@1800)	
MG-5114A	1.03, 1.20, 1.48, 1.75, 1.92	503(675)	652(875)
	2.50	503(675)	626(840)
MG-514C & MG-514M*	1.51, 2.00, 2.50, 3.00	380(510)	485(650)
	3.50	336(450)	418(560)
	4.13, 4.50, 5.16	380(510)	—
	6.00	(283(380)@1800)	
MG-5141	1.17, 1.53, 1.71, 1.96	559(750)	746(1000)
	2.50	522(700)	671(900)
MG-516	3.07, 3.50, 4.40, 4.52, 5.50, 6.00	(405(543)@1800)	
MG-5161	5.86, 6.53, 7.00	(405(543)@1800)	
MG-518-1	1.48, 2.00, 2.47, 2.94, 4.06, 4.48, 5.07, 5.92	(447(600)@1800)	
	6.48	(410(550)@1800)	
MG-520-1	2.02, 2.51, 2.97, 3.44, 4.03, 4.49, 5.00, 6.11	(552(740)@1800)	
	7.00	(477(640)@1800)	
MG-5202	1.17, 1.53, 1.76, 2.03, 2.48, 2.92	671(900)	947(1270)
	3.48	641(860)	746(1000)
MG-530	1.59	947(1270)	—
	1.95	895(1200)	—
	2.34	846(1135)	—
	3.13	794(1065)	—
	4.04	753(1010)	—
	4.94	832(1115)	—

TWIN DISC MARINE TRANSMISSION

Model	Reduction Ratio (:1)	kW Intermediate @2100 rpm	hp Pleasurecraft @2300 rpm
MG-530	6.06	(701(940)@1800)	
	7.27	(637(855)@1800)	
MG-530M*	1.59, 1.95, 2.34	832(1115)	—
	3.13	794(1065)	—
	4.04	753(1010)	—
	4.94	832(1115)	—
	6.06	(701(940)@1800)	
	7.27	(637(855)@1800)	
MG-540	1.92, 2.58, 2.90	(940(1260)@1800)	
	3.26	1156(1550)	—
	3.91	1037(1390)	—
	4.60	(925(1240)@1800)	
	5.17	1115(1495)	—
	6.18	(802(1075)@1800)	
	7.00	(746(1000)@1800)	
	7.47	(701(940)@1800)	
MGN-80	1.57, 1.79, 1.97, 2.52	526(705)	671(900)
	2.96	509(683)	628(843)
	3.52	477(639)	601(806)
MGNV-232E	1.54, 1.73, 1.96	600(805)	895(1200)
	2.43	544(729)	746(866)
MGN-232E	1.29, 1.50, 1.76, 1.96	724(972)	895(1200)
	2.48	565(757)	699(937)
MGN-233E	1.57, 1.79, 1.97, 2.52	761(1020)	895(1200)
	2.96	663(890)	774(1038)
	3.52	558(749)	652(874)
MGN-272	1.18, 1.50, 1.74	868(1164)	1103(1479)
	2.04	819(1099)	1103(1479)

TWIN DISC MARINE TRANSMISSION

Model	Reduction Ratio (:1)	kW Intermediate @2100 rpm	hp Pleasurecraft @2300 rpm
MGNV-272E	1.66, 1.81, 2.07	868(1164)	1103(1479)
	2.46	793(1063)	1006(1349)
MGN-273E	1.64, 1.83, 2.03, 2.55	862(1156)	1103(1479)
	3.12	725(972)	955(1280)
MGN-332G	1.00, 1.45, 1.71	1166(1563)	1430(1917)
	2.04	1118(1499)	1430(1917)
	2.36	1006(1349)	1306(1751)
MGNV-332G	1.53, 1.72	1004(1346)	1430(1917)
	1.93	954(1279)	1430(1917)
	2.43	780(1046)	1306(1751)
MGN-334	2.52, 3.00, 3.46, 4.04	1089(1461)	1430(1917)
MGNV-432	1.52, 2.03	1450(1945)	1798(2412)
	2.53	1164(1561)	1455(1937)
MGN-433G	1.18	1472(1974)	—
	1.53, 1.71, 2.06	1579(2118)	—
	2.52, 3.00	1487(1994)	—
MGN-472	1.53, 2.11	2008(2693)	—
	2.52	1809(2426)	—
MGNV-472	1.52, 1.95	2017(2705)	—
	2.46	1708(2290)	—

* Special operating limits apply. Consult Twin Disc.
A = Down Angle
V = V-drive
M = Omega Power Control
The V in Twin Disc MGN Series transmission designations indicates 10° down angle output. C-drive and V-drive configurations are also available

UPDATED

AIR PROPELLERS

Company Listing by Country

Germany
Hoffmann Propeller GmbH & Company KG
MT-Propeller Entwicklung GmbH & Company KG

United Kingdom
Air Vehicles Ltd
Dowty Aerospace Propellers

United States of America
Ardco
Pacific Propeller Inc

GERMANY

HOFFMANN PROPELLER GmbH & COMPANY KG

PO Box 100339, Küpferlingstrasse 9, D-8200 Rosenheim 2, Germany

Telephone: +49 (8031) 32011
Telex: 525811 HOCO D
Telefax: +49 (8031) 15832

Richard Wurm, *Proprietor*
Johann Sterr, *Managing Director*

Hoffmann Propeller GmbH and Company KG was founded in 1955 by Ing Richard Wurm, starting with six employees. Now Hoffmann has 70 employees and the company is not only involved in the field of general aviation propellers but also in that of hovercraft. Propellers absorbing an input power up to 2000 kW are designed and manufactured for these craft. Besides this, blades for wind energy converters, blowers and large fan blades for wind tunnel application in the automotive industry are in current production. Propeller overhaul and service is provided for all types of Hoffmann propellers and also for other manufacturers' propellers.

The company covers the following certifications: LBA EC-2 for design and development of aircraft propellers; LBA I-C 14 for production of aircraft propellers and equipment; LBA II-A 35 for repair of aircraft propellers and governors of all types; FAA BV5Y-767M for repair and overhaul of aircraft pro-

pellers and accessories; CAA Hovercraft Approval for design and production of hovercraft propellers.

After completing the enlargement of the factory in 1990 the company now covers an area of 5700 m², enabling Hoffmann not only to increase production but also to engage in new product design and research. Hovercraft propellers manufactured by Hoffmann incorporate various special features. The excellent erosion resistance of the composite materials used is far superior to that of aluminium alloy. The wood laminations are reinforced with carbon or glass fibre which adds torsional strength and offers resistance to impact of particles entering the propeller disc.

For improved erosion protection the blades optionally have a special Irathane coating. The leading edge protection is made of stainless steel totally integrated into the airfoil profile. Additional protection against erosion is guaranteed by different kinds of erosion strip.

Since 1960 fixed-pitch, ground-adjustable and either hydraulically or mechanically controlled variable and reverse pitch propellers have been continuously built for air propeller driven boats, snow sledges and hovercraft.

Chaconsa, VCA-2/3; two two-blade ground-adjustable propellers, free, driven by about 150 kW, 2 m diameter.
Wärtsilä Larus; four four-blade hydraulically controlled propellers, forward and reverse pitch, driven by about 550 kW, 3 m diameter.

BHC AP1-88; two four-blade ground-adjustable propellers per craft, ducted, driven by approximately 370 kW, 2.75 m diameter.
Chaconsa VCA-36; two five-blade hydraulically controlled, forward and reverse pitch propellers (one left-hand, one right-hand rotation), free, driven by 1000 kW, 4 m diameter.
Slingsby, Tropimere 6; two three-blade ground-adjustable propellers, 1.10 m diameter.
Slingsby SAH 2200 (ex 1500); one three-blade reversible-pitch propeller, ducted, 1.40 m diameter.
Marineswift Thunderbolt 30; one five-blade ground-adjustable propeller, driven by approximately 200 kW, 1.12 m diameter.
CIS; two hydraulically controlled propellers, ducted, driven by 257 kW, 3 m diameter and for a 25 m Hovercraft a five-blade hydraulically controlled propeller, ducted, driven by 1800 kW, 3.6 m diameter.
Griffon 2000 TDXs for the Swedish Coast Guard; two four-blade variable-pitch propellers, mechanically controlled, 1.80 m diameter, driven by 239 kW Deutz V8 diesel engines.
Several new Hovercraft propellers are in development. By the enlargement of the factory, Hoffmann Propeller is now in a position to fully engage in new projects and to explore new paths of technology.

VERIFIED

Canadian Coast Guard BHC AP1-88 hovercraft propelled by Hoffmann ducted propellers HO-V254 **1990**

Hoffmann 3.6 m diameter five-blade propeller **1990**

MT-PROPELLER ENTWICKLUNG GmbH & COMPANY KG

PO Box 0720, Airport D-94307 Straubing, Germany

Telephone: +49 (9429) 8433
Telefax: +49 (9429) 8432

Gerd Mühlbauer, *President*

This company was formed in 1982 and is involved mainly in the production of propellers for aircraft. It has developed a range of electric variable-pitch propellers and hydraulic constant speed propellers. Some of the propellers are LBA approved. The largest diameter propeller built by the end of 1986 was 2.9 m for 800 shp, but designs can be undertaken up to 3.5 m 2000 shp and above.

UPDATED

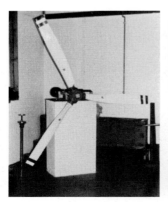

Examples of recent MT-Propeller Entwicklung propellers **1987**

UNITED KINGDOM

AIR VEHICLES LTD

Head Office and Factory: Unit 4, Three Gates Road, Cowes, Isle of Wight, UK

Telephone: +44 (1983) 293194
Telex: 86513 HVWORK G
Telefax: +44 (1983) 291987

C B Eden, *Director*

Air Vehicles Limited has been involved in hovercraft since 1968 and manufactures specialist components for fully amphibious hovercraft, SES and other types of fast ferries.

Air propellers: Propellers are normally custom-designed to suit the application. Sizes up to 2.2 m diameter of fixed- and variable-pitch types have been produced. Larger sizes are available.

Propeller ducts: Associated propeller ducts are designed and manufactured up to propeller diameter of 3.6 m and absorbing 2900 hp.

Fans: Axial, mixed flow and centrifugal fans are produced for hovercraft and SES vessels. They are usually manufactured in marine aluminium alloy giving a robust fan with good fatigue life. Systems requiring high flow and pressure such as SES are often supplied complete with lightweight volute and transmission system. As the main supplier of fans to the UK hovercraft industry, all fans are designed and manufactured to comply with the British Hovercraft Safety Requirements. This will usually ensure compliance with all other classification societies.

Skirt systems: The design and manufacture of SES and amphibious hovercraft skirt systems.

Bulkheads and doors: Design and manufacturer of lightweight bulkheads and partitioning systems for fast ferry interiors. Lightweight, easy fit door and surround assemblies.

Seating: Air Vehicles Limited designs and manufactures seating systems under the name of Advanced Seating Technology for hovercraft, SES and fast ferries.

AST 2000: UK Civil Aviation Authority type approved hovercraft seating, tested to 6 *g* and complying with CAA8 issue 3 fire regulations.

AST 3000: Lightweight high performance fast ferry seating tested to comply with IMO strength and fire regulations.

UPDATED

Typical centrifugal fans and propeller manufactured by Air Vehicles

1993

DOWTY AEROSPACE PROPELLERS

Anson Business Park, Cheltenham Road East, Gloucester GL2 9QN, UK

Telephone: +44 (1452) 714888
Telex: 43246
Telefax: +44 (1452) 711333

D G M Davis, *Managing Director*
R G Nailer, *Commercial Director*
J D Kemp, *Engineering Manager*

A R Cooper, *Marketing Manager*
G C Hanson, *Marketing Manager*

Dowty Aerospace Propellers, an operating business of Dowty Aerospace Gloucester Limited and a member of the TI Group, has been designing and manufacturing propellers for aircraft since 1937 when the company was originally formed as Rotol Airscrews Ltd. For over 30 years the company has been actively engaged in propulsion systems for air cushion vehicles.

The company is at present working on the production of propellers for the Textron Marine LCAC vehicles, together with its more recent C-7 air cushion vehicle project.

In support of Dowty Aerospace products world-

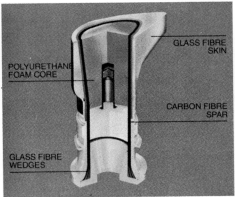

Dowty blade root retention features   *1988*

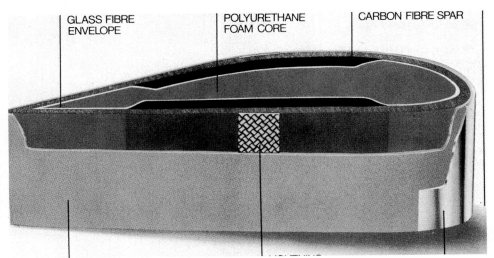

Dowty all-composite blade construction   *1988*

Dowty ducted propeller installation on the Textron Marine LCAC   **1990**

wide, a network of repair and overhaul facilities are available. These facilities are strategically placed in the USA, Europe and South-east Asia.

Dowty Aerospace Aviation Services
Cheltenham Road, Gloucester GL2 9QH, UK

Telephone: +44 (1452) 713111
Telex: 43246
Telefax: +44 (1452) 711954

Dowty Aerospace Aviation Services
21 Loyang Crescent, Loyang Industrial Estate, 1750 Singapore

Telephone: +65 545 9455
Telex: 21447
Telefax: +65 542 3936

Dowty Aerospace Aviation Services
PO Box 5000, Sully Road, Sterling, Virginia 22170, USA

Telephone: +1 (703) 450 8200
Telex: 824459
Telefax: +1 (703) 430 9060

Hovercraft installations (Air cushion vehicles)
British Hovercraft Corporation SR. N5, SR. N6, 2.744 m diameter, four-blade hydraulic pitch control with reversing, single propeller installation, produced in aluminium alloy and composite material construction

Dowty all-composite propeller for the Textron Marine LCAC   **1986**

British Hovercraft Corporation SR. N6 Mk 6, 3.049 m diameter, four-blade, hydraulic pitch control with reversing, two-propeller installation, aluminium alloy blades
Mitsui PP15 3.201 m diameter, four-blade, hydraulic pitch control with reversing, single propeller installation, aluminium alloy blades
Vosper Thornycroft VT2 4.116 m diameter, seven-blade, two-propeller installation (ducted), composite material blades
Textron Marine LCAC 3.582 m diameter, four-blade, two-propeller installation (ducted) composite material blades
Textron Marine C-7 2.438 m diameter, four-blade, two-propeller installation (ducted), composite material blades

The extensive corrosion and erosion problems associated with air cushion vehicles led Dowty to develop composite blades with all-over erosion protection. These blades, the latest of which incorporate advanced technology aerofoil sections unique to Dowty, offer the following advantages: low weight combined with high strength, internal carbon fibre spars for high integrity, freedom from corrosion and they are easily repairable.

Dowty propellers for air cushion vehicles are designed to combine simple construction with safe operation. Techniques proven on ACVs have in turn been applied to and certificated on new generation general aviation, executive and commuter aircraft.

UPDATED

UNITED STATES OF AMERICA

ADVANCE RATIO DESIGN COMPANY INC

2540 Green Street, JEN Industrial Campus, Chester, Pennsylvania 19013, USA

Telephone: +1 (215) 494 3200
Telefax: +1 (215) 494 5079

Carl L Aley, *President*
David F Thompson, *Technical Director*
Craig D Thompson, *Vice President*

ARDCO specialises in composite airfoil blading and structures. The ARDCO team has designed and produced blades for turboprops, ducted propulsion fans, hovercraft compressors and helicopter main and tail rotors, also model blades for advanced unducted fan testing. Over the past few years ARDCO has done extensive design work on large ducted props for the Westinghouse naval airship programme. Materials include glass fibre, graphite and/or Kevlar/epoxy, oriented linear-filament reinforced materials, compression moulded with low density cores of honeycomb or foam plastic and flush co-bonded metal leading edge erosion strips. ARDCO produces blades to fit existing hubs or complete rotor assemblies, as required. The company also uses Resin Transfer Moulding (RTM) techniques where unusually massive (some hollow-ribbed) composite structures of hundreds of pounds weight are required, such as for marine propellers. Complete vehicle airframe structures are also custom-designed and fabricated.

HIGH PERFORMANCE SURFACE-CRAFT PROPELLER

ARDCO is in the process of developing a specialised fan/propeller series useful for a variety of high performance surface craft which utilises ducted propulsion, such as hovercraft and airboats. The family of fan/propellers to be made available will offer a spread of characteristics as follows:
Diameters: 914-1321 mm
Number of blades: 2,3,4,6,12 with equi-spaced patterns
Pitch angle: ground-adjustable pitch
Power input: approx 134 kW
Rotational tip speeds: 122-167 m/s

The objective for this propeller series is quiet operation while giving efficient performance and hence, operating at moderate tip speeds, these propellers require large blade area and/or a larger number of blades.

The blades with relatively thin aerofoils are solid glass-filament epoxy, pressure-moulded and featuring integrally bonded stainless steel leading-edge abrasion caps to protect against water spray environments.

The hub is pressure moulded in glass fibre-reinforced composite material and features ground-adjustable blade pitch, allowing power absorption versus rpm to be fine tuned.

The propeller is designed for long life and minimal maintenance in a marine environment and towards this end total elimination of metal-to-metal contact is embodied as well as minimisation of exposed metal surfaces.

UPDATED

ARDCO all-composite surface-craft propeller
1990

PACIFIC PROPELLER INC

5802 South 228th Street, Kent, Washington 98032-1187, USA

Telephone: +1 (206) 872 7767
Telex: 32-0368
Telefax: +1 (206) 872 7221

Dennis Patrick, *President*
Gary Bottoms, *Director of Business Development*

Pacific Propeller manufactures, overhauls and sells propeller systems for aircraft and hovercraft use, having been in this business since 1946. PPI has manufactured over 10 000 metal propeller blades for single and multi-engine installations and is the current supplier of propellers for the Canadian Coast Guard SR. N5, SR. N6 and Voyageur hovercraft. In addition, PPI designed and manufactured propeller blades are the only current production units approved for installation on the US Army LACV-30 hovercraft. By the Autumn of 1991 over 500 AG200-1S blades had been supplied to the US Army for use on the LACV-30.

HC200-1S PROPELLER BLADE

This is a hard alloy derivative of the AG-series blades manufactured for aircraft use. It is designed to be tougher and more erosion-resistant to the effects of salt and sand spray. Typical hovercraft installations use the three-bladed HSP 43D50 hub coupled to the Pratt & Whitney ST6 TwinPac or the Rolls-Royce Gnome turbine engines. Propeller diameter is 2.72 m. This configuration has been tested in excess of 1600 hp and is safe for operation up to 2300 rpm. Each blade weighs 22.22 kg and can be overhauled using standard propeller overhaul facilities.

UPDATED

MARINE PROPELLERS

Company Listing by Country

Australia
Veem Engineering Group

Denmark
Hundested Motor and Propeller Fabrik A/S

Germany
Schottel-Werft
Sulzer-Escher Wyss GmbH

Italy
Eliche Radice SpA
LA. ME Srl

Japan
Kamome Propeller Company Ltd

Netherlands
Lips BV

Norway
Servogear A/S
Ulstein Propeller A/S

Sweden
Berg Propulsion AB
KaMeWa AB

Switzerland
Rolla SP Propellers SA
Rolla (USA)

United Kingdom
Brunton's Propellers Ltd
Stone Manganese Marine Ltd
Teignbridge Propellers Ltd

United States of America
Bird-Johnson Company
Michigan Wheel Corporation
T-Torque Drive System Inc

AUSTRALIA

VEEM ENGINEERING GROUP

10 Ballantyne Road, Kewdale 6105, Western Australia, Australia

Telephone: +61 (9) 351 8388
Telefax: +61 (9) 350 5302

M Miocevich, *Manager*

Manufacturer of propellers from 250 to 2550 mm in diameter in three-, four- or five-blade designs. Materials include 88/10/2 gun metal, CX3 manganese bronze, AB2 aluminium bronze or CMAI bronze.

The company works to quality assurance standard ISO 9002 and provides propellers for a wide variety of craft in Australia and New Zealand including many fast commercial craft.

Propellers can be supplied with up to five, six or seven blades and finished to ISO 484/2-1981 (E) to Class 2, 1 or S standards as required.

UPDATED

DENMARK

HUNDESTED MOTOR AND PROPELLER FABRIK A/S

Skansevej 1, DK-3390 Hundested, Denmark

Telephone: +45 0233 7117
Telex: 40245 HMF DK
Telefax: +45 0233 9902

Designers and manufacturers of controllable-pitch propellers since 1929. The 20 knot RMI SD-60 *Halcyon* Swath vessel is fitted with Hundested 1143 mm diameter fully reversible (Type FR-H) propellers.

VERIFIED

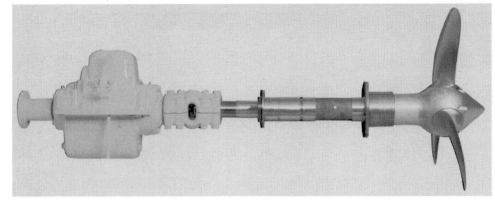

Hundested Type FR-H controllable-pitch propeller system as fitted to the RMI Halcyon   *1993*

GERMANY

SCHOTTEL-WERFT
Josef Becker GmbH & Co KG
Mainzer Strasse 99, D-56322 Spay/Rhein, Germany

Telephone: +49 (2628) 610
Telefax: +49 (2628) 61300

Uwe Gragen, *Director, Sales and Marketing*

SCHOTTEL manufactures and supplies marine propulsion systems. The company also provides consultancy services using experience gained from the engineering and installation of more than 20 000 Rudderpropellers and pump jets.

The first two (of a planned series of 10) passenger catamarans for Sydney Harbour, Australia, have gone into operation. Both vessels are fitted with SCHOTTEL SRP 132/131 Rudderpropellers and control systems. The vessels, named *Dawn Frazer* and *Betty Cuthbert*, were built by NQEA and are operated by the State Transit Authority of New South Wales on a regular service on the Parramatta River.

VERIFIED

Dawn Frazer *and* Betty Cuthbert *fitted with* SCHOTTEL *Rudderpropellers*
1993

SULZER-ESCHER WYSS GmbH

PO Box 1380, D-88183 Ravensburg, Germany

Telephone: +49 (751) 830
Telex: 732901
Telefax: +49 (751) 833274

Sulzer-Escher Wyss has considerable experience in the design and production of controllable-pitch propellers, many supplied for frigates, corvettes, patrol boats, mine countermeasure vessels and special purpose vessels. A particularly interesting feature developed in 1970 by Sulzer-Escher Wyss for higher speed propellers is an air ejection system to reduce the noise consequences of cavitation. Compressed air is led to channels in the leading edges of the blades and vented through a multiplicity of small holes at face and back, blade root and tip, therefore creating an air cushion over the blade. This air cushion reduces the noise generated by a cavitating propeller considerably. Over 140 propellers have been supplied with this system. A further promising development investigated by Sulzer-Escher Wyss is an increase in the number of blades to seven. Extensive model tests have shown that an interesting increase of the cavitation inception speed can be obtained without a penalty in efficiency: a disadvantage expected from the resultant slightly larger hub ratio is compensated by a reduction of the induction losses (approach to a propeller with an infinite number of blades). The mechanical hub design has been completed on the basis of the same loads and safety factors as have proven reliable in five-bladed propellers. The first seven-bladed frigate propellers are in operation.

A recent seven-blade controllable-pitch propeller design was supplied for the Blohm+Voss Corsair SES. The semi-submerged propellers for this vessel have the following characteristics:

Diameter: 1200 mm
Hub ratio: 0.32
Design pitch ratio: 1.75
Max shaft power: 2560 kW
Rotational speed: 940 rpm

VERIFIED

One of the two Sulzer-Escher Wyss 1.2 m diameter controllable-pitch propellers fitted to the Blohm+Voss 52 knot Corsair SES
1992

ITALY

ELICHE RADICE SpA

Via Valtellina 45, I-20092 Cinisello Balsamo, Milan, Italy

Telephone: +39 (2) 6604 9348
Telex: 332352 RADPRO I
Telefax: +39 (2) 6612 7688

Alfredo Radice, *Proprietor*
Carlo Radice, *Proprietor*

Manufacture of fixed-pitch propellers for high-speed craft. Early Hovermarine HM2 craft were fitted with Radice propellers in stainless steel. Bronze propellers with two to five blades and diameters up to 3.5 m can be supplied.

VERIFIED

LA. ME Srl

Via Della Fornace 4, Dosso Cavalino, I-20090 Opera, Milan, Italy

Telephone: +39 (2) 5760 2441
Telex: 3802831 I
Telefax: +39 (2) 5760 3549

Marco Lazzati, *Managing Director*
Ing Giovanni Patrone Raggi, *Sales and Marketing Manager*

LDU

LDU is an evolution of the 'Step Drive' offering the advantages of the conventional 'Z' drive with the increased performance of surface propulsion; it is claimed to maintain all the advantages of the surface propeller and eliminates completely the negative aspects which have plagued and prevented the acceptance of this excellent system of propulsion for many years.

During its short life the LDU has been successfully fitted on hundreds of craft in pleasure, workboat and military categories.

The engine may be fitted amidships or right aft without the added complication of a costly V-drive and transmission shaft. The tunnel rudders over the top half of the propellers have been employed to overcome some of the disadvantages of conventional rudders or propeller power steering. The two vertical rudder blades which are a continuation of the shroud act as sidewalls and, operating below the hull, give positive control as required as well as protecting the propeller in shallow water.

To enhance the reverse thrust capabilities of a fixed-pitch propeller a new blade section profile has been devised giving, on the back of the blade, a concave area towards the trailing edge, producing improved section lift coefficient and hence thrust when in reverse rotation.

The propeller incorporating this profile is called the Diamond Back surface propeller and overcomes the poor astern thrust associated with surface propellers.

The present range of LDU units extends from 37 to 2980 kW (indicative power limits).

Principal Features
Body of LDU: monocoque structure in 316L stainless steel, welded and heat-treated
Rudder: of semi-circular design together with reinforcing plate and stock of 316L stainless steel plate and bar respectively
Rudder linkage: consisting of yoke, dummy tiller and tie rod terminals in cast 316L stainless steel, or Nickel-Aluminium-Bronze

Diamond Back surface propeller　　*1987*

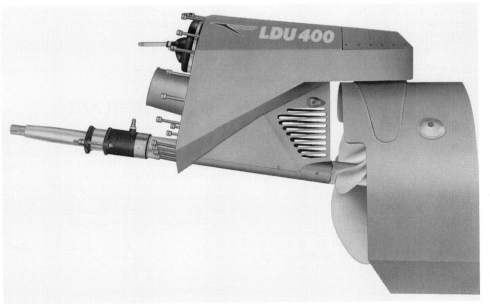

LDU, Model 400　　*1992*

LDU Model data

Model	LDU100	200PL	300	400	600	1000PL	2400PL	3000PL
Max torque, shaft, kg/m	45	105	175	205	270	470	850	1500
rpm/hp indicative limits	120 hp at 1950 rpm to 292 hp at 4760 rpm	280 hp at 1920 rpm to 380 hp at 2600 rpm	380 hp at 1554 rpm to 600 hp at 2460 rpm	438 hp at 1540 rpm to 700 hp at 1850 rpm	500 hp at 1460 rpm to 800 hp at 2130 rpm	700 hp at 1070 rpm to 1200 hp at 1850 rpm	1200 hp at 1010 rpm to 2200 hp at 1650 rpm	2200 hp at 1050 rpm to 3500 hp —
Max torque, rudder stock, kg/m	30	75	125	150	150	250	500	800
Exhaust, outside diameter mm	120	130	168	168	168	200	300	460
Fitting to transom (studs)	22	22	22	22	22	22	22	24
Lubrication, linkage	molybdenum grease	molybdenum grease	molybdenum grease	molybdenum grease	molybdenum grease	molybdenum grease	molybdenum grease	molybdenum grease
Lubrication, shaft	water	water	water	water	water	water	water	water
Dimensions: A, mm	806	878	1030	1117	1117	1356	1596	1995
Dimensions: B, mm	670	805	961	1019	1019	1231	1450	1845
Dimensions: C, mm	526	635	735	798	798	952	1120	1400
Weight, excluding propeller, kg	85	140	240	265	600	1100	2200	

Propeller shaft: Armco Aquamet 17-18-22 or monel k 500

Surface propeller: four-blade with Diamond Back sections cast in Nickel-Aluminium-Bronze (NAB). For the Model 2400PL and above propellers are five- and seven-blade

Shaft bearings: Water-lubricated in synthetic fibre

Recent Applications

LA. ME Srl propellers have recently been fitted to a number of larger high-speed marine craft: the Brooke Marine 33 m, 50 knot pleasure boat *G-Whiz*; the Brooke Marine 50 knot *Virgin Atlantic Challenger II*, Italian custom patrol boat 16.5 m, 49 knots, 14 other custom boats and three patrol craft for the UAE.

UPDATED

LDU dimensions, see table
1988

JAPAN

KAMOME PROPELLER COMPANY LTD

690 Kamiyabe-cho, Totsuka-ku, Yokohama 245, Japan

Telephone: +81 (45) 811 2461
Telefax: +81 (45) 811 9444

Hiroshi Itazawa, *President*

Design and manufacture of a wide range of controllable-pitch propellers from 224 to 11 186 kW. Installations have included 1750 mm diameter, 1400 mm pitch CPC-53F propellers on the Mitsui 20.5 knot *Kotozaki*, a 27 m Swath vessel.

UPDATED

NETHERLANDS

LIPS BV

PO Box 6, NL-5150 BB Drunen, Netherlands

Telephone: +31 (4163) 88115
Telex: 35185 LIPS NL
Telefax: +31 (4163) 73162

Lips was established in 1934 and is the world leader in the field of marine propellers, covering fixed-pitch, controllable-pitch, side-thruster and systems to their own design. There are 500 employees in the Netherlands company.

The company has provided propellers for a number of high-speed craft including Fjellstrand catamarans for Turkey and Norway and the FBM Marine FDC 400 fast displacement catamaran.

VERIFIED

Lips transcavitating CP propeller that was designed for the US Navy SES Sea Viking
1988

NORWAY

SERVOGEAR A/S

N-5420 Rubbestadneset, Norway

Telephone: +47 (53) 427380
Telex: 40909 N
Telefax: +47 (53) 427783

Leif M Endresen, *Technical Manager*

Designers and manufacturers of controllable-pitch propellers (up to 2000 hp) and drive systems. Servogear propellers are on a number of high-speed craft including the Westamarin S80 monohull vessel *Vøringen* and the Westamarin W95 *Sunnhordland*.

A new V-drive system, Type VD 250A, specifically for high-speed craft was announced in 1986. This unit has a built-in clutch and a servo for controllable-pitch propellers. The gearbox has the following characteristics:
Max continuous power input: 590 kW at 2300 rpm
Reduction ratio: 1.96:1
Torque: 2500 Nm
Dry weight: 160 kg

Servogear propellers are manufactured in manganese bronze for the bosses and nickel-aluminium-bronze for the blades, but other materials can be used if requested.

UPDATED

Servogear propulsion system with 'Power Rudder'

1990

ULSTEIN PROPELLER A/S

N-6065 Ulsteinvik, Norway

Telephone: +47 (700) 14000
Telex: 42 848 UP N
Telefax: +47 (700) 14017

Stig Ulstein, *Managing Director*
Jarle Hessen, *Sales Manager*

Designers and manufacturers of controllable-pitch propellers, tunnel thrusters, compass thrusters and the Speed-Z Propulsion System. The Speed-Z system is marketed in the output range of 700 to 2800 kW with controllable- and fixed-pitch propellers. Orders for the Speed-Z system have been received from the following shipyards: Westamarin A/S, Fjellstrand A/S, Broward Marine Inc and Baglietto Shipyard. High-speed applications have included a controllable-pitch installation on the Fjellstrand high-speed catamaran, *Asie III* and two Speed-Z four-blade propulsion units, Type CPZ, for the Westamarin W5000 *Anne Lise*, 49.5 m high-

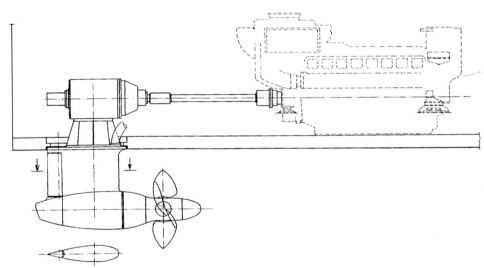

Layout of the Speed-Z Propulsion System Type CPZ

1988

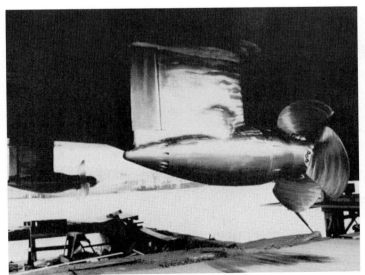

Ulstein Speed-Z Propulsion Systems Type CPZ 60/40-125 fitted to the Westamarin 5000 Anne Lise, *28 knot thermo-cargo catamaran. More recently Ulstein controllable-pitch propellers have been fitted to the Swath vessel* Navatek 1

1988

speed thermo-cargo catamaran, delivered June/July 1987. These units each absorb 2040 kW and position the propellers in undisturbed free-stream flow. In comparison with conventional propeller systems an efficiency gain of 10 per cent is claimed. The system combines propulsion and steering functions. Other advantages of the Speed-Z propulsion system are reduced vibration and noise onboard, a cost-efficient compact installation, effective load control for protection of the drive motors and good manoeuvring capability.

Since Speed-Z is a traction (pulling) propeller there are no appendages in front of it and therefore the propeller acts in a homogeneous velocity field. These are ideal conditions for efficiency and avoidance of damaging cavitation. This has been substantiated by cavitation tests and prototypes in operation which produce no noticeable noise or vibration in the hull.

Another major advantage is the right angle drive which allows the propeller to be installed in line with the water flow. A conventional propeller installation is always a compromise between keeping the shaft angle low to avoid harmful root cavitation and ensuring sufficient clearance between the propeller and the hull to avoid noise and vibration from the high pressure pulses created by the propeller. The Speed-Z unit has, as mentioned, the best possible conditions of flow to the propeller giving stable cavitation conditions and minimal fluctuating forces.

A comparison has been made, based on model test tank results with the Speed-Z unit, with a conventional installation with sloping shaft, brackets and rudder. The propeller on the conventional installation had a diameter of 1.6 m with a maximum speed of 525 rpm, while the Speed-Z unit has a diameter of 1.25 m at 769 rpm. Even though the Speed-Z unit is higher loaded, that is, the power per unit area is greater, the propeller efficiency is 76 per cent at an engine output of 2040 kW and ship speed of 28 knots. The corresponding efficiency of a conventional installation is about 72 per cent. When the resistance of the appendages was taken into account the improvement in efficiency was even more significant. The result of the model tests showed that the overall propulsive efficiency of the model fitted with the Speed-Z was 66 per cent at 28 knots which compared with 58 per cent for the conventional system as described previously. In this case the new Speed-Z gave an improvement in efficiency of eight per cent, that is to say a saving in installed power of 13.8 per cent to achieve the same speed.

UPDATED

Ulstein Speed-Z Propulsion Unit showing the top reduction gear with clutch and the lower 90° reduction gear with rudder flap and propeller mounting
1988

SWEDEN

BERG PROPULSION AB

S-430 90 Öckerö, Gothenburg, Sweden

Telephone: +46 (31) 969020
Telex: 2401 8206027
Telefax: +46 (31) 969456

Berg Propulsion AB is one of the world's leading companies in the design, development and manufacture of controllable-pitch propellers. Since 1928 Berg has manufactured and delivered more than 5000 propulsion systems.

Berg Propulsion AB offers a new line of propellers manufactured in composite materials. The materials are cheap and easily available and very simple production techniques have been developed. The main idea behind the concept of the FLEXPROP, as these new propellers are known, is to make use of the elastic properties of the blades in reducing load variations when they are operating in irregular flow at the stern of a vessel.

VERIFIED

KaMeWa AB

PO Box 1010, S-681 29 Kristinehamn, Sweden

Telephone: +46 (550) 84000
Telex: 66050 KAMEWA S
Telefax: +46 (550) 84778

Ingar Jensen, *Managing Director*
Claes Rudling, *Sales Director*
Olof Malmquist, *Public Relations Manager*

KaMeWa has accumulated experience from over 50 years of activity in the marine field. The company is also the only manufacturer of propellers to possess a cavitation laboratory with comprehensive facilities for advanced testing of various forms of marine propulsion device.

The KaMeWa design and manufacture of propellers for high-speed craft covers super-cavitating designs, which are modified to meet quiet and high efficiency cruising conditions, wide-blade design for these conditions, skewed wide-blade propellers for extremely quiet cruising and the same design for ventilated blades. These propellers are manufactured in either stainless steel or nickel-aluminium-bronze. Propellers for patrol boats have been supplied over many years. Some of the most recent installations are for patrol boats and corvettes for

Finnish Navy's Turku *equipped with three KaMeWa featherable controllable-pitch propellers, 3000 kW per shaft*
1993

Finland, Greece, Italy, South Korea, Malaysia, Morocco, Spain and Thailand.

The water-jet unit is becoming an ever increasing alternative for high-speed craft propulsion. KaMeWa is leading in this field (please see the KaMeWa entry in the *Water-jet units* section).

UPDATED

SWITZERLAND

ROLLA SP PROPELLERS SA

Via Silva 5, PO Box 251, CH-6828 Balerna, Switzerland

Telephone: +41 (91) 439361
Telefax: +41 (91) 430653

Remo Cattaneo, *President*
Philip Rolla, *Managing Director*
Mark Wilson, *Director of Production*
Marzio Porro, *Research and Development*
Franco Gotta, *Applications Engineer*
John Rose, *Director of Rolla USA*

ROLLA (USA)

4030 Mustang Road, Melbourne, Florida 32934, USA

Telephone: +1 (407) 242 7552
Telefax: +1 (407) 242 7771

The company was founded in 1963 by Philip Rolla. The services, consultation and designs include: performance and power prediction for displacement and planing craft; propeller design; one-off propeller design; estimation of complete hydrodynamic characteristics of the propeller geometry, and propeller cavitation characteristics through exclusive lifting surface and panel method programmes; manufacturing of propeller models; model basin tests in the Berlin University cavitation tunnel and at the IMHEF cavitation tunnel at Lausanne; full-scale tests; propeller re-calculation and redesign for existing vessels; designing and manufacturing of propeller prototypes and pre-series; designing of conventional and unconventional propulsion systems; and consultation on propulsion problems.

Propellers are specially designed to be dedicated to the craft's projected operational profile by using the Rolla proprietary lifting surface and panel method programmes and manufactured using CAD/CAM 'CATIA' programme from Dassault aerospace. A Rolla associated manufacturing facility is able to mill propellers up to a 3 m diameter with a 5 axes 'MECOF' M 1000 milling machine.

Rolla also offers a complete design service for those interested in the application of surface propellers, not wanting to use a commercially available drive, but wanting to realise their own proprietary system. Rolla will collaborate with constructors in the design of their own system and make available over 30 years of experience in surface propellers and installation.

Surface-piercing, super-cavitating, transcavitating and sub-cavitating propellers are designed and produced to any required geometry and with up to eight blades.

As part of its dedication to research in 1993, Rolla became a member of the MIT/Navy/Industry Consortium on Cavitation Performance of High-Speed Propulsors. One of the principal objectives was to develop efficient computational optimisation techniques for the automated design, in the presence of cavitation, of innovative high-speed propulsive configurations. In 1994 Rolla became a member of Lausanne University consortium for testing.

For given design requirements and constraints, the geometry of the cavitating propulsor will be determined by the computer rather than by the designer. The most efficient cavitating propulsor will thus be selected among all possible solutions rather than among the limited number of solutions which are usually considered in a manual design procedure. It is also an objective to improve the present cavity model performing computational and experimental research in order to address several fundamental aspects of the model.

Integrating these improvements in the design process will result in a new generation of propulsor, meeting the design requirements and thus reducing model testing cost and time.

In general, propellers are produced in high tensile stainless steel (using investment casting and forging) for very high-speed craft and traditional casting in steel or Nibral for commercial, military, workboats, luxury boats and pleasure boats up to 80 knots. The Rolla families of stainless steel and Nibral surface-piercing propellers include lines specifically designed for Arneson Drives, Levi Drive Units, T-Torque Drive System, Mondrive System and Trimax. Also interesting is the recent design and production of Rolla forged steel blades for controllable-pitch surface propellers. The Rolla results obtained at the Technische Universitat Berlin constitute the first systematic series of surface propellers available in the world and permit Rolla to supply the torque and thrust coefficients and efficiency, horizontal and vertical force figures for different shaft inclinations and propeller immersions. The Rolla stainless steel propellers for stern drives include lines specifically designed for ZF-MPM, Volvo Penta, MerCruiser, Kiekhaefer, Yamaha and OMC.

Concerning the latest research programmes, diversified cavitation tunnel tests were carried out on the latest family of Rolla propellers in stainless steel. Other members of this latest family have included some of the most recent propellers and some that are already veterans of intensive application. Concerning the latest technology and the production, Rolla has recently introduced three new special models, known as Super-Propellers. They are investment cast in 17-4-PH and ERO, available in five, six and seven blades, have an extremely high performance, and a maximum diameter of 870 mm. They are the largest investment cast steel propellers in the world, actually designed and constructed.

It is worth noting that the Swiss company is presently custom designing and manufacturing surface-piercing propellers for military projects worldwide. The listed vessels are produced in series, confirming Rolla's past and continuing research and dedication to surface propellers. Rolla has also intensified the design and construction of special propellers for all applications, submerged as well as surface.

Recent applications of Rolla propellers to military vessels

IAI-RAMTA, Israel
Super-Dvora Mk II 2 × MTU 8V/Arneson ASD-14 &
2 × MTU 12V/ASD-16

TRINITY, USA
for US Navy and Mexico *XFPB* 3 × GM 16V/ASD-14

PETERSON BUILDERS, USA
US Navy Mk V 2 × MTU 16V 396 TB 94 21 m Cougar Cat/Fixed Surface Drives

ASTAFERSA, Spain
Spanish Customs 2 × MTU 16V 396 TB 94 21 m Cougar Cat/Fixed Surface Drives

FB MARINE, Italy
Italian Customs 3 × 600 hp Seatek/Trimax Drives

UK MoD
3 × 600 hp Seatek/Trimax Drives

SWEDE SHIPS, Sweden
Swedish Customs 3 × 600 hp Seatek/Mercury No 7 Drives

McDONNELL DOUGLAS, USA
Magnum 40 2 × CAT 600 hp/ASD-10

SIMONNEAU, France
Star Naja 2 × Cat 425 hp/Trimax Drives

SILKINE, Thailand
18 m Foil-assisted Catamaran 2 × MAN 820 hp/ASD-12

COUGAR, UK
38' Kuwait 2 × 375 hp/ASD-8

US NAVY, USA
HSAC 2 × 550 hp/Speedmaster III A Drives

JAPANESE COAST GUARD, Japan
12 m PBs 3 × 340 hp/ASD-8

UPDATED

Rolla REXPSC90/91-6 propeller
1994

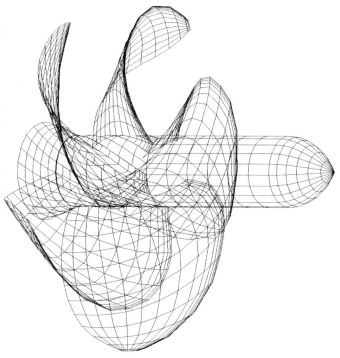

Panel method design for submerged propulsors **1995**

UNITED KINGDOM

BRUNTON'S PROPELLERS LTD

Station Road, Sudbury, Suffolk CO10 6ST, UK

Telephone: +44 (1787) 373611
Telex: 98400 PROPS G
Telefax: +44 (1787) 881019

Brunton's Propellers Ltd is a specialist company in the design and manufacture of propellers for high performance craft such as patrol boats, surface effect ships, hydrofoils, catamarans and so on, where the propellers have to work in very exacting conditions. The design requirements in such cases can be extremely critical and manufacturing to very close tolerances is required: ISO 484 Class 'S' and better. Brunton's parent company is Stone Manganese Ltd, designers and manufacturers of ship propellers.

As well as meeting commercial requirements, Brunton's Propellers Ltd supplies the British MoD and navies around the world.

Propellers may be manufactured in high tensile manganese bronze, nickel-aluminium-bronze, Novostron (a manganese-aluminium-bronze alloy), Superstron 70 and gun metal, though this last material is now seldom used.

Brunton's associated company, Stone Propellers Ltd, manufactures extremely accurate model propellers for test and research work in test tanks and cavitation tunnels.

VERIFIED

Brunton five-blade propeller for twin-propeller 33.5 m patrol boat **1986**

1 m diameter propellers (Dr Kruppa design) for HM527 surface effect ship
1988

STONE MANGANESE MARINE LTD

(A member of the Langham Industries group)

Dock Road, Birkenhead, Merseyside L41 1DT, UK

Telephone: +44 (151) 652 2372
Telex: 629270 SMMBH G
Telefax: +44 (151) 652 2377

J M Langham, *Chairman*
J R Wilson, *Deputy Chairman*
G Patience, *Managing Director*
B N Preston, *Director*

Stone Manganese Marine has been manufacturing propellers for more than 100 years. The company and its associates operate 10 manufacturing units throughout the world and the product range covers all sizes of fixed-pitch marine propellers for all types of ships, including high-speed marine craft.

The main factory is at Birkenhead, which includes the technical department, offering a comprehensive technical service to customers and the preparation of the company's proprietary Meridian design.

The company has a long established connection with the University of Newcastle upon Tyne, collaborating in the operation of the cavitation tunnel where the KCA design, specifically to suit high-speed craft, was developed and tested. The KCA design has been adopted for high-speed marine applications worldwide.

UPDATED

Stone Manganese Marine Ltd KCA design propellers for high-speed craft **1986**

TEIGNBRIDGE PROPELLERS LTD

Forde Road, Brunel Industrial Estate, Newton Abbot, Devon TQ12 4AD, UK

Telephone: +44 (1626) 333377
Telex: 42976 TEPROP G
Telefax: +44 (1626) 60783

D A Duncan, *Chairman*
D A Hunt, *Managing Director*
T Hughes, *Sales Director*
R P Madle, *Engineering Director*
A P Bonnell, *Company Secretary*
M Izzo, *Designer, High Speed Applications*

Operating out of three separate manufacturing facilities in the UK, Teignbridge offers, a complete design and manufacturing service to naval architects, operators and builders of all types of vessels from high-speed craft such as fast ferries, hydrofoils, patrol boats and superyachts to fishing vessels, tugs and inland vessels.

For the manufacture of high definition propellers to ISO Class I and Class S tolerances, the most up to date CAD/CAM technology is employed.

Teignbridge also produces a range of standard

and custom designed sterngear, rudders, shaft brackets and associated equipment. All products can be designed and manufactured to comply with the rules of any classification society.

Complete sterngear systems are produced up to 300 mm shaft diameter. Shaft materials used are Temet 25 duplex stainless steel, conventional stainless steels AISI316 and 304, mild steel and Temet 17, a high strength stainless steel. Sterntubes are manufactured to suit GRP, aluminium, steel and wooden vessels and supplied with bearings and shaft seals for water or oil lubrication.

Shaft brackets and rudder systems are supplied either cast in nickel-aluminium bronze or fabricated in carbon or stainless steels. Sterngear components are produced in purpose built machine shops on modern CNC machinery.

STANDARD RANGE PROPELLERS

For fast vessels Teignbridge produces a standard series of 'sub-cavitating' propellers manufactured in nickel-aluminium bronze and manganese bronze. This range of propellers is manufactured as standard from 305 mm diameter to 1020 mm diameter covering all common P/D ratios.

For non-planing applications propellers are generally manufactured to ISO Class 2 tolerances. For faster vessels Class 1 tolerances are applied.

CUSTOM DESIGNED PROPELLERS

These are specified for applications where standard series propellers cannot be used. Teignbridge custom designed propellers fall into three categories: highly skewed; propellers for optimum performance in terms of speed, noise and vibration; and propellers for surface-piercing applications.

High-speed propellers are manufactured to Class S tolerances and are designed using the 'lifting surface' theory to optimise propeller geometry to suit each vessel's particular application.

Teignbridge's surface propellers are the result of many years experience in designing partially sub-

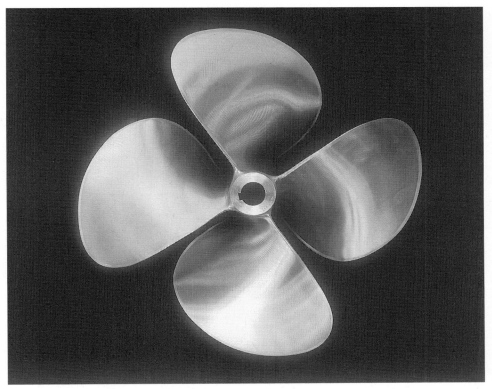

Aquaquad four-bladed standard high-speed propellers   *1995*

merged super-cavitating propellers. This has culminated in the design of a series of four- and five-blade propellers using the revolutionary 'cascade theory' for section design. This has allowed the design of very efficient, thin sections using nickel-aluminium bronze and Temet 25 duplex stainless steel. This propeller series has been optimised for use on high-speed, diesel powered ferries and military vessels between 30 and 55 knots. The four-blade series is used on highly loaded, high-speed applications.

UPDATED

Teignbridge seven-bladed, highly skewed low noise and vibration propeller, three of which are fitted to a luxury passenger vessel operating on the Rhine   *1994*

Aquaquin five-bladed standard high-speed propellers   *1995*

UNITED STATES OF AMERICA

BIRD-JOHNSON COMPANY

Pascagoula Operations
3719 Industrial Road, Pascagoula, Mississippi 39567, USA

Telephone: +1 (601) 762 0728
Telex: 589938
Telefax: +1 (601) 769 7048

Peter J Lapp, *Manager*

110 Norfolk Street, Walpole, Massachusetts 02081, USA

Telephone: +1 (617) 668 9610
Telex: 6817294
Telefax: +1 (617) 668 5638

Peter J Gwyn, *Chief Executive Officer and President*
Joseph J Riley, *Chief Financial Officer and Vice President, Finance and Accounting*

Gary W Dayton, *Director, Marine Marketing and Services*

Bird-Johnson Company is a leading supplier of fixed- and controllable-pitch propeller systems for naval application. In-house capabilities include design, foundry, hand and NC finishing, assembly, test and repair. All products are backed by logistic support including a 24 hour emergency service network.

VERIFIED

MICHIGAN WHEEL CORPORATION

1501 Buchanan Avenue SW, Grand Rapids, Michigan 49507, USA

Telephone: +1 (616) 452 6941
Telefax: +1 (616) 247 0227

Stan Heide, *President*
Martin Ronis, *Vice President Marketing*
Thomas Siler, *Vice President Finance*
Gary Palmowski, *Vice President Manufacturing*
William Herrick, *Director/Marketing Services*

Established in 1903, Michigan Wheel produces a wide range of fixed-pitch propellers, including the Machined-Pitch type, with a diameter up to 2.44 m, and the Dyna-foil type, diameter up to 2.44 m. These propellers can be made in manganese bronze alloy, nickel-bronze, aluminium-bronze and stainless steel.

VERIFIED

T-TORQUE DRIVE SYSTEM INC

3333 NE 188th Street, North Miami Beach, Florida 33180, USA

Telephone: +1 (305) 937 5064
Telefax: +1 (305) 937 5071

Adam Erdberg, *President*

T-TORQUE DRIVE SYSTEM

The T-Torque Drive System (US Patent No 4 919 630) is an advanced heavy-duty marine propulsion system based on surface-piercing operation of super-cavitating propellers. The system provides the recreational, commerical or military diesel-powered craft operator with high manoeuvrability, high speed and shallow water operation capability. The system is highly reliable due to its construction in the highest marine grade polished stainless steel (316L) and simplistic concept. The shafts connect directly to the engine transmissions and pass through the transom supported by heavy-duty struts which are mounted above the bottom of the boat. Since the propeller shafts directly penetrate the transom, the shaft angle is far less than conventional inboard systems, thereby providing greatly reduced appendage drag and increased efficiency. Shaft centres are at normal separations depending upon the particular vessel and engines. This configuration allows the vessel to have the low-speed dockside precision manoeuvrability of a conventional inboard-powered vessel. The T-Torque rudder system is supported by a polished stainless steel T-Strut securing the rudders behind the propellers. The rudders turn via a hydraulic power steering system with hydraulic lines built into the T-Strut (see illustration).

The system has been in service since 1984 on various recreational, commercial and military vessels up to 26 m (85 ft) in length.

VERIFIED

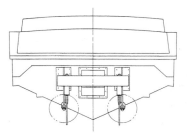

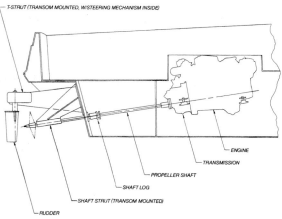

Main features of T-Torque drive system   *1992*

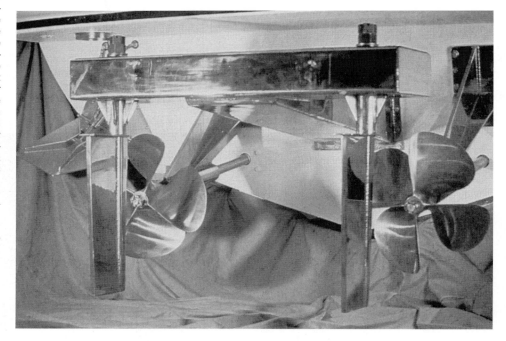

T-Torque model drive system
1992

WATER-JET UNITS

Company Listing by Country

Finland
FF Jet Ltd AB

Italy
Castoldi SpA

Japan
Kawasaki Heavy Industries Ltd (Prime Mover Division)
Mitsubishi Heavy Industries Ltd
Niigata Engineering Company Ltd

Netherlands
Lips Jets BV

New Zealand
C W F Hamilton & Company Ltd (Hamiltonjet)

Norway
Kværner Energy A/S
Ulstein Propeller A/S

Sweden
Kamewa AB
MJP

United Kingdom
PP Jets
Ultra Hydraulics Ltd

United States of America
Amjet
North American Marine Jet Inc

 **LIPS JETS** ▪▪▪▪▪▪▪▪▪▪▪▪▪▪
Leaders in Propulsion Systems

SEE OUR EDITORIAL ON PAGES 436, 437 and 438

FINLAND

FF JET LTD AB

PO Box 79, SF-67101 Kokkola, Finland

Telephone: +358 (68) 822 1505
Telefax: +358 (68) 822 1435

In 1994 KaMeWa of Sweden acquired FF Jet Ltd AB which has consolidated its position as the leading supplier of water-jets to this industry. The KaMeWa/FF Jet product range, manufactured by FF Jet Ltd AB in Kokkola, Finland is marketed through the KaMeWa sales network (see KaMeWa entry under Sweden).

FF-JET 240
Designed for planing craft up to four tonnes and displacement craft up to seven tonnes. Power range 40 to 230 kW. Max 4000 rpm. Dry weight 100 kg.

FF-JET 310
Designed for planing boats up to seven tonnes and displacement boats up to 12 tonnes. Power range 40 to 300 kW. Max 3000 rpm. Dry weight 190 kg.

FF-JET 375
Designed for planing boats up to 11 tonnes and displacement boats up to 22 tonnes. Power range 80 to 450 kW. Max 2500 rpm. Dry weight 290 kg.

FF-JET 410
Designed for planing craft up to 15 tonnes and displacement craft up to 28 tonnes. Power range 200 to 1000 kW. Max 2300 rpm. Dry weight 380 kg.

FF-JET 450
Designed for planing boats up to 18 tonnes and displacement boats up to 35 tonnes. Power range 200 to 1000 kW. Max 2100 rpm. Dry weight 370 kg.

FF-JET 550
Designed for planing craft up to 35 tonnes. Power range 300 to 1500 kW. Max 1600 rpm. Dry weight 780 kg.

UPDATED

Application of FF-Jet 410 units **1994**

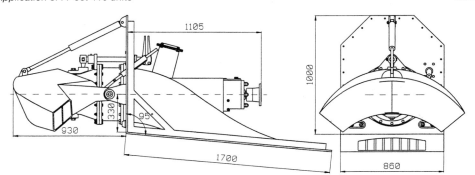

Arrangement of FF-Jet 410 unit
1994

ITALY

CASTOLDI SpA

Viale Mazzini 161, I-20081 Abbiategrasso, Milan, Italy

Telephone: +39 (2) 94821
Telex: 330236CAST I
Telefax: +39 (2) 9496 0800

Dr Franco Castoldi, *Managing Director*

Castoldi SpA is associated with BCS SpA, the leading European manufacturer of self-propelled agricultural machines, and MOSA SpA, manufacturer of mobile electric welding machines. The development of Castoldi water-jet units began in

1958 and they are now available for fast craft in the range of 4 to 28 m.

Castoldi manufactures a range of axial flow water-jet units, the JET 03 for powers up to 40.5 kW, the JET 05 for up to 150 kW, the Turbodrive 238 for up to 220 kW, the JET 06 for 330 kW, Turbodrive 337 for 480 kW and the JET 07 for up to 883 kW. All the

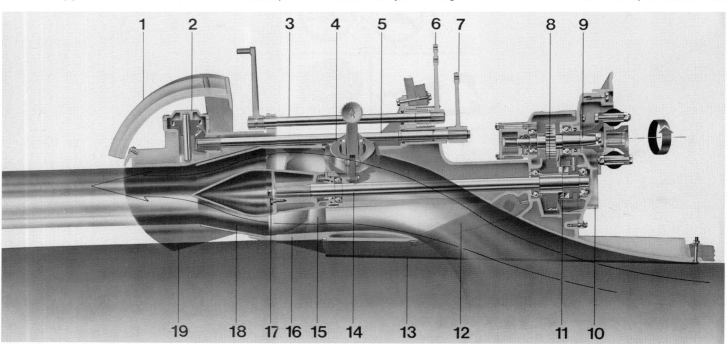

Components of a Castoldi JET 05 water-jet unit **1** *Reversing deflector;* **2** *Rudder control gears;* **3** *Reversing deflector control shaft;* **4** *Inspection port;* **5** *Steering deflectors control shaft;* **6** *Reversing deflector control lever;* **7** *Steering deflectors control lever;* **8** *Gear coupling;* **9** *Primary shaft;* **10** *Gearbox flange;* **11** *Disconnecting clutch;* **12** *Movable debris screen rake;* **13** *Body of unit;* **14** *Impeller shaft;* **15** *Impeller;* **16** *Impeller housing;* **17** *Impeller retaining bolt;* **18** *Nozzle;* **19** *Steering deflectors*
1987

Castoldi units feature a single stage axial flow impeller; the casings are built in lightweight aluminium alloy which is very durable being hard anodised up to 80 microns. The impeller, the impeller shaft and many other parts are made in stainless steel.

The Castoldi drives (except for the JET 03) have several features that make them stand out from other water-jet units: a built-in gearbox with 25 gear wheel ratios for adapting the power and rpm characteristics of the engine to the jet drive; an integral disconnecting clutch allowing a true neutral condition; a remotely operated movable debris screen rake for cleaning the water intake; all oil lubricated bearings; and other refinements. The Castoldi water-jet units are equipped with especially designed mechanical/hydraulic controls which make them extremely easy to operate.

VERIFIED

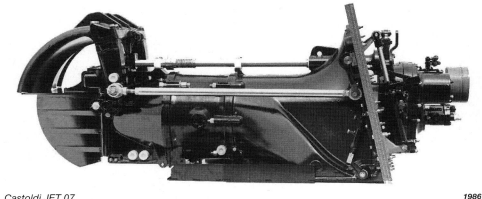

Castoldi JET 07   1986

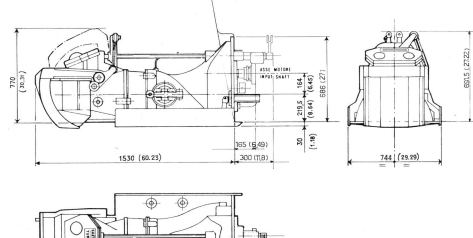

Castoldi Turbodrive 337 water-jet capable of absorbing up to 480 kW
1990

JAPAN

KAWASAKI HEAVY INDUSTRIES LTD (PRIME MOVER DIVISION)

1-1 Higashi Kawasaki-cho 3-chome, Chuo-ku, Kobe 650-91, Japan

Telephone: +81 (78) 682 5535
Telex: 5623931 KHIKOB J
Telefax: +81 (78) 682 5530

H Shida, *Director, General Manager*
H Kitaura, *Senior Manager, Hydraulic Machinery Department*

Kawasaki has been manufacturing PJ-20 Water-jet Propulsors for Jetfoil since 1989 and has developed a KPJ-A series of water-jet propulsors for high-speed displacement vessels. The first KJP-A unit was delivered in 1993 and four KJP-169A units were delivered in 1994.

PJ-20

This unit was designed to match the Rockwell International Corporation units supplied for hydrofoils such as the Jetfoil, and this business was transferred to Kawasaki in 1987.

Maximum continuous input power for these units is 2795 kW at 2060 rpm.

Kawasaki PJ-20 water-jet propulsor   1988

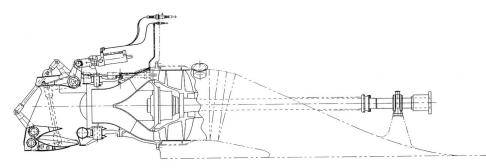

Section through Kawasaki KPJ-169A waterjet unit
1995

KPJ-A SERIES

Kawasaki completed the first unit and made an actual load test in Kawasaki's dry dock to prove its efficiency and strength in 1993.
Model: KPJ-1A (43A equivalent).
Type: Single stage axial flow, flush inlet.
Input power: 515 kW.

Four units were installed on the AMD1500 Mk II Kawasaki Jet Piercer in 1994:
Model: KPJ-169A.
Type: Single stage axial flow, flush inlet.
Input power: 5420 kW.

The KPJ-A series accepts power inputs from 200 to 20 000 kW.

UPDATED

Kawasaki KPJ-169A water-jet unit
1995

MITSUBISHI HEAVY INDUSTRIES LTD

5-1 Marunouchi 2-chome, Chiyoda-ku, Tokyo, Japan

Telephone: +81 (3) 3212 9414
Telefax: +81 (3) 3212 9777

The Mitsubishi company has produced water-jet units for Japanese monohull fast ferries and for the Mitsubishi Super Shuttle 400 diesel driven hydrofoil catamaran. These latter units are designated MWJ-5000A and have a shaft input of 2125 kW each. A novel feature of the units is the use of a double-cascade type of impeller and a vane cascade arrangement for reverse thrust.

NIIGATA ENGINEERING COMPANY LTD

4-1 Kasumigaseki 1-chome, Chiuoda-ku, Tokyo 100, Japan

Telephone: +81 (3) 3504 2473
Telefax: +81 (3) 3595 2645

NIIGATA-MJP

Licensed by MJP Marine Jet Power AB of Sweden in 1991, Niigata Engineering markets the range of water-jet units as specified in the MJP Marine Jet Power AB entry and in the accompanying table.

Niigata has an extensive marine engineering business base and a broad range of engineering support divisions and subsidiaries worldwide.

Water-jet type	Max input power		Max input speed rpm	Weight kg
	kW	hp		
J550R	1500	2039	1290	1180
J650R	2100	2855	1100	1600
J750R	2800	3807	950	2100
J850R	3700	5031	845	3300
J950R	4600	6254	750	4200
J1100R	6500	8887	670	6100
J1250R	8900	12 100	600	7400
J1500R	12 000	16 315	480	11 500

UPDATED

NETHERLANDS

LIPS JETS BV

Lipsstraat 52, 5150 BB Drunen, Netherlands

Telephone: +31 4163 88115
Telex: 35185 lips nl
Telefax: +31 4163 73162

Lips Jets BV was established at Drunen in the Netherlands in June 1993 as a wholly owned subsidiary of Lips BV, the only major propeller manufacturer in the world to produce fixed-pitch propellers, controllable-pitch propellers, side thrusters, steerable thrusters, water-jets and control systems to its own design. Lips Jets BV is a continuation of the former Riva Lips Srl, which was a joint venture between Riva Calzoni and Lips.

The main features of the Lips water-jet are:
(1) Lips water-jets are fabricated in welded stainless steel. Stainless steel in a welded construction has a high resistance against corrosion and fatigue, provides optimum design flexibility for

optimisation, guarantees material properties by using certified plates
(2) For each specific application the optimum inlet is designed to match the required flow at the craft design speed and power with the optimum inlet velocity ratio to ensure a high efficiency in a cavitation free condition
(3) The axial bearing is located inside the craft which makes it easily accessible for inspection or maintenance without dry docking and bowl dismantling, eliminates the risk of water penetration into the lubricating oil and eliminates the risk of water pollution by lubricating oil
(4) The mixed flow pump design has a high pump efficiency, optimum hydraulic balancing to reduce the axial loading of the bearing, excellent cavitation characteristics and is casted in high resistant Duplex type stainless steel

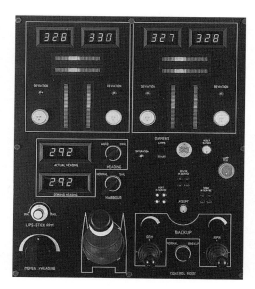

Wing control panel of LIPSTRONIC/w control system
1995

Typical cross-section of Lips water-jet unit

1995

(5) Inside the hub the shaft/impeller is supported by a water lubricated radial bearing. A very high reliability is hereby achieved by avoiding complex mechanical components outside the craft which require critical sealing in order to safeguard oil lubrication. The bearing can be inspected without dry docking, is not subject to sudden failure and has proven to be a reliable long-life component

(6) The hydraulically operated steering and reversing bucket has been designed such that it executes its task in the most efficient way while achieving a high reliability by limiting the number of moving parts.

LIPSTRONIC/W

Under the name LIPSTRONIC/w, an extensive range of integrated propulsion and navigation control systems is available, specially designed for the control of fast water-jet propulsed craft. As this system is of modular design, for each specific propulsion configuration and craft requirement the optimum control system can be designed.

The main features of the LIPSTRONIC/w controls are:

(1) The LIPSTRONIC/w is based on microcontroller technology. In conjunction with optional fieldbus technology this allows for weight savings

(2) Integrated propulsion and navigation control

(3) High redundancy with high degree of safety as designs are based on Failure Mode Effect Analysis

Four steerable water-jets type LJ-115-DL for Stena Sea Lynx II

1995

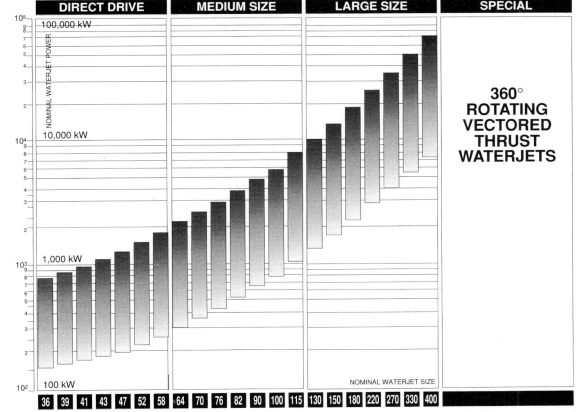

Power range of Lips water-jet units

1992

(4) Lips Jets designed its own autopilot especially for fast water-jet propulsed craft
(5) Combined follow-up control of bucket and impeller speed as well as steering angle
(6) The highest possible degree of manoeuvrability

by use of fully co-ordinated control by means of a three-axis joystick. This allows for short turn-around times
(7) The LIPSTRONIC/w control system can be easily extended with fully integrated diesel or gas-

turbine control of remote starting, local control, electronic governing, monitoring and alarming.

UPDATED

NEW ZEALAND

C W F HAMILTON & COMPANY LTD (HAMILTON JET)

Lunns Road, PO Box 709, Christchurch, New Zealand

Telephone: +64 (3) 348 4179
Telefax: +64 (3) 348 6969
Telex: NZ2938 SYNET (Attn: HamJet)

Designers and manufacturers of water-jets since the mid-1950s, HamiltonJet now offers models capable of absorbing power inputs up to 3000 kW. With in excess of 20 000 units installed worldwide in many types of craft such as fast ferries, police patrol craft, naval troop carriers, fishing boats, crew boats, rescue craft, pleasure cruisers and fire boats, HamiltonJet will liaise with designers, builders and operators from conceptual design stages through to final commissioning. Computer speed predictions, detailed installation advice, commissioning assistance and training programmes are available to support each project. Full logistic support for all installations is provided by HamiltonJet's extensive worldwide network of factory trained distributors, who are supported by a factory based Ready Reaction Force on permanent stand-by to fly anywhere at short notice.

The current HamiltonJet product range includes the HJ Series, HM Series and HS Series jets.

Design Features

All HamiltonJet models are designed and manufactured to meet the standards of the world's leading certifying authorities, primarily Lloyd's Register or American Bureau of Shipping. Robustly constructed from corrosion resistant materials, each model incorporates matched intake transition duct with protection screen, high efficiency mixed flow style pump, optimised tailpipe and discharge nozzle and integral steering and split duct astern thrust deflectors.

Intake Transition/Intake

Configured to mount inboard at the stern, Hamilton water-jets draw water through a factory supplied intake transition which is manufactured to suit the hull. Damage to internal components is eliminated by incorporating a highly developed intake screen and, unlike some water-jets, this screen is engineered into the total package so that operational parameters such as thrust generation and cavitation resistance are unaffected by its presence. At planing speeds, this screen is largely self-cleaning.

The HamiltonJet design is such that the force of the generated thrust is transmitted to the hull bottom through this transition, eliminating the fore and aft propulsor loads from the transom structure and engine.

The main thrust bearing is incorporated in the intake, which is a one piece casting unaffected by the hull structure and movement, providing the bearing with a rigid housing to ensure life long alignment.

Pump

Mounted on a precision stainless steel mainshaft, the mixed flow style impeller is designed to pump large volumes of water at relatively low pressures. The impeller in each application is rated to absorb full engine power at full shaft rpm and this power is constantly absorbed regardless of boat speed, eliminating the possibility of overloading the engine. Good cavitation resistance is exhibited throughout a wide speed range, allowing full engine power to be applied at low boat speeds for quick acceleration.

While optimised for fast vessel speeds, the flexibility of the HamiltonJet design is evidenced in its ability to operate effectively in off-design conditions, such as those experienced below the planing

HamiltonJet Model 321 water-jet

30.5 m Alaskan passenger ferry with quadruple HM422 jets

threshold, in adverse sea conditions or when the hull is fouled.

Stator and Nozzle

Water flow exiting the pump unit passes through the stator vanes where the rotation velocity components are removed to ensure a straight uniform flow is presented to the discharge nozzle. Nozzle size is a key component in achieving maximum propulsive coefficients and the nozzle sizes of Hamilton water-jets are optimised for each application.

Control Functions

Steering in response to helm commands with a Hamilton water-jet is affected by the deflection of the jetstream to port or starboard by the integral balanced steering deflector. The steering deflector is designed to maximise lateral thrust with minimum loss of forward thrust while maintaining lightest operating loads.

Ahead/astern function is achieved with the integral split duct astern deflector, designed to provide maximum astern thrust under all conditions of boat speed, water depth and throttle opening. The split duct design angles the astern jetstream down to clear the transom and to the sides to retain a steering thrust component, an arrangement which vectors the jetstream away from the jet intake, avoiding recycling and resulting in astern thrust generation up to 60 per cent of ahead thrust which can be maintained up to high throttle settings.

On Hamilton water-jets these steering and astern functions are separate and have independent

effects, but, when used in conjunction with each other, can affect complex vessel manoeuvres.

With the astern deflector fully raised, full forward thrust is available. With the deflector in the lowered position, full astern thrust is generated. In both positions, full independent steering effect is available for rotating the craft. By setting the deflector in the intermediate 'zero-speed' position; the ahead and astern thrusts are equalised for holding the craft on station but, with full steering effect still available for rotational control. Infinitely variable adjustment either side of the 'zero-speed' position enables the craft to be crept ahead or astern and, in multiple jet installations, true sideways movement can be induced.

Control Systems

A number of HamiltonJet packaged control systems to interface between the helm station and the jet is available to maximise the inherent manoeuvring capabilities of the design.

Depending on the jet model, options available include simple manual cable, hydraulic, electric or electronic systems. The latter options can be interfaced with other vessel systems. All systems are designed to be fully proportional, where the appropriate deflector movement follows that initiated by the controller at the helm station.

HJ SERIES

These are high efficiency single stage units, typically for work and patrol boats, fast ferries and pleasure cruisers of up to 20 m. A large number of models and impeller rating combinations means these jets can be directly driven by many common gasolene and diesel engines.

MODEL 211
Maximum power input: 260 kW.
Impeller diameter: 215 mm (8 rating options).
Typical 211 Jet application (single)
Vessel: 7.62 m fire/rescue craft
Displacement: 2.20 t
Speed: 29 knots
Engine: Single Volvo TAMD 41A diesel, 149 kW at 2800 rpm
Drive: Direct
Operator: Verplanck Fire Dept, New York, USA.

MODEL 273
Maximum power input: 225 kW.
Impeller diameter: 270 mm (11 rating options).
Typical 273 Jet application (twin)
Vessel: 10.6 m riverine assault craft
Displacement: 7.5 t
Speed: 38 knots
Engines: Twin Cummins 6BTA5.9M2 diesels, 224 kW at 2800 rpm each
Drive: Direct
Operator: US Marine Corps.

MODEL 291
Maximum power input: 375 kW.
Impeller diameter: 290 mm (11 rating options).
Typical 291 Jet application (twin)
Vessel: 11.65 m police patrol craft
Displacement: 11 t
Speed: 29 knots
Engines: Twin Volvo TAMD 71A diesels, 262 kW at 2500 rpm each
Drive: Direct
Operator: Swedish Marine Police.

MODEL 321
Maximum power input: 480 kW.
Impeller diameter: 320 mm (12 rating options).

Typical 321 Jet application (single)
Vessel: 10.6 m fishing boat
Displacement: 6.4 t
Speed: 32 knots
Engine: Single Volvo TAMD 72WJ diesel, 328 kW at 2600 rpm
Drive: Via reduction/reversing gearbox.

MODEL 362
Maximum power input: 580 kW.
Impeller diameter: 360 mm (9 rating options).
Typical 362 Jet application (twin)
Vessel: 14.6 m fast rescue craft
Displacement: 11.5 t
Speed: 34 knots
Engines: Twin Volvo TAMD 122D diesels, 336 kW at 2000 rpm each
Drive: Direct
Operator: Spanish Rescue Authority.

HM SERIES
This is an extension to the HJ range and comprises a number of units suitable for power inputs ranging from 1200 kW to 3000 kW.

Models included in this range are:
HM422, HM521, HM571, HM651, HM721 and HM811.

These models would normally be driven via a reduction gearbox. As with all the models in the HamiltonJet range, vital control components are mounted inboard where they are protected from the elements and impact damage. All HM Series jets feature integral hydraulic power packs driven off the jet mainshaft and they are designed for the efficient propulsion of fast ferries, work and patrol boats typically in the 20 to 60 m range.
Typical twin HM Series application
Vessel: 22 m customs patrol craft
Displacement: 56 t
Speed: 32 knots
Jets: Twin HamiltonJet HM571s
Engines: Twin MTU 396 12V TE 84 diesels, 1270 kW at 1940 rpm each

Operator: Royal Malaysian Customs & Excise.
Typical triple HM Series application
Vessel: 28.5 m crew boat
Displacement: 63 t
Speed: 25 knots
Jets: Triple HamiltonJet HM521s
Engines: Triple MAN D2848 LE diesels, 520 kW at 2300 rpm each
Operator: Syarikat Borcos Shipping, Malaysia.
Typical quadruple HM Series application
Vessel: 30.5 m catamaran passenger ferry
Displacement: 62 t
Speed: 33 knots
Jets: Quadruple HamiltonJet HM422s
Engines: Quadruple Caterpillar 3412 V12 diesels, 560 kW at 2100 rpm each
Operator: Alaska Catamaran Inc, Alaska, USA.
Hamilton HM Series water-jets are also widely used in loiter/boost applications in conjunction with other propulsors.

HS SERIES
The models in this range are optimised specifically for craft operating in the 45 to 65 knot speed range. Featuring multi-stage pump units which allow high power inputs to be applied to a relatively small jet, they exhibit outstanding cavitation resistance and hydrodynamic efficiencies. Suitable for powering by high-speed diesel or gas-turbine engines in high performance pursuit or assault craft.
Typical HS Series Jet application
Vessel: 13.4 m prototype pursuit craft
Displacement: 6.6 t
Speed: 60 knots
Jets: Single HamiltonJet HS363
Engines: Twin Allison C30 gas-turbines, 485 kW each, driving the single jet through a combining gearbox.

UPDATED

NORWAY

KVÆRNER ENERGY A/S

PO Box 9277, Grønland, N-0134 Oslo, Norway

Telephone: +47 (22) 666666
Telex: 71650 KV N
Telefax: +47 (22) 193765

Odd Sandøy, *General Manager, Marketing*

Kværner Energy supplies the high-speed craft market with complete propulsion modules including gas-turbines and water-jets.

Kværner Energy has developed a new range of water-jets for the high-speed craft market.

The new Kværner water-jet has been designed to provide a propulsion system for all kinds of vessels. Kværner Energy's experience and long traditions with hydrodynamic equipment, turbines and pump design has resulted in an advanced water-jet that is optimised with respect to simplicity, low weight and high efficiency. The present Kværner water-jet programme covers output between 50 kN of thrust to 400 kN of thrust, corresponding to prime mover needs of 1500 to 23 000 kW.

The company has supplied water-jets to Kværner Fjellstrand for the *Flying Cat* and to Kværner Mandal for the nine mine countermeasure vessels for the Norwegian Navy.
Water-jet description: The water-jet pump is optimised with respect to high efficiency, simplicity, low weight and low suction pressure requirement.

A six-blade impeller is mounted on the impeller shaft tube. The shaft sleeve is supported by a conical roller bearing at the front end, and a spherical axial bearing at the rear end.

The static bearing holder is firmly bolted on to the hub of the pump bowl which is bolted to the pump house. This ensures that the impeller is in a fixed position in relation to the pump walls. This type of design allows the pump to operate with a very small

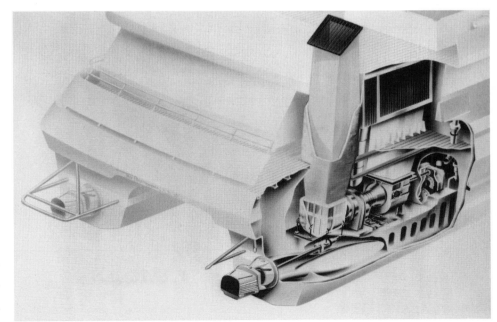

Example of Kværner integrated propulsion system   *1994*

clearance between the impeller and the pump house, thus increasing the efficiency and reducing the risk of cavitation.

Pump bearings are oil lubricated. The oil system is under permanent pressure in order to avoid water leakage into the lubricating system in case of a mechanical seal failure. When the unit is not operating this pressure is maintained by the oil accumulator.

A nozzle ring is separately mounted and can be changed to alter the discharge area.

The primary shaft is connected to the impeller through a spline coupling. This gives the shaft a certain degree of freedom in relation to the location of the pump. A mechanical seal is provided where the shaft penetrates the water duct. The shaft runs free through the water intake duct.

Steering and reversing are provided for by a hydraulically operated steering nozzle and reversing bucket. When activated the steering nozzle is lifted out of the water-jet allowing the water to impinge on the reversing mechanism, bending the jet downwards. Further activating of the reversing mechanism will move a lower flap up and into the water-jet, forcing the jet to complete a 145° turn.

When not activated the lower flap on the reversing mechanism rests in a horizontal position below the jet, ensuring minimum resistance in the water.

Kværner Energy supplies drawings specifying the inner contour and location of the inlet duct. The purchaser designs and builds the mechanical structure of the inlet duct, and, where the shaft penetrates the water intake duct, prepares a foundation for the mechanical seal.

The hydraulic system consists of the following main parts:
Main hydraulic pump
Stand-by hydraulic pump with electrical motor
Proportion valves
Instrumentation (local and transmitter)
Piping, tubes and fittings
Oil tank
Oil accumulator pressure compensation
Filters.
Both main and stand-by hydraulic pumps are of the variable displacement variable pressure type. The main pump is mechanically driven from gearbox or engine, while the stand-by pump is driven from a standard electric motor. Oil is then delivered

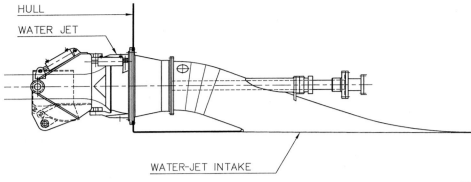

Kværner water-jet features

1994

through a filter to the two proportional valves. From the steering proportional valves, oil is transferred through the stern to the two hydraulic cylinders mounted on the water-jet. From both steering and reversing cylinders, oil is returned through the proportion valve back to the pump suction side. An accumulator assures a pump suction pressure of approximately 3 bar.

The lubricating oil system is pressure compensated, with a constant overpressure on the return side. This prevents water leakage into the oil.

An electronic control and manoeuvring system is provided to take advantage of the flexible manoeuvring capabilities of water-jet propulsion systems.

VERIFIED

ULSTEIN PROPELLER A/S

N-6065 Ulsteinvik, Norway

Telephone: +47 (700) 14000
Telex: 42 848 UP N
Telefax: +47 (700) 14017

Stig Ulstein, *Managing Director*
Jarle Hessen, *Sales Manager*

Ulstein Propeller A/S will be manufacturing water-jets in the power range 300 to 5000 kW covered by four units: WJ450, WJ560, WJ630 and WJ710. Trials on the first water-jet model, the WJ630, started on 21 January 1992. This unit is being tested for application to the Ulstein UT 904 SES.

The prototype unit WJ630 is designed to absorb 2400 kW at 40 knots and at an impeller speed of 1025 rpm. Several options of intake design have been analysed in two and three dimensions by solving the Navier-Stokes equations at the Norwegian Institute of Technology. This enables the details affecting the noise and vibration characteristics as well as the propulsive efficiency to be studied.

UPDATED

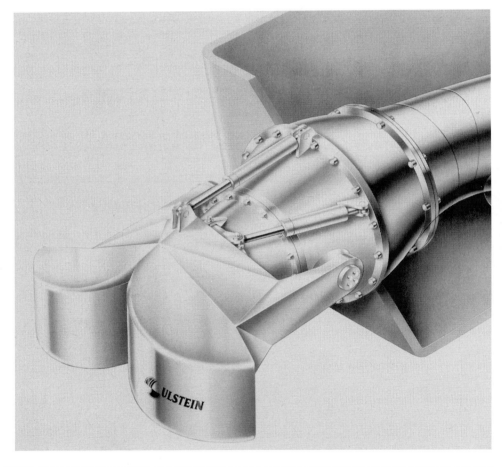

External features of the Ulstein water-jet unit
1991

SWEDEN

KaMeWa AB

A Vickers plc company

PO Box 1010, S-681 29 Kristinehamn, Sweden

Telephone: +46 (550) 84000
Telex: 66050 KAMEWA S
Telefax: +46 (550) 18190

Ingar Jensen, *Managing Director*
Björn H Svensson, *Manager, Marketing and Sales, Jet propulsion systems*

Since the beginning of this century KaMeWa in Sweden has designed and manufactured hydro-

turbines and large pumps of various types. In the 1930s the first KaMeWa propeller of controllable-pitch type was delivered. A vast amount of experience in the marine propulsion field has since then been collected at KaMeWa. In the last two decades KaMeWa has been a major supplier of controllable-pitch propellers and thrusters. The company uses a well developed international network for sales and after sales service.

In the mid-1960s KaMeWa built two prototype jet propulsion systems for small craft. The first larger units, however, were delivered in 1980 and since then KaMeWa has systematically established itself as the dominant producer of larger systems for water-jet propulsion.

An appreciable amount of research and develop-

ment in hydrodynamics, mechanics and electronics constitutes the basis for the KaMeWa jet propulsion system. Significant benefits for vessels with this system are high propulsive efficiency, even at part load; insensitivity to floating debris; suitability for shallow draught operation; good manoeuvrability; low hydro-acoustic and vibration levels and low magnetic signature.

These features make water-jet propulsion suitable for example in medium and high-speed vessels such as corvettes, patrol boats, landing craft, passenger ferries, motor yachts and workboats.

Design: Principally, the water-jet consists of an inlet duct leading the water to the impeller, a pump casing and an outlet nozzle, forming the jet. Steering is accomplished by a steering nozzle, directing the jet

±30° which redirects the jet of water issuing from the nozzle. Astern thrust is achieved by a reversing bucket incorporated in the steering nozzle.

The most effective propulsion will be with the jet just above the dynamic waterline. However, to secure priming of the pump at start up, the pump shaft centre must not be higher than the waterline at rest.

Inlet duct: In order to improve efficiency and to avoid excessive cavitation in the pump (the impeller and its casing), the velocity head of the inlet flow must be used to the largest possible extent. Thus, the inlet channel should lead the water to the pump with only small losses. Unsuitable inlet shapes not only cause losses but also result in choking, which can disturb the pump.

To be able to meet these demands, tests at correct cavitation numbers have been made in the KaMeWa Marine Laboratory with models of various inlet designs. Based upon these model tests the inlet duct can be given an efficiency of about 75 to 80 per cent in relation to the inlet velocity head.

The inlet duct is preferably integrated into the hull and normally built by the shipyard according to KaMeWa drawings. The inlet at the hull surface is well rounded to avoid vortices entering the pump at low speeds. Debris is prevented from entering the inlet by a grid. Should the pump get clogged it can be cleaned through the inspection openings in front of the impeller. The inlet duct ends at the transom with a connecting flange for the pump.

Pump: The pump is of the mixed flow type and the six-blade impeller is bolted to a stub shaft carried in the stator hub by one radial and one axial roller bearing. The bearings are spherical with the same centre of sphere, so that they are unaffected by minor deviations from the theoretically correct centreline of the pump shaft. Movements of a semi-elastically mounted gearbox will thus not affect the bearings.

The pump unit also contains the stationary guide vanes and the outlet nozzle forming the jet.

The thrust of the pump unit is taken up and transferred to the transom of the vessel.

The impeller hub is filled with oil to lubricate and cool the bearings. The thrust bearing also acts as a

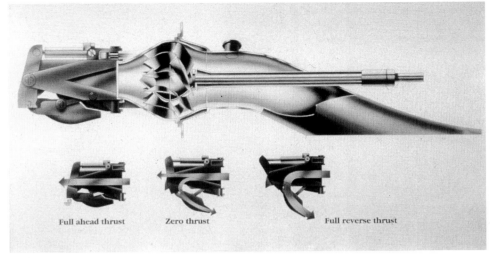

Full ahead thrust   Zero thrust   Full reverse thrust

KaMeWa water-jet system, basic form   **1994**

centrifugal pump circulating the oil within the hub. The temperature of the oil is thus kept within about 20°C above the water temperature without any extra oil cooler. To minimise the risk of water leakage into the hub, the oil pressure is kept above the water pressure by a circulating pump and a gravity tank.

The pump unit as well as the pump shaft and the steering/reversing gear are made of acid-proof steel. Sacrificial zinc anodes are fitted within the space between the impeller chamber and the conical aft part of the inlet duct to protect the hull and inlet.

Steering and reversing gear: Steering forces are achieved by deflecting the jet sideways turning the steering nozzle 30° port or starboard. The steering nozzle also incorporates the reversing device. Jet reversal is obtained by turning the bucket under the nozzle, where it gradually enters the jet from below and finally gives full reverse thrust. By setting the bucket in intermediate positions the thrust can be

continuously and smoothly varied from zero to maximum ahead and astern.

The fact that the bucket is coming from under the jet means that a very low vibration level is achieved on the gear since only that part of the jet which needs to be deflected is affected while the remaining part of the jet is undisturbed.

The bearings for the steering as well as for the reversing bucket are of the self-lubricating type. On top of the steering nozzle are two supports for the pivoted hydraulic cylinders for steering. The reversing bucket consists of upper and lower parts linked together by bearings at the aft end. The movement of the two parts is controlled by a yoke welded to the upper part and journalled in the steering nozzle. The lower part is coupled to the steering nozzle by one link on each side of the nozzle. The yoke is connected to the pivoted hydraulic cylinder for reversing positioned on top of the steering nozzle. When reversing, the upper part closes the steering

KaMeWa water-jet unit deliveries 1993 onwards
KaMeWa delivered over 500 units between 1989 and 1993

Delivery	Name of Ship	Type of Ship	Owner	Shipyard	Yard No	Number of units	kW/ shaft	Size of unit
1993	—	Catamaran	Aquajet, Japan	MIHO, Japan	334	2	1920	63S
1993	—	SES	—	SEC, Viareggio, Italy	774	2	2×19850	180S
1993	Universal Mk III	Catamaran	—	Kværner Fjellstrand (S) Pte Ltd, Singapore	0010	2	2000	63S
1993	—	Catamaran	—	Kværner Fjellstrand, Omastrand, Norway	1618	2	2000	63S
1993	—	Catamaran	—	Kværner Fjellstrand (S) Pte Ltd, Singapore	0006	2	2000	63S
1993	—	Catamaran	—	Kværner Fjellstrand (S) Pte Ltd, Singapore	0007	2	2000	63S
1993	Lada Satu	Catamaran	Lada-Langkawi Development Authorities, Malaysia	SBF Shipbuilders, South Coogee, Australia	LK32-1	2	1435	56S
1993	Lada Dua	Catamaran	Lada-Langkawi Development Authorities, Malaysia	SBF Shipbuilders, South Coogee, Australia	LK32-2	2	1435	56S
1993	—	Catamaran	Lada-Langkawi Development Authorities, Malaysia	SBF Shipbuilders South Coogee, Australia	LK32-3	2	1435	56S
1993	—	Catamaran	—	Wavemaster International Pty Ltd, Henderson, Australia	47	4	1960	63S
1993	Hui Yang	Catamaran	Yuet Hing, Hong Kong	Austal Ships Pty Ltd	100	2	1920	71S
1993	Tai Shan	Catamaran	Yuet Hing, Hong Kong	Austal Ships Pty Ltd	101	2	1920	71S
1993	—	Monohull	—	Rodriquez Cantieri Navali SpA, Messina, Italy	251	2	2000	71S
1993	—	Motoryacht	—	Brödrene Aa Marine A/S, Hyen, Norway	230	2 1	2×2410+ 1×736	63S 40B
1993	—	Monohull ferry	—	Rodriquez Cantieri Navali SpA, Messina, Italy	256	2 1	2×3565+ 1×20 800	100S 180B
1993	—	Patrol boat	MSA, Japan	MHI Shimonoseki,	984	1	1820	80S
1993	—	Catamaran	—	Wavemaster International Pty Ltd, Henderson, Australia	32	2	1940	71S
1993	Peng Jiang	Catamaran	—	Wavemaster International Pty Ltd, Henderson, Australia	35	2	1960	63S
1993	—	Motoryacht	—	Brödrene Aa Marine A/S, Hyen, Norway	231	2 1	2×2410+ 1×736	63S 40B
1993	—	Monohull	Rok Navy	KangNam Corp, Pusan, Korea	—	2	755	56S
1993	—	Patrol boat	MSA, Japan	Hitachi, Japan	7104	1	1820	80S
1993	—	SES	—	Samsung, Kyungnam, Korea	H4001	2	2000	63S
1993	Gang Zhou	Catamaran	Yuet Hing, Hong Kong	Austal Ships Pty Ltd	102	2	1960	71S
1993	Gao Ming	Catamaran	Yuet Hing, Hong Kong	Austal Ships Pty Ltd	103	2	1960	71S
1993	—	SES	—	SEMO Co Ltd, Kyungnam, Korea	PMS-02	2	1970	63S
1993	—	SES	—	SEMO Co Ltd, Kyungnam, Korea	PMS-03	2	1970	63S
1993	—	Monohull	Palton Services Ltd, Dublin, Ireland	CODECASA, Viareggio, Italy	103	2	2560	63S
1993	—	Monohull fast ferry	Transmediterraneo, Spain	Empresa Nacional Bazan, San Fernando, Spain	315	2 2	2×5000+ 2×5000	100S 100B
1993	—	Catamaran	—	Kværner Fjellstrand (S) Pte Ltd, Singapore	0008	2	2000	63S
1993	—	Catamaran	—	Kværner Fjellstrand (S) Pte Ltd, Singapore	0009	2	2000	63S
1993	Gui Feng	Catamaran	Yuet Hing, Hong Kong	Austal Ships Pty Ltd	109	2	1960	71S
1993	—	Catamaran	Yuet Hing, Hong Kong	Austal Ships Pty Ltd	110	2	1960	71S
1993	—	Catamaran	Yuet Hing, Hong Kong	Austal Ships Pty Ltd	105	2	3130	71S
1993	—	Catamaran	Yuet Hing, Hong Kong	Austal Ships Pty Ltd	106	2	3130	71S
1993	—	Catamaran	Yuet Hing, Hong Kong	Austal Ships Pty Ltd	108	2	3130	71S
1993 1993	—	Catamaran	—	Kværner Fjellstrand, Omastrand, Norway	1619	2	2000	63S
	—	SES	—	Beliard Polyship, Oostende, Belgium	8822	2	1841	63S
1993	—	Catamaran	—	Austal Ships Pty Ltd	168	2	1960	71S
1993	—	Catamaran	—	Kværner Fjellstrand, Omastrand, Norway	1620	2	2000	63S
1993	—	Monohull ferry	—	Leroux et Lotz	621	2 1	2×2243+ 1×4486	80S 90B
1993	Marwin	Open power boat	—	Baglietto Shipbuilders, Varazze, Italy	C63	2	1570	50S
1993	—	SES	—	SEMO Co Ltd	PMS-04	2	1970	63S
1993	—	Catamaran	Alameda, San Francisco, USA	Nichols Brothers Boat Builders Inc, Freeland, WA, USA	108	2	970	50S
1993	—	Foil-assisted catamaran	—	Daewoo Shipbuilders, Kyungnam, Korea	—	2	2000	63S

KaMeWa water-jet unit deliveries 1993 onwards (continued)
KaMeWa delivered over 500 units between 1989 and 1993

Delivery	Name of Ship	Type of Ship	Owner	Shipyard	Yard No	Number of units	kW/ shaft	Size of unit
1993	—	Catamaran	—	Wavemaster International Pty Ltd, Henderson, Australia	48	4	2000	63S
1994	—	Catamaran	Stena Rederi AB	Finnyards OY.	404	4	17 035	160S
1994	—	—	—	Trinity Marine, New Orleans, USA	1393	2	1680	50S
1994	—	Catamaran	—	MIHO, Japan	338	2	1980	63S
1994	—	Tricat	CTS Parkview	FBM Marine Ltd	1407	2	4200	90S
1994	—	Tricat	CTS Parkview	FBM Marine Ltd	1408	2	4200	90S
1994	—	Tricat	CTS Parkview	FBM Marine Ltd	1409	2	4200	90S
1994	—	Tricat	CTS Parkview	FBM Marine Ltd	1410	2	4200	90S
1994	—	Tricat	CTS Parkview	FBM Marine Ltd	1411	2	4200	90S
1995	—	Catamaran	Stena Rederi AB	Finnyards OY	405	4	17 035	160S
1994	—	Monohull	SPI Maritime, Tahiti	Austal Ships Pty Ltd, Henderson, Australia	35	2	2×1960+	63S
						1	1×1960	63B
1994	—	Monohull	—	Hitachi, Japan	7313	2	1745	56S
1994	—	—	MSA, Japan	Mitsui, Japan	—	1	1820	80S
1994	—	Catamaran	—	Kværner Fjellstrand, Omastrand, Norway	1621	2	2000	63S
1994	—	Monohull fast ferry	Transmediterraneo, Spain	Empresa Nacional Bazan, San Fernando, Spain	316	2	2×5000+	100S
						2	2×5000	100B
1994	—	Catamaran	—	Wavemaster International Pty Ltd, Henderson, Australia	69	4	1960	63S
1994	—	Monohull	Corferry	Rodriquez	—	2	6000	112S11
						1	12000	160S11
1994	—	Catamaran	Stena Rederi AB	Finnyards OY	406	4	17035	160S11
1994	—	Catamaran	Buquebus	Incat Tasmania	—	2	5300	80S11
							5300	80S11
1994	—	Monohull	European Ferries	Mjellan and Karlsen	—	4	5800	112S11
1994	—	Catamaran	Sea Containers	Austal Ships	—	4	4950	100S11
1995	—	Monohull	SNCM	Leroux et Lotz	—	2	6000	112S11
						2	6000	112B11
1995	—	Catamaran	Mols-Linien	Danyard	—	4	6200	112S11
1995	—	Catamaran	Mols-Linien	Danyard	—	4	6200	112S11

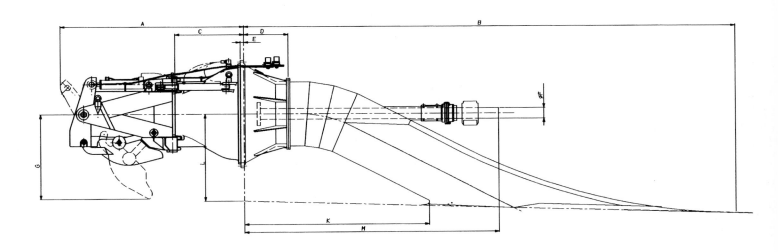

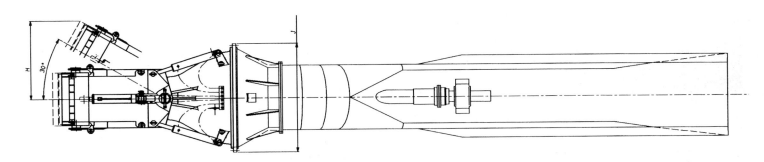

Size options for KaMeWa Type 62 water-jet units

1995

nozzle and deflects the jet down to the lower part which further changes the jet direction to forward/down, resulting in astern thrust.

For feedback and position indication, there are cables connected to the steering nozzle and to the reversing bucket. The cables are drawn through the transom and connected to potentiometers.

Hydraulic and lubricating system: A separate hydraulic power pack for each unit is used for manoeuvring. Normally the load-compensated main pump is PTO-driven and for start and stand-by a small electric motor driven pump is used. The control valves are mounted on top of the power pack.

The power pack also contains the lubricating system. A small pump is used for circulating the oil as well as to maintain a pressure higher than the waterhead outside the seal. The pack should be positioned above the waterline in order to keep a static head at standstill.

Electronic remote-control system: The positions of the steering nozzle and the reversing bucket as well as engine speed are set by the electronic remote-control system. Usually the reversing bucket and the engine speed are controlled by a common combinator lever. When in transit all jet units are normally controlled simultaneously regarding steering angle, reversing and shaft rpm. To achieve optimum manoeuvrability during docking, station keeping and under low-speed manoeuvring the different water-jet units are individually controlled. After some practice an operator can select steering angle, reverse flap position and shaft rpm of each individual unit to achieve the desired manoeuvre. However, KaMeWa has also developed a computerised system that calculates and orders the optimum combination of settings of the water-jets and side thrusters. By means of an azimuth lever the operator selects a desired force and its direction in relation to the vessel. With a special knob the turning moment on the vessel can be controlled.

The KaMeWa water-jet units have the following advantages and characteristics:

(1) They are designed to give high performance at high ship speeds as well as at low cruising speed. The efficiency has been verified in a number of full-scale installations, please see accompanying graph
(2) For medium-speed vessels with a top speed of 20 to 25 knots, the fuel economy is in general competitive with that achieved with propellers
(3) For fast patrol boats fuel economy may be improved compared with fixed-pitch propeller installation from top speed down to the 10 to 15 knots region
(4) The water inlets have a very low drag when idling during cruising which makes the KaMeWa water-jet units attractive as booster units, also in combination with propellers
(5) The thrust/weight ratios of the KaMeWa water-jet units are optimised for most common hull forms, that is, planing and semi-planing hulls, catamarans and sidewall hovercraft (SES)
(6) KaMeWa's modern marine laboratory provides the testing facility required for inlet design, cavitation and performance studies

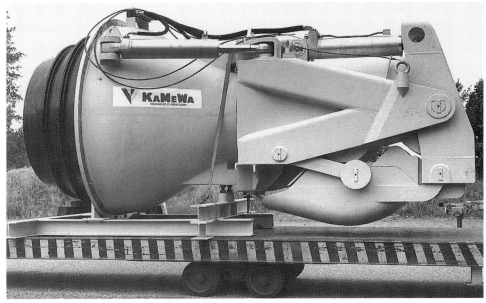

One of four KaMeWa size 160 water-jet units to be installed in Stena's High Speed Sea Service Ferry. With an output of 16 354 kW each, these units are the most powerful water-jets with steering and reversing gear built in the world to date *1995*

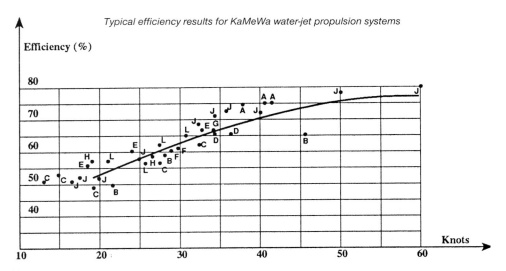

Typical efficiency results for KaMeWa water-jet propulsion systems

Key:

A	100 t	catamaran,	full-scale tests, resistance tested, torque measurements
B	240 t	monohull,	full-scale tests, resistance tested, torque measurements
C	130 t	monohull,	full-scale tests, resistance tested, fuel rack
D	85 t	monohull,	full-scale tests, resistance tested, torque measurements
E	230 t	monohull,	full-scale tests, resistance tested, torque measurements
F	135 t	catamaran,	full-scale tests, resistance tested, torque measurements
G	100 t	SES,	full-scale tests, R from trials with propellers
H	360 t	monohull,	model tests in towing basin and cavitation tunnel
J	930 t	monohull,	model tests in towing basin and cavitation tunnel
K	1000 t	monohull,	model tests in towing basin and cavitation tunnel
L	400 t	monohull,	full-scale tests, resistance tested, fuel rack

1992

Destriero, *the Atlantic Blue Riband holder* *1994*

Guizzo, *the Tirrenia Aquastrada* *1994*

(7) Fixed geometry inlets can be designed to operate satisfactorily at full engine load from low cruising speeds (when running on a reduced number of shafts) up to the top speed of the vessel

(8) The pump shaft speed is practically independent of ship speed at constant power output. This means that the water-jet unit will never overload a diesel engine as the power absorption is always approximately proportional to rpm^3. Reduced maintenance costs due to prolonged MTBO for the diesels may be achieved in certain installations

(9) Due to the absence of appendages and the rugged design of the KaMeWa water-jet units the costs for maintenance and off-hire time due to damages from floating debris can be reduced

(10) In multi-shaft installations CODAG/CODAD propulsion is possible without complex gearing and control systems. Full diesel power is always available irrespective of increased ship resistance due to bad weather and fouling or at extreme light displacements. This means an increased top speed for the vessel

(11) The KaMeWa water-jet units are designed to simplify maintenance and overhaul. The units can be mounted and dismounted from outside the ship

(12) The KaMeWa water-jet installations are characterised by low noise and vibration levels

(13) Excellent manoeuvrability over the whole speed range of the vessel. Full engine torque is always available for manoeuvring and acceleration

(14) Years of operating in the debris-laden waters of the Hong Kong area have proved that the units are very reliable and insensitive to sand and floating debris in the water.

Very low hydro-acoustic noise combined with high efficiency make the KaMeWa water-jets attractive for navy craft. Two 63S units capable of absorbing 2040 kW each are used for the propulsion of the Swedish Navy SES stealth craft.

Destriero

On the 9 August 1992 this vessel completed the 3106 nm from New York to Bishops Rock (the Scilly Isles), off the west coast of England, in 58 hours and 34 minutes, winning the coveted Atlantic Blue Riband. The vessel maintained an average speed of 53.09 knots with maximum speed intervals of more than 65 knots.

The Destriero has a fuel capacity of 750 tonnes. It is equipped with three KaMeWa size 125 water-jet units powered by gas-turbines with a total rating of 60 000 bhp.

Aquastrada

The Rodriquez Aquastrada monohull's three engines deliver a total output of about 38 000 bhp. In the centre, a gas-turbine transmits 27 880 bhp to a KaMeWa 180 water-jet that acts as a booster for high-speed operation. On each side a high-speed diesel engine rated at 4850 bhp drives a KaMeWa 100 wing water-jet. This arrangement ensures high manoeuvrability, short stopping distance and a cruising speed of 20 knots.

Stena HSS

The Finnyards Stena HSS catamaran is the largest high-speed water-jet-propelled catamaran built to date and is propelled by four KaMeWa 160 water-jet units. With an output of 16 354 kW each, these units are the most powerful water-jets with steering and reversing gear in the world.

The new ferry will have a service speed in the region of 40 knots and accommodation for 1500 passengers and 375 cars. Scheduled for delivery in 1995, the vessel will operate in the Irish Sea.

UPDATED

MJP

MARINE JET POWER AB
ÖSTERBY GJUTERI AB

S-740 63 Österbybruk, Sweden

Telephone: +46 (295) 20785
Telefax: +46 (295) 21383

Torbjörn Ahlbäck, *Managing Director*
Gerard Törneman, *Managing Director and General Manager*
Björn Hanberg, *Sales Manager*
Michael Näsström, *Service Manager*

MJP Marine Jet Power AB is a Swedish company developing and designing advanced propulsion systems for high performance vessels in commercial operations. MJP is also a division of Österby Gjuteri AB, responsible for the marketing and production of the MJP water-jets for the European, Asian, Australian and American markets. The MJP water-jet units are also marketed and produced by Niigata Engineering in Japan under licence from MJP Marine Jet Power AB. MJP is developing water-jets to absorb up to 10 000 kW and the range covers jet propulsion systems for double, triple and quadruple drive installation between 600 kW and 10 000 kW.

The new models are named S92 and they include all design developments and experience gained from over 150 000 operating hours in various types of vessels and environments.

Manoeuvring capability: The system includes jet propulsors, steering/reversing units, electro-hydraulic controls and a computerised Remote Manoeuvre Controller (RMC), which is claimed to be the first digital control system in this field. With the computerised RMC the crew's learning period for advanced water-jet operation has been reduced to a minimum and the risk for mistakes in critical situations has been minimised. The RMC includes control levers for steering, speed/forward/reverse and a single combinator for cruising/harbour mode. Normally a twin installation of water-jets requires two combinators, one for each unit, but with the digital control system advanced manoeuvres are made with one single combinator. The combinator can be used in two ways: in cruising mode for different speed setting on each unit, and in harbour mode for lateral movement of the vessel without the need of bow thrusters and rotation around the vessel's centre of flotation.

The different settings of the water-jets, that is forward/neutral/reverse, outward/inward inclination and speed are controlled by the computer and can be adjusted for different vessels and loading conditions by the crew.

For steering purposes hydraulic rotary actuators are used which allow full nozzle turning from one side to the other within 2.5 seconds. The feedback to the electrohydraulic controls and the inclination to the mimic panel in the wheelhouse are done through double built-in electrical transmitters in the hydraulic actuators.

The complete steering and reversing unit is made of stainless steel castings and the reverser is positively balanced, this allows a stepless redirection of the jetflow from full speed ahead to full speed astern.

Efficiency: To achieve predicted efficiency and speed a new type of mixed-flow pump was developed. The blade-to-blade flow analysis was carried out on a computer together with the finite element strength analysis of the impeller. This design technique is ensuring low drag and high freedom from cavitation.

To further increase the efficiency a new type of impeller bearing was designed including a continuous bearing monitoring system. This careful design also increases vessel comfort due to freedom from vibration of impeller and shaft.

Operating reliability: Many of today's high-speed surface craft are constructed in light alloy plate, and therefore a new type of intake including plastic parts has been designed to avoid corrosion problems by insulating the stainless steel pump unit from the hull.

MJP water-jet unit mounted on the 41 m Marinteknik monohull ferry Rosaria Lauro *1989*

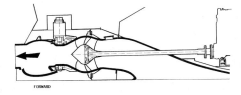

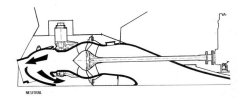

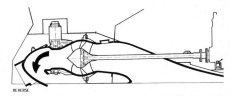

Mechanism of flow redirection on MJP water-jet units *1988*

MJP Marine Jet Power AB deliveries 1993 onwards (MJP delivered over 100 water-jets prior to 1993)

No	Water-jet model	Output kW	Engine make	Shipowner	Area of operation	Yard/Hull	Name of vessel	Classi-fication	Hull type	LOA (m)	Speed (knots)	Delivery
41	J650R-DD	2 × 1880	MTU	Sealink	France	Marinteknik B 88	*Saint Malo*	BV	Catamaran	41	35	1993
42	J650R-DD	2 × 1920	MTU			Kværner Fjellstrand (S)		DnV	Catamaran	40	37	1993
43	J650R-DD	2 × 1470	MTU	Tropic Charters of Singapore	Indonesia	Austal 15	*Bali Hai II*	DnV	Catamaran	36	29	1993
44	J750R-DD	2 × 1435	MTU	Universal Boss	Hong Kong	FBM 1332	*Universal Mark VI*	DnV	Catamaran	32	35	1993
45	J650R-DD	2 × 1839	Niigata	Fuke Kaiun	Japan	Hitachi Zosen C	—	JG	Catamaran	31.5	38	Apr 1993
46	J650R-DD	2 × 1839	Niigata	Ishizaki Kisen	Japan	Hitachi Zosen C	—	JG	Catamaran	31.5	38	May 1993
47	J650R-DD	2 × 1839	Niigata	Fuke Kaiun	Japan	Hitachi Zosen C	—	JG	Catamaran	31.5	38	Jun 1993
48	J650R-DD	2 × 1839	Niigata	Seto Inland	Japan	Hitachi Zosen C	—	JG	Catamaran	31.5	38	Jul 1993
49	J650R-DD	2 × 1839	Niigata	Ishizaki Kisen	Japan	Hitachi Zosen C	—	JG	Catamaran	31.5	38	Nov 1993
50	J650R-DD	2 × 1839	Niigata	Seto Inland Sea Lins	Japan	Hitachi Zosen C	—	JG	Catamaran	31.5	38	Jan 1994
51	J650R-DD	2 × 1839	Niigata	Fuke Kaiun	Japan	Hitachi Zosen C	—	JG	Catamaran	31.5	38	Feb 1994
52	J500S-DD	2 × 735	MTU	Swedish Coast Guard	Swedish Coast	Karlskronavarvet	*KBV 302*	DnV	Monohull	20	33	1994
53	J500s-DD	2 × 735	MTU	Swedish Coast Guard	Swedish Coast	Karlskronavarvet	*KBV 303*	DnV	Monohull	20	33	1994
54	J500S-DD	2 × 735	MTU	Swedish Coast Guard	Swedish Coast	Karlskronavarvet	*KBV 304*	DnV	Monohull	20	33	1994
55	J500S-DD	2 × 735	MTU	Swedish Coast Guard	Swedish Coast	Karlskronavarvet	*KBV 305*	DnV	Monohull	20	33	1995
56	J500S-DD	2 × 735	MTU	Swedish Coast Guard	Swedish Coast	Karlskronavarvet	*KBV 306*	DnV	Monohull	20	33	1995
57	J500S-DD	2 × 735	MTU	Swedish Coast Guard	Swedish Coast	Karlskronavarvet	*KBV 307*	DnV	Monohull	20	33	1995
58	J500X-DD	2 × 735	MTU	Swedish Coast Guard	Swedish Coast	Karlskronavarvet	*KBV 308*	DnV	Monohull	20	33	1995
59	J500S-DD	2 × 735	MTU	Swedish Coast Guard	Swedish Coast	Karlskronavarvet	*KBV 309*	DnV	Monohull	20	33	1995
60	J500S-DD	2 × 735	MTU	Swedish Coast Guard	Swedish Coast	Karlskronavarvet	*KBV 310*	DnV	Monohull	20	33	1995
61	J500S-DD	2 × 735	MTU	Swedish Coast Guard	Swedish Coast	Karlskronavarvet	*KBV 311*	DnV	Monohull	20	33	1995
62	J650R	4 × 1415	MTU	Surf	Caribbean	Marinteknik Singapore	*H 130*	DnV	Catamaran	41	42	1994
63	J650R-DD	2 × 1970	MTU	Cheerful Prospects Ltd	Hong Kong	Marinteknik Singapore	*H 118*	DnV	Catamaran	34	39	1994
64	J650R-DD	2 × 1920	MTU	Bintan Resort	Singapore	Kværner Fjellstrand	*H 017*	DnV	Catamaran	40	37	1994
65	J650R-DD	2 × 1935	MWM	Hong Kong Resort Co Ltd	Hong Kong	Marinteknik Singapore	*H 137*	DnV	Catamaran	42	34	1994
66	J650R-DD	2 × 1935	MWM	Hong Kong Resort Co Ltd	Hong Kong	Marinteknik Singapore	*H 138*	DnV	Catamaran	42	34	1995
67	J650R-DD	2 × 1935	MWM	Hong Kong Resort Co Ltd	Hong Kong	Marinteknik Singapore	*H 139*	DnV	Catamaran	42	34	1995
68	J650R-DD	2 × 2000	MTU		India	Kværner Fjellstrand	*H 016*	DnV	Catamaran	40	37	1994
69	J650-DD	2 × 1720	MTU	Daikyo	Australia	Lloyd's Ship Yard	*Reef Prince*	DnV	Catamaran	36	30	1994
70	J650R-DD	2 × 2000	MTU			Kværner Fjellstrand	*H 019*	DnV	Catamaran	40	37	1994
71	J650R-DD	2 × 2000	MTU			Kværner Fjellstrand	*H 020*	DnV	Catamaran	40	37	1994

All other components and materials are also chosen to avoid corrosion and mechanical wear in the demanding marine environment.

The monitoring system for the RMC has built-in measuring points which give fast fault indication and considerably shorten the servicing time.

RMC-DD
Advanced manoeuvring system for water-jets

Background: During the last five years, MPJ has delivered over 35 advanced manoeuvring systems installed in high-speed catamarans and monohull ferries, in the range of 33 to 42 m length and with speeds between 20 and 40 knots.

This system, the 'Remote Manoeuvre Controller — Dual Drive' (RMC-DD) is unique on the market, with two preselectable modes of 'cruise' and 'harbour' for open sea and confined harbour operations respectively.

New generation: The two separate combinator levers for direction and thrust control in the older system are now combined in one two-axis single combinator of joystick type with some special mechanical tracking control facilities to give the operator an improved sense of direction control during cruise as well as in confined harbour manoeuvres.

This leaves the other hand free for steering control or to switch over to the autopilot.

MJP J500R-DD water-jets for the Swedish Coastguard

1995

The autopilot makes the harbour manoeuvres easier; by switching it to control the steering in harbour mode during lateral (sideway) movement, the helmsman can leave the parallel steering control to the autopilot. In this case, the autopilot will provide automatic parallel steering when leaving or approaching a pier in transversal direction. By setting the autopilot course parallel to the pier and activating it, the helmsman needs only to concentrate his attention on controlling the sideway propulsive thrust and make required adjustment of the forward/reverse power that may be needed depending on current and wind affecting the movement, or when moving in diagonal fashion, still under 'parallelism' with the preset course. All these thrust control adjustments can now be done with the single hand combinator lever.

If the helmsman wants to take over the steering for a short adjustment or turning during the transversal movement, without switching the autopilot control off, he can override the autopilot by turning the lever in the desired direction. Retransmitting the control to the autopilot is done by setting the steering lever in neutral position (electrical autopilot interface) or by letting go of the lever, if the autopilot interface is driven by a friction coupled DC motor directly on the steering lever shaft. (Alternative optional AP-interface.)

Upgrading of the first-generation of RMC-DD: A retrofit kit for upgrading the earlier deliveries of RMC-DD equipped with the older manoeuvring lever system, is available on request.

Remote Manoeuvre Station (RMS)

The RMS can be easily moved to different positions such as the bridge wing, the fly bridge or the aft deck if required. The possibility to operate more than one RMS with an advanced and safe 'takeover' routine is incorporated in this development.

The RMS will be accumulator powered, and communicate with the main RMC-DD system by a non-galvanic ('contactless') adaptor to a simple communication net.

When not in use, the RMS unit(s) is connected to a charger, preferably placed on the main manoeuvre bridge. A highly sophisticated internal self-check and communication protocol and a very safe 'takeover routine' assure safe handling and operation of the overall system.

Even the first generation of RMC-DD can be modified and upgraded with RMS units since it is pre-adapted with input/output channels for that use.

MJP J450R, J550R, J650R and J750R

Four types of complete propulsion systems, single or double, including water-jets, hydraulics and computerised remote-control system.
Output: 200-3500 kW per unit
Speed range: 18-60 knots
Material: stainless steel in water-jets

Weight: 600-2000 kg
Manoeuvring: electrohydraulic servo system
Remote-control: computerised control including combinator for lateral movement and rotation

Size	*Nom kW	Max kW	A	B	⌀C	⌀D	E	F	G	H	Weight per unit kg**	
											Steerable	Booster
500	1200	1800	510	1290	855	500	2050	3400	575	460	815	575
550	1500	2250	560	1412	940	550	2250	3790	630	505	1090	710
650	2100	3150	665	1680	1120	650	2675	4510	750	600	1560	1035
750	2800	4200	765	1900	1255	750	3075	5180	860	690	2105	1460
850	3700	5550	880	2100	1440	850	3540	5890	990	795	3145	2125
950	4900	7350	1010	2460	1610	950	4070	6590	1100	915	4330	3000
1100	6950	9750	1200	2845	1890	1100	4820	7630	1350	1090	6040	4080
1350	9200	13800	1355	3490	2110	1350	5560	9370	1555	1250	8450	5830
1550												
1750												
2050												

* Above figures are nominal, final data in accordance to technical specification.
** Weight figures incl hydraulics, excl shafting & intake.

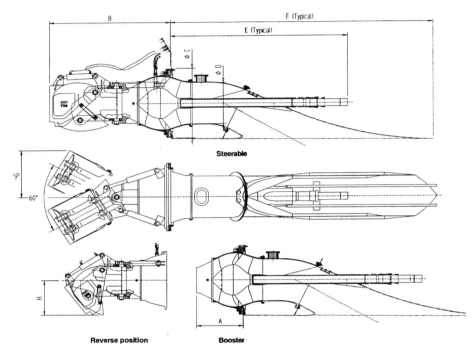

Dimensions of MJP water-jet units 1995

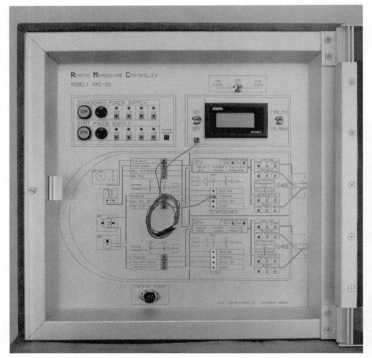

Computerised MJP Remote Control System 1988

Bridge installation of Remote Control System 1990

UNITED KINGDOM

PP JETS

A subsidiary of Vosper Thornycroft Hydraulic Power Division

Northarbour Road, Cosham, Portsmouth, Hampshire PO6 3TL, UK

Telephone: +44 (1705) 383311
Telex: 86860 VTHYPO G
Telefax: +44 (1705) 325133

R Forhead, *Sales and Marketing*
R G Parker, *Technical Consultant*
M J Breeze, *Technical Consultant*

PP Jets was acquired by Vosper Thornycroft Hydraulic Power Division in 1993.

The company offers a range of jet units up to its Model PP 300 of 762 mm impeller diameter suitable for powers up to 3000 kW (4000 hp).

PP Jets have for a number of years successfully used GRP for the major fixed components of their water-jet units. The range of jet units from Model PP 115 upwards is now being built with a mixture of glass fibre, Kevlar and carbon fibre reinforcement. These materials are totally corrosion resistant and give excellent structural properties. All metal parts exposed to the water can be made in stainless steel or, for special applications, in more exotic materials eliminating problems associated with dissimilar metals in contact with salt water.

The method of construction allows the form of the jet to be made to match the hull contour with comparatively simple additions to the mould. Further, the moulded surface presents a highly polished finish for the water flow.

An adjustable trim facility is available on most models giving up and down nozzle movement of ±10°.

In 1992, Kort Propulsion Company Ltd announced that it was marketing PP Jets water-jet systems from 150 to 3000 kW.

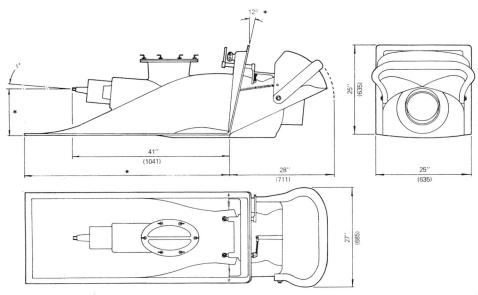

Cutaway version of PP 115 water-jet **1992**

PP 140

PERFORMANCE EXAMPLES
At max quoted power levels:
 Thrust at 10 knots, 400 shp, 1650 kg
 Thrust at 20 knots, 400 shp, 1320 kg
 Thrust at 40 knots, 400 shp, 770 kg

UPDATED *Model PP 140 water-jet unit* **1986**

PP type number	65	90 90G	100	115	140	170	210	250	300
Engine size (hp)									
petrol	40-200	60-350	—	—	—	—	—	—	—
diesel	10-50	40-250	60-350	70-400	100-600	200-900	400-3000	600-2000	1500-4000
Impeller diameter at inlet	165	229	254	292	356	431	533	635	762
Materials									
Jet unit body	aluminium LM25 hard anodised (PP 90G-GRP)	composites	composites	composites	composites	composites	composites	composites	composites
Impeller	Aluminium bronze	Aluminium bronze	Aluminium bronze	Superston 70	Superston 70	Superston 70	Superston 70	Superston 70	Superston 70
Weight (kg)	30	60 (PP 90G-70)	100	125	200	350	600	900	1500

ULTRA HYDRAULICS LTD

An Ultra Group Company

Anson Business Park, Cheltenham Road East, Staverton, Gloucester GL2 9QN, UK

Telephone: +44 (1452) 857711
Telex: 437452 G
Telefax: +44 (1452) 858222

D Burton, *Managing Director*
R J Scarborough, *Director*
M J Lane, *Engineering Manager, Marine Products*
C R G Ellis, *Sales Manager*

Ultra Hydraulics, an Ultra Group company, is a high technology engineering company based in the UK with overseas representation in Canada, Germany and the USA.

The product range of Ultra Hydraulics includes water-jets, developed over a 30 year involvement in the marine field, starting with the Dowty Turbocraft jet boats of the 1950s. Ultra water-jets are now among the most numerous water-jet units in the world.

Water-jets have been produced for defence markets and are principally designed to produce very high thrust at relatively low speed, without suffering from cavitation.

The basic component of the water-jet is an axial flow impeller (single or two stage) made of stainless steel, set within a stainless steel reaction casing. The intake and outlet ducts are of cast aluminium.

The control mechanisms are simple and are designed to be robust and reliable. Both the steering and reversing actuator arms penetrate the transom plate and are readily adapted to match the boat's control systems. The zero thrust condition is achieved by the downward vectoring of the jet.

The control of the unit is identical to conventional rudder practice, requiring no retraining of crew. The jet can be directed 33° either side of the central position and the pivot arrangement ensures a high level of flow efficiency, in all conditions.

The components are all made from high quality materials and require minimal maintenance. Ingested debris can be cleared from within the boat by means of an access hatch, or simply discharged by back-flushing the unit.

Typical high-speed craft utilising Ultra water-jets include combat support boats (bridge erection boats).

The Water-jet 300 is installed in over 500 craft, including combat support boats for the Far Eastern, Greek, NATO, UK and US armies. Versions of the basic unit have also been installed in army amphibious vehicles, where space constraints have dictated changes to the unit's layout.

There are also applications in the field of auxiliary or loitering propulsion for larger craft, such as patrol boats, where good manoeuvrability and slow speed economy are required.

A recent development is the rotating nozzle jet which is capable of being directed through 360°. Another development utilises a high solidity stainless steel impeller which results in a craft speed increase combined with smaller unit size and hence weight reduction.

Water-jets are purpose-built to meet customer requirements. Production has included units from 250 to 450 mm, capable of absorbing up to 1 300 bhp and the company is prepared to investigate other sizes and powers to suit special applications. Development is proceeding on higher thrust water-jets.

UPDATED

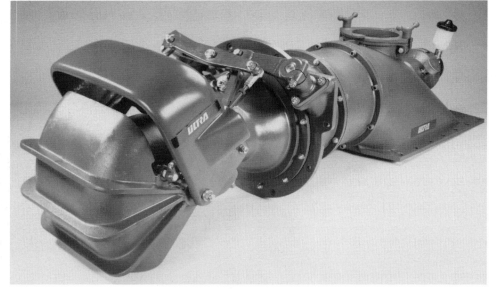

Dia 300 two stage water-jet for marine craft applications   **1991**

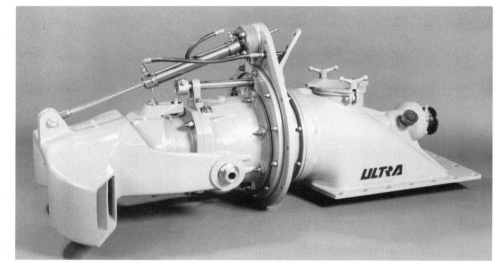

The new Ultrajet 300 mm water-jet unit
1994

UNITED STATES OF AMERICA

AMJET

AMERICAN HYDRO JET CORPORATION

2033-F West McNab Road, Pompano Beach, Florida 33069, USA

Telephone: +1 (305) 978 8996
Telefax: +1 (305) 978 6597

P W Roos, *President*
R Filippino, *Vice President, Manufacturing*
A L Cohen, *Marketing Manager*

American Hydro Jet Corporation began the design and manufacture of water-jet units in 1988.

AMJET presently supplies water-jets in six ranges to absorb power levels up to 3750 kW. The six ranges are designated J-1200, J-1400, J-1700, J-2200, J-2700 and J-3500.

AMJET J-3500 SERIES HYDRO JET DRIVE

The AMJET J-3500 series jet drive is designed for power inputs of 1120 kW (displacement hulls) to 5250 kW (high-speed planing hulls). The impeller diameter can be selected from 71 to 88 cm. The maximum shaft speed is 1200 rpm and the weight range is up to 2000 kg. The power steering and reverse systems provide for efficient steering, especially at high speeds, as well as conventional reverse direction steering with excellent manoeuvrability.

AMJET J-3580   **1992**

The complete water-jet propulsion system is modular in concept and designed with flexibility, allowing many applications from displacement speed to very fast planing hulls, each with highest efficiency possible. The use of the reduction gear as the forward pump shaft support eliminates the need for a double universal drive line and allows the engine to be placed further aft. It makes possible the prefabrication of modules, and customer fabrication of the intake duct as an integral part of the hull. All modules (except intake duct) are pre-assembled, tested and all controls adjusted at the factory so that reassembly in the field requires no further adjustment. It allows for effective cost control during manufacture and installation in the field. All hydraulic controls are placed inside the vessel and the lubrication oil, void space and water pressure ducting are internal to the pump, eliminating all external hose and tubing connections.

UPDATED

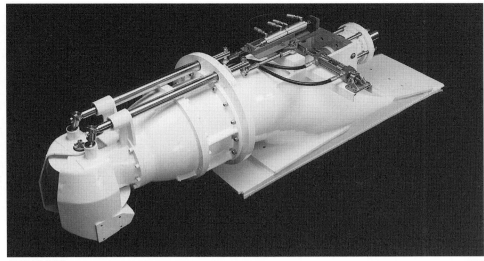

AMJET 1700   *1995*

AMJET 1700 triple arrangement
1995

NORTH AMERICAN MARINE JET INC

PO Box 1232, Benton, Arkansas 72018, USA

Telephone: +1 (501) 778 4151
Telefax: +1 (501) 778 6381

Established in 1980, this company manufactures water-jets for high-speed craft for the power range 110 kW to 560 kW. The company also supplies high thrust, low-speed units. Water-jets have been supplied to a variety of craft including US Navy patrol boats, fishing boats, workboats, dive boats, crew boats, fire boats and excursion boats.

The company has in-house facilities for the fabrication of steel, stainless steel and aluminium, backed up by analytical design software, and a CAD system.

The Nomera range is offered to the high-speed craft market, and a new 300 kW unit for high-speed craft of 30 to 60 knot speeds is soon to be introduced.

NOMERA 14

Designed to operate with diesel or petrol engines at 2400 to 3000 rpm, this unit provides high thrust and maneuvrability. Straightforward construction allows for easier maintenance and increased reliability. There are two models, the Nomera 14A and the

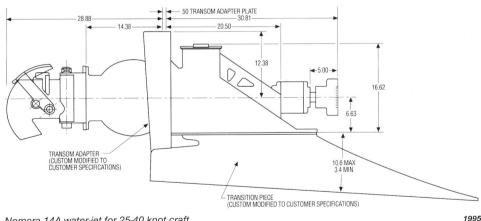

Nomera 14A water-jet for 25-40 knot craft   *1995*

Nomera 14-OB offering the same performance but a slight variance in unit dimensions.
Principal Particulars
Dry weight: 180 kg
Length: 1.56 m (Nomera 14A); 1.57 m (Nomera 14-OB)
Power: 120-224 kW
Shaft speed: 2400-3000 rpm
Impeller diameter: 0.29 m

NOMERA 20
Principal Particulars
Dry weight: 500 kg
Length: 2.19 m
Power: 186-560 kW
Shaft speed: 1800-2400 rpm
Impeller diameter: 0.40 m

NEW ENTRY

AIR CUSHION SKIRT SYSTEMS

Company Listing by Country

France
Aerazur SA
Pennel & Flipo

Spain
Neumar SA

United Kingdom
Air Cushion Ltd
Avon Technical Products Division
British Hovercraft Corporation Ltd
Greengate Polymer Coatings Ltd
Northern Rubber Company Ltd

United States of America
Bell Avon Inc

FRANCE

AERAZUR SA

Division Applications des Elastomères, 58 boulevard Gallieni, F-92137 Issy-Les-Moulineaux Cedex, France

Telephone: +33 (1) 41 23 23 23
Telex: 631891 F
Telefax: +33 (1) 46 48 74 85

F Menard, *Department Manager*

In January 1990, Aerazur (the aerospace subsidiary of the Zodiac group, active in flexible material technologies and a world leader in inflatable boats) purchased the Coated Fabric Division of Kléber Industrie (part of the Michelin Group). The activities of this division and the corresponding division of Aerazur have been merged into a new 'Division Applications des Elastomères'.

The synergy between Aerazur (in charge of air cushion seal design on various French SES programmes since 1980, including Molenes and Agnes 200), and the extensive coated fabrics development and manufacturing capabilities of the former Coated Fabric Division of Kléber, resulted in the creation of a significant industrial base in the design and manufacturing of SES seals.

Design expertise is available within the company for various SES and hovercraft seal designs (loop and segments and full height segments or innovative designs such as a proprietary self-adjusting front-seal design used on Agnes 200). Various simulation software and computer-assisted design systems have been developed and are used for preliminary design, full-scale development or test data analysis. Installation services and full-scale test and maintenance support are available.

The division is one of the world's major producers of coated fabrics, specialising in high quality products, conforming to the rigorous standards and specifications prevailing in the aerospace and marine (notably liferafts and military inflatables) fields.

For hovercraft and SES seals, a range of fabrics has been specially developed, using advanced base fabrics and rubber compounds (based on Hypalon, neoprene or natural rubber, according to the projected use). These products are tested and qualified on specially designed test rigs, reproducing the conditions encountered in real use. Various materials are available in surface weights ranging from 170 to 4000 g/m².

Development of these materials and assembly procedures, especially for increasing life of the seals, is constantly pursued, based on operational experience.

These materials are used on the seals designed and manufactured by Aerazur or are sold to other

Agnes 200 at high speed, fitted with Aerazur skirt systems (French Navy)   *1992*

skirt manufacturers like Griffon Hovercraft Ltd and Air Vehicles Ltd in the UK. Recently, Aerazur has designed, manufactured and installed the seal system for the French SES Agnes 200 and a new aft seal design for the Blohm+Voss Corsair SES.

During the Summer of 1992, Agnes 200 was used commercially for a scheduled trans-Channel service between Brighton and Dieppe, a 770 nm crossing in often difficult sea conditions (diagonal or transverse seas, waves over 2 m height being encountered 17 per cent of the time). Normal service and full operational speed (35 knots) were maintained up to Sea State 5, with several crossings in Sea State 6. More than 500 hours of cushionborne service were logged, with negligible wear on the aft seal and very little on the front seal. The side fingers were replaced for inspection, as a precautionary measure, every 200 hours and returned to service within a week; the central fingers remained on the ship and showed no wear after 500 hours. All the inspection and replacement was conducted without dry-docking; due to

the modular design the side fingers were replaced in less than four hours, between two trips. Of particular interest is the fact that the good performance of the seal system resulted in a stable and comfortable ride, confirming the design option that no ride control system is needed with these seals (Agnes 200 has no RCS installed), and the good pressure retention characteristics allowed frequent operation on a single supply fan. Subsequent design activity has resulted in an improved design with more than 500 hours of service life possible without maintenance.

The Division is also one of the world leaders in flexible fuel cells and fuel systems for aerospace and armoured vehicles and this technology has been applied to various high-speed marine vehicles. An example of this is that Aerazur has designed, manufactured and installed the complete fuel system of the French Blue Ribbon challenger *Jet Ruban Bleu* and supplied the fuel cells for the Spanish Chaconsa hovercraft.

VERIFIED

PENNEL & FLIPO

384 rue d'Alger, F-59052 Roubaix Cedex 1, France

Telephone: +33 20 36 92 60
Telex: 820373F
Telefax: +33 20 24 55 10

Philippe Lemyze, *Export Manager*

Pennel & Flipo, a subsidiary of Vev Prouvost, employs 600 people. This 60 year old company has concentrated its considerable experience in developing a diverse range of products, and coatings based on the calendering and laminating of rubber, PVC and polyurethane.

Hypalon rubber-coated fabrics are produced for inflatable boats, either on a polyamide-base enka nylon or on a high-tenacity polyester trevira. A whole

range of neoprene-coated fabrics has been produced for general use including hovercraft skirt applications. Finished weights for the various materials are in the range of 950 to 2500 g/m².

Polyurethane-coated fabrics are available from 145 to 1500 g/m².

VERIFIED

SPAIN

NEUMAR SA

La Rinconada, B-6, E-28023 Madrid, Spain

Telephone: +34 (1) 548 2071
Telefax: +34 (1) 547 4696

M de la Cruz, *Technical Director*
J A Barbeta, *Manufacturing Manager*

Neumar SA specialises in the research, development and design of air cushion lift systems, and in the manufacture of flexible structures for hovercraft. The company was formed to bring together a group

of engineers and technicians all of whom had previous experience in hovercraft technology. Of this previous experience it is worth mentioning the research and development, design and manufacture of the hovercraft lift system and skirt for the company Chaconsa under a contract for the Spanish Ministry of Defence.

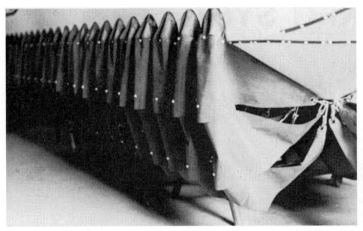 

Two views of the Neumar skirt system developed to secure high stability with low power requirements **1986**

Neumar has developed a hovercraft lift system offering very high stability with low power requirements and reduced manufacturing and maintenance costs. It has been called an Automatic Transversal Air Distribution or ATAD lift system because of the main function it performs. Several two-dimensional models and two prototypes have been built and tested, with which the viability of this new lift system has already been demonstrated. The ATAD lift system is described in detail in the *Air cushion vehicles* section under the Neumar SA entry.

VERIFIED

UNITED KINGDOM

AIR CUSHION LTD

Unit 4SW, Marchwood Industrial Park, Marchwood, Southampton, Hampshire SO40 4PB, UK

Telephone: +44 (1703) 870077
Telefax: +44 (1703) 870044

J D Hake, *Chairman (USA)*
P Auston, *Director*
G Westerling, *General Manager*

Air Cushion Limited (ACL) specialises in the manufacture of flexible structures, mainly for the hovercraft industry. The company produces skirts for hovercraft manufacturers all over the world, for craft ranging from small two-seaters to large hoverbarges.

As hovercraft skirts are an integral part of a system, the ACL design contribution varies from skirt design to full-scale development of the craft manufacturer's own design. In all cases, templates are produced and held by ACL. As a result of the company's long period of involvement with the hovercraft industry, it is able to advise on material suitability, manufacturing techniques and assembly methods.

The new ACL factory in Southampton has equipment capable of making hot bonded (vulcanised) seams up to 5.18 m long and bonding areas up to 2.44 × 1.22 m in one operation. The workshops are fitted with an extraction system which allows large areas to be safely coated with adhesives associated with cold bonding. The company also possesses long-arm sewing machines and HF welding equipment which is in continuous use for the manufacture of flexible tanks and inflatables for use in boats and other applications. These are marketed under the trade name 'Stowaway'.

A wide range of material is stocked coated with neoprene, natural rubber, hypalon, nitrile, polyurethanes, PVC and others. Material weights range from 170 to 3500 g/m².

VERIFIED

AVON TECHNICAL PRODUCTS DIVISION

Melksham, Wiltshire SN12 8AA, UK

Telephone: +44 (1225) 791823
Telex: 44142 AVOMEL G
Telefax: +44 (1225) 705585

P D Miller, *Managing Director*
J E Fitzgerald, *General Manager*
P S Smart, *Sales Manager, ACV*
M E Prentice, *Design Engineer, ACV*

Avon Technical Products Division has facilities to provide the comprehensive design, development, manufacture and material supply services to craft manufacturers and operators. Present development programmes include investigations relating to the design of seals for SES vehicle ferries and fast cargo craft.

The majority of Avon air cushion skirt materials are coated with natural synthetic rubber blends, or neoprene rubber calendered on to specially selected base fabrics. Avon can also provide plied materials from their range, with two or more layers of base fabrics to increase the mechanical properties to satisfy the requirements of certain components within the structure of the skirts.

Avon can offer special experience in the design of the attachments of skirts to craft and attachments between flexible components. Mechanical fastenings for these purposes are stocked and can be offered when these form part of a seal. In the design of skirt components Avon provides for the rapid attachment and removal of all parts during maintenance periods.

Applications of Avon skirt materials include the following:

SR. N4 Mk 2 and Mk 3 (BHC)

Avon has been sole supplier of fingers (segments) for all of the SR. N4 Mk 2 and Mk 3 craft, operated by Hoverspeed, having first supplied to Hoverspeed's predecessors (Hoverlloyd and Seaspeed) in 1972. Avon also supplied and developed fingers for Hoverlloyd and Seaspeed SR. N4 Mk 1 craft dating back to 1969. Avon's involvement over the years has led to major increases in finger life, and has provided a high throughput test-bed for the development of improved coated fabric materials and bonding systems.

LCAC (Textron Marine Systems)

Involvement with this programme started in 1980. Avon is an approved supplier of materials for the skirt system on this craft and, in conjunction with Bell Avon, has been heavily involved in the development and manufacture of components for all ship sets to date.

HM5/HM2 (Hovermarine International)

Avon developed the new bow and stern seals for the four HM5 SES craft which operate on the route between Hong Kong and Macau and has supplied materials and components.

LACV-30 (Textron Marine Systems)

In 1983 Avon manufactured a prototype spray suppression skirt as a direct contract for the US Army. Avon has also supplied materials for these craft since 1979.

BH 110 SES-Bell Halter (now Textron Marine Systems)

Avon has been sole supplier of bow and stern seals for Bell Halter's BH 110 craft since development craft were produced. It has also been manufacturing and developing components for the prototype since 1979, until the establishment of Bell Avon in the USA.

CIRR 105 (Brødrene Aa A/S)

The detailed design of seals for the *Norcat* fast ferry air cushion catamaran (SES) was undertaken in 1984 and included the geometric and structural design of the flexible components and their attachments to the craft. Since then Avon has manufactured seals for all successive craft of this type and supplied seals to their customers for operation in various parts of the world.

UT904 (Ulstein International A/S)

Supplier of bow and stern seals for the UT904 vessels (first delivered in 1991), using novel materials to improve stability of the stern seal.

Karlskronavarvet AB

Avon was awarded a contract in 1987 for the design and supply of the seal system for the two Jet Rider 3400 craft, followed by contracts for the SES 4000 vessels built by Westmarin A/S.

AP1-88 (Westland and licensees)

Avon has supplied all types of material for this craft since its inception, and now manufactures skirts under contract to Westland Aerostructures.

SES SEASWIFT 23 (Royal Schelde)

Design and supply of seals in 1988-89.

CORSAIR (Blohm+Voss AG)

Design and supply of seals for the Corsair SES test craft.

SMYGE (Karlskronavarvet/Kockoms AB)

Development of materials with special underwater signature properties and the manufacture of seals for the SMYGE Test Craft 1990-91, plus spares and replacements.

MCMV (Royal Norwegian Navy)
Supply of bow and stern seals plus spares and replacements.

Samsung Heavy Industries
Supply of bow and stern seals plus spares for 37 m SES.

UT 928 (International Shipyards Pty Ltd)
Supply of bow and stern seals.

UPDATED

BRITISH HOVERCRAFT CORPORATION LTD

Division of Westland Aerospace

East Cowes, Isle of Wight PO32 6RH, UK

Telephone: +44 (1983) 294101
Telex: 86781 WAD G
Telefax: +44 (1983) 298872

C C Gustar, *Managing Director, Westland Aerospace*
J M George, *Commercial Director*

BHC has been producing hovercraft for over 35 years, which has involved a great deal of research, particularly in the design and manufacture of flexible skirts. BHC has also designed skirt systems for other builders and, most notably, was responsible for the design of the skirts for the LACV-30 and LCAC.

BHC continues to design flexible skirt systems and conduct hydrodynamic testing. The manufacturing of the company's skirts is now subcontracted, under strict BHC quality control, to specialist rubber fabricators, principally SMR Technologies Inc and Avon Industrial Polymers.

UPDATED

GREENGATE POLYMER COATINGS LTD

Greengate Works, Greengate, Manchester M3 7WS, UK

Telephone: +44 (161) 834 5652
Telefax: +44 (161) 834 1497

J Redmond, *Director and General Manager*
E J Thomas, *Sales and Marketing Director*
R Wisner, *Manufacturing and Personnel Director*
R W Collier, *Technical Manager*
A Yorke-Robinson, *Technical Sales Manager*

GPC manufactures many high performance fabrics for hovercraft uses including buoyancy tubes, skirt, finger (segment) and ancillary applications.

VERIFIED

Example materials:

GPC quality	Composition	Total weight (g/m²)	Breaking strength (kg/50 mm width)	Tear strength (kg)
1188	Neoprene/Nylon	375	100	57.5
6816	Natural rubber/Nylon	620	250	20
2026	Neoprene/Nylon	1040	275	20
3144	Neoprene/Nylon	1200	450	35
3504	Hypalon/Nylon	1300	300	25

Tiger 4 hovercraft with GPC skirt
1986

NORTHERN RUBBER COMPANY LTD

A Member of the Tomkins plc Group

Retford, Nottinghamshire DN22 6HH, UK

Telephone: +44 (1777) 706731
Telefax: +44 (1777) 709739

D E P Owen, *Managing Director*
W J Newbold, *Technical Director*
M Thompson, *Sales and Marketing Director*
K D Bacon, *Assistant Director Sales*
J Stanfield, *Sales*

The Northern Rubber Company has worked in co-operation with many major constructors of hovercraft around the world, supplying skirt materials, components and complete fabrications for lightweight sport vehicles to some of the largest craft currently in service.

Experience gained during initial development of skirt fabrics in the UK, together with continuing development closely matched to the requirements of constructors and operators, has led to an established range of materials used for the complete requirements of skirt structures. This includes fingers (segments), cones, loops, doublers, spray suppressors, anti-bounce webs and so on.

Recent applications for Northern Rubber's materials include:

Royal Schelde Seaswift 23 SES

Northern Rubber has supplied the skirt bow segments for this SES. The material used is a multi-layer construction of natural rubber/polybutadiene, sand-

Seaswift 23 SES fitted with Northern Rubber natural rubber/polybutadiene coated nylon skirt　*1992*

wiched with a specially designed nylon fabric producing a tough semi-flexible material 3 mm thick.

SR. N4 Series British Hovercraft Corporation (BHC)

Northern Rubber supplies materials used extensively on the above series, having been closely involved with BHC during the development of the

skirt system for the SR. N4 Mk 1 which came into service in 1969. Hoverspeed as operators continue to use Northern Rubber materials in the maintenance of these skirts.

SR. N6 Series (BHC)

Both civil and military variants of this series have incorporated skirt materials from the Northern Rubber range. The abilities of the materials to withstand the most rigorous operating conditions has contributed to the development of the SR. N6 Mk 6 which features significantly enhanced all-weather performance and improved manoeuvrability partly due to skirt construction in which Northern Rubber materials feature.

AP1-88 (BHC)

Northern Rubber currently supplies skirt component materials to the UK and overseas constructors and operators of the AP1-88.

HM5/HM2 Series (Hovermarine International)

Many of these craft are in service in the Far East with the Hong Kong and Yaumati Ferry Company on routes to Macao and China, where Northern Rubber skirt fabrics perform under conditions of high utilisation.

PUC 22 C (*Larus*) (Wärtsilä)

The complete skirt system for *Larus* was fabricated by Northern Rubber, and completed in a restricted period to schedule. On transfer to Canada, the craft underwent modification to allow operation in temperatures as low as −50°C, temperatures which caused no detrimental effects on the skirt or the flexibility and integrity of its materials.

Materials: The range of composite flexible materials is manufactured in combinations of natural rubber or neoprene polymer and nylon substrates. All materials are tested in accordance with the highest standards covered by BS 4F100, but to properly demonstrate the adhesive properties of the hovercraft materials, Northern Rubber has developed a system of testing the materials which gives results related to closely monitored representative conditions.

Neoprene composite materials have outstanding oil and ozone resistance, and good low temperature flexibility down to −30°C. Natural rubber composite materials combine excellent abrasion resistance and lower temperature flexibility to −51°C.

UPDATED

Properties of Northern Rubber Skirt Materials

	Breaking Strength	Tear Strength Across	Adhesion Peel	Total Weight	Width
NR-11 520-12 ozs (410 g/m²) Neoprene					
Use: Skirt and finger segments for use on two- and four-seated Hovercraft					
Warp	1200 N/25 mm	225 N	44 N/25 mm	410 g/m²	1370 mm
Weft	1200 N/25 mm	225 N	44 N/25 mm	410 g/m²	1370 mm
NR-11 323-28 ozs (950 g/m²) Neoprene					
Use: Segment fabric for hover trailers and also inflatable craft					
Warp	1780 N/25 mm	310 N	66 N/25 mm	950 g/m²	1370 mm
Weft	1780 N/25 mm	310 N	66 N/25 mm	950 g/m²	1370 mm
NR-11 111-40 ozs (1360 g/m²) Neoprene					
Use: Finger segments for use on sidewall hovercraft					
Warp	2200 N/25 mm	880 N	110 N/25 mm	1360 g/m²	1270 mm
Weft	2000 N/25 mm	830 N	110 N/25 mm	1360 g/m²	1270 mm
NR-C11 569-40 ozs (1360 g/m²) Neoprene					
Use: Skirt segments for hovercraft. Water skates and heavy load trailers					
Warp	2200 N/25 mm	620 N	110 N/25 mm	1360 g/m²	1370 mm
Weft	2000 N/25 mm	570 N	110 N/25 mm	1360 g/m²	1370 mm
NR-C11 533-60 ozs (2040 g/m²) Neoprene					
Use: Finger segments for sidewall hovercraft, also segments for water skates					
Warp	2200 N/25 mm	800 N	110 N/25 mm	2040 g/m²	1320 mm
Weft	2000 N/25 mm	800 N	110 N/25 mm	2040 g/m²	1320 mm
NR-C10 863-74 ozs (2515 g/m²) Neoprene					
Use: Skirt and finger fabric for commercial passenger-carrying vehicles					
Warp	2450 N/25 mm	800 N/25 mm	130 N/25 mm	2515 g/m²	1270 mm
Weft	2200 N/25 mm	800 N/25 mm	130 N/25 mm	2515 g/m²	1270 mm
NR-C11 843-83 ozs (2800 g/m²) Natural Rubber					
Use: Skirt and finger fabric for commercial passenger-carrying vehicles					
Warp	3800 N/25 mm	800 N/25 mm	200 N/25 mm	2800 g/m²	1270 mm
Weft	3800 N/25 mm	800 N/25 mm	200 N/25 mm	2800 g/m²	1270 mm
NR-C11 184-85 ozs (2890 g/m²) Neoprene					
Use: Skirt and finger fabric for commercial passenger-carrying vehicles					
Warp	4000 N/25 mm	2200 N	222 N/25 mm	2890 g/m²	1270 mm
Weft	3800 N/25 mm	2000 N	222 N/25 mm	2890 g/m²	1270 mm
NR-C11 828-90 ozs (3000 g/m²) Natural Rubber					
Use: Skirt and segment fabric for heavy load transporters and passenger-carrying vehicles					
Warp	3800 N/25 mm	2200 N	200 N/25 mm	3000 g/mW	1270 mm
Weft	3550 N/25 mm	2200 N	200 N/25 mm	3000 g/mW	1270 mm
NR-C11 748-95 ozs (3220 g/m²) Neoprene					
Use: Segments for heavy load transporters and passenger-carrying vehicles					
Warp	4000 N/25 mm	2200 N	222 N/25 mm	3220 g/m²	1270 mm
Weft	3800 N/25 mm	2000 N	222 N/25 mm	3220 g/m²	1270 mm
NR-C11 549-100 ozs (3400 g/m²) Natural Rubber					
Use: Segments for heavy load transporters and passenger-carrying vehicles					
Warp	5300 N/25 mm	3100 N	222 N/25 mm	3400 g/m²	1270 mm
Weft	5300 N/25 mm	3100 N	222 N/25 mm	3400 g/m²	1270 mm
NR-C11 580-110 ozs (3740 g/m²) Natural Rubber					
Use: Segments for heavy load transporters and passenger-carrying vehicles					
Warp	6000 N/25 mm	4000 N	222 N/25 mm	3740 g/m²	1270 mm
Weft	6000 N/23 mm	4000 N	222 N/25 mm	3740 g/m²	1270 mm

UNITED STATES OF AMERICA

BELL AVON INC

1200 Martin Luther King Jr Blvd, Picayune, Mississippi 39466-5427, USA

Telephone: +1 (601) 799 1217
Telefax: +1 (601) 799 1360

Keith D Smith, *President*
P Gene Smith, *Works Manager*
Peter Inch, *Technical Manager*
David Poole, *Sales Office Manager*
Mark Toler, *Sales Administrator*

Bell Avon Inc is a joint venture between Avon Rubber Company Ltd and Textron Marine and Land Systems. As a subsidiary of Avon, Bell Avon has full access to the resources of the world's largest and most experienced manufacturer of hovercraft skirt materials. Avon has been producing coated fabrics since the 1920s and has been developing materials for hovercraft systems and other sophisticated applications since the 1960s. The company has a diverse background in the development of materials and products utilising polymer technologies.

In April of 1985, Bell Avon opened its facility in Picayune, Mississippi, as the only specialised manufacturer of hovercraft skirt systems in North America. In 1991, Bell Avon became the premier manufacturing facility for Avon's flexible fabrications. Bell Avon continues to expand its base of specialised products for use in the military, industrial and commercial sectors, utilising Avon's high quality materials together with state-of-the-art thermoplastics.

Facilities: Bell Avon's facility in South Mississippi currently occupies over 50 000 ft² of manufacturing space, with plans to further expand on its six acre site. Specific manufacturing equipment includes:
High precision hydraulic presses
Large beam presses
A range of "C" frame presses
Thermoplastic welding machines
Dialectic welding equipment
Surface preparation machines
Die cutting presses
Specialised mixing equipment.

Manufacture and assembly is carried out at this purpose built plant, which is located conveniently for shipping by rail, highway, air and sea. A wide range of coated fabrics is kept in inventory to satisfy short lead time orders. Bell Avon utilises state-of-the-art bonding processes to produce an extremely well integrated composite structure. The proprietary thin adhesive layer provides considerably better flexural fatigue properties than bonding tapes.

Design capability: Bell Avon's pre-production engineering capabilities offer major benefits in terms of improved cost and enhanced operational performance. Engineers work closely with customers to bridge the gap between theoretical design and final cost. Utilising the latest design technology and software, Bell Avon, and its parent, Avon, offer full skirt design, including stress analysis, design appraisal, finite element analysis and reduced or full scale model testing.

Refurbishment: Bell Avon is able to offer customers many refurbishment options for prolonging the life of skirt components, often at a fraction of the cost of a new component. This repair work is carried out to the exacting standards required on new components and all incoming parts are reviewed for compatibility with the repair programme. Customers are issued with a detailed report indicating style of repair and firm cost proposal, assessing both the financial and structural viability of such work.

LCAC: The LCAC skirt comprises more than 80 different components, and is supplied to craft manu-

Textron Marine Systems Landing Craft, Air Cushion (LCAC) for which Bell Avon has now become a major supplier of skirt systems and components **1995**

facturers as assembled segments for ease of installation. The skirt is developed from the conventional bag and finger design, utilising lock bolts to facilitate the changing of worn or damaged components. The skirt design embraces many differing weights of coated fabric and calendered sheet to arrive at the optimum combination of weight, flexibility and operational life. Coated fabric weights vary between 1390 g/m^2 and 3050g/m^2, and both natural and synthetic rubbers are used. Compounding and processes are designed to meet the unusual environmental and operating systems which face this craft.

Bell Avon has rapidly become a major supplier of original equipment and spares for this program. Since its inception, Bell Avon has produced, or has orders in hand to produce, over 72 of the original skirt sets used on the 91 LCACs currently operated or scheduled for construction.

Surface Effect Ships (SES): Bow fingers and stern seal components manufactured and assembled by Bell Avon have been installed on Bell Halter commercial craft operated in Egypt and South America, on US Coast Guard craft formerly based in Key West, Florida, on the US Navy's SES 200 and on the US Army corps of Engineers survey boat, *Rodolf*.

In 1990, the US Navy's SES 200 was upgraded by Textron Marine and Land Systems to include water-jet propulsion and a new three-lobe stern seal. The seal was designed utilising the vast experience gained from supplying the European SES market

Textron Marine Systems LACV-30 for which Bell Avon has manufactured a new stern seal skirt configuration **1987**

and in conjunction with Avon a new seal was fabricated. This seal has consistently exceeded all specification and craft requirements.

Commercial hovercraft: Bell Avon regularly works with customers on skirt design for both military and commercial ACVs. Skirt systems, utilising the vast range of coated fabrics available, have been produced for the Utility Air Cushion Vehicle (UACV) and

the C7/FR7 craft designed and produced by Textron Marine and Land Systems. The C7 hovercraft is a commercial craft operating in Asia as a passenger craft for Freeport McMoran and the FR7 is used as a fire/rescue craft by the Singapore Aviation Authority.

UPDATED

RIDE CONTROL SYSTEMS

Company Listing by Country

Japan
Hitachi Zosen Corporation

Norway
Kværner Fjellstrand A/S
Ulstein Marine Electronics A/S

United Kingdom
Brown Brothers and Company Ltd

United States of America
MDI
SES Ride Controls Inc

JAPAN

HITACHI ZOSEN CORPORATION

Head Office: 3-28 Nishikujo 5-chome, Konhana-ku, Osaka, 554 Japan

Telephone: +81 (6) 466 7546
Telex: 63376 J
Telefax: +81 (6) 466 7578

Hitachi Zosen developed a ride control system with Supramar for the PTS 50 type hydrofoil, *Housho,* a PTS 50 Mk II which was delivered to Hankyu Kisen KK on 19 January 1983.

The underside of the bow foil is fitted with two flapped fins to improve ride comfort. Operated by automatic sensors, the fins augment stability and provide side forces to dampen rolling and transverse motions.

VERIFIED

Flapped roll-stabilisation fin on Housho   *1992*

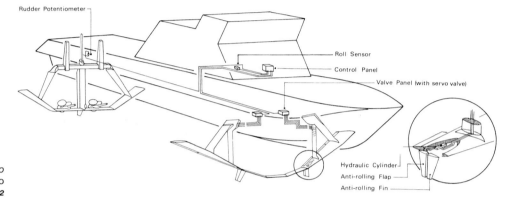

PTS 50 Mk II roll-stabilising system as fitted to Housho
1992

NORWAY

KVÆRNER FJELLSTRAND A/S

N-5632 Omastrand, Norway

Telephone: +47 (5) 554100
Telex: 42148 FBOAT N
Telefax: +47 (5) 554244/4268

Erling Berge, *Vice President, Business Development*
Knut Eide, *Marketing Manager*
Alf Steine, *Financial Manager*

CLIPPER MOTION DAMPENING SYSTEM (MDS)

Kværner Fjellstrand developed the Clipper Motion Dampening System (MDS) in order to improve the sea-keeping characteristics of their high-speed catamarans in rough seas. By counteracting the impact of the waves on the hull, Clipper MDS minimises slamming, pitching and rolling.

The Clipper MDS comprises a strut carrying the controlling fins, a hydraulic transmission system, a control system and sensors.

Struts on which the controlling fins are mounted are installed at the forward end of each hull at the point where they can provide maximum dampening effect. An adjustable fin with a surface area corresponding to 2 m² is mounted on each strut. Vessel motion data are acquired by sensors and then passed to a computer which in turn continuously adjusts the angle of the fins to counteract the motion of the vessel.

The system can be installed on Kværner Fjellstrand's 38.8 m Advanced Slender Catamarans and 40 m Flying Cats. Retrofitting is also possible on existing models.

The first Clipper MDS was mounted on *Victoria Clipper,* operated by Clipper Navigation Inc of Seattle, USA.

One of the hull installations of Kværner Fjellstrand's first Clipper Motion Dampening System mounted on Victoria Clipper   *1994*

Experience with the 38.8 m *Victoria Clipper* and other craft has shown that bow accelerations in 1.5 to 2 m significant wave heights are reduced by 36 per cent and with the Clipper MDS in use in lower wave heights of 0.5 to 1 m the reduction is as much as 46 per cent. The operator has found that the Clipper MDS dramatically reduces motion discomfort in 2.4 m seas (6.2 per cent of craft length) and that in following seas it is possible for the first time to continue on autopilot.

VERIFIED

ULSTEIN MARINE ELECTRONICS A/S

Kjopmannsgt. 23, N-6025 Alesund, Norway

Telephone: +47 (71) 29929
Telefax: +47 (71) 21225

Stig Ulstein, *Managing Director*

The company is the result of a merger between the two Ulstein companies Ulstein Marine Electronics A/S and Peilo Teknik A/S. Manufacture of electronic equipment for the marine industry is the main activity. In addition to the well-known remote-control systems for ship manoeuvring, propulsion control systems, tank measuring systems and alarm systems, Ulstein Marine Electronics is also involved in cockpit design for high-speed craft and is developing a ride control system for these craft.

UPDATED

UNITED KINGDOM

BROWN BROTHERS AND COMPANY LTD

Broughton Road, Edinburgh EH7 4LF, UK

Telephone: +44 (131) 556 2440
Telex: 72151
Telefax: +44 (131) 556 3253

M Conway, *Managing Director*
W Reid, *Director/General Manager*
D J McNeill, *Sales and Marketing Director*
J R Jamieson, *Technical Director*
G G Moir, *Commercial Director*

Brown Brothers offers a range of ride control systems for high-speed vessels, including: non-retractable fin stabilisers and trim tabs, controlling pitch and roll for monohulls and Swath motion control equipment comprising non-retractable fin stabilisers with a multi-variable gain control for independent or simultaneous control of pitch, roll and heave.

Both systems permit stabilisation of up to 90 per cent.

VERIFIED

UNITED STATES OF AMERICA

MARITIME DYNAMICS, INC

424X Great Mills Road, Lexington Park, Maryland 20653, USA

Telephone: +1 (301) 863 5499
Telefax: +1 (301) 863 0254

Clarence A Lysdale, *President*
John D Adams, *Vice President*
Mark E Lindler, *Director of Operations*
Charlotte R Sebra, *Sales and Marketing*
Robert L Chandler, *Service Manager*

For over 15 years, Maritime Dynamics, Inc (MDI) has designed, developed and manufactured ride control systems for advanced marine vehicles. MDI's capability includes the analysis and simulation of ship motions, control system design, software development, hardware fabrication, installation and crew training. MDI control systems are in operation on Surface Effect Ships (SES), Air Cushion Vehicles (ACV), Catamarans (CAT), Small-Waterplane-Area Twin-Hull (SWATH) ships and monohulls. See table of MDI Ride Control System Installations.

Maritime Dynamics cushion vent valve assembly for use in SES ride control systems   1991

Surface Effect Ships

MDI ride control systems for SES provide motion control and real-time data for optimisation of overall craft performance. In 1980, MDI designed and supplied a ride control system for the USN XR-1D SES. This was the first active ride control system to demonstrate significant improvements in SES ride quality under rough sea conditions. MDI has continued the development of SES ride control systems and currently manufactures microprocessor-based systems for both military and civilian craft.

The ride control system minimises wave-induced pressure changes in the air cushion, to reduce the craft motions and vertical accelerations caused by 'wave pumping' of the cushion volume. The resulting attenuation of the vertical accelerations can significantly reduce fatigue and discomfort during moderate and high-speed cushionborne operations. Control is provided by an Electronic Control Unit (ECU) which controls hydraulically driven cushion vent valves and/or variable flow fans dynamically regulating the net cushion airflow to maintain a constant pressure.

Components for a typical SES ride control system installation consist of pressure, attitude, and acceleration sensors; a microprocessor-based ECU with applicable control algorithms; a hydraulic system;

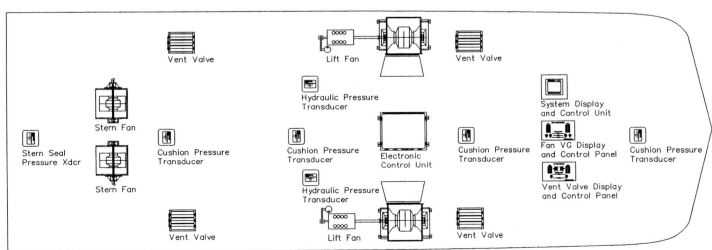

Major components of a typical Maritime Dynamics ride control system for an SES

1991

Ride Control System Installations

Type	Builder	Hull no	Length	Commission date	Vessel name
SES	Bell Halter, Inc	—	50 m	1982	SES-200
SES	Bell Halter, Inc	—	33 m	1982	Sea Hawk
SES	Brødrene Aa	170	32 m	1984	Ulstein Surfer (ex Fjordkongen ex Norcat)
SES	Brødrene Aa	184	35 m	1986	Santa Lucia (ex Ekwata)
SES	Bell Halter, Inc	—	50 m	1986	SES-200 (with additional lift fans)
SES	Brødrene Aa	190	35 m	1988	Talieh (ex Wight Queen, ex Virgin Butterfly ex Ekwata II)
SES	Brødrene Aa	199	35 m	1988	Express La Paz (ex Santa Maria)
SES	Brødrene Aa	201	35 m	1989	Wight King (ex Sant' Agata)
SES	Eikefjord Marine	202	35 m	1989	San Pietro
SES	Blohm+Voss	—	37 m	1989	Corsair
SES	Royal Schelde	—	23 m	1989	Wight Prince (ex Seaswift 23)
SES	Brødrene Aa	210	35 m	1989	San Frangisk
SES	Eikefjord Marine	200	35 m	1989	San Pawl
SES	Eikefjord Marine	219	35 m	1990	Fjordkongen I
SES	Eikefjord Marine	211	35 m	1990	Catamaran II (ex Golden Olympics, ex Supercat One)
SES	Brødrene Aa	218	35 m	1990	Yasuda Ocean Liner
SES	Eikefjord Marine	213	35 m	1990	Perestroika
SES	Brødrene Aa	212	35 m	1990	La Vikinga
SES	Brødrene Aa	204	35 m	1991	Sea Flower
SES	Karlskronavarvet	—	30 m	1991	Smyge
SES	Ulstein	208	38 m	1991	Ocean Flower
SES	Brødrene Aa	226	35 m	1991	Catamaran I
SES	Semo Co Ltd		35 m	1992	Democracy
SES	Ulstein	205	38 m	1992	Santa Eleonora
SES	Karlskronavarvet	—	30 m	1993	Smyge
SES	Beliard Polyship	—	30 m	1993	Manto
SES	Kværner Mandal	—	55 m	1993	MCMV
SES	Kværner Mandal	—	55 m	1994	MCMV
SES	Samsung Heavy Industries	—	37 m	1994	Dorado
SES	Semo Co Ltd	PMS-02	40 m	1994	Democracy II
SES	Semo Co Ltd	PMS-03	40 m	1994	Democracy III
CAT	International Catamarans, Tasmania	023	74 m	1990	Seacat Calais (ex Seacat Tasmania)
CAT	Aluminium Shipbuilding, Ltd		49 m	1990	Condor 9
CAT	International Catamarans, Tasmania	025	74 m	1990	Hoverspeed Great Britain
CAT	International Catamarans, Tasmania	026	74 m	1990	Seacat Boulogne (ex Sardegna Express, ex Hoverspeed France)
CAT	International Catamarans, Tasmania	027	74 m	1991	Hoverspeed Boulogne
CAT	International Catamarans, Tasmania	028	74 m	1992	Seacat Scotland
CAT	International Catamarans, Tasmania	024	74 m	1992	Patricia Olivia
CAT	Nichols Brothers		37 m	1992	SeaJet I (ex Nantucket Spray, ex Metro Atlantic)
CAT	International Catamarans, Tasmania	030	74 m	1993	Condor 10
CAT	International Catamarans, Tasmania	031	74 m	1993	Stena Sea Lynx
CAT	International Catamarans, Tasmania	032	74 m	1993	Juan L
CAT	Hyundai Heavy Industries	—	45.5 m	1993	—
CAT	WaveMaster International	048	45 m	1994	Fei Long
CAT	International Catamarans, Tasmania	033	74 m	1994	Stena Sea Lynx II
Swath	Hyundai Heavy Industries	—	37 m	1993	
Swath	Swath Ocean Systems	—	20 m	1993	Houston
Swath	Swath Ocean Systems	—	27 m	1993	Chubasco
Swath	USCG Yard - Curtis Bay, Maryland	—	27 m	1994	Kaimalino
Monohull	WaveMaster International	034	45 m	1993	Super Flyte
Monohull	Westport Shipyard	8501	30 m	1994	Catalina Express
Monohull	Westport Shipyard	8502	30 m	1994	Islander Express

and a set of vent valves that are connected to the ship's air cushion. Each vent valve assembly consists of aerodynamically shaped louvres driven by a servo-controlled hydraulic cylinder.

The ECU uses a 16 bit microprocessor to implement sampled data control algorithms using cushion pressure and ship motion feedback signals, and to output servo control signals to each vent valve or fan inlet guide vane selected for active control. Fault monitoring of the system's electronic, hydraulic and mechanical components is performed between each control algorithm computation. MDI ride control systems installed on SESs operating from 35 to 45 knots consistently achieve a 50 per cent reduction in heave accelerations and have demonstrated reductions as high as 70 per cent.

The ride control display also provides a menu-driven real-time display of measured craft parameters relating to air cushion and craft operating conditions (for example, means and standard deviations of trim, roll, cushion pressure, vent valve position and vertical acceleration). These data have proven to be extremely valuable to the vessel operator for optimising overall performance in different sea conditions.

The ECU can be used on any SES or Air Cushion Vehicle (ACV) equipped with either vent valves or variable flow fans by programming it with appropriate control algorithms. MDI has developed a systematic technique for deriving these control algorithms which is based on classical and optimal control theory as well as extensive experimental testing.

Ride control systems have been installed on over 30 SES craft, including the following vessels: USN SES-200, USCG WSES Sea Hawk, the CIRR 120P class of passenger ferries, Royal Schelde's 23 m SES, the Blohm+Voss SES Corsair, SEMO's 37 m Democracy, the Swedish Navy's Smyge, Beliard Polyship's 30 m Manto and the Norwegian Navy's Mine Countermeasures Vessel.

Future systems are expected to utilise actively controlled bow T-foils to further improve motion reduction and enhance ride quality.

Catamarans

In 1991, MDI introduced the first ride control system to improve passenger comfort on catamarans. The system consists of a microcomputer-based controller that measures the vessel's motions and commands hydraulically actuated fins to reduce wave-induced pitch, roll and heave motion. MDI's first installation was on Condor 9, an Incat Design 49 m wave-piercing catamaran built by Aluminum Shipbuilders Ltd. This 450 passenger vessel is operated on the western end of the English Channel by Condor Ltd between Weymouth, UK and St Malo, France. The vessel has bow fins mounted inboard and outboard on each hull and a stern fin that is mounted inboard on each hull.

During tests in February 1992, in measured seas of 2.4 m significant wave height, the ride control system installed on Condor 9 consistently reduced the vessel's pitch and roll motions by 50 per cent relative to the uncontrolled case. In head seas, the vertical accelerations at the forward, mid and aft passenger seats were reduced by 45 per cent, 35 per cent and 20 per cent respectively.

In co-operation with Vosper Thornycroft (UK) Ltd, MDI has provided a similar system for SeaJet I, a 37 m wave-piercing catamaran built by Nichols Brothers. This vessel has operated successfully in Hawaii and is currently operating between San Diego, California and Catalina Island.

MDI ride control systems have been installed on nine 74 m wave-piercing catamarans built by International Catamarans Tasmania. The controller commands two very large hydraulically actuated stern flaps (such as trim tabs) mounted on the transom of each hull. The hydrodynamic, mechanical and hydraulic design of these flaps has been jointly developed by International Catamarans and MDI. Without increasing the vessel's resistance, these flap systems substantially reduce the pitch and roll accelerations that cause motion sickness.

The ride control system installed on the 74 m wave-piercing catamaran Condor 10 utilises both stern flaps and bow T-foils. The bow T-foil design was designed jointly by MDI and Condor Ltd and produced by MDI. This system provides Condor 10 with satisfactory ride quality to operate all year round on the western end of the English Channel.

Swath

MDI ride control systems for Swath provide trim and list stabilisation (such as mean attitude control) and pitch, roll and relative bow motion control.

Components for a typical Swath installation consist of ship motion sensors; a microprocessor-based ECU with applicable control algorithms; a fin control panel; a hydraulic system; a pair of forward fins or canards; and a pair of aft fins or stabilisers. Control of rudders for manoeuvring is provided if desired.

The Swath ECU and control panels provide automatic and manual control of the fins; real-time display of vessel pitch, heave, roll and fin motions; and display of mean values for trim and list.

MDI ride control systems are currently installed on the Houston, a 65 ft pilot vessel, and Chubasco, a 90 ft high performance yacht, both built by Swath Ocean Systems of San Diego. A third system is installed on a 37 m Swath vessel built by Hyundai Heavy Industries for the Korean Agency for Defence Development and a fourth system was delivered to the USN for installation on the test ship Kaimalino in 1994.

Monohulls

In early 1993 MDI introduced a ride control system for high-speed monohulls. The monohull system integrates steering, trim and list stabilisation and pitch, roll and yaw motion damping to provide superior control of craft motions during high-speed operation in calm and rough water. This is possible through integrated control of the craft's rudders and

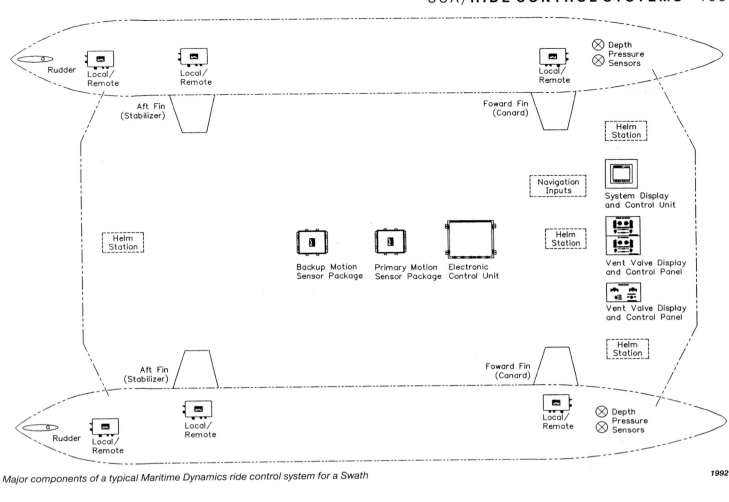

Rudder
Local/ Remote
Local/ Remote
Aft Fin (Stabilizer)
Foward Fin (Canard)
Local/ Remote
Depth Pressure Sensors
Helm Station
Navigation Inputs
Helm Station
System Display and Control Unit
Vent Valve Display and Control Panel
Vent Valve Display and Control Panel
Helm Station
Helm Station
Backup Motion Sensor Package
Primary Motion Sensor Package
Electronic Control Unit
Aft Fin (Stabilizer)
Foward Fin (Canard)
Local/ Remote
Depth Pressure Sensors
Rudder
Local/ Remote
Local/ Remote

Major components of a typical Maritime Dynamics ride control system for a Swath

1992

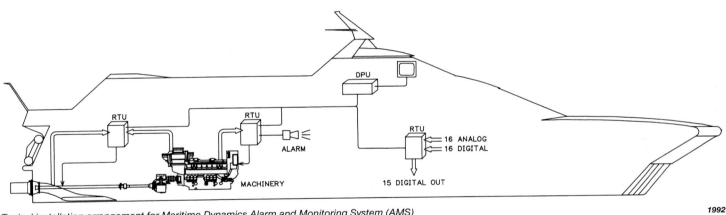

DPU
RTU
RTU
ALARM
RTU
16 ANALOG
16 DIGITAL
MACHINERY
15 DIGITAL OUT

Typical installation arrangement for Maritime Dynamics Alarm and Monitoring System (AMS)

1992

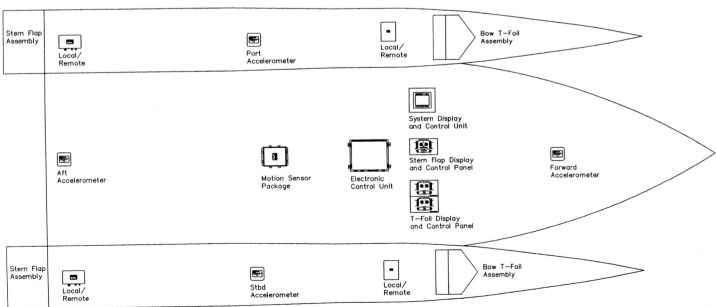

Stern Flap Assembly
Local/ Remote
Port Accelerometer
Local/ Remote
Bow T–Foil Assembly
System Display and Control Unit
Stern Flap Display and Control Panel
Aft Accelerometer
Motion Sensor Package
Electronic Control Unit
Forward Accelerometer
T–Foil Display and Control Panel
Stern Flap Assembly
Local/ Remote
Stbd Accelerometer
Local/ Remote
Bow T–Foil Assembly

Major components of a typical Maritime Dynamics ride control system for a catamaran

1992

Major components of a typical Maritime Dynamics ride control system for a monohull   *1994*

active stern-mounted flaps in response to ship motions and helm commands. MDI's first monohull installation is on WaveMaster International's 40 m monohull *Super Flyte*. In 1 to 2 m bow seas, the system has consistently demonstrated 60 per cent roll reduction and 40 per cent pitch motion reduction.

Alarm and monitoring systems

MDI manufactures a machinery Alarm and Monitoring System (AMS) for mid-size vessels designed for flexibility in installation, software programming and operation. It consists of up to 12 Remote Transmitter Unit (RTU) modules on a multiplexed databus which is controlled by a bridge-mounted Data Processing/display Unit (DPU). Dual DPUs may be installed in separate locations and operated in parallel for full time on-line redundancy. Alternatively, since the system is designed to utilise standard PC compatible computers, one redundant (backup) DPU can run commercial software for electronic charts, voyage accounting, fax reception and so on.

The system is capable of monitoring 192 analogue channels and 192 discrete channels, and can also control 180 digital outputs.

The AMS is installed on SES and catamaran ferries and high-speed monohull yachts. It has been approved by both Det Norske Veritas and the Korean Register of Shipping.

VERIFIED

SES RIDE CONTROLS INC

15840 S W 84th Avenue, Miami, Florida 33157, USA

Telephone: +1 (305) 233 4306
Telefax: +1 (305) 233 1339

Don Burg, *President*
Steve Zarzecki, *Control Systems Design*

AIR-SUPPORTED CRAFT RIDE CONTROL SYSTEM

SES Ride Controls Inc offers a new Ride Control System (RCS) for air-supported craft such as the SES, hovercraft and GEM. Wave-induced pressure pulses in the air cushions supporting such craft can produce an uncomfortable bouncy or 'cobblestone' ride effect. This bouncy ride can be reduced by decrease in power to the powered fan that supplies the air cushion, however, a significant reduction in vessel speed results. It has been demonstrated that an active RCS results in dramatic reductions in craft motions with little speed reduction.

This new RCS uses brushless electric servo motors that drive specially constructed vanes at very high operational speeds. These vanes are mounted in valve assemblies that vent the pressure peaks as they occur and/or occlude airflow into the fan inlet to avoid formation of pressure peaks.

Vent valve operation is directed by a pilot-house-mounted microprocessor-based controller that processes dynamic changes in air cushion conditions and other parameters. There is a fully automatic mode setting and there are operator-selectable input parameters for fine tuning. Data presented on a high resolution display screen include cushion pressure, hull roll and pitch, and *g* forces (accelerations). This information is invaluable to the operator for monitoring ride and trim control and for other operational purposes.

Particular attention has been given in the design to ensure maximum reliability and simplicity of operation, as is evident by the use of brushless electric motors and the elimination of linkages and hydraulics. There is an individual servo motor for each vane, thus eliminating high wear linkages. The only movable contacting components are the vane support and motor bearings. All bearings are sealed and self-lubricated, they are also fully rotated several times at each start up to insure a random change of bearing and race contact points and good distribution of bearing lubrication. The vanes are made of Type 316 stainless steel and the valve housings of Type l5086 marine aluminium to ensure maximum life in a salt spray environment.

A pneumatically energised vane-locking system is included which automatically locks the vanes in a closed position in the event of power failure. This ensures the craft can operate without the RCS, if such an unlikely power failure occurs.

The smaller component is the pilot-house control

Components for a typical SES Ride Controls Inc RCS for an air cushion vehicle installation   *1991*

Controller (right-hand side) for SES Ride Controls Inc RCS   *1992*

and high resolution display module while the larger electronic module houses servo motor control and drive components. The larger flanged units are two identical vane assemblies with one showing two vane drive motors and their driven vanes, and the other showing the pneumatic vane locking components. It can be seen from these vane assemblies that simple flange mounting is provided for in-craft vent ducts. An entire vane can be easily removed from a vane assembly with no requirement to remove the vane assembly from the craft vent duct.

This new patent-pending RCS concept offered by SES Ride Controls Inc has application to all types of air cushion craft. It has been designed for easy installation, low power consumption, maximum life and reliability and ease of maintenance. Power requirements are only 5 to 8 kW for a typical 35 m SES.

The new Air Ride 'Dual-Air' SES (see the *Air cushion vehicles* section under USA) with fore-and-aft air cushions used in each side hull will enable trim and pitching control to be obtained by varying fore-and-aft air cushion pressures. Control will be achieved using an SES Ride Controls Inc ride control system similar to that presented here.

VERIFIED

SERVICES

Marine craft regulatory authorities
Consultants and designers
Societies involved with high-speed craft

MARINE CRAFT REGULATORY AUTHORITIES

ARGENTINA
Prefectura Naval Argentina
　Avenida Madero 235
　1106 Buenos Aires
　Argentina

Telephone: +54 (1) 331 7001/9
Telex: 18581 PREFEC AR
Telefax: +54 (1) 331 2876/5750

Prefecto General Jorge Humberto Maggi, *Argentine
Coast Guard Commandant*
Prefecto General Jorge Arnoldo Gentiluomo,
Deputy Commandant

AUSTRALIA
ACVs and Hydrofoils
*Covers interstate and international voyages. Smaller
craft come under jurisdiction of state or local
authorities.*

Australian Maritime Safety Authority
　Ship and Personnel Safety Services
　PO Box 1108
　Belconnen ACT 2616
　Australia

Telephone: +61 (62) 279 5048
Telefax: +61 (62) 279 5966

T Rose, *Chief Marine Surveyor, Survey Operations*

New South Wales
The Maritime Services Board of NSW
　Maritime Centre
　207 Kent Street
　Sydney
　New South Wales 2001
　Australia
　or
　PO Box 32
　Sydney
　New South Wales 2001
　Australia

Telephone: +61 (2) 364 2111
Telex: 24944 MSBSY AA
Telefax: +61 (2) 364 2064

Wayne L Gilbert, *Chief Executive*

Northern Territory
Department of Transport and Works
　Marine Branch
　PO Box 2520
　Darwin
　Northern Territory 0801
　Australia

Telephone: +61 (89) 895285
Telefax: +61 (89) 895300

Chris Bigg, *Director*

Queensland
Department of Primary Industries
　PO Box 46
　Mineral House
　George Street (Cnr Margaret Street)
　Brisbane
　Queensland 4001
　Australia

Telephone: +61 (7) 224 2111/8690
Telex: 40760 HARBRS AA
Telefax: +61 (7) 229 6079

A W Regan, *Manager*

South Australia
South Australian Ports Corporation
　PO Box 19
　Port Adelaide
　South Australia 5015
　Australia

Telephone: +61 (8) 470611
Telex: 82525 AA
Telefax: +61 (8) 470605

Tasmania
Navigation and Survey Authority of
　Tasmania
　1 Franklin Wharf
　PO Box 202B
　Hobart
　Tasmania 7001
　Australia

Telephone: +61 (02) 347122
Telefax: +61 (02) 341329

Captain J W Lewis, *Superintendent*

Victoria
The Port of Melbourne Authority
　PO Box 4721
　Melbourne Victoria 3001
　Australia

Telephone: +61 (3) 611 1777
Telex: 34211 AA
Telefax: +61 (3) 611 1905

Kingsley Culley, *Chairman*
John King, *Chairman/Chief Executive*
Peter Olszak, *General Manager Port Operations*
Mike McCarthy, *General Manager Finance and
Admin*
Anthony Honeyborne, *Manager Port Operations*

Western Australia
Department of Marine and Harbours
　1 Essex Street
　PO Box 402
　Fremantle
　Western Australia 6160
　Australia

Telephone: +61 (09) 335 0888
Telex: 94784 SMHFRE
Telefax: +61 (09) 335 0850

Stuart Hicks, *Executive Director*

BELGIUM
Ministere des Communications et de l'Infrastructure
　Administration des Affaires Maritimes et de la
　Navigation
　rue d'Arlon 104
　B-1040 Brussels
　Belgium

Telephone: +32 (2) 233 1211
Telex: 61880 VERTRA B
Telefax: +32 (2) 230 3002

CANADA
Transport Canada
　Director General
　Maritime Regulation Branch
　Canadian Coast Guard
　Canada Building
　344 Slater Street
　Ottawa
　Ontario K1A 0N7
　Canada

Telephone: +1 (613) 998 0660
Telefax: +1 (613) 991 5670

R G Wade, *Superintendent*
K Tue-Fee, *Senior Surveyor Hulls*
M Andrades, *Senior Surveyor Machinery*

　Design approval and safety certification of all craft
and operators complying with the IMO High-Speed
Craft Code, and certification of personnel.

DENMARK
Danish Maritime Authority
　Vermundsgade 38C
　DK-2100 Copenhagen Ø
　Denmark

Telephone: +45 (39) 271515
Telex: 31141 SOFART DK
Telefax: +45 (39) 271516

EGYPT
Egyptair
　Cairo International Airport
　Heliopolis
　Cairo
　Egypt

Telefax: +20 (2) 245 3861

FIJI
Director of Marine
　Marine Department
　PO Box 326
　Suva
　Fiji

Telephone: +679 315266
Telex: 2486 FM SAS FJ
Telefax: +679 303251

W Salu, *Director*
A Vata, *Assistant Director*

FINLAND
Board of Navigation
　Vuorimiehenkatu 1
　PO Box 158
　SF-00141 Helsinki
　Finland

Telex: 12-1471

FRANCE
Ministère de L'Equipment des Transports et
Tourisme
　3 Place de Fontenoy
　F-75700 Paris 07SP
　France

Telephone: +33 (1) 44 49 80 00
Telex: 250 823 (Mimer Paris) F
Telefax: +33 (1) 44 49 80 52 (général du Ministère)
Telefax: +33 (1) 44 49 83 47 (Bureau de la Documen-
　tation et de l'Information)

GAMBIA
Gambia Ports Authority
　Wellington Street
　PO Box 617
　Banjul
　The Gambia

GERMANY
See-Berufsgenossenschaft
　Ships Safety Department
　Reimerstwiete 2
　D-20457 Hamburg
　Germany

Telephone: +49 (40) 361370

GHANA
Shipping Commissioners
    Division of Shipping and Navigation
    Ministry of Transport and Communications
    PO Box M38
    Accra
    Ghana

GREECE
Ministry of Mercantile Marine
    Merchant Ships Inspectorate
    Palaiologou 1 str
    GR-18535 Piraeus
    Greece

Telephone: +30 (411) 1214
Telex: 212581 GR

V Stauropoulos, *Commodore*

HONG KONG
Director of Marine
    Marine Department
    Harbour Building
    38 Pier Road
    PO Box 4155
    Hong Kong

Telephone: +852 852 4512
Telex: 64553 MARHQ HX
Telefax: +852 545 0556

HUNGARY
General Inspection for Transport
    PO Box 102
    H-1389 Budapest 62
    Hungary

Telephone: +36 (1) 22800/24290

István Tóth, *General Director*

ICELAND
Directorate of Shipping
    PO Box 7200
    Hringbraut 121
    IS-127 Reykjavik
    Iceland

Telephone: +354 (1) 25844
Telefax: +354 (1) 29835

INDIA
Directorate General of Shipping
    Jahaz Bhavan
    Walchand Hirchand Marg
    Ballard Estate
    Bombay 400 038
    India

INDONESIA
Department of Transport, Communications and
    Tourism
    8 Medan Merdelka Barat
    Jakarta-Pusat
    Indonesia

IRELAND
Department of the Marine
    Leeson Lane
    Dublin 2
    Ireland

Telephone: +353 (1) 785444
Telex: 618214

G Honet, *Manager*

ISRAEL
Ministry of Transport
    Administration of Shipping and Ports
    PO Box 33993
    102 Ha'atzmauth Road
    Haifa 33411
    Israel

Telephone: +972 (4) 520241
Telex: 46632
Telefax: +972 (4) 511161

J Lapidas, *Chief Naval Architect*

ITALY
Ministero della Marina Mercantile
    Ispettorato Tecnico
    Viale Asia
    I-00100 Rome
    Italy

IVORY COAST
Ministère des Travaux Publics et des Transports
    BP V6
    Abidjan
    Ivory Coast

JAMAICA
The Marine Board
    c/o The Port Authority
    15-17 Duke Street
    Kingston
    Jamaica

Telephone: +1809 922 0290/8

Carrol Pickersgill, *Secretary Marine Board*

JAPAN
Japanese Ministry of Transportation
    2-1-3 Kasumigaseki
    Chiyoda-ku
    Tokyo
    Japan

KOREA, SOUTH
Bureau of Marine Transportation
    Ministry of Transportation
    1-3 Do Dong
    Choong-ka
    Seoul
    South Korea

KUWAIT
Department of Customs and Ports
    PO Box 9
    Kuwait

Telephone: +965 481 4371/2
Telex: US PTT 22197 KT

LEBANON
Ministère des Travaux Publics
    Direction des Transports
    Beirut
    Lebanon

LUXEMBOURG
Ministère des Transports
    19-21 boulevard Royal
    L-2938 Luxembourg

Telephone: +352 478-1
Telex: 1465 CIVAIR LU
Telefax: +352 467790

Commissariat aux Affaires Maritimes
    19-21 boulevard Royal
    L-2938 Luxembourg

Telephone: +352 479 4521
Telefax: +352 465753

Service de la Navigation
    36 route de la Macum
    L-6753 Grevenmacher
    Luxembourg

Telephone: +352 75048
Telex: 3727 NAVLU
Telefax: +352 758822

MADAGASCAR
Direction des Transports Maritimes
    101 Tananarive
    BP 581
    Madagascar

Telephone: +261 25860
Telex: 22301 MTMT MG
Telefax: +261 24001

MALAWI
Ministry of Transport and Communications
    Chief Surveyor of Vessels
    Private Bag 322
    Lilongwe 3
    Malawi

Telephone: +265 730122 (Marine Department)
Telefax: +265 733826

MALAYSIA
The Ministry of Transport
    Wisma Perdana
    Jalan Dungun
    Damansara Heights
    50616 Kuala Lumpur
    Malaysia

Telephone: +60 (3) 254 8122
Cables: MINCOM, KL
Telex: 30999 MA
Telefax: +60 (3) 255 7041

MEXICO
Departamento de Licencias
    Direction de Marina Mercante
    SCT
    Luerpo A
    2 Piso
    Mexico 12
    Mexico

MOROCCO
Ministère de l'Equipement
    Direction des Affaires Techniques
    Rabat-Chellah
    Morocco

NETHERLANDS
Ministry of Transport, Public Works and Water
    Management
    Director General of Shipping and Maritime Affairs
    PO Box 5817
    NL-2280 HV Rijswijk
    Netherlands

Telephone: +31 (70) 395 5555
Telefax: +31 (70) 399 6274

NEW ZEALAND
Maritime Safety Agency
    1st Floor, Transport House
    271-281 Upper Cuba St
    PO Box 27006
    Wellington
    New Zealand

Telephone: +64 (4) 382 8198
Telefax: +64 (4) 385 6035

Hydrofoils and surface effect ships are subject to
the Ship Construction and Safety Equipment (Code
of Practice for Hydrofoil Ships and Surface Effect
Ships) Notice 1989. The Hovercraft Act 1971 is
administered by the Division but no regulations have
been enacted to date to give effect to the Act.

NORWAY
Sjøfartsdirektoratet
    Norwegian Maritime Directorate
    Holbergs Terrasse
    Stensberggt. 27
    Oslo
    Norway

Telephone: +47 (22) 454500
Telex: 21557 SDIR N
Telefax: +47 (22) 568780

SOUTH AFRICA
The Director General
    Department of Transport
    Chief Directorate Shipping
    Private Bag X193
    Pretoria 0001
    South Africa

Telephone: +27 (12) 290 2913
Telefax: +27 (12) 290 2040

SPAIN
Dirección General de la Marina Mercante
C/ Ruiz de Alacrón, num 1
E-28014 Madrid
Spain

Telephone: +34 (1) 580 1400
Telex: 43579 MAMER E
Telefax: +34 (1) 522 2752

D Rafael Lobeto Lobo, *Director General*

SWEDEN
The National Maritime Administration
Sjofartsverket
S-601 78 Norrkoping
Sweden

Telephone: +46 (11) 191000
Telex: 64380 SHIPADM S
Telefax: +46 (11) 191049

K Janerus, *Director*

SWITZERLAND
Lake Constance
Kantonspolizei Thurgau Seepolizei
Bleichestrasse 42
PO Box 660
CH-8280 Kreuzlingen
Switzerland

Telephone: +41 (72) 752222
Telefax: +41 (72) 752284

Strassenverkehrs und Schiffahrtsamt des Kantons
St Gallen
Abr. Schiffahrt
CH-9400 Rorschach
Switzerland

Telephone: +41 (71) 411474

Kantonale Schiffahrtskontrolle
Rosengasse 8
CH-8200 Schaffhausen
Switzerland

Telephone: +41 (53) 827604

Lake Geneva
République et Canton de Genève Service de
la Navigation
Route de Veyrier 86
CH-1227 Carouge
Switzerland

Telephone: +41 (22) 319 2754

Lake Lucerne
Strassenverkehrsamt des Kantons Luzern
Schiffsinspektorat
Obergrund
CH-6000 Luzern 4
Switzerland

Telephone: +41 (41) 246111

Lake Lugano and Lake Locarno
Sezione della Circolazione
Ufficio amministrativo
Capo Servizio Navigazione
CH-6528 Camorino
Switzerland

E Regazzi, *Director*

Lake Neuchatel
Departement de Police
CH-2000 Neuchatel
Switzerland

Lake Thoune, Lake Brienz and Lake Biel
Strassenverkehrs-und Schiffahrtsamt des Kantons
Bern
Schermenweg 5
PO Box 3001
Bern
Switzerland

Telephone: +41 (31) 634 2111
Telex: 911520 sabe CH
Telefax: +41 (31) 634 2680

Dr R Netzer, *Director*

Lake Zürich
Kantonspolizei Zürich
Seepolizei/Schiffahrtskontrolle
Seestrasse 87
CH-8942 Oberrieden
Switzerland

Telephone: +41 (1) 720 7021

Oblt R Hotz, *Chief*

TURKEY
T C Ulaştirma Bakanliği
Ministry of Transport
General Directorate for Maritime Transport
90 Sokak No 5 Emek
Ankara
Turkey

Telephone: +90 (4) 212 4633/4576/4573
Telex: 44068 LDID
Telefax: +90 (4) 212 4485

T C Ulaştirma Bakanliği
Istanbul Bölge Müdürlüğü
Karaköy
Istanbul
Turkey

UNITED KINGDOM
Civil Aviation Authority
Hovercraft Certification, Issue of Type, Safety, Experimental and Export Certificates. Approval of persons or organisations from whom the CAA may accept reports on the design, construction, maintenance or repair of hovercraft or elements thereof. Approval of hovercraft items and equipment.
Publication of 'British Hovercraft Safety Requirements'
Technical enquiries to:

A C G Seal
Design Liaison Surveyor
Rotorcraft & Hovercraft Section
CAA Safety Regulation Group
Aviation House
Gatwick South
Gatwick
West Sussex RH6 OYR
UK

Telephone: +44 (1293) 573294
Telex: 878753
Telefax: +44 (1293) 573976

Publications:

Civil Aviation Authority
Printing and Publication Services
Greville House
37 Gratton Road
Cheltenham
Gloucestershire GL50 2BN
UK

Telephone: +44 (1242) 35151
Telefax: +44 (1242) 485139

Department of Transport
Hovercraft Operating Permits and Registration
High-Speed Marine Craft

Marine Safety Agency
Spring Place
105 Commercial Road
Southampton
Hampshire SO15 1EG
UK

Telephone: +44 (1703) 329140
Telefax: +44 (1703) 329161

S G N Firth, *Principal Marine Surveyor*

UNITED STATES OF AMERICA
Department of Transportation
Commandant (G-MTH-4)
US Coast Guard
Washington DC 20593-0001
USA

Telephone: +1 (202) 267 2997
Telefax: +1 (202) 267 4816

VENEZUELA
Ministerio de Transporte y Comunicaciones
Dirección General Sectorial de Transporte
Acuatico Dirreccion de Navegacion Acuatico
Caracas
Venezuela

YUGOSLAVIA (Serbia and Montenegro)
Federal Economic Secretariat
Transport Department
Bulevar AVNOJ-a 104
Belgrade
Serbia

CONSULTANTS AND DESIGNERS

Company Listing by Country

Australia
Advanced Multihull Designs Pty Ltd
Australian Maritime Engineering CRC Ltd
Crowther Multihulls Pty Ltd
International Catamaran Designs Pty Ltd (InCat)
Kamira Holdings Pty Ltd
Laubreaux Marine Design
Mark Ellis Design
Phil Curran Design
Stolkraft Pty Ltd

Belgium
Eurosense Hoversounding NV

Canada
D F Dickins Associates Ltd
Promaxis Systems Inc
Robert Allen Ltd
The Mariport Group Ltd

Commonwealth of Independent States
Forma Ltd
Kort
Sudoexport
Transal-Aks Engineering Co

Croatia
Brodoprojekt

Denmark
Jan Kjærulff Yacht Design

France
Bertin & Cie
Ifremer
Techni Carène

Germany
MTG Marinetechnik GmbH

Greece
National Technical University of Athens

Italy
Sciomachen

Japan
Masaru Ikeda Ship Consulting Office

Korea, South
Korea Research Institute of Ships and Ocean Engineering

Netherlands
Nevesbu

Norway
Amble & Stokke A/S
Camo
Cirrus Ship Design A/S
Ola Lilloe-Olsen
Otto L Scheen Jr A/S
Paradis Nautica

Singapore
Swan Hunter Singapore Pte Ltd

Spain
Neumar SA
Ur Tekniks S.L.

Sweden
SSPA Maritime Consulting AB

Switzerland
Dr Ing E G Faber Marine Engineering Consultant
Dipl Ing E Schatté
Supramar AG

United Kingdom
Air Cushion Ltd
Air Vehicles Ltd
Associated & Marine Technology Ltd
Blyth Bridges Marine Consultants Ltd
BMT Group Ltd
Lorne Campbell
Maritime Services Ltd
Nigel Gee and Associates
Hovercraft Consultants Ltd
Hovercraft Development Ltd
Hovercraft Sales and Marketing
Hoverwork Ltd
Independent Maritime Assessment Associates Ltd
JCL High Speed Marine Craft Consultancy
John McNeece Ltd
Seaspeed Technology Ltd
SWATH International Ltd
Robert L Trillo
Wolfson Unit for Marine Technology and Industrial Aerodynamics, University of Southampton
W S Atkins Marine & Structural Technology

United States of America
Aero-Marine Engineering
Air Craft Corporation
Air Ride Craft Inc
Aquamarine, Inc
Band, Lavis & Associates Inc
Donald L Blount & Associates Inc
CGZ Design Inc
Davidson Laboratory Stevens Institute of Technology
Elliott Bay Design Group Ltd
Fast Hulls International Inc
Fryco Inc
Gibbs & Cox Inc
The Harbor Consultancy International
J B Hargrave Naval Architects Inc
J W Johnson Naval Architects
Raymond Hunt Associates Inc
MDI
Payne Associates
Quadrimaran International
M Rosenblatt & Son Inc
TGMD Inc

AUSTRALIA

ADVANCED MULTIHULL DESIGNS PTY LTD

55 Grandview Street, Pymble, Sydney, New South Wales 2073, Australia

Telephone: +61 (2) 488 9877
Telefax: +61 (2) 488 8144 (Administration)
Telefax: +61 (2) 488 8466 (Technical)

John Szeto, *Managing Director*
Allan Soars, *Technical Director*
Bahram Ossivand, *Financial Controller*

Advanced Multihull Designs Pty Ltd was formed in late 1989 to specialise in the design of conventional fast catamarans, wave-piercing catamarans and foil-assisted multihull craft.

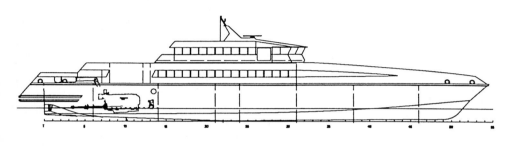

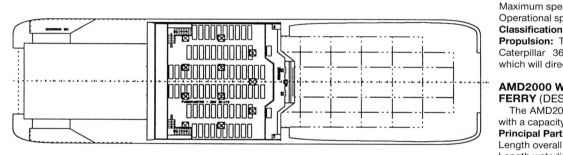

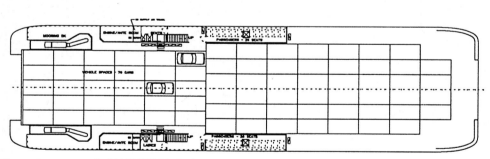

General arrangement of AMD K40 (design)
1995

The company has licensed six builders in six countries to build their designs, they are: Kawasaki Heavy Industries Ltd (Japan), Van der Giessen-de Noord NV (Netherlands), Constructions Mecaniques de Normandie (France), A Fai Engineers and Shiprepairers (Hong Kong), Astra Bay Enterprises (Australia), and Hang Tong High-Speed Ship Development Co (China).

As of early 1995 the company had three catamarans operating to its designs with a further six either under construction or on trials.

The largest wave-piercing catamaran built to date, the AMD/Kawasaki Jet Piercer, was launched by Kawasaki in late 1994. The fastest car-carrying catamaran to date, the K55 ferry built by InCat Australia in Hobart, was also launched in late 1994. Although the original concept design of this latter craft was produced by InCat designs of Sydney, the final and detail designs were undertaken by AMD.

A larger vessel of a similar design to the K55, code-named the K50, has also been designed by AMD for InCat Australia, for delivery to Dae A Gosh Ferry Company of South Korea in mid-1995.

An AMD350 passenger-only wave-piercing catamaran is under construction at Astra Bay Enterprises in Fremantle, Australia, also for delivery in 1995. This is a 42.5 m vessel capable of carrying 350 passengers at speeds of up to 36 knots.

An AMD150 is currently being built by the Chinese licensee and an AMD80 by A Fai in Hong Kong.

The company has a number of other designs available including the AMD2000, a 97 m wave-piercing catamaran and the K40, a 68 m, 43 knot car-carrying design.

Details of AMD craft can be found under the headings of their builders/licensees.

K40 CAR AND PASSENGER FERRY

In January 1994 Incat Australia commissioned Advanced Multihull Designs Pty Ltd to design a budget car ferry design which would be suitable for short routes (10 to 30 nautical miles), where there is a volume of light vehicle and passenger traffic.

Principal Particulars

Length overall	68 m
Beam	19 m
Draught	2.5 m
Passengers	400
Vehicles	70 cars
Propulsive power	2 × 5420 kW
Maximum speed	43 knots
Operational speed	36 knots

Classification: +1A1 HSLC R3 Car Ferry "B" EO.
Propulsion: The vessel will be powered by two Caterpillar 3616 medium-speed diesel engines, which will directly drive KaMeWa water-jets.

AMD2000 WAVE-PIERCING CATAMARAN FERRY (DESIGN)

The AMD2000 is the largest of the AMD designs with a capacity for 900 passengers and 200 cars.

Principal Particulars

Length overall	96.75 m
Length waterline	86 m
Beam	29.6 m
Draught	2.5 m (normal)
	3.3 m (max)
Crew	24
Passengers	874
Vehicles	196 cars or
	10 buses and 149 cars
Fuel capacity	240 000 l
Water capacity	20 000 l
Propulsive power	2 × 16 850 kW
Maximum speed	45 knots
Operational speed	40 knots

Classification: Lloyd's Register + 100 A1 HSC WPC Group 3.
Propulsion: Engines: two Rolls-Royce Spey SM1C gas-turbines, 16 850 kW each.
Thrust devices: four KaMeWa 125 SII water-jets.

UPDATED

AUSTRALIAN MARITIME ENGINEERING CRC LTD

PO Box 986, Launceston, Tasmania 7250, Australia

Telephone: +61 (03) 354875
Telefax: +61 (03) 266261

Don Lennard, *Executive Director*

The Australian Maritime Engineering Cooperative Research Centre (AMECRC) was established in July 1992 with the support of the Australian Government, Australian maritime engineering industries and a number of academic institutions. The centre provides a scientific and technological base for research and development in maritime engineering. It combines the specialist skills and resources of its participants and its work covers a wide range of Australia's maritime engineering services. The research programmes are driven by the users of the research.

Recent export successes by Australia's burgeoning high-speed craft industry require stepped up research and development to underpin further advances into the large replacement market for world ocean ferry fleets.

Present areas of research include:

Calm water performance of marine vehicles: Research in this field covers the hydrodynamic performance, both surface and subsurface, of marine vehicles and devices. This includes investigation of innovative high-speed craft forms, propellers and water-jets.

Ocean influence on ships and maritime structures: Research here includes dynamic loading, seakeeping, motion sickness and survivability.

Structural design and fabrication of ships and maritime structures: Included in this research topic are problems of lightweight maritime structures, the durability of these structures and new approaches to design and fabrication with the intention of enabling design to be optimised and innovative solutions to be developed and their merits properly assessed.

Ongoing research work includes the testing of a series of high-speed displacement ship hull forms and the prediction of wave making resistance of a catamaran in restricted water. AMECRC also carries out contract research: one major contract involved the design and installation of a ride control system for high-speed vessels including catamarans and monohulls in the Asia Pacific region, and the new 79 m catamaran for Europe.

Research Facilities

Cavitation Tunnel: working section 0.6 × 0.6 m, maximum speed 12 m/s.

Towing tank: 60 × 3.5 × 1.5 m (Australian Maritime College), maximum speed 4.5 m/s. Full-scale prediction can be carried out for powering in calm water and in waves, for seakeeping ability and for squat and bank interaction in shallow water.

Full scale trials: motions data acquisition system; ocean wave recorders; shaft power measurement; stabilised accelerometer platform; strain gauge suite.

A number of extensive pieces of computer software is available and others are being developed by Centre participants. These provide a theoretical backup to the experimental facilities listed above.

NEW ENTRY

CROWTHER MULTIHULLS PTY LTD

PO Box 35, Turramurra (Sydney), NSW 2074, Australia

Telephone: +61 (2) 979 9599
Telefax: +61 (2) 979 9614

Brett Crowther, *Director*

Crowther Multihulls has vast experience in all aspects of multihull design from efficient, high performance catamaran ferries and large, luxurious power and sailing yachts through to smaller cruising craft and high performance racing sailboats.

The company is an Australian Government approved research organisation and clients can be eligible for government grants (in Australia) on research and development work carried out by the office.

Designs completed in recent years include:

DMB, 22.4 m ketch-rigged pearling/diving catamaran (design no 73) of exceptional performance under sail and power;

Tafua, four 18 m luxury charter motor sailers (design no 58);

Southern Spirit, 29.9 m luxury motor sailer/yacht (design no 96 Mk II);

Ocean Spirit, 32 m tourist motor sailer yacht (design no 126);

Sunbird, Sunseeker and *Quickcat*, three 34 m high-speed passenger ferries (design nos 109, 117 and 132);

Kimberley Explorer, 34 m mini passenger liner catamaran (design no 120);

Xin Ning and *Shun Feng*, (lines, powering and developmental design for Precision Marine Holdings) two 39.7 m 36 knot water-jet passenger ferries (design no 155) for China;

Melanesian Discoverer, 35 m mini passenger liner catamaran for Papua New Guinea;

Reef Adventurer II, 33 m high-speed ferry (design no 136);

Capricorn Reefseeker, 35 m high-speed passenger ferry (design no142);

Majistic, 25 m 28 knot water-jet luxury motor sailer (design no 161 Mk II);

Equator Dream, 35.6 m 25 knot luxury cruise catamaran (design no 160) for Singapore;

Princess of Rhodes, 35.6 m 33 knot high-speed ferry (design no 157) for Greece;

Micronesian Dream, 33.5 m cruise catamaran (design no 153/3);

Island Pearl, 34.2 m high-speed ferry (design no 192);

Peisunna, 16.8 m motor catamaran yacht;

Aussie One, 30 m ketch-rigged day-charter catamaran (design no 167);

Blade Runner, 43 m 29 knot 400 passenger ferry (design no 201);

Tai An, 35 m 33 knot 250 passenger *Blade Runner* style high-speed ferry for Hong Kong;

Reef Queen, design by Lock Crowther Designs, superstructure styling by Hydronautics Australia and Lloyd's Ships. A 38 m 31 knot 380 passenger water-jet fast tourist ferry (design no 218);

On The Edge, a 20 m 60 passenger sloop rigged fast day charter catamaran (design no 223);

Aussie Magic, a 26 m 150 passenger day charter (or 110 passenger formal dining sloop rig catamaran (design no 213);

Tara Vana, a 50 m sail/game fishing charter catamaran for Bora Bora, French Polynesia (design no 222);

Reef Prince, a 38 m 31 knot 380 passenger water-jet fast tourist ferry (design no 250). Hull and structural design are by Lock Crowther Designs, superstructure styling, general arrangement and systems engineering by Lloyd's Ships Australia;

Qu Er Hao, a 35 m 33 knot, 250 passenger *Blade Runner* style high-speed ferry for Hong Kong.

UPDATED

Lloyd's Ship Reef Queen   *1994*

Tai An   *1995*

INTERNATIONAL CATAMARAN DESIGNS PTY LTD (InCat)

1 Mafeking Avenue, Lane Cove, Sydney, NSW, Australia 2066

Telephone: +61 (2) 427 2822
Telefax: +61 (2) 427 7238

Philip Hercus, *Director*
Tony Armstrong, *Technical Manager*

International Catamaran Designs Pty Ltd, better known as InCat Designs, was formed in 1988 as a result of the restructuring of International

Catamarans Pty Ltd. Even prior to that time International Catamarans, which was formed in 1977, was one of the world's leading catamaran designers and builders. In 1995 InCat Designs is still the world's leading catamaran design company, having designed over 130 catamaran craft which are operating in over 15 countries. The company is possibly best known as the designer of the wave-piercing catamaran, the 30 m prototype of which was launched in 1985 as *Spirit of Victoria*.

A turning point for InCat Designs and as a consequence for the fast ferry industry, was the delivery of *Hoverspeed Great Britain* in 1990. This was at that time by far the largest and fastest catamaran to have been designed and built, and was ordered by Sea Containers for operation across the English

Channel. Subsequently eight further 74 m wave-piercing catamarans were built with a further three 78 m versions built to date.

A noticeable achievement of the 74 m *Hoverspeed Great Britain* was a crossing of the Atlantic in June 1990 during its delivery voyage, at an average speed of 36.6 knots, hence qualifying for the Blue Riband award.

To date, over 25 wave-piercing catamarans have been constructed. The company is currently designing their largest craft at over 100 m which will be built in Vancouver for operation by British Columbia Ferries.

The ship designs from InCat designs are largely marketed and built by licensees around the world. A notable development in 1994 was the formation of

The InCat 74 m Hoverspeed Great Britain, *the first of the world's large fast ferries* (Hoverspeed)

1993

South Australia Ships Pty Ltd, the most recent licensee which has been specifically organised to build the large freight catamarans. Such designs at present cover vessels carrying 1000 tonnes deadweight at speeds of up to 50 knots.

Licensees of InCat Designs Pty Ltd:
Aluminium Shipbuilders Ltd, UK
Gladding Hearn Inc, USA
InCat Australia Pty Ltd, Australia
Nichols Brothers Inc, USA
South Australia Ships Pty Ltd, Australia

UPDATED

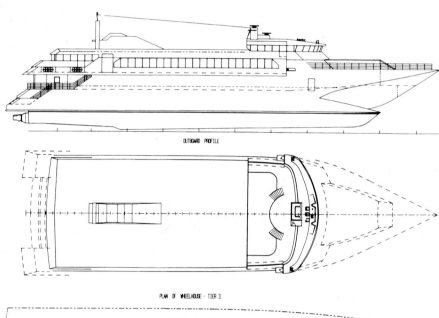

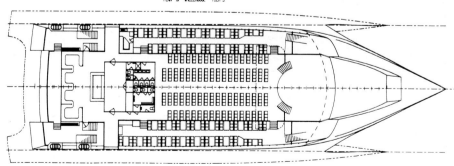

General arrangement of InCat 74 m wave-piercing catamaran
1993

KAMIRA HOLDINGS PTY LTD

PO Box 118, Stockton, NSW 2295, Australia

Telephone: +61 (49) 201344
Telefax: +61 (49) 201344

Greg Cox, *Managing Director and Naval Architect*

Kamira Holdings is a firm of naval architects and engineers specialising in the custom design of high-speed monohull craft in the 12 to 30 m range. The company has a building partner, Macquarie Inter-

national Motor Yachts, which has a range of Greg Cox designed craft under construction.

UPDATED

LAUBREAUX MARINE DESIGN

PO Box 637, Spit Junction NSW 2088, Australia

Telephone: +61 (612) 968 4177
Telefax: +61 (612) 960 1499

Tony Laubreaux, *Director, Naval Architect*
David Lyons, *Director*

Laubreaux undertakes complete design and project management for high-speed passenger vessels and other commercial and paramilitary craft. It also acts as a consultant on the structural design of high-speed marine vehicles in aluminium and advanced composites.

Recent designs have included the following:
Seaflyer 750, a 7.5 m, 40 knot catamaran fisheries vessel built in aluminium.
Multipurpose Catamaran An 8 m, 20 knot vessel

built in fibreglassed plywood for a Pacific Island. Current projects include:
A 72 passenger, 25 knot, 17 m aluminium catamaran; a 110 passenger, 30 knot, 21 m aluminium catamaran; a 250 passenger, 30 knot, 38 m aluminium catamaran; and work on a new high-speed river catamaran for Sydney harbour, which will be launched shortly.

UPDATED

MARK ELLIS DESIGN

11 Mews Road, Fremantle, Western Australia 6160, Australia

Telephone: +61 (9) 430 5270
Telefax: +61 (9) 430 5601

Mark Ellis, *Naval Architect*

Designers of high-speed catamaran and monohull craft. Recently built designs include the Fremantle Volunteer sea rescue catamaran, a 20 m oil spill response catamaran, a 15 m Pilot catamaran for Burrap and *GAC Shamal,* a 23 m monohull offshore supply vessel. A 23 m monohull passenger ferry is presently under construction to a Mark Ellis design.

UPDATED

Oil spill response catamaran
1994

PHIL CURRAN DESIGN

Lot 300 Sparks Road, Henderson, Western Australia 6166, Australia

Telephone: +61 (09) 410 2988
Telefax: +61 (09) 410 2553

Phil Curran, *Director, Naval Architect*
Steve Bruyn, *Design Manager, Naval Architect*

Phil Curran designs range from 6 m vessels to high-speed private luxury yachts over 65 m. Phil Curran Design has produced nearly 500 designs since first commencing business some 16 years ago.

Commercial and pleasure craft are designed in all forms of construction, specialising in modern high technology construction materials such as aluminium, composites, foam sandwich, carbon fibre and Kevlar.

Phil Curran Design has now developed a range of computer cut designs, up to 45 m high-speed

catamarans (*Moecca*). This process offered by its subsidiary CDM, provides boat builders with a cost-effective package.

Designs have included the following craft:
Customised, 21 m, 38 knot, 15 tonne planing vessel with water-jet propulsion.
PM 17, built by Precision Marine Holdings Pty Ltd. This 17 m power boat design has received numerous orders and won the 1986 and 1988 Power Boat of the Year awards and the Australian Design Award. With a 24 tonne displacement the boat is capable of 40 knots.
PM 40, Precision Marine 40' sports fisherman. This production vessel is capable of 35 knots and has proved a very successful design with 37' and 43' vessels added to the range.
Numerous high-speed fishing vessels with speeds ranging from 20 to 50 knots built of aluminium and composites.
Oceanfast 2800 *Mercedes,* 27 m, 30 knot luxury motor yacht with twin water-jets, operating out of Florida waters.

Oceanfast 3000 *Never Say Never,* 33.3 m, 30 knot luxury charter vessel operating in the Caribbean.
Oceanfast 3000/2 *Antipodean,* sister ship to Oceanfast 3000, *Never Say Never.*
Oceanfast 4000 *Parts VI,* 46.69 m, 30 knot, 150 tonne (light ship) luxury motor yacht used by the Royal Perth Yacht Club as their flagship during the 1986-87 America's Cup Regatta in Fremantle, Western Australia.
Oceanfast 5000 *Mystique,* 49.5 m, 34 knot, 180 tonne, planing vessel with water-jet propulsion operating out of New York waters.
Wilderness Seeker, 100 seat, 19.95 m, 30 knot ferry with water-jet propulsion, built for Gordon River operations in Tasmania.
Moecca, 44.5 m, 29 knot, 270 tonne (lightship) pleasure catamaran with water-jet propulsion for worldwide cruising.

VERIFIED

STOLKRAFT PTY LTD

Level 10, Seabank, 12 Marine Parade, Southport, Queensland 4215, Australia

Telephone: +61 (75) 329722
Telefax: +61 (75) 911023

J D Aitkenhead, *Managing Director*

Stolkraft is the registered trademark for an innovative hull form, conceived by the late Mr Leo Stolk and subsequently developed in Australia for high-speed applications. The hull form makes use of both hydrodynamic and aerodynamic lift at high speeds

achieved solely by the forward speed of the craft.

Performance has been proven by a number of model and prototype tests. Commercial applications to date include a 13 m pilot boat for the Port of Auckland and a series of water taxis for river use.

NEW ENTRY

BELGIUIM

EUROSENSE HOVERSOUNDING NV

Main office: Nerviërslaan 54, B-1780 Wemmel, Belgium

Telephone: +32 (2) 460 7000
Telex: 26687B
Telefax: +32 (2) 460 4958

E Maes, *Managing Director*
J Van Sieleghem, *Project Leader*

BEASAC (Belfotop Eurosense Acoustic Sounding Air Cushion platform)

Since 1983 Eurosense has been under contract with the Belgian Ministry of Public Works, Coastal Services, for the constant monitoring of the access channels to the major Belgian seaports, and for the study of the coastal morphology. For this purpose, Eurosense has used a hydrographic survey technique based on the use of a fully amphibious hovercraft.

Nearshore bathymetric surveys by hovercraft ensure an overlap with beach observations (executed by aerial or terrestrial survey), thus enabling a complete coverage of the coast and near-shore sea bottom to be achieved. Furthermore, the manoeuvrability of the hovercraft and the high survey speed (up to 55 km/h, or 30 knots) result in measurements being obtained up to four times faster than those with classic hydrographic vessels.

This new concept in the field of hydrography was developed by Eurosense and called BEASAC (Belfotop Eurosense Acoustic Sounding Air Cushion platform). The first BEASAC was developed using the SR. N6 Mk 1S hovercraft. A second version, the twin-propeller SR. N6 Mk 6, was named BEASAC III.

BEASAC

The first BEASAC hovercraft is a modified SR. N6 Mk 1S.

There are two hydraulically operated arms mounted on each side deck to bring acoustic transducers in and out of the water. Eurosense has developed an automatic retraction and deployment system allowing the measurements to be performed up to the last available metre of water depth.

In front of the pilot, a navigation screen shows the predefined tracks and harbour planimetry. This screen is continuously updated with the position of the craft, its speed, direction and the distance off track.

BEASAC III

The BEASAC III is based on the twinpropeller SR. N6 Mk 6. In the centre of the craft a hydraulically operated arm lowers the acoustic transducers into the water through a moon pool in the floor of the craft. The longitudinal and transverse cushion dividers of the skirt are modified to allow for this movement. As for BEASAC, a mechanical weak link construction and an automatic retraction and deployment system are installed.

Operations equipment: The data are acquired by a computer system extended with interfacing networks to gather all sensor registration. Graphical navigation screens inform the pilot and surveyor of track, planimetry and quality control of the data. Computer hardware and software, developed by Eurosense, enable continuous chart production to be achieved, as well as further data processing, for example Digital Terrain Modelling, differential map production, volume computation and refraction calculation.

UPDATED

The Eurosense SR. N6 Mk 6, BEASAC III   *1991*

CANADA

D F DICKINS ASSOCIATES LTD

4-124 Valhalla Road, Salt Spring Island, British Columbia V8K 2V1, Canada

Telephone: +1 (604) 537 4492
Telefax: +1 (604) 537 2310

David Dickins, *President*

D F Dickins Associates Ltd is actively involved in marine transportation studies. The company provides a variety of services including route evaluation, conceptual design and testing, technical and economic feasibility studies and environmental impact studies. The firm offers a diverse range of consulting expertise through affiliations with hovercraft manufacturers, naval architects and marine biologists.

From 1981 to 1984 Dickins Associates acted as technical director of Sohio's ACV research programme. This involved the co-ordination of an international design team to develop the concept for a 1000 tonne ACV. During the last year of this programme, Dickins directed the testing of the 200 tonne JEFF(A) at Prudhoe Bay.

A project completed for Gulf Canada Resources in 1986 involved the conceptual design of large self-propelled hovercraft up to 845 tonnes gross weight. During the same year, Dickins Associates worked with the Canadian Coast Guard Hovercraft Base in Vancouver to test an SR. N6 as a potential platform for spraying dispersants on oil slicks at sea.

A number of studies has examined the feasibility

Chominco's AP1-88 during loading at the Snip gold mine   *1993*

of using hovercraft in resupply and emergency response roles. In 1989, Dickins assisted Chominco Metals in an environmental, technical and economic evaluation of hovercraft servicing their Snip gold mine in northern British Columbia. Chominco proceeded with procurement of an AP1-88 during the Summer of 1990. Operations to date have been very successful and were detailed in a paper presented in Washington at HPMV 92.

A project for the Municipality of Anchorage examined the technical feasibility and demand for a hovercraft operating as an emergency response vessel in Cook Inlet. This study concluded that the AP1-88 would satisfy the mission requirements.

In 1991 the company evaluated the feasibility of operating a successful tourist hovercraft service in the Kluane National Park region of Canada's Ukon Territory.

Recent publications are included in the bibliography section of this edition.

UPDATED

PROMAXIS SYSTEMS INC

2385 St Laurent Boulevard, Ottawa, Ontario K1G 4J3, Canada

Telephone: +1 (613) 737 2112
Telefax: +1 (613) 737 0229

James D Beer, *President*

SWATH CPV (DESIGN)

Promaxis has developed a design for a Swath coastal patrol vessel for use in search and rescue, fisheries patrol, defence surveillance, MCM and other related missions in rough seas such as those that exist off the east and west coasts of Canada.

This 360 tonne all-aluminium vessel is arranged to facilitate handling and treatment of survivors by providing dedicated rescue zones, recessed into the port and starboard sides of the upper hulls. At each zone 15 m² of deck space is provided leading to a triage area and treatment room amidships. Within the accommodation, seating and bunks are provided for up to 25 survivors. A helicopter landing pad is designed to enable landing and take off of a Jet-Ranger helicopter in up to Sea State 5 conditions. For ship external fire-fighting two monitors are located between the funnels.

The vessel will be driven at 15 knots in Sea State 5 head seas by two medium-speed diesels, developing a total of 3600 hp. The main engines are located within the main deck structure with a mechanical transfer of drive to controllable-pitch propellers.

Accommodation, all above main deck level, provides for a mixed 14 person crew with officers forward and ratings aft. Stores, fuel and water requirements are designed for 15 days' endurance at economical speed.

The design minimises development risks by employing standard, proven systems technology. The vessel will be built to Transport Canada regulations and classed with an international classification society.

Dimensions
Length overall: 34.6 m
Max beam: 15.50 m
Draught, full load: 3.5 m
Weight
Displacement, full load: 360 t
Performance
Speed in Sea State 5: 15 knots

VERIFIED

ROBERT ALLEN LTD

1690 West Second Avenue, Vancouver, British Columbia V6J 1H4, Canada

Telephone: +1 (604) 736 9466
Telefax: +1 (604) 736 9483

Robert Allen, *Director*

Well known for the company's tug designs, Robert Allen Ltd has also been closely involved in the development of high-speed craft in Canada.

The company has specialist experience in the use of CAD and CAM technology to assist shipyards in the planning and construction process.

NEW ENTRY

THE MARIPORT GROUP LTD

3425 Harvester Road, STE 215, Burlington, Ontario L7N 3N1, Canada

Telephone: +1 (416) 333 8171
Telefax: +1 (416) 333 1162

Christopher Wright, *President*
John Cowah, *Senior Consultant*

The Mariport Group Ltd conducts marine systems analysis and work has included projects for: Toronto Waterbus, Busan-Yeosu Ferry (South Korea), High-Speed Ferry (S E Alaska), Mine Supply and Personnel Vessel (Alaska, Newfoundland and China).

VERIFIED

COMMONWEALTH OF INDEPENDENT STATES

FORMA LTD

15 Lahtinskaya Street, 197136 St Petersburg, Russia, CIS

Telephone: +7 (812) 230 2672
Telefax: +7 (812) 230 8112

Igor Mizin, *President*

Incorporated in 1991 in St Petersburg, Forma Ltd is one of the first Russian private companies specialising in the research and design of high-speed vessels. The firm unifies about thirty specialists who for many years had worked in leading research and design centres, and have experience in the design of practically all fast craft built in the former USSR. At present Forma provides support to the Russian design bureaus.

The company develops and uses calculation methods and analytical software for hydrodynamic predictions. Model testing services are also offered.

The company's experience includes the design of the largest dynamically supported ships (500 t hydrofoil with fully submerged foil system with foilborne speed of 50 knots in Sea State 5; 750 t SES with speed of 40 knots in Sea State 4; 400 t ACV with speed of 55 knots). For the design of the hydrodynamic aspects of these projects (including foil systems, lift systems, and high pressure head waterjets), Forma Ltd used mathematical modelling of 3-D motion, and automatic control system algorithms.

Specialists of the company have obtained several author patents for inventions concerned with high-speed craft. They have presented over thirty technical reports at international conferences and symposiums.

NEW ENTRY

KORT

Moscow, Russia, CIS

Telephone: +7 (095) 153 1477
Telefax: +7 (095) 153 1477

V G Moulev, *Chairman*
S A Yendrikhovsky, *General Director*

The key task of Kort is the integration of CIS high-speed ship manufacture into the world market. This process has already involved enterprises such as the Central Hydrofoil Ship Design Office (Nizhny Novgorod), Poti Shipyard and other businesses. Companies in Cyprus, Germany and Greece have indicated interest in this integration programme.

VERIFIED

SUDOEXPORT

11 Sadovaja-Kudrinskaja St, 123231 Moscow, Russia, CIS

Telephone: +7 (095) 252 4491
Telex: 411116
Telefax: +7 (095) 200 2250

Vladimir A Chnyr, *General Director*
Vjacheslav V Yanchenko, *Director of Imports*
Yuri I Fomichev, *Export Director*

Sudoexport is a Russian organisation engaged in the export and import of all kinds of sea-going and riverine ships and ship's equipment, and the export and import of technological equipment for shipbuilding and associated engineering activities.

Sudoexport offers skilled services in shiprepair including repair for the naval-defence fleet. The company is also an investor in various joint ventures and has a worldwide agent network.

VERIFIED

TRANSAL-AKS ENGINEERING CO

3 Sovetskaya Pl, Nizhny Novgorod, 603106 Russia, CIS

Telephone: +7 (831) 268 4989
Telefax: +7 (831) 268 0574

TRANSAL-AKS is a research, design and consultancy company specialising in the field of high performance marine and amphibious craft. Only limited information concerning its military and commercial designs is currently available, although it is clear that fast passenger transportation is one of the main markets being considered. The craft illustrated here has a speed of over 300 knots with a passenger capacity of 50. The range is 250 nm with a payload of 5 tonnes. Fuel consumption is predicted to be 0.054 kg/seat.nm.

NEW ENTRY

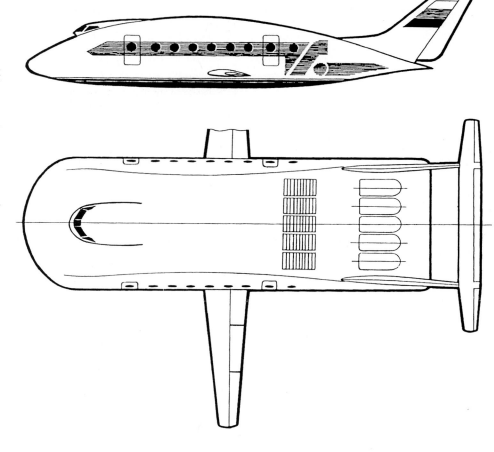

Proposed arrangement of wing-in-ground-effect craft
1995

CROATIA

BRODOPROJEKT

Ship Design & Marine Engineering
Ciottina 17a, 51000 Rijeka, Croatia

Telephone: +38 (51) 38188
Telex: 24335 BROPRO YU
Telefax: +38 (51) 211318

Sinila Reljie, *Naval Architect, Marketing Manager*

This organisation is developing a number of high-speed catamaran designs.

VERIFIED

DENMARK

JAN KJÆRULFF YACHT DESIGN

Engvej 9, DK-2960 Rungsted Kyst, Denmark

Telephone: +45 (42) 867215
Telefax: +45 (42) 867215

Jan Kjærulff, *Naval Architect*

Jan Kjærulff Yacht Design is a firm of consulting naval architects and marine engineers involved in the design and survey of fast craft. Recent projects have included two 16 m craft, a fast catamaran ferry and a 16 m fast crew boat. The company has also completed a 70 m fast ferry design for Danish State Railways. The company works closely with Temex, the owner of the specialist marine craft operator Supply-Trans.

Current designs include a 13 m, 12 passenger ACV, with a speed of up to 60 knots. Trials for this craft took place during November 1994.

A 16 m fast car and passenger catamaran ferry has also been designed for services to Danish islands.

UPDATED

FRANCE

BERTIN & CIE

PO Box 3, F-78373 Plaisir Cedex, France

Telephone: +33 (1) 34 81 85 00
Telex: 696231 F
Telefax: +33 (1) 30 54 04 14

Hervé Hamon, *Chairman*
Alain Pirovano, *Secretary*

Bertin has been engaged in developing the Bertin principle of separately fed multiple plenum chambers surrounded by flexible skirts since 1956. A research and design organisation, the company employs a staff of more than 500, mainly scientists and design engineers who are involved in many areas of industrial research, including air cushion techniques and applications.

The Bertin principle of multiple air cushions has led to the development of the Aérotrain high-speed

tracked transport system and to numerous applications in the area of industrial handling and aeronautics. These applications, developed by Bertin, are described in the sections devoted to Air Cushion Applicators, Conveyors and Pallets and Air Cushion Landing Systems in *Jane's Surface Skimmers 1980* and earlier editions.

UPDATED

IFREMER

INSTITUT FRANÇAIS DE RECHERCHE POUR L'EXPLOITATION DE LA MER

Centre de Brest, PO Box 70, F-29280 Plouzané, France

Telephone: +33 98 22 40 40
Telex: 940627 OCEAN F
Telefax: +33 98 22 41 35

Philippe Marchand, *Director*

IFREMER was formed in 1984 from the merger between CNEXO (National Centre for Sea Development) and ISTPM, Scientific and Technical Institute for Sea Fisheries. IFREMER is commissioned by the French Government to conduct studies for the evaluation of unconventional ships, for example amphibious hovercraft, surface effect ships, hydrofoil craft, catamarans and Swath vessels and may participate in any development of these concepts. Test facilities are located at Brest in Brittany. The largest part of the unconventional ship research programme of IFREMER is concerned with air cushion technology and the relevant patents have been acquired from the former SEDAM company. Since 1985 IFREMER has been mainly involved in the design of the ADOC 12 hovercraft and the NES 24 surface effect ship. Since December 1991 IFREMER has been involved in a national programme called MENTOR.

MENTOR

The objective of the MENTOR (Modele Explorative de Navire de Transport Oceanique Rapide) national programme is to study three types of high-speed ferries with the following characteristics; a payload of 250 tonnes (including 500 passengers and 100 cars), a speed of 50 knots on Sea State 5 and a range of 300 miles. There are three types of ferries under evaluation, SES, Swath and slender monohull with stabilisation.

ADOC 12

In 1986 IFREMER conducted complete performance tests on the ADOC 12 craft from its establishment at Brest. In 1988 the craft was improved with diesel engines and a new propulsion system for better manoeuvrability.

VERIFIED

TECHNI CARÈNE

6 Route de Bû, Les Christophes, F-28260 Sorel Moussel, France

Telephone: +33 16 37 41 80 38
Telefax: +33 37 41 73 81

Philippe Nineuil, *Director*

Techni Carène is a naval architecture and engineering office established in 1979 by Philippe Nineuil, naval architect and a member of the Institut Français des Architectes Navals (IFAN).

The company is involved in the design of all types of ships from 15 m up to 60 m in length, in all materials and adopted to a wide range of operation programmes such as: passenger transport, hydrographic, diving support, fishing, patrol, and offshore supply.

It has also developed a range of displacement and medium-speed catamarans named CATATRANS, which include fishing, hydrographic and passenger units.

Two examples of high-speed craft built to Techni Carène designs are: *Azenor*, a 25 m, 200 passenger aluminium catamaran operated in Brittany, France, delivered in 1992; and *Dravanteg*, a 27 m mixed cargo and passenger catamaran, powered by 2 × 895 kW diesels driving KaMeWa water-jets, operated in Brittany, France. Both of these vessels were built by the shipyard Navale Aluminium Atlantique, Saint-Nazaire.

NEW ENTRY

GERMANY

MTG MARINETECHNIK GmbH

Wandsbeker Königstrasse 62, PO Box 701249, D-2000 Hamburg 70, Germany

Telephone: +49 (40) 65830
Telex: 215200
Telefax: +49 (40) 658 3392

Franz-Josef Görgen, *Managing Director*
Werner Kurz, *Commercial Director*

MTG Marinetechnik GmbH was founded in 1966 at the instigation of the Federal German MoD as a central planning and design office for naval systems, especially naval surface craft and general naval technology. MTG shareholders are major shipyards and electronics companies. MTG designs naval systems, prepares tender documents for naval projects and is involved in all project development phases with particular emphasis on the early planning stages. The company is staffed by some 120 employees, the majority of whom are technical/scientific engineering graduates. MTG is renowned for its competence and impartial consulting services.

For several years now MTG has been working on the design of unconventional marine platforms. Initial basic studies have led to the design of the Fast Test Craft SES 700 and a Swath design for a research vessel.

In the years 1984 to 1988 a design study for naval fast test craft was worked on in the Federal Republic of Germany. The selected vessel is a large steel-

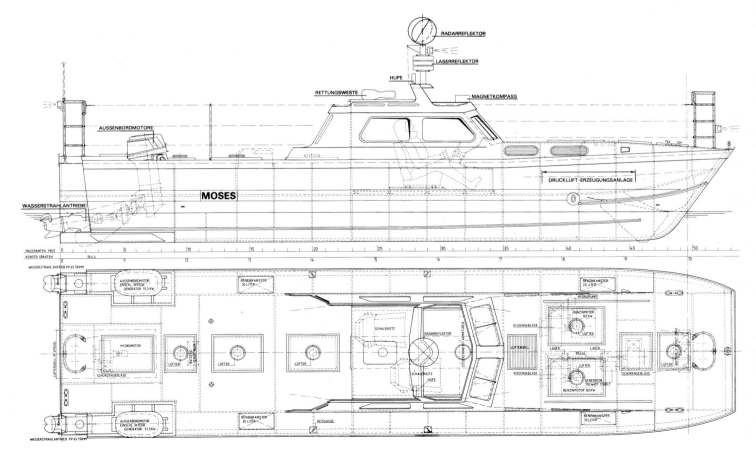

MTG Marintechnik MOSES manned test craft

hulled surface effect ship, with a full load displacement of 720 tonnes and a maximum speed in excess of 50 knots. The design study was managed by MTG Marinetechnik GmbH in Hamburg, on behalf of the German Ministry of Defence in close co-operation with the US Naval Sea System Command under a Data Exchange Agreement. Extensive model tests were performed at the David Taylor Model Basin (DTRC), leading to the development of manned model, MOSES. MTG integrated into the overall design, contributions from Maritime Dynamics Inc for a seal and lift system design and a ride control system.

During the last few years extensive investigations have been performed by MTG on Swath technology leading to the design of a naval research vessel. This design is intended to replace the 2000 tonne conventional monohull, *Planet,* which is currently in operation for the German Navy. The Swath 3200 tonne, 13 to 15 knot vessel has been designed to meet the operational requirements of the German MoD for the tasks which are anticipated in the field of naval research in the year 2000. The basic missions and tasks are related to: underwater acoustics, maritime geology and geophysics, and meteorology and aerology.

MTG has developed a high standard of expertise in the design of unconventional craft which can be readily exploited for a wide range of naval and commercial applications.

VERIFIED

GREECE

NATIONAL TECHNICAL UNIVERSITY OF ATHENS

LABORATORY OF SHIP DESIGN

9 Heroon Polytechniou Str, GR-15773 Athens, Greece

Telephone: +30 (1) 7484 622/625/626
Telex: 221682 NTUA GR
Telefax: +30 (1) 7484 627

Apostolos Papanikolaou, *Professor, Director*

AEGEAN QUEEN (DESIGN)

This 1000 tonne displacement Swath passenger/car ferry design, able to carry approximately 750 passengers and 88 cars at a speed of 30 knots, was announced in 1989 and has been designed by the Laboratory of Ship Design at the National Technical University of Athens, Department of Naval Architecture and Marine Engineering. Resistance and seakeeping model testing has been performed at the Towing Tank of NTUA, Laboratory of Naval and Marine Hydrodynamics.

The concept of Aegean Queen is to develop a rapid, safe and comfortable marine transportation system for connecting the Greek mainland with the surrounding and even more distant islands in the Aegean and Ionian Sea. A prototype design for the route Piraeus to Heraklion (Crete) proved the technical and economic feasibility of the proposed concept.

The main structure of Aegean Queen is to be made from steel and the superstructure from aluminium alloys. A preliminary structural design proved the validity of the initial weight assumptions of the proposed design.

Recently completed designs include a 600 tonnes displacement Swath multipurpose research vessel (so called SMURV) for the Mediterranean area and a 60 TEU high-speed Swath multipurpose container carrier (so called SMUCC) for short sea shipping operations in Europe.

The latter concept, including an innovative terminal facility for fast loading and unloading of high value deck containers, was first presented at the Shipbuilding and Machinery Exhibition SMM '94 in September 1994, Hamburg, Germany.

UPDATED

ITALY

SCIOMACHEN

NAVAL ARCHITECTS

Via Massarenti 410, I-40138 Bologna, Italy

Telephone: +39 (51) 533043
Telefax: +39 (51) 531304

Franco Sciomachen, *Director*
Ernesto Sciomachen, *Director*
Aldo Sciomachen, *Director*

The Sciomachen name has been associated with yachts and boats since 1951. After being devoted to mainly sailing craft in the early years, the company's projects today encompass a full range of marine designs from high-speed power yachts to fast ferries, excursion vessels, fishing vessels and displacement yachts, as well as racing and cruising sailboats. Construction materials include fibreglass, steel, aluminium and wood, with sizes from about 7 m to over 45 m.

The company's yacht design experience is reflected in the design of its commercial vessels, where functionality is always matched with aesthetically pleasing lines.

Sciomachen's European headquarters are in Bologna, Italy, with an office in San Diego, California, serving the Pacific Rim.

VERIFIED

JAPAN

MASARU IKEDA SHIP CONSULTING OFFICE

2-1-8-907 Benten, Minato-ku, Osaka, Japan

Telephone: +81 (6) 574 1658
Telefax: +81 (6) 574 1658

Masaru Ikeda, *Surveyor and Consulting Engineer*

Masaru Ikeda is a representative surveyor, registered consulting engineer for the Scientific Technology Department, Reg No 8533. Projects have included a catamaran research boat, a high-speed fishery patrol boat and a high-speed passenger vessel.

VERIFIED

KOREA, SOUTH

KOREA RESEARCH INSTITUTE OF SHIPS AND OCEAN ENGINEERING

PO Box 1, Taeduk Science Town, Taejon 305-606, South Korea

Telephone: +82 (42) 8617401
Telefax: +82 (42) 8687711

This company was founded in 1989 and is supported by the South Korean government, but has been affiliated with companies working in the shipbuilding industry since 1973.

KRISO is a research institute specialised in high performance ships, offshore structures, deep sea submersibles and underwater robots.

A towing tank (216 m × 16 m × 7 m) is used for evaluation of hull and propulsor technology, seakeeping and manoeuvring, and other purposes; for high-speed craft such as SESs, catamarans, hydrofoil catamarans and hybrid ships. Computational fluid dynamics is also widely used.

Other areas of interest being researched include advanced ship design technology, strength and vibration technology, and marine machinery performance evaluation using physical testing and theoretical computer techniques.

NEW ENTRY

NETHERLANDS

NEVESBU

B. V. Nederlandse Verenigde Scheepsbouw Bureaus, (Netherlands United Shipbuilding Bureaus)

PO Box 16350, 2500 BJ The Hague, Netherlands

Telephone: +31 (70) 3497979
Telefax: +31 (70) 3854460

This marine engineering company was founded in 1935, and concentrates on ship design, maritime technology and marine engineering. It is a private company, with an average (last four years) net turnover of DFl 15 million. Its shareholders are: Royal Schelde Group of Vlissingen, Rotterdam Dockyard, Wilton-Fijenoord of Schiedam, Stork of Naarden and Signaal of Hengelo. Nevesbu provides research, design and engineering services to customers all over the world. Among these customers are several navies, including the Royal Netherlands Navy, shipowners, shipyards, dredging companies, offshore industry, petro/chemical industry and government organisations. Consultancy activities include feasibility and reliability studies, engineering software development and probabilistic risk analyses.

Nevesbu employs approximately 85 dedicated people of which more than 30 are highly qualified specialists holding MSc and BSc degrees in various fields of engineering such as naval architecture, marine engineering and information technology. Nevesbu also counts many experienced design engineers and draftsmen. In addition, the close cooperation with technical universities, research institutes and industry is a valuable asset.

Two examples of high-speed craft designed by Nevesbu are a 46 m coastguard vessel (design), of 22 knots speed; and a 66 m customs patrol boat of 30 knots speed, delivered in 1988.

NEW ENTRY

NORWAY

AMBLE & STOKKE A/S

PO Box 1616, Valhalla, N-4602 Kristiansand, Norway
Office: Kongsgaard Alle 53, N-4632 Kristiansand S, Norway

Telephone: +47 (380) 95803
Telefax: +47 (380) 95871

Eivind Amble, *Naval Architect*
Tor Stokke, *Naval Architect*

Specialists in the design of high-speed marine craft and related research and development. With 20 years' experience as naval architects, their reference list ranges from luxury Mega motor yachts to small dinghies, from offshore racing power boats to military craft and to high-speed commercial vessels.

During recent years Amble & Stokke A/S has been involved in a variety of design tasks. In 1991 the company received an award for 'The Best Engineered Motoryacht 1991' as the naval architects of the 76 m motor yacht *Golden Odyssey*, teamed with Platou Ship Design and Veritas Marine Services and builders Blohm+Voss. They designed the latest generation of high-speed rescue craft for the Norwegian Society for Sea Rescue, and the latest pilot cutter for the Norwegian Coastal Directorate.

Amble & Stokke has been involved in the design of the Sea Lord high-speed passenger catamarans built by the Båtservice Group, and in some of the SES projects undertaken by the Kværner Mandal yard. During the last few years, Amble & Stokke has been involved in the high-speed craft research and development programme initiated by the Royal Norwegian Council for Scientific and Industrial Research, both as naval architects and through its sister company CETEC (Consultancy - Engineering - Technology) in structural design and studies on the application of advanced composites. On specific projects, the firm works in association with IMAA (Independent Maritime Assessment Associates) of Romsey, UK.

VERIFIED

CAMO

COMPUTER-AIDED MODELLING A/S

Jarlev 4, N-7041 Trondheim, Norway

Telephone: +47 (7) 514966
Telefax: +47 (7) 514257

CAMO was established in 1984 by a group of leading experts in the control engineering field and early in 1993 12 people were employed.

FoilCat 2900 is a Norwegian high-speed foilborne catamaran. At normal cruising speed the foils of the Westamarin FoilCat 2900 will lift both hulls above the water surface. The vessel is stabilised in flight condition by a control system that ensures extremely good passenger comfort even in 3 to 4 m waves. The control system is developed by CAMO.

By dynamic simulation of the vessel expensive prototype development and the overall time for system development can be significantly reduced.

FoilCat 2900 is a 29 m catamaran with fully submerged foils fore and aft. In flight condition at 50 knots, the system is unstable and has to be stabilised by a control system.

A mathematical model of the hydrodynamic properties of the vessel was developed in close cooperation with Marintek, Trondheim. The model was programmed in the Cypros simulation programme ESIM.

A control system was developed based on the simulation model. Its purpose is to stabilise the vessel in three degrees of freedom: heave, roll and pitch. The control system is based on modern theories for non-linear and multi-variable control. All failure modes were tested against the simulator, and a comprehensive Failure Mode Effect Analysis was worked through before going on sea. The control system handles all sensor and servo errors by detecting and isolating any erroneous device.

A model of a conventional catamaran was achieved by removing the foils from the FoilCat model. A simulation experiment was carried out comparing the performance of the two vessels at 37 knots in 1 m seas. The mean vertical acceleration for the catamaran was approximately 0.7 g (1 g 9.8 m/s^2), compared to 0.05 g for the FoilCat, and pitch motion similarly reduced. All parts of the system were tested on the simulator prior to sea trials. This approach uncovered several potential problems in time before the final installation on board. As a result development time and cost was considerably lower than if the system had been tested and tuned exclusively on board.

The simulation system was used to verify vessel design details; specify sensors; develop the control system; perform failure mode effect analysis; specify sea trial test programme and prepare documentation for the shipyard and the authorities.

VERIFIED

CIRRUS SHIP DESIGN A/S

Våkleiva 133, PO Box 130, N-5062 Bønes, Bergen, Norway

Telephone: +47 (5) 513 5400
Telex: 40422 CIRR N
Telefax: +47 (5) 513 5411

Dick Vinkler, *President*
Atle Ulvesæter, *Vice President*

Cirrus Ship Design A/S is the leading designer of air cushion catamarans (SES).

There are 15 Cirrus air cushion catamarans in operation worldwide. These are CIRR 105 and 120P designs with a capacity up to 330 passengers and a top speed of approximately 50 knots.

The range of Cirrus air cushion catamarans also includes both naval vessels such as mine-hunters and patrol craft, as well as large ferries with capacity for cars and buses.

The Royal Norwegian Navy is currently building nine 56 m mine-hunters based upon the Cirrus air cushion catamaran design. This is the largest SES project in the world. For this project Cirrus Ship Design A/S also supplies all cushion-related hardware, computers, skirts and so on.

Cirrus Ship Design A/S has provided Blohm+Voss AG with the CIRR 200PO air cushion design as a basis for the Corsair 600 car ferry. This vessel, which has a capacity for 400 passengers and 56 cars (or eventually a combination of buses and cars), will have a top speed of about 47 knots.

Cirrus Ship Design A/S is also co-operating with the Tencara yard of the Montedison Group, Italy, for building of the CIRR 120P type passenger vessels under licence. Through the introduction of advanced FRP production technology the performance of this vessel has now been further improved.

The latest design from Cirrus Ship Design A/S is the CIRR HSPC 42. This is an advanced patrol craft based upon the proven technology of the CIRR 120P and designed to meet NATO requirements. The vessel incorporates stealth design and the Cirrus patented missile silent launch system. Top speed is in the range of 65 knots.

VERIFIED

OLA LILLOE-OLSEN

N-6780 Hyen, Norway

Telephone: +47 (57) 69805
Telefax: +47 (57) 69925

Ola Lilloe-Olsen, *Director*

Having built up and run Teknisk Modell-Senter A/S for 12 years, Ola Lilloe-Olsen established a design office in July 1991, Teknisk Modell-Senter being closed later.

Work and projects now being undertaken include the following: revision work on the IMO 373 (x) Code, particularly for craft below 30 m; the use of high-speed catamarans as fishing vessels; the development of two 32 m catamarans for carrying Royal Norwegian Mail between Stavanger and Aalesund and intermediate towns; and a further project, the development of a new generation of ambulance vessels.

UPDATED

38.4 m longliner high-speed fishing vessel (design)

1993

OTTO L SCHEEN JR A/S

Holterteigen 5, N-1440 Drøbak, Norway

Telephone: +47 (64) 930775/0341
Telefax: +47 (64) 930775

Otto L Scheen Jr, *Principal*

Designers of high-speed monohull vessels for a wide variety of applications, many in the range of 15 to 30 m.

Otto Scheen has been responsible for the design of nearly 100 monohull fast craft up to 30 m in length with speeds over 40 knots; a considerable number of these have been passenger or ambulance boats.

Designs have included the 20 m, 75 passenger, 35 knot *Sea Princess*; the 16.1 m, 41 knot ambulance *Solund*; four 30 knot rescue vessels of the Norboat class; and a 28 m, 160 passenger, 25 knot monohull vessel for a Korean yard.

Most recently, Otto L Scheen Jr A/S was responsible for the complete design and project management of a 34 m rescue vessel, with a speed of 20 knots and bollard pull of 20 tonnes.

UPDATED

PARADIS NAUTICA

PO Box 171, N-5040 Paradis, Bergen, Norway

Telephone: +47 (55) 910010
Telefax: +47 (55) 910009

Asbjørn Tolo, *Director*
Hans J Runshaug, *Director*
Eirik Neverdal, *Director*

Kåre Angell Hamnes, *Director*
Eilev Instanes, *Director*

Paradis Nautica is a marine consultancy based in Bergen, Norway. The partners have a total of 80 years of experience in various aspects of the the fast ferry industry, and offer services to ship owners, operators, investors, yards and government agencies.

Some examples of the services offered by Paradis Nautica include: craft feasibility studies, evaluation of contracts and companies, market studies, charter assistance, new building tenders, ship concept development and design, technical support, and engineering design.

NEW ENTRY

SINGAPORE

SWAN HUNTER SINGAPORE PTE LTD

750E Chai Chee Road 07-01, Chai Chee Industrial Park, Singapore 1646

Telephone: +65 449 9388
Telex: 21219 RS
Telefax: +65 449 6738

T J Bearder, *Managing Director*
Teo Yeow Soon, *Finance and Commercial Director*
R K Williams, *Manager Technical Services*
M Liew, *Manager Logistics Support*
Lim Siew Koon, *Design Services Manager*

This company has a history in Singapore dating back to 1923. The company specialises in the following fields: logistic support and supply, planned maintenance systems, international procurement, general marine services, design of high performance naval vessels, design of quasi-military craft for police and customs duties and technology transfer using designs based on a range of model-tested hull forms. Supply of technical manpower teams can also be provided. The company acts as the local representative for various marine agency lines and backs these with follow-up services.

Together with the parent company in the UK, the firm has experience of a complete range of warships from small patrol boats to frigates and aircraft carriers. The company also has the facilities to design and build landing craft and fleet auxiliary vessels of all types from 30 to 300 m long.

Over the years, vessels have been supplied to government organisations in 15 countries in the Middle and Far East as well as to many commercial companies in the region.

VERIFIED

SPAIN

NEUMAR SA

La Rinconada B-6, E-28023 Madrid, Spain

Telephone: +34 (1) 548 2071
Telefax: +34 (1) 547 4696

J Peire, *General Manager*
M de la Cruz, *Technical Director*
J A Barbeta, *Manufacturing Manager*

Neumar SA was founded in 1983 as a consulting engineers and designers company for air cushion technology. The services it offers include research and development with an emphasis on lift systems; hovercraft design; project management, which can comprise construction subcontracting with collaborating shipyards; hovercraft skirt design; and manufacturing, technical and economic feasibility studies.

The company offers a range of hovercraft designs which are based on a new lift system that it has recently developed and patented. This has been called an Automatic Transversal Air Distribution (ATAD) lift system because of the main function it performs in providing very high stability with low power requirements and reduced manufacturing and maintenance costs. To prove the viability of this lift system, several two-dimensional models and two prototypes have been built and tested.

The ATAD lift system has been developed with the aim of obtaining high stability values with low lift power requirements. It is a pressure-stability, fully segmented system that is based on a longitudinal flexible keel which has the inherent ability to increase the pressure difference between the two chambers into which it divides the air cushion, while keeping the pressure ratio between the air distribution duct and the air cushion at a very low level.

A by-product of this lift system is a hull design which further increases the hovercraft sea-keeping qualities. The hull bottom cross-section has the form of a 'W', both 'Vs' ending in conical surfaces which at the bow are prolonged upwards and forward forming a planing surface to prevent adverse consequences of any plough-in phenomena. This hull form greatly reduces water impact loads and at the same time it has a high structural efficiency that in turn leads to a lower structure weight.

Please see the 1992-93 edition of this book for details of the Neumaran NM-6 three- to four-seat hovercraft.

VERIFIED

Trials of the Neumaran NM-6 prototype over mud and reeds
1988

UR TEKNIKS S. L.

Amézqueta 10, Entlo E, 20010 San Sebastián, Spain

Telephone: +34 (43) 472396/472144
Telefax: +34 (43) 472271

Xavier Urkiola, *Director*

UR Techniks is a firm of naval architects specialising in construction projects for fast catamaran vessels. The company has already had 15 and 20 m catamarans built for the tourist trade in Spain and

has designs for cargo, fishing and oceanographic survey craft.

NEW ENTRY

SWEDEN

SSPA MARITIME CONSULTING AB

PO Box 24001, S-400 22 Göteborg, Sweden

Telephone: +46 (31) 639500
Telex: 20863 SSPAGBGS
Telefax: +46 (31) 639624

Hans Broberg, *Managing Director*

Claes Källström, *Technical Director*
Bo Jansson, *Chief Naval Architect*

SSPA has been involved in the testing of high-speed craft designs and their associated equipment for many years. Noted for their contribution to the success of the Royal Swedish Navy's high-speed vessels, the company has also been closely involved in the testing and development of commercial high-

speed craft, notably the Italian *Destriero,* the Stena HSS catamaran, and the Fast Ship project for transatlantic freight shipping.

The main areas of consulting expertise offered by the company are engineering design, fluid mechanics and naval system design.

VERIFIED

SWITZERLAND

DR ING E G FABER MARINE ENGINEERING CONSULTANT

Gratstrasse 20, CH-8472 Seuzach, Switzerland

Telephone: +41 (52) 533040
Telefax: +41 (52) 533040

Consultant in application engineering with special emphasis on the field of interaction between hull,

propulsor and engine. A writer of engine matching software.

VERIFIED

DIPL ING E SCHATTÉ

Amlehnstrasse 33, CH-6010 Kriens (Lucerne), Switzerland

Telephone: +41 (41) 412794

Consultant in hydrodynamics, aerodynamics , marine technology and high-speed craft.

VERIFIED

SUPRAMAR AG

Seestrasse 78, CH-8703, Erlenbach, Switzerland

Telephone: +41 (41) 1912 1808
Telefax: +41 (41) 1912 1809

Dipl Ing Volker Jost, *President*
Dipl Ing Harry Trevisani, *General Manager*
Dr Ing Herrmann de Witt, *Hydrodynamics*
Dr Ing Otto Münch, *Stabilisation and Control*

(PATENT HOLDERS AND DESIGNERS)

Since its foundation in 1952, Supramar has provided a worldwide consultancy service, covering not only its hydrofoil vessels but also other aspects of fast marine transport. Its scientists have delivered

papers to most of the world's leading professional bodies.

The company has been under contract to many governments and military services.

Supramar developed on a commercial basis the hydrofoil system introduced by the Schertel-Sachsenberg Hydrofoil syndicate and its licensee, the Gebrüder Sachsenberg Shipyard. The development started in the 1930s and led to the realisation of a number of military hydrofoils of up to 80 tonnes displacement and 41 knots in speed.

The inherently stable, rigid surface-piercing V-foil system which is typical for the Supramar type craft was developed by the late Baron Hanns von Schertel.

In May 1953 the world's first passenger hydrofoil service started on Lake Maggiore in Italy with a Supramar type PT 10 craft *Freccia d'Oro.* She was

later transferred to Lake Lucerne. A larger craft, the PT 20, was built by Lürssen Shipyard in 1953 and named *Bremen Pioneer.* Since then many Supramar type hydrofoils have been built under licence from Supramar, mainly by Rodriquez, Hitachi and Westermoen. Full details of all Supramar designs are given in *Jane's Surface Skimmers 1985* and earlier editions. Many Supramar PT 20 and PT 50 hydrofoil vessels are still in service.

Supramar Ltd is also engaged in new designs of high-speed craft such as fast monohulls and catamarans as well as general engineering services. The company has been involved in re-equipping Kometa type hydrofoils with MTU high-speed diesel engines.

UPDATED

UNITED KINGDOM

AIR CUSHION LTD

Unit 4SW, Marchwood Industrial Park, Southampton, Hampshire SO40 4PB, UK

Telephone: +44 (1703) 870077
Telefax: +44 (1703) 870044

J D Hake, *Chairman (USA)*
P Auston, *Director*
G Westerling, *General Manager*

Air Cushion Ltd is the largest supplier of skirts for medium size passenger hovercraft in the world and has been in business for 25 years. ACL can offer experience on designing skirts and associated parts for a variety of air-propelled passenger craft, from two-seat leisure craft to large passenger craft.

ACL has also designed many industrial and non-passenger carrying applications of the fluid cushion principle. These include water skate heavy load moving system, tank moving equipment and heavy lift platforms and trailers.

The firm can provide a complete consultancy design and manufacturing service on all aspects of ACV design and performance, as well as inflatable or flexible structures.

Skirts manufactured include those for all Griffon hovercraft.

UPDATED

AIR VEHICLES LTD

Head Office and Factory: Unit 4, Three Gates Road, Cowes, Isle of Wight, UK

Telephone: +44 (1983) 293193
Telex: 86513 HVWORK G
Telefax: +44 (1983) 291987

C B Eden, *Director*

Air Vehicles Ltd, formed in 1968, has a wide experience of all types of hovercraft and hovercraft operations and can offer a full range of services as consultants. Particular fields in which it has specialised knowledge are the design of hovercraft up to 20 tonnes payload, the design and manufacture of ducted propeller systems for installations up to 3.6 m in diameter and the design and manufacture of lift fans for amphibious hovercraft and SES vessels.

Approved by the Civil Aviation Authority, the company can design and undertake modifications to existing craft. Typical examples are the conversion of SR. N5 and SR. N6 to flat deck layout for logistic operations, the addition of high-speed, dunking hydrographic equipment to SR. N6 and Tiger 12 craft and various modifications for seismic surveying operations. The company also has hovercraft available for charter.

Air Vehicles Ltd also undertakes feasibility studies and was responsible for an original design concept leading to the AP1-88 80 passenger diesel craft operated by Hovertravel Ltd.

VERIFIED

ASSOCIATED & MARINE TECHNOLOGY LTD

Six Oaks House, Rudd Lane, Upper Timsbury, Romsey, Hampshire SO51 0NU, UK

Telephone: +44 (1794) 368988
Telefax: +44 (1794) 368967

Eur Ing Anthony Marchant, *Director*
John Walker, *Director*
David Kendall, *Director*

AMTEC continues to provide independent technical and commercial consultancy to all sectors of the marine industry, especially builders and operators of high-speed, high performance craft in all materials, sizes and configurations.

The consultancy and its principals are best known for their wide ranging experience and innovative solutions in the optimisation of designs, to give minimum weight structures and solving complex structural problems. Recently updated CAD and FEA software databases ensure that their practical solutions are backed by the most modern drafting and presentation skills, designed to interface with other design input and modern manufacturing needs.

AMTEC offers advice on all aspects of new vessel design, including detailed reference to all major Classification Society Rules, and regularly undertakes structural design from first principles. The company has a specialist survey division for high performance craft of all types and purposes and advises on all aspects of upgrading and refit.

The firm has current experience in the structural design of high-speed amphibious hovercraft, mono-hull, catamaran, SES and Swath configurations in aluminium alloys, FRP composites and steel. Additionally AMTEC offers specialist skills and experience in turnkey project management and is currently involved in the specification, design and completion of luxury yachts.

The consultancy offers technical advice in matters of contract and litigation, maintains a detailed and comprehensive database of information and is frequently retained to advise on projects which extend beyond regular design practice.

VERIFIED

BLYTH BRIDGES MARINE CONSULTANTS LTD

8 Manor Court, Barnes Wallis Road, Fareham, Hampshire PO15 5TH, UK

Telephone: +44 (1489) 574432
Telefax: +44 (1489) 578862

Andrew G Blyth, *Director*
David C Bridges, *Director*

Independent naval architecture and marine engineering services for high-speed conventional and unconventional surface craft. The company was formed in 1990 by the joining of two established independent consultants.

The directors between them have 50 years experience in the research, design and construction of advanced monohulls and multihulls, including Surface Effect Ships (SES) and Small-Waterplane-Area Twin-Hull (SWATH) ships. Both are graduates

and Chartered Engineers and spent a significant part of their careers working for the innovative warship builders, Vosper Thornycroft.

Andrew Blyth is a naval architect whose clients include SSPA Maritime Consulting AB in Sweden, for the design and testing of SES for a wide international clientele; Swath International Ltd, on the design of a range of Swath ships; the International Standards Organisation, as convenor of a working group writing criteria for stability of all types of small craft; the Civil Aviation Authority, for work on SES stability criteria and Westland Aerostructures Test Facilities; for technical direction of a research programme into SES stability for the UK Department of Transport and US Coast Guard.

David Bridges is a marine engineer with particular experience in the conceptual and detailed design and commissioning of gas-turbine and high-speed diesel machinery installations for fast patrol boats, SES, Swath ships and large monohulls, for military, recreational and commercial applications. His clients include well-known shipyards all over the world.

The company offers clients an objective, independent marine consultancy service, based on a unique combination of practically oriented ship construction and research, and capable of realistic advice from the conceptual stage, through model testing to detail design of arrangement, structure and machinery, oversight of construction and conduct of performance trials.

The company was formed in order to provide specialist expertise to Societa Esercizio Cantieri SpA in Viareggio, Italy, in connection with the design and construction of large (over 1000 tonnes) SES passenger/vehicle ferries in high tensile steel and propelled by gas-turbines and water-jets. This involvement has extended from preliminary parametric powering, stability and weights investigations, self-propelled water-jet model tests to determine propulsion and lift system requirements, to the arrangement of machinery and fan installations, and advising on seal and ride control system parameters.

VERIFIED

BMT GROUP LTD

Orlando House, 1 Waldegrave Road, Teddington, Middlesex TW11 8LZ, UK

Telephone: +44 (181) 943 5544
Telex: 263118 MARFEL G
Telefax: +44 (181) 943 5347/977 3622

Dr I W David, *Manager*

The vessel hydrodynamics section of BMT Group offers extensive services in consultancy, centred mainly on its capabilities in the fields of physical and mathematical modelling.

The company manages the hydrodynamic facilities at Haslar which are one of the largest in Europe. Hydrodynamic and aerodynamic studies are undertaken for clients in the field of high-speed craft, ferries, small craft and ships.

Major tank testing studies have been undertaken

for the Department of Transport Marine Directorate into ship safety (notably that of ro/ro passenger ferries) and the RNLI for the design of new high-speed lifeboats. Resistance, propulsion, sea-keeping and manoeuvring experiments are offered as a standard service and the company has a long history of such work for high-speed planing and semi-displacement craft. The well-known NPL Round-Bilge Displacement craft series stems from a forerunner of the company.

Work has been carried out for sailing yachts, mainly in connection with the America's Cup and this, in common with many studies carried out by the company, has been accomplished with a blend of physical and mathematical modelling, allied to design expertise.

Mathematical models relating to resistance, sea-keeping, propeller design and manoeuvring simulation are available to clients, supported by CAD systems which are compatible with those used in the high-speed and small boat industry.

As part of the BMT Group, the company can help clients by access to its wider expertise, ranging from environmental studies in the sea and air to CAD/CAM, available throughout the Group.

VERIFIED

LORNE CAMPBELL

Poole Boat Park, West Quay Road, Poole, Dorset BH15 1HX, UK

Telephone: +44 (1202) 666179
Telefax: +44 (1202) 666179

Lorne F Campbell, *Principal*

Design, naval architecture and consultancy in the area of high-speed power craft.

The principal, Lorne Campbell, has been working in the area of high-speed marine craft for nearly 30 years.

Much experience has been gained in the design of high-speed offshore racing powercraft and numerous successes have been gained over the years with monohull, hydroplane, catamaran and trimaran configurations, including six offshore world championships and three world speed records, an interesting one being the current world speed record for electrically powered craft at 52.82 mph.

Much has been learned about the complicated aerodynamic and hydrodynamic interaction affecting high-speed craft working close to the air/water interface, and the design and handling of craft which have to maintain high speeds in rough water.

The company can offer a unique blend of practical and theoretical experience in the design, performance and naval architecture of high-speed craft for both calm and rough conditions. Both wind tunnel and free running scale models are used during the design of craft which have no previous 'parent' form to work from. Considerable experience has been gained in the area of propulsion systems in general and surface propellers in particular. Propellers have been designed in-house when nothing suitable has been available.

A service is offered ranging from concept design and preliminary investigation through general arrangement, layout and styling, resistance, propulsion and stability, up to project management.

UPDATED

NIGEL GEE AND ASSOCIATES

The High-Speed Craft Design Centre, 9 Mitchell Point, Ensign Way, Hamble, Southampton, Hampshire SO31 4RF, UK

Telephone: +44 (1703) 456433
Telefax: +44 (1703) 456438

Nigel Gee, *Senior Partner*
John Bonafoux, *Partner*

Nigel Gee and Associates offers a totally comprehensive service for all aspects of high-speed marine craft technology. A staff of 12 engineers and naval architects specialise in the complete range of high-speed craft design and consultancy activities. Over the last eight years the company has designed in excess of 100 high-speed vessels, of which over 60 are either built or currently being built.

Recent design and consultancy activities by the company include:

Bazan Group, Spain - design and consultancy work for the *Mestral* 98 m car and passenger ferry

DB Catafoil Ltd, UK - concept, preliminary and detail design for a 40 knot, 36 m, foil-assisted catamaran

Samsung Heavy Industries, South Korea - concept, preliminary and detailed design for a 50 knot, 37 m surface effect ship passenger vessel

Beliard Polyship, Belgium - concept, preliminary and detail design for a 45 knot, 30 m surface effect passenger vessel

Textron Lycoming Gas-Turbines, USA - consultancy and market research for applications of marine gas-turbines to high-speed ferries and other vessels.

British Columbia Ferry Corporation (BCFC) - consultancy for the selection of high-speed, car and passenger ferry designs for BCFC's routes in British Columbia

National Marine services, Abu Dhabi - design of a fleet of high-speed water taxis

Leeward Islands Ferry Transport Project - concept design studies for a high-speed monohull.

The package of services offered to the high-speed marine industry include:

Initial concept design and production of specifications for quotation purposes

Preliminary design and naval architecture

Design of tank test models and tank test supervision

Structural design from first principles or to classification society rules

Engineering design - machinery, systems and electrics

Detailed fitout design

Presentation drawings, artist's impressions, interior artwork and so on

Technical assistance to clients, pre- and post-contract, including building supervision

Specialised surveys.

Beliard Polyship 30 m SES   **1994**

Samsung 37 m SES

The NGA partners, Nigel Gee and John Bonafoux, have a combined 40 years of experience in the high-speed marine craft field and in particular, have recent experience relevant to the new markets for large, high-speed car and freight carriers, and in applications of gas-turbine technology to these and similar vessels.

UPDATED

36 m Chief Flying Sun *Catafoil*
1993

HOVERCRAFT CONSULTANTS LTD

22 Nash Road, Dibden Purlieu, Hythe, Hampshire SO4 5RS, UK

Telephone: +44 (1703) 843178
Telefax: +44 (1703) 814292

M J Cox, *Managing Director*
J F Cox, *Secretary*
J E Rapson, *Associate*

Hovercraft Consultants Ltd (HCL) was founded in 1981 by members of the air cushion research company, Hovercraft Development Ltd, to provide commercial design and advisory services to the hovercraft and related industries.

HCL specialises in providing design expertise in those areas of air cushion technology which are not covered by conventional naval architecture. HCL is often involved at the start of new hovercraft projects, providing performance, weight, cost and general arrangement projections. Skirt and seals, lift systems and air propulsors form the main part of HCL's detailed design work.

Skirt systems have been designed for a great variety of craft, both amphibious and SES, with design speeds from the lowest to over 70 knots. Design payloads have ranged from two people to 300 tonnes and climatic conditions from the tropics to the Arctic. Much of the design process is now computer-based which has eliminated the need for three-dimensional skirt models and full-scale manual lofting. This has reduced design time and has made possible the direct, computer-controlled laser cutting of full-scale components. Computer programs developed in-house are also used for craft performance prediction, thrust estimation and fan performance.

HCL is currently developing a new type of lift fan which is intended to provide characteristics better suited to air cushion devices than the more conventional backward curved foil blade type in common use. The new fan is designed to provide substantially more airflow per intake while maintaining the high efficiency levels of traditional designs.

Many design projects undertaken by HCL have involved the use of scale models to predict behaviour and performance. Such models have varied from simple static skirt inflation rigs to fully dynamic models for use on towing tanks, in wind tunnels and for free-flight radio control tests.

Since HCL has no affiliation with any manufacturer or operator, it is able to provide unbiased appraisals of existing and projected craft. The suitability of such craft for particular routes and duties is assessed both technically and economically. The company keeps records of both technical and commercial aspects of high-speed water-borne transport.

VERIFIED

HOVERCRAFT DEVELOPMENT LTD

101 Newington Causeway, London SE1 6BU, UK

Telephone: +44 (171) 403 6666
Telex: 894397 G
Telefax: +44 (171) 703 7586

M L Martin, *Chairman*

D J Veasey, *Director*
J Williams, *Secretary*

(PATENT HOLDING AND LICENSING ORGANISATION)

Hovercraft Development Ltd (HDL) was formed in January 1959 by the National Research Development Corporation (NRDC), the assets of which are now owned by the British Technology Group Ltd.

The company uses its portfolio of patents as the basis of licensing agreements with hovercraft manufacturers to manufacture and sell in the USA and Canada.

HDL's patents concern the HDL skirt shift system. Licences are available to all companies in the industry.

UPDATED

HOVERCRAFT SALES AND MARKETING

PO Box 7, Sarisbury Green, Southampton, Hampshire SO31 8YS, UK

Telephone: +44 (1703) 403547
Telefax: +44 (1703) 406747

Graham A Gifford, *Managing Director*

Hovercraft Sales and Marketing (HOVSAM) undertakes general hovercraft consultancy work, specialising in the recommendation of various amphibious and non-amphibious hovercraft for particular routes and applications. In the 0.5 to 7 tonne payload range of amphibious hovercraft, HOVSAM acts as consultant to Griffon Hovercraft Ltd; for the Surface Effect Ship (SES) range of craft, HOVSAM is consultant to Hovermarine International Ltd. Graham Gifford has placed many hovercraft and SES into various countries around the world and will advise on route feasibility and economics, and the suitability of both commercial and military hovercraft for particular areas and applications.

UPDATED

HOVERWORK LTD

12 Lind Street, Ryde, Isle of Wight PO33 2NR, UK

Telephone: +44 (1983) 565181
Telex: 86513
Telefax: +44 (1983) 812859

C D J Bland, *Managing Director*
E W H Gifford, *Director*

R H Barton, *Director*
R K Box, *Director*
G M Palin, *Director*
B A Jehan, *Operations Manager*

Hoverwork Ltd was formed in 1966 to provide support to the high-speed marine industry. The services offered include route analysis and feasibility studies, the charter of hovercraft and crews, logistic duties, crew changes and many types of survey work in shallow water areas often difficult for other forms of transport. Full maintenance and spare parts can be provided to support services worldwide. Within the company there is a recognised training school which offers comprehensive courses to operational crews and the training of engineering personnel for other operators.

VERIFIED

INDEPENDENT MARITIME ASSESSMENT ASSOCIATES LTD

35 Knights Bank Road, Hill Head, Fareham, Hampshire PO14 3HX, UK

Telephone: +44 (1329) 663202
Telefax: +44 (1329) 668176

Anthony Marchant, *Structural Design Engineering*
John Lewthwaite, *Naval Architecture*
David Bridges, *Marine Engineering*

Darrol Stinton, *Aeromarine Operations*
Klaus Suhrbier, *Hydrodynamics*
Anthony Wardle, *Project Management*

IMAA is an amalgam of advanced design and commercial talents drawing together experience from marine and aeronautical engineering. Its purpose is to offer a completely integrated consultancy service to designers, builders, operators and underwriters of high-speed, high technology vessels.

The consultancy offers expertise in naval architecture, marine engineering, advanced structural design, aeronautical engineering, risk analysis, operational analysis, turnkey project management and commercial marketing disciplines.

IMAA's principals' collective experience covers all configurations from conventional fast monohulls and catamarans to hovercraft, Surface Effect Ships (SES), Swath and surface effect aircraft (RAM-WING) designs, and are collectively equipped to offer technical audit on existing designs or a fully integrated design service from inception and planning stages.

UPDATED

JCL HIGH SPEED MARINE CRAFT CONSULTANCY

35 Knights Bank Road, Hill Head, Fareham, Hampshire PO14 3HX, UK

Telephone: +44 (1329) 663202
Telefax: +44 (1329) 668176

John C Lewthwaite, *General Manager*

The JCL consultancy offers concept design, and research and development skills based on thirty years of experience in the fast craft business. A wide range of activities is covered and includes SES, fast monohull, catamaran and hovercraft types. Work is carried out on both commercial and military applications and the consultancy advises companies in several European countries.

NEW ENTRY

JOHN McNEECE LTD

2 Holford Yard, Cruikshank Street, London WC1X 9HD, UK

Telephone: +44 (171) 837 1225
Telefax: +44 (171) 837 1233

John McNeece, *Chairman*
Mark T Hilferty, *Design Director*
Erol Aziz, *Planning Director*
Gordon Craigmyle, *General Manager*

McNeece was formed in 1963 and is an acknowledged leader in the design of ferry and cruise ship interiors, with three UK national design awards. It has extensive experience covering monohulls, catamarans and Swath vessels.

The most recently completed contracts include work on two 400 seat high-speed catamarans for Wightlink Ferries and a 1400 passenger cruise ship, the *MV Zenith*, for Chandris Celebrity Cruises. McNeece is interior design consultant for Swath International Ltd for its Super Regency and Swath Ocean 4000 vessels.

McNeece design is targeted to the end user; the passenger. At the outset, it establishes a clear understanding, with the co-operation of the owners, of the passenger profile and their aspirations. This strategic guidance enables the firm to focus on the marketing aspects of the design. An important factor, essential for the success of the interior design as a motivational tool in the process of earning revenue and adding value to the product.

CAD facilities are available, as are layering and three dimensional modelling capabilities. Services include the production of general arrangements; full colour artist's impressions; working drawings; interior fit-out specifications; schedules of fixtures and finishes; weight calculations and budgeted fit-out costs.

VERIFIED

MARITIME SERVICES LTD

Stone Lane, Gosport, Hampshire PO12 1SS, UK

Telephone: +44 (1705) 524490
Telefax: +44 (1705) 524498

Ian C Biles, *Managing Director*

Vessel refit, repair, new building and refit supervision, feasibility studies, route evaluation and vessel management.

Maritime Services International Ltd was set up seven years ago to provide an expert technical service to owners and operators of fast craft worldwide.

Recent projects have included a hull damage repair supervision and full refit of two Cirrus 120P SES catamarans, proposal of a fast patrol boat conversion for an oil company operating on the west coast of Africa and feasibility study into the repair of the badly damaged *Catamaran 1*. In addition to the technical side of their work the company has carried out economic evaluations of possible fast ferry routes in the Persian Gulf and South America, either using existing vessels or recommending new vessels.

Current work includes a full economic and technical feasibility study into a long distance route in the Indian Ocean.

NEW ENTRY

SEASPEED TECHNOLOGY LTD

The Old Mill Business Centre, Botley, Southampton, Hampshire SO3 2GB, UK

Telephone: +44 (1489) 795222
Telefax: +44 (1489) 795333

S J Phillips, *Director*
T B Ramsay, *Naval Architect*

Seaspeed Technology Ltd is a totally independent company specialising in the technology of high-speed marine craft.

A worldwide multi-disciplinary marine consultancy and design support service is provided in both the commercial and military industry sectors. The company offers a high level of academic, professional and practical experience over the complete range of design, build and operational technologies.

The main activities of the company include:
Speed, manoeuvring and seakeeping predictions
Structural design and materials selection
Computer simulations
Model construction, testing and data analysis
Ship sea trials and instrumentation
Risk and FMEA analysis
Design assessments
Market analysis.

Seaspeed Technology has provided consultancy services to major companies around the world, generally in the field of high-speed craft design, production and operation.

Recent contracts have included:
Fast catamaran research for the UK Defence Research Agency
Stability of workboat research for the UK Marine Safety Agency
Risk analysis for the Department of Transport and industrial companies
Market research for the UK based Marine Technology Directorate
Radio controlled model construction and testing
Shallow water testing of fast multihull vessles
Fast craft manoeuvring and sea-keeping simulations for a range of companies
Advanced material developments
Marine escape system design and simulation for a range of companies
Design and technology assessments and patent developments

UPDATED

SWATH INTERNATIONAL LTD

8 Manor Court, Barnes Wallis Road, Fareham, Hampshire PO15 5TH, UK

Telephone: +44 (1489) 579900
Telefax: +44 (1489) 576757

Captain Nicholas G Pearson, *Marketing Director (Europe)*

4061 Powder Mill Road, Calverton, Maryland 20705, USA

Telephone: +1 (301) 595 9850
Telefax: +1 (301) 595 9854

Swath International Ltd is a ship design company specialising in the technology of Swath craft, particularly those with a fast operational speed. A wide range of designs is marketed by the company which also has agreements with shipyards worldwide to build their vessels. Nichols Brothers of Seattle, USA, commenced construction of a Super 4000 Class high-speed passenger Swath in 1993 which is now scheduled for delivery in mid-1995.

The range of designs covers passenger and ro-ro ferries, cruise ships, supply ships, hydrographic survey vessels and pilot/patrol craft ranging in size from 18 to 100 m

The baseline designs cover: the 80 m Super Regency Class carrying 876 passengers and 258 cars at 37 knots; and the 37 m Super 4000 Class which can be configured as a ro-ro or passenger only ferry. The vessel of this class currently under construction at Nichols Brothers is designed as a casino ferry carrying 384 passengers at 27 knots; the 33 m Euro 4000 has been configured in a number of arrangements such as a cruise vessel, supply vessel and passenger ferry. The smallest design offered is the 18.7 m Channel Class craft carrying 100 passengers at a speed of 25 knots.

The design of these craft offers extremely low ship motions and minimal degradation in speed performance in rough weather compared to all other multi-hull craft, these aspects being clear advantages of the Swath concept.

80 m SUPER REGENCY CLASS (DESIGN)
Ro-ro passenger ferry.
Principal Particulars

Length overall	80 m
Beam	33.2 m
Draught	7.1 m
Passengers	1400
Vehicles	365 cars or
	10 coaches + 265 cars
Maximum speed	40 knots
Operational speed	40 knots

UPDATED

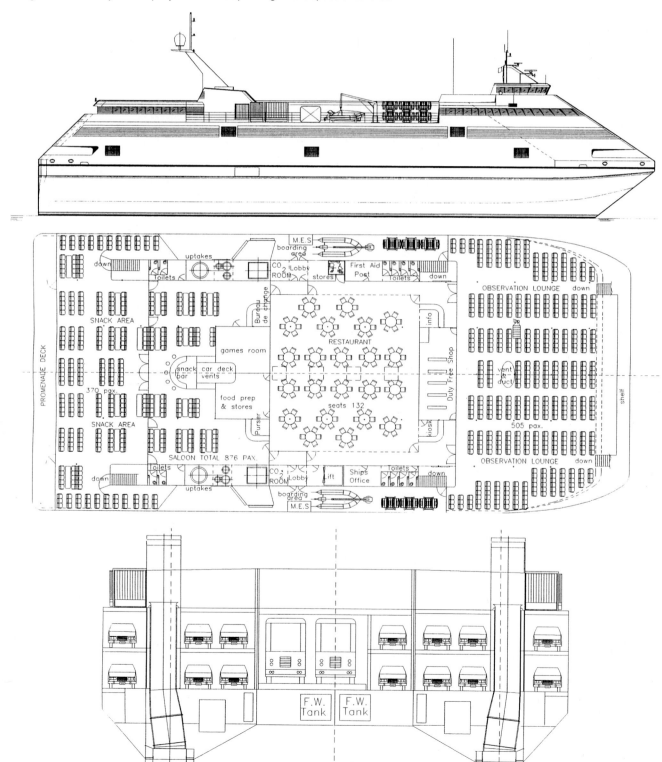

General arrangement of Super Regency Class Design

ROBERT L TRILLO

Broadlands, Brockenhurst, Hampshire SO42 7SX, UK

Telephone: +44 (1590) 622220
Telefax: +44 (1590) 622220

Eur Ing Robert L Trillo, *Principal*

An independent consultancy formed in 1969, since when work has been undertaken in many countries throughout the world, principally concerned with the introduction of new concepts and innovation in advanced forms of marine transport.

Capabilities:
Consultancy and design work on all forms of high-speed water-borne transport (urban transport and sea-going) including catamarans, hovercraft and Surface Effect Ships (SES). Feasibility studies and appraisal of projects for development financing and supervision of programmes from preliminary design through to production.

High-speed ferry evaluation:
Engineering capabilities of specific relevance to high-speed water-borne urban transport systems including the design of quiet air propulsion systems (designs of Robert Trillo ducted propellers are now employed on over a dozen types of hovercraft), and the development of techniques for the avoidance or minimisation of vessel wash.

An extensive database of statistics and information on all types of high-speed ferries is available to assist in feasibility studies concerned with the choice of vessels and power-plants.

The principal has been engaged as an expert witness on arbitration cases and is the author of the book *Marine Hovercraft Technology*.

Projects:
High-speed river craft innovation and development for minimum wash and minimum noise in relatively calm and sheltered waters. A catamaran concept with extremely slender hulls and introduced as the RTL Hydrocat, is now patented and has been actively taken up by FBM Marine Ltd, Isle of Wight, UK, as their Thames Class catamaran.

Further work has continued on the development of propulsion systems for amphibious vehicles for use in swamps and canal restoration work and the development of quiet amphibious hovercraft.

A particularly interesting low-speed project has been the preliminary design and project management for an Italian air cushion vehicle for rice cultivation work, two prototypes having been built by Griffon Hovercraft Ltd.

VERIFIED

WOLFSON UNIT FOR MARINE TECHNOLOGY AND INDUSTRIAL AERODYNAMICS, UNIVERSITY OF SOUTHAMPTON

Southampton, Hampshire SO9 5NH, UK

Telephone: +44 (1703) 585044
Telefax: +44 (1703) 671532

W J Allday, *Director*

The Wolfson Unit is the Industrial Advisory Unit of the Department of Ship Science at the University of Southampton. The Unit was established in 1967 to provide a comprehensive consultancy service in marine technology and industrial aerodynamics. It is staffed by full-time qualified consulting engineers, with a wide range of academic and industrial experience. It is also able to draw on the experience of academic staff and other consulting engineers throughout the university to widen the scope of consultancy.

The work of the unit includes development work for clients on powered craft of all types from ships and coasters to high-speed catamarans and fast patrol boats. Much of this work takes place in the towing tank including the measurement of resistance and the study of ship motions and sea-keeping in head seas. The wind tunnel is used to study airflow over superstructures, aerodynamic forces on high-speed craft and flow into propellers. Radio-controlled models are used in the study of sea-keeping and of manoeuvring.

Recent work has included resistance and sea-keeping tank tests on FBM Marine's Fast Displacement Catamaran, and the comparison of two high-speed craft under survival conditions in breaking waves in the tank.

The Unit does not work only with models. Using portable computerised data acquisition systems, trials data have been collected from as far away as the Grand Banks and the Barrier Reef. With many ferry operators evaluating high-speed catamarans for their routes, this has included comparing the sea-keeping ability and passenger comfort of these craft with existing ferries.

Advice can be given on aluminium welding standards and construction methods and inspections carried out for quality assurance purposes and problem solving or failure analysis. The Unit has developed and sells an acceleration monitor which displays RMS accelerations in a seaway. This measures accelerations at a selected position in the vessel and displays it in the wheelhouse.

The Wolfson Unit sells a wide range of computer programs to naval architects, including hydrostatics and stability, lines fairing, ship motions, manoeuvring and powering. These programs have been sold worldwide to customers from small design offices to government organisations such as the Department of Transport. They also run a bureau service, including stability booklets for fast ferries.

VERIFIED

W S ATKINS MARINE & STRUCTURAL TECHNOLOGY

Division of WS Atkins Consultants Ltd

Woodcote Grove, Ashley Road, Epsom, Surrey KT18 5BW, UK

Telephone: +44 (1372) 726140
Telex: 266701 ATKINS G
Telefax: +44 (1372) 740055

W S Atkins is a very large, international, multi-disciplinary consultancy offering a wide range of services useful to designers, builders and operators of fast craft. Although a relatively recent entrant into the fast craft arena, the company has been established for many years in the offshore industry.

Structural and naval architectural work is carried out by the Marine and Structural Technology division which specialises in engineering analysis, using software which has been developed in-house. The main areas of work are analysis of hydrodynamic loads and motions in regular and irregular waves; linear and non-linear structural analysis, including fracture mechanics; fatigue analysis.

There have been two major software packages developed; AQWA deals with hydrodynamic analysis whilst ASAS is a finite element package. Both have been widely used by the company and others for analysis of fixed and floating marine structures, including offshore platforms, VLCCs and fast catamarans.

The Marine and Structural Technology division is supported by the other divisions in the group which offer a range of relevant skills, including computational fluid dynamics; noise and vibration; design of port and harbour facilities; safety and reliability; planning of transport systems and cargo management systems.

Recent experience has included work on large wave-piercing catamarans, in which hydrodynamic analyses were performed with waves from various directions to compare sea-keeping and loads on different vessels. This was followed by extensive structural analysis involving global stress distribution, design of fatigue resistant details and investigation of superstructure mounting systems.

VERIFIED

UNITED STATES OF AMERICA

AERO-MARINE ENGINEERING

9727 Hagel Circle, Lorton, Virginia 22079, USA

Telephone: +1 (703) 550 1236
Telefax: +1 (703) 550 1236

Harold Ginsberg, *President*

Mr Harold Ginsberg founded Aero-Marine Engineering in 1994. Aero-Marine Engineering is a technical consulting firm for the aerospace and marine industry and performs project management, design, development and engineering support of advanced marine vehicles. It specialises in hovercraft, surface effect ships, hydrofoils, wing-in-ground-effect craft and high-speed catamarans.

Prior to starting this firm Mr Ginsberg was a project engineer at the US Army's Belvoir RD&E centre's Marine Division and designed, developed and provided engineering support to the US Army's hovercraft programmes.

NEW ENTRY

AIR CRAFT CORPORATION

4112 Victoria Blvd, Hampton, Virginia 23669, USA

Telephone: +1 (804) 722 6994

Ronald Gorton, *President*
Simon T Gorton, *Vice President*

Steven G Doleac, *Project Manager*

Air Craft Corporation is a consulting, manufacturing and marketing company that was formed to fill a need in the industry for affordable air cushion vehicles. Air Craft is involved in the development of ACV design and analysis software, the development of light hovercraft, and the fabrication of lightweight marine structures made of composite materials and corrosion resistant metals. In addition, the company develops and fabricates tooling for composite parts.

Using moulded fibreglass construction techniques, Air Craft has developed a hovercraft, called Ranger, which is capable of carrying a 545 kg payload, or up to 6 passengers. Uses for this craft include cargo and passenger transport, and recreation. The craft is designed for use in salt water, has 0.6 m freeboard, is propelled by two ducted fans, and is supported on cushion by a single independently controlled lift fan. Ranger is available as a low-cost kit product as well as a fully assembled turnkey product.

Air Craft has developed a variety of low cost fabrication techniques for constructing lightweight composite structures that have foam core and/or blade stiffened geometries. Composite fabrication techniques include hand lay-up, spray up, vacuum bagging and adhesive bonding. Fabrication techniques used to construct lightweight metal structures include SMAW, GTAW and adhesive bonding. Air

Craft also has expertise in the fabrication of master and production tooling. The materials used to construct the tooling include composites and industrial plasters. Production tooling structures, measuring up to 9 ft by 23 ft, have been built.

NEW ENTRY

AIR RIDE CRAFT INC

15840 SW 84th Avenue, Miami, Florida 33157, USA

Telephone: +1 (305) 233 4306
Telex: 6974096 LARAMIE
Telefax: +1 (305) 233 1339

Don Burg, *President*

The Air Ride concept, designed and patented by Don Burg, has been configured in a number of ways on mono- and multihull designs. The concept is based on supporting a percentage of the craft weight on a cushion of air thereby reducing frictional resistance. In the catamaran designs it is reported that 85 per cent of the weight of the craft would be supported by the air cushion.

A number of models, prototypes and operational craft have been built using Air Ride designs, the first test craft having been built in 1978 with a 12.8 m demonstration craft built in 1980. A 19.8 m crew/supply craft was launched in 1983 and by 1991 two other Air Ride craft for passenger transportation had been built by Avondale.

There is a number of associated patents held by Don Burg, possibly the most interesting of which is a locking docking system, which uses the variation in height of the vessel in the water produced by variation in air cushion pressure.

Air Ride is currently marketing a number of designs including a 26 m, 40 knot ferry; a 26 m, 55 knot private yacht; a 49 m, 50 knot, 500 passenger ferry; a 100 m car and vehicle ferry; and a 215 m, 44 knot freighter.

UPDATED

The second Avondale-built Air Ride 33.23 m 368 passenger SES ferry
1993

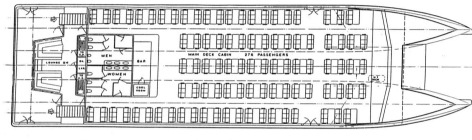

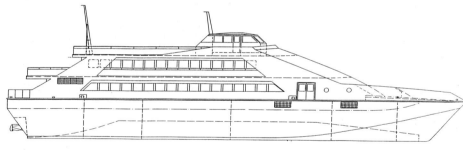

General arrangement of the 49 m SeaCoaster 50 knot ferry
1994

AQUAMARINE, INC

33 Sharon Avenue, Piedmont, California 94611-3511, USA

Telephone: +1 (510) 654 4448
Telefax: +1 (510) 654 2650

P Michael Watson, *President*

Aquamarine provides management services and consultation to passenger vessel operators, for ferry, tourist and dining yacht businesses. The company specialises in financial evaluations, operations and services analysis and standards, guest services organisation and vessel design and construction.

Recent work includes the management of dining cruise and tourist sightseeing operations in San Diego, Newport Beach, Long Beach, Los Angeles,

San Francisco and Hawaii; contract and construction management of numerous passenger vessels; analysis and planning for high-speed ferry services in San Francisco Bay and between San Diego and Mexico; and analysis for cruise-ferry operations in California and from Seattle to Canada.

UPDATED

BAND, LAVIS & ASSOCIATES INC

Corporate Office: Ritchie Highway, Severna Park, Maryland 21146, USA

Telephone: +1 (410) 544 2800, +1 (301) 261 1030
Telefax: +1 (410) 647 3411

UK Office: 1631 Parkway, Solent Business Park, Whiteley, Fareham, Hampshire, UK
Model Shop: 1244-50 Ritchie Highway, Unit 19A, Arnold, Maryland 21012, USA

David R Lavis, *President and Chief Executive Officer*
Shirley A Wilson, *Vice President, Finance*
Brian G Forstell, *Vice President, Systems Analysis*
Daniel L Wilkins, *Vice President, Engineering*

John L Allison, *Chief Engineer*
Daniel G Bagnell, *Chief Naval Architect*
Philippe Goubault, *Special Projects*

Band, Lavis & Associates Inc is an independent engineering firm offering a comprehensive range of advanced and conventional marine engineering and naval architectural services. Since 1977, the company has pioneered advanced marine vehicle design and technology development, principally for US military applications. The company provides considerable technical support to the US Navy's ACV and SES programmes, including ship and subsystem design, engineering, analysis, model testing, full-scale tests and trials, computerised performance and motion simulation, and finite element static and dynamic structural analysis. Similar work

is performed for the US Army's ACV programmes and for the US Coast Guard's patrol boat and cutter programmes. Company personnel have worked continuously on ACV and SES design and development for more than 30 years. The staff has made significant contributions to all major ACV and SES programmes in the USA and a large number of earlier programmes in the UK.

The company's dedication to quality was recognised in 1991 with the presentation of two US Small Business Administration (SBA) awards for excellence in contributing to the SBA goal of building America's future.

The company offers particular expertise in the design of high-speed marine craft. Since 1977, the company has been developing a comprehensive range of unique computer software to support this capability, including procedures for the design of hull structure, propulsion systems and the analysis of craft resistance, stability, sea-keeping, manoeuvrability, structural loads and structural design.

The company has also developed four extensive computer-aided design-synthesis models, one each for SES, ACVs, catamarans and monohulls, all of which permit whole-ship design trade-offs to be examined with respect to cost and craft performance. The software has been extensively validated and has, to date, been used to support 29 separate design projects. Ship designs and detailed hardware designs are developed on the company's CAD system. The company also has a library containing over 10 000 documents comprising one of the most extensive computer-catalogued repositories of reference material on advanced marine vehicles.

Throughout the course of its involvement in military and commercial projects, the company has collected a large database of cost estimates and actual cost data covering the development, construction and operation of conventional and unconventional vessels. The company has integrated this database into a series of cost estimator programmes that allow comprehensive development, acquisition and operating cost estimates to be produced at an early stage of a design.

The technical design and cost analysis capabilities of the company have been incorporated into the design synthesis models used by the company to conduct parametric design optimisation. As a result, the company has the capability of developing preliminary designs on the basis of life-cycle cost optimisation. For a military vessel, the hourly cost of operations (including the amortisement of investment cost as well as all associated 'programmatic' costs) may be used as the optimisation criteria. For a commercial vessel, the retail ticket price to the passenger may be considered. As the design progresses, refined estimates are made by replacing early assumptions with actual data in the model inputs.

The company has extensive experience in the design, fabrication, test planning, testing and data analysis of subscale models. Its experience in model fabrication and testing covers a wide range of ACVs, SESs, Planing Hulls and other types of vessels and marine structures. The company has a long history of work related to the design, analysis and testing of inflated structures, principally in connection with the skirts and seals of ACVs and SESs, but more recently with the design of a series of inflatable boats.

Recent Projects:

The company has developed, through full-scale fabrication and operation, vehicles and systems for the US Army aimed at improving the Army's capability to off-load vehicles and cargo over undeveloped shorelines during amphibious operations.

The Pontoon Air Cushion Kit (PACK) was developed to be installed on existing platforms formed of standard 40 × 8 ft pontoons. The prototype PACK ACV system was designed for an 80 × 32 ft platform and provides the platform with an amphibious capability. The prototype platform with the PACK installed has carried a payload of 140 tonnes with an endurance of 10 hours. Model tests were completed in 1989 and full-scale trials were conducted in 1990 and 1991. The PACK also has secondary uses in combat and non-combat missions relating to construction and salvage operations over marginal terrain and to general heavy-lift and amphibious operations. The company was responsible for the concept, design, fabrication, field assembly and operation of this ACV. In support of this and other projects, the company also designed and model-tested in their test facility a high capacity, high efficiency, low noise lift fan with characteristics suitable for various ACV and SES applications.

The High Seastate Container Transfer System (HISEACOTS) was developed to facilitate the off-loading of containers from container ships to LACV-30 ACV lighters. The LACV-30 flies onto the HISEACOTS platform where it is straddled by a gantry crane which has accepted cargo from the crane ship. Offloading operations can continue in higher sea states than has previously been possible. The HISEACOTS was subject to subsystem tests in 1989 and two series of full-scale trials in 1991 and 1992.

In 1991, the company was awarded a US Navy Small Business Innovative Research (SBIR) contract to develop the design of an improved Combat Rubber Raiding Craft (CRRC) with enhanced performance, increased survivability and reduced detectability for US Navy SEALs. As a direct result of this development, the company was contracted to develop designs for a production series of recreational inflatable boats for a new commercial venture. Designs in the size range of from 9 to 12 ft, both have straight and curved tubes that are developed with flat pattern layouts produced directly by the company's CAD system.

In 1991, the company began the design of a unique planing craft referred to as the Advanced Materiel Transporter (AMT) for, and in co-operation with, the US Navy's Carderock Division of the Naval Surface Warfare Center (NSWC). In early 1992, the design of a one-third scale GRP model, 44 ft long, was completed and constructed by Seemann's Composites in Gulfport, Mississippi.

In addition to work for the US Department of Defense and the Department of Transportation, the company has become increasingly involved during the last few years in SES and ACV projects in France, Germany, Italy, Japan, South Korea, Norway, Singapore and SwedenUPDA

UPDATED

DONALD L BLOUNT & ASSOCIATES INC

2550 Ellsmere Avenue, Suite K, Norfolk, Virginia 23513, USA

Telephone: +1 (804) 857 1943
Telefax: +1 (804) 857 4160

Donald L Blount was design manager for *Destriero*, the 67.7 m vessel which succeeded in achieving the Blue Riband prize for the fastest Atlantic crossing at an average speed of 53.09 knots. Details of *Destriero* are given in the *High-speed monohull craft* section of the book.

UPDATED

Destriero (Will Cofnuk)
1994

CGZ DESIGN INC

201D Eastbrook, Greenville, North Carolina 27858, USA

Telephone: +1 (919) 768 8000

Jim Caldwell, *Chief Designer*
Dr Andrew Zborowski, *President*

ECLIPSE PROJECT (DESIGN)

Designers of monohull and catamaran craft employing a patented 'Constant Lift Hull Configuration,' Jim Caldwell and Andrew Zborowski have established design and model test facilities concentrating on the development of highly efficient hull forms over very wide speed ranges: 20 to 100 knots. Caldwell designed and developed the first true offshore Tunnel Boat in 1979 and holds a patent for the constant lift bottom concept. Zborowski has degrees in naval architecture from The Technical University of Gdansk and has also studied experimental naval architecture at The Hydro and Aerodynamic Laboratory at Lyngby, Denmark. Their latest projects include the Eclipse 140 CAT megayacht and the Fluid Travel 146 CAT high-speed ferry.

VERIFIED

DAVIDSON LABORATORY STEVENS INSTITUTE OF TECHNOLOGY

711 Hudson Street, Hoboken, New Jersey 07030, USA

Telephone: +1 (201) 216 5345
Telefax: +1 (201) 216 8214

Dr Michael S Bruno, *Director*

Organised in 1935 as the Experimental Towing Tank, the Laboratory is active in basic and applied hydrodynamic research, including smooth water performance and manoeuvrability, sea-keeping, propulsion and control of marine vehicles including ACV, SES, hydrofoil craft, planing craft and so on. Special model test facilities are available to investigate the dynamic behaviour of all types of vessels and platforms in smooth water and waves.

Recent projects have included:
Towing tank studies of various seaplane model con-

figurations for the analysis of bow spray, porpoising, high-speed resistance and impact loads.

An experimental investigation into the stability, course-keeping and manoeuvring characteristics of planing hulls, performed primarily in the Laboratory's rotating arm facility.

VERIFIED

ELLIOTT BAY DESIGN GROUP LTD

5301 Shilshole Avenue, NW Suite 200, Seattle, Washington 98107, USA

Telephone: +1 (206) 782 3082
Telefax: +1 (206) 782 3449

John Waterhouse, *President*
Kenneth Lane, *Vice President*
Douglas Wolff, *Chief Naval Architect*
Brian King, *Senior Marine Engineer*
Annette Grimm, *Business Manager*

Elliott Bay Design Group is a firm dedicated to providing naval architecture, marine engineering

and shipyard support services. Using microcomputer technology and an extensive reference library, the company offers a wide range of services. The firm handles projects ranging from concept design of high-speed hulls to numerical lofting of structure. The full time staff of 22 includes six naval architects, three marine engineers and one electrical engineer.

As the successor to Nickum & Spaulding Associates, the firm's design experience is focused on commercial workboats and passenger boats. High-speed vessel designs up to 45 m and 50 knots have been created using both high-speed diesels and gas-turbines. The firm has completed work on hydrofoils, catamarans, planing hulls and Swaths. The staff are knowledgeable about the requirements

of various regulatory bodies including USCG, ABS, IMO and DnV.

Projects undertaken within the past two years include: the design of an 18.6 m aluminium pilot boat, performance analysis of a 12.8 m high-speed survey boat, design of a harbour service craft with firefighting and oil spill recovery capabilities, and a ferry transportation study for Cook Inlet, Alaska. The company has also lofted a variety of hulls from other designers including a 76.5 m tuna seiner, a 17.7 m high-speed limit seiner, a 39.6 m steel crab boat and a 6.7 m aluminium seine skiff.

VERIFIED

FAST HULLS INTERNATIONAL INC

3020 Daurine Court, Gilroy, California 95020, USA

Telephone: +1 (408) 842 8913

Bryan Duffty, *President*
Raymond Villareal, *Vice President, Marketing*
Christopher Barry, *Vice President, Engineering*

Fast Hulls International, Inc (FHI) was formed to further develop an advanced hybrid hydrofoil system for general maritime use. The concept was originally developed at FMC Corporation for the US Marine Corps Advanced Amphibian Assault Vehicle (AAAV) programme. FMC has sub-licensed the original inventors to use their patents for non-amphibious vehicles.

The basic concept uses one or more stepped planing hulls forward and a fully submerged hydrofoil aft. The planing hull provides the surface reference for the hydrofoil and the hydrofoil provides lift at high efficiency for a portion of the vessel weight. The vessel centre of gravity is well forward of the hydrofoil so that it provides substantial pitch damping. This eliminates the pitch instability common in many hybrid hydrofoil designs, improving sea-keeping without compromising efficiency. The vehicle design can be optimised for efficiency, speed, load carrying and sea-keeping by suitable proportions and design of the planing components and foils and the lift contributed by each.

In late 1992 FHI was testing a sub-scale manned test-bed and smaller self-propelled free models to investigate six degree of freedom dynamic behaviour. FHI is also developing a generalised computer

simulation of vehicle dynamics and sea-keeping to evaluate ride quality, structural loads and economics for various services.

Current design projects include a recreational version in the 7 m size range, a human-powered demonstrator to attempt the 20 knot Du Pont prize and a conceptual design for a 149 passenger catamaran ferry.

FHI intends to license their technology to US and international builders when it is fully developed and proven.

VERIFIED

FRYCO INC

7107 Silver Leaf Lane, Houston, Texas 77088, USA

Telephone: +1 (713) 931 5911
Telefax: +1 (713) 931 5168

Edward D Fry, *President*

Edward Fry established FRYCO in 1978 after 22 years of building experience. He has supervised the design and construction of over 700 commercial, military and pleasure craft including: US Navy high-speed combatants for Navy SEAL Teams, cata-

marans for commercial and US Army use, monohull yachts up to 50 knots and rig service vessels up to 30 knot speed. He has also conducted scale model tests at various institutions and has data available for design study, designed equipment and written training manuals for oil pollution recovery equipment at five major ports and supervised Middle East licensee shipyard for US builder for four years.

FRYCO designs vessels up to 50 m and specialises in high-speed craft. The company is experienced in gas-turbine engine packaging and installation as well as diesel and petrol engines. Computer models are used for speed prediction and hydrostatics. Hulls are created with computer graph-

ics making fully developed offsets available to the builder for automatic CAD/CAM cutting. Fry's building background assures practical, economic designs with emphasis placed on reliability and serviceability.

Fryco currently has more than a dozen building projects in five countries ranging from fibreglass yachts of 18 m up to aluminium and steel passenger vessels of 70 m. The newest project under development is a 70 m Swath fast ferry vessel. The design is for 1000 passengers, at 35 knots, and will be model tested by Stevens Institute, Hoboken, New Jersey.

VERIFIED

GIBBS & COX INC

50 West 23rd Street, New York, New York 10010, USA

Telephone: +1 (212) 366 3900
Telefax: +1 (212) 366 3916

Anthony P Romano, *Chairman of the Board*
Henry E Buttelmann, *President*

Arlington Office: 1235 Jefferson Davis Highway, Arlington, Virginia 22202, USA

Telephone: +1 (703) 979 1240

Bath Office: 46 Church Road, Brunswick, Maine 04011, USA

Telephone: +1 (207) 721 8200

Project management, co-ordination and consultation on conceptual and preliminary designs, contract drawings and specifications and construction drawings for commercial or naval ships of the SES/ACV or submerged hydrofoil systems, destroyers, escorts, frigates, corvettes and VTOL/Helo carriers.

VERIFIED

THE HARBOR CONSULTANCY INTERNATIONAL

34 Otis Hill Road, Hingham, Massachusetts 02043, USA

Telephone: +1 (617) 749 0078
Telefax: +1 (617) 749 0078

Martha A Reardon, *Managing Director*

The Harbor Consultancy International, founded by Martha A Reardon in 1987, provides ferry transit system consultancy to public agencies and private businesses and individuals. Services range from the initial development of ferry concepts, public participation programmes (including the establishment and management of Water Transportation Task Forces and Ferry Conferences), use of ferries for the relief of traffic congestion, investigation of environmental considerations and constraints, historic research, slide presentations of existing international ferry systems, government liaison, troubleshooting, the development of marketing proposals and project management. THCI provides liaison services between technical specialists and local government planners and redevelopment authorities. Services also include written grant proposals, project documentation, and surveys of issues such as Harbour Traffic, Risk Management and Emergency and Contingency Plans. THCI works with consultant teams of transportation planners, naval architects and mechanical engineers. THCI associates have extensive experience in fast ferry system management and operations. Recent projects have included the San Francisco Bay Area Ferry Study, the Massachusetts Water Resources Authority Water Transportation programme, the Rhode Island Water Transportation Master Plan for the year 2000 and the Boston-Halifax ferry study for the Massachusetts Port Authority. Recent presentations have included: "Initiatives and Opportunities in Water Transportation", American Planning Association regional meeting, Newport, October 1994; "Fast Ferries: Some Environmental Considerations", 4th International Conference on High-Speed Marine Craft, Kristiansand, September 1994; "Connections by Water in Harbors around the World", Harbour Visions Charette: Bringing the City to the Sea, Boston, September 1994; "Water Transportation and the Urban Environment", Citta d'Acqua, Venice, March 1993; Conference Moderator, "Ferries '93", *Marine Log*, Fort Lauderdale, March 1993.

UPDATED

J B HARGRAVE NAVAL ARCHITECTS INC

205½ Sixth Street, West Palm Beach, Florida 33401, USA

Telephone: +1 (407) 833 8567
Telefax: +1 (407) 833 7791

J B Hargrave, *President*

Designers of a wide range of medium to high-speed monohull craft. A 36.5 m fibreglass yacht is presently under construction and is scheduled for completion in January 1996.

Preliminary designs include several 39 m fibreglass motor yachts. In addition design work for production vessels is still continuing.

The company has over 35 years of experience in the design of passenger ferries, commercial vessels and custom motor yachts. These designs range in size from 5.5 m runabouts to 190.5 m chemical tankers.

UPDATED

J W JOHNSON NAVAL ARCHITECTS

2135 Whispering Sands Lane, Virginia Beach, Washington, USA

FAST-1, *Wild Thing*

Designed by J W Johnson and built by Todd Marine in Norfolk Virginia, *Wild Thing* is a fast air-supported trimaran. The craft was launched in mid-1993 and operates tourist excursion trips.

The vessel is constructed from Airex composite material and is classed to operate under the US Coast Guard regulations for less than 150 passengers and less than 20 miles offshore.

The design will be marketed and built by Bollinger Shipyard on a non-exclusive basis.

Larger aluminium or steel models are possible, and a patrol boat derivative has been proposed.

Principal Particulars

Length overall	30 m
Beam	11 m
Draught	1.2 m
Displacement, maximum	80 t
Crew	3
Passengers	149
Fuel capacity	4500 l
Propulsive power	3 × 750 kW
Maximum speed	45 knots

Propulsion: The main engines are 3 × Caterpillar 3512 rated at 750 kW; driving J W Johnson designed JSD-1 surface drives, via ZF 195A 2:1 gearboxes.

UPDATED

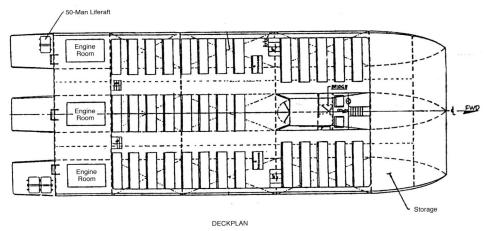

General arrangement of Wild Thing

1994

RAYMOND HUNT ASSOCIATES INC

69 Long Wharf, Boston, Massachusetts 02110, USA

Telephone: +1 (617) 742 5669
Telefax: +1 (617) 742 6354

John H Deknatel, *President*
Winn Willard, *Manager Commercial and Military Projects*

C Raymond Hunt Associates created the deep-V hull design in 1959 and has been refining the concept since. Specialising in the design of deep-V fast yachts and commercial and military craft, the company's in-house capabilities include the full range of design and engineering services. The present staff of seven includes naval architects and engineers with expertise in all construction materials and methods of propulsion.

Other commercial applications of the Hunt deep-V concept have included:
Sandy Hook, a 20 m, 24 knot, aluminium pilot boat for Port of New York and New Jersey built by Gladding-Hearn Shipbuilding Corporation
P-150, a 24 m, 27 knot FRP patrol vessel for Western Australia syndicate, now a fisheries patrol vessel in the Solomon Islands
TPB-86, a 26 m, 30 knot FRP water-jet patrol vessel built in Thailand by Technautic Company Ltd

1988, study for Massachusetts Port Authority concerning water transportation in Boston Harbor and Logan Airport focusing on high-speed ferry
1990, design of 22 and 30 knot 18.3 m FRP patrol boats for India
1990 design of 18 m very fast patrol and pursuit craft for Boston Whaler Commercial Products Division.

Recent projects include the 20 m, 25 knot *Golden Gate* pilot boat for San Francisco, and the 29 m, 32 knot FRP sportsfishing yacht *Golden Odyssey II*.

VERIFIED

MARITIME DYNAMICS INC

424X Great Mills Road, Lexington Park, Maryland 20653, USA

Telephone: +1 (301) 863 5499
Telefax: +1 (301) 863 0254

Clarence A Lysdale, *President*
John D Adams, *Vice President*
Mark E Lindler, *Director of Operations*
Charlotte R Sebra, *Sales and Marketing*
Robert L Chandler, *Service Manager*

Maritime Dynamics Inc (MDI) was founded in 1972 to provide engineering services for the design, development and testing of advanced ships and their subsystems, including: Surface Effect Ships (SESs), Air Cushion Vehicles (ACVs), hydrofoils, catamarans and Small-Waterplane-Area Twin-Hull (SWATH) vessels.

During its 23 year history, MDI has developed simulations to predict the motions of the following types of craft, operating in random seas, with and without active ride control:
Surface Effect Ships
Air Cushion Vehicles
Catamarans
Hydrofoil Catamarans
Monohulls.

MDI offers engineering services in support of conceptual, preliminary, contract and detail design of high-speed craft and related systems in the following areas:
Sea-keeping predictions with and without ride control
Control surface design and hull integration
Lift system design for SES, ACV and foil-supported craft
Structural design and stress analysis

Electronics design of machinery, monitoring and craft control systems
Vibration analysis
Instrumentation systems
Model fabrication, testing, analysis and full-scale prediction
Full-scale testing and analysis.

MDI's engineering capabilities are backed by direct participation in military and commercial high-speed craft that are in operation in various parts of the world. Many of these vessels are fitted with MDI ride control systems, see the Ride control systems section of this book. This participation provides continuous feedback to improve design methods and simulation programmes.

VERIFIED

PAYNE ASSOCIATES

300 Park Drive, Severna Park, Maryland 21146, USA

Telephone: +1 (410) 647 4943
Telefax: +1 (410) 647 0954

Advanced high-speed ship design and modifications for improved performance. Computer simulation of high-speed ship motions and performance in a seaway, including ride comfort and kinetosis (seasickness) evaluation. Advanced hydrodynamic research, as evidenced by Mr Payne's many archival publications and his book *Design of High-Speed Boats, Volume 1: Planing,* Fishergate Publishing Inc, 2521 Riva Road, Anapolis, Maryland 21401, USA (1988).

Mr Payne is also an authority on the biodynamics of ride comfort and a US member of the International Standards Organization committees responsible for standards in this field.

Payne designed and launched the first two experimental Swath vessels (FICATs I and II) in 1964-65, the first supercritical planing hulls (GAYLE Boats) in 1968, the first Seaknife in 1971 and the first foil-

supported catamaran (the Wavestrider) in 1983. Modern Swath designs have tended to follow Dr Tom Lang's configuration, but all these boats have had an impact on the more advanced designs recently appearing around the world. Because foil supported craft occasionally 'plough-in', no matter how active their control systems, and are not considered smooth riding enough for speeds above 40 knots, Payne started developing an improved configuration in 1989. A three tonne prototype was launched in Spring 1994, and preliminary trials have been conducted successfully.

In 1990, Payne Associates introduced the first time-domain personal computer programme for high-speed boats. BOAT3D replicates all the capabilities of a sophisticated towing tank for calm water or any kind of random seaway. Estimates of ride comfort and probability of kinetosis are part of the programme's printed output, utilising all known methodologies. BOAT3D can also calculate the pressure distribution and peak plating stress throughout the hull, once typical scantlings are defined. The programme has a number of internal hull algorithms which can replicate the vast majority of lines by adjusting a few coefficients. Lines are

plotted automatically when required, on a laser jet or dot matrix printer. User-supplied lines which are incompatible with these internal algorithms can be inserted via a user-written subroutine, such as a list of offsets.

The programme can also utilise 'external forces' not generated by the hull in the main programme. It has been used in this way to add the aerodynamic forces and moment of a wingship, in the study of take off, landing and occasional wave impacts while cruising over a seaway. The forces and moments from the hydrofoils of Payne Associates' Dynafoil prototype were also coupled to BOAT3D for an extensive optimisation and evaluation of the boat in a seaway prior to commencing construction.

BOAT3D will accept engine, transmission and propeller data so that the correct rpm and thrust is calculated at any speed and position of the propellers with respect to the water surface. To assist in selecting an efficient propeller, a separate standalone programme uses the same information to automatically plot engine rpm and propeller thrust against speed, for a range of user-selected variables.

UPDATED

QUADRIMARAN INTERNATIONAL

c/o Baltimore Steam Packet Company Inc, PO Box 1959, Williamsburg, Virginia 23185, USA

Telephone: +1 (804) 220 2355
Telefax: +1 (804) 253 8110

Trond Conradi, *President*

The Quadrimaran, a four-hulled fast multihull craft, was designed by Daniel Tollet of France, and developed using a large scale prototype craft. An 18.5 m vessel was constructed in France in 1991 and has since then been operational in the Mediterranean. Two 27 m, 28 knot vessels were delivered in 1994 and a 60 knot prototype is currently under construction in Portsmouth, Virginia, USA.

The benefits of the craft are reported to be related

to low fuel and running costs and a high level of stability and sea-keeping ability.

Designs are offered from 22.5 m to 175 m with payloads ranging from 5 to 3000 tonnes.

NEW ENTRY

M ROSENBLATT & SON INC

350 Broadway, New York, New York 10013, USA

Telephone: +1 (212) 431 6900
Telefax: +1 (212) 334 0837

Lester Rosenblatt, *Chairman and Chief Executive Officer*
P W Nelson, *President and Director*
A M Stein, *Vice President, Operations and Director*
B Rosenblatt, *Vice President and Director*
S Halpern, *Vice President and Manager, Western Division*
N M Maniar, *Vice President and Technical Director*
D M Krepchin, *Vice President and Manager, San Diego Branch*
A Baki, *Vice President and Manager, Washington DC Area Branch*
C Laviola, *Vice President and Design Manager, Eastern Division*
P B Kimball, *Vice President*

M Rosenblatt & Son Inc is an established naval architectural and marine engineering firm with nearly 50 years of proven experience in all phases of ship and marine vehicle design.

With offices in nine US cities and abroad, the firm is close to the entire shipbuilding community and has a thorough understanding of its problems and needs. Its experience covers programme management, inspection of construction and integrated logistics support, as well as design.

A major portion of the company's design activities has been and is for the US Navy. Completed assignments are of the broadest possible variety, covering research and development, feasibility studies, preliminary, contract and detail design for all classes of major combatants, auxiliaries and high performance craft. In addition, the company has provided extensive design services for the conversion, overhaul and repair of naval combatants, auxiliaries, submarines, amphibious warfare supply and landing craft.

The service to the maritime industry includes a wide variety of tasks covering the new and modification design of oceanographic ships, container ships, tankers, general cargo ships, dredgers, bulk

carriers, drilling platforms and ships, survey vessels, pipe-laying barges and a great variety of supporting craft.

Typical high-speed marine craft and ACV assignments have included:
Concept designs of a 20 tonne wheeled ACV and a 60 tonne wheeled hydrofoil for the US Army
Preliminary and detail design of a 30 m combat hydrofoil for a foreign army
Steering and manoeuvring system design for a tracked ACV for Bell Textron
Surface Effect Ship Advanced Design and Technology handbook for US Navy
PHM design producibility and cost reduction review for US Navy
Development of Advanced Marine Vehicle (AMV) bibliography for US Navy.

ARPA Advanced Surface Effect Vehicles
Conceptual studies, parametric studies and propulsion machinery analysis for phase 'O' studies of Advanced Surface Effect Vehicles for Advanced Research Project Agency. Work performed for American Machine and Foundry Company.

JSESPO Surface Effect Ship Test Craft

Conceptual and feasibility design studies of candidate SES vehicles for the JSESPO sizing study for second-generation SES test craft in the 1000 to 3000 tonne range. The work included studies of various candidate versions of SES to identify and evaluate their unique operational and design capabilities; technological assessment of various structural materials and systems; and preparation of a proposed development programme with required supporting research and development. Work performed for Joint Surface Effect Ship Program office.

AAV(P) Advanced Assault Amphibious Vehicle Personnel

Assistance to FMC Corporation with development of alternative concepts for proposal to the US Navy.

VERIFIED

TGMD INC

211 North Third Avenue, PO Box 290, Sturgeon Bay, Wisconsin 54235, USA

Telephone: +1 (414) 743 5092
Telefax: +1 (414) 743 7936

Timothy Graul, *Principal*

TGMD Inc, was incorporated in 1994, continuing the naval architecture, marine engineering, design and consulting practice begun when the firm was established in 1981 as Timothy Graul Marine Design. A separate branch, Timothy Graul Marine Surveys, offers surveys and appraisals. Graul is a non-exclusive surveyor for DnV.

The design of patrol boats, ferries, pilot boats, tugs, fire boats, military vessels, research boats, passenger craft and river tow boats and barges remain specialities of TGMD, particularly those less than 61 m (200 ft) in length. As a result, the staff are especially skilled in design techniques and applications of rules and regulations applicable to small ships. All staff have hands on experience in vessel construction and operation.

TGMD uses computer programs for stability, powering and performance analyses; for structural design optimisation and for configuration control. Computer-aided drafting is employed whenever it is appropriate.

Major projects completed by TGMD in 1994 include a 600 passenger dinner/excursion boat, a 300 passenger transfer boat, an aluminium cata-maran, several dinner/cruise boats, a crew/supply boat and a ferry barge/tug combination. In addition, the firm assisted builders of many other craft with engineering services, regulatory body approval assistance and working plans.

Timothy Graul, president of TGMD Inc, is a graduate of the University of Michigan and a registered Professional Engineer. He is a member of SNAME and its small craft committee and is Chairman of panel SC-5 (small passenger vessels). He is assisted by a staff of five designers and engineers.

UPDATED

SOCIETIES INVOLVED WITH HIGH-SPEED CRAFT

Company Listing by Country

Canada
Canadian Air Cushion Technology Society

Norway
International Marine Transit Association

United Kingdom
The Hovercraft Society
Joint Aero-Marine Group

United States of America
The International Hydrofoil Society

CANADA

CANADIAN AIR CUSHION TECHNOLOGY SOCIETY

Canadian Aeronautics and Space Institute, 222 Somerset Street West, Suite 601, Ottawa, Ontario. K2P 2G3, Canada

Telephone: +1 (613) 234 0191

Carson Payne, *Chairman*
A J S Timmins, *Executive Director*

The Canadian Air Cushion Technology Society (CACTS) is a constituent society of the Canadian Aeronautics and Space Institute (CASI). It is devoted to the development and application of air cushion technology, principally with regard to the transportation domain, but also in industry and in other fields

where this technology may be of benefit. The goal of the society is to keep its members abreast of developments in the field through information dissemination and exchange. This is done through periodic conferences to which participants from various countries involved in air cushion technology and hovercraft are invited.

VERIFIED

NORWAY

INTERNATIONAL MARINE TRANSIT ASSOCIATION

Incat Designs, 1 Mafeking Avenue, Lane Cove, Sydney, NSW 2066, Australia

Telephone: +61 (2) 427 2822
Telefax: +61 (2) 427 7238

Philp C Hercus, *President*

Martha A Reardon, *Secretary, Treasurer*
34 Otis Hill Road, Hingham, Massachusetts 02043, USA

Telephone/Fax: +1 (617) 749 0078

IMTA was formed in 1977 "to research and collect information on developments within and affecting the ferry service industry; to exchange information and technical data through an international network of members; and to stimulate industry co-operation and advancement by providing a forum for people to share experiences and learn from others". Annual conferences have been held in Europe, Asia and North America. The agenda includes subjects of interest to large and small ferry operators of conventional and high-speed craft, passenger-only, ro/ro ferry systems and public and private agencies.
Conferences during the last three years were held in Hong Kong, San Francisco and Bergen, and managed by the IMTA President in the host city.

The membership of IMTA includes ferry operators, naval architects, shipbuilders and equipment manufacturers, government agencies, support service companies, marine engineering and planning consultants, academia and specialists in maritime training.
Future conference venues include: Sydney, Australia in 1995; Victoria, Canada in 1996; Helsingborg, Sweden in 1997.

UPDATED

UNITED KINGDOM

THE HOVERCRAFT SOCIETY

15 St Mark's Road, Gosport, Hampshire PO12 2DA, UK

Telephone: +44 (1705) 601310

Lord Romsey, *Patron*
Sir Christopher Cockerell, *President*
R L Wheeler, *Vice President*
J E Rapson, *Vice President*
E G Tattersall, *Vice President*
M A Pinder, *Vice President*
N MacDonald, *Chairman*
W Jacobs, *Hon. Secretary*

Formed in 1971, The Hovercraft Society (THS) was the UK constituent of the 'International

Air Cushion Engineering Society'. Membership is open to persons engaged in hovercraft related fields and to those having a *bona fide* interest in hovercraft in the UK and overseas. Current membership is drawn from ACV manufacturers, ferry operators, design groups, government departments and agencies, financial and insurance organisations, consultants, journalists and universities. Current fees for ordinary membership are £16 per annum.

THS organises regular meetings at which talks are given on technical, commercial and military design and operation of amphibious craft, SES and other air cushion devices. It also produces a monthly Hovercraft Bulletin available to all members, containing information and news on air cushion related topics. Occasionally THS organises visits and social events for its members.

A collection of books, periodicals, papers and reports on the subject of hovercraft has been accumulated by the Society and these are housed at the address. Access to these documents is by prior arrangement with the Secretary.
THS has introduced an annual student award (presently up to £500). This will be granted to a chosen applicant proposing to carry out a project or thesis in the UK on a subject connected with the design, construction or operation of a hovercraft, SES or some other air cushion device (details from the Secretary).
Details of the Hovercraft Museum Trust, now housing a wide range of hovercraft and associated equipment, can be obtained from THS.

UPDATED

JOINT AERO-MARINE GROUP

c/o SUT, 76 Mark Lane, London EC3R 7JN, UK

Telephone: +44 (171) 481 0750
Telefax: +44 (171) 481 4001

S J Philips, *Chairman*
D R Wardle, *Secretary*

The Joint Aero-Marine Group (JAMG) was founded in 1982 as an intersociety group of professional engineers with a mutual interest in aero and marine technologies, particularly in the cross-fertilisation of ideas and techniques. It is linked within the Group/Committee structure to The Royal Aeronautical Society, The Royal Institution of Naval Architects and the Society for Underwater Technology.

The objective of the JAMG is to act as a catalyst for the exchange of ideas and information within the sectors of government, industry and academia involved with aero marine technology. High-speed marine craft are of particular relevance and interest to the JAMG.

UPDATED

UNITED STATES OF AMERICA

THE INTERNATIONAL HYDROFOIL SOCIETY

PO Box 51, Cabin John, Maryland 20818, USA

John R Meyer, *President*
Mark R Bebar, *Vice President*
Capt John W King, *Secretary, Treasurer*
Patsy N Jackson, *Recording Secretary*

A quarterly newsletter is published by the International Hydrofoil Society and is available from

Captain John King, USN (Ret), 4313 Granada Street, Alexandria, Virginia 22309, USA
The membership fee for this society is US$ 20.00.

IHS Board of Directors
1991-94
Mark R Bebar
George Jenkins
Capt John W King
Wade Webster
1992-95
John R Meyer

John Monk
Dr James R Wilkins Jnr
Phillip Yarnall
1993-1996
Barney C Black
James H King
Mark Rice
Kenneth B Spaulding Jr

VERIFIED

ADDENDA

AUSTRALIA

WAVEMASTER INTERNATIONAL PTY LTD

Lot 500 Cockburn Road, Henderson, Western Australia 6166, Australia

Telephone: +61 (9) 410 1422
Telex: 93356 AA
Telefax: +61 (9) 410 2089

Glen Williams, *Director*

52 m Car/Passenger Ferry

Two of these craft are scheduled for delivery in mid-1996, although final financing deals are currently still being negotiated.

Principal Particulars

Length overall	52.5 m
Length waterline	45.1 m
Beam	16.8 m
Draught	2 m
Crew	12
Passengers	450
Vehicles	46
Fuel capacity	46 000 l
Water capacity	3000 l
Propulsive power	4 × 1941 kW

Classification: DnV, +1A1 HSLC R2 Passenger Car Ferry EO; IMO Code of Safety for Dynamically Supported Craft.

Structure: MIG welded marine grade aluminium.

Propulsion: The main engines are 4 × Deutz MWM TBD 620 V16 diesels, each rated at 1941 kW at 1800 rpm; driving 4 × KaMeWa 71 water-jets; via ZF BU55D or Reintjes VLJ930HL/HR gearboxes.

Control: The craft will be fitted with a stabiliser system consisting of two transom flaps and two "T" foils at the bow.

NEW ENTRY

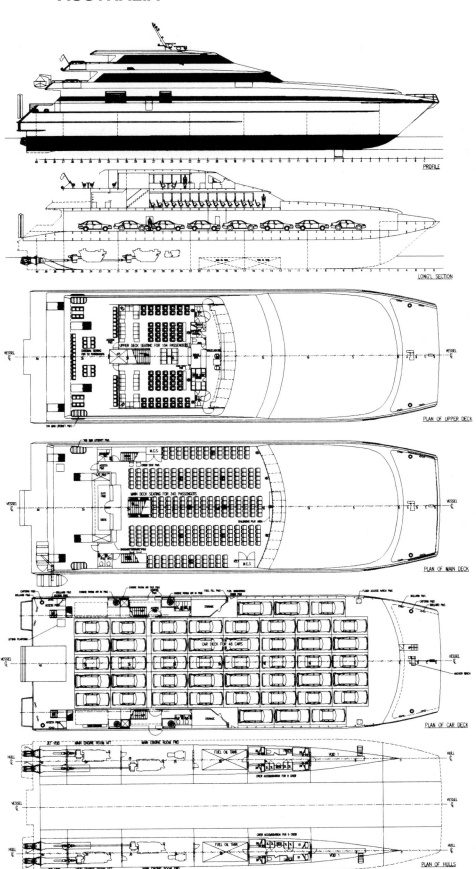

WaveMaster 52 m Car/Passenger Ferry
1995

CHINA, PEOPLE'S REPUBLIC

HANG TONG HIGH SPEED SHIP DEVELOPMENT CO LTD

Fenjiang Road, Xinhui City, Guangdong Province, People's Republic of China 529100

Telephone: +86 (0750) 661 0966 / 663 2967
Telefax: +86 (0750) 666 6547 / 661 0966

Hang Tong is a joint venture company that specialises in the development of high-speed craft. At present they are producing hovercraft, backed by the advanced technology of Chinese aerospace industry.

These hovercraft (the "HT" range), are built in several shipyards around China, and are claimed to offer high reliability and good survivability at low prices.

All the craft in the range are constructed using welded corrosion resistant aluminium alloy. The propulsion systems all use a simple toothed belt transmission device for the lift fans and drive propellers, the craft also have bow thrust ports to assist low-speed manoeuvres.

Typical uses for craft in the HT range include: Passenger ferry, patrol craft, amphibious assault craft, survey and exploration.

HT-904

This is the smallest craft in the range, capable of carrying 20 passengers, or a payload of 1.5 tonnes.

Principal Particulars

Length overall	10.5 m
Beam	4.5 m
Weight, maximum	6 t
Payload	1.5 t
Passengers	20
Propulsive power	230 kW
Lift power	230 kW
Maximum speed	32 knots
Operational limitation	1 m wave height

Structure: Welded aluminium alloy
Propulsion: The main engine is a single Deutz BF12L 513C diesel, maximum output 230 kW; driving a 1.8 m diameter propeller, and the lift fan.
Control: Air rudder, bow thrusters.

HT-901

Two versions of this design have been built: A passenger ferry, of which two have been built; and an open well-deck amphibious transporter.

Principal Particulars

Length overall	17.9 m
Beam	7.7 m
Weight, maximum	21 t

HT-901 open well-deck hovercraft   **1995**

Payload	6 t
Passengers	50
Propulsive power	4 × 190 kW
Lift power	4 × 190 kW
Maximum speed	32 knots
Operational limitation	2 m wave height

Structure: Welded aluminium alloy.
Propulsion: The main engines are 4 × Deutz BF8L 413 diesels, powering both the lift fans and the two 2.3 m diameter drive propellers.
Control: Air rudders and thrust ports.

HT-903

Two versions of this design are offered, the 24 m HT-903B, and the 28 m HT-903A.

HT-903B

One of these craft made a 1000 mile voyage from the South China Sea to the East China Sea.

Three craft operate on a busy service across the entrance of the Yangtze river. A HT-903B for Hangzhou Gulf Ferries, is under construction.

Principal Particulars

Length overall	24.35 m
Beam	8.8 m
Weight, maximum	40 t
Payload	12 t

Passengers	100
Propulsive power	4 × 360 kW
Lift power	4 × 360 kW
Maximum speed	45 knots
Operational limitation	2.8 m wave height.

Structure: Welded aluminium alloy.
Propulsion: The engines are 4 × Deutz BF12L 413 diesels, maximum output 360 kW each; driving 2 × 3 m diameter air propellers, and the lift fans.
Control: Air rudders and bow thrusters.

HT-903A

Principal Particulars

Length overall	27.95 m
Weight, maximum	55 t
Payload	18 t
Passengers	150
Propulsive power	5 × 360 kW
Lift power	5 × 360 kW
Maximum speed	40 knots

Structure: Welded aluminium alloy.
Propulsion: The engines are 5 × Deutz BF12L 413 diesels, maximum output 360 kW; driving three 3 m propellers and the lift fans.
Control: Air rudders and thrust ports.

NEW ENTRY

FRANCE

IRIS CATAMARANS

Zone Industrielle, F-17290 Aigrefeuille, France

Telephone: +33 46 35 70 40
Telefax: +33 46 35 50 10

Maarten Mostert, *Director*

The IRIS (InteR Islands Shuttle) project is a new multpurpose catamaran concept for the transportation of passengers, containers, or special cargo services; although is designed for relatively short voyages (maximum four hours).

The catamaran design consists of an open platform suspended between the two hulls, with the bridge situated at the forward end of this platform. Passenger modules having the dimensions of 40 ft containers, or of course containers, can be mounted on this platform.

Three designs are offered, all using the same hulls but different bridgedeck structures and propulsion packages.

IRIS 4

This version can carry four container sized modules.

Principal Particulars

Length overall	38 m
Length waterline	36.28 m
Beam	11 m
Draught	1.15 m
Payload	38 t (includes modules)
Passengers	160
Fuel capacity	5.3 t
Water capacity	750 l
Propulsive power	2 × 720 kW
Maximum speed	31 knots
Operational speed	25 knots
Range	300 nm

Classification: DnV 1A1 HSLC R1 Passenger.
Structure: The main construction material is vacuum bagged GRP-Sandwich. This method is used to construct the hulls, control station, after deck and passenger modules; but all shock sensitive areas are single skin laminate. The transverse beams that support the bridgedeck structure are to be built from aluminium alloy and joined to the hulls on heavily reinforced watertight bulkheads. Longitudinal deck girders are positioned under the container edges providing.
Propulsion: The main engines are 2 × Deutz MWM TBD 616 V12 diesels, each producing 720 kW; driving 2 × Lips LJ 56 DL water-jets.

IRIS 6

This version can carry six container sized modules.

Principal Particulars

Length overall	38 m
Length waterline	36.28 m
Beam	12.16 m
Draught	1.27 m
Payload	55 t (includes modules)
Passengers	240
Fuel capacity	7.1 t
Water capacity	1100 l
Propulsive power	2 × 960 kW
Maximum speed	34 knots
Operational speed	26 knots
Range	315 nm

Classification: DnV 1A1 HSLC R1 Passenger.
Structure: The construction is similar to the IRIS 4.
Propulsion: The main engines are 2 × Deutz MWM TBD 616 V16 diesels, each producing 960 kW; driving 2 × Lips LJ 64 DL water-jets.

IRIS 8

This version can carry eight container sized modules.

Principal Particulars

Length overall	38 m

Length waterline	36.28 m	Water capacity	1500 l
Beam	14.71 m	Propulsive power	2 × 1524 kW
Draught	1.37 m	Maximum speed	36 knots
Payload	70 t (includes modules)	Operational speed	31 knots
Passengers	320	Range	370 nm
Fuel capacity	8.3 t		

Classification: DnV 1A1 HSLC R1 Passenger.

Structure: The construction is similar to the IRIS 4.
Propulsion: The main engines are 2 × Deutz MWM TBD 620 V112 diesels, each producing 960 kW; driving 2 × Lips LJ 70 DL water-jets. A gas-turbine version is being investigated for the IRIS 8.

NEW ENTRY

KOREA, SOUTH

SEMO COMPANY LTD

Shipbuilding Division, 1 Jangiri Donghaemyun, Kosungkun, Kyungnam, South Korea

Telephone: +82 (556) 723535
Telefax: +82 (556) 723570

Bok-Hoon Lee, *Vice President*

Known for their ferry operating division which includes in a fleet of 30 ferries, three hydrofoils, three amphibious hovercraft and now four SESs, Semo has reportedly started construction of a composite designed catamaran ferry for addition to its fleet in late 1995. No comprehensive details of this vessel were available at the time of publication.

NEW ENTRY

NORWAY

WESTAMARIN A/S

Andøyveten 23, PO Box 115, Vågsbygd, N-4602 Kristiansand, Norway

Telephone: +47 (38) 088200
Telex: 21514 WRIN N
Telefax: +47 (38) 085012

Westamarin A/S is a subsidiary of the Swedish company Addum AB. The shipyard was established in 1855 and has been associated with the design and production of ships and offshore structures since that time. With a prior association with Westamarin West A/S, the yard has been developing large fast catamaran craft since 1990. The company holds the ISO-9001 quality assurance standard. In early 1995 Stena Line placed a contract worth US$110 million with Westamarin A/S for two large fast catamaran ferries codenamed HSS 900. The first ferry is scheduled to be delivered in mid-1996 with the second for delivery in late 1996. It is understood that the proposed route for the craft is between Gothenburg and Fredrikshavn.

NEW ENTRY

SINGAPORE

MARINTEKNIK SHIPBUILDERS (S) PTE LTD

31 Tuas Road, Singapore 2263

Telephone: +65 861 1706
Telex: 53419 MARJET RS
Telefax: +65 861 4244

David C H Liang, *Group Chairman*
Patrick Cheung, *Managing Director*
Andrew Yeo, *Director, Technical Manager*
Susan Sim, *Business Manager*

Marinteknik Shipbuilders (S) Pte Ltd was established in 1984 for the building of high-speed vessels. To date, the yard has built more than 30 vessels of both monohull and catamaran type as passenger vessels and crew boats for customers worldwide. In early 1995 the company received an order for a third quadruple engine 41 CPV Catamaran for delivery to the Chambon Group this year. An 85 m monohull design is also being marketed which is understood to be currently under negotiation.

85 m Monohull Car/Passenger Ferry (design)
Principal Particulars

Length overall	85 m

85 m Monohull Car/Passenger Ferry   *1995*

Beam	15 m
Draught	3 m
Passengers	584
Vehicles	104 cars
	7 buses
Maximum speed	36 knots
Operational speed	35 knots
Range	750 nm

Classification: The car deck is designed to the latest Scandinavian safety requirements.

Structure: The hull can be built from either high tensile steel with aluminium superstructure, or using all aluminium construction.
Propulsion: The main engines are 3 × MTU 1163 equivalent, each powering a KaMeWa or MJP water-jet.
Control: The vessel will have an active stabiliser system to aid sea-keeping.

NEW ENTRY

BIBLIOGRAPHY

In general only papers specifically concerned with high-speed marine craft are included in this bibliography. In a few instances some of the papers listed may not be available in published form.

CONFERENCE PROCEEDINGS 1990-1995

Papers presented at the Seventh International High-Speed Surface Craft Conference, 11-12 January 1990, and published by High-Speed Surface Craft Ltd, UK.
Design for Speed Economy and Comfort - The Role of the Independent Designer in the Design of High-Speed Surface Craft, Nigel Gee (Nigel Gee and Associates).
The Development of Efficient Composite (FRP) Structures for High-Speed Vessels by Full-Scale Testing, Anthony Marchant and Kenneth T Stevens (Associated & Marine Technology Ltd).
High-Speed Water Transportation on Corpus Christi Bay, Steve Ortmann (Corpus Christi Regional Transportation).
Can Fast Ferries Relieve Urban Congestion? Roger M Mabbot (Small Ferry Systems).
Fast Ferry Enhancement Through Innovative Marketing - A Case History, Merideth Tall (Clipper Navigation Inc).
Legal Liabilities of a Fast Ferry Carrier to its Passengers, Alan P R Walls, Holman, Fenwick & Willan).
Fincantieri SES Designs, L De Martini and E Belli (Fincantieri CNI).
The Case for Surface Propulsion, Renato Levi.
SES Model Tests - An Integral Part of the Design Process, Andrew G Blyth (Consultant Naval Architect), and Dr Olle Rutgersson (SSPA Maritime Consulting AB).
The Development of the Speed Z Propulsion System, Svein O Halstensen and Per A Leivdal (Ulstein Propeller AB).
The Case for Engine-Speed Water-Jets in High-Speed Craft, G H Davison (C W F Hamilton & Company Ltd).
Combination and Application of Multiple Water-jet Propulsion Systems, Gerard Torneman (MJP Marine Jet Power AB).
MTU Series 396 High Performance Engines for Fast Passenger and Utility Craft, Dipl-Ing Burkart Feurer (MTU Friedrichshafen).
The World's First 30 knot Fast Displacement Catamaran (SWATH) Ferry, Robert Milner (FBM Marine Ltd).
Performance Comparisons of Selected Fast Ferries, Timothy D Kelley (Swath Ocean Systems Inc).
SuperOutrigger - Less Pitch - Less Roll - Less Drag - Less Cost - Less Complex, Nathan I Daniel and Howard E Daniel (SuperOutrigger).
The Use of Novel Fabrics as Bases for Hovercraft Skirts, Dr Carol J Lewis (Avon Rubber plc).
The Development of a New Range of Passenger and Cargo Hovercraft, John H Gifford (Griffon Hovercraft Ltd).
Aspects on High-Speed Craft Propulsion, Eric Bjarne (SSPA Maritime Consulting AB).

Papers presented at the International Marine Transit Association Conference, 'Marine Transit, the Way of the Future...', Quebec, Canada, 23-30 September 1990.
A Service for Washington, DC, F C Rummage (Aqua Line Inc, Landover, Maryland.)
FBM Marine Limited's FDC 400: The World's First 30 knot Fast Displacement Catamaran (SWATH) Ferry, T Arnold, P Eyre, (CPF Systems Limited).
Experience with a Catamaran Commuter Ferry in New York Harbor (Year Round Operations), Mark J Stanisci (Hydrolines).
Boston Harbor Ferries: A New Awareness, Martha A Reardon (The Harbor Consultancy International).
Fast Passengers Sea Transportation: Monohull or Twin Hull?, Vincenzo Ruggiero (University of Genoa, Italy).
Assessment of the Risk and Other Implications of Hijacking for the Underwriters, Anthony J Murphy (Thomas Miller P & I, London).
A Response to the Herald of Free Enterprise Tragedy: The UK Legislation to Bring Ferry Operations up to a Basic Minimum Standard, C J Parker (The Nautical Institute, London).
The Seabus System in Vancouver, BC (BC Transit), Rod Morrisson (BC Ferry Corporation).
Recent Ferry Tragedies, Implications for the Shipowners/Ferry Operators, Peter A Heathcote (Marine Atlantic, Canada).
Ferry Operations in Ice Conditions, Jacques Clavelle (Canadian Coast Guard).
Ferry Operations in Hong Kong, Edward Young (Consultant, Hong Kong).
The Golden Gate Bridge Integrated Transit System and the 1989 Loma Prieta Earthquake, Gene P Rexrode (Golden Gate Bridge, Highway and Transportation District).
Ferries, Fixed Links and Flexilink, J F Sloggett (Dover Harbour Board).
Economic Aspects of a Fixed Link with Prince Edward Island, Murray Ryder (Marine Atlantic).
The Cruise and Ferry Industry in Alaska, John Halterman (Alaska Marine Highway System, Juneau, Alaska).
Environment and Antifouling - What Is the Future?, Mark Morris (International Paint World Headquarters, England).
A Review of the Achille Lauro Hijacking, Francesco Siccardi, (Studio Legale Siccardi & C, Genoa, Italy).

Ferries in a Seamless Transport Network, prepared by: Jack M Davis, David Phraner; presented by: George Cancro (The Port Authority of NY & NJ, Office of Ferry Transportation, New York, USA).
High-Speed Diesel Engine for Catamaran Ferries - Experience with Installation and Operation, Helmut Pleimling (MWM Motoren-Werke Mannheim AG, Mannheim, Germany).
Air Supported Catamarans from Norway, Erik Hakonsholm, (Ulstein of Norway SES Ships).
SWATH Ferry Development Program, Michael Schmicker (Navatek Ships Ltd).
Cruise Ferries in the Baltic, Gustaf Myrsten (Redery AB Slite, Nacka, Sweden).
Security Requirements for Cruiselines, Ferries and Ports, B A H Parritt (International Maritime Security, Ashford, Kent, UK).

Papers presented at the Second Conference on High-Speed Marine Craft 1990, Kristiansand, Norway, Norwegian Society of Chartered Engineers, 3-6 September 1990.
Operation of High-Speed Marine Craft, Stig Vaular (Hardanger Sundhordalandske Dampskipsselskap, Norway).
Design Tool for High-Speed Catamaran, Per Werenskiold (Norwegian Marine Technology Research Institute).
High-Speed Marine Craft Structures - a Personal Viewpoint, A Marchant (CETEC/AMTEC).
Safety - Rules and Regulations, Karl Wicklund (Det Norske Veritas, Norway).
Norwegian High-Speed Marine Craft Research Programme, Kjell Holden (Norwegian Marine Technology Research Institute).
Development of MCMV SES Platform, Bjørn Krohn and Arne Wangsholm (Royal Norwegian Navy).
Propulsion Systems for High-Speed Marine Vehicles, Dr Ing C Kruppa (Technical University of Berlin, Germany).
Structural Design Considerations of High-Speed Marine Craft, Sverre Valsgard (Det Norske Veritas, Norway).
Diesel Engine Operation Conditions in Propulsion of High-Speed Vehicles, Bard Meek-Hansen (Norwegian Marine Technology Research Institute).

Papers Presented at Cruise + Ferry 91 Conference, London, UK, 29-31 May 1991.
Car Ferries - Looking to the Future, B Langford (P & O European Ferries Ltd, Dover, UK).
Ferry Routes, Ship Motions and Passenger Comfort - Analysing the Relationship, J R MacGregor, G R Lamb, T D Kelley (SWATH Ocean International, USA).
Human Comfort Onboard Fast Passenger Ferries, E Brubakk, F Tellsgaard (Det Norske Veritas Classification, Norway).
Fast Craft and the Competition on the London to Paris and London to Brussels Routes. Time and Cost Comparisons City-to-City, J Charlier (Institute of Geography UCL, Belgium).
A 50 knot Gas Turbine Powered Foilcat for 300-400 Passengers, E Instanes (Kværner Fjellstrand A/S, Norway).
The DB Catafoil - A New Foil-Assisted Catamaran Passenger Ferry. Breaking the 40 knot Barrier at Minimum Cost, N Gee (Nigel Gee & Associates, Southampton, UK).
Application of Light Alloy on Passenger Vessels, G Bacicchi, A Maccari (Fincantieri, Trieste, Italy).
Regulatory Considerations for SWATH Ships, A P Ritola (American Bureau of Shipping, USA).
Service Experience of the Seamaster Fast Displacement Catamaran (SWATH) Ferry, R Milner (FBM Marine Ltd, Isle of Wight, UK).
Compact Diesel Engines for Fast Ferries, G Haussmann (MTU, Friedrichshafen, Germany).
The Impact of New High Performance Fast Ferries on Port Facilities - the Design Process, D Byrne (Transmarine Ltd, UK).
Port Opportunities for Maximising the Use of High-Speed Catamaran Ferries, J Rose (Marine Development Ltd, Scotland).

Papers presented at the Fast '91, First International Conference on Fast Sea Transportation, The Norwegian Institute of Technology, Trondheim, Norway, 17-21 June 1991.
High-Speed over Water, Ideas from the Past, the Present and for the Future, R L Trillo (Robert Trillo Limited, UK).
Waves and Wave Resistance of a High-Speed River Catamaran, L J Doctors (University of New South Wales, Australia).
A Fundamental Study on a Flow Field around a Submerged Body of Revolution with Surface-Piercing Struts, T Fuwa, N Hirata, T Hino (Ship Research Institute, Japan).
Computational Fluid Dynamics Applied to High-Speed Crafts with Special Attention to Water Intake for Water-Jets and Super Structure Aerodynamics, M Førde, H Norstrud, N Kubberud (Norwegian Institute of Technology, Norway).
Concept of a Large Surface Effect Ship for Fast Ocean Transport, D W Czimmek, B H Schaub (Newport News Shipbuilding, USA).

A Review of Current Fast Wave-Piercing Car Ferries, P C Hercus (INCAT Designs, Australia).

The Catafoil - a Foil-Assisted Catamaran for Fast Ferry and Yacht Applications, N Gee (Nigel Gee and Associates, UK).

The Effect of an Advanced Spray Rail System on Resistance and Development of Spray of Semi-Displacement Round Bilge Hulls, B Müller-Graf (Berlin Model Basin, Germany).

Aspects of Hydrofoil Design; with Emphasis on Hydrofoil Interaction in Calm Water, H J B Mørch, K J Minsaas (Marintek, Norway).

A Submerged Hull and Foil Hybrid Super-High-Speed Liner, N Yamanaka, O Yamamoto, R Satoh, T Nagatsuka, T Arii, T Fuwa (Kawasaki Heavy Industries Ltd, Japan).

SES 500 - Fincantieri - Design Criteria, L De Martini (Fincantieri, Italy).

Development and Trials of Experimental Craft SES 'Corsair', N Schlichthorst, J Wessel (Blohm+Voss AG, Germany).

A Concept Design Study of 'Techno-Superliner', Y Kunitake, H Ozawa, S Morishita, R Oimatsu (Mitsui Engineering & Shipbuilding Company, Japan).

Sea-keeping of Foilcatamarans, S Falch (Kværner Båtservice, Norway).

Research on Hydrodynamic Aspects of TSL-A, M Hirano, N Toki, Y Kusaka, Y Wada (Akishima Laboratories Inc, Japan).

Experimental Investigation of Resistance and Sea-keeping Characteristics of a Catamaran Design, A Incecik, B F M Morison (The University of Glasgow, UK).

Economy and Speed in Commercial Operations, B Foss (Møre and Romsdal College, Norway).

Synthetic Aspects of Transport Economy and Transport Vehicle Performance with Reference to High-Speed Marine Vehicles, S Akagi (Osaka University, Japan).

Comparison of a Cargo Catamaran with a Container Ship and a Transport Aircraft, A Kraus, A Naujeck (Howaldtswerke-Deutsche Werft, Germany).

A State of the Art of Fast Sea Transportation in Japan, T Koyama (Tokyo University, Japan).

A Calculation of Free-Surface Flows Generated by Planing Craft, T Hino, N Hirata, T Hori (Ship Research Institute, Japan).

On Dynamic Stability of Fast Planing Craft, M Simeone (Istituto Universitario Navale, Italy).

Open Ocean Operation and Manoeuvrability at High Speed, S Hellstroem, D Blount, P Ottosson, L Codega (SSPA Maritime Consulting AB, Sweden).

Assessment of Long Term Effects of Slamming Loads on FRP Sandwich Panels, L Buene, A T Echtermeyer, O E Sund, M K Nygård, B Hayman (A S Veritas Research, Norway).

Response of Fast Craft Hull Structures to Slamming Loads, B Hayman (Veritas Marine Services, Norway).

Enhanced Shock Performance of FRP Sandwich Structures, R P Reichard (Florida Institute of Technology, USA).

Hydrodynamic Analysis and Performance of Surface Effect Ships (SES), D Nakos, A Nestegård, T Ulstein, P D Sclavounos (MIT, USA).

A New Method for Analysing the Sea-keeping of SWATH Ships, D Kring, P D Sclavounos (MIT, USA).

The Motion Response of an ACV with a Bag-Finger Skirt in Waves, G J Lee, K P Rhee (Seoul National University, South Korea).

FRP-Sandwich as Construction Material for High-Speed Craft, A Mortenson (Ulstein International A/S, Norway).

Structural Optimisation of a High Performance GRP-Sandwich Ship Hull, O Gullberg, O Romell (Karlskronavarvet AB, Sweden).

Design and Manufacturing of NES 24 Structure, J F Rolin, A Ifremer (Ifremer, France).

On the Potential of SWATH Ships for Very High-Speed Operations, R C McGregor, J R McGregor, H H Chun (The University of Glasgow, UK).

Hydrodynamic Optimisation of High-Speed SWATH, A Papanikolaou, M Androulakakis (National Technology University of Athens, Greece).

Hydrodynamic Design of Fast Ferries by the Concept of Super-Slender Twin Hull, R Sato, H Nogami, Y Shirose, A Ito, H Miyata, K Masaoka, E Kamal (Ishikawajima-Harima Heavy Industry, Japan).

The Design, Delivery, Trial and Operation of Hovercraft Ferry 'Hong Xiang', L Hu (MARIC, China).

Romanian Experimental Hovercraft 1960-1990, K Matei (ICEPRONAV-Galatz, Romania).

'DESTRIERO': The Realisation of a Technological Challenge, M Parodi, L Grossi (Fincantieri Cantieri Navali, Italy).

Experimental Investigation on Air Cushion Catamarans, Y Liang, Q S Huang (MARIC, China).

Hydrodynamic Analysis of Surface Effect Ships: Experiences with a Quasi-Linear Model, G McHenry, P Kaplan, F Korbijn, A Nestegård (DnV Classification A/S, Norway).

High-Speed Long-Range Catamaran Design, K S Min (Hyundai Heavy Industries, South Korea).

A Production Model of WIG as a High-Speed Marine Craft: 'Marine Slider μsky-2', S Kubo, T Matsubara, T Matsuoka, T Kawamura (Tottori University, Japan).

Hybrid Hydrofoil Technology - An Overview, J R Meyer (David Taylor Research Center, USA).

Basic Principles for Choosing Skirt Arrangements for Amphibious ACV's, V V Klichko (Krylov Shipbuilding Research Institute, CIS).

EKRANOPLAN - A High-Speed Marine Vehicle of New Type, B Chubikov, V Pashin, V Treshchevsky (Hydrofoils Design Bureau, CIS).

Research and Development Program of Techno-Superliner, K Sugai, M Yamaguchi (Technology Research Association Techno-Superliner, Japan).

Added Resistance in Waves of a Catamaran at High Froude Number, M Ohkusu (Kyushu University, Japan).

The Prediction of Resistance of Surface Effect Ships, H Oehimann, J C Lewthwaite (MTG Marinetechnik GmbH, Germany).

Speed Loss and Operability of Catamarans and SES in a Seaway, O Faltinsen, K Minsaas, R Zhao, J B Helmers (Norwegian Institute of Technology, Norway).

Structural Design of an Aluminium Missile Boat, P Olkinuora, E Knuuttila, M K Hakala, S Rintala, J Vuorio (Hollming Ltd, Finland).

Structural Analysis and Design of Hydrofoils and Struts, T Moan, B Skallerud, O Skjåstad (Norwegian Institute of Technology, Norway).

Methods of Avoiding Common Problems with Aluminium Structures, W J Allday (University of Southampton, UK).

Structural Loads on Advanced Marine Vehicles, including Effects of Slamming, P Kaplan (Hydromechanics Inc, USA).

Offshore Measurements of Design Loads on Large Scale Self-Propelled Model of a High-Speed Monohull SAR Vessel, J Talvia, R Wiefelspuett (RWTH, Aachen, Germany).

Prediction of Sea-keeping Performance of a SWATH Ship and Comparison with Measurements, T E Schellin, A Papanikolaou (Germanischer Lloyd, Germany).

Vertical Motions and Wave Loads of Large Sized High-Speed Ships with Hydrofoils, H Ohtsubo, A Kubota (The University of Tokyo, Japan).

A 4000 Horsepower Marine Gas Turbine, Installation and Control in High-Speed Commercial Craft, T B Lauriat, R DiGiovanni (Textron Lycoming, USA).

Engine Running Conditions During High-Speed Marine Craft Operation, B Meek-Hansen, H Engja (Marintek, Norway).

Interfacing the LM 1600 Gas Turbine Module with Advanced Marine Vessels, J M Thames (GE Marine & Industrial Engines, USA).

Prime Movers for High-Speed Vehicles, C Günther (MTU, Germany).

The German High-Speed Research Programme. Unconventional and Fast Seaborne Vehicles, H Wilckens (Forschungzentrum Schiffbaus, Germany).

Roll Damping Due to Lift Effects on High-Speed Monohulls, J J Blok, A B Aalbers (MARIN, Netherlands).

Performance and Dynamic Stability of a High-Speed Semi-Submersible Vehicle with Wings, K Mori, Y Doi (Hiroshima University, Japan).

Feasibility Study on a High-Speed Hydrofoil Catamaran of Lesser Pitching, M Nakato, O Matsumoto, Y Osawa, H J Nobukawa, M Tamashima (Hiroshima University, Japan).

The Design Process for Military Vessels, A Wangsholm (Royal Norwegian Navy Material Command, Norway).

Comparative Parametric Studies of Monohull and Surface Effect Ships, P Goubault, H Oehlmann, D R Lavis, W Goetsch (Band, Lavis & Associates Inc, USA).

AGNES 200: Description of the Development Programme and Presentation of Initial Results from Sea Trials, J P Guezou, P Letty, Y P Picart (STCAN, France).

The Development of an Automatic Control System for a Submerged Hull and Foil Hybrid Super-High-Speed Liner, T Itoko, S Hitashino, Y Yamagami, T Ikebuchi (Kawasaki Heavy Industries Ltd, Japan).

The Rough Water Capabilities of Fully Submerged Hydrofoil Craft 'Jetfoil', Y Saito, M Ika, T Ikebuchi, M Asao (Kawasaki Heavy Industries Ltd, Japan).

New Method for Improvement of Performance and Sea-keeping Characteristics of High-Speed Craft, A V Ponomarev (Krylov Shipbuilding Research Institute, CIS).

Non-linear Behaviour of Single-Skin and Sandwich Hull Panels, M Hentinen, M Hildebrand (VTT, Ship Laboratory, Finland).

Lightweight Propeller Shaft Made of FRP for High Performance Vessel, G Behrens, M Eklund (Karlskronavarvet AB, Sweden).

Fire Safety - Principles and Priorities in Future Rules and Regulations, S E Jacobsen (DnV Classification A/S, Norway).

Safety of Collision Avoidance Manoeuvre under High-Speed Navigation, K Hara (Kobe University of Mercantile Marine, Japan).

Safe and Comfortable Operation of Foil catamarans, E Instanes, P Werenskiold, J T Pedersen (Kværner Fjellstrand, Norway).

Noise and Vibration Aspects of High-Speed Passenger Vessels, K A Abrahamsen, P T Gravastrand (Det Norske Veritas, Norway).

Surface-Piercing Propellers - Methodical Propellers Series Model Test Results, J C Rose, C F L Kruppa (Rolla SP, USA).

The Effect of Water-jet-Hull Interaction on Thrust and Propulsive Efficiency, T van Terwisga (MARIN, Netherlands).

A Description of the Water-jets Selected for the 'DESTRIERO', R Svensson (KaMeWa AB, Sweden).

Design Research of SES Ride Control System, T Ma, W L Zhou, Y N Xie (Marine Design & Research Institute of China, China).

Dynamic Analysis and Control of Air-Cushion and Bag Systems of SES, S Steen, A Sørensen, O Egeland, O Faltinsen (Marintek, Norway).

Full-Scale Experiments by the First Hydrofoil Catamaran WINGSTAR 12 'Exceller', H Kawaguchi, H Miyata, H Yamato, T Takai (Setouchi Craft Company Ltd, Japan).

The Maximum Attenuation of Seaway Induced Motions, within a Given Set of Constraints, Possible for Hydrofoil Supported Ships, W C O'Neill, USA.

Power Shaft Hydrostatic Transmission for Propulsion of High-Speed Craft, H Speich, A Cappiello (Rexroth SpA, Italy).

Computer Programs in the Feasibility Design of New SES Projects, P Ottosson, O Rutgersson (SSPA Maritime Consulting AB, Sweden).

The Prediction of the Hydrodynamic Performance of Hydrofoil Craft in Waves, F van Walree, C Buccini (Maritime Research Institute Netherlands, Netherlands).

The Take-Off Characteristics of Hydrofoil and its Optimum Hullform Design, B J Zhong (China Ship Scientific Research Center, China).

Some Considerations on Rules and Regulations for Fast Sea Transportation in Japan, K Ogawa (Ministry of Transport, Japan).

Safety of Fast Sea Transport, Sandvik (Norwegian Maritime Directorate, Norway).

Papers presented at the 16th Annual Conference, International Marine Transit Association, 29 September to 3 October 1991, Estoril, Portugal.
Planning for Commuter Ferry Systems, Mark Conway (Toronto Harbour, Canada).
An Environmental Problem: Ferry Wakes in Puget Sound, Kenneth Fox (Ferry Services, Art Anderson Associates, Seattle, Washington, USA).
The New Westfoil 25 m, Randy Rust (Westport Shipyard Inc, Westport, Washington, USA).
Emissions and Alternative Fuels - Engine Design Considerations, P B Palmer (Caterpillar Overseas, Geneva, Switzerland).
Access Issues for the Handicapped, Terry Ivany (Marine Atlantic, New Brunswick, Canada).
Venice: The New Electric Ferry and Introduction to the Ferry System, Bruno della Logia (Cetena, Venice, Italy).

Papers presented at the International Symposium on Hydro- and Aerodynamics in Marine Engineering, Hadmar '91, 28 October to 1 November l991, Varna, Bulgaria.
Hydrofoils for Stabilizing Fast Ships - A Concept with Future?, E Mohr and V Bertram (Technische Beratungen Mohr and Institut fur Schiffbau, Hamburg, Germany).
Empirical Formulae to Presume the Resistance Performance of High-Speed Craft, Y Yoshida (Japan Defence Agency, Japan).
The Method for Calculating Hovercraft Motion Characteristics Taking into Account Dynamics of the Flexible Skirt, E A Paravjan (Krylov Shipbuilding Research Institute, CIS).
Computational Investigations of Airfoils Characteristics for Wing-in-Ground-Effect Vehicles, A R Besyadovsky, N V Kornev, N B Plisov, V K Treshkov (Leningrad State Marine University, CIS).

Papers presented at IMAS 91, Sixth International Maritime and Shipping Conference, High-Speed Marine Transportation, 11-13 November 1991, at the University of New South Wales, Sydney, Australia by The Institute of Marine Engineers in association with The Institute of Marine Engineers (Sydney Branch), The Royal Institution of Naval Architects (Australian Division) and the University of New South Wales (Naval Architecture Section).
The Sea-keeping Comfort of Large Fast Catamarans, P C Hercus, N A Armstrong and B K Egan (International Catamaran Designs Pty Ltd).
Speed Loss and Operational Limits of High-Speed Marine Vehicles, O M Faltinsen (Norwegian Institute of Technology), K O Holden and K J Minsaas (Marintek).
Fast Ferry by Super-Slender Twin Hull, H Miyata (Tokyo University), H Nogami, M Shiria and Y Shirose (IHI Company Ltd).
Research and Development Programme of Techno-Superliner, M Yamaguchi (Technological Research Association of Techno-Superliner).
The Design, Development and Construction of a 35 m Low-Wash Fast Catamaran River Ferry, N Hornsby (State Transit Authority), G Parker (Grahame Parker Design Pty Ltd), L J Doctors (University of New South Wales) and M R Renilson (The Australian Maritime College).
sResearch and Development of Super-Conducting Magnetohydrodynamic Ship Propulsion, S Motora (University of Tokyo), S Takezawa and H Tamama (Ship & Ocean Foundation, Japan).
Development of the Surface Effect Ship 500, A Cordano and L de Martini (Fincantieri).
Agnes 200: an Outline for a Future Surface Effect Ship, J P Guezou, P Letty and Y P Picart (DGA Direction des Construction Navales).
A Concept for a Fast Ship Stabilised by Hydrofoils, V Bertram (HSVA) and E Mohr (Technische Beratungen Mohr).
The Development of a 50 knot 40 m FoilCat, J H Jorde (Kvaerner Fjellstrand).
A Three Dimensional Structural Analysis of a Large Wave-Piercing Catamaran Design, J A Morris (Lloyd's Register).
Classification of High-Speed Marine Transportation with Particular Emphasis on Structural Strength, E H Olbjorn, C T Hughes and B V Govindasamy (Det Norske Veritas Classification Sydney Plan Approval Centre).
Marine Grade Aluminium Alloys for High-Speed Craft Construction, J T Callahan (Alcan Australia Ltd).
Propulsion of Small-Waterplane-Area Twin-Hull Ships, J R MacGregor, D C Bridges and A G Blyth (Swath Ocean International).
Two-Stage Water-Jets for High-Speed Commercial Craft, K Alexander (CWF Hamilton and Company Ltd).
Water-Jet Propulsion of High-Speed Craft, R Svensson (KaMeWa AB).
Engines for Fast Passenger and Utility Craft, G Haussmann (Motoren- und Turbinen-Union Friedrichafen GmBH).
Engine Parameters for High-Speed Marine Transportation, R M Halleen (Caterpillar Inc).
Medium-Speed Engine Designs Meet the Requirements of High-Speed Ships, M Whattam (Ruston Diesels Ltd).
Requirements of Diesel Engines and their Application for the Propulsion of High-Speed Craft, W A Sprogis (Motoren-Werke Mannheim AG, MWM).
Gas Turbine Propulsion for Large Fast Ferries, P Sweatman (Rolls Royce Industrial & Marine Gas Turbines Ltd).
Aeroderivative Gas Turbine Propulsion for High-Speed Craft, P A Dupuy and R E Reid (GE Marine & Industrial Engines).
Considerations in Applying Gas Turbines to High-Speed Vessels, J E Horne (Turbo Power and Marine Systems Inc) and J Taschner (MAN/GHH).
The Marine Transportation System between Kobe City and Kansai

International Airport Utilising the High-Speed Passenger Ship Jetfoil, T Yagi (Kawasaki Heavy Industries).
Lessons to be Learned from the Apollo JetCat Casualty in Hong Kong, Ck A Jenman (Global Maritime (London) Ltd) and M H Rowe (Global Maritime (Sydney) Pty Ltd).
The Administration's Role in the Development and Implementation of Safety Standards for High-Speed Craft, W A Graham (Department of Transport (UK)).
Certification of a High-Speed Craft - an Administration's View, R C Gheling and I M Williams (Australian Maritime Safety Authority).
Keeping Up with High-Speed Commercial and Passenger Craft Development - Legal and Insurance Implications for Owners and Certifying Authorities, C Jenman (Global Maritime Ltd) and D Coleman (Mills Oakley McKay).
Safe and Economic Operation of High-Speed Craft with Special Attention to the Diesel Engine Running Conditions, B Meek-Hansen and P Werenskiold (Marintek A/S).
Do Fast Car Ferries Have a Profitable Future?, R M Mabbott (Ferrysystems Ltd).

Papers presented at the Eighth International High-Speed Surface Craft Conference, 21-23 January 1992, Heathrow, London, UK, published by High-Speed Surface Craft, 69 Kings Road, Kingston-upon-Thames, Surrey KT2 5JB, UK.
Fast Ferry Economy - Development of the Harding 35.5 m Catamaran, Kjartan Stensones and Emil Abry (Harding Verft and Abry & Tandberg Industrial Design).
Operational Experience with Hydrofoils on the Danube, Kiroslav Gerhat (CSPD Division of Passenger Transport).
Capacity, Speed and Economy, Bjorn Foss (More & Romsdal College, Norway).
Motion Sickness Evaluation on Ships, Allan Soars and Julius Schmidt (Advanced Multi-Hull Designs).
The Reliability of Aero-derived Marine Gas Turbines, Tim and Brian Wilkinson (Rolls-Royce Industrial & Marine Gas Turbines).
Application of the FT8 Marine Gas Turbine to Large High-Speed Surface Craft, J E Horner and T W Prete (Turbo Power & Marine Systems) and Joachim Taschner (MAN/GHH).
Cats at the Cape of Storms, Bob van Niekerk (Bobkat, Antwerp).
The Practical Application of Hybrid Design Techniques to Fast Ferries for the 1990's, Nigel Gee (Nigel Gee and Associates).
Hydrostatic Transmissions - New Proposals for the Propulsion of High-Speed Craft, Hanno Speich and Alessandro Cappiello (Mannesmann Rexroth and Hydromarine).
Some Issues in Water-jet Design and Selection, Rik Hothersall (CWF Hamilton).
Modern Manoeuvring of Ships with Water-jets, Kurt Nilsson and Henry Holmberg (Styr-Kontroll Teknik).
25 Years of SES Development and the Future, Ted Tattersall (Hovermarine International).
Is Big Beautiful?, John Lewthwaite, David Bridges and Tony Marchant (Independent Maritime Assessment Associates).
Aquastrada - A Complete Model Testing and Numerical Evaluation of a New Deep V Monohull Design, Bruno Galtier and Claudio Buccini (Bassin d'Essais des Carenes and Rodriquez Cantieri Navali).
Computer Aided Design and Development of a High-Speed Catamaran, Grant Firth (Firth Marine Design/Coastdesign UK).
The SeaCockpit Bridge Concept - A Functional Analytic Design Approach to Safe Operation, Svein Kristiansen (Norwegian Marine Technology Research Institute/Norwegian Institute of Technology - Division of Marine Systems Design) and Arild Tomter (Norsk Forsvarsteknologi).
Bridge and Systems Integration on High-Speed Ferries, Noel Hogg (Vosper Thornycroft, UK).
Trials of the New 23 m Thames Class Catamaran, Nigel Warren and Robert Milner (FBM Marine Group).
The Economics of Designing High-Speed Ferries, Max Martin (International Maritime Transportation Advisory Services) - (not presented at the Conference).

Papers presented at the Fifth International Symposium on Practical Design of Ships and Mobile Units, PRADS '92, 17-22 May 1992, the University of Newcastle upon Tyne, UK.
Motion Control and Wave Loads of High-Speed Ships with Hydrofoils, H Ohtsubo and A Kubota (University of Tokyo, Japan).
Development of a Practical Swath Ship with High Performance, H Hwan Chun and R C McGregor (Hyundai Research Institute, Korea and University of Glasgow, UK).
Structural Loading Aspects in Designing Swath Ships, H S Chan, E B Djatmiko, A F Miller and L Blyth (University of Glasgow, UK).
Global Wave Loads on High-Speed Catamarans, O Faltinsen, J R Hoff, J Kvalsvold and R Zhao (Norwegian Institute of Technology and Marintek, Norway).

Papers Presented at ATMA Conference, Navires a Grande Vitesse, 20-21 May 1992, Paris, France, by Association Technique Maritime et Aeronautique
L'ACQUASTRADA, Une Evaluation Numerique et Experimentale Complete d'un Nouveau Concept de Monocoque en V Profond, B Galtier ("Navires de Commerce", Bassin d'Essais des Carenes de Paris) and C Buccini (Rodriquez Cantieri Navali, Italy).
The Sea-keeping Comfort of Large Fast Catamarans, C Hercus, T Armstrong and B K Egan (International Catamaran Designs Pty Ltd, Sydney, Australia).

Ride Quality of Fast Ferries, B Lamb and D Holcomb (Swath Ocean International Limited, Fareham, Hampshire, UK).

Essais d'Evaluation des Performances du Navire a Effect de Surface "AGNES 200", S Skorupka, P Perdon and D Le Coz (Bassin d'Essais de Carenes de Paris).

Navire Semi-Submersible Trimaran, J-C Nahon (Bureau d'Etudes Mauric, Marseilles) and M Bourgeois-Gaffie (Direction des Recherches Etudes et Techniques, Paris).

HYDRAIR: Une Nouvelle Generation de NES, Nguyen Manh Khanh (Societe Khanh Hydrair, Garches).

Developpement de Navires Rapides en Europe, Y Rouille (Constructions Mecaniques de Normandie, Cherbourg, France).

Criteres Operationnels pour les Navires a Grande Vitesse, L De Martini and L M Martini (Departement Commercial et Marketing, Division des Navires Militaires, Fincantieri, Genes, Italy).

Navires a Grande Vitesse: Marches Potentiels et Reponses Esquissees, H Michea, (Departement Offshore, Barry Rogliano Salles, Paris).

Water-Jet Propulsion of High-Speed Passenger Vessels, R Svensson, (KaMeWa AB, Sweden).

Aeroderivative Gas Turbine Propulsion for High-Speed Craft - an Update, J J Ferrera, P A Dupuy and R E Reid (General Electric, Marine and Industrial Engines, Cincinnati, Ohio, USA).

Propulsions a Hautes Performances pour Navires a Passagers Rapides, V Jost and G Haussmann (MTU-Friedrichshafen) and M Gorce (SEMT- Pielstick, Saint-Nazaire).

Transmission Electrique pour Navires Rapides du Futur, J-L Sabrie (GEC ALSTHOM Belfort), H Godfroid (CEGELEC Belfort) and P Asselin (ALCATEL ALSTHOM International Mission Marine).

Etude d'un Catamaran a Faibles Remous, M R Milner (FBM Ferries, FBM Marine Group, Isle of Wight, UK).

A Three Dimensional Structural Analysis of a Large Wave-Piercing Catamaran Design, J-A Morris (Class Computational Group - Shipdivision, Lloyd's Register of Shipping, London, UK).

Aspects Reglementaires de la Classification des Navires Rapides et Legers par le Bureau Veritas, J-N Babinet, (Division Nouvelles Constructions, Bureau Veritas, Paris La Defense).

Evaluation de la Structure d'AGNES 200 - Presentation du Programme - Premiers Resultats, Y-P Picart, (Service Technique des Constructions et Armes Navales, Groupe Materiaux Structures Navales, Paris).

Navires a Grande Vitesse. L'Aspect Reglementaire, D Allain, (Bureau de la Reglementation, Secretariat d'Etat a la Mer, Paris).

Papers presented at HPMV '92, Intersociety High Performance Marine Vehicle Conference and Exhibit, 24-27 June 1992 at Arlington, Virginia, USA, by Flagship Section American Society of Naval Engineers.

Hydrofoil Development and Applications, John R Meyer and James R Wilkins, Jr. (USA).

Hybrid Hydrofoil Technology Applications, John R Meyer (USA).

Recent PHM Operational Experience, L J Jackson (USA).

Jetfoil Operational Experience in Japan, T Yagi, Y Saito, T Ikebuchi and M Asao (Japan).

Numerical Simulation of some Manoeuvrability Characteristics for a Surface Piercing Hydrofoil Craft, Igor Prislin (former Yugoslavia).

An Estimation Method of the Motions in Waves for a Submerged Hull and Foil Hybrid High-Speed Ship, Y Yamagami, T Ikebuchi, Y Saito and T Itoko (Japan).

Hydro-Numeric HYSWAS Design, Volker Bertram and Ernst Mohr (Germany).

Offshore Minibases for Small Naval Combatants, M D Van Orden, (USN, Retd) and Roy D Gaul (USA).

Hovercraft Development, David R Lavis (USA).

Dynamic Response of an Air Cushion Lift Fan, Philip A Sullivan, F Gosselin and M J Hinchey (Canada).

The Research of Resistance and Motion Characteristics of ACV with Responsive Skirt, Zhou Weilin, Ma Tao and Zheng Nan (China).

Operational Experience with a Very High Stability Skirt System for Amphibious Hovercraft, Mariano de la Cruz (Spain).

Air Cushion Vehicle Simulation: The First Full Mission Trainer, Mark E Donner, Jeanne Class and Mary R Sabo (USA).

The Evolution of Chinese ACV/SES, Yun Liang and Peng Guihua (China).

On the Operation of an Experimental Hovercraft for the Antarctic, Rinichi Murao, Sadao Takeuchi and Minoru Inaba (Japan).

COMINCO's AP.1-88 Operation: A Successful Application of Hovercraft in the Mining Industry, David Dickins, Merlyn Royea and Paul Morrison (Canada).

LCAC: A Systems Evolution, John Auzins and U H (Jack) Rowley (USA).

Summary of Recent Developments in the Recreational and Commercial Light Hovercraft Industry, Kevin D Bedsworth (USA).

Recent Development of Air Cushion Vehicles in Japan, S Ono, S Yamashita, I Yoshino, H Ozawa and M Inaba (Japan).

The LCAC in Tests & Trials, Daniel F Bobeck (USA).

The Evolution of Crew Training in US Navy Landing Craft, Air Cushion (LCAC) Operations, David C Braa and David M Eakin (USA).

Air Cushion Vehicles and Oil Spills, Daniel L'Heureux, CCG (Canada).

Frequency Response Characteristics of an ACV Bag-Finger Skirt, Xie You Nong (China).

Model C-7: Amphibious Transportation for the 1990s, Frank P Higgins (USA).

The Evolution of the US Navy SES-200, Robert C Moore and Gregory L Bender (USA).

The BES 16 - A Spanish Surface Effect Ship, Jose A Alaez and Juan Ponce (Spain).

Cobblestone Effect on SES, Asgeir Sorensen, Sverre Steen and Odd M Faltinsen (Norway).

The SES - Optimum Hullform for Patrol Boats, Gregory L Bender (USA).

US Coast Guard WSES: Nine Years Old and Going Strong, Peter J DiNicola (USCG) (USA).

Long Range Maintenance Planning for USCG WSES, Dwight G Hutchinson, (USCG) and Mark R Schwender (USA).

The Use of Pressure Distributions to Model the Hydrodynamics of Air Cushion Vehicles and Surface Effect Ships, Lawrence J Doctors (Australia).

A Collection of Simplified Field Equations for SES Design, Chris B McKesson (USA).

Optimization of SES Designs by Use of Calculations and Model Tests, Olle Rutgersson (Sweden) and Andrew G Blyth (UK).

An Experimental Study on Air Drawing of a Water-jet Inlet for Surface Effect Ships, Shigenori Mishima (Japan).

Seal System of a Large Surface Effect Ship (Japan), Yasumi Toyama, Shirou Ono and Seichiro Nishihara (Japan).

Buoyantly Supported Multi-Hull Vessels, B-O Jansson (Sweden) and G Robert Lamb (USA).

Design and Comparison of Long Hull SWATHs and Overhanging Strut SWATHs for Oceanographic Survey Missions, Jeffery A Peters (USA).

Wave Cancellation Multihull Ship Concept, Michael B Wilson and Chun Che Hsu (USA).

An Experimental Study of Automatic Pitch Control on a SWATH Model, Edward M Lewandowski and James A White (USA).

Full-Scale Experiment and Advanced Design of SSTH Fast Ferries, A Abe, Y Shirose, A Ito, H Nogami, R Michida, H Miyata and T Ohmori (Japan).

Main Hydrodynamic Features and Performance Characteristics of SWATH Ships, V A Dubrovsky (Russia).

Design of a Tandem Canted Strut Commercial SWATH, Jonathan M Ross and Manfred J Zapka (USA).

The "Surfing TRIS" Concept, Design and Performances, Alfredo Magazzu (Italy).

Design & Operation of the 400-Passenger SWATH Ship NAVATEK I, Ludwig H Seidl, William F Clifford and James P Cummins (USA).

Three-Hulled Ships; Distinctive Features and Applications, Victor A Dubrovsky (Russia).

Hydroaviation, Stephan F Hooker and Michael R Terry (USA).

Power Augmentation of Wing-in-Ground-Effect Craft, Roger W Gallington (USA).

Matched Asymptotics in Aerodynamics of WIG Vehicles, K V Rozhdestvensky (Russia).

Numerical Simulation of Wingships, J M Elzebda (UAE), D T Mook and A H Nayfeh (USA).

Numerical Investigation of Non-linear Unsteady Aerodynamics of the WIG Vehicle, N V Kornev and V K Treshkov (Russia).

Modelling of Smart Structures for Wingships, P F Pai, A H Nayfeh and D T Mook (USA).

USSR Research & Design Efforts in the Development Marine Ekranoplans and their Transportation Capability in Various Water Areas, L D Volkov, V M Pashin, A V Ponomarev, D N Sinitsin and B V Chubikov (Russia).

Amphibian "A-40" - A Step in the Future of Hydroaviation, G S Panatov and G P Kobyzev (Russia).

Overview of Planing Craft Developments, Daviel Savitzky (USA).

Structural Developments in High-Speed Offshore Powerboats, Ronnal P Reichard (USA).

The Development of Composites for Fast Rescue Craft, F D Hudson (UK).

Optimized Designs for Stepped Planing Monohulls and Catamarans, Eugene P Clement and Joseph G Koelbel, Jr. (USA).

Sea Trials & Model-Ship Correlation Analysis of the High-Speed Gas Turbine Vessel "DESTRIERO", D L Blount (USA), L Grossi and G Lauro (Italy).

Amphibious Warfare Vehicles - Challenges, Development and Progress, Michael A Gallagher (USA).

Side-by-Side Testing of Hard Chine and Round Bilge Semi-planing Models in Waves, John J Zseleczky, Bruce C Nehrling and Roger H Compton (USA).

The Efficient Use of Simulation in Planing Hull Motion Analysis, Armin W Troesch & John D Hicks, USCG (USA).

Model Tests and Numerical Drag Prediction for a Water-jet Powered Planing Hull with a Full Beam Stern Extension, Michael T Musatow and Gregory Lee (USA).

Underway Inclining Experiments Performed on a Planing Hull Model, Roger H Compton, John J Zseleczky and William S Abrams, USN (USA).

An Assessment of Advanced Naval Vehicles for the Rapid Route Surveillance MCM Role, J Goodwin, R G Heather, J Cook, P R James, N D T Smith (UK).

Transport Effectiveness in HPMV Design, Michael R Terry (USA).

The Integration of Operating Economics in the Early Design of High-Speed Passenger Vessels, Philippe Goubault and Brian Forstell (USA).

"When it Absolutely, Positively Has to Get to the Beach." - Technology Demonstrators that Meet the LOTS Challenge, Brian J David and Daniel L Wilkins (USA).

SWATH Ships in a Monohull World, Roy D Gaul (USA).

Progress of Some High-Speed Marine Vehicles: Analysis of Prospects, V B Latyshenko, S A Otlov and V V Pleshivtcev (Russia).

The Achievement of High Performance in Marine Vehicles over the Period of 1970-1990, Robert L Casanova & Robert Latorre (USA).

Well Deck Deployable Naval Combatants, Michael Bosworth, USN, Scott Black and John R Meyer (USA).

Matching Vehicle Characteristics to Seaway Environments, William H Buckley (USA).

Sea-keeping Evaluation of High Performance Marine Vehicles, Nere Skjomedal, Jan V Aarsnes and Sigurd Falch (Norway).

Advanced Marine Vehicle Structural Loads - Present State of the Art, Paul Kaplan (USA).
Non-linear Heave and Pitch Motions of Fast Ships in Irregular Head Seas, J A Keuning (Netherlands).
An Alarm and Monitoring System for High Performance Marine Vehicles, Timothy A Pannone and J Steven Goss (USA).
Applications of the "Air Drive" Ventilated Tunnel/Surface-Piercing Propeller Propulsion System, Gary W van Tassel (USA).
Ship Propulsion Systems with High-Speed Diesel Engines, Christian Gunther (Germany).
Dynamic Aspects of Marine Propulsion Systems with Diesel Engines, G Venturini (Italy).
Gas Turbine Control in High Performance Marine Vehicles, T B Lauriat (USA).

Papers presented at the Third Conference on High-Speed Marine Craft, 8-10 September 1992, Kristiansand, Norway, by the Norwegian Society of Chartered Engineers.
Alternative Concepts in Transportation Sea/Air/Road, Bjorn Foss, (Consultant, Norway).
New Concepts in Sea Transportation, Norwegian Shipping Company (Norway).
High-Speed Cargo Ships Market Trends, Types of Ships, Critical Technology Economy, Nere Skomedal (Kvaerner Mandal, Norway).
Classification Societies - are they up-to-date?, Douglas Faulkner (University of Glasgow, UK).
FOILCAT 2900 Design and performance, Egil Svennesby (Westamarin West A/S) and Knut Minsaas (Norwegian Technology Research Institute).
Rules and Regulation - IMO, Ivar Manum (Norwegian Maritime Directorate, Norway).
SeaCat Accident, Konrad M. Havig, (Norwegian Maritime Directorate, Norway).
Safety of Operation of HSMC, Terje Steen (SINTEF, Norway).
Operational Performance and Limitations, Per Werenskiold (Norwegian Technology Research Institute, Norway).
Human Performance Factor, Bjarne Dahl (Consultant, Norway).
Practical Operative Experience from Hong Kong, C A Jenman (Global Maritime London, UK).
How do I as a Passenger Experience a Passage?, Knut F Ramstad and Trond H Overland (Oslo Business School, Norway).
Operational Procedures and Training, Ole Fredriksen and Terje Solberg (Braathen Safe), Arild Nybakk (AS Bundefjorden DS).
Bridge Resource Management, Eric Wahren (SAS Flight Academy AB, Sweden).
Bridge Design for Improved Safety, Per Aanestad (Norwegian Defence Technology).
Operational Safety - Influence on Design, Frode Klepsvik (Det Norske Veritas, Norway).
Progress in Navigational Equipment, Lars Mathisen (Norwegian Technology Research Institute, Norway).
Reliability Failure Analysis for High-Speed Marine Craft and their Safety Equipment, Stephen Phillips (Seaspeed Technology Ltd, UK).

Papers presented at the International Marine Transit Association 17th Annual Conference, 26-29 October 1992, Hong Kong.
The Responsibility of a Marine Administration for Operational Safety under the Dynamically Supported Craft Code, A C Pyrke (Marine Department, Hong Kong).
Operation of Boeing Jetfoil, David Hill (Far East Hydrofoil Company Ltd, Hong Kong).
Discovery Bay Ferry Service, Jeremy C H Marriott (Hong Kong Resorts International Ltd , Hong Kong).
The Development and Current Use of Night Vision Equipment for High-Speed Passenger Craft in Hong Kong, P R Owen, (Marine Department, Hong Kong).
High Performance Propulsion Systems, Technical representative (MTU Motoren- und Turbinen-Union, Friedrichshafen GmbH, Germany).
Spanning the Golden Gate - The Bridge and the Ferry System, Gene Rexrode (Golden Gate Bridge, Highway & Transportation District, San Francisco, USA).
Textron C-7 Amphibious Transportation for the 90's, Frank Higgins (Textron Marine Systems, New Orleans, USA).
The Seaswift Series High-Speed SES Ferries of Royal Schelde, M J H Slegers (Vlissingen, Netherlands).

Papers presented at the High-Speed Surface Craft Conference, 9-11 March 1993
Regulating high-speed and novel craft, A Blyth (Independent naval architect).
The semi-planing ship, a new concept for large high-speed ferries, J Lewthwaite (JCL High-Speed Marine Craft).
Why class?- classification society contributions to the structural design of multihull craft, A J Williams (Lloyds Register of Shipping).
Optimized gear drives for high-speed surface craft, H Sidler (MAAG Gear Co Ltd).
The bubbly water-jet - a promising high-speed marine propulsion concept, Professor A Gany (Technion Israel Institute of Technology).
Speed Z propulsion - advantages/full-scale experience, S O Halstensen (Ulstein Propeller AS).
Profit from pleasure, M Burgess (Quicksilver Connection).
Motions of high-speed vessels and their effect on passengers and crew, P A Weynberg and I M C Cambell (Wolfson Unit).
Regression analysis applied to model testing, J-H Jorde (Bergen College of Engineering).
Modern diesel engines for high-speed surface craft, G Haümann (MTU Friedrichshafen).

Fast ferry engines of choice - Caterpillar 3600 engines, R M Halleen, (Caterpillar).
Recent work on water-jet/hull interaction - K Alexander (CWF Hamilton).
The use of simulation in training for high-speed operation, R J Syms (Australian Maritime College).
Refurbishment of old hydrofoils for operation today, C Jenman and J Halligan (Global Maritime).
The rebirth of the amphibious hovercraft, G A Gifford, Griffon Hovercraft).
Intermediate technology catamarans, B Fehrenbach (F. Tech).
The speed competitive Swath fast ferry, T Kelley (Swath International).

Papers presented at the Symposium on High-Speed Marine Vehicles, 25-26 March 1993, at Naples, Italy.
Innovazioni, alte velocità, transporti, U Marchese.
Power prediction based on model tests for high-speed craft, G Jensen and V Bertram (Hamburg Ship Model Basin HSVA).
Computer-aided design techniques applied to a fast ferry, V Bertram (HSVA, Hamburg, Germany).
Full-scale manoeuvring trial results of two planing hulls, G Capurro (CETENA).
Study of service performances of surface effect ships, M Gronda (Studio Technico Navale Ansaldo, Genoa, Italy).
Advantages and Experiences with Load Profile-related and On-Condition Maintenance Concepts for High-Performance Diesel Engines, G Rechtsteiner.
Sistema do controllo digitale Rodriquez MEC1-FS, S Crupi.
A New Proposal of Performance Evaluation and Analysis for Flush-Inlet Water-jet Crafts, L Iannone and R Rocchi (INSEAN, Rome).
Structural Design Aspects of High-Speed Hulls, E Fasano and S Arena (Dipartimento di Ingegneria Navale, Naples, Italy).
A Case for the Viability of Fast Vehicle / Passenger Ferries, C Norman (Austal Ships, Western Australia).
On the Propulsion Plants of High-Speed Displacing Vessels, A Bisceglia and A Paciolla (University "Frederico II", Naples).
MDV 1200 Fincantieri - Analysis on the effects of ship motions on passenger comfort, S Saione and S Vaccarezza (Fincantieri CNI).
L'impresa del Destrieo, A Pietropaolo (Sperry Marine).
Technological Process for Big and Fats Ship Building, R Lembo (Cantieri di Baia).
Il nuovo 75 m della Kværner Fjellstrand: Con le auto a 35 nodi, P Johannesen.
Structural design and safety criteria for fast catamarans and Surface Effect Ships, A Pittaluga and G Casella (Registro Italiano Navale).
Flying the sea into the future, C G Biancardi (Instituto Universitario Navale, Naples).
Ship motion and passenger comfort of a high-speed SSC during service operation, H Yagi et al (Mitsui Engineering and Shipbuilding Co Ltd, Japan).
Classification of catamarans, A J Williams (Lloyd's Register of Shipping, London).
Technical economic evaluation of Diesel against gas turbine propulsion in passenger-carrying hydrofoil boats, E Gugliemino and R Sinatra (Università degli Studi di Catania).
The influence of Froude number calculated by displacement on the form of the Hydrodynamic comples of surface ships, M A Basin (Forma Ltd, St Petersburg, Russia).
Life Cycle Cost-Choosing Fast Ferry Engines, R M Hallen and D P Davis (Caterpillar Inc).
A back drived "sub-jet" as hydrofoil propeller, V Quaggiotti (University of Padua, Italy).
International Requirements for High-Speed Craft, G Pattofatto (Registro Italiano Navale).
Development of foil sections with delayed cavitation inception, M Ferrando et al (University of Genoa).
Analysis of partially cavitating profiles, M Caponetto (Univsersity of Genoa).
The nex 1300 Engine family: a proposal for high-speed commercial transport, G Besio et al.
Deutz MWM marine engines for applications on high-speed vessels, A Gasparri.
Comparison and experimental validation of performance analysis procedure for high-speed propellers, E J Glover et al (Newcastle University, UK).
Sea-keeping: comparazione fra aliscafo, catamarano e monostab, C Buccini and M Sferrazza (Rodriquez Cantieri Navali SpA).
Structural optimization of a Swath design, M Chiaverini et al (CETENA SpA).
Hull interference in wave resistance of catamarans, R Nabergoj and R Prever (Department of Naval Architecture, Trieste, Italy).
Efficient solution of the multiattribute design problem applied to fast passenger vessels, G Trincas et al (University of Zagreb, Croatia).

Papers presented at Cruise & Ferry 93 Conference, 11-13 May 1993, at Olympia 2, London.
Cruise Ferries v Channel Tunnel, B Langford (P&O European Ferries, UK).
Changes in traffic and operation strategies from new fast ferries entering the Scandinavian market, T Hagman and K Lumsden (Chalmers University of Technology, Gothenburg).
Developments of the Newbuilding and Secondhand Market for Fast Ferries, D Moe (Sea Service International Oslo).
Market Potential for Fast Ferries between Italy and Greece, O Vederhus and H Heijveld (Centre for International Shipping & Transport, University of Plymouth, UK).
Fast Ferry RORO Berths - Improving their Investment Profile by Providing a Range of Utilisation Options, D Byrne and S Hodgson (Transmarine Ltd, UK).
Ferry Rapido 92: a Monohull Solution for Trasmediterranea, H Sierra (E N Bazan, Spain).

Development of a Fast Monohull Ferry, P Viergutz (Blohm+Voss AG, Hamburg, Germany).

A New High-Speed SWATH, J Gollenbeck and J Holland (Schichau Seebeckwerft AG, Germany).

A Semi-Swath Catamaran Car Ferry, J V Jensen (Danyard, Denmark).

REAL Fast Car Ferries - Experience from 74 m Craft and Designs up to 115 m, P Hercus (Incat Designs, Sydney).

Can Superliners be fast and profitable?, K Levander (Kværner Masa-Yards, Finland).

Passenger Comfort and Safety (Interior Design and Craft Performance Related to New IMO 373 Code), P Werenskiold (Marintek, Norway).

Passenger and Furniture Restraints in the Collision Case. A New Look at the Deck Attachment, C Eden (Air Vehicles Ltd, UK).

The Problem of External Noise from Fast Ferries, L Thiele (Odegaard & Danneskiold-Samsoe ApS, Copenhagen).

Keeping Fast Ferries Quiet - New Developments in Propulsion Plant Silencing Systems, K Hall (Industrial Acoustics Company, UK).

Papers presented at the International Marine Transit Association 18th Annual Conference, 18-21 October 1993, San Francisco.

'Back to the Future'. Ferry Operations as part of a Regional Transportation Network, Rod McMillan (MTC Oakland, California).

The Oaklands Alameda Ferry: Competing with cars, buses and light rail mass transit, Roger Murphy (Blue and Gold Fleet, San Francisco).

Ferries as a Marketing Tool for a Land Development, Paul Bishop (Harbor Bay Express, Alameda, California).

Improving Finatial Results: Blending Commuter and Visitor/Attraction Services, Terry Koenig (Red and White Fleet, California).

High-Speed Ferries, (DnV, Norway).

Using Computer Technology to Enhance Passenger Comfort and Marketing, Merideth Tall (Clipper Navigation, Seattle).

Why Water Jets on Modern High-Speed Ferries, Bjorn Svensson (Kamewa AB, Sweden).

Papers presented at FAST '93, 13-16 December 1993, at Yokohama, Japan.

Comfort Inquiry and Motion Measurement During Commercial Passenger Service on the French SES *Agnes 200*, S Skorupka and P Perdon (Bassin d'Essais des Carènes de Paris, France).

Agnes 200: Structural Evaluation, Y-P Picart (DCN, France).

Agnes 200: Up-to-date Technical Information and Potential Use for Commercial and Military Applications, J-P Guezou (DCN, France).

The Second Stage of TSL-A Program, H Ozawa et al (Mitsui Engineering and Shipbuilding, Japan).

Integrated Structural Design and Strength Evaluation System for *TechnoSuperliner-A*, H Sueoka (Mitsubishi Heavy Industries, Japan).

Research on Hydrodynamic Performance of TSL-A, Y Kusaka et al (Mitsui Engineering and Shipbuilding, Japan).

The Norwegian High-Speed Marine Vehicle Research Programme, K O Holden (MARINTEK, Norway).

Design and Development of Hydrofoil Catamarans in Norway, K J Minsaas (MARINTEK, Norway).

The Future for High-Speed Light Craft, K M Wiklund (Det Norske Veritas, Norway).

A Study on the Structural Design of the Hydrofoil System for High-Speed Foil Catamaran Ships, K-S Min et al (Hyundai Heavy Industries, Korea).

A Study on the Prediction Method of Motion Characteristics for the High-Speed Catamaran Ship, K-S Min et al (Hyundai Heavy Industries, Korea).

Diesel Driven Fully Submerged Hydrofoil Catamaran: Mitsubishi Super-Shuttle 400, *Rainbow*, K Kihara et al (Mitsubishi Heavy Industries, Japan).

Model Tests and the Development of Control System for the Super-Shuttle 400 *Rainbow*, N Toki et al (Mitsubishi Heavy Industries, Japan).

Design and Manufacturing of the Foil Structure for Mitsubishi Super-Shuttle 400 *Rainbow*, H Sueoka et al (Mitsubishi Heavy Industries, Japan).

The Real-Time Simulation to Verify the Automatic Control System for a Submerged Hull and Foil Hybrid Super-High-Speed Liner, T Itoko (Kawasaki Heavy Industries, Japan).

A submerged Hull and Foil Hybrid Super-High-Speed Liner, R Ogiwara (Kawasaki Heavy Industries, Japan).

Structural Analysis of a Submerged Hull and Foil Hybrid Super-High-Speed Liner, I Neki (Ishikawajima-Harima Heavy Industries, Japan).

SUS-A: The State-of-the-Art of the German Research Program for Fast Catamarans, A Kraus and A Naujeck (Howaldtswerke, Germany).

SUS-A: The Scope of the VWS Hard Chine Catamaran Series '89, B Müller-Graf (VWS, Germany).

SUS-A: The Effect of Section-Symmetry on Resistance, Performance and Sea-keeping Qualities of Fast Hard Chine Catamarans, B Müller-Graf (VWS, Germany).

SUS-B: First Results of the German Research Project for Swath Ships, A Nitz (EMIT, Germany).

SUS-B: A Computational Fluid Dynamics Method for SWATH Ships, V Bertram (University of Hamburg, Germany).

SUS-B: Numerical Simulation and Validation for SWATH Ships in Waves, P Blume and H Söding (HSVA, Germany).

Waveloads of a 30 m SSTH in Sea, A Ito et al (Ishikawajima-Harima Heavy Industries, Japan).

A Study on Manoeuvrability of the Super Slender Twin Hull, T Ishiguro (Ishikawajima-Harima Heavy Industries, Japan).

Development of a Foil-Assisted Catamaran *Superjet-30*, T Arii et al (Hitachi Zosen, Japan).

Development of a Motion Control System for a Foil-Assisted Catamaran *Superjet-30*, T Arii et al (Hitachi Zosen, Japan).

R&D of a Displacement-Type High-Speed Ship, N Takarada et al (Sumitomo Heavy Industries, Japan).

Sea-keeping Assessment of a Displacement Type Super High-speed ship in Directional Spectrum Waves, S Takezawa et al (Yokohama National University, Japan).

Experimental Study on Performance of V-CAT Hull Form by Sea Trial, O Yamamoto et al (NKK, Japan).

Design, Trial and Operation of Mitsui MightyCat 40, S Yamashita et al (Mitsui Engineering and Shipbuilding, Japan).

The Systematic Test of Wedge on Flat Plate Planing Surface, C S Chen et al (National Taiwan University, Taiwan, China).

Scale Effects on the Resistance Components of a High-Speed Semi-Displacement Craft, S Cordier and F X Dumez (Bassin d'Essais des Carènes, France).

Numerical Simulation of Free-Surface Flows around an Advancing Twin Hull Form, M-S Shin et al (KRISO, Korea).

Experimental and Numerical Investigation into Wave Exciting Surge Forces in Large Following Seas, J A Keuning et al (Deft University of Technology, Netherlands).

Design and Construction of a Seawater Survey Ship Built Using Aluminium Honeycomb Panels, Y Kaneko et al (Nagasaki Institute of Applied Science, Japan).

The Response of Various Ships Hull Plating Materials to Pressure Loads Caused by Slamming, R G Wraith et al (University of Melbourne, Australia).

Multiple Criteria Synthesis Technique Applied to the Reliability Based Structural Design of Hull Components of a Fast Swath Ship, P K Das et al (University of Glasgow, UK).

Structural design of Large, Fast Marine Vehicles Based on First Principals, O F Hughes et al (Virginia Poly. Institute, USA).

An Integrated Propulsion Lift-Control Design for Large High-Speed Hydrofoil Craft, P Kaplan (Hydromechanics Inc, USA).

On the application of Fuzzy Ride Control System to a Surface Effect Ship in Waves, K P Rhee et al (Seoul National University, Korea).

Attitude Control System for a High-Speed Catamaran with Hydrofoils in Waves, C-G Kang et al (KRISO, Korea).

Longitudinal Control of the SES based on Fuzzy Control Technique, H Yamato (University of Tokyo).

Study on Flow Characteristics and Resistance Components of Simple Planing Hull Forms, S Hirano and T Himeno (University of Osaka Prefecture, Japan).

A Consideration on Wave Loads Acting on High-Speed Monohulls in Irregular Waves by Non-linear Simulation Method, S K Chou et al (United Ship Design & Development Center, Taiwan, China).

Simulation of Running Attitude and Resistance of a High-Speed Craft Using a Database of Hydrodynamic Forces Obtained by Fully Captive Model Experiments, Y Ikeda (University of Osaka Prefecture, Japan).

Wave-Induced Motions and Loads on Fast Monohulls - Correlation of Theoretical Predictions with Model and Full-Scale Experiments, T Karppinen et al (VTT Ship Laboratory, Finland).

Structural Analyses of Composite Materials for Watercraft, T Kosugi and M Kashikawa (YAMAHA, Japan).

Loads and Responses of Steel and GRP Naval Ships in Random Seas, W G Price and P Temarel (University of Southampton, UK).

Residual Strength of Sandwich Structured - a Finite Element Study, M Heder (Chalmers University of Technology, Sweden).

Improvement with Hydrodynamic Characteristics of Catamaran with Hydrofoil, B-S Kim et al (DSHM, Korea).

Heave and Pitch Motions of a Catamaran Advancing in Waves, M Kashiwagi (Kyushu University, Japan).

Prediction of Relative Motion of a High-Speed Catamaran in Oblique Seas, M Ohkusu and G-C Wen (Kyushu University, Japan).

A Comparison of an Extended Strip Theory with a Three-Dimensional Theory for Computation of Response and Loads, R Tønnesen et al (Det Norske Veritas, Norway).

Hydroelastic Modelling of Slamming against Wetdeck of a Catamaran, J Kvålsvold and O M Faltinsen (Norwegian Institute of Technology, Norway).

Hydroelastic Analysis of Ship Hulls at High Forward Speed, M K Wu et al (Norwegian Institute of Technology, Norway).

A Simplified and Design-Orientated Method for Impacted Plated Structure Analyses, S-R Cho et al (University of Ulsan, Korea).

Slamming Impact Loads and Hull-Girder Response of a Large High-Speed Craft in Waves, H Takemoto et al (Ship Research Institute, Japan).

Completely Submerged Propellers for High-Speed Craft, E Bjärne (SSPA, Sweden).

Theoretical Analysis of Contra Rotating Propeller Systems and Experimental Validation, H Streckwall (HSVA, Germany).

A Contribution on the Performance of Partially Submerged Propellers, N Olofsson (KaMeWa, Sweden).

Performance of a Supercavitating Propeller with Lip-Cup, H Kato et al (University of Tokyo, Japan).

Hydrofoil Research: Model Tests and Computations, F van Waltree and K Yamaguchi (MARIN, Netherlands).

Turning Motion and Directional Stability of Surface-Piercing Hydrofoil Craft, M Hamamoto et al (Osaka University, Japan).

Reduction of Hull Resistance with Hydrofoils, R Tasaki and R Sato (Ship and Ocean Foundation, Japan).

Validation of Hydrofoil Design Programme HYF3, R Latorre and D Bourg (University of New Orleans, USA).

On the Pressure Distribution of a Water-Jet Intake Duct in Self-Propulsion Conditions, Y Okamoto et al (NKK, Japan).

Hull-Water-jet Interaction Mechanisms: Theory and Validation, H G Coop and A J Bowen (University of Canterbury, New Zealand).

Surface-Piercing Propellers - Propeller/Hull Interaction, J C Rose et al (Rolla SP Propellers, USA).

Methods for Regulatory and Design Assessment of Planing Craft Dynamic Stability, P Werenskiold (MARINTEK, Norway).

Exhaust Emission Measurements on the High-Speed craft M/S Salten, B Meek-Hansen and O Bergh (MARINTEK, Norway).

Development of the ABS Guide for Building and Classing High-Speed Craft, C Morlan (ABS, USA).

Towards the Adoption of an IMO High-Speed Craft Code, F Plaza and K Sekimizu (IMO, UK).

A Study of Performance Predictions for High-Speed Slender Ship with Twin Wing Hulls, L Zhou et al (Hiroshima University, Japan).

Motion Responses of Air Cushion Catamaran in Regular Waves, Y Xie et al (Marine Design and Research Inst. of China).

A Study on the Hydrodynamic Aspects of Hybrid Hydrofoil Catamaran, K Shimizu et al (Mitsui Engineering and Shipbuilding, Japan).

A Numerical Solution of Three-Dimensional Gliding Plates, M Bessho and S Sakuma (Nihon University, Japan).

A Theoretical Model for the Powering Characteristics of Water-jet-Hull Systems, T van Terwisga (MARIN, Netherlands).

A Non-linear Simulation Method for Vertical Motions of Surface Effect Ships, H Ohtsubo et al (University of Tokyo, Japan).

Numerical Computations of the Non-linear Steady Waves Generated by a Two-Dimensional Hydrofoil, K J Bai (Seoul National University (Korea).

The TF40 Marine Gas Turbine, Some Recent High-Speed Applications, T B Lauriat (Textron Lycoming, USA).

Marine Propulsion with Industrial Derivative Gas Turbines, C M Waldheim (Solar Turbines Inc, USA).

Diesel Engine Behaviour Subject to Transient Loading in High-Speed Vessels, P O Moksnes and H Engja (Norwegian Institute of Technology, Norway).

Fast Vessel Engines-Environmentally Superior Power for Highly Reliable Transportation, R M Halleen et al (Caterpillar, USA).

Resistance and Motion Properties of Air Cushion Assisted Catamarans, H Miyata et al (University of Tokyo, Japan).

Sea-keeping and Comfort of Large SES, S Steen et al (MARINTEK, Japan).

Sea-keeping of an SES Experimental Craft. A Comparison between Computation and Measurements, N G Skomedal and S Falch (Kvaerner Mandal, Norway).

Sea-keeping Behaviour of an SES in Different Wave Directions, G K Kapsenberg (MARIN, Netherlands).

Operational and Cost Analysis of Fincantieri's Fast Ferries, G Arena and L De Martini (Fincantieri, Italy).

A Study of Transport Economy and Market Research for High-Speed Marine Passenger Vehicles, S Akagi (Osaka University, Japan).

Fast Sea Transportation System in the Aspect of Logistics, T E W Hagman and K R Lumsden (Chalmers University of Technology, Sweden).

Fast Sea Transportation - The Effect of Present and Future Technical Developments on Operating Economies, N I Gee and E Dudson (Nigel Gee and Associates, UK).

Global Strength Analysis of Wave-Piercing Catamarans, M Yamamoto et al (Kawasaki Heavy Industries, Japan).

Introducing Eurofast, G Arena and V Farinetti (Fincantieri, Italy).

Lift Fans Stability for SES, K C Witt (Witt & Sohn, Germany).

Bottom Plating Strength of High-Speed Fishing Craft, N Umeda et al (National Research Institute of Fisheries Engineering, Japan).

Fundamental Study on Optimum Position of Outriggers of Trimaran from View Point of Wave Making Resistance, K Suzuki and M Ikehata (Yokohama National University, Japan).

The Influence of Demihull Separation and River Banks on the Resistance of a Catamaran, L J Doctors and M R Renilson, AMECRC, Australia).

Experimental Investigations on Resistance and Sea-keeping Qualities of High-Speed Catamarans, S Matsui et al (West Japan Fluid Engineering Laboratory).

High-Speed Semi-Submersible Vehicle with Wing - Hydrodynamic Characteristics and Free-Running Experiments, K Mori et al (Hiroshima University, Japan).

Fast Ferry Mestral, J A Moret et al (E N Bazan, Spain).

Fast Slender Monohull Vessels for Cargo Transport, K Levander (Kvaerner Masa-Yards, Finland).

Dynamic Performance of Jet Skating Ship, S Naito et al (Osaka University).

Hydrodynamic Analysis and Design of a SWATH Multipurpose Research Vessel, A Papanikolaou et al (National Technical University of Athens, Greece).

Experimental Investigations on SWATH Models, V A Subramanian and C P Vendhan (Indian Institute of Technology, India).

One Fast Semi-Submersible Catamaran Vessel to Support Offshore Platforms, T Tachibana and O Caltabeloti (San Paulo State Institute of Technology (Brazil).

Assessment of High-Speed Navigation in a Congested Area by Traffic Simulation, A Nagasawa et al (Marine Safety Academy, Japan).

Safety Assessment of Advanced Marine Transportation System including High-Speed Vessels with Safety Margin as an Index, M Numano et al (Ship Research Institute, Japan).

Experimental Study of Fire Protection of a WPC Car Ferry, M Yamamoto et al (Kawasaki Heavy Industries, Japan).

Operational Procedures and Standards for the Operating Compartment, T Solberg et al (Braathen, SAFE, Norway).

High-Speed Monohulls in Extreme Sea Conditions: A Study of Operational Limits, J Lundgren (SSPA, Sweden).

Experience from Operation of Large Water-Jet Units, R Svensson (KaMeWa, Sweden).

Flyable Hydrofoil Catamaran - A New Seaplane Concept, K Akashi (ShinMaywa Industries, Japan).

Motions of a Small Racing Boat Running in Steady Wind and Encountering Waves, M Nakato and M-K Ha (Hiroshima University, Japan).

On the Manoeuvring Simulation and the Steering Tests of an ACV Model, R Murao and H Kasai (Aoyama-Galuin University, Japan).

New IMO High-Speed Craft Code and the Problems of Ekranoplanes Certification, A I Bogdanov and D N Synitsin (Central Marine Res & Des Institute, Russia).

Optimization Tools for Ship resistance and Sea-keeping Problems, J J Maisonneuve (SIREHNA, France).

Performance and Behaviour of the Large Slender Monohull, E Jullunstrø et al (MARINTEK, Norway).

Optimization of Design Parameters of Water-Jet Propulsion System, K Matsumoto et al (Toshiba Corporation, Japan).

Water-Jet Propulsion Unit for High-Speed Hydrofoil Catamarans, T Kawakami (Mitsubishi Heavy Industries, Japan).

Some Notes on SES Hull Structural Design According to Classification Rules, T Jastrzebski and Z Sekulski (Technical University of Szczecin, Poland).

Integrated FEM Computer Program for Dynamic Analysis of Hovercraft Structure and its Machinery and Propulsion System, G X Yu et al (Shanghai Jiao Tong University, China).

Parametric Design Trade-Off Study and Preliminary Design of an SES Passenger Car Ferry, Y R Joo et al (Samsung Heavy Industries, Korea).

Structural Analysis of SEC's SES, J F Garside et al (ABS, USA).

WIGSIM-Wing-In-Ground-Effect Vehicle Flight Simulator, N Kornev (St Petersburg Marine Technical University, Russia).

Note on Prediction Aerodynamic Lift/Drag Ratio of WIG at Cruise, S Ando (Tokushima Bunri University, Japan).

A Concept of Wing-In-Surface-Effect Ship (WISES), T Fuwa et al (Ship Research Institute, Japan).

Design Philosophy and Design Procedures for Large High-Speed Craft, T E Svensen and S Valsgård (Det Norske Veritas, Norway).

Electric Manoeuvring and Drive Systems for Advanced Craft, R A Gellatly and D L Blount (EML Research, USA).

Propulsion Systems for Fast Ferries, G Haussmann (MTU, Germany).

Prospects for Hard Chine Monohull Vessels, D L Blount (Donald L Blount and Associates, USA).

State-of-the-Art and Perspectives of Development of Ekranoplans in Russia, K V Rozhdestvensky and D N Synitsin (Marine Technical University, Russia).

Prospect of High-Speed Marine Vehicles in China in the 21st Century, L Yun (Marine Des and Res Institute of China).

Some Aspects of Efficient Structural Design of Future Fast Multi-Hull Ships, D Faulkner (University of Glasgow).

Papers presented at the 10th Fast Ferry International Conference, 22-24 February 1994, London

Experience from the first operational season of the Rodriquez Aquastrada, E Tripiciano (Terrenia Navigazione).

Condor - Innovation by experience, A R White (Condor).

Superfast sea transport, V Airaksinen (Finnyards).

Design of an SES high-speed passenger and car ferry and development of a new ride control system, J Reischauer (MTG Marinetechnik).

Design philosophy behind the deep vee monohull MDV 1200 Pegasus, V Farinetti et al (Fincantieri).

A quarter century of high-speed craft safety development - A Canadian perspective, R Wade (Canadian Coast Guard).

The IMO code of safety for high-speed craft, A Blyth.

Performance standards for large high-speed craft, J Holland and A Kraus (Schicau Seebeckwerft and HDW).

30 years of Copenhagen to Malmo service, L Carlin (Dapskibsselskabet Oresund).

Operating a profitable commuter service in New York, M Stanisci and G Dunzelman (TNT Hydrolines).

Trials and tribulations of a shipbuilder, R Clifford (Incat Australia).

A formidable fast vehicle ferry, C Norman, Austal Ships.

Port facilities for fast ferries, K Fear (Posford Duvivier).

When do gas turbines make sense for passenger vessels, T Lauriat (Textron Lycoming).

Economical marine gas turbines, D Dunlevy (Caterpillar Solar Turbines).

Meeting the exacting propulsion demands of commercial operator of fast ferries, O Sandoy (Kvaerner Energy).

Stretching high-speed ferries - technical and economic considerations, N Gee and A Marchant (N Gee and Associates and AMTEC).

Tricat - the development of a 45+ knot ferry, M McSorley (FBM Marine Ltd).

New hydrofoil-assisted catamarans, N de Waal (Teknicraft Design).

Crew training - High-speed passenger craft, P Owen (Hong Kong Marine Dept).

Risk factors in high-speed craft operations - A study on Hong Kong to Macau routes, S Singh (Hong Kong Polytechnic).

Likely developments in large high-speed ferries by the year 2000, J Lewthwaite et al, (IMAA).

Papers presented at INEC '94 Cost Effective Maritime Defence, 31 August - 2 September 1994, London.

On the design of a propulsion power plant of high speed vessels, Prof A Paciolla, (University of Naples, Italy).

High speed and seaworthy small-displacement craft for coastal fleet, E A Aframeev, (Krylov Shipbuilding and Research Institute, Russia).

Papers presented at Ausmarine '94, November 22-24 1994, Fremantle Australia.
Trading ships, Captain Bill Bolitho, (Australian Shipowners' Association).
Patrol boats - their design and a way of buying them, Superintendant Arnie Highfield, (Royal Hong Kong Police).
Developments in South East Asia in the next decade, Commodore P K Nettur (Rtd), (Royal Malaysian Navy).
Requirements for naval vessels until the turn of the century, Commodore Peter Purcell, (Royal Australian Navy).
Fishing boats, P Talley, (Talley fisheries Ltd and Amaltal Fisheries Ltd).
Developing a maritime culture in Australia, Commodore Sam Bateman (Rtd), (Royal Australian Navy).
The changing enviroment - a shipowners expectations of a shipyards approach to safety and enviromental awareness, R Fletcher, (P&O Towage and Salvage Pty Ltd).
Owners requirments for pilot vessels, Captain Robert Hall (Fremantle Port Authority).
Development of specialised oil and gas support vessels in Australia, Mr. Kenny Macleod, (M & P Subocean).
Requirements of Japanese passenger ferry operators, Mr. Naoki Hashimoto, (Diamond Ferry Co. Limited).
Company profile of Advanced Multi-hull Design, Paul Miller, (Advanced Multi-hull Design).
Designing around the bottom line, Stuart Ballantyne, (ASDMAR).
AMECRC research activities & consulting services, Giles Thomas, (Australian Maritime Engineering CRC Ltd).
Always an Austal vessel, Chris Norman, (Austal ships).
New joining technologies for steel aluminium fibre reinforced marine structures, Mike Turner, (Co-operative Research Centre for Materials Welding and Joining).
New high speed safety code - legal implications, Ian Morison, (Sly and Weigall).
Some notes on 100 years of the use of aluminium in shipbuilding, Stuart Ridland, (Lloyds Register).
Future trends for fast water transportation of cargo, Iwane Takahara, (NEC Logistics Ltd, Japan).
The Solar Taurus Gas Turbine Package, Thornton Lauriat, (Solar Turbines).
The evolution of the Caterpillar 3500 family of high performance marine propulsion engines, Jack Laird, (Caterpillar).
A new high speed diesel engine for high speed craft propulsion, (GEC Alsthom).
Gas turbine experience in Hong Kong, Carroll Oates, (Textron Lycoming).
Future thrust - optimum propulsion solutions towards the twenty first century, Philip Rae, (CWF Hamilton & Co Ltd).
Twin disc transmission and propulsion systems, Mark Dougall, (Twin Disc Transmission and Propulsion Systems).
Marine gears for propulsion systems of high-speed craft, Graeme Miller, (ZF Australia).
The Veem Enngineering Group, Paul Kay, (Veem Engineering).
Centa flexible couplings and driveshafts, Borre Karlsrud, (Centa Transmissions).

Papers presented at the International Symposium on Waterjet Propulsion - Latest developments, 1-2 December 1994, London.
The evolution of the modern waterjet propulsion unit, S Roy, (Southampton Institute of Higher Education).
Waterjet testing in the SSPA towing tank, Dr G Dyne and P Lindell, (SSPA Maritime Consulting AB, Sweden).
Waterjet propulsion - experience from high powered installations, R Svensson, (KaMeWa AB, Sweden).
Waterjet propulsion: a shipbuilders view; N Warren, N Simms, J Ketchmar, (FBM Marine Group).
The medium speed diesel and waterjet propulsion, R G Hunt, (GEC Alsthom Ruston Diesels Ltd).
The waterjet as an engine dynamometer, Dr K Alexander, (CWF Hamilton and Co Ltd, New Zealand).
Steering and reversing gear for very large waterjets, J Allison and Dr C Dai, (Band, Lavis & Associates Inc, USA).
Jet drive steering and reversing: a new approach, P Roos, (American Hydro Jet Corporation, USA).
Influence of waterjet forces on ship design, R Verbeek, (Lips Jet BV, Netherlands).
An operators requirements for waterjet installations & control systems in high speed ferries, A Way, (Marine and General Engineers Ltd, Guernsey).
Practical considerations on waterjets with flush intakes, Dr J English, (Maritime Technology).
Some important factors in waterjet development; J G Stricker, A J Becnel and J G Purnell, (Naval Surface Warfare Centre, USA).
The importance of high manoevrability for efficient operation, G Torneman, (MJP Waterjets, Sweden).

Papers presented at the 11th Fast Ferry International Conference, 21-23 February 1995, Hong Kong
A management information system as an estimating tool, D Hill, (Far East Hydrofoil Company).
30 Year's experience of maintaining high speed surface craft for the Hong Kong Macao route, C K ff Nobbs, (CTS-Parkview Shipyard).

Real and Imaginary problems with the new IMO HSC Code, C A Jenman, (Global Maritime).
Caterpillar 3600 engine - Life cycle costs open non-traditional markets, J G Stevenson and R M Halleen, (Caterpillar).
Night vision equipment and its use, P R Owen, (High speed craft consultant.)
Analyzing and troubleshooting poor vessel performance: Techniques available to operators using contemporary performance prediction software, D M MacPherson, (Hydrocomp).
The first twenty one year's experience of Hovermarine craft operations in Hong Kong, P J Hill and D C S Ho, (Hovermarine International and The Hong Kong & Yaumati Ferry Company respectively).
The fast ferry service between Central Hong Kong and Discovery Bay, Lantau Island; J Marriot, (Discovery Bay Transportation Services).
Looking after the customer, A M Whyte, (Red Funnel Group).
Hayabusa - the world's largest high speed wavepiercing catamaran car ferry (Kawasaki Jet Piercer), Y Saito et al, (Kawasaki Heavy Industries).
Developing a cargo carrying high speed ro-ro monohull; M Garguet (Euroyards), J de No (Astlleros Españoles), D Klug (Bremer Vulkan), M Garguet (Chantiers de L'Atlantique), V Farinett (Fincantieri), L Kinneman (Howaldtswerke-Deutsche Werft).
Developing a composite hull for a large high speed catamaran, H Enlund, (Finnyards).
The development of advanced and cost effective HT Hovercraft in China, Z H Wang, (Hang Tong High Speed Ship Development).
FMEA and the human element, R G Wade, (Canadian Coast Guard).
An evaluation of a fast ferry operation after one year of operation, T E W Hagman, (Chalmers University of Technology).
Operational experience with multiple waterjet installations, P Rae, (C W F Hamilton).
A novel approach to the improvement of fast catamaran seaworthiness, A D Kruglov, (Advanced Transportation Technologies).
Gas Turbines in today's passenger vessels, D Dunlevy, (Solar Turbines).
MTU 396 experience in fast passenger vessels, MTU 1163 the choice for large passenger vehicle ferries; G HauBman, (Motoren-und Turbinen-Union Friedrichshafen)
The Hong Kong experience, F C Chan, (Hong Kong Marine Department).
The law of fast ferries; Paul Turner (Clifford Chance), and Timothy Kelley (Jones, Waldo, Holbrook & McDonough).

Papers presented at the International Conference on Seakeeping and Weather, 28 February and 1 March 1995, London.
Weather and warships; past, present and future, D K Brown.
Measurement of encountered waves and ship motions during full scale seakeeping trials; A Rantanen, J Holmberg and T Karppinen, (VTT Manufacturing Technology, Finland).
Seakeeping for design: development and application of an inverse analysis design methodology to multihull forms; Grant Hearn, Peter Wright and Bill Hills, (University of Newcastle, UK).
Head sea slamming tests on a fast surface ship hull form series; J Colwell, I Datta and R Rogers, (Institute for Marine Dynamics, Canada).
Analysis of non-linear vessel motions: experiments and predictions; J Boyd, K Klaka and G Thomas, (Australian Maritime Engineering CRC Ltd).
A note on the effect of non-linearity on the prediction of vertical motions of a small high speed craft, G J Macfarlane and M R Renilson, (Australian Maritime Engineering CRC Ltd).

Papers presented at the International Maritime Defence Conference, 28-31 March 1995, London.
Future ASW frigate concept study of a trimaran variant, Andrew B Summers and John Eddison, (US Department of Defense, UK Ministry of Defence).
The trimaran frigate - recent research and and potential for the next generation, Professor David Andrews and J H Hall, (University College London, Defence Research Agency).
SMYGE-YS 2000 - future projects. Swedish development of state-of-the-art surface combatants; Commander Magnus Bergman, Carl Fagergren, Urban Mathiasson, Anders Lönnö.
The design of the FF-21 multi mission frigate, John Paul Mabry and Leonid Afanasieff, (Newport News Shipbuilding, John J McMullen Associates Inc).
Novel propulsion systems for future surface warships; Christopher Elliot, E S Matthews, T&EE Pyestock, (Ministry of Defence).
Ship design implications of the ICR marine gas turbine, Gordon Price and Elizabeth R Watson, (Rolls-Royce Industrial and Marine Gas Turbines Ltd).
The Ingalls Corvette; Chester A Hard, Kermit B Pethtel Jr, James P Brooks, (Litton Ingalls Shipbuilding).
Proposal for a frigate innovative propulsion system, Captain Alfio Todde, (Italian Navy).
The OKSØY Class MCMV; Commander Johs Instefjord, Nere Skomedal and Thomas Kjaer, (Royal Norwegian Navy, Kvæner Mandal Shipyard).

Papers presented at the Cruise and Ferry Conference, 16-18 May 1995, London.
SuperFast Ferries - 500 miles in 20 hours, K-W Brraun, Schichau Seebeckwerft.
Impact of the new IMO Code, Frode Klepsvik, (DnV, Norway).
Stena HSS - the coming of age for marine evacuation systems, (ML Lifeguard, UK).
The importance of system reliability, E. Kroto, (Lyngso Marine, Norway).
Operational experience from Hayabusa, Hisao Manabe, (Kawasaki, Japan).
A Giant Mestral - the Alhambra will carry 1250 passengers and 246 cars, Honorio Sierra, (Bazan, Spain).

The world's fastest car ferry Juan Patricio - breaking the 50 knot barrier, P. Miller, (AMD, Australia).
Tricat in service, M. McSorley, (FBM Marine, UK).
The seakeeping performance of fast single and multihull passenger ferries, T. Karppinen et al, (VTT, Finland).
High speed propellers or waterjets?, H. Bouwman, Lips BV, Netherlands).
Beyond 5 MW, D. Dunlevy, (Solar Turbines, USA).
Keeping fast ferries in service, G. Rechtsteiner, (MTU, Germany).

Papers presented at the International Symposium Warship '95 - Offshore Protection Vessels, 14-15 June 1995, London.
The new generation Aviso patrol vessel; V Martinot-Lagarde, M Maynard and J M Grenier, (Ministere de la defense, DCN Ingenierie, France).
The new Danish OPV's based on the standard flex concept, I B Rodholm RADM (Ret) RDN, (IBRO Consult, Denmark).
Europatrol 250 - protecting the maritime frontiers of the EC, B Morrison, (Vosper International Ltd, UK).
"Protector III" - a new fisheries protection vessel for Eastern Sea Fisheries Joint Committee; D M Cannell & J R Pratt, S C Amos, (D M Cannell Naval Architects, Eastern Sea Fisheries Joint Committee, UK).
HM Customs - recent new ship procurement, R Farrer, (HM Customs and excise, UK).
Propeller tip vortex cavitation noise (on OPV's), K Brannstrom, (Karlskronavarvet AB, Sweden).
Measured seakeeping on an Australian offshore patrol boat, K J Hope, (Australian Defence Force Academy).
ABS M-10: Third Generation Hovercraft, A F White & Lt-Col E Southby-Tailyour RM (Ret), (ABS Hovercraft, UK).
SWATH ships for offshore protection, R Holcomb and A Blyth, (Swath International Ltd, Blyth Bridges Marine Consultants Ltd, UK).
Design, build and trial of the 20 m Ultra Fast Patrol Boat, S S C Huang, (Lung Teh Shipbuilding Co Ltd, Republic of China).
Very Slender Vessels, A Thompson, (Paragon Mann Ltd, UK).

ADDITIONAL PAPERS PUBLISHED 1990-1995
The Rolls-Royce Spey Marine Gas Turbine, J Ferrie, The Institute of Marine Engineers, London, 20 February 1990.
Jetfoils on the Ostend-Dover Route: a Technical and Commercial Appraisal, Jacques J Charlier (Institute of Geography, Catholic University of Louvain, Belgium), MARIT POL MGMT, 1990, Vol 7, No 2, pages 123-132.
An Evaluation of the SWATH Vessel Frederick G Creed in the Canadian North Atlantic, J E Goodyear, D Nicholson (Canadian Hydrographic Service, Science Branch Department of Fisheries and Oceans, St John's, Newfoundland) D J Hussey, C D Roushorn (RDS Donelad Limited, Bedford, Nova Scotia) and A Hayes (Geo-Resources Inc, St John's, Newfoundland), Proceedings of US Hydrographic Conference '90, Norfolk, Virginia, 1-3 May 1990, The Hydrographic Society of America.
Hydrostatic Propulsion Systems or Main Drives Now in the Water, Hanno Speich (Mannesmann Rexroth), presented for the Shipbuilding Seminar at Mannesmann Rexroth GmbH in Lohr am Main, 29-30 May 1990.
An Investigation into the Stability and Survivability of Passenger Carrying Catamaran Craft, S A Roberts, J Cook and B Matthewson (Vosper Thornycroft UK Ltd and UK Department of Transport) 28 November 1990, Meeting of the Royal Institution of Naval Architects at Southampton, UK.
Producibility Benefits of the Swath Configuration, Richard L De Vries, (US Navy) Marine Technology, Vol 28, No 1, January 1991, pages 23-29.
An Engineering Approach to Predicting the Hydrodynamic Performance of Planing Craft Using Computer Techniques (W5 1990), D Radojcic (Royal Institution of Naval Architects).
Drag Reduction by Riblets for Marina Applications (W6 1990), Kwing-So Choi (Royal Institution of Naval Architects).

MEC1 Hydrofoil and Hydrostatic Transmission, presented to Hydraulic und Elektronik im Schiffbau and Offshore-Berich Conference, Stadhalle Lohr/Main, 29 April to 3 May 1990.
Power Transmission Systems for Advanced Ships the Hydrostatic Powershaft System, Hanno Speich, Mannesmann Rexroth GmbH, & Alessandro Cappiello, Hydromarine Srl, Marin Jubilee Meeting 11 to 15 May 1992, Wageningen, Netherlands.
Pitch-Heave Dynamics Models for an Air Cushion Vehicle, Teremce Arthur Graham, University of Toronto Institute for Aerospace Studies (UTIAS), 4925 Dufferin Street, Downsview, Ontario, Canada.
Snelle Schepen voor Passagiersvervoer - een Overzicht (Fast Ships for the Carriage of Passengers, an Overview), G Delhasse, (Scheepswerf Beliard Polyship, Ostend) presented to Belgian Naval Architects Association, 3 November 1992.
The Economics of Designing High-Speed Ferries, Max Martin (International Maritime Transportation Advisory Services Pty Ltd, Sydney, Australia) at Eighth International High-Speed Surface Craft Conference, London, 22 January, 1992.
Propulzija Vodenim Mlazom (Water Jet Propulsion), Tomo Agustinovic, Bureau Veritas, Rijeka, published in Brodogradnja, Zagreb, No 3-4, 1992.
The Influence of Variations in Thickness of Joined Hydrofoil Shell Plates on the Stressed State, I K Tarasov, published in Sudostroenie (Shipbuilding), Russia, October 1992.
Safety Study of High-Speed Marine Craft, Marintek, SINTEF Group, Trondheim, Norway, 1992.
Surface Effect Ship (SES) Developments Worldwide, D R Lavis and K B Spaulding, SNAME, March 1991.
The Design and Comparison of High Performance Marine Craft, A Rational Approach to Selection, D R Lavis and R S Sippel, Band, Lavis & Associates, Inc, MARIN Jubilee Conference, Wageningen, Netherlands, May 1992.
Scaling SES Motions, D R Lavis, Band, Lavis & Associates, Inc, 23rd American Towing Tank Conference, New Orleans, Louisiana, USA, June 1992.
Marine Water-jet Propulsion, J L Allison, Band, Lavis & Associates, Inc, presented at the Chesapeake Section of the Society of Naval Architects and Marine Engineers, 15 September, 1992.
A Methodology Designed to Help Ferry Operators Define the Best Vessel for a Route, P Goubault, Band, Lavis & Associates, Inc, Ferries '92, Boston, 1992.
Gas turbine or CODAG/CODOG propulsion for high-speed ferries, Thornton B Lauriat (Marine Gas Turbine Marketing, Textron Lycoming), given at Ferries '93, 28-30 March, Fort Lauderdale, USA.
FT8-55, A New High Performance 25 MW Mechanical Drive Aero Derivative Gas Turbine, Aldo Prario (Turbo Power & Marine Systems Inc) and Heinrich Voss (MAN Gutehoffnungshutte AG), presented at the Gas Turbine and Aeroengine Congress and Exposition, 11 to 14 June 1990, Brussels, Belgium.
The Advancing Technical Innovation In Water Transport, Robert L Trillo, Consultant, Aquapolis No 6 November/December 1992, Centro Internazionale Città d'Acqua, S Marco 4403/A, I-30124 Venice, Italy.
Design Aspects Of 162 Passenger Air Cushion Catamaran, Sun Yong Quan, MARIC, presented at Cities on Water and Transport Conference, Venice, 17-19 March 1993, Centro Internazionale Città d'Acqua, S Marco 4403/A, I-30124 Venice, Italy.
Riverbus - An Urban Transportation System for Rivers, Harbours and Lakes. M McSorley, FBM Marine Ltd, presented at Cities on Water and Transport Conference, Venice, 17-19 March 1993, Centro Internazionale Città d'Aqua, S Marco 4403/A, I-30124 Venice, Italy.
The Safety Challenge Of High-Speed Navigation—how should we meet it? Arild Tomter, Norsk Forsvarsteknologi A/S, Norway.
High-Speed Marine Vehicles, A National R&D Programme 1989 to 1992, MARINTEK, N-7002 Trondheim, Norway.
High-Speed Unconventional Craft, Miroslav Sambolek and Darko Bandula, Brodogradnja, Quarterly Journal of Naval Architecture and Shipbuilding Industry (No 1-2,1992), Brodarski Institute, Godina 40, 41000 Zagreb, Slavonia
The wash of boats on recreational waterways, G E Godd, RINA 1994.

REFERENCE PUBLICATIONS, BOOKS AND PERIODICALS

BIBLIOGRAPHIES AND GLOSSARIES
Glossary for High-Speed Surface Craft, The Society of Naval Architects and Marine Engineers, 1 World Trade Center, Suite 1369, New York, New York 10048, USA.

Bibliography on Hovercraft (ACV), Compiled by H G Russell, TIL Reports Centre, UK, September 1968, TIL/BIB/101.

ITTC Dictionary of Ship Hydrodynamics, Maritime Technology Monograph No 6, 1978. The Royal Institution of Naval Architects, London, August 1978.

Bibliography and Proposed Symbols on Hydrodynamic Technology as Related to Model Tests of High-Speed Marine Vehicles, SSPA, Public Research Report No 101, 1984, SSPA, PO Box 24001, S-400 22, Gothenburg, Sweden.

High-Speed Waterborne Passenger Operations and Craft: Bibliography, US Department of Transportation, Urban Mass Transportation Administration, Washington DC, USA, UMTA-IT-32-0001-84-2, August 1984.

GENERAL INTEREST BOOKS
A Quest for Speed at Sea, Christopher Dawson. Hutchinson & Company Ltd. ISBN 0 09 109720 7.

Hovercraft and Hydrofoils, Roy McLeavy. Blandford Press Ltd. ISBN 0 7137 07674, pp 215.

Hovercraft and Hydrofoils, Jane's Pocket Book 21, Roy McLeavy. Jane's Publishing Company.

The Interservice Hovercraft (Trials) Unit, B J Russell. Hover Publications, 1979. ISBN 0 9506 4700 4.

The Law of Hovercraft, L J Kovats. Lloyd's of London Press Ltd, 1989.

Amazon Task Force, Peter Dixon. Hodder and Stoughton, London, UK, 1981. ISBN 0 340 32713 8 and 0 340 34578 0 Pbk.

The Great Himalayan Passage, Adventure Extraordinary by Hovercraft, Michel Peissel. William Collins Sons & Company Ltd, London, UK, 1974. ISBN 0 00 211841 6.

Hydrofoils and Hovercraft, Bill Gunston. Aldous Books, London, UK, 1969. ISBN 490 00135 1 and 490 00136 X.

An Introduction to Hovercraft and Hoverports, Cross & O'Flaherty. Pitman Publishing/Juanita Kalerghi.

Light Hovercraft Handbook, (ed) Neil MacDonald. Hoverclub of Great Britain Ltd (available from 45 St Andrews Road, Lower Bemerton, Salisbury, Wiltshire), 1976.

Hover Craft, Angela Croome. 4th edition, 1984 Hodder and Stoughton Ltd. ISBN 0-340-33201-8, ISBN 0-340-33054-6 Pbk.

Twin Deliveries, J Fogagnolo. International Catamarans Pty Ltd, Hobart, Tasmania. Paperback, 1986.

Ships and Shipping of Tomorrow, Rolf Schonknecht, Jurgen Lusch, Manfred Schelzel, Hans Obenaus, Faculty of Maritime Transport Economics, Wilhelm-Pieck University, Rostock, Germany. MacGregor Publications Ltd, Hounslow, UK, pp 240, 1987.

Power Boat Speed, Racing and Record-Breaking: 1897 to the Present, Kevin Desmond. Conway Maritime Press Ltd, London, UK, 1988. ISBN 0 85177 427 X, pp 256.

Hurtigbåten (The Fast Craft), Bjørn Foss, Published by: Nordvest Forlag, Norway, 1989, pp 160. In colour. ISBN 82 90330 464.

The Law of Shipbuilding Contracts, Simon Curtis (Partner, Watson, Farley & Williams, London) Lloyds of London Press Ltd, Sheepen Place, Colchester, Essex C03 3LP, UK, pp330, 1991. ISBN 10 85044 334 3.

The Hoverspeed Story, Miles Cowsill & John Hendy, Ferry Publications, 12 Millields Close, Pentlepoir, Kilgetty, Pembrokeshire SA68 0SA, UK.

Worldwide High-Speed Ferries, Paul Hynds (Hoverspeed), Conway Maritime Press Ltd, 101 Fleet Street, London EC4Y IDE, UK, pp 160, 1992. ISBN 0 0 85177 587 X.

From Sea to Air - the Heritage of Sam Saunders, A E Tagg and R L Wheeler, Crossprint, Daish Way, Dodnor Industrial Estate, Newport, Isle of Wight, UK, pp 316, 1989. ISBN 0 9509739 3 9.

TECHNICAL BOOKS

High-Speed Small Craft by P du Cane. Temple Press Books Ltd, London, 3rd edition 1964, pp 470.

Jane's Surface Skimmers (annual 1967-1985) compiler and editor: Roy McLeavy, published by Jane's Publishing Company.

Jane's High-Speed Marine Craft (annual 1986-1995) compiler and editor: Stephen J Phillips, published by Jane's Information Group.

Hovercraft Design and Construction, Elsley & Devereaux. David & Charles, Newton Abbot, UK, 1968, pp 262.

Dynamics of Marine Vehicles, Rameswar Bhattacharyya (US Naval Academy, Annapolis, Maryland, USA). John Wiley & Sons, 1978, ISBN 0 471 07206 0, pp 498.

Air Cushion Craft Development (First Revision), P J Mantle (Mantle Engineering Company, Inc, Alexandria, Virginia, USA). David W Taylor, Naval Ship Research and Development Center DTNSRDC-80/012, January 1980, pp 593.

Transport Ships on Hydrofoils, Blumin, Massejef and Ivanof Isdatelstvo Transport, Basmannij Tupik, D 6a, Moskowsaja Tipografija Nr 33, Glawpoligrafproma, Moscow, CIS, 1964.

Marine Hovercraft Technology, Robert L Trillo, pp 245, 1971. ISBN 0 249 44036 9. Available from Robert L Trillo, Broadlands, Brockenhurst, Hampshire SO42 7SX.

Resistance and Propulsion of Ships, Svend Aage Harvald (The Technical University of Denmark). John Wiley and Sons, 1983, ISSN 0275 8741 and ISBN 0-471-06353-3, pp 353.

Industrial Fans-Aerodynamic Design, Papers presented at a seminar organised by the Fluid Machinery Committee of the Power Industries Division of the IMechE, held London, 9 April 1987. Published: MEP Ltd.

Global Wave Statistics, N Hogben (British Maritime Technology Ltd). Unwin Brothers Ltd, Woking, UK, 1987, pp 656, £295.

Fibre Reinforced Composites 1986, Institution of Mechanical Engineers publication 1986, ISBN 0 8529 8589 4/297, pp 262.

Encyclopaedia of Composite Materials and Components, Editor: M Grayson, 1983. pp 1100, Available from: AIAA, order number 57-8, ISBN 0 471 87357 8.

Marine Gas Turbines, J B Woodward. Wiley-Interscience (1-95962-6), 1975, pp 390.

The Marine Encyclopaedia Dictionary (2nd Edition), E Sullivan, May 1988, ISBN 1 85044 180 4, pp 468.

Design of High-Speed Boats. Vol 1 Planing, P R Payne. Fishergate Inc, Annapolis, Maryland, USA, pp 244, 1988. ISBN 0 942 720 06 07.

Hovercraft Technology, Economics and Applications. Editor: J R Amyot, Elsevier Science Publishers BV, l989, ISBN 0-444-88152-2 & 0-444-41872-5, pp 770, DFl.395.00.

Mechanics of Marine Vehicles, B R Clayton and R E D Bishop, Gulf Publishing Company, Houston, USA (not available in Bangladesh, Europe, Ireland or the United Kingdom).

The Leading Star of Future Overwater Commuter Transport - WIG, Shigenori Ando, Professor of Aeronautical Engineering, Nagoya University, Japan (In Japanese).

Theory and Design of Hovercraft, Professor Yun Liang, Marine Design & Research Institute of China (MARIC), Shanghai, China, pp 344, ISBN 7-118-00745-5/U.62. National Defence Industry Press, China, June 1990 (In Chinese). Industry Press, China, June 1990.

PERIODICALS

Fast Ferry International, (10 issues annually) ISSN 0954 3988, High-Speed Surface Craft Ltd, 69 Kings Road, Kingston upon Thames, Surrey KT2 5JB, UK.

Hovercraft Bulletin, (monthly) The Hovercraft Society, 24 Jellicoe Avenue, Alverstoke, Gosport, Hampshire PO12 2PE, UK.

Light Hovercraft, (monthly) The Hoverclub of Great Britain Ltd, 45 St Andrews Road, Lower Bemerton, Salisbury, Wiltshire, UK.

Work Boat World, (monthly) ISSN 1037-3748, Baird Publications Ltd 1993, 4A Carmelite Street, London EC4Y OBN, UK and 10 Oxford Street, South Yarra 3141, Melbourne, Australia.

Ship and Boat International, (ten times a year) 10 Upper Belgrave Street, London SW1X 8BQ, UK.

Small Ships, (bi-monthly) ISSN 0262 480X, International Trade Publications Ltd, Queensway House, 2 Queensway, Redhill, Surrey RH1 1QS, UK.

Cruise Ferry Info, ISSN 1102-934X. Marine Trading AB, Brogantan 7, S-302 43, Halmstad, Sweden.

Index of Organisations

Index of Craft Types

Index of Craft Names

DATE DUE			

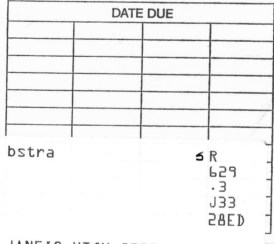

JANE'S HIGH-SPEED MARINE
CRAFT